The figure on the cover is *Instruction in Music and Grammar in an Attic School* by Douris, a red-figured painting on the exterior of a kylix. *c.*470 B.C.

Frontispiece, Raphael. *School of Athens*, Detail. Fresco. 1509–1510. Stanza della Segnatura, Vatican, Rome (Vatican Photographic Archive). The architect Bramante is portrayed as Archimedes (figure bending over slate); holding globes are the astronomers Zoroaster (bearded figure) and Ptolemy (with crown); Raphael (in profile) and his colleague Sodoma appear at the extreme right.

REVISED EDITION

ARTS AND IDEAS

WILLIAM FLEMING

Professor of Fine Arts, Syracuse University

HOLT, RINEHART AND WINSTON

New York · Chicago · San Francisco · Toronto · London

CONTENTS

INTRODUCTION TO THE
REVISED EDITION

THIS REVISED EDITION took shape during two years of intensive travel, study, and teaching abroad. The search for new illustrations led from Istanbul to Santiago de Compostela, from London to Sicily. Many of the new descriptions were written *in situ* during extended stays in Athens, Rome, Florence, Paris, and Madrid. Since nearly a decade separates the writing of the first edition and the appearance of this one, a new look is clearly in order.

Recent scholarly research has shed more light on some of the darker spots of art history, and the trial of the text in the fire of the classroom has also suggested certain clarifications and refinements. The Ravenna synthesis of early Christian art, it has been found, could better be understood by drawing a sharper distinction between the Early Roman Christian and the Byzantine styles and by flashbacks to such prototypes as Old St. Peter's in Rome and Hagia Sophia in Constantinople. The monastic Romanesque, while still centered at Cluny, has been updated with Professor Kenneth Conant's new plan and his bird's-eye view of the abbey as it was at the end of the period, and has been expanded by references to such other monuments along the pilgrimage roads as St. Sernin at Toulouse and Santiago de Compostela. The early Renaissance picture has been enlarged to include the Siennese painters. The scope of the Florentine Renaissance has been broadened to bring in Paolo Uccello and Piero della Francesca as well as Flemish paintings by Jan van Eyck and Hugo van der Goes that were commissioned by Medici bankers. The transition from Renaissance to baroque has an added dimension by coming to grips with mannerism as found in Venetian architecture and painting. The Counter-Reformation baroque now includes developments in Rome itself as well as in Spain. The 19th century has been reorganized into more clearcut divisions among the neoclassic, romantic, realistic, and impressionistic styles. Finally, a new design for the book has allowed for greater flexibility, making it possible to expand the chronologies and place the illustrations to greater advantage. Space has been found for 93 additional illustrations, bringing the total to 455, while many illustrations in the first edition have been replaced with new engravings made from recent photographs especially collected for this edition.

Like its predecessor, this revised edition is a study of the principal styles of Western art as mirrored in selected masterpieces of architecture, sculpture, painting, literature, and music. As before, specific works of art are placed in the foreground, but they are seen also in their relationships one to another and against the background of ideas that motivate the life of their times. Since an artist must, perforce, represent his world, his society, and his place in the universe as he himself sees it, his work becomes a representation of his times from a particular point of view. His temple, statue, picture, or poem is an indication of how a sensitive member of that society thinks, feels, dreams, imagines, communicates. A building in this light is not a mere pile of sticks and stones, no matter how interesting the shape these may assume, but an environment for the ordered activity of his fellow men. Sculpture and painting represent the visage of an age, as well as man's fears and hopes in symbols and images. In poetry and music the inner rhythms, the joys and sorrows, of the human heart are heard. In the creative process the artist starts with the vanishing point of the void—empty space and undefined time—then *composes* in the literal sense of selecting materials, placing them together, building them up. The procedure is from the singular toward the plural, from unrelatedness to relatedness, and eventually toward the order and unity of a style.

The search for unity within historical periods, or at least for a coherent grouping of diversities, is crucial for both style definition and art criticism. Cultural expressions, in the manner of the classical unities of Greek drama, usually occur within definite limits of time, place, and action. Seeking for the underlying ideas that motivate human activities can often reduce to basic simplicity what appears on the surface as a confusing multiplicity of directions. And since the arts are usually experienced simultaneously not separately, often it is wiser to seek understanding on a multi- rather than a single-directional basis. If a common configuration of ideas can be found, then aspects that previously proved baffling suddenly may fall into place and acquire meaning.

Such ideas may be initiated by artists themselves either individually or as a group or by single or collective patrons endowed with sufficient discernment, means, and energy to pursue projects to completion. Such a patron might be a ruler with the vision of Pericles, who presided over the cultural climax of ancient Athens; an enterprising medieval abbot or bishop, who envisaged a great monastery or cathedral complex; a family of merchant princes, such as the Medici, who brought Renaissance Florence to its creative peak; or a religious order like the Jesuits, who spread the Counter-Reformation baroque style in the wake of their missionary endeavors. The 20th century has witnessed the Commonwealth of India commissioning Le Corbusier to construct Chandigarh, an entirely new capital city complete with every public and private facility. In New York, the heirs of a modern industrialist have contributed an architectural complex in

Rockefeller Center that compares in grandeur with the imperial forums of ancient Rome. And many public agencies and private contributors have joined forces to erect the Lincoln Square "acropolis" that embraces an opera house, several concert halls, a repertory theater, a library, an educational center, and cooperative apartment houses.

Whenever a center has attained a degree of civilization, has developed a prosperous economy, has given birth to a number of promising individuals, has fostered an adequate educational system, has in its midst groups of artists and master craftsmen, a significant cultural expression may occur. When this happens, it is usually because some personality of powerful convictions has reacted so strongly to the challenge of his time that he is catapulted into a dominating position. Various explanations have been advanced, such as the "great-man theory," which holds that outstanding persons stamp their image upon an age, and that genius is the primary causal influence on history. Social realists, contrariwise, contend that environmental forces shape the characters and actions of the individuals involved. The truth probably lies somewhere between these extremes of nature and nurture, and the interplay between powerful personalities and the stimulus of their times brings about the explosion commonly described as genius.

Art history, as presented in these pages, will be seen as a reflection of personal preferences, social conflicts, the rivalries of cities and states, and the ambitions of public and private patrons quite as much as a record of the rise of men of genius, the development of skilled craftsmen, or the production of specific works. The human urge to make order and build, to decorate and depict, to impress and express are the constants of art production, while the shifts of taste, the evolution of techniques, the fluctuation of forms, and the momentum of art movements are the variables.

Techniques of production are, and always will remain, private problems of the particular craftsman, whether he be architect, poet, or musician. Composition, however, is common to them all. An architect puts bricks together, a poet words, a musician tones. But contrary to some purist views, they do not do so in a vacuum of self-expression but to communicate thoughts, free fantasies, social comments, satirical observations, self-revelations, images of order, and the like. Their works—temples, statues, murals, odes, sonatas, or symphonies—are addressed not to themselves but to their fellow men. Highly important is the fact that their viewpoints are shaped and colored by their historical and social environment.

The artist's choice of medium, his way of handling materials, the language with which he expresses himself, his personal idioms and idiosyncrasies, his mode of vision, his manner of representing his world, all add up to a vocabulary of symbols and images that define his individual style. In a broader sense, however, a style must include similar expressions in many media, whether in visual, verbal, or tonal imagery. Since artists, working within a given time and place, share a sociocultural heritage, it follows that each has a common point of departure. In the arts, as in politics, there are conservatives who try to preserve traditional values, liberals who are concerned with current trends, and progressives who point to coming developments. The individual artist may accept or reject, endorse or protest, conform or reform, construct or destroy, dream of the past or prophesy the future, but his taking-off point must be his own time. The accents with which he and his contemporaries speak, the vocabularies they use, the symbols they choose, the passion with which they champion ideas, all add up to the larger synthesis of a style.

A positive approach, then, can be established on the coincidence of *time*, *place*, and *idea*. A given group of artists, while working in their separate fields, are an integral part of a society, living within a certain geographical and temporal center, and collaborating to a greater or less extent. The closer the coincidence, the closer the relationship will be. Composite works of art—forums, monasteries, cathedrals, operas—are always collaborative in nature and must to a considerable degree have mutual influences. Liturgical needs, for instance, must be taken into account in the design of a cathedral, and the sculptural and pictorial embellishments must fit into the plan and iconography of the structure. Hence, in one *time* and in one *place*, the arts of architecture, sculpture, painting, music, and liturgy share a common constellation of *ideas* in relation to the contemporary social order and its spiritual aspirations.

Through the study of the arts in relation to the life and time out of which they spring, a richer, broader, deeper humanistic understanding can be achieved. The past, as reflected in the arts, exists as a continuous process, and any arbitrary separation from the present and future disappears in the presence of a living work. True critical appraisal of art, or indeed any other human activity, can never be a catalogue of minutiae, a record of isolated moments. Understanding can come only when one event is related to another, and when their sum total is absorbed into the growing stream of universal life from which each particular moment derives its significance. In their natural relationship, the arts become the study of people reflected in the ever-changing images of man as he journeys across historical time, as he expresses his attitudes toward himself, his fellow men, and the universe, as he searches restlessly for reality, and as he ceaselessly strives to achieve the ideals that create meanings for life.

Greek Altar (the "Ludovisi Throne"), Side Panel. Marble. 32¼" high at left side. *c.*460 B.C. Museum of Fine Arts, Boston

Part 1
THE CLASSICAL
PERIOD

CHRONOLOGY:

Athens, 5th Century B.C.

General History
B.C.

c.1600–c.1100		Mycenaean Period
c.1184		Fall of Troy to Achaeans
c.1100		Dorians and Ionians invaded Greek peninsula, conquered Achaeans. End of Mycenaean Period, beginning of Hellenic civilization
c.950–	c.800	Period of Homeric epics
c.800–	c.500	Archaic Period
	c.756	First Olympiad. All Greeks competed in ceremonial games
	c.494	Persians under Darius invaded Greece
	c.490	Athenians defeated Persians at Marathon
	480	Persians under Xerxes defeated Spartans at Thermopylae. Athens sacked and burned. Athenians defeated Persian fleet at Salamis
	477	Delian League founded under Athenian leadership
c.461–	429	Pericles (490–429) ruled Athens
	454	Delian League treasury moved to Athens
437–	404	Peloponnesian Wars between Athens and Sparta
	413	Athenians defeated at Syracuse, Sicily
	404	Athens fell to Sparta. End of Athenian empire
	387	Plato founded Academy
	335	Aristotle founded Lyceum

Architecture and Sculpture

c.650	Ionic temple of Artemis built at Ephesus
c.600	Kouros from Sounion carved
c.550	Hera of Samos carved
c.530	Archaic Doric temples built at Athens, Delphi, Corinth, Olympia
c.489	Doric temple (Treasury of Athenians built at Delphi

c.468–	457	Temple of Zeus built at Olympia
c.460–	440	Myron and Polyclitus active
	450	Phidias appointed overseer of works on acropolis
449–	440	Temple of Hephaestus (Theseum) built
447–	432	Parthenon built by Ictinus and Callicrates. Parthenon sculptures carved under Phidias
437–	432	Propylaea built by Mnesicles
427–	424	Temple of Athena Nike built by Callicrates
421–	409	Erechtheum built by Mnesicles
c.350–	300	Lysippus active
	334	Choragic monument of Lysicrates built

A.D.

	c.100	Plutarch (c.46–c.125) wrote *Parallel Lives*
c.140–	150	Pausanius visited Athens. Later wrote description of Greece

Philosophers

c.582–	c.507	Pythagoras
500–	428	Anaxagoras
469–	399	Socrates
427–	347	Plato
384–	322	Aristotle

Historians

c.495–	425	Herodotus
c.460–	395	Thucydides
c.434–	c.355	Xenophon

Sculptors

c.490–	c.432	Phidias
c.460–	c.450	Myron active
c.460–	c.440	Polyclitus active
c.390–	c.330	Praxiteles
c.350–	c.300	Lysippus active

Painters

c.480–	c.430	Polygnotus (noted for perspective drawing)
	c.440	Apollodorus, the "shadow painter," flourished (modeled figures in light and shade)

Dramatists and Musicians

525–	456	Aeschylus
496–	406	Sophocles
480–	406	Euripides
c.444–	380	Aristophanes

I

THE HELLENIC STYLE

ATHENS, 5TH CENTURY B.C.

In a small city-state in the land of Hellas more than four centuries before the Christian era, a new spirit was astir—a spirit destined to quicken the hearts and minds of mankind then and now and in times yet to come. Here, in Athens, for a brief span of time were concentrated the creative activities of many men of genius—leaders who made Athens victorious in the struggle for control of the Mediterranean world, statesmen who had made Athens the first democracy in a world of tyrants, philosophers who were seeking to understand the world in which they lived, and artists who conceived daring expressions in stone, word, and tone. Here, in 480 B.C., the Athenians had turned the tide against the powerful Persians, but only after their city had been reduced to rubble. Here, without hereditary rulers, government rested on the shoulders of the citizen class, and the rule of the *demos*, the people, became the order of the day. Here the statesman Pericles and the future philosopher Socrates heard the wisdom of Anaxagoras, who taught that the universe was governed by a supreme mind that brought form out of the chaos of nature and that man, as the measure of all things, by thinking for himself could likewise bring order into human affairs. And here, after the destruction of their city, the Athenians, boldly facing the future, instead of reconstructing their old temples and statuary launched a new building program that surpassed anything the world had ever seen and that was to serve as a classical model for all generations to come.

3

Like many other ancient cities, Athens had developed around an *acra*, or hill, that had first served as a military vantage point. As in other cities, a long-ago victory on this fortified hilltop, known as the *acropolis* (Fig. 1:1), had been attributed to divine intervention, and in the popular mind the acra had become a sacred place, to be crowned with a suitable monument—just as the brow of the warrior responsible for the heroic deed had been adorned with the kingly diadem. Civic buildings, palaces, and temples had been erected, and the people in the city below looked up with pride toward the acropolis that recorded their history, represented their aspirations, and had become the center of their religious and civic ceremonies. From the beginning, the Athenian acropolis was never static, and its successive buildings reflected the city's changing fortunes. Once it had been the site of the palace of Erechtheus, an early hero and legendary king. Its shift from a military citadel and royal residence to a religious shrine especially sacred to Athena as the city's protectress, is described by Homer when he notes in the *Odyssey:* "Therewith grey-eyed Athene departed over the unharvested seas, left pleasant Scheria, and came to Marathon and wide-wayed Athens, and entered the house of Erechtheus."

Spreading out from the base of the acropolis was the *agora* (Fig. 1:2), or marketplace, with its colonnades, public buildings, market stalls, gardens, and shade trees. This 10-acre square was the center of the city's bustling business, social, and political life. Here could be found country folk selling their wares, citizens discussing the news, foreign visitors exchanging stories, and magistrates conducting routine city affairs. "You will find everything sold together in the same place at Athens," wrote the poet Eubolus in a humorous vein, "figs, witnesses to summonses, bunches of grapes, turnips, pears, apples, givers of evidence, roses, . . . honeycombs, chickpeas, lawsuits, . . . myrtle, allotment-machines, irises, lamps, water-clocks, laws, and indictments." And he could well have added "philosophies of life," for the agora was the place to find spiritual as well as material goods, the place where philosophers settled the problems of the universe. On a typical day, Socrates could be heard arguing with the sophists, whom he called "retailers of knowledge," for, as his pupil Plato was to point out, the merchandising in the agora was "partly concerned with food for the use of the body, and partly with food of the soul which is bartered and received in exchange for money." The sophists were primarily concerned with the art of persuasive speech, but some professed to teach wisdom as well. As manipulators of public opinion, they often became intellectual opportunists who would use any line of reasoning so long as it turned their trick. In his disputations, Socrates showed that sophistry was more a matter of quibbling on the surface over words than of penetrating profoundly into the deeper world of ideas. By pricking some of their pomposities with the sting of his wit, Socrates gained his immortal reputation as the "gadfly" of Athens.

Fig. 1:1. The Acropolis, Athens. View from the southwest (Stournaras)

On the southern slope of the acropolis was the theater of Dionysus, the sanctuary dedicated to the god of wine and frenzy and patron of the drama, and where the ancient poetic festivals were held. Here, more than 2000 years before Shakespeare, the people of Athens gathered to enjoy the plays that mirrored their world in dramatic form and, annually, through their applause to pick the winner of the coveted poetry prize that had been won no less than 13 times by Aeschylus, the founder of heroic tragedy. Sophocles, his successor and principal poet of the Periclean period, quickened the pace of Greek drama by adding more actors and actions; Euripides, last of the great tragic poets, ran the gamut of emotions, endowing his plays with such passion and pathos that they plumbed the depths of the human spirit. After the great Periclean age was past, the comedies of Aristophanes proved that the Athenians still were able to see the humorous side of life.

Above the theater, on the rocky plateau of the acropolis, was a leveled site, about 1000 feet long and 445 feet wide, where the temples were constructed. Under Pericles, this was a place of ceaseless activity by builders, sculptors, painters, and other craftsmen. The necessary materials were available in abundance: Paros and other Aegean islands yielded good stone; from nearby Mt. Pentelicus came the fine-grained, cream-colored marble ideal for building and carving; Mt. Hymettus in Athens itself had a blue-white stone, excellent for embellishments; while the dark-gray limestone of Eleusis could be used for contrasting effects. As the buildings rose stately in size and fair in form, the craftsmen, declares Plutarch in his biography of Pericles, were "striving to outvie the material and the design with the beauty of their workmanship, yet the most wonderful thing of all was

Fig. 1:2. Ruins of the Ancient Agora with Reconstruction of the Stoa of Attalus II of Pergamon (159–138 B.C.). Athens (Royal Greek Embassy)

the rapidity of their execution. Undertakings, any one of which singly might have required, they thought, for their completion, several successions and ages of men, were every one of them accomplished in the height and prime of one man's political service."

Pericles had the wisdom to foresee that the unity of a people could rest on philosophical idealism and artistic leadership as well as on military might and material prosperity. A seafaring people, the Athenians had always looked beyond the horizon for ideas as well as goods to add luster to their way of life. In the Delian confederation, now that the Persian threats were ended, they joined with the broader community of Greek-speaking peoples of the mainland, Aegean islands, and the coast of Asia Minor to achieve a cultural rather than a territorial or political unity. With the Delian treasury brought to Athens and its ample funds available for her building program, the city was assured leadership in the arts as well as in other practical and idealistic enterprises. Thus Athens became a city whose acknowledged wealth was in its dramatists (Aeschylus, Sophocles, and Euripides), its architects (Ictinus, Callicrates, and Mnesicles), its sculptors (Myron, Polyclitus, and Phidias), and such painters and craftsmen as Polygnotus and Callimachus.

The acropolis was, then, both the material and spiritual treasury of the Athenian people, the place which held both their worldly gold reserves and their religious and artistic monuments. Work continued with unabated enthusiasm until by the end of the 5th century B.C. the acropolis had become a sublime setting, worthy of the goddess of wisdom and beauty, and the pedestal that proudly bore the shining temples dedicated to her.

ARCHITECTURE

The Acropolis and the Propylaea

On festive occasions, the Athenians would leave their modest homes to walk along the Panathenaic Way, the main avenue of their city, toward the acropolis. As the procession moved diagonally across the agora, all could see the small Doric Hephaesteum, known also as the Theseum (Fig. 1:3), on a low hill to their right. Now the best preserved of all Greek temples, it was dedicated to Hephaestus (Vulcan), god of the forge and patron of metalworkers. He shared his temple with Athena in her role as protectress of arts and crafts that brought fame to the artisans who lived in the adjoining potters' quarter, known as Ceramicus. But ahead, towering above them, was the supreme shrine—the acropolis where they worshiped their gods, commemorated their heroes, and recreated themselves. Accessible only by a single zigzag path up the western slope, the ascent was never easy. In Aristophanes' *Lysistrata*, a chorus of old men bearing olive branches to kindle the sacred fires chant as they mount the hill: "But look, to finish this toilsome climb only this last steep bit is left to mount. Truly, it's no easy job without beasts of burden and how these logs do bruise my shoulder!"

As the procession neared the summit (Fig. 1:4), the exquisite little temple of Athena Nike (Fig. 1:12) appeared on a parapet to the right, and in front was the mighty Propylaea. Built entirely of Pentelic marble except for some dark contrasting Eleusinian stone in the frieze, this imposing structure was in the form of a spacious gateway with wings extending on either side to an over-

Fig. 1:3. Hephaesteum ("Theseum"). Pentelic and Parian marble. 104′ × 45′. Begun *c.* 449 B.C. Athens (Royal Greek Embassy)

Fig. 1:4. The Acropolis, Athens. Restoration after Lambert and D'Espouy

all width of about 156 feet. An enclosure on the left was a picture gallery, and an open room on the right contained statuary. In the center was the portico consisting of six Doric columns with the middle two spaced more widely apart as if to invite entrance. Between the columns facing the city and the corresponding ones on the opposite side facing the acropolis plateau was an open vestibule with columns of the more slender Ionic order that permitted greater height and more open interior space. The axis of the Propylaea paralleled that of the Parthenon, an exception to the usual self-containment of Greek buildings of the Hellenic period but justified by the Propylaea's function of gateway rather than of a building independent in its own right.

Through the portals of the Propylaea the procession entered the sacred area. Looming above amid the revered monuments to the gods and heroes was the colossal statue of Athena Promachus, said to have been cast by Phidias from the bronze shields of defeated Persian enemies, the tip of her spear gleaming brightly enough to guide homecoming sailors over the seas toward Athens. On the right was the majestic Parthenon; on the left the graceful Ionic Erechtheum (Fig. 1:8).

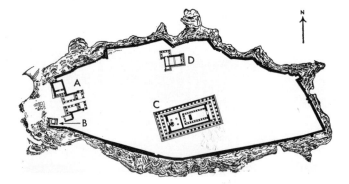

Fig. 1:5. The Acropolis, *Plan*. A, Propylaea; B, Temple of Athena Nike; C, Parthenon; D, Erechtheum

The Parthenon

At first glance, the Parthenon (Fig. 1:6) seems to be a typical Greek temple. Such a shrine was originally conceived as an idealized dwelling to house the image of the deity to whom it was dedicated. Under a low-pitched gabled roof, the interior was a windowless oblong room called the *cella*, in which the cult statue was placed. The *portal*, or door, to the cella was on one of the short ends, which extended outward in a *portico*, or porch, faced with columns to form the façade. Sometimes columns were erected around the building in a series known as a *colonnade*. The method of construction was simple: a platform of three steps, the top one known as the *stylobate*, from which rose the upright *posts* that supported the *lintels*, or cross beams. When these columns and lintels were of marble, the weight and size of the superstructure could be increased and the *intercolumniation*, or span between the supporting posts, widened. The history of Greek temple architecture was largely the refining of this *post-and-lintel* system, which permitted the architects a steadily increasing freedom.

The capital of the Doric column is in three parts: the necking, the echinus, and the abacus (Fig. 1:7). The purpose of any capital is to mediate between the vertical shaft of the column and the horizontal entablature above. The *necking* is the first break in the upward lines of the shafts, though the fluting continues up to the outward flair of the round, cushionlike *echinus*. This, in turn, leads to the *abacus*, a block of stone that squares the circle, so to speak, and smoothly effects the transition between the round lower and rectangular upper

Fig. 1:6. Ictinus and Callicrates. Parthenon. Pentelic marble. *c.*228′ × 104′. Columns 34′ high. 447–432 B.C. Athens (Stournaras)

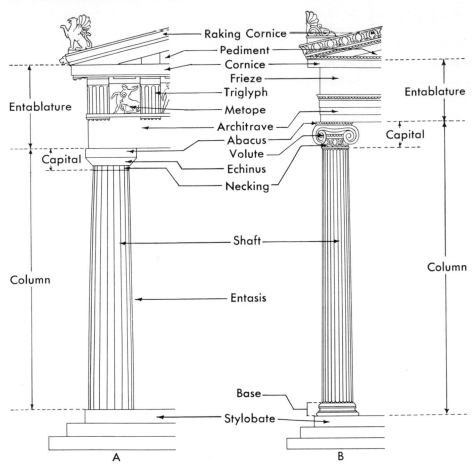

Raking Cornice
Pediment
Cornice
Frieze
Triglyph
Metope
Architrave
Abacus
Volute
Echinus
Necking
Shaft
Entasis
Base
Stylobate

Entablature

Capital

Column

Entablature

Capital

Column

A   B

Fig. 1:7. Comparison of Doric and Ionic Orders

members. Above the columns and below the roof is the *entablature* (see Fig. 1:7). Directly above the abacus is the *architrave*, a series of plain rectangular blocks stretching from the center of one column to that of its neighbor to form the lintels of the construction and to support the upper parts of the entablature —frieze, cornice, and pediment. At this point, sculpture is called into play for decorative purposes, beginning with a decorative band known as a *frieze*. In the Doric order, the frieze is made up of alternating triglyphs and metopes. The rectangular *triglyphs* are so named because of their three grooves (glyphs), two in the center and a half groove on either side. They are the weight-bearing members, and by rule one is placed above each column and another in the interval between. The sameness of the triglyphs contrasts with the differently carved relief panels of the *metopes*. This alternation results in an interesting visual rhythm, which illustrates the classical principle of harmonizing the opposites of unity and variety. The frieze is protected by the overhanging *cornice* (and enhanced by its shadow), and the *raking cornice* rises gablelike from the side angles to the apex in the center. The triangular space enclosed by the cornices is called the *pediment*, which is about three feet deep, thus creating an indented space in which free-standing sculpture can be placed to climax the decorative scheme.

On closer inspection, the Parthenon is not so much a typical Greek temple as it is the culmination of the long evolution of the Doric order with variations adapting it to the needs of its time and place. Since the Parthenon was to serve both as a shrine to Athena and the treasury of the Delian League, the plan called for a double cella. The larger room on the east was to house Phidias' magnificent gold-and-ivory cult statue of Athena and that on the west was to be the treasury. It was this western cella that technically was called the *parthenon*, or chamber of the virgin goddess; later the name was given to the whole building. The outer four walls of the cella were embellished by a continuous frieze, a decorative device borrowed from the Ionic order. A *peristyle*, or colonnade, of free-standing columns completely surrounded the temple, the columns being placed far enough outward from the cella walls to permit an *ambulatory*, or passageway. Along its 228 feet of length were 17 columns on each side, and along the 104-foot width in front and back were eight columns—hence the Parthenon is called octastyle. (The number of columns used on the portico of a Greek temple was determined by the size of the building rather than by any rigid rule, six being the usual number although some temples had as many as 10 and 12.) On both the east and west ends of the Parthenon, between the outer colonnade and the entrance portals to the cella, were six additional columns that formed the inner porticos.

Except for such details as the timbered roof beneath the marble tiles and the wooden doors with their frames, the entire Parthenon was built of Pentelic marble. When freshly quarried, this fine-grained stone was cream colored, but as it has weathered through the centuries its minute veins of iron have oxidized so that today the color varies from light beige to darker sepia tones depending on the light. In the original design, bright colors played an important part. The triglyphs were tinted dark blue and parts of the molding were red, as is known from ancient sources. The sculptured parts of the metopes were left cream-colored, but the backgrounds were painted. In the frieze along the cella walls, the reins of horses were bronze additions, and the draperies of figures here and on the pediments were painted. Such facial features as eyes, lips, and hair were done in natural tints.

For sheer technical skill, the workmanship of the Parthenon is astonishing. No mortar was used anywhere; the stones were cut so exactly that when fitted together they form a single smooth surface. The columns, which appear to be monoliths of marble, actually are constructed of sections called *drums*, so fitted and held tight by square plugs in the center that the joinings are scarcely visible. To insure harmonious proportions, the design is based on the mathematical principle of the golden section, a flexible system of dividing lines into extreme and mean rations. Just how it was applied is now unknown, but far from being a cut-and-dried formula, the golden section obviously allowed much latitude in actual practice.

The orderly organization of verticals and horizontals, the relationship of length and breadth to height, the ratio of the solid masses of the columns to the open voids between them—all are according to tradition. A unit of measure known as the *module* was used to assure the orderly relation of parts and whole. Such modules were not fixed measures like yards and feet but flexible units, such as the diameter or radius of a column. In keeping with the Greek ideal of the structural integrity of single buildings, the module was varied from case to case.

While the Parthenon was built according to geometrical laws, many subtle variations from the norm reveal that it was a living geometry based on experience rather than on a textbook. Further examination will reveal that what appears to be straight and correct is in reality a complex system of convex and concave curves. To accommodate the building to its rocky site, to correct certain optical illusions, as well as to create the appearance of vitality and flexibility in what otherwise would become a cold exercise in geometry, the architects Ictinus and Callicrates found a solution that is psychologically and aesthetically rather than mathematically correct. If completely level, for instance, the long straight line of the stylobate would seem indefinite and, to the eye, might even appear to sag slightly under the weight of the masonry. To give it a feeling of having a beginning, a middle, and an end (as well as to correct a possible optical distortion), the architects caused the stylobate to rise slightly upward and flair outward on each of the four sides. From the corners to the center on the short ends the rise is about 2¾ inches and on the long sides, about 4 inches.

If all columns were equal in diameter, those on the corners when seen against the sky would appear slimmer and weaker than those viewed against the cella walls. Hence, to promote the feeling of structural solidity and the effect of a closed composition, the corner columns are thicker and closer together than those in the center. Each of these columns, in the process called *entasis*, swells slightly to a point about one third of its height and then tapers gradually toward the top. This entasis creates an impression of elasticity as if, by analogy, the "muscles" of the columns bulge a bit as they carry their load. The outer surfaces of the columns have 20 grooves, called *flutes*, which form concave vertical channels from the bottom to the top of the shaft. Fluting serves two purposes, the first being to correct an optical illusion. When seen in bright sunlight, a series of ungrooved round columns appears flattened. The fluting maintains the round appearance and provides a constant play of light and shadow. The second purpose is an aesthetic one: to provide a number of graceful scalloped curves to please the eye; also, by increasing the number of vertical lines, the visual rhythm is quickened, and the eye is led upward toward the sculpture of the entablature.

No column, moreover, is exactly parallel to its neighbors, and the columns as well as the cella walls slant slightly inward to avoid the appearance of top-heaviness and promote the feeling of stability. It has been estimated that if the lines of columns and walls were continued upward, they would meet at a point about a mile above. Columns and walls thus seem to come together in a communal effect of converging cooperation. That all was part of the original subtle design is known from the writings of the Roman architect Vitruvius, who apparently had access to the lost book on the Parthenon by Ictinus. More than mere dimensions, however, the Parthenon has proportions. With its deviations from mathematical exactness, all rigidity is banished, and the temple becomes an example of active equilibrium and mobile stability rather than a static study in geometry. It is, in short, a work of art rather than a case of skillful engineering.

In its time, the Parthenon stood out as a proud monument to Athena and her people and a realization of Pericles' ideal of "beauty in simplicity." Begun in 447 B.C. as the first edifice in that great statesman's building program, it was dedicated during the Panathenaic festival 10 short years later at a time when the star of Athens was still in ascendancy. It, as well as its companion buildings on the acropolis, would be standing today with only the usual deteriorations due to the passage of time were it not for a disaster in the year 1687. At that time, a Turkish garrison was using the Parthenon as an ammunition dump, and during a siege by the Venetians a random bomb ignited the stored gunpowder, blowing out the central section. From that time on, the Parthenon has been a noble ruin. Today, after numerous partial restorations, its outline is still clear, and in its incomparable proportions and reserved poise it remains one of the imperishable achievements of the mind of man.

The Erechtheum

After Phidias' gold-and-ivory statue was so handsomely housed in the Parthenon, the city fathers wished to provide a place for the older wooden statue of Athena that was thought to have fallen miraculously from the sky. They also wished to venerate the other heroes and deities that formerly shared the acropolis with her. Hence a new building of the Ionic order (Fig. 1:8) was undertaken. It was described in the city records as "the temple in the acropolis for

the ancient statue." The site chosen was that where Erechtheus, legendary founder of the city, had once dwelled. As recounted by Homer: "And they that possessed the goodly citadel of Athens, domain of Erechtheus the high-hearted, whom erst Athene daughter of Zeus fostered when Earth, the grain giver, brought him to birth;—and she gave him a resting place in Athens in her own rich sanctuary; and there the sons of the Athenians worship him with bulls and rams as the years turn in their courses. . . ."

This was also the spot where Athena and the sea god Poseidon were supposed to have held their contest for the patronage of the land of Attica and the honors of Athens, and which is depicted in the sculptures on the west pediment of the Parthenon. As they asserted their claims, Poseidon brought down his trident on a rock whereupon a horse, his gift to man, sprang out. A spring of salt water also gushed forth to commemorate the event. When Athena's turn came, she brought forth the olive tree, and the gods awarded her the victory. Later, Erechtheus, whom she protected, tamed the horse and cultivated the olive that gave the Athenians food and oil with which to cook, light for their lamps, and oil for anointing their skins. Since the sacred olive tree, the salt spring, the mark of Poseidon's trident on the rock, and the tomb of Erechtheus were all in the same sacred precinct, the architect Mnesicles had to plan the temple around them, a fact that makes the plan of the Erechtheum (Fig. 1:5) as complex as that of the Parthenon is simple. The rectangular interior, some 31½ feet wide and 61¼ feet long, had four rooms for the various shrines on two different levels, one 10½ feet higher than the other. Projecting outward from three of the sides were porticos, each of different dimensions and design. That on the east has a row of six Ionic columns almost 22 feet high. The north porch (Fig. 1:9) has a like

Mnesicles (?). Erechtheum. Pentelic marble. 37' x 66'. *c.*421–409 B.C. Athens. Fig. 1:8 (*opposite*). View from the southeast (Stournaras). Fig. 1:9 (*right*). North Porch (Royal Greek Embassy). Fig. 1:10 (*below*). South Porch with caryatid figures. Caryatids 7' 9" high (Royal Greek Embassy)

number but with four in front and two on the sides; while the smaller porch on the south (Fig. 1:10) is distinguished by its six sculptured maidens, the famous caryatids, who replace the customary columns.

Unlike those of the Doric order, Ionic columns (Fig. 1:7) are more slender and have their greatest diameter at the bottom. Their shafts rest on a molded base instead of directly on the stylobate, and they have 24 instead of 20 flutings. Most striking, however, is the Ionic capital with its scroll-like volutes. The fine columns of the north porch (Fig. 1:9) rest on molded bases carved with a delicate design. The necking has a band decorated with a leaf pattern; above this comes a smaller band with the egg-and-dart motif, and after the volutes a thin abacus carved with eggs and darts. The columns support an architrave divided horizontally into three bands stepping slightly inward, a continuous frieze rather than the alternating Doric triglyphs and metopes; and above rises a shallow pediment without sculpture. A greatly admired and much-imitated doorway leads into the cella of the Erechtheum. Framed with a series of receding planes, the lintel above combines each of the decorative motifs that appear elsewhere in the building. As seen in the band that runs around the cella (Fig. 1:11), these include (from lower to upper) the honeysuckle, bead-and-reel, egg-and-dart, bead-and-reel, and leaf-and-tongue.

Facing the Parthenon, the south porch of the Erechtheum, with its caryatids (Fig. 1:10), is smaller than the others, measuring only some 10 by 15 feet. Above three steps rises a 6-foot parapet on which the six maidens, about one and a half times larger than life, are standing. In order to preserve the proportions of the building and not appear to overburden the figures, the frieze and

Fig. 1:11. Erechtheum, Decorative Band showing honeysuckle, bead-and-reel, egg-and-dart, bead-and-reel, and leaf-and-tongue motifs (Hege)

Fig. 1:12. Callicrates. Temple of Athena Nike. Pentelic marble. 18½′ x 27′. *c.*427–423 B.C. Athens (Royal Greek Embassy)

pediment were omitted. Grouped as if in a procession, the figures infer a stately forward motion, with three on one side lifting their right legs and those on the other, their left. The folds of their draperies suggest the fluting of columns; and, while the maidens seem solid enough to carry their loads, there is no hint of stiffness in their stances. And just as the cella frieze of the Parthenon re-enacts the Panathenaic festival, so these maidens well may be related to the ritual of the Erechtheum. A sculptural fragment from an older temple on the acropolis shows a priestess leading a procession in which four maidens bear a long chest on their heads. Since the temple bears the name of their warrior king, the caryatids seem to suggest a ceremony honoring the heroic dead.

Here on their acropolis, the Athenians brought to the highest point of development two distinct Greek building traditions—the Doric with the Parthenon, and the Ionic with the Erechtheum and the Temple of Athena Nike (Fig. 1:12). That the two architectural orders should be combined in the Propylaea and enshrined separately in these three temples reflected the fact that Athens was the place where the Dorian people of the western Greek mainland and the Ionians of the coast of Asia Minor across the Aegean Sea had for centuries lived together in peace and harmony and through the generations had become one

18

Fig. 1:13. *Choragic Monument of Lysi-crates.* Pentelic marble. Podium 13′ high, 9½′ square; shrine 20′ high, 7′ in diameter. 334 B.C. Athens. Drawing after Stewart and Revett

Fig. 1:14 (*below*). Ruins of the Temple of Olympian Zeus. Pentelic marble. Columns 56½′ high. 174 B.C.–A.D. 130. Athens (Royal Greek Embassy)

people. In the following century, another order was added: the Corinthian. Taller and more treelike than the Ionic, the columns of the Corinthian order are distinguished by their ornate capitals with double rows of acanthus leaves and fernlike fronds rising from each corner and terminating in miniature volutes. The oldest surviving Corinthian structure in Athens is the choragic monument of Lysicrates (Fig. 1:13), now located at the foot of the acropolis. Too ornate for the generally restrained Hellenic taste, the Corinthian had to wait for Roman times to reach its full development, as seen in the ruins of the Temple of Olympian Zeus (Fig. 1:14).

SCULPTURE

The Parthenon Marbles

The Parthenon sculptures have a special significance, since they rank high among the surviving originals of the 5th century B.C. Otherwise, the Hellenic style has to be seen through later Hellenistic and Roman copies. The extant Parthenon statuary falls into three groups: the high-relief metopes of the Doric frieze, the free-standing pediment figures, and the low-relief cella frieze. Phidias' celebrated gold-and-ivory cult statue of Athena has long since disappeared, and inferior later copies convey little of the splendor attributed to it by the ancients. As architectural sculpture, the friezes and pediments should not be judged apart from the building they embellish. By providing diagonal lines and irregular masses as well as figures in motion, they offset the more static vertical and horizontal balances of the structural parts. The original location of these sculptures must also be kept in mind by the modern viewer: they were intended to be seen outdoors in the intense Greek sunlight and from the ground some 35 feet below (not out of context in the artificial light of a museum and at eye level).

Since the entire Parthenon project was completed in little more than a decade, Phidias, its presumed designer, could have had time to do little more than make sketches for his assistants to work from. He may have done some examples in each group, and the best of the sculptures are sometimes attributed to him. The result is a model of simplicity and restraint, and the marbles complement the building as a whole rather than assert themselves independently. The workmanship reveals the unevenness common to all group jobs. Some sculptures show the hand of a master; others are routine products of artisans. But the fact that the metopes were finished first, were surpassed by the cella frieze, and that both, in turn, were eclipsed by the later pedimental sculptures shows that the work did not aim at standardization but rather at a continuous approach to the ideal of excellent craftsmanship.

Fig. 1:15. Phidias (?). *Lapith and Centaur*, metope from Parthenon frieze. Marble. 3′ 11″ x 4′ 2″. 447–441 B.C. British Museum, London

The metopes of the Doric frieze play an important part in the architectural design of the Parthenon by providing a welcome variety of figures to relieve the structural unity, and their diagonal lines contrast well with the alternating verticals of the triglyphs and the long horizontals of the architrave and cornice just below and above. In order to take full advantage of the bright sunlight, these metopes were done in *high relief*, a technique by which the figures are deeply carved so as to project boldly outward from the background plane. In one of the most skillfully executed (Fig. 1:15), the rich spreading folds of the mantle form a fine frame for the human figure, and, in turn, both make a striking contrast with the awkward angularity of the grotesque centaur.

The inner frieze that ran along the outer walls of the cella was a continuous band about 3¼ feet high, over 500 feet in length, and included some 600 figures. Since this frieze was placed behind the colonnade and directly below roof level, where it had to be viewed close by at a steep upward angle, some sculptural adjustments were called for. The technique, of necessity, was *low relief*, in which the figures are shallowly carved. Because shadows in this indirect light are cast upward, the frieze had to be tilted slightly and cut so that the lower parts of the figures project only 1¼ inches from the background plane, with the relief gradually becoming bolder toward the top where the figures extend outward about 2¼ inches. The handling of space, however, is so deft that as many as half a dozen horsemen are depicted riding abreast without confusing the separate planes. The horses, when seen at eye level, are too small in comparison

Fig. 1:16 (*above*). Parthenon, Frieze of West Cella Wall. Marble. *c.*440 B.C. (Hirmer).

Fig. 1:17 (*below*). Detail (Royal Greek Embassy)

Fig. 1:18. Parthenon, Frieze of East Cella Wall, *Poseidon and Apollo*. Marble. 43″ high. *c*.440 B.C. Acropolis Museum, Athens (Stournaras)

with their riders. When viewed from below and in indirect light, however, they would not seem out of proportion. The use of color and metal attachments for such details as reins and bridles also helped accent details and protected the clarity of the design. All the heads, whether the figures are afoot or on horseback, are kept on the same level in order to preserve the unity of the design as well as to provide a parallel with the architectural line. (This principle, known as *isocephaly*, will also be encountered in later Byzantine art [see Figs. 4:10, 4:21, and 4:22].)

The cella frieze, unlike the traditional mythological subjects elsewhere in the Parthenon sculptures, depicts the Athenians themselves participating in the festival of their goddess. The scene is the Greater Panathenaea that took place every four years. Larger than the annual local procession because it included delegations from other Greek cities, the Greater Panathanaea was also the prelude to more elaborate poetical and oratorical contests, dramatic presentations, and games. On the western side (Figs. 1:16 and 1:17), which is still in place, last-minute preparations for the parade are in progress as the riders ready their mounts. The action, appropriately enough, starts just at the point where the live procession, after passing through the Propylaea, would have paused to regroup. The parade then splits in two, one file proceeding along the north and the other along the south side. After the bareback riders come the charioteers; and, as the procession approaches the eastern corners, the marshals slack the tempo to a more dignified pace. Here are musicians playing lyres and flutes, youths bearing winejugs for libations, and maidens walking with stately tread. The two files then converge on the east side, where magistrates are waiting to begin the ceremonies. Even the immortal gods, as seen in the panel depicting Poseidon and Apollo (Fig. 1:18), are present to bestow their Olympian approval on the proceedings. The high point of the ritual comes in the center of the east side with the presentation of the *peplos*, the saffron and purple-tinted mantle woven and embroidered by chosen maidens to drape the ancient wooden image of Athena.

The pedimental sculptures, in contrast to the friezes, are free-standing figures, carved in the round. The themes of both pediments have to do with Athena, that on the west (Fig. 1:19), facing the city, depicting her triumph over Poseidon (see page 14) and that on the east pediment (Fig. 1:20) recounting the story of her miraculous birth, the event that was celebrated each summer at the Panathenaea. While but a few fragments of the western pediment remain, enough survive of its eastern counterpart to convey a good idea of its original state (Figs. 1:21 and 1:22).

From various sources it is known that the eastern scene is Mt. Olympus, and Zeus, father of the gods, was seated in the center. On one side stood Hephaestus, cleaving open the head of Zeus to let Athena spring forth in full battle array. The sudden appearance of the goddess of wisdom, like a brilliant idea from the mind of its creator, disturbs the Olympian calm. As the news spreads from the center to the sides, each figure is in some way affected by the presence of divine wisdom in their midst. Iris, the messenger of the gods (Fig. 1:21), rushes toward the left with a rapid motion as revealed by her windswept drapery. Seated on a chest, Demeter and Persephone are turning toward her, and the rich folds of their costumes bespeak their attitudes and interest. The reclining Dionysus, with his panther skin and mantle spread over a rock, is awakening and looking toward the sun god Helios, the horses of whose chariot are just rising from the foaming sea at break of day. On the opposite side are three goddesses (Fig. 1:22) whose postures bring out their relationship to the composition. The one nearest the center of the pediment, aware of what has happened, is about to rise, while the middle figure is starting to turn toward her. The reclining figure at the right, still in respose, is as unaware of the event as is her counterpart Dionysus on the far left. Like the feminine group on the left, these figures constitute a unified episode in the composition, and their relation to the whole is made clear in the lush lines of their flowing robes. This flowing linear pattern, and the manner in which it transparently reveals the anatomy of the splendid bodies beneath, mark a high point in the art of sculpture. At the far right, the chariot of the moon goddess Selene was seen descending. Now only the expressive downward-declining horse's head remains to show by his spent energies that it is the end of the day.

Perhaps the most admirable aspect of the whole composition is the ease and grace with which each piece fulfills its assigned space. Fitting suitable figures

Fig. 1:19. Parthenon. West Pediment Reconstruction, *Contest of Athena and Poseidon for the Land of Attica*. Metropolitan Museum of Art, New York

Fig. 1:20. Parthenon. East Pediment Reconstruction, *Birth of Athena*. Metropolitan Museum of Art, New York

East Pediment Figures. Marble. *c*.438–432 B.C. Fig. 1:21 (*below*). (Far left) *Sun God's Horses*, lifesize; (center) *Dionysus*, 5′ 8″ long, *Demeter* and *Persephone*, 4′ 10½″ high; (right) *Iris*, 5′ 8″ high. Fig. 1:22 (*opposite below*). *Three Goddesses*, over lifesize, and *Moon Goddess' Horse*, lifesize. British Museum, London

Fig. 1:23. Temple of Zeus, Olympia. West Pediment Figures, *Battle between Lapiths and Centaurs*. Marble. Center figure of *Apollo* over lifesize. *c.*460 B.C. Museum, Olympia (Stournaras)

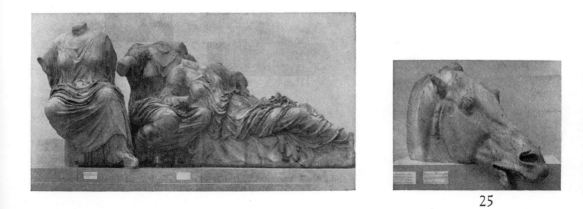

25

into a low isosceles triangle and at the same time maintaining an uncrowded yet unified appearance was a problem that long occupied Greek designers. As in the earlier temple at Olympia (Fig. 1:23), one overlife-size figure, such as Apollo, usually dominated the center, with seated or crouching figures on either side and reclining ones in the acute side angles. The pediment space of the Parthenon stretched about 90 feet and rose over 11 feet in the center. The rising and setting sun and moon chariots defined the time span as that of a single day, while the setting of Mt. Olympus and the single event supplied the identity of place and action in keeping with the classical unities (a principle that will be treated more fully in the section on Drama). The ascending and descending chariots gave a contrasting upward and downward movement on the extreme ends, while the reclining and seated figures led the eye to the apex where the climax took place. The subsequent action dispersed the middle figures centrifugally once more toward the sides. The varied postures, rich plastic modeling, and flowing lines connect all the figures with such a unified motion that, even though the center ones are now missing, the meaning is quite clear.

Taken as a whole, the Parthenon marbles present a picture of the Greek past and present plus aspirations for the future. The attempt to interpret the dark ancient myths of a people into more enlightened contemporary terms is to be found here in the sculptures as well as in Greek philosophy, poetry, and drama. The metopes on the east portray the primeval battle of the gods and giants for control of the world, and the triumph of the Olympians hailed the coming of cosmic order out of chaos. The metopes on the south show the Lapiths, oldest Greek inhabitants of the peninsula, subduing the half-human centaurs with the aid of the Athenian hero Theseus. This victory signals the ascendancy of human ideals over the bestial side of human nature. In the north group, the Homeric epic of the defeat of the Trojans is told, while in the west metopes the Greeks are seen overcoming the Amazons, those ferocious women warriors who symbolized

Fig. 1:24. *Athena Lemnia*, Detail. Marble. Roman copy of head of Phidias' original of *c*.450 B.C. Civic Museum, Bologna (German Archeological Institute)

the Asiatic enemies and, in this case, allude to the Athenian defeat of the Persians at Marathon. In the east pediment, the birth of the city's patroness Athena is seen; while the west pediment tells the story of the rivalry of Athena as goddess of the intellect and Poseidon, patron of maritime trade, suggesting the conflict of two ways of life—the pursuit of enlightenment and of material wealth. The Panathenaic procession of the cella walls brings history up to date by depicting a contemporary subject. Here the proud Athenians could look upward and see their own images carved on a sacred temple, an echo of the living procession that marched along the sides of the temple on feast days. The climax came after they had gathered at the east portico and the portals of the temple were opened to the rays of the rising sun, revealing the image of the goddess herself. Shining forth in all her gold-and-ivory glory, Athena was the personification of the eternal truth, goodness, and beauty for which her faithful followers were striving. With her help, the forces of Greek civilization had overcome the ignorance of the barbarians. The bonds between the goddess and the citizens of her city were thus periodically renewed, and the Parthenon as a whole glorified not only Athena but the Athenians as well.

The Course of Hellenic Sculpture

The tremendous distance traversed by the art of sculpture from the archaic, or preclassical, phase prior to the 5th century B.C. to the end of the Hellenic style period in the mid-4th century can be seen clearly when examples are compared. The *Kouros* (Fig. 1:25) represents the archaic type of youthful athletes, victors in the games, moving toward the temple to dedicate themselves. The advancing left foot provides the only suggestion of movement in the otherwise rigid posture. The anatomy of the torso is severely formal and very close to the block of stone out of which it was carved. The wide shoulders and long arms attached to the sides provide a quadrangular framework; the long vertical line from the neck to the navel divides the chest; while the diamond-shaped abdomen is defined by four almost straight lines. The dreamy facial expression as well as the conventional geometry of the body points toward Oriental and Egyptian origins.

The *Doryphorus*, or *Spearbearer*, by Polyclitus (Fig. 1:26), in contrast, moves with greater poise and freedom. Originally in bronze, it is now known only through routine marble copies. The sculptor was renowned in ancient times for his attempts to formulate a canon, or rational theory of proportions, for the human figure. The exact way Polyclitus' theory operated is not known, but the Roman architect Vitruvius mentions that beauty consists "in the proportions, not of the elements, but of the parts, that is to say, of finger to finger, and of all the fingers to the palm and wrist, and of these to the forearm, and of the forearm to the upper arm, and of all the parts to each other, as they are set forth in the

28

Fig. 1:25 (*left*). *Kouros* from Sounion. Marble. Over lifesize. *c.*615–590 B.C. National Museum, Athens (Royal Greek Embassy)

Fig. 1:26 (*below left*). Polyclitus. *Doryphorus* (*Spear Bearer*). Marble. 78″ high. Roman copy of Polyclitus' original of *c.*450–440 B.C. National Museum, Naples (Alinari). Fig. 1:27 (*below right*). Praxiteles. *Hermes and the Infant Dionysus*. Marble. 85″ high. *c.*350 B.C. Museum, Olympia (Royal Greek Embassy)

Fig. 1:28 (*above left*). *Charioteer* from Sanctuary of Apollo, Delphi. Bronze. 71″ high. *c.*470 B.C. Museum, Delphi (Hirmer). Fig. 1:29 (*above*). *Zeus* (*Poseidon* ?). Bronze. 82″ high. *c.*460–450 B.C. National Museum, Athens (Hirmer). Fig. 1:30 (*left*). Myron. *Discobolus* (*Discus Thrower*). Marble. Roman copy found at Castel Porziano of Myron's bronze original of *c.*460 B.C. Terme Museum, Rome (Soprintendenza)

Fig. 1:31. *Charioteer of Delphi*, Detail (Hirmer)

Canon of Polyclitus." Just as the Parthenon had its module derived from a unit of the building, so Polyclitus took his module from a part of the body. Whether it was the head, the forearm, or the hand apparently varied from statue to statue. Once adopted, however, the whole and all its parts were expressible in multiples or fractions of the module. As Vitruvius illustrated the canon, the head would be ⅛ of the total height; the face ¹⁄₁₀, subdivided, in turn, into three parts: forehead, nose, and mouth and chin. The forearm would be ¼ the height, and the width of the chest equal to this length of forearm. Like the optical refinements of the Parthenon, however, Polyclitus' canon was not a mechanical formula but one that allowed for some flexibility so that the dimensions could be adjusted for a figure in movement or for one designed to be seen from a certain angle.

Praxiteles' *Hermes and the Infant Dionysus* (Fig. 1:27), coming at the close of the Hellenic period, is the epitome of elegance and grace. Unlike the rather studied *Doryphorus*, Hermes rests his weight easily on one foot, and the relaxed stance throws the body into the familiar S curve, a Praxitelean pose widely copied in later Hellenistic and Roman statuary. From the stiffness of the stolid archaic Kouros and the strength of the stocky Doryphorus, sculpture under the masterly hand of Praxiteles has arrived at complete plasticity. Through the soft modeling and suave surface treatment, Praxiteles has given his cold marble material the vibrance and warmth of living flesh.

The *Charioteer of Delphi* and the *Zeus* found at Artemision (Figs. 1:28 and 1:29)—two of the rare Hellenic bronze originals—and the Roman marble copy of Myron's lost bronze *Discobolus*, or *Discus Thrower* (Fig. 1:30), reveal a similar evolution in style from quiet monumentality to energetic action within a 20-year timespan in the mid-5th century. The splendid charioteer once was part of a larger group that included several horses, and although in action, the figure is given something of the monumentality and equilibrium of a fluted column by the vertical folds of its lower garment. The commanding figure of *Zeus*, poised to throw a thunderbolt, reveals in its powerful musculature the massive reserves of strength of a truly godlike physique. In Myron's *Discobolus*, the taut yet resilient muscles of the athlete are poised momentarily between a backward movement and forward thrust. The vigorous motion is admirably contained by the curved arms that both enclose the composition and confine the activity to a single plane.

Much the same line of development can be seen in three female figures. The archaic *Hera of Samos* (Fig. 1:32), a severely cylindrical figure, is quite abstract in that everything extraneous has been eliminated and only the essential formal and linear elements retained. The rhythmically repeated vertical lines of the skirt contrast with the ingenious curves of the upper drapery to create a pattern of dignity befitting the queen of Olympus. The *Athena Lemnia* (Fig. 1:33) is a superior marble copy of Phidias' original bronze statue that once stood on the

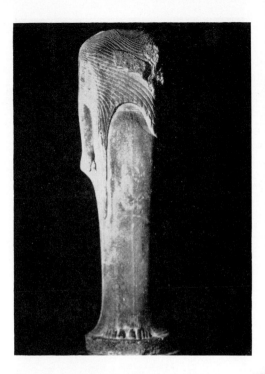

Fig. 1:32 (*above*). *Hera of Samos.* Marble. *c.*63″ high. *c.*550 B.C. Louvre. Paris (Archives Photographiques). Fig. 1:33 (*above right*). *Athena Lemnia.* Marble. *c.*72″ high. Roman copy of Phidias' original of *c.*450 B.C. Body from Albertina Gallery, Dresden, with head from Civic Museum, Bologna

Fig. 1:34 (*right*). Praxiteles. *Aphrodite of Cnidos.* Marble. Over lifesize. Roman copy of Praxiteles' original of *c.*320 B.C. Vatican Museum, Rome (Vatican Photographic Archive)

Fig. 1:35 (*above*). *Athena*. Relief from Acropolis. Marble. 18″ high. c.445 B.C. Acropolis Museum, Athens. Fig. 1:36 (*right*). *Goddess Adjusting Sandal*. Relief from balustrade of Temple of Athena Nike. Marble. 42″ x 20″. 427–424 B.C. Acropolis Museum, Athens (Royal Greek Embassy)

Athenian acropolis. Omitting the usual helmet, he created a mood that is lyrical rather than epical, and in ancient sources the statue was referred to regularly as "the beautiful." The serene profile, softened by the subtle modeling, surely approaches the ideal of chaste classical beauty. Praxiteles' *Aphrodite of Cnidos* was proclaimed by Greco-Roman critics as the finest statue in existence. Now known only through such an inferior copy as Figure 1:34, the "soft melting gaze" and noble demeanor attributed to the original can only be imagined. Praxiteles, however, departed from the draped goddesses of the previous century by boldly portraying the goddess of love in the nude. By so doing, he created a prototype that influenced all subsequent treatment of the undraped female figure.

Two reliefs from the acropolis illustrate the course of sculpture's development in yet another way. One can observe how the noble restraint of the panel portraying *Athena* (Fig. 1:35) yields half a century later to the informal treatment of the *Goddess Adjusting Her Sandal* (Fig. 1:36). The dignified calm of the erect Athena has melted into the graceful relaxed posture of the goddess bending downward. Whatever rigidity there was in the perpendicular lines of the earlier example has given way to the rippling drapery of the later relief where it creates a sense of movement and transparently reveals the contours of the body beneath.

DRAMA

Greek drama was a distillation of life in poetic form, represented (or imitated, to use the ancient term) on the stage. In these vivid presentations, members of the audience through their representatives in the chorus became vicarious participants in events happening to a group of people at another time and in another place. Like all great works of art, Greek drama can be approached on many different levels. At one, it can be a thrilling story of violent actions and bloody revenge. At another, it is a struggle between human ambition and divine retribution, or a conflict of free will and predestined fate. At still another level, it becomes a moving experience that ennobles through lofty language and inspired poetry. Plots were always taken from mythology, heroic legends, or stories of royal houses. Since these age-old themes were forms of popular history known in advance, the dramatist could concern himself with more purely poetic functions than plot development. He could provide dramatic commentaries on old tales, reinterpreting them in the light of recent events. He could thus inspire by conjuring up the heroic past, as did Aeschylus in *The Persians*; express individual sentiments in the light of universal experience, as did Sophocles in *Antigone*; invite re-examination of ancient superstitions, as did Euripides in *The Bacchants*; or remind that present difficulties had parallels in time past and, by showing that it has ever been thus, place current problems in broader historical perspective.

The origins of the Greek dramatic form were rooted in the religious rites associated with the worship of Dionysus (the Bacchus of Roman mythology), the god of wine and revelry, whose cult festivals coincided with spring planting and fall harvesting seasons. From primitive magical practices, the rituals gradually grew in refinement until they became a vehicle for powerful creative expression. When theaters came to be built, they were located in a precinct sacred to Dionysus. His altar occupied the center of the circular *orchestra* where the chorus sang and danced, and the audience which gathered paid their tribute to him by their presence.

In the beginning, Greek drama had only a chorus, whose function, according to the philosopher Nietzsche, was to conjure up the divine vision in which it "beholds its lord and master Dionysus . . . [and] sees how he, the god, suffers and glorifies himself." The vision beheld by the chorus eventually came to be acted out, and the alternation between group *choruses* and individually declaimed *episodes* became the basis of the dramatic form. Put another way, the choral songs were at first a group narration of great deeds. Later, the words attributed to the hero were sung and mimed by the leader of the chorus. Then a second and a third actor was added, and the dialogue of the enacted episodes achieved parity with the alternating choruses. Hellenistic and Roman drama were to upset this classic balance by emphasizing the action and roles of individ-ual performers, but in Hellenic times the collective voice of the chorus and that of the principal actors were equal in importance. As the group chanted its *stro-phes* and *antistrophes* (turns and counterturns), it effected transitions from scenes, reminded of the past and foretold the future, reflected public opinion, voiced the dramatist's own commentary, and, above all, by acting as its proxy, made the audience feel a part of the play.

The theater of Dionysus at Athens, like the better preserved one at Epidaurus (Fig. 1:37), had an *auditorium* hollowed out of a hillside to accommodate about 18,000 spectators. The semicircular tiers of seats half surrounded the orchestra and faced the *skene*, a scene building or raised platform, on which the actors played their roles. The skene had a permanent architectural façade with three doors for the actors, while the chorus entered and exited at the corners below. The stylized face of the skene, suggesting a temple or palace, was suitable for most dramatic situations, since the action almost always took place in the open. The chorus, for example, usually represented worshipers at a shrine, townspeople or petitioners before a palace, a mob, or a group of prisoners, while the actors moving in and out of the portals above took the parts of priests, heroes, or mem-bers of royal families. When the situation demanded another setting, the chorus or an actor would paint the scene with a few words so that other sets were un-necessary.

A typical Greek play opens with a *prologue*, spoken by one of the actors. The prologue sets the scene, outlines the plot, and provides a taking-off point for the action that is to follow. The substance of the drama then unfolds in a sequence of alternating choruses and episodes (usually five episodes enclosed by six cho-ruses) and concludes with the *exodus* of the chorus and an *epilogue*. Actors wore masks of general types that could be recognized instantly by the audience. The size and outdoor location of the theaters made facial expressions ineffective, and the swift pace of Greek drama requires the player of a king or peasant to estab-lish immediately a type and character. The masks were equipped with mega-phones that helped project the voices, though the acoustics of the bowl-shaped theaters are generally excellent. Masks also proved useful when an actor took more than one part, bringing him immediate acceptance in either role.

Restraint and simplicity were the rule in Greek staging. As with the later Elizabethan theater, scenic spectacle was conspicuous by its absence. The only visual illusions seems to have been the *mechane*, a crane that lowered to the stage those actors portraying gods. This *deus ex machina*, or god from the machine, in later times became a convenient way of solving dramatic problems that were too complex to be worked out by normal means. Direct action, moreover, never occurred on stage. Any violent deed took place elsewhere and was reported by a messenger or another character. The plays proceeded by narration, commentary,

Fig. 1:37. *Theater at Epidaurus.* 373′ in diameter, orchestra 66′ across. Late 4th century B.C. (German Archeological Institute)

speculation, dialogue, and discussion. All these devices—plot known in advance, permanent stage setting, use of masks, offstage action—served two principal purposes: to accent the poetry of the play and to give the freest possible scope to the spectator's imagination. But while Greek drama is a complex of choral song, group dances, mimed action, and dialogue coordinated into a dramatic whole, poetry always is the central dramatic agent. It should also be noted that the Athenians experienced their plays and poetry only in oral presentations. While manuscript copies of literary and philosophical works were available to scholars, books in the modern sense did not exist. Much of the beauty and power of the plays was derived from the heightened experience of poetic declamation as well as from the Greek tongue itself. Not an accentual language, Greek admits of a wide variety of metrical patterns capable of expressing every nuance of action and mood. In reading a Greek drama in translation, therefore, one must let one's imagination supply the melody, color, and flowing rhythms of the original language as well as the missing factors associated with a live theatrical production.

The scope of Greek drama was tremendous, extending from majestic tragedy of heroic proportions, through the pathos of *melodrama* (in its proper meaning of drama with melody) and subtle satires (or satyr plays), all the way to the riotous comedies of Aristophanes. Conflict is always the basis for dramatic action, and the playwrights set up tensions between such forces as murder and revenge, crime and retribution, cowardice and courage, protest and resignation, human pride and humility. When, for instance, a hero is confronted with his destiny, the obstacles he encounters are at once insurmountable and necessary to surmount. In the conflict that follows, the play runs a gamut of emotion and explores the heights to which human life can soar and the depths to which it can sink. In Sophocles' *Oedipus Rex*, the hero starts at the peak of his kingly powers and ends in the abyss of human degradation. Each character in a true drama, moreover, is drawn three-dimensionally so as to reveal a typically human mixture of attractive and repulsive, good and bad, traits. The *protagonist*, or central character, can fulfill the necessary conditions of tragedy only when he portrays some noble figure —one "highly renowned or prosperous," as Aristotle puts it—who is eventually brought to grief through some flaw in his own psychological make-up and by some inevitable stroke of fate. The reasons for this must gradually be made apparent to the audience through the process of "causal necessity." A common man's woes might bring about a pathetic situation but not a tragic one in the classical sense. When a virtuous hero is rewarded or the evil designs of a villain receive their just deserts, obviously there is no tragic situation. When a blameless man is brought from a fortunate to an unfortunate condition or when an evil person rises from misery to good fortune, there is likewise no tragedy because the moral sense is outraged.

Under Aeschylus, its founder, Greek tragedy sought to comprehend the mystery of the divine will, often so inscrutable to man—as in his *Agamemnon*. By establishing a working relationship between man and his gods, Aeschylus tried to reconcile the conflict between the human and the divine and find a basis for personal and social justice. The implications of the early Aeschylean tragedy were thus strongly ethical, showing clearly that the drama was still identified in his mind with theological thought. The forms of Sophocles' plays were distinguished by their impeccable craftsmanship, while their lofty content was based on the course of human destiny as seen in the light of the moral law of the universe.

Euripides, said the philosopher Aristotle, sought to show men as they are, while Sophocles had depicted men as they ought to be. In some ways, the works of Euripides may not be so typical of the Hellenic style as those of Aeschylus or Sophocles, but his influence on the subsequent development of the drama, both in Hellenistic and later times, was incalculably greater. *The Bacchants*, the last of his 90-odd plays, was written at a time when the darkness of disillusionment was descending on Athenian intellectuals toward the end of the disastrous Peloponnesian war, and in it he gives voice to some of the doubts and uncertainties of his time. Like most masterpieces, it is in some respects atypical, while in others it seems to stem from the deepest traditional roots of the theater's origin. Despite some inner inconsistencies and a certain elusiveness of meaning, *The Bacchants* has all the formal perfection and grandeur of utterance of the loftiest tragedies.

Fig. 1:38. School of Scopas (?). *Dionysian Procession.* Marble. 4th century B.C. National Museum, Athens (Alinari)

The strange wild beauty of the choruses, the magic of its poetry, and the complex interplay between the human and divine wills endow it with all the necessary ingredients of the theater at its best.

After the great days of Aeschylus, Sophocles, and Euripides were over, Aristotle, with knowledge of their complete works instead of the relatively few extant examples known today, wrote a perceptive analysis of tragedy in his treatise *Poetics*. According to him, true drama, as indeed all other works of art, must have form in the sense of a beginning, a middle, and an end. Unity of time, place, and action is also desirable. Sophocles' *Oedipus Rex*, for example, takes place in a single day (albeit a busy one); all the scenes are set in front of the palace at Thebes; and the action is direct and continuous without subplots. Other Greek plays encompass a longer span of time and have several settings. But, as Aristotle pointed out, these unities were useful but by no means hard and fast rules. In the episodes, convention held that three actors on stage at one time was the maximum. If the play required six parts, the roles were usually apportioned among three actors. As the action proceeds, the conflict between *protagonist* and *antagonist* emerges, and the play should rise to its climax in the middle episode. Through the proper tragic necessity, the hero's downfall comes because he carried the seeds of his own destruction within his breast. After this turning point, the well-planned anticlimax resolves the action once more into a state of equilibrium. Tragedy, according to Aristotle, had to be composed of six necessary elements which he ranked as follows: Plot, "the arrangement of the incidents"; Character, "that which reveals moral purpose"; Thought, "where something is proved to be or not to be"; Diction, "the metrical arrangement of the words"; Song, "melody holds the chief place among the embellishments"; and Spectacle. Finally, Aristotle summed up his definition of tragedy as "an imitation of an action that is serious, complete, and of a certain magnitude; in language embellished with each kind of ornament, the several kinds being found in separate sections of the play; in the form of action, not of narrative; with incidents arousing pity and fear, wherewith to accomplish its *katharsis* [purgation] of the emotions."

MUSIC

The word *music* today carries with it the connotation of a fully mature and in-dependent art. It must be borne in mind, however, that symphonies, chamber music, and solo instrumental compositions, where the focus is almost entirely on abstract sound, are relatively modern forms. The word *music* is still used to cover the union of sound with many other elements, as in the case of popular songs, dance music, military marches, and church music. It also describes the combina-tion with lyric and narrative poetry, as in songs and ballads; with bodily move-ments, as in the dance and ballet; and with drama, as in opera.

In ancient Greece, *music* in its broadest sense meant any of the arts and sciences that came under the patronage of the muses, those imaginary maidens who were the daughters of the heavenly Zeus and the more earthly Mnemosyne. Since Zeus was the creator and Mnemosyne, as her name implies, the symbol of memory, the muses and their arts were considered to be the results of the union of the creative urge and memory, half divine, half human. This was simply a fan-ciful way of saying that music was recorded inspiration. As Greek civilization progressed, the muses, under the patronage of Apollo, god of prophecy and en-lightenment, gradually increased to nine, and the arts and sciences over which they presided came to include all the intellectual and inspirational disciplines that sprang from the fertile minds of this highly creative people—lyric poetry, tragic and comic drama, choral dancing, and song. Astronomy and history were also included. The visual arts and crafts, on the other hand, were protected by Athena and Hephaestus—intelligence tempered by fire. Plato and others placed music in opposition to gymnastic or physical pursuits, and its meaning in this sense was as broad as our use of the words *liberal arts* or *culture*.

The Greeks also used *music* more narrowly in the sense of the tonal art. But music was always intimately bound up with poetry, drama, and the dance and was usually found in their company. At one place in the *Republic*, Socrates asks: "And when you speak of music, do you include literature or not?" And the an-swer is in the affirmative. Thus, while it is known that the Greeks did have inde-pendent instrumental music apart from its combination with words, evidence points to the fact that the vast body of their music was connected with literary forms. This does not imply, of course, that music lacked a distinct identity or that it was swallowed up by poetry, but rather that it had an important and honored part in poetry. Plato, for example, inquires: "And I think that you must have observed again and again what a poor appearance the tales of the poets make when stripped of the colours which music puts upon them, and recited in simple prose. . . . They are like faces which were never really beautiful, but only blooming; and now the bloom of youth has passed away from them?"

Greek music must therefore be considered primarily in its union with literature. The clearest statement of this again is found in the *Republic*, where it is
pointed out that "melody is composed of three things, the words, the harmony
[by which is meant the sequence of melodic intervals], and the rhythm." In discussing the relative importance of each, Plato states that "harmony and rhythm
must follow the words." The two arts thus are united in the single one of *prosody*
—that is, the melodic and rhythmic setting of a poetic text. The Greek melodies
and rhythms are known to have been associated with specific moods, which enabled poets and dramatists to elicit various emotional responses from their audiences. And while ethical and emotional orientations have changed over the centuries, the basic modal and metrical system of the Greeks has, in effect, continued
through all subsequent periods of Western music and poetry.

Music, in both its broad and narrow senses, was closely woven into the fabric
of the emotional, intellectual, and social life of the ancient Greeks, and the art
was considered by them to have a fundamental connection with the well-being
of individuals personally as well as with their social and physical environment.
Surely no more eloquent tribute to the power of art in public affairs has ever
been made than that quoted by Socrates to the effect that music is so fundamentally related to government that "when modes of music change, the fundamental
laws of the State always change with them." Education for young people in
Greece consisted of a balanced curriculum of music for the soul and gymnastic
for the body. The broad principle of building a sound mind in a sound body is
still one of the ideals of education. Even the welfare of the soul after death had
musical overtones, since immortality to many Greeks meant being somehow in
tune with the cosmic forces, and being at last able to hear the "music of the
spheres." All these notions had to do with the idea of the physical nature being
somehow in harmony with the metaphysical, and the soul being an attunement
of the body. This thought found an enduring place in Western literature, and no
writer has expressed it more sensitively than Shakespeare in a passage (Act V,
Scene 1) in *The Merchant of Venice:*

> . . . look, how the floor of heaven
> Is thick inlaid with patines of bright gold:
> There's not the smallest orb which thou behold'st
> But in his motion like an angel sings,
> Still quiring to the young-eyed cherubins;
> Such harmony is in immortal souls;
> But, whilst this muddy vesture of decay
> Doth grossly close it in, we cannot hear it.

The most important Greek contribution to music is without doubt a theoretical one—that of coordinating the mathematic ratios of melodic intervals with

their scale system. The discovery, attributed to Pythagoras, showed that such intervals as the octave, fifth, and fourth had a mathematical relationship. This can easily be heard when a tuned string is stopped off exactly in the middle. The musical interval between the tone of the unstopped string and the one which is divided into two equal parts will then be the octave, and the mathematical ratio will be 1:2. Then if a segment of the string divided in two parts is compared with one of a string divided into three parts, the resulting interval will be the fifth, and the ratio 2:3. If one compares the tone of the triply divided string with one divided into four parts, the interval will be the fourth, and the ratio 3:4. Hence, mathematically 1:2 equals the octave; 2:3, the fifth; 3:4, the fourth; 8:9, the whole tone; and so on. Music to Pythagoras and his followers thus was synonymous with order and proportion and rested on a demonstrably rational basis. This tremendous discovery seemed to be a key that might unlock the secrets of the universe, which, they reasoned, might likewise be reduced to numbers and be constructed according to the principles of a musical scale. This idea found its way into all aspects of Greek intellectual life, and even Plato built up a conception of the cosmic harmony of the world on these musical principles in his *Timaeus*. It is possible that the architects also incorporated these laws into the proportions and designs of their buildings. The Roman architect Vitruvius, for instance, was thoroughly familiar with Greek musical theory.

Knowledge of Greek music must be gleaned from a variety of sources, such as occasional literary references, poetry and drama, visual representations of musical instruments and music-making in sculpture and painting, theoretical treatises, and some very fragmentary surviving examples of the music itself. When all the separate sources are combined, a faint notion of what Greek music actually was like can be gleaned. From them, it is apparent that music's highest development undoubtedly was found in its union with the drama. The Athenian dramatist was by tradition responsible for the music, the training of the chorus, and the staging of his play as well as for the writing of the book. In addition to all this, he often played one of the roles. The great dramatists, therefore, were composers as well as poets, actors, playwrights, and producers.

In reconstructing the Greek drama, one must imagine a Greek audience to whom the drama was a lively aural and visual experience of choral singing and dancing, of vocal and instrumental music, as well as of dialogue and dramatic sequence. Today, with all the choruses and dances missing, a play such as *The Suppliants* of Aeschylus is like the libretto of an opera without the musical score. It is so clearly a lyric drama that the music itself must have been the principal means by which the poet conveyed his meaning. Euripides' *The Bacchants*, on the other hand, has far greater intrinsic dramatic substance, but even here the emotional intensity of the individual scenes often rises to such a pitch that music had to take over where the words left off—just as when a person is so overcome with feeling that words fail and he resorts to inarticulate sounds and gestures.

The weight of the musical expression fell primarily on the chorus, which was the original basis of the dramatic form and from which all the other elements of the drama evolved. We have at last realized, said Nietzsche in his analysis of Greek drama, "that the scene, together with the action, was fundamentally and originally conceived only as a *vision*, that the only reality is just the chorus, which of itself generates the vision and speaks thereof with the entire symbolism of dancing, tone, and word." The chorus performed both in stationary positions and in motion, accompanied by mimetic gestures as it circulated about the orchestra where the choral songs, dances, and group recitatives took place around the altar of Dionysus. The forms of the choruses were metrically and musically very elaborate and were written with such variety and invention that repetitions either within a single play or in other plays by the same poet were very rare.

Interestingly enough, the sole surviving relic of Greek music from the 5th century B.C. is a fragment of a choral *stasimon*, or stationary chorus, from Euripides' *Orestes*. All ancient Greek manuscripts come down through the ages from the hands of medieval scribes who omitted the musical notation of the earlier copies because it was no longer comprehensible to them. In this instance, the musical notation was included, but all that is left is a single sheet of papyrus now perforated with age. From ancient accounts, however, it is known that the music of Euripides differed considerably from that of his predecessor Aeschylus and his contemporary Sophocles. Euripides was educated in the "new" music by Timotheus, while Sophocles received his instruction from the more conservative rival Lampros. The new music was considered more ornate and was criticized because it was so complex that the words were unintelligible. The text was thus on its way to becoming of as little consequence as that of an opera chorus of today, while traditionally it had dominated the music. Evidence to support this development is found in the literary content of Euripidean choruses, which sometimes have little or no direct connection with the action.

Fragmentary though this scrap of evidence is, these few notes from Euripides' *Orestes* are enough to tell their own story. Since the intervals called for are in half and quarter tones, it means that Euripidean choruses were musically complex enough to demand highly skilled singers. The mode is mixolydian, which is described by Aristotle in his *Politics* as being "mournful and restrained." The words that accompany the fragment perfectly express this sentiment, and, when properly performed, it still conveys this mood. Other than this single relic of choral recitative, the music of the 5th century must remain mute to our ears, and we can only echo the words of Keats in his "Ode on a Grecian Urn": "Heard melodies are sweet, but those unheard are sweeter."

IDEAS

Each of the arts—architecture, sculpture, painting, poetry, drama, and music—is, of course, a distinct medium of expression. Each has its materials, whether of stone, bronze, pigments, words, or tones. Each has its skilled craftsmen who have disciplined themselves through years of study so they can mold their materials into meaningful forms. But every artist, be he architect, sculptor, painter, poet, dramatist, or musician, is also a child of his time, who in youthful years is influenced by the social, political, philosophical, and religious ideas of his period and who, in turn, during his maturity contributes creative leadership in his special field. No art exists apart from its fellows, and it is no accident that the Greeks thought of the arts as a family of sister muses. Architecture, to complete itself, must rely on sculpture and painting for embellishments; sculpture and painting, for their parts, must search for congenial architectural surroundings. Drama embraces poetry, song, and the dance in the setting of a theater. This was all quite clear in ancient times, as Plutarch quotes Simonides as saying "Painting is silent poetry; poetry is painting that speaks." When the philosophers Plato and Aristotle discoursed on the arts, they looked for common elements applicable to all. And they were just as keen in their search for unity amid the multiplicities of art as they were for unity among all the other aspects of human experience.

Certain recurring themes appear in each of the arts of the Hellenic period as artists sought to bring their ideals to expression. Out of these themes emerges a trio of ideas—humanism, idealism, and rationalism—that recur continually in Athenian thought and action. These three ideas, then, provide the framework that surrounds the arts and encloses them in such a way that they come together into a significant unity.

Humanism

"Man," said Anaxagoras, "is the measure of all things." And, as Sophocles observed, "Many are the wonders of the world, and none so wonderful as man." This, in essence, is humanism. With himself as yardstick, Hellenic man conceived his gods as perfect beings, immortal and free from physical infirmities but, like himself, subject to very human passions and ambitions. The gods likewise were personifications of human ideals: Zeus stood for masculine creative power, Hera for maternal womanliness, Athena for wisdom, Apollo for youthful brilliance, Aphrodite for feminine desirability, and so on down the list. And because of his resemblance to the gods, Hellenic man gained greatly in self-esteem. When gods were more human, as the saying goes, men were more divine.

The principal concern of the Greeks was with human beings—their social relationships, their place in the natural environment, and their stake in the universal scheme of things. In such a small city-state as Athens, civic duties devolved on each individual. Every responsible person had to concern himself with politics, which Aristotle considered to be the highest social ethics. Participation in public affairs was based on the need to subordinate personal aspirations to the good of the whole state. A man endowed with great qualities of mind and body was honor-bound to exercise his gifts in the service of his fellow men. Aeschylus, Socrates, and Sophocles were men of action who served Athens on the battlefield as well as in public forums and theaters. One responsibility of a citizen was to foster the arts, and under Athenian democracy the state itself, meaning the people as a whole, became the principal patron of the arts.

Politically and socially, the Athenian's life was balanced between an aristocratic conservatism and a liberal individualism, which were maintained in equilibrium by the democratic institutions of his society. His art reflects a gravitational pull between this aristocratic tradition, which resisted change and emphasized austerity, restraint, and stylization in the arts, and the new dynamic liberalism, which opposed conservatism with greater emphasis on emotion, a desire for greater ornateness, and naturalism. The genius of Phidias was that he was able to achieve a golden mean between these opposites, and the incomparable Parthenon and its sculptures were the result.

Humanism also expressed itself in kinship with nature. By personifying all things, animate and inanimate, the Greeks tried to come to terms with unpredictable natural phenomena and to explain the inexplicable. With their forests populated with elusive nymphs and satyrs, their seas with energetic tritons, and their skies with capricious zephyrs, they found an imaginative way of explaining some of the forces beyond their control. These personifications, as well as the conception of the gods as idealized human beings, created a happy condition for the arts. By increasing his understanding of nature in all its aspects, Hellenic man also enhanced his own humanity. To create an imaginary world that is also a poetic image of the real world will always be one of the pursuits of the artist. And the Greeks thought of art as a *mimêsis*—that is, an imitation or representation of nature. Since this also included human nature, it implied a re-creation of life in the various mediums of art.

Particularly congenial to this humanistic mode of thought was the art of sculpture. With the human body as the point of departure, such divinities as Athena and Apollo appeared as idealized images of perfect feminine and masculine beauty. Equally imaginative were such deviations from the human norm as the goat-footed Pan, the half-human half-horse centaurs, and the myriads of fanciful creatures and monsters that symbolized the forces of nature. The Greeks were more thoroughly at home in the physical world than the later Christian peoples who believed in a separation of flesh and spirit. The Greeks greatly admired the beauty and agility of the human body at the peak of its development. In addi-

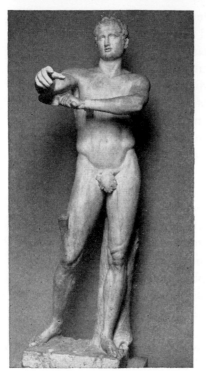

Fig. 1:39. Lysippus. *Apoxomenos* (Scraper). Marble. 81″ high. Roman copy after Lysippus' original of *c*.330 B.C. Vatican Museum, Rome (Vatican Photographic Archive)

tion to studies in literature and music, Greek youth was trained from childhood for competition in the Athenian and Olympic games. Since it was through the perfection of their bodies that men most resembled the gods, the culture of the body was a spiritual as well as a physical activity. The nude body in action at gymnasiums was a fact of daily experience, and sculptors had ample opportunity to observe its proportions and musculature. The result is embodied in such well-known examples as the *Discobolus* (Fig. 1:30) by Myron, statues of athletes attributed to Polyclitus, such as the *Doryphorus* (Fig. 1:26), and the *Scraper* by Lysippus (Fig. 1:39). As an instrument of expression, the male nude reached a high point in the 5th century B.C., but the female form had to wait for similar treatment until the succeeding century.

Any humanistic point of view assumes that life here and now is good and meant to be enjoyed. This attitude is the opposite of medieval asceticism, which denied the joys of this life as snares of the devil, believing that true good could be attained only in the unseen world beyond the grave. While the Greeks had no single belief about life after death, the usual one is found in the underworld scene of Homer's *Odyssey* when the shade of the hero's mother explains that "when first the breath departs from the white bones, flutters the spirit away, and like to a dream it goes drifting." And the ghost of Achilles tells Odysseus that he would rather be the slave of the poorest living man than reign as king over the underworld.

The spiritual kingdom of the Greeks was definitely of this world. They produced no major religious prophets, had no divinely imposed creeds, no sacred scriptures as final authority on religious matters, no organized priesthood. Such mottoes inscribed on the sacred stones of Delphi as "Know thyself" and "Nothing in excess" were suggestions that bore no resemblance to the thunderous "Thou Shalt Nots" of the earlier Ten Commandments. Knowledge of their gods came from Homer's epics and Hesiod's book of myths. The character and action of these gods, however, were subject to a wide variety of interpretations, as is clear from the commentaries of the 5th-century drama. This nonconformity bespoke a broad tolerance that allowed free speculation on the nature of the universe. Indeed, the Greeks had to work hard to penetrate the divine mind and interpret its meaning in human affairs. Ultimately, their ethical principles were embodied in four virtues—courage, meaning physical and moral bravery; temperance, in the sense of nothing too much or, as Pericles put it, "our love of what is beautiful does not lead us to extravagance"; justice, which meant rendering to each man his due; and wisdom, the pursuit of truth.

Just as the Greek religious outlook sought to capture the godlike image in human form, so also did the arts try to bring the experience of space and time within human grasp. Indefinite space and infinite time meant little to the Greeks. The modern concept of a nation as a territorial or spatial unit, for instance, did not exist for them. Expansion of their city-state was not concerned with lines on a map but with a cultural unity of independent peoples sharing common ideals. The continuous flow of time also seemed unreal, and their unconcern with a precise historical past is evidenced in the imperfection of their calendar and in the fact that their historians were really chroniclers of almost-contemporary events. Their geometry was designed to measure static rather than moving bodies, and their visual arts emphasized the abiding qualities of poise and calm. Greek architecture humanized the experience of space by organizing it so that it was neither too complex nor too grand to be fully comprehended. The Parthenon's success rests on its power to humanize the experience of space. Through its geometry, such visual facts as repeated patterns, spatial progressions, and intervallic distances are brought within easy optical and intellectual grasp. The simplicity and clarity of Greek construction was always evident to the eye, and by imposing a sense of order on the chaos of space, architects made it clearly intelligible.

Just as architecture humanized the perception of space, so the arts of the dance, music, poetry, and drama humanized the experience of time. These arts fell within the broad meaning of *music*, and their humanistic connection was emphasized in the education of youth, because, as Plato says, "rhythm and harmony find their way into the inward places of the soul, on which they mightily fasten, imparting grace, and making the soul of him who is rightly educated graceful." The triple unities of time, place, and action observed by the dramatists brought the temporal flow within definite limits and is in striking contrast to the shifting scenes and continuous narrative styles of later periods. The essential humanism of Greek drama is found in its creation of distinctive human types; in its making of the chorus a collective human commentary on individual actions of gods and heroes; in its treatment of human actions in such a way that they rise above individual limitations to the level of universal principles; and, above all, the creation of tragedy, in which the great individual is shown rising to the highest estate then plunging to the lowest depths, thereby spanning the ultimate limits of human experience. In sum, all the arts of Greece became the generating force by which Athenian man consciously or unconsciously felt himself identified with his fellow citizens and with the entire rhythm of life about him. Through the arts, human experience is raised to its highest level; refined by their fires, the individual is able to see his world more clearly in the light of universal values.

Idealism

When an artist faces the practical problems of representation, he has two main courses open to him: he can choose to represent objects as they appear to the physical eye or as they appear to the mind's eye. In one case, he emphasizes nature, in the other, imagination; the world of appearances as opposed to the world of essences; reality as contrasted with ideality. The avowed realist is more concerned with concretion—that is, with rendering the actual, tangible object that he sees with all its particular and peculiar characteristics. The idealist, on the other hand, accents abstraction, which is to say he eliminates all extraneous accessories and concentrates on the inner core, the essential qualities of things. A realist, in other words, tends to represent things as they are; an idealist, as they might or should be. Idealism as a creative viewpoint gives precedence to the idea or mental image, tries to transcend physical limitations, aspires toward a fulfillment that goes beyond actual observation, and seeks a concept closer to perfection.

Both courses were followed in the Hellenic style. One of Myron's most celebrated works was a bronze cow said to be so natural that it caused amorous reactions in bulls and calves tried to suckle her. Such a work would certainly have been in line, in the literal sense at least, with the Greek definition of art as the imitation of nature. In contrast, the painter Parrhasius agreed with Socrates that, since it was impossible to find perfection in a single human model, it was necessary to "combine the most beautiful details of several, and thus contrive to make the whole figure look beautiful."

The case for idealism is argued in Plato's dialogues. He assumes perfect truth, beauty, and goodness can exist only in the mental world of forms and ideas. Phenomena observed in the visible world are but reflections of these invisible forms. By way of illustration, parallelism is a concept, and two exactly parallel lines will, in theory, never meet. It is impossible, however, to find anything approaching true parallelism in nature, and, no matter how carefully a draftsman draws them, two lines will always be unparallel to a slight degree and, hence, will meet somewhere this side of infinity. But this does not destroy the concept of parallelism, which still exists in the mental image or idea of it. Plato's *Republic*, to cite another example, is an intellectual exercise in projecting an ideal state. No one knew better than the author that such a society did not exist in fact and probably never would. But this did not lessen the value of the activity, and the important thing was to set up goals that would approach his utopian ideal more closely than did any existing situation. "Would a painter be any the worse," he asks, "because, after having delineated with consummate art an ideal of a perfectly beautiful man, he was unable to show that any such man could ever have existed? . . . And is our theory a worse theory because we are unable to prove the possibility of a city being ordered in the manner described?" His idealistic theory, however, leads Plato into a rather strange position regarding the activities of artists. When, for instance, they fashion a building, a statue, or a painting, they are imitating, or representing, particular things that, in turn, are imitations of the ideal forms, and hence their products are thrice removed from the truth. The clear implication is, of course, that art should try to get away from the accidental and accent the essential, to eliminate the transitory and seek the permanent.

Aristotle, for his part, distinguished between various approaches in art. In his *Poetics*, he observes that "it follows that we must represent men either as better than in real life, or as worse, or as they are. It is the same in painting. Polygnotus depicted men as nobler than they are, Pauson as less noble, Dionysius drew them true to life. . . . So again in language, whether prose or verse unaccompanied by music. Homer, for example, makes men better than they are; Cleophon as they are; Hegemon the Thasian, the inventor of parodies, . . . worse than they are." Aristotle also applied the same standard to drama, pointing out that "Comedy aims at representing men as worse, Tragedy as better than in actual life." In the visual arts, the distinction, then, is between making an idealized image, a realistic image, or a caricature. And it is clearly implied that the true artist should be concerned only with the ideal.

At its high point in the latter half of the 5th century B.C., the Hellenic style was dominated by the idealistic theory. The Greek temple was designed as an idealized dwelling place for an idealized being, and by its logical interrelationship of lines, planes, and masses, it achieves something of permanence and stability in the face of the ephemeral and haphazard state of nature. In portraying an athlete, a statesman, or a god, the Hellenic sculptor concentrated on typical or general qualities rather than on the unique or particular. This was in line with

the Greek idea of personality, which it was felt was better expressed in the dominating traits and characteristics than in individual oddities or peculiarities. In
sculpture, as well as in all the other arts, the object was to rise above transitory
sensations to capture the permanent, the essential, the complete. Thus the sculptor avoided representing the human being in infancy or old age, since these extremes of immaturity and postmaturity implied incompleteness or imperfection
and hence were incompatible with the projection of ideal types. The range of
representations extends from athletes in their late teens through images of Hermes, Apollo, and Athena, who are conceived in their early maturity, to Zeus,
father of the gods, who appears as the fully developed patriarch in all the power
of mature manhood. It must also be remembered that few of the Hellenic sculptor's subjects were intended to represent human beings as such. The majority
were fashioned to represent gods, who, if they were to be cast in human form,
must have bodies of transcendent beauty.

In some way, even the intangible tones of music participated also in the ideal
world by reason of the mathematical relationships on which they are based. A
melody, then, might have something more permanent than its fleeting nature
would indicate. One of the main functions of the drama was to create ideal types,
and, while the typical was always opposed to the particular, somehow the one
arose from the other. The interpretation of this interplay was assigned to the
chorus, and the drama as a whole shared with the other arts the power of revealing how the permanent could be derived from the impermanent; how the formula could be extracted from the process of forming; how an abiding quality
could be distilled from the state of universal flux; how the type could be found
in the many specific cases; and how the archetype could arise from the types.

In the extreme sense, the real and ideal worlds represent blind chaos and
perfect order. Since the one was intolerable and the other unattainable, it was
necessary to find a middle ground somewhere along the line. Glimpses of truth,
beauty, and goodness could be caught occasionally, and these intimations should
help man to steer a course from the actual to the ideal. By exercising the faculties
of reason, judgment, and moral sense, man can subdue the chaotic conditions of
his existence and bring closer into view the seemingly far-off perfection.

The Socratic theory of education, expressed in the balance between gymnastic for the body and music for the soul was designed as a curriculum leading
toward this end. The Greek temple, the nobly proportioned sculptural figures,
the hero of epic and tragedy, and the orderly relationships of the melodic intervals in music are one and all the embodiments of this ideal. Politician, priest,
philosopher, poet, artist, and teacher all shared a common responsibility in trying
to bring it closer to realization. As Socrates said: "Let our artists rather be those
who are gifted to discern the true nature of the beautiful and graceful; then will
our youth dwell in a land of health, amid fair sights and sounds, and receive the

good in everything; and beauty, the effluence of fair works, shall flow into the eye and ear, like a health-giving breeze from a purer region, and insensibly draw the soul from earliest years into likeness and sympathy with the beauty of reason."

Rationalism

Rational and irrational forces exist within every society as well as every person. The question remains whether the state or individual tries to solve problems by reason or emotion. "Things are numbers," Pythagoras is supposed to have said, and by this statement to affirm that something solid and permanent underlies the shifting appearances of things. A few generations later, Anaxagoras went a step farther by stating that "mind has power over all things that have life." His disciple Socrates continued the argument and kindled in his followers a burning love of truth, not because truth was useful for worldly success but because it is an ideal to be pursued for its own sake. The good life in the heyday of Greek civilization embraced not only the ethical principles of courage, temperance, and justice but also wisdom, a virtue achieved by the free exercise of man's rational faculties.

In the Hebraic and Christian traditions, mortal error lay in transgressions of the moral law, but to the Greeks, original sin was a lack of knowledge. The tragedy of Oedipus in Sophocles' drama *Oedipus the King* is his ignorance that does not permit him to know when he is murdering his father, marrying his mother, and begetting children who are also his own brothers. His downfall therefore comes through his ignorance, and his fate is the price he has to pay. In *The Bacchants*, the general theme is the conflict between the known and the unknown. Agave is led to murder her own son because she voluntarily surrenders her reason to an irrational cult. Her son Pentheus' downfall comes because his reason was not strong enough to comprehend the emotional and irrational forces that motivated the lives of the members of his family and his subjects. In order to bring these factors under control, they had first to be understood, and therefore Pentheus lacked the wisdom and tolerance necessary in a successful ruler. The entire Greek philosophical tradition concurred in the assumption that, without the knowledge and the free exercise of the faculty of reason, there is no ultimate happiness for mankind.

By thinking for themselves in the spirit of free intellectual inquiry, the Greeks in considerable measure succeeded in formulating reasonable rules for the conduct of life and its creative forces. This faith in reason also imparted to the arts an inner logic of their own, since when a craftsman's hands are guided by an alert mind, his work can penetrate the surface play of sense impressions and plunge to deeper levels of experience. For all later periods, this balance between the opposites of reasons and emotion, form and content, reality and appearance becomes the basis for any classical style. For such subsequent classical movements as the Renaissance and 19th-century neoclassicism, the guiding principle is symmetry, proportion, and unity based on the interrelationship of parts with one another and with the whole.

The qualities of balance, clarity, and simplicity that the Greeks set up as standards of excellence in all the arts depended upon the selective faculty of a well-ordered mind. As Plato put it, "beauty of style and harmony and grace and good rhythm depend on simplicity,—I mean the true simplicity of a rightly and nobly ordered mind and character." Plato's attitude toward the arts that did not meet these specifications was highly critical. And since inspiration as well as rule is a necessary condition of creativity, Plato was afraid that some works of art tended to be more the product of divine madness than of reason. Aristotle, without compromising his rational position, was able to distinguish between historical and poetic truth, fact and fancy. But poetic license was severely criticized by Plato. He was disturbed, for instance, by such architectural refinements as the entasis of columns and the tilting of walls for purposes of creating the appearance of perfection by carefully calculated distortions. Since only the world of mathematics seemed fixed and logical, the world of appearances was deceptive, as proved by such illusions as a straight stick appearing bent when thrust into water. The artist, to Plato, was one who sometimes seemed to minister to the deficiencies rather than the strengths of human nature. "Thus," he writes, "every sort of confusion is revealed within us; and this is that weakness of the human mind on which the art of conjuring and of deceiving by light and shadow and other ingenious devices imposes, having an effect like magic." The philosopher also pointed out that "in works either of sculpture or painting, which are of any magnitude, there is a certain degree of deception; for if artists were to give the true proportions of their fair works, the upper part, which is farther off, would appear to be out of proportion in comparison with the lower, which is nearer; and so they give up the truth in their images and make only proportions which appear to be beautiful, disregarding the real ones." Furthermore, that which is true of the deviations of visual lines applies also to the variations in the rhythms of recited poetry and performed music. If mathematical regularity prevails, the result is dull and mechanical. In music, pitch must also waver slightly in order to approximate the human voice and sound natural and interesting. This Plato also considered irrational, and he felt that the only hope was for "the arts of measuring and numbering and weighing [to] come to the rescue of human understanding." It follows that the excellence or inferiority of the several arts then depends upon the manner in which they make use of mathematical principles.

In spite of the suspicions of the philosophers, the Hellenic artists were no less concerned than Plato with the pursuit of an ideal order, which they felt could be grasped by the mind through the medium of the senses. Greek architecture, in retrospect, turns out to be a high point in the rational solution to building problems. The post-and-lintel system of construction, as far as it goes, is eminently reasonable and completely comprehensible. All structural members fulfill their logical purpose, and nothing is hidden or mysterious. The orderly principle of repetition on which Greek temple designs are based is as logical in its way as one of Euclid's geometry propositions or Plato's dialogues. It accomplishes for the eye what Plato was trying to achieve for the mind. The tight unity of the Greek temple met the Greek requirement that a work of art be complete in itself. Its carefully controlled but flexible relationships of verticals and horizontals, solids and voids, structural principles and decorative embellishments give it an inexorable internal consistency. And the harmonic proportions of the Parthenon reflect the Greek image of a harmoniously proportioned universe quite as much as a logical system.

Sculpture likewise avoided the pitfalls of rigid mathematics and succeeded in working out principles adapted to its specific needs. When Polyclitus said "the beautiful comes about, little by little, through many numbers," he was aiming at a rational theory of art in which the parts and whole of a work could be expressed in mathematical proportions. But he also allowed for flexible application of the rule, depending on the pose or line of vision. By such a reconciliation of the opposites of order and freedom, he reveals the sculptor's kinship with his philosophical and political colleagues who were trying to do the same for other aspects of Athenian life.

Rational and irrational elements were present in both the form and content of Greek drama, just as they were in the architecture of the time. In the Parthenon, the structurally regular triglyphs were interspersed with panels showing centaurs and other mythological creatures. The theme of these sculptures was the struggle between the Greeks as champions of enlightenment and the forces of darkness and barbarism. In the drama, the rational Apollonian dialogue existed alongside the inspired Dionysian chorus. However, even in the latter, the composition of intricate metrical schemes and the orderly and complex arrangements of the parts partake of rationalism and convey the dramatic content in highly orderly form. In the dialogue, the action of the episodes must by rule lead inevitably and inexorably toward the predestined end, just as the lines and groupings of the figures must do in a composition like that on the east pediment of the Parthenon. In the union of mythological and rational elements, tragedy could mediate between intuition and rule, the irrational and rational, the Dionysian and Apollonian principles. Above all, it achieves a coherence that meets Aristotle's critical standard of "a single action, one that is a complete whole in itself with a beginning, middle, and end, so as to enable the work to produce its proper pleasure with all the organic unity of a living creature."

Just as the harmony of the Parthenon depended on the module taken from the Doric columns, so Polyclitus derived his proportions for the human body from the mathematical relationship of its parts. In similar fashion, melodic lines in music were based on the subdivisions of the perfect intervals derived from the mathematical ratios of the fourth, fifth, and octave. So also the choral sections of the Greek drama were constructed of intricate metrical units that added up to the larger parts on which the unity of the drama depended. In none of these cases, however, was a cold crystallization the desired effect. In the architecture of the Hellenic style, in the statues of Polyclitus, in the dramas of Aeschylus, Sophocles, and Euripides, and in the dialogues of Plato, the rational approach was used principally as a dynamic process to suggest ways to solve a variety of human and aesthetic problems.

It was also the Greeks who first realized that music, like the drama and other arts, was a mean between the divine madness of an inspired musician, such as Orpheus, and the solid mathematical basis on which the art rested acoustically. The element of inspiration had to be tempered by an orderly theoretical system that could demonstrate mathematically the arrangement of its melodic intervals and metrical proportions. Finally, it should always be remembered that the chief deity of the city was Athena, goddess of knowledge and wisdom. Even such a cult religion as that of Dionysus, through the Orphic and Pythagorean reforms, tended constantly in the direction of increased rationalism and abstract thought. While Athena, Dionysus, and Apollo were all born out of a myth, their destinies found a common culmination in the supreme rationalism of Socrates and Plato, who eventually concluded that philosophy was the highest music.

CONCLUSION

As the Athenians looked into the mirror of their arts, they well could have reflected on the long road they had traveled from the dark past of prehistory, with all its primitive practices and mythological superstitions. In the light of their radiant present, they confidently shared the direction of their world with their gods who, to be sure, were immortal but not all-powerful. Since even deities had limitations, man's help was urgently needed. The constant search for justice and wisdom was bringing the divine and human worlds closer together into a single universal harmony, and in the process, the gods were humanized and men reached out toward divinity.

The Socratic notion of truth, for instance, was not brought down from a mountain or imposed from above by either god or man. It was evolved with practice and effort by the application of rational principles in a dialectical, or give-and-take, process. Since the arts of the Athenians were addressed to reasonable beings, they were more persuasive if they possessed the qualities of balance, order, and proportion than if they attempted to impress by the ponderous mass of a pyramid or the colossal height of a projected tower of Babel. Athenian idealism found expression in a trinity made up of the eternal verities of truth, beauty, and goodness, each in its way a facet of the ideal oneness attainable by the mind of man. The approach to these ideals was not through mystical rites but through the process of dialectics, aesthetics, and ethics. Through these avenues, it was possible to discern on the distant horizon an intellectual, beautiful, and moral living space, broad enough to insure the expansion of Athenian institutions and arts into a sphere of excellence seldom equalled and never excelled by men before or since.

Such, then, was the remarkable configuration of historical, social, and artistic events that led to this unique flowering of culture. Circumstances, however, conspired to bring about a decline of political power, although Athens was destined to remain the teacher of Greece, Rome, and all later peoples of Western civilization. And the words of Euripides still sound a ringing note down the corridors of time:

> Happy of old were the sons of Erechtheus,
> Sprung from the blessed gods, and dwelling
> In Athens' holy and untroubled land.
> Their food is glorious wisdom, they work
> With springing step in the crystal air.
> Here, so they say, golden Harmony first
> Saw the light, the child of the Muses nine.

Fig. 1:40. *Grave Stele of Hegeso*. Marble. 59″ high. *c*.420–410 B.C. National Museum, Athens (Royal Greek Embassy)

CHRONOLOGY:

Pergamon, 2d Century B.C.

General Events
B.C.

359–	336	Philip of Macedon gained control of Greece
	336	Philip assassinated; succeeded by son, Alexander the Great
334–	323	Alexander's conquests in Near East, Persia, and Far East
	331	City of Alexandria, Egypt, founded
	323	Alexander the Great died
323–	275	Alexander's generals divided empire: Ptolemies in Egypt, Seleucids in Syria and Palestine, Attalids in Pergamon
241–	197	Attalus I ruled as king of Pergamon
		Defeated Gauls in Galatia
		Allied kingdom with Rome
		Erected monument commemorating victory over Gauls
		Patron of First School of Pergamene sculpture
197–	159	Eumenes II, king of Pergamon
		Defeated Gauls
		Power of kingdom at zenith
		Founded Pergamene Library
		Commissioned Altar of Zeus
		Patron of Second School of Pergamene Sculpture
159–	138	Attalus II, king of Pergamon
		Patron of painting
	146	Roman conquest of Greece
138–	133	Attalus III, king of Pergamon
		Willed kingdom to Rome
	129	Pergamon became a Roman province

Architecture and Sculpture

359–	351	Mausoleum at Halicarnassus built; frieze by Scopas and School
323–	146	Hellenistic Period proper; 146–27 transitional Greco-Roman period; great centers of culture at Alexandria, Pergamon, Antioch, Rhodes
	c.306	*Winged Victory of Samothrace*
	c.250	*Venus de Milo* (*Aphrodite of Melos*)
	c.228	First School of Pergamon Attalus I's monument celebrating victory over Gauls
183–	174	Second School of Pergamon Eumenes II's Great Altar of Zeus
	c.100	*Laocoön Group* done at Rhodes by Agesander, Athendorous, and Polydorus

Philosophers and Scientists

c.341–c.270	Epicurus, founder of Epicureanism
c.336–c.264	Zeno of Citium, founder of Stoicism
c.321	Aristoxenus of Tarentum, musical theorist, flourished
c.300	Euclid flourished
c.287– 213	Archimedes

Painters and Sculptors

c.359–c.351	Scopas active
c.330	Apelles, court painter to Alexander, flourished
c.200	Boethos active

2

THE HELLENISTIC STYLE

PERGAMON, 2D CENTURY B.C.

Like the earlier city of Athens, Pergamon developed around its acra, the military stronghold that became the residence of its rulers and a sanctuary. The Pergamene acropolis was a geographical site with even greater natural advantages than that of Athens, and it played a significant role in the growth of the city. The town that grew up around it was as far from the Aegean Sea as necessary to avoid surprise naval attack yet near enough to a harbor to permit a thriving export trade. The fertile plain, formed by the confluence of three rivers, was easily defensible from the hill; and the city itself, surrounded as it was by the wide sea on one side and high mountains and precipitous ravines on the other, was impregnable except from its southern approach. Here, in a situation of unusual beauty, grew the city that was to play such an important role in the Hellenistic period.

After Athens fell to Sparta, Greece veered away from the small democratic city-state as the basic political unit to more autocratic forms of government. Philip of Macedon first succeeded in bringing the mainland of Greece into a single kingdom; then his son Alexander the Great embarked on a course of

55

conquest leading to a short-lived world empire. With its great centers separated as widely as Syracuse on the island of Sicily, Alexandria on the banks of the Nile, and the cities of Asia Minor on the east coast of the Aegean, Greek thought and attitudes became more varied and international in scope. The Hellenistic period proper covers the two centuries between the death of Alexander in 323 B.C. and the Roman conquest of Greece in 146 B.C., but in effect it continued through a transitional Greco-Roman era down to 27 B.C., the beginning of the Augustan Age in Rome. Throughout these two centuries, cultural leadership remained in the hands of the Greeks, but as they came in contact with such a variety of native influences, their culture became progressively more cosmopolitan. Hence the distinction is drawn between the earlier and purer Hellenic and the later more diffused Hellenistic styles.

In the Asia Minor region, significant art centers developed at Halicarnassus, Ephesus, Rhodes, and especially at Pergamon. The unique position of the latter was largely owing to the energy and political sagacity of the Attalid kings, whose early recognition of the rising power of Rome led to an advantageous alliance with that city of the future. Pergamon was thus both an important center of civilization in its own right and one of the principal bridges over which the Greek tradition passed into the Roman Empire.

A planned Greek city rather than an improvised jumble of buildings and houses apparently goes back no further than the middle of the 5th century B.C. The fame of "wide-wayed Athens" rested on its Panathenaic Way, a street about 12 feet broad. Just wide enough for five or six men to walk abreast, it facilitated the processions to the acropolis, theaters, and market place. Otherwise the streets of Athens were narrow alleys barely broad enough for a man with a donkey cart. Without pavement of any kind, they must have been as dry and dusty in summer as they were damp and muddy in winter and spring. The Athenian residential section was only a mass of mud-brick houses in which rich and poor lived side by side in relative squalor. Only in the agora and on the acropolis was there a sense of spaciousness. But even here buildings were planned with full attention to their individual logic and little or none to their relationship as a group. Each building thus existed independently rather than communally.

Such Greek cities in the vicinity of Pergamon as Milesia and Priene are known to have been laid out in gridiron fashion with streets criss-crossing at right angles and with city blocks of regular size. A writer of the time describes a Roman military camp as being "four-sided and equal-sided, while details of its street planning and its general arrangement are precisely parallel to those of a city." From this it is evident that he was comparing the camp with a normal Greek city of his time. St. John also adopted this gridiron plan for his visionary new Jerusalem, which he described in *Revelation* as being surrounded by a great wall with 12 gates, three on each side. "And the city," he wrote, "lieth four-square, and the length is as large as the breadth" (Rev. 21:12).

These Greek city plans, while a vast improvement on their haphazard predecessors, were based on the application of an inflexible geometrical pattern that paid little or no attention to the irregularities of the natural site. When a hill was within the city limits, the streets sometimes became so steep that they could be negotiated only by precipitous stairways. While the residential sections of the ancient city of Pergamon have yet to be excavated, it is inferred that they must have followed some such regular system. Under Eumenes II, the city reached its largest extent, and the thick wall he built around it enclosed over 200 acres of ground—more than four times the territory included by his predecessor. A system of ducts that brought in an ample water supply from nearby mountain springs was sufficient for a population of 120,000 and was the greatest of its kind prior to the Roman aqueducts.

The main entrance to Pergamon was from the south through an impressive arched gateway topped by a pediment with a triglyph frieze. Traffic was diverted through several vaulted portals that led into a square, where a fountain refreshed travelers. From here, the road led past the humbler dwelling places toward the large lower market place, which bustled with the activities of peddlers and hucksters of all sorts. This market was built in the form of a large open square surrounded on three sides by a two-story colonnade enclosing rows of rooms that served for shops. Moving onward, the road went past buildings that housed the workshops and mills in which pottery, tiles, and textiles were produced. Homes of the wealthier citizens were located on promontories off the main streets overlooking the rest of the city. At the foot of the acropolis another square opened up, which could boast of a large city fountain and a fine view.

On a dramatic site almost 1000 feet above the surrounding countryside rose the Pergamene acropolis, a commanding citadel that ranked among the most imposing in the Greek world. Up the slopes of the hill, on a system of rising levels supported by massive retaining walls and fortifications, were the buildings and artifacts that gave the city its reputation as a second Athens. By ingenious use of natural contours, the Pergamenes had developed settings for a number of buildings, which were not only outstanding as individual edifices but which, by means of connecting roadways, ramps, and open courtyards, were grouped into a harmonious whole. Here on a succession of rising levels were gymnasiums, athletic fields, temples, assembly places, public squares, wooded groves, and an amphitheater. Above them all, flanked by watch towers, barracks, arsenals, storage houses, and spacious gardens, stood the royal residence.

Fig. 2:1. The Acropolis, Pergamon. Reconstruction of H. Schlief (German Archeological Institute)

ARCHITECTURE

On the three lowest of the artificially created terraces of the Pergamene acropolis were a series of open grounds, enclosed by colonnades and buildings, which comprised a triple gymnasium—one for each general age group. The spacious outdoor areas included a playground for boys, an athletic field, and a racecourse. Provision was also made for dressing rooms, baths, and indoor sports. And, as the education center of the city, the gymnasium also included classrooms and lecture halls. It is significant that such gymnasiums provided mental as well as physical exercise. Their pleasant locations in gardens and groves, in fact, were responsible for the names of such famous schools of philosophy as the Academy and Lyceum, just as the *stoa*, or shady colonnade facing a public building, became the name of the Stoic school of thought. At the Pergamon gymnasium, statues have been found of such mythological figures as Asclepius, son of Apollo and physician of the gods, and Hygeia, daughter of Asclepius and guardian of the health of growing youths, as well as sculptured representations of athletes at their games. A small adjacent temple was dedicated to one of the patron deities of sports, possibly Hermes, the fleet-footed messenger of the gods, or Heracles, mythological paragon of strength; and nearby were statues of Nike, goddess of victory, altars for votive offerings, and busts of prominent athletes who won the Olympic and other Greek games.

Above the gymnasium was the upper agora, an open square that served both as an assembly place and as the market where such merchandise as the famous Pergamene pottery and textiles were sold. The top three levels start with the broad marble-paved terrace on which stood the Altar of Zeus as seen in Figure 2:1 at the extreme right. Dating from about 180 B.C., this artistic triumph of the Eumenian period was proclaimed by many ancient authorities as one of the seven wonders of the ancient world. Since both its structure and sculptures are of major importance, this building will be discussed in detail in the following section.

On the next level was the precinct dedicated to Athena Polias, patroness of Pergamon. Her shrine (Fig. 2:1, center above) was a graceful Doric temple, smaller than the Parthenon, with six-columned porticos on either end and ten columns on each side. This level was framed by an L-shaped, two-storied colonnade that formed an open courtyard in which stood the bronze monument that celebrated the victory of Attalus I, father of Eumenes, over the Gauls. Fragments of this group survive in such marble copies as the *Dying Gaul* (Fig. 2:2 and 2:3) and *Gaul and His Wife* (Fig. 2:4). This colonnade served also as the façade of the great library of Pergamon, which was appropriately placed here in the precinct of Athena, goddess of reason, contemplation, and wisdom. The most precious part of the library was housed on the second-story level in four rooms stretching about 145 feet in length and 47 in width. On their stone shelves, some of which are still extant, rested the ancient scrolls, estimated to have numbered about 200,000 at the time of the Attalids. The Pergamon library ranked with that of Alexandria as one of the two greatest libraries of antiquity. Later, after the major portion of the Alexandrine collection of half a million volumes had been burned in an uprising against Caesar, Mark Anthony made a gift to Cleopatra of the entire library of Pergamon.

One of the principal industries of the city, incidentally, was that of the preparation of the skins of sheep and calves for writing purposes. The product was called by the Romans *pergamena*, from which our English words *pergamenous* and *parchment* are derived. Thus both the city and one of its main products were synonymous with writing materials and books. Parchment still continues to be identified with scholarship and learning in the traditional sheepskins of college diplomas. In ancient times, great commercial as well as scholarly rivalry raged over the comparative merits of Alexandrian papyrus (or paper) and the Pergamene parchment. Owing to its greater permanence, posterity has reason to be grateful for the more enduring quality of parchment.

Below the Athena precinct was the theater (Fig. 2:1, center below), which was constructed under Eumenes II about 170 B.C. The auditorium, with its 78 semicircular tiers of stone seats that could accommodate 10,000 spectators, was carved out of the hillside. Below was the traditional circular section of the orchestra, where the chorus performed around a small altar dedicated to Dionysus, and the rectangular scene building for the actors. Glancing upward toward the auditorium as in Figure 2:1, one could see the principal groups of acropolis buildings spreading fanwise outward. On the lower right was the Altar of Zeus; above center was the temple of Athena and the library; and on the high plateau at the left were the buildings and fortifications of the royal palace.

Just as the Attalid kings dominated the life of their city and constituted the apex of the social pyramid of their kingdom, so their royal residence crowned the highest point in their capital city. (Later, when the realm came under the domination of Rome, the royal palace was replaced by a large Corinthian temple in honor of the Emperor Trajan [Fig. 2:1, top left].) From their hilltop summit the kings of Pergamon could survey much of their rich domain. From the mountains to the north came the silver and copper that furnished the metal for their coins—so necessary in promoting trade and paying soldiers. From the same region came also supplies of pitch, tar, and timber—greatly in demand for the building of ships—as well as marble for their buildings and sculptures. A panorama thus unfolded around them, starting with the heights of Mt. Ida and the surrounding range (down whose slopes flowed the streams that watered the fertile valleys and broad plains), all the way to the bright waters of the shining Aegean Sea, beyond which lay the shores of the Greek motherland.

Along with Croesus, the Attalids of Pergamon were famed for their fabulous wealth, and "rich as an Attalid" was a phrase used by Horace and other Roman writers. But by later standards, the Attalids lived comparatively modestly, and the residence generally referred to as the "royal palace" was in actuality a loose constellation of small buildings, set amid wooded groves and gardens, that shifted from time to time with the changing fortunes and dignities of the kings. Included in the group were living rooms opening out into columned courtyards, chambers devoted to the dynastic cult, a barracks for the royal guard, a treasury, and various storerooms for goods, grain, and arms. At its grandest, the palace was no more pretentious than some of the better houses at Pompeii. While Hellenistic architects were restricted by ancient traditions in the building of temples, they were known to have excelled at such residences as these. Unfortunately, all the important examples of Hellenistic houses have perished, but since they were a link in an unbroken chain of Mediterranean architecture, it is not difficult to reconstruct them after later models.

Outlines and fragments of the group of buildings reveal the successive stages of the palace complex at Pergamon. An idea of the decorative scheme at the time of Eumenes II can be seen in the mosaic floor, Figure 2:15. The love of display, however, was not found in such royal residences so much as in the great public buildings the Attalids erected and in the ostentatious gifts they made to such cities as Athens and Rome. More important to the Attalid kings than the size and luxury of their dwelling was the close link with the temples of the gods that the location afforded. Both symbolically and practically, their residence was located here in order to dominate the city that spread out below them. From there all eyes would be attracted to the magnificent group of edifices, thus causing the populace to look upward both psychologically as well as actually toward the place of the kings and gods who ruled over their lives.

The planning of the town thus cleverly promoted the idea of the monarchy towering above it. There, topographically as well as politically, stood the king, aloof from his people and associated with the gods. Even while living, he was accorded such divine prerogatives as a cult statue with perfumed grain burning on an altar before it and an annual celebration in his honor. This semidivine status, connected with his right to rule, served the practical social purposes of commanding obedience to his laws, facilitating the collection of taxes (often under the guise of offerings to the gods), and uniting the peoples and factions who lived under him. Assisting in this deification were the intellectuals and artists he attracted to his court, whose works were regarded with awe by the multitude. The vast impressiveness of the architecture and sculpture was enough to overwhelm native and foreigner alike.

The pomp and display that marked Hellenistic life was a distinct departure from the simplicity and nobility of the more austere 5th century B.C. Grandeur became the grandiose, and many monuments were erected not to revere the gods but to honor kings who, even in their own lifetimes, assumed semidivine status. The accent was no longer on the abstract idealism and universality of the earlier period but on the glorification of individuals. With the changing times, however, definite advancements in the art of building were taking place. Pergamene architects went beyond the simple post-and-lintel method of the Hellenic period and employed the arch-and-vault in city gates, in underground water and sewer systems, and in a domed building that appears to have been the model for the Roman Pantheon (Fig. 3:19). Architecturally as well as culturally, Pergamon forged the link between the Greek and Roman periods. Such was the picture of the brilliant city with thousands of statues, sculptured reliefs, painted murals, and books; and peopled with philosophers, scholars, writers, artisans, and pursuers of luxury and pleasure.

SCULPTURE

While sculptural works of all kinds are known to have existed in profusion throughout the city of Pergamon, the examples that claim the attention of posterity were located on two of the terraces of the acropolis. In the Athena precinct just below the palace, bounded by the temple on one side and the L-shaped colonnades of the library on two others, was a spacious courtyard in which Attalus I erected the sculptural monuments commemorating his victories. The groups he commissioned were in place during the last quarter of the 3d century B.C. On the terrace below, in the first quarter of the 2d century B.C., his son and successor Eumenes II built the Altar of Zeus (Fig. 2:5) with its famous frieze. Historically, the two periods have been distinguished as the First and Second schools of Pergamon, but since they were separated by less than half a century, some sculptors may have worked on both projects, and if not, they must have had a hand in training their successors. The bronze originals of the First School have all disappeared and can be studied only in the marble copies made by later Hellenistic or Roman artists. Owing to the fortunate results of the late 19th-century German excavations, many of the sculptures from the Second School may be seen in the originals.

The principal works of the First School were two large monuments in bronze, each of which was composed of many figures. One commemorated the victories of Attalus over the neighboring Seleucid kingdom, but only a few details of this group survive. The other honored his earlier and greater victory over the nomadic tribes of Gauls, which swept down from Europe across the Hellespont into the region north of Pergamon. From this province, called Galatia after them, the Gauls were a constant threat to the Greek cities lying to the south. While his predecessor had bought them off by paying tribute, Attalus I refused this expedient and met their subsequent invasion with an army. The battle was fought about 30 miles to the east of Pergamon, and the outcome was decisive enough to drive back the Gauls for a generation. The consequences were felt far and wide, and all the cities and kingdoms of the Greek world breathed a little easier.

The fierce Gauls had inspired such general terror that their defeat was associated in the popular mind with something of a supernatural character. The name of Attalus was everywhere acclaimed as *Soter* (Savior), and after incorporating the lands he had gained, he assumed the title of king. Thereafter, as King Attalus the Savior, he continued to capitalize on his fortunes by embarking on a program of beautifying his city with the services of the best available Greek artists. Sharing the same patroness, Pergamon proudly began to bear the appellation of a second Athens, and its ruler that of a political and cultural champion of Hellenism over the barbarians. Not content with adding to the renown of his own city, Attalus made donations of treasure and works of art to other Greek centers, especially Athens. There he paid tribute to the ancient capital by erecting on its acropolis a monument celebrating four great victories—that of the gods over the giants, the early Greeks over the Amazons, the 5th-century Athenians over the Persians, and, of course, his own over the Gauls—thus linking his kingdom more closely with the long unbroken chain of Greek culture. The copies and fragments of struggling giants, dead Amazons, wounded Persians, and dying Gauls that have been found all over the Mediterranean region testify to the fame of this Athenian group. It is a curious commentary on the taste and temper of Roman times that replicas only of the unfortunate victims were made, while the proud victors, probably riding in triumph on horseback, were overlooked. At Pergamon, however, Attalus' monument was devoted solely to the occasion on which he was the victor. It was a large collective group that rested on a circular platform some 10 feet in diameter. In the center rose a cylindrical base, about 7 feet high, on which were placed the victorious Pergamenes and their leader, while their vanquished opponents were found below on three descending steps. Parts of the monument can be seen in numerous museums, the *Dying Gaul*, and the *Gaul and His Wife* being the most famous of the parts.

The *Dying Gaul* (Figs. 2:2 and 2:3)—often erroneously called "Dying Gladiator" because it was the inspiration of Byron's poem of that name—is a fine example of Hellenistic pathos. The mortally wounded warrior has agonizingly dragged himself out of the thick of the battle to struggle alone against death. His dying eyes are fixed on the ground where his sword, the trumpet he has sounded for aid, and other pieces of his equipment are lying. He supports himself weakly with one arm, proud and defiant to the end, while his life's blood flows slowly out of the gaping wound in his side. The anguished expression in the face is portrayed with an intensity not hitherto encountered in Greek art. The strong but rude musculature of his powerful body, so different from that of the supple Greek athletes, marks him as a barbarian. Further contrast is found in his hair, which is greased so heavily that it is almost as thick as a horse's mane; in the moustache, which was never worn by the Greeks or Romans; and in the collar of twisted gold worn around his neck. All these carefully recorded details show the interest of the period in individuals as such, in the features that distinguished one people from another, and, above all, in the artist's desire to awaken the sympathies of the observer. The sculptor thus invites by the process of empathy the involvement of the observer in the situation. The contemporary audience would have felt both attraction and repulsion toward such a subject and hence would have experienced a strong emotional reaction. The litter of the battlefield beside him, as well as other realistic details, is not used so much for its own sake as to convey a sense of immediacy in the experience of the beholder. At the same time the viewer was invited to look beyond the physical wounds and behold the spiritual anguish of the proud but defeated warrior, who is so reluctant to accept his fate.

The impressive impact of the *Gaul and His Wife* (Fig. 2:4) is no less powerful. The custom of the Gauls was to take their women and children with them on their campaigns. Realizing his defeat, and too proud to be taken a slave, this Gaul has just killed his wife and is looking apprehensively over his shoulder

at the approaching enemy as he plunges his sword into his own neck. The mood of despair is heightened by the sweeping lines of the woman's drapery, which droops downward in deep folds and casts dark shadows. In both these surviving representations, strong feeling is aroused by the noble figures who stare death so courageously in the face.

To the Second School of Pergamon are assigned all the works that fall within the reign of Eumenes II, the patron under whom Pergamon achieved the highest point of its power and glory. Like his father before him, Eumenes II had his victories over the Gauls, and he continued the tradition of erecting votive works with the Altar of Zeus (Fig. 2:5). It was at once the greatest single monument of the city and one of the few top-ranking architectural and sculptural works of the Hellenistic period. It too was intended to glorify the position of the king and to impress the entire Greek world with his contribution to the

(*Opposite*) Fig. 2:2 (*top*). Dy-ing *Gaul*. Marble. 75″ long. Ro-man copy after bronze original of *c*.225 B.C. Capitoline Museum, Rome. (Fig. 2:3 (*lower*). *Dying Gaul*, back view (Soprinten-denza)

Fig. 2:4. *Gaul and His Wife*. Marble. 83″ high. Roman copy after bronze original of *c*.225 B.C. Terme Museum, Rome (Gabri-netto Fotografico Nazionale)

cause of Hellenism in the struggle against the barbarians. Because of the as-siduous efforts of the German excavators, it is possible to appraise the work of this period from the originals. Beginning in 1878, piece by piece each fragment was painstakingly unearthed, and after a half-century of study, the entire monu-ment was reconstructed in the Pergamon Museum in Berlin. Famed throughout the ancient world, the Altar was described in the early years of the Christian era by St. John as "Satan's seat" (Rev. 3:13). The reference seems to have been prompted by the resemblance of the structure to an immense throne and by the pagan gods and demons depicted in the frieze. While the principal interest is focused on the sculpture, the building also commands architectural interest. The actual altar on which animal sacrifices and other offerings were burned was a large stone podium standing in the inner courtyard. As seen in the ground plan (Fig. 2:6), the altar was surrounded by a U-shaped enclosure known as a

Fig. 2:5. *Altar of Zeus*, Pergamon. Marble. 120′ wide, 112′ long. Podium including frieze 18′ high. *c*.180 B.C. Reconstruction formerly in Pergamon Museum, Berlin (Marburg)

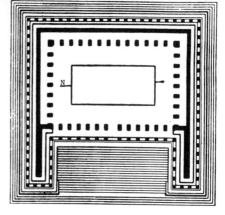

Fig. 2:6. *Altar of Zeus. Plan*

temenos. The building as a whole rested on a platform with four steps, above which was the great frieze over 7 feet in height and 450 in length, running continually around the entire podium, bending inward on either side of the stairway, and diminishing in size as the steps rose (Fig. 2:7). Below, the frieze was framed by a molding and above, by a *dentil range.* These bricklike blocks served also to support an Ionic colonnade that surrounded the structure and paralleled the frieze. Above the colonnade was a friezeless entablature with a second dentil range supporting the roof, and crowning the whole was a series of free-standing statues of gods and mythological animals placed at various points along the outer edges of the roof.

The structure reveals a distinct difference from the 5th-century concept of space as defined against a background plane. In the earlier period, the altar was placed outside the temple and rituals took place against the exterior colonnades. The Hellenistic concept of space, by way of contrast, shows an interest in depth. In the case of the Altar of Zeus, the spectator looked not toward a flat background but into the interior of a courtyard that enclosed the altar. The wider space between the columns also invited the eye toward the interior, whereas the closer intercolumniation of the 5th century promoted the continuity of the plane. Since the Hellenistic concept uses the same structural members as the previous Greek style, the Altar of Zeus is more a variation on 5th-century forms than a radical departure from them. The columns, entablatures, and interior walls, consistent with the Greek tradition, clearly define the spatial limits, and there is as yet no hint of the unbounded or infinite.

The general effect produced by the Altar of Zeus as a whole is that of a traditional Greek temple—the Parthenon, for example—turned upside down. The simple dignity of the older Doric temple depended upon its structural integrity. The columns served the logical purpose of supporting the upper members, and the sculptured sections were high above where they embellished but did not dominate the design. Here at Pergamon, however, the traditional order is inverted. Since the frieze is considered more important, it is put below where it can be seen more easily at almost eye level; above, for the sake of tradition, appears the colonnade, where it has no structural purpose. Structurality as a guiding principle has here yielded to decoration for its own sake, and the art of architecture has, in effect, given way to that of sculpture. In the case of the Parthenon, the decorative frieze was included to give some variety to what might otherwise have been a monotonous unity. The Altar of Zeus, on the other hand, with the overwhelming variety of the frieze, has the regularity of a colonnade to preserve the unity. The quiet Greek architectural drama, in other words, has now become an architectonic melodrama.

The subject of the frieze is the familiar battle of the gods and giants, and it was usual to include just the 12 Olympians and an equal number of opponents. But here the unprecedented length demanded a much larger array, and it seems certain that the scholars of the library were called upon to compile a catalogue of divinities, together with their attendants and attributes, in order to have enough figures to go around. This mythological proliferation, however, apparently taxed the knowledge of the average Greek, because visual footnotes were provided by carved names over the unfamiliar figures. Further intellectual influence is found in the allegorical treatment of the ancient battle theme. Literal belief in the gods as such was largely a thing of the past, and the local scholars interpreted them as personifications of the forces of nature, the gods standing for orderly and benign phenomena and the giants for such calamities as earthquakes, hurricanes, and floods.

On the inner part of the podium, facing the stairs, the action starts with the divinities of the earth who are summoned forth to take part in the struggle that

Altar of Zeus. c.180 B.C. Formerly Pergamon Museum, Berlin

Fig. 2:7 (left). Detail, West Bastion (Titzenthaler)

Fig. 2:8 (below). Detail of frieze, Zeus Hurling Thunderbolts. Marble. 90″ high (Staatliche Bildstelle)

Fig. 2:9. Detail of frieze, *Athena Slaying a Giant*. Marble. 90″ high. (Staatliche Bild-stelle)

Fig. 2:10 (*right*). Detail of frieze, *Goddess Throwing Jar of Snakes*. Marble. 90″ high (German Archeological Institute)

is to decide the overlordship of the world. Zeus and his fellow gods are locked in mortal conflict with his father Chronus, who is supported by the wicked titans. Moving outward along the tongue parallel with the stairs, the action proceeds along the south. Here, in the brightest sunlight, the giants are depicted as forces of darkness in combat with the spirits of light. Helios, the sun god, is shown as a charioteer driving four horses. Fighting with him are Hemera, winged goddess of day, her brother Aether, spirit of air, the moon goddess, and others. From this side the transition is made to the realm of the sky, and around the corner on the east, as the climax of the composition, the Olympians are found. First among them is Hecate, accompanied by her dog, which is biting one of the giants. Next is Artemis, the heavenly huntress, who fells her foe with an arrow. Then comes Zeus himself, to whom the altar was dedicated, and nearby is Heracles, father of Telephus, the legendary founder of Pergamon. In keeping with his Olympian position, Zeus is the only god who takes on three titans simultaneously. In a series of four slabs (Fig. 2:8), his powerful figure, wrapped in a swirling mantle, is rearing back to smite the giants with his spear and thunderbolts. While most of Zeus' arm is missing, his hand is seen in the upper left corner of the panel. The titan in the lower left has already been overcome by a thunderbolt, which is depicted as a pointed spear with a handle of acanthus leaves. The second giant is on the other side, his body tense with terror before the blow falls. In the slab to the right, Porphyrion, king of the titans, is shown from the back. From his animal ears to his serpent legs, he is a fearsome sight as he shields himself with a lion skin from both Zeus' eagle above and the forthcoming thunderbolts.

Next comes the fine group depicting the part played by Athena, protectress of the city (Fig. 2:9). Her figure is shown in the second slab, with a shield on her left arm while she grasps a winged giant by the hair with her right and forces him to earth where her sacred serpent can inflict the mortal wound. A moment of pathos is provided by the giant's mother, the earth goddess Gaea, who is seen as a torso rising from the ground. Though she is on the side of the gods, the earth mother implores Athena with her eyes to spare the life of her rebellious son. Gaea's attributes are seen in the horn of plenty she carries in her left hand, a cornucopia filled with the rich fruits of the earth—apples, pomegranates, and grapes with vine leaves and a pine cone. Over her hovers the goddess Nike, symbolizing the victory of Athena.

From this climax in the sky, the action on the shadowy north side gradually descends into the realm of the water spirits, who drive the fleeing giants around the other corner of the stairway into the sea where they drown. Here are the representations of the rivers of Greece. Among the latter is a goddess who is generally identified as Styx (Fig. 2:10), the spirit of the river that separates the realm of the living and the dead. In her hand is a jar of snakes that she is about to hurl against her adversary. It is possible that here reference is made to an incident in a naval battle in which the fleet of Eumenes II was opposed by that of the famous Hannibal. The Carthaginians resorted to a unique method of warfare by collecting poisonous snakes, packing them in terracotta jars, and hurling them onto the decks of the Pergamene ships. Finding their vessel filled with writhing serpents, the sailors jumped overboard and swam for shore. This historical episode, while not very flattering to local pride, nevertheless was in keeping with the theme of the frieze. Whatever the explanation, this fine figure with her flowing drapery and vigorous attitude is one of the best realized of the entire frieze. Around the face of the west side and up the stairs are other creatures of the sea. The tumultuous action thus opens and closes on the terrestrial plane, starting on the other side of the stairway with the divinities of the land and ending here with those of the sea. They are separated by the expanse of the wide steps as well as by their placement at the beginning and the end of the dramatic conflict.

The frieze as a whole is a technical feat of the first magnitude executed by a school of sculptors, many of whose names are inscribed below as signatures for their work. In addition to the figures, such details as swords and belt buckles, saddles and sandals, and the cloth for costumes are carved and polished to simulate the textures of metal, leather, and textiles, respectively. The bold high-relief carving, deep undercutting that allows the figures to stand out almost in the round, and rich modeling effects that make full use of light and shadow reveal complete mastery of material. To sustain such a swirl of struggling forms and violent movement over such a vast space is a minor miracle. The traditional Doric frieze could depend for unity on the momentary action in the metopes regularly interrupted by the static triglyphs. Here the unity relies on the continuity of the motion itself. The slashing diagonal lines and sharp contrasts of movement are grouped into separate episodes by the device of coiling snakes. Winding in and out they become the connecting links of the composition, leading the eye from one group to another and promoting a sense of constant writhing motion.

Facing the inner court where the altar stood was a later and less-pretentious frieze that told the story of Telephus, the mythological founder of Pergamon, whom the Attalids claimed as an ancestor. Just enough fragments remain to tell of its manner and treatment. The narration is handled like an epic poem, and its design shows unmistakable signs of literary influence. While the great frieze maintained the unities of time, place, and action, the Telephus frieze is subdivided into a sequence of biographical episodes set in a variety of locations. Since the flow of time and shift of locale are closer to actual experience than were the stylized classical unities, the frieze takes yet another step in the direction of realism. It is also the earliest known example of such treatment and points toward such later Roman narrative friezes as that on Trajan's Column (Fig. 3:22).

Fig. 2:11. "*Farnese*" *Hercules.* Marble. Over lifesize. National Museum, Naples (Bromofoto)

Comparing the great frieze with the earlier *Dying Gaul* and *Gaul and His Wife*, one can note a style trend between the First and Second schools. Both allude to the perennial wars between the Pergamenes and Gauls. But, in contrast to the almost morbid preoccupation with pain in the earlier monument, the gods on the Altar of Zeus slay the giants with something approaching gaiety and abandon. Instead of sympathy for the victims, the viewer's reaction is wonder at the marvelously ingenious ways the gods invent to dispatch their enemies. Both accent pathos, but in the earlier examples the compassion of the observer is elicited simply and directly. While the great frieze deals with the battle of the gods and giants, it is a thinly disguised allegory of the war between the Pergamenes and Gauls. But the Pergamenes in the guise of the gods have become superhuman figures, while the giants, whose features bear close resemblance to the Gallic types of the earlier period, are now monsters. Instead of the frank realism of the previous generation, the tale is told in the language of melodrama accompanied by visual grandiloquence. It is put on the stage, so to speak, and done with theatrical gestures and histrionic postures. The emotional range is enormous, beginning with the stark horror of monsters with enormous wings, animal heads, snaky locks, long tails, and sepentine legs, which recall the grotesque prehistoric creatures who inhabited the primordial world. After the terror of seeing such bestial forms, the contemporary audience must have melted into sympathy for the earth mother pleading mercy for her monstrous offspring, and then gone from tears to laughter at the inept antics of some of the clumsy giants. And after hissing the villains, the rescuing gods would have brought hearty applause. Yet it is good theater since it includes dramatic oppositions, such as the graceful figure of Styx and other beautiful feminine forms amid the carnage of the battlefield. The simple realism of the First School, however, has become exaggerated. In the case of bodily types, the functional physique of the Dying Gaul has become the Herculean power of the professional strong man who is more at home in the arena than on the battlefield. The continuation of this trend is seen in the later example of the muscle-bound figure of the Farnese Hercules (Fig. 2:11).

Previously in the case of the whole structure of the Altar of Zeus, it was pointed out that the perception of depth entered into the architectural composition, with the eye being drawn into an enclosed interior. Likewise with the sculpture, the eye does not move only from side to side, as in a plane, but is constantly led back and forth into spatial depth. Because it is painted blue, the marble background is no longer a solid boundary but dissolved into atmosphere. To escape the plane, some of the figures of the great frieze project outward in such high relief as to be almost in the round; others even step outward from the frieze and support themselves by kneeling on the edge of the steps (Fig. 2:7). The heavy shadows cast by the high-relief carving further intensify this effect. Thus the two-dimensional plane of the Hellenic style was expanded here to suggest some recession in depth. A general comparison of Hellenistic with the Athenian art of the 5th century B.C. leaves one with the impression of discord rather than harmony; a magnitude that overwhelms rather than dimensions constrained within limited bounds; a wild emotionalism in the place of a rational presentation; virtuosity triumphing over dignified refinement; melodrama superseding drama; variety in ascendance over unity. The Athenian culture, in short, placed its trust in man; the Hellenistic period, in superman. No longer the master of his fate, Hellenistic man is now engulfed in the storms and stresses of grim circumstances beyond his control.

PAINTINGS, MOSAICS, AND THE MINOR ARTS

Owing to the enduring qualities of stone, more ancient sculpture has survived than art works in any other form. Buildings were torn down for their materials and replaced by others. Statues in bronze, precious metals, and ivory were intrinsically too valuable to survive as such. Libraries of antiquity either were burned or had their volumes disintegrate in the course of time, so that their books survive only in imperfect copies made by medieval scribes or as fragmentary quotations in other volumes. The musical notation contained in ancient manuscripts was not understood by these copyists and eventually was omitted. Mosaics and pottery have fared better, but they too were either broken up or carried off by conquerors and collectors. Of all the major visual arts in antiquity, however, painting has suffered most from the ravages of time, and the number of surviving examples is sufficient to give only a hint of what this art must have been at its best. Because of this situation, the impression is easily gained that sculpture was the most important of all the arts. Literary sources, however, attest to the effectiveness and the high esteem in which painting was held by the ancients. The fame of individual painters and the critical praise for their works make it clear that painting was considered on a par with architecture and sculpture.

Two renowned painters were known to have been active in Athens during the 5th century B.C. One was Polygnotus who worked out the principles of perspective drawing, so that his pictures created the illusion of three dimensions and the recession of planes in depth. Apollodorus, "the shadow painter," was the other, who was famed for his use of light and shade and the finer gradations of color. Pausanias, a writer in Roman times, described some murals of Polygnotus, which were in the Propylaea at Athens and elsewhere, and gave longer and more detailed accounts of them than he did of the sculptures on the Acropolis. He also mentions many paintings at Pergamon and describes an especially famous one of the Three Graces (Fig. 2:12). The influence of these painters, however, survives to a limited extent in the copies that were made of their masterpieces, and in the vase painting that was done by ceramic craftsmen in imitation of their methods. The latter is, however, only a by-product of the main art and must be considered the work of artisans rather than that of independent artists.

The excavated fragments at Pergamon reveal that the walls of temples and public buildings frequently were painted with pictorial panels and had streaks of color that realistically imitated the texture of marble. Other scattered fragments of paintings show that the Pergamenes loved bright colors, such as yellows, pinks, and greens that contrasted with deep reds, blues, and browns. The palace paintings used motives of actual animals, such as lions and charging bulls, and of imaginary ones, such as tritons and griffins. Interiors of rooms were often decorated with painted friezes similar to sculptural ones; and walls, especially of small rooms, were painted with panels, columns, and pilasters, which cast realistic shadows in order to create the illusion of spaciousness. The writers of antiquity also attest to paintings drawn from such literary sources as the *Odyssey* and the like. It is also known that Hellenistic painting often dealt in *genre* scenes—that is, casual informal subjects from daily life.

Fig. 2:12. *Three Graces*. Fresco. Early 1st century A.D. Probably a copy of a Pergamene original of the 2d century B.C. National Museum, Naples (Soprintendenza)

While Attalus I and Eumenes II were both closely identified with the great sculptural developments of their times, their successor Attalus II was primarily interested in painting. He acquired a large collection by purchase and by sending his artists to various centers to copy famous works that he could not buy. An inscription reveals that Eumenes II sent artisans to Delphi to assist in the repair of its theater; and that Attalus II in 140–139 B.C. dispatched three painters to restore a famous painting there, possibly one which he had previously caused to be copied.

Although the original paintings no longer exist, and only fragments of mosaics and vase painting survive, well-preserved copies of Pergamene work have been found in the Greek cities of southern Italy, notably Herculaneum. This city supposedly was founded by Hercules, whose son Telephus founded Pergamon, and a "family" relationship existed between the two centers. Herculaneum, in fact, became a later middle-class edition of the earlier richer and aristocratic Pergamon. During the earthquake of A.D 79 and the accompanying tidal wave and eruption of Mt. Vesuvius, Herculaneum was suddenly buried under tidal mud and volcanic ash and Pompeii under molten lava. Hence many paintings and mosaics have been preserved almost intact. The taste of both cities was Hellenistic in orientation, and their well-to-do patrons, preferring tried-and-true traditional subjects, usually commissioned copies of famous paintings rather than original works.

The *Three Graces* (Fig. 2:12) and *Hercules Finding His Infant Son Telephus* (Fig. 2:13) are adaptations of Pergamene originals. In the latter, the winged

Fig. 2:13. *Hercules Finding His Infant Son Telephus*. Fresco from Herculaneum. Early 1st century A.D. Probably a copy of a Pergamene original of the 2d century B.C. National Museum, Naples (Alinari)

figure in the upper right is pointing out to Hercules his son Telephus, who is seen in the lower left among wild animals and suckling a doe. The place is Arcadia, personified by the stately seated figure. Beside her are the fruits of the land, and at her back a playful faun is holding a shepherd's crook and blowing the panpipes. The coloring for the most part is sepia and reddish brown, relieved by lighter blue, green, and whitish tints. The figures appear against the background plane of the sky that projects them forward in the manner of relief sculpture. The drapery and modeling of the flower-crowned Arcadia recall the carving of a marble relief, while the powerful musculature of Hercules' body is cast in the manner of a bronze statue in the round.

Since sculpture itself was painted in vivid colors, and sometimes landscapes were painted in the backgrounds of reliefs, the two arts obviously were closely identified in the Hellenistic mind, and they should perhaps be thought of more as complementary arts than as independent media. Paintings were more adaptable to interiors, while weather-resistant stone made marble reliefs better for out-of-doors. From the extant evidence, it is clear that the visual intention and expressive effect of both arts were closely associated, and that neither could claim supremacy over the other.

Mosaics, the art of which goes back to remote antiquity, were highly favored at Pergamon for the flooring of interiors and wall-panelling. As with later Roman work, geometrical patterns were preferred for floors, while representations of mythological subjects, landscapes, and informal genre scenes were used for murals. Copies of many Pergamene designs have been found at Herculaneum, Pompeii, Naples, and Rome. According to Pliny the Elder, the most renowned mosaicist of antiquity was Sosus, who was active at Pergamon. Among his most widely copied designs was one of doves drinking from a silver dish, and another favorite was for a dining-room floor (Fig. 2:14) that showed vegetables, fruit, fish, a chicken leg, and a mouse gnawing on a nut.

One of the best-preserved Hellenistic mosaics comes from the palace of Eumenes II (Fig. 2:15) where it covered the entire floor of a room. The center has a square geometrical design made up of small cubes of black, gray, red, yellow, and white marble. Surrounding it was a border about a yard wide with a foliated pattern of such variety that in the 40 feet that have been excavated there is no repetition. Against a black background colored flowers, exotic lilies, vine leaves, and various fruits, all with delicate shadings, are intertwined. In some places grasshoppers are feeding on acanthus leaves, in others small boys are playing among vines. An interesting touch is provided by the signature of the artist with the words "Hephaiston made it," that appears as if on a piece of parchment with three corners fastened down by red sealing wax, while the other curls up casting a shadow on the floor.

Pergamon was noted for its textiles, particularly the woolens used for carpets and curtains. A rich brocaded cloth with interwoven gold threads was known all over the ancient world as *vestes attalicae*, a name that indicated its manufacture in the royal mills. Special chemical and mineral dyes made Pergamene cloth unique. Metal work, such as silver bowls, bronze medallions, and coins, reveal the Pergamene craftsmen as being adepts in the art of embossing and chasing, as did also their cameos—gems engraved with miniature portraits.

Pergamon was also known as a ceramic center. The clay of the region was well adapted to the making of everything from bricks and tiles to pottery of all sorts. A type of pottery, known as Pergameneware, originated here and was distinguished by its bright varnished surfaces in colors of rich reds with variations in coral, orange, and brownish shades. The large quantities of terracotta figurines, varying from a few inches to a full foot in height indicate their popularity in individual homes. The usual reproductions of famous statues as well as those depicting mythological figures have been found, but, in general, the heroic subjects were left to the large monuments. The figurine medium, being particularly adaptable to informal treatment, was used largely for genre scenes, such as children playing, mothers nursing their young, intoxicated satyrs, and grotesque old men going to market with their wares. Such a work as Boethos' *Boy*

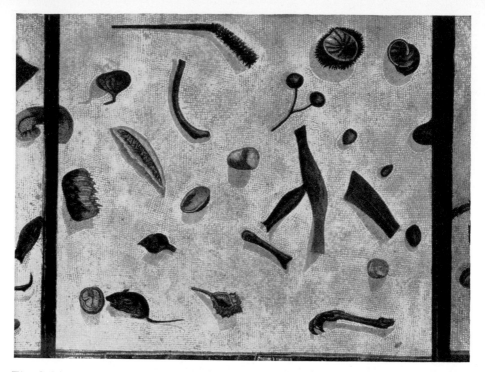

Fig. 2:14. Sosus. *Unswept Dining Room Floor*. Mosaic. Later Roman copy of 2d-century B.C. original by Sosus of Pergamon. Lateran Museum, Rome (Vatican Photographic Archive).

Fig. 2:15. Mosaic from Palace of Eumenes II, Pergamon. 28′ square. 2d century B.C. (Altertümer von Pergamon)

Fig. 2:16. Boethos. *Boy with Goose.* Marble. *c.*36″ high. Roman copy of original of *c.*200 B.C. Capitoline Museum, Rome (Soprintendenza)

with Goose (Fig. 2:16) shows a humorous treatment, as the boy is pretending he is Hercules, and, in proportion to his size, the goose becomes a giant. In common with the practice of the time, artisans and craftsmen traveled about between various centers, and those trained in Pergamon were in wide demand and enjoyed a particularly high reputation.

MUSIC

Pergamon was identified with the musical tradition of that nearby northern Asia Minor region known as Phrygia, which had its own characteristic idioms, modes, rhythms, scales, and instruments. As early as the 5th century B.C., the Greeks in Athens were divided in their musical views as to the relative merit and propriety of their native Dorian tradition and the increasing influence coming from foreign centers. In particular, the wild and exciting music of Phrygia was gaining in popular favor. The melodies in the Phrygian mode apparently induced strong emotional reactions, and the introduction of a musical instrument called the Phrygian pipe had a similar effect in inflaming the senses. This pipe was a double-reed instrument with a peculiarly penetrating sound, somewhat like the modern oboe. Properly it is known as the *aulos* when used singly and the *auloi* when the player used a double version of the instrument. In English versions of ancient Greek works it is often incorrectly translated as the flute. The Dorian music, on the other hand, was associated with such stringed instruments as the lyre and the cithara, the latter of which is inaccurately rendered as the harp.

Fig. 2:17. *Contest of Apollo and Marsyas*. Marble. 38¼ high. *c*.350 B.C. Relief from Manteneia, Greece. National Museum, Athens (Alinari)

Both the lyre and the cithara in the Dorian music and the aulos in the Phrygian were used principally to accompany the songs, melodies, and choruses of the two modes and only to a much lesser extent were played as solo instruments by skilled performers. Lyre-playing was especially associated in the Dorian tradition with the Apollo cult, and the Greeks attributed to this body of music the quality of *ethos*, or ethical character; the aulos, as the instrument of Dionysus, was associated with *pathos*, or strong feeling, and had a sensuous quality conducive to enthusiasm. To the Athenians, this meant a division in their aspirations and ideals—one instrument and mode of singing were associated with clarity, restraint, and moderation; the other with emotional excitement and aroused passions.

The resultant division of opinion was expressed in the many sculptural representations of the musical contest between the Olympian Apollo and the Phrygian satyr Marsyas. According to an ancient myth, Athena was the inventor of the aulos. One day as she was playing, however, she caught sight of her reflection in a pool of water. So displeased was she with the facial grimaces the aulos caused her to make that she threw it away in disgust. Marsyas, happening along, found it and was so enchanted by its sounds that he challenged Apollo, the immortal patron of the muses, to a contest. The god chose to play on the dignified lyre, won the contest handily, and proved once again that mortals are no match for the gods. As a punishment he had his challenger flayed alive.

Fig. 2:18. *Knife Sharpener* and (*right*) *Marsyas*, Marble. Roman copies of Pergamene originals. Uffizi, Florence (Soprintendenza), and Louvre, Paris (Archives Photographiques).

A 5th-century representation of the myth attributed to Myron shows Athena, calm and disposed, disdainfully throwing away the instrument which distorted her fine features, while Marsyas raises his hands in surprise. A 4th-century relief from Mantineia of the school of Praxiteles (Fig. 2:17) represents the contest in progress. On one side, calmly awaiting his turn, is the seated Apollo with his lyre; on the other, Marsyas is ecstatically blowing on the auloi. Between them is the judge, or music critic, standing patiently but with knife in hand. The Pergamene versions left out the contest and showed the victorious Apollo on one side, the unfortunate loser in the center strung up by the wrists to a tree, and on the other side the crouching figure of a Scythian slave (Fig. 2:18), whetting a knife with keen anticipation. The choice of the punishment as the part of the myth to be represented—and the evident enjoyment with which this Hellenistic artist tackled his sinister subject—was obviously designed to tear the emotions to shreds.

The disapproval of Phrygian music shown by the punishment of Marsyas must have reflected the view of those who wished to preserve ancient traditions. Yet the power and popularity of the aulos and the Phrygian melodies associated with it grew constantly. One measure of its hold on the people is found in the attitude of the philosophers who were concerned with maintaining balance and order in the state. Plato, for instance, would not admit aulos players into his ideal state, because he considered the instrument "worse than all the stringed instruments put together." He was most emphatic about his preference for "Apollo and his instruments to Marsyas and his instruments." But even the complex stringed instruments were eliminated in favor of the simple lyre and cithara for use in the city, and the pipe to keep the shepherds happy in the country. But while he rejected the aulos, Plato made a curiously human concession in retaining the Phrygian melodies. The two musical modes allowed in the ideal state were the Dorian, which he called the "strain of necessity," and the Phrygian, which was the "strain of freedom." The first was "warlike, to sound the note or accent which a brave man utters in the hour of danger and stern resolve"; clearly a type of military music is implied by this. However, maintaining such heroic resolve at all times was apparently too much to expect even of the citizen of his utopia, and Plato therefore allowed the Phrygian music "to be used by him in times of peace and freedom of action, when there is no pressure of necessity."

Aristotle, while for the most part agreeing in his musical views with Socrates and Plato, took exception to this, and said: "The Socrates of the *Republic* is wrong in retaining only the Phrygian mode along with the Dorian, the more so because he rejects the [aulos]; for the Phrygian is to the modes what the [aulos] is to musical instruments—both of them are exciting and emotional. Poetry proves this, for Bacchic frenzy and all similar emotions are more suitably expressed by the [aulos] and are better set to the Phrygian than to any other mode." It must be pointed out that Aristotle did not reject the Phrygian mode altogether, but only in the case of the education of youth. For this he strongly recommended only the Dorian music, since it was the "gravest and manliest." The Phrygian might produce too much enthusiasm, while the Dorian was more likely to result in a "moderate and settled temper."

In spite of the philosophers and their dire warnings, the stimulating Phrygian music made rapid headway, and in Hellenistic times it was the dominant musical style. The calm, simple, and dignified Dorian tradition, which Plutarch called the age of "beautiful music," was a thing of the past, and the wilder, more frenzied strains of Phrygia had taken its place. Their effects can readily be seen in the sculptural representation of a *Satyr Playing the Scabellum* (Fig. 2:19). The satyr cult was a Phrygian phenomenon, and this statue as well as other satyr types have been traced to a Pergamene origin. Holding the

Fig. 2:19. *Satyr Playing Scabellum.* Marble. Roman copy of Hellenistic original. Uffizi, Florence (Soprintendenza)

clashing metal *scabellum,* or cymbals, in his hands and stamping on a castenet-like percussion instrument attached to one foot, the satyr is performing an orgiastic dance with wild abandon. The physical tension seen in the lines of the torso reflects the frenzied Dionysian rhythm that seems to electrify his whole body. This image of youthful passion makes it easy to understand why the austere thinkers felt that the music that produced such a reaction lacked ethos.

While historical facts about the actual musical life of Pergamon are few, it is known that here, as in other Hellenistic centers, the practice of music was accorded a high place in the arts. Both boys and girls received musical instruction in their educational institutions, and sang hymns as they marched in processions or participated in religious observances. The curriculum included the teaching of musical notation and the chanting of poetry to the accompaniment of the cithara. The chief educator of the city, the gymnasiarch, was also expected, among his other duties, to arrange for the appearances of visiting poets and musicians.

The Hellenistic era was one of increasing professionalism in activities that had previously been performed by free citizens as part of their public duties and honors. Participation in athletic contests and performances of certain dances, which earlier had been done only by those of noble birth, were taken over by specialists who often commanded high fees for their services. Professional associations, known as the Dionysiac *technites*, had a membership made up of stage managers, actors, mimes, dancers, and musicians who participated in theatrical productions. These groups functioned as guilds, or unions, and the master craftsmen accepted talented apprentices who understudied them. The Attalids and other Hellenistic monarchs promoted and protected these technites with an eye toward improving and maintaining the quality of their theatrical and musical performances.

While evidence of musical activity at Pergamon is quite sketchy, Tralles, one of the cities of the Pergamene kingdom, provides some general information and one of the best musical examples of antiquity. Less than 100 miles from Pergamon as the crow flies, Tralles was a subject-city of the Attalids, who there maintained a residence which usually was occupied by the high priest of the city as their representative. This Phrygian town was saved from the threat of defeat and enslavement at the hands of the Gauls by the victory of Eumenes II in 168 B.C. Like many other cities of the region, Tralles was so grateful for its deliverance that it instituted annual gymnastic and musical festivals in honor of the Pergamene kings. One of these was the Panathenaea, which honored Athena as the protectress of Pergamon; another was the Eumenaia, which feted the monarch himself. From inscriptions it appears that the Eumenaia was principally a musical contest.

At Tralles, in the latter part of the 19th century, a tombstone was unearthed that had an inscription of some four lines of poetry accompanied by clear musical notation. It was an epitaph inscribed on a slab of stone by a man named Seikolos for the grave of his wife Euterpe. On transcription it turned out to be the words and music of a short but presumably intact tune in the Phrygian mode from the 2d century B.C. After hearing about the wild and orgiastic character of Phrygian music, the reader will find this short song a model of sobriety. The mood, in fact, is more melancholy than intoxicating, and since it was carved on a tombstone, the elegiac character is quite appropriate.

Skolion of Seikolos (2d or 1st century B.C.)　　　　　　　　(After Kunkel)

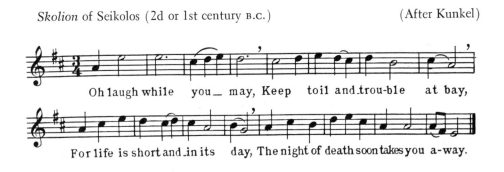

Oh laugh while you_ may, Keep toil and trou-ble at bay,

For life is short and in its day, The night of death soon takes you a-way.

This delightful little song, well over 2000 years old, was of a popular type known as a *skolion*, or drinking song, which was sung after dinner by the guests themselves as the cup was passed around for toasts and libations to the gods. The word *skolion* is derived from the Greek meaning zigzag and referred to the manner in which the lyre and cup were passed back and forth, crisscrossing the table as each of the reclining guests sang in his turn. The simplicity of this example marks it as the type of song expected to be in the social repertory of every acceptable guest rather than as one of the more elaborate ballads intended to be sung by professional entertainers. In spirit and mood it is not unlike the familiar "Auld Lang Syne," and the occasions on which it was sung would parallel those when we sing the venerable Scottish air. The substance of the words is the universal one of eat, drink, and be merry for tomorrow we die, which expresses a convivial philosophy of the Epicurean type. Technically, it is in the Phrygian mode with the upper and lower extremes falling on e' and e, thus spanning an octave. The tone most often stressed is a, which thus becomes the mean between the higher and lower reaches of the melody and consequently functions as its tonal center.

IDEAS

Many striking differences have been noted between the Hellenistic and earlier Hellenic style. As the names indicate both are Greek; but the Hellenic was a more concentrated development of the small city-states of the Greek mainland, whereas the Hellenistic is a combination of native Greek and such regional influences as those of the Near East, North Africa, Sicily, and Italy. The very diffusion of Hellenistic art over several centuries and the entire Mediterranean world makes the quest for stylistic unity the more difficult. It is remarkable, in fact, that there is any unity at all. The style contrast between Hellenic and Hellenistic, moreover, is never one of polar extremes but rather a tilting of the cultural scale in one direction or another. The universal and social humanism of Athens becomes the particular and personal *individualism* of Pergamon and other centers. The noble Hellenic idealism breaks down into a *realism* that looks at the world more in terms of immediate experience than under the aspect of eternity; the uncompromising rationalism of Socrates, Plato, and Aristotle yields to an *empiricism* of scientists, scholars, and artists interested more in the development of methods and techniques and the application of knowledge to practical affairs than in the adventurous spirit of free inquiry. The tendencies that underly the various art enterprises at Pergamon in particular and the Hellenistic period in general, then, are to be found in a pattern of interrelated ideas, of which individualism, realism, and empiricism are component parts.

Individualism

As one phase of humanism, the individualistic bias of Hellenistic life, thought, and art contrasted strongly with the broader social accent of the Hellenic period. In politics, the rough-and-tumble public discussions of free citizens and decisions arrived at by voice vote were superseded by the rule of an inner circle of oligarchs headed by a king who enjoyed semidivine status. The cult of personal hero worship that started with Alexander the Great and continued with the kings that succeeded him in the various parts of his far-flung empire was reflected in the popular biographies of great men; in the building of lavish temples and monuments glorifying not the ancient gods but monarchs and military heroes, such as the famous mausoleum for King Mausolus of Halicarnassus (Fig. 2:20); in the sculptor's accent on individual characteristics, diverse personality traits, and racial differences. In the earlier Hellenic centers, poets, playwrights, and musicians were mainly skilled amateurs; even in sports the accent was on active participation. In the Hellenistic period, however, a rising spirit of professionalism is noted in the fame of individual writers, actors, virtuosos, and athletes, with the result that people became passive spectators more than active participants.

The search for truth in Athens was a gregarious activity of argumentation participated in by all comers in public squares or in the shady groves of an academy or lyceum where Plato and Aristotle discoursed with colleagues and students. Truth, it was felt, could not be arrived at individually but only through give and take, question and answer, examination and cross-examination, dialogue or dialectical process. In Hellenistic times, these strenuous mental gymnastics gave way to the more personal contemplation and self-reflection of the Stoic and Epicurean philosophies. The thought of Epicurus found ready acceptance in the rich and flourishing cities of Asia Minor. Epicurus had taught that the highest good was "freedom from trouble in the mind and from pain in the body" and that the pursuit of pleasure was the goal of life. The austere idealism of Socrates thus gave way to a comfortable hedonism. But since some pleasures exceed others, the mind and critical faculties are needed to distinguish among those that give more lasting satisfaction. Epicurus also held that happiness for the individual lay in the direction of the simple life, self-containment, and withdrawal from public affairs. This, in effect, denied the social responsibilities of citizenship and encouraged escapism and extreme individualism.

Since the state controlled so much of his public life, Hellenistic man found greater enjoyment in his personal and home life. Poverty had been deemed an honorable estate in ancient Athens where rich and poor lived as neighbors in modest homes. Hellenistic wealth, however, allowed a more luxurious standard of living for a larger percentage of the population. Hellenistic architects, then, took special interest in domestic dwellings; painters and mosaicists were called upon to embellish the houses of the well-to-do; sculptors created figurines with informal, sometimes humorous, subjects, such as Boethos' *Boy with Goose* (Fig. 2:16), because they were more adaptable to the home than monumental formal works; together with potters and other craftsmen, all worked to contribute to the life of luxury and ease of a frankly pleasure-loving people.

The Hellenistic artist was more interested in exceptions than rules, in the abnormal than the normal, in types than archetypes, in diversity than unity. In portraiture, he noted more the physical peculiarities that set an individual apart, not those that united him with others. Even the gods were personalized rather than generalized, and the choice of subjects from daily life showed the artist's increased preoccupation with informal, casual, everyday events. He was also more concerned with environmental influences on man than with man's being able to rise above his limitations. The Hellenistic artist, by recognizing the complexity of life, gave his attention to subtle shades of feeling and to representing the infinite variety of the world of appearances.

Hellenistic thought entered on a new emotional orientation. Instead of looking for the universal aspects of experience that could be shared by all, Hellenistic philosophers held that each man has his own feelings, ideas, and opinions entirely different from those of others. In this every-man-for-himself attitude, each

Fig. 2:20. Reconstruction of Mausoleum at Halicarnassus. 359–351 B.C. (German Archeological Institute)

must decide what is good and evil, true and false. Instead of seeking a golden mean between such opposites as harmony and discord as did their Hellenic predecessors, Hellenistic philosophers became psychologists analysing the self and laying bare the causes of inner conflict. The joy, serenity, and contentment of the Hellenic gods and athletes were social emotions that could be shared by all. The sorrow, anguish, and suffering of Hellenistic wounded warriors and defeated giants were private, subjective feelings that separated man from his fellows and invited inward reflection. It was an old variation on the theme—laugh and the world laughs with you, weep and you weep alone. Artists turned from the ideal of self-mastery to that of self-expression, from the concealment of inner impulses to outbursts of feeling—in short from ethos to pathos. It was said of Pericles that he was never seen laughing and that even the news of his son's tragic death did not alter his dignified calm. A strong contrast to this Olympian attitude is provided by the late Hellenistic *Laocoön Group* (Fig. 2:21), where the balance of reason and emotion is replaced by a reveling in feeling for its own sake. What is lacking in self-restraint and regard for the limitations of the sculptural medium, however, is amply made up for by the vigor of treatment and virtuosity of execution.

The preoccupation of Pergamene artists with such painful and agonizing subjects as the defeated Gauls, the punishment of Marsyas, and the battle of gods and giants reveals the deliberate intention of involving the spectator in a kind of emotional orgy. Misfortune here becomes something that can be enjoyed by the fortunate who participate in the situation with a kind of morbid satisfaction. La Rochefoucauld said: "We all have the strength to endure the misfortunes of others"; and Aldous Huxley observed that when the belly is full men can afford to grieve, and "sorrow after supper is almost a luxury." In the spirit of Stoic philosophy, life and suffering were to be endured with a sort of grim satisfaction akin to a form of morbid enjoyment. The artists of the great frieze of the Altar of Zeus, for instance, show incredible inventiveness in the ways and means they found for the gods to inflict pain and death. The composition approaches an almost encyclopedic inclusiveness in the various modes of combat by the gods and the capacity for suffering by the giants. Nothing like it appears again in art until the Romanesque *Last Judgments* and Dante's *Inferno*.

Realism

The increasing complexity and quicker pulse of Hellenistic life weakened the belief in the underlying unity of knowledge and abiding values that produced the poise of Hellenic figures and the impassive calm of their facial expressions. The world of concrete experience was more real to Hellenistic man than one of remote abstract ideals. In his more realistic view of things, he looked to variety

Fig. 2:21. Agesander, Athenodorus, and Polydorus. *Laocoön Group*. Marble. *c.*50 B.C. 95″ high. Vatican Museum, Rome (Vatican Photographic Archive)

rather than unity and took into account individual experiences and differences. Hellenistic artists sought to present nature as they saw it, to render minute details and ever finer shades of meaning. The decline of idealism was not necessarily the result of decadence, as is so frequently stated, so much as it was a matter of placing man's activities in a new frame of reference, re-examining his goals and redefining basic human values. Confronted with the variety and multiplicity of his world, the Hellenistic artist made no attempt to reduce its many manifestations to the artificial simplicity of types and archetypes. The Hellenic way was to portray man standing aloof and rising above his environmental limitations, but in Hellenistic art man is right in the midst of the natural and social forces that beset him on all sides, and he is inevitably conditioned by them. The writhing forms on the great frieze reveal some of the conflicts and contradictions of Hellenistic man. His gods became projections of his own psychological problems. The earlier Hellenic gods, for instance, appeared to have the world well under control, and the Apollo of the Olympia pediment (Fig. 1:23) shows no sign of stress or strain as he directs the course of battle with a wave of his arm. The deities of the Altar of Zeus, on the other hand, are fighting furiously, and things seem to verge on getting out of hand.

In the Athenian architecture of the 5th century B.C., each building, however well in harmony with its site, was an independent unit, and the architects were little concerned with any precise relation to nearby buildings. Indeed, to have admitted that one structure was dependent upon another in a group would have diminished its status as a self-contained whole and thus rendered it incomplete by Hellenic standards. On the Athenian acropolis, each temple had its own axis and its independent formal existence—in keeping with the conception that each separate work of art must be a logical whole made up only of the sum of its own parts. Only such concessions to nature as were necessary for structural integrity were made. To man alone belonged the power of creating symmetrical form and balanced proportion, and the perfection of each building had to stand as a monument to the mind of man and, as such, to rise above its material environment rather than be bound by it. Hellenistic architecture moved away from the isolated building in the ideal sense of its being a self-contained unit toward a realistic recognition that nothing is complete in itself but must always exist as part of an interrelated pattern. City planning is therefore in this sense a form of realism, and Hellenistic buildings were considered in their relation to the community as a whole. In the case of the Pergamene acropolis, the relationship of each building was carefully calculated not only in regard to its natural surroundings but to its place in the group.

In sculpture, the members of each group were likewise subject to their environment, and man is portrayed as an integral part of his surroundings. In such reliefs as the Telephus frieze, the painting-in of a natural background places man

Fig. 2:22. *Aphrodite of Cyrene*. Marble. Roman copy of *c*.100 B.C. after Praxitilean original, found at Cyrene, North Africa. Terme Museum, Rome (Soprintendenza)

constantly in reference to specific locations. By using higher relief, Hellenistic sculpture becomes more dependent on changing light and shade for its expressive effect, allows for movement in more than one plane, and suggests greater depth in space. In earlier sculpture, a figure always bore the stamp of a type and personality was subordinate to his place in society. A warrior, for example, had a well-developed physique, but his face and body bore no resemblance to any specific person. He could be identified by a spear or shield and was more a member of a class than a person in his own right. The Hellenistic desire to render men as unique personalities and not as types necessitated a masterly technique capable of reproducing such particular characteristics as the twist of a mouth, wrinkles of the skin, physical blemishes, and individualized facial expressions. Faces, furthermore, had to appear animated and lifelike, so that the subject of a realistic portrait could be distinguished from all others. Fidelity to nature also meant the accurate rendering of anatomical detail. Like a scientist, the sculptor observed the musculature of the human body with precision so as to render every nuance of the flesh. In the handling of materials, the older Hellenic sculptors never forgot that stone was stone. But the realistic zeal of the later Hellenistic craftsmen often led them to force stone to simulate the softness and warmth of living flesh. The story of the legendary sculptor Pygmalion who chiseled his marble maiden so realistically that she came to life could have happened only in the Hellenistic period, and the sensuous figure of the *Aphrodite of Cyrene* (Fig. 2:22) surely bears this out.

In all Hellenistic sculpture, the human subject is related to the forces that shape his character and mold his flesh. All the minute physical and psychological conditions that vary the bodies and minds of men, women, and children are taken into account. Yet the end result was managed so that the dignity and status of the art was maintained by rising above the letter of realism in order to portray the spirit of the subject or theme represented. Hellenistic emphasis on realism appealed greatly to the forthright Roman conquerors of Greece, and its appeal to these men of action was largely responsible for the ultimate survival of these Pergamene sculptures.

Empiricism

The rationalism of Hellenic thought as developed by Socrates, Plato, and Aristotle had emphasized the spirit of free intellectual inquiry in a quest for universal truth. Epicureanism and Stoicism, by contrast, were practical philosophies for living. The abstract logic of the earlier period, in short, yielded to an empiricism that was concerned more with science than wisdom, in bringing together the results of isolated experimentation, and in the application of knowledge to the solution of practical problems. More broadly, Hellenistic empiricism stressed fact-gathering, the cataloguing of source materials in libraries, scholarly research, collecting art works, and developing critical criteria for judging the arts.

Epicurus, by eliminating the notion of divine intervention in human affairs, and by his physical explanations of natural phenomena, laid the philosophical basis for a scientific materialism. Such astronomers and physicists as Archimedes and Hero of Alexandria knew the world was round, had a solar calendar of 365¼ days, invented a type of steam engine, and worked out the principles of steam power and force pumps. Indeed, the modern mechanical and industrial revolutions might well have taken place in Hellenistic times had not slave labor been so cheap and abundant. The progressiveness of the period is also seen in its commercial developments that led to new sources of wealth.

This scientific attitude found brilliant expression in the musical field by the development of the theoretical basis of that art. While philosophers and mathematicians of the earlier period had made many discoveries and had had brilliant insights into the nature of music, it remained for the Hellenistic mind to systematize them and construct a comprehensive and coherent science of music. Under Aristoxenos of Tarentum, a disciple of Aristotle, and under Euclid, the theory of music reached a formulation so complete and comprehensive that it became the foundation for Western music. While it is impossible to go into the intricacies of the Greek musical system here, one should keep in mind that it was in this theoretical field more than any other that a lasting musical contribution was made.

After establishing his great library, Eumenes II gathered about him many of the outstanding Greek scholars of his day. They were dedicated to the task of preserving the literary masterpieces of bygone days, making critical editions of the works of ancient poets and dramatists, selecting material for anthologies, cataloguing collections, copying manuscripts, writing grammatical treatises, and compiling dictionaries. In their scholarly endeavors, they upheld the works of the ancients above the writers of their own time, and as a consequence their literary production began to be addressed more to other scholars than to the people at large. Such a restricted audience of cultivated readers could not be supplied by Pergamon alone but had to be sought for all over the scattered Greek world. By mutual consent, the pure and majestic Attic Greek of Pericles, Euripides, and Plato became their "common dialect" and the artificial medium of communication between the cultured classes. With this emphasis on a tongue that was no longer spoken, the living language in which writers could address their fellow citizens began to be regarded as a local dialect.

This was the period of classifiers and organizers in all departments, and the spirit of research was in the air. As a result, creativity in the arts began to be stifled by a growing spirit of antiquarianism. The literary life of Pergamon, for instance, was devoted more to scholarly pursuits than to creative writing, and erudition eventually became a substitute for inspiration. The influence of the library and its scholars was felt in the visual arts as well. The magnitude of the design of the great frieze of the Altar of Zeus demanded the collaboration of scholars, and the completeness of the undertaking shows evidence of the spirit of research. It is, in fact, a catalogue of mythology, which even includes the obscure names of the individual giants. The labeling of the figures of the frieze in the manner of visual footnotes and annotations contrasts markedly with that of the Parthenon. At that time, any Greek would have recognized the principals in the cast, and the supporting members were left to the imagination, since they served mainly in the aesthetic capacity of filling in the extra space. As in the case of literature, the Hellenistic visual arts no longer stemmed from the experience of a local community by deriving their spirit and substance from the spoken word and the common religious experience. They were addressed, on the contrary, to an educated class who were sophisticated enough to understand it. The theory of art for art's sake therefore took over.

Like their literary colleagues, the sculptor and the painter were confronted for the first time with a museum filled with noted works from the glorious past that commanded increasing admiration from their contemporaries. In their zeal for collection, the Attalid kings had even carried on extensive excavations which brought to light many works that the 5th century B.C. had thought better to bury. Fortunately, this spirit of looking to a past golden age was not carried to the point of entirely excluding contemporary creative activity. Many artists of the time, however, had to devote their energies to making copies of famous works of the past, such as those by Myron, Phidias, and others, which were placed in the halls of the great library.

The interest of the patrons extended also to the historical and critical aspects of the visual arts, just as it had done in the case of literature and music. This had the positive result of formulating aesthetic standards and setting up critical criteria so necessary in the evaluation process. In the earlier period artists did not enjoy the high social position they had in Pergamon and other Hellenistic cities at this time. Hence the theorizing about taste and the development of aesthetic judgment proved that now, in contrast with the earlier period, artistic products were at last worthy of the attention of the highest intellectual and social circles. The collector became a judge and connoisseur, and hence engendered a state of mind in which standards of value and aesthetic expression were regarded as important intellectual pursuits.

The Road to Rome

A reputation for learning had direct bearing on the political purposes of the Pergamene government. The more renowned their capital became for its intellectual and cultural enterprises, the higher its prestige in the Greek world would be. The career of Eumenes II's brother, who eventually succeeded him as Attalus II, is a case in point. As a skillful general, he was invaluable to the Pergamene regime; yet at the conclusion of a successful war, he took five years off to study philosophy at the academy in Athens. Furthermore, the proudest boast of the Attalids after their military victories was that they were the saviors of Hellenism from the barbarians. This claim, of course, had to be fortified by

Fig. 2:23. *Imperial Procession*, detail of Fig. 2:24 (*opposite*). Marble. 63" high

the development of their capital as a center of arts and letters. To advertise the cultural achievements of his realm, Eumenes II chose his librarian, the famed grammarian Crates of Mallos, as his ambassador to Rome. By his championship of humanistic learning, and by stimulating Roman desire for more knowledge about Greek philosophy, literature, and art, Crates made a lasting impression on the future world capital.

With literary talents being diverted into the editing of manuscripts, scholars delving into the history of the past, art collectors digging for buried treasure, and musicians writing theoretical treatises, Pergamon was well on its way toward becoming an archive and a museum. In time, this antiquarianism was bound to lead artistic developments into a stylistic eclecticism and to reduce aesthetic procedures to academic formulas and rules—all of which is symptomatic of artistic hardening of the arteries and the eventual decline of the creative powers. When, therefore, in 133 B.C. Attalus III willed his kingdom to Rome, he was actually presenting that city with a living museum. The vast art holdings of the Attalids soon were on their way to Italy where the interest and admiration they commanded, when they were shown in public exhibitions, were destined to have a powerful effect on the taste of the Roman people.

Fig. 2:24 (*below*). *Augustus' Altar of Peace* (*Ara Pacis Augustae*). Marble. *c.*35′ square. *c.*13 B.C. Rome. The form is a smaller version of the Altar of Zeus at Pergamon. The carving shows the continuity of Hellenistic craftsmanship into the Roman period. (See also p. 130)

CHRONOLOGY:
Rome, 2d Century A.D.

General Events

B.C.

100–	44	Julius Caesar
29–	19	Vergil wrote *Aeneid*
27–A.D.14		Augustus reigned

A.D.

c.16	Maison Carrée at Nîmes built
c.50	Pont du Gard at Nîmes built
54– 68	Nero reigned
70	Titus captured Jerusalem; temple destroyed
79	Eruption of Vesuvius; Pompeii and Herculaneum destroyed
c.80	Vitruvius wrote *On Architecture*
81	Arch of Titus, Rome, built
82	Colosseum, Rome, finished
c.93	Quintilian wrote *Institutes of Oratory*
96–180	Antonine Age; Roman Empire reached pinnacle of power and prosperity
96– 98	Nerva, emperor
98–117	Trajan, emperor
c.100	Suetonius wrote *Lives of Twelve Caesars*
100	Pliny the Younger delivered *Panegyric* to Trajan before Roman Senate
100–102	Trajan's first Dacian campaign
105–106	Trajan's second Dacian campaign
110	Via Traiana built between Benevento and Brindisi Baths of Trajan built
113	Forum of Trajan built Column of Trajan erected
114	Arch of Trajan built at Benevento
117–138	Hadrian, emperor
120–124	Pantheon, Rome, built
138–161	Antoninus Pius, emperor
c.150	"House of Diana," Ostia, built
161–180	Marcus Aurelius, emperor
217	Baths of Caracalla, Rome, built

B.C.80–A.D.14 "Golden Age of Literature"

B.C.106–43	Cicero
c.96 –55	Lucretius
87 –57	Catullus
70 –19	Vergil
65 – 8	Horace
59–A.D.17	Livy
43–A.D.17	Ovid

A.D. 14–117 "Silver Age of Literature"

3B.C.–A.D.65	Seneca
23– 79	Pliny the Elder
c.66	Petronius died
c.90	Epictetus flourished
35– 95	Quintilian
40–c.102	Martial
c.46– 120	Plutarch
55–c.117	Tacitus
c.60–c.135	Juvenal
62– 113	Pliny the Younger
75–c.150	Suetonius
c.160	Apulius flourished
c.200	Tertulian flourished

3

THE ROMAN STYLE

ROME, 2D CENTURY A.D.

The Antonine Age was, according to Gibbon, "the period in the history of the world during which the condition of the human race was most happy and prosperous. . . ." Under Trajan, Hadrian, and Marcus Aurelius, continues the great historian, "the Empire of Rome comprehended the fairest part of the earth and the most civilized portion of mankind." This benign state of affairs Gibbon attributed to the Romans' genius for law and order, their cultivation of tolerance and justice, and their capacity for wise government.

The Arch of Trajan at Benevento (Fig. 3:1) recalls some of this vanished grandeur by proclaiming the virtues and accomplishments of the first great emperor of Gibbon's chosen period. Commissioned by the Roman Senate to celebrate the completion of the Via Traiana, a 200-mile highway over the mountains that linked Rome with the large port of Brindisi, the Arch honored an outstanding achievement in engineering as well as the chief engineer of the Empire. Such a gateway, marking as it did the start of the long road toward the East, challenged the Romans' imaginations to envisage lands that lay beyond the seas and reminded them that their city was not a self-contained unit. Roman awareness that their individual destinies, as well as those of their city and state, were closely bound up with the surrounding territories found logical expression in just such a monument. Among ancient city-states Rome was unique in its solution of the problem of how to maintain its municipal integrity and at the same time manage a far-flung empire. In evolving the institutions by which this political unity could be made compatible with such wide human diversity, the Romans achieved their greatest social distinction.

Such arches usually marked the conclusion of a successful military campaign, by which distant barbarian tribes were subdued or some new civilized people was brought into the Roman orbit. In the case of the Arch of Titus in Rome, the returning conqueror, together with his army, a train of captives, and the trophies of war, passed through the arch with the plaudits of the multitudes ringing in his ears. In keeping with this martial theme, the sculptural panels on one side of the passageway of the arch show Titus after his conquest of Palestine, driving his chariot in the grand procession, preceded by the goddess Roma and followed by Senators and representatives of the Roman people. On the other side are servants bearing the seven-branched golden candelabra and the sacred trumpets he had plundered from the temple at Jerusalem (Fig. 3:3).

Trajan's Arch was modeled architecturally after that of Titus, including such details as the attached *Composite* columns, a Roman combination of the Ionic and Corinthian orders. It differs in spirit from the Arch of Titus, however, in that the sculptures celebrate the arts of peace rather than those of war. The reliefs that so liberally cover its surface were arranged in characteristic Roman fashion so as to inform and instruct as well as to delight the eye. On the side facing the town of Benevento and more-distant Rome (Fig. 3:1), the panels deal with Trajan's domestic policy. He is seen making land grants in the newly conquered Danube region to veterans of his wars; standing in the midst of prosperous merchants grateful for the new harbor he built for them at Ostia, the port of Rome; and receiving the acclamation of the Senate and the people in the Roman Forum. Across the lintel moves a triumphal procession, and on either side of the keystone hover victories with crown and banners. Above, Jupiter and Juno and Minerva (known in Roman mythology as the Capitoline Triad) are seen extending their welcome to the Emperor. As a gesture of approval, Jupiter is turning over his thunderbolt to Trajan, a recognition of his great power as well as a sign that the adulation of the emperor was replacing the worship of the old Olympian deities. This group is placed next to the inscription, which adds to Trajan's usual string of titles that of *Optimo*, the best, which is said to have pleased him especially since he shared it only with Jupiter.

On the side toward the seaport are the scenes pertaining to Trajan's foreign policy. Germany is seen taking the oath of allegiance; various Oriental rulers are sending tributes through their envoys; and the Emperor is establishing state-sponsored benefits for the relief of poor children. Above, a figure symbolizing Mesopotamia is paying him homage, and the divinities of the Danube territory are welcoming him. The inside passage of the archway is similarly decorated. One

Fig. 3:1. *Arch of Trajan*. A.D. 114. Benevento (Anderson)

Fig. 3:2. *Arch of Tra-
jan*. Detail, *Trajan
Sacrificing* (Ander-
son)

Fig. 3:3. *Arch of Titus*. Detail, *Spoils of Jerusalem*. Marble. 94′ high. A.D. 81. Rome (Vatican Photographic Archive)

side shows a group of happy, well-fed children and their parents, all grateful for the benefits bestowed upon them. The other shows Trajan participating in a sacrificial observance before setting out on the new highway for eastern conquests (Fig. 3:2). Although each panel depicts a separate episode, unity is achieved in the repetition of the imperial personage. Variety is obtained by shifting the human and geographical environment. Changes of place are indicated partly by the activities and partly by the backgrounds, which signify a setting in Rome by some familiar buildings, a country place by trees, and a remote locality by exotic river gods. The subject matter is obviously propaganda for imperial rule—even to the extent of sometimes showing Trajan as a figure of superhuman size—but the restrained manner of presentation keeps this aspect from becoming too blatant. The actual sculpture is technically well handled, though there is a tendency to accent linear detail at the expense of unity and repose.

While monumental arches were nonutilitarian in purpose, their form exemplifies the building principle that underlies the Roman achievements in architecture. With the arch the Romans constructed their vaults and domes that carried architecture forward well into modern times. The fact that Trajan's Arch was built in a provincial town south of Rome on the road to and from the great centers of the East—Athens, Pergamon, Alexandria, Ephesus, and Antioch— is a reminder of the route by which the heritage of the classical Mediterranean world became a part of Western cultural tradition. By military conquest, by annexation, by inheritance, and by voluntary action—one by one the proud old city-states and kingdoms became a part of greater Rome. Likewise all the ideas, institutions, and art forms of this vast region were sifted through the ingenious Roman mind, and, together with notable contributions of her own, Rome gradually achieved a culmination of culture, expressed in her literature, architecture, and sculpture, that could compare favorably with the political eminence of her great empire.

ARCHITECTURE

Forum of Trajan

Shortly after his accession as emperor in A.D. 98, Trajan began a grandiose project in Rome: the construction of a new forum. Just as the empire had grown in his time to its greatest extent, so the population of Rome had risen to over a million, creating a need for larger and more imposing public buildings. The old Forum Romanum of the Republic had long been inadequate, and several extensions had been undertaken in the early years of the Empire. But Trajan's project was so ambitious that it equaled all previous forums combined, bringing the total area covered by such structures to over 25 acres. Needless to say, its magnificence was in every way comparable to its size. Trajan entrusted the project to Apollodorus, a Greek architect-engineer from Damascus, famous for the construction of a bridge over the widest part of the Danube during Trajan's second Dacian campaign. But Apollodorus' Greek origin did not necessarily indicate a Hellenistic bias on the emperor's part; all other known architects in Rome at this time (including those who collaborated on the project) were Romans, and Apollodorus was thoroughly conversant with the current Roman building tradition.

A forum is actually a typically Roman conception, combining a system of open courtyards and buildings grouped in a specific relationship. A glance at the plan of the Athenian acropolis (Fig. 1:5) shows that the Parthenon and Erechtheum had little more in common than the site on which they stood. But no part of a forum existed in isolation, and in this instance everything was conceived from the beginning on a large scale and with an eye to symmetry. From the ground plan (Fig. 3:4), one can see that the whole was bisected by a central axis running from the center of the arched gateway, through the middle of the square, through the entrance to the basilica (whose axis is at right angles to the whole forum), to the base of the column, and finally up the steps of the temple to the altar at the back.

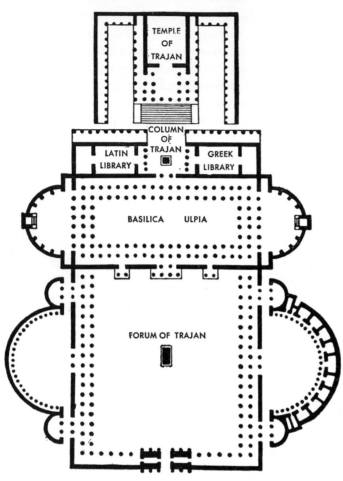

Fig. 3:4. Forum of Trajan, Rome. *Plan* (Based on Helen Gardner. *Art Through the Ages,* 3d ed. New York, Harcourt, Brace, 1948. p. 177. By permission)

Fig. 3:5. Forum of Trajan. Northeast Exedra and Market Hall. A.D. 113. Rome

The forum idea apparently evolved from an open city square that combined the facilities of a market and a meeting place. By degrees, the buildings around it were put to administrative uses, and space was allotted for political centers, law courts, triumphal arches, commemorative monuments, and temples. Various historians have pointed to prototypes in the older agoras of Greek cities, in the city plans of smaller Roman settlements, and in Roman military camps. As these facilities developed, however, they became a typical Roman institution. And because the Senate met in the Roman Forum, the center of political debate, a forum has since been identified with parliamentary bodies and a meeting of minds.

The problems confronting Apollodorus in the case of the Forum of Trajan were by no means simple. Clearing such a large space in a densely populated city meant demolishing many blocks of houses. His site, moreover, was the valley between the Quirinal and Capitoline hills. If the usual interpretation of the inscription on Trajan's column is accepted, that monument was erected "to show posterity how high rose the mountain leveled by the Emperor." In practical terms, this would mean that more than 100 feet was cut off the Quirinal hill and carted away to make room for the courtyard and basilica. The remaining part was then terraced as a site for the market buildings, which extended up the hillside.

Entrance to the Forum was made through a majestic triple archway into the large paved quadrangle, enclosed on three sides by a wall and colonnade and on the fourth by the Basilica Ulpia, whose entrances stood opposite those of the archway. Standing in the exact center was an impressive bronze statue of Trajan on horseback. Though no longer extant, it is known to have resembled the surviving bronze equestrian portrait of Marcus Aurelius (Fig. 3:9). With the baton of command firmly in his hand, this last of the Antonine emperors sits astride his splendid mount with an equilibrium worthy of the patient Stoic philosopher and the thoughtful mien of the author of the widely read *Meditations*. Flanking the square on the east and west sides were semicircular *exedrae* outlined by tall Doric columns. Similar in shape were the series of market stalls rising upward into the two hills. The best preserved are those on the Quirinal side, which were six stories in height and constructed of brick (Fig. 3:5). On the forum floor were more than 150 booths—for vegetables, fruits, and flowers; above were large vaulted halls where wine and oil were stored; spices and imported delicacies were sold on the third and fourth floors; the fifth was used to distribute food and money out of the imperial treasure; and on top were tanks supplied by fresh water from an aqueduct where live fish could be bought.

Adjacent to the open square (Fig. 3:4) was the Basilica Ulpia, of which only the rows of broken columns now mark the site (Fig. 3:6). The term *basilica* was applied rather generally to large public buildings and is approxi-

Fig. 3:6. Ruins of *Column of Trajan* and Basilica Ulpia. Marble. Rome (German Archeological Institute)

mately equivalent to the modern use of the word *hall* to refer to a place for meetings. Since court sessions were also held in such places, the term *hall of justice* is likewise related to one of its functions. As an architectural form, the Roman basilica is one link in the long chain of Mediterranean structures that began with domestic dwellings, Egyptian hypostyle halls, and Greek temples and continued later with Christian basilican churches.

The large rectangular interior of the Basilica Ulpia (Fig. 3:7), named for Trajan's family, was marked by a double colonnade in the Corinthian order that ran completely around the building, supporting a balcony and a second tier of columns that, in turn, supported the beams of the timbered roof. This large central hall served as a general meeting place as well as a business center. The semicircular apses, possibly roofed over with hemispherical vaults and set apart from the central hall by screens or curtains, housed the courts of law. The decorative scheme of the building included the lavish use of polychrome marbles. The steps at the entrances were of *giallo antico* stone, and the flanking columns were of matching yellow marble. The exterior and interior walls were liberally faced with varicolored marble panels, and the floor was done in rich mosaic patterns. In the double colonnade the shafts of the columns on the ground floor were of red granite, while their Corinthian capitals were carved from white stone. Pausanias' description of the "roof of bronze" probably meant that the decorative scheme had been completed with some form of metal embellishments.

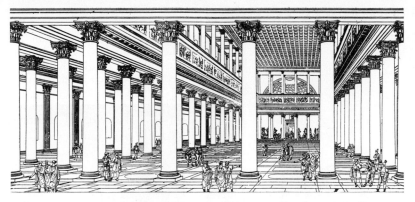

Fig. 3:7. Reconstruction of Basilica Ulpia, Interior. A.D. 113. Rome

Beyond the basilica were two libraries, one for Greek and the other for Latin books, separated by a courtyard that enclosed the base of Trajan's Column (Fig. 3:8), the sculpture of which will be discussed shortly.

After Trajan's death his adopted son and successor, Hadrian, built at the end of the main axis of the Forum the Corinthian temple that climaxed the grand design. Architecturally, it was a large-scale version of the Maison Carrée (Fig. 3:15) at Nîmes in southern France. Like other Roman temples, this temple honoring Trajan and the Maison Carrée rested on podiums and had porticos in the front, which were much more prominently featured than those in Greek temples. The well-preserved example at Nîmes likewise shows only the columns of the portico standing free, while the rest are attached to the cella, indicating that columns were needed less for structural strength than for embellishment.

Fig. 3:8. Reconstruction of Court surrounding base of *Trajan's Column.* A.D. 113. Rome

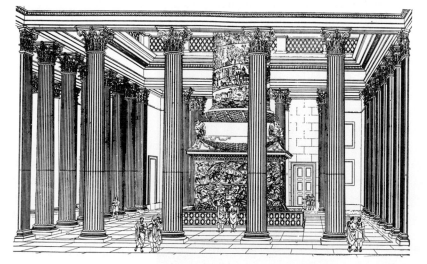

Fig. 3:9 (*left*). *Equestrian Statue of Marcus Aurelius.* Gilt bronze. Over lifesize. A.D. *c.*161–180. Rome (Gabinetto Fotografico Nazionale)

Fig. 3:10 (*above*). *Augustus.* Marble. 80″ high. *c.*20 B.C. Found at Primaporta near Rome. Vatican Museum, Rome (Vatican Photographic Archive)

Fig. 3:11 (*left*). *Roman Married Couple, "Portia and Cato"* (?). Marble. 27″ high. *c.*1st century B.C. Vatican Museum, Rome (Vatican Photographic Archive)

The practice of deifying rulers and building temples to them was already widespread in Hellenistic times, and in Rome it began as early as the reign of Augustus. The type of statue that stood in such temples can be seen in the *Portrait of Augustus* (Fig. 3:10), which was found near Prima Porta. He stands in the imposing attitude of an imperator addressing his troops. Carved on the cuirass, or metal breastplate of his armor, are scenes in low relief recounting the outstanding achievements of his reign and pictures of the gods and goddesses who conferred their favors upon him. At his side is a cupid astride a dolphin, which alludes to the divine origin of the Julian family. Vergil, the principal poet of his period, traced Augustus' ancestry all the way back to Aeneas, the legendary founder of Rome, whose father was the mortal Anchises but whose mother was none other than the immortal Venus. Much of the Roman religion was a family affair, honoring the living *pater familias* as well as the nearer and more remote ancestors. A room in every household was set aside for this purpose, and the custom was responsible for a whole genre of sculpture, such as the portrait busts of *Porcia and Cato* (?) (Fig. 3:11). In contrast to the generalized and somewhat idealized portrait of Augustus as the statesman and imperator, the unpretentious portrait of these ordinary citizens is remarkably realistic. Both sculptures, however, served essentially the same purpose—one as the image of the father of a family in a simple household, the other for the veneration of a great man in a temple. The paternalistic emperors were felt to deserve the universal reverence of the whole Roman family, since they were considered *pater patriae*, or fathers of their country. Erecting a temple to a distinguished Roman emperor was not unlike building the Washington Monument or the Lincoln Memorial in Washington, D. C. Certain days were set aside for the offering of food and drink in simple family ceremonies; on the day for honoring the emperor, the rites at his temple were more formal, occasionally including animal sacrifice, a procession, festivities, and amusements. Religion to the Romans thus represented the tradition and continuity of the family and, in the larger sense, the history and destiny of Rome itself.

With the exception of this temple, the Forum of Trajan was completed in the Emperor's lifetime and was dedicated by him for the use of the people of Rome in A.D. 113. The whole, then, is made up of parts—the triumphal entrance archway, the courtyard and its equestrian statue, the mercantile buildings, the Basilica Ulpia, two libraries, a monumental column, and the temple—all adding up to an architectural composition on a grand scale, designed to accommodate a hierarchy of activities. Beginning with a shopping center and place to transact business, the Forum continued with a general meeting place and the halls of justice, moved on to places for quiet contemplation, study in the libraries and the reading of history in visual form on the column, and, finally, came to rest in the precinct for the veneration of the Emperor and the worship of the Roman gods.

Imperial Baths

While the forums took care of the more serious pursuits of his people, Trajan never forgot that circuses were often as important as bread in promoting the happiness of his subjects. One of every emperor's duties, in fact, was to provide for public amusement out of his private purse. Only the very wealthy could afford entertainment in their own homes, so the people as a whole had to look for their recreation outside. To this end many baths, theaters, amphitheaters, arenas, and stadiums had been built all over the city. The variety they encompassed has never been surpassed, and to this day the highest praise that can be given an elaborate public festival is to call it a "Roman holiday."

Imperial baths provided the people with far more than hot, cold, and tepid swimming pools. They offered such other facilities as dressing rooms, gymnasiums, restaurants, bars, and shady walks. Guests also could listen to public lectures, read in one of the libraries, or stroll about the galleries where statuary and paintings were exhibited. The baths were, in short, the people's palaces where the sociable citizenry could enjoy together the things that only the rich could afford separately. Favored also as places to show the booty and souvenirs carried off during foreign conquests, the baths have been sites where much ancient statuary has been found, notably the *Laocoön Group* (Fig. 2:21). These baths also had important hygienic advantages; and with the habit of daily bathing firmly established, the people of Rome probably were cleaner than those of any other city, before or since.

Fig. 3:12. *Groined Vaults*. Drawing by Choisy

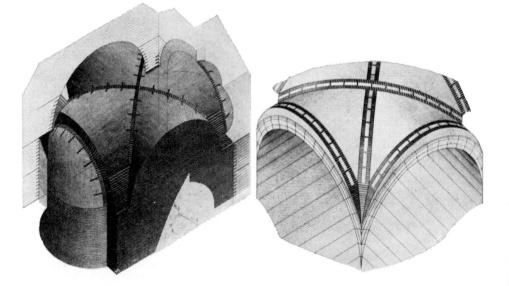

Fig. 3:13. Baths of Caracalla. *Great Hall*, restored by Spiers. 183′ long, 79′ wide, 108′ high. A.D. 211–217. Rome (Anderson and Spiers, Architecture of Ancient Rome. London, B. T. Batsford, 1927. Plate XLIX)

Trajan added to the already-existing public baths a large establishment also built by Apollodorus. Although the ruins of his Thermae (Baths) are not so well preserved as the later baths of Caracalla and Diocletian, enough is known to establish a clear picture of what they were like. Only a degree smaller than the later examples, their facilities were on a comparable scale. The large central hall was the earliest known use of concrete cross vaulting, the principle of which can be studied in Figure 3:12 and in the similar central hall of the Baths of Caracalla (Fig. 3:13), which measured 183 feet in length with an open space between the walls of 79 feet. From the illustration, it can be seen that the barrel vault that runs lengthwise is three times intersected at right angles by shorter vaults extending across the width of the hall. Besides spanning larger interior spaces without the obstruction of supporting piers and columns, this type of construction had the additional advantage of ample lighting through the clearstory windows, which were provided with thin strips of translucent yellow marble in lieu of glass. Modern architects, when erecting such huge plants as the Union Station in Washington, D. C., and Grand Central terminal in New York City, found no better models among large secular structures than these Roman baths.

Colosseum, Aqueducts, and Apartment Houses

Other places, such as the Colosseum (Fig. 3:14) which dates from the late 1st century, were the scene of more garish forms of mass amusement, including gory gladiatorial contests between men and wild beasts. The oval form of the Colosseum covers about 6 acres and could seat about 50,000 spectators at one time. Around its circumference run some 80 archways, which served so efficiently as entrances and exits that the entire bowl could be emptied in a matter of minutes. The Roman talent for organization is not only evident here in such practical respects but extends to the structure and decorative design. Three architectural orders are combined in the successive stories of the same building. The attached columns on the lower range are the "home-grown" variation of the Doric, known as the Tuscan; those on the second tier are Ionic; on the third, Corinthian; while on the fourth, which rises to a height of 157 feet, are found flat Corinthian pilasters between which run a row of sockets, for the poles over which a canvas awning was stretched to protect the spectators from sun and rain. The building material was a concrete made from broken pieces of brick, small rocks, volcanic dust, lime, and water. It could be poured into molds of any desired shape and when dry was as hard as natural stone. The exterior was originally covered with marble facing, and the entire structure would be in good condition today had it not been used as a quarry for building materials right up to the 18th century. In spite of this, the Colosseum is still one of the most

Fig. 3:14. Colosseum. Long axis 620′, short axis 513′, height 160′. A.D. 72–80. Rome

Fig. 3:15. "Maison Carrée." Marble. 59' x 117'. Podium 11' high, columns 30½' high. *c.*16 B.C. Nîmes, France

imposing ruins to survive from Roman times, and its popularity as a prototype can be seen in the numerous football stadiums on college campuses today.

In order to assure an ample water supply for his thermae, Trajan found it necessary to improve the old system of aqueducts and to add a new one, 35 miles long, that is still in use today. One of the most beautiful examples of a Roman aqueduct is the Pont du Gard at Nîmes (Fig. 3:16), which survived from the 1st century A.D. A system of underground and open concrete channels was constructed to bring water from its mountain source to the town 25 miles away. Functioning on the principle of gravity, the ducts were sloped in the de-

Fig. 3:16. Pont du Gard. *c.*880' long, *c.*160' high. A.D. *c.*50. Nîmes, France

Roman Apartment House at Ostia, "House of Diana." 2d century A.D. Fig. 3:17 (*left*). Ruins. Fig. 3:18 (*right*). Restoration by Gismondi

sired direction, and in this instance the water was carried almost 300 yards across the valley at a height of more than 160 feet. The graceful lower range of arches support a bridge that is still in use, while the upper series of large and small arches support the water channel.

The most ambitious of Trajan's civil-engineering projects, however, was the construction of a port at Ostia about 15 miles from Rome. It was a complicated system of breakwaters and canals connected with Rome by the Tiber River, and it provided facilities for export and import trade as well as an anchorage for the Roman fleet. Ostia rapidly grew into one of the most important commercial centers of the 2d century, and recent excavations have uncovered some of its warehouses, theaters, baths, and many other public and private buildings. Of major interest are the ruins of apartment houses that reveal the type of multiple-family dwelling place in use at this time both in Ostia and Rome. In contrast to the more leisurely and rambling Mediterranean country villas found at Pompeii, the so-called "House of Diana" (Fig. 3:17) shows a close-knit, eco-nomically spaced, well-planned building of five stories, which has a strikingly modern look. Because the house was located on a street corner, the ground floor had rows of shops along two sides. The second floor provided small apart-ments for the shopkeepers and their families, and each apartment was connected by separate steps to a shop below. In the reconstruction drawing (Fig. 3:18) two entrances can be seen on the right. One led into the center courtyard, which provided light for the inner rooms and a fountain. The other led to a staircase, which gave access to the upper floors. The most desirable apartments would have been those with the balconies on the third floor. In the time of Constantine, two centuries later, Rome was known to have had almost 50,000 apartment houses, some of which rose as high as eight stories, and only about 1700 private town houses.

Fig. 3:19. Pantheon. *Portico,* 101′ wide, 59′ high. Walls 20′ thick. A.D. *c.*115–125. Rome (Foto Unione)

The Pantheon

With their highly developed sense of social organization, the Romans hit upon the idea of a pantheon as a temple for all the gods. This religious conception was an interesting extension of their political experience, and the Olympian deities were considered in this context as a sort of super senate which legislated on such cosmic matters as thunderstorms and earthquakes and on any odd matter that was outside the jurisdiction of the otherwise efficient and conscientious Roman senators and emperor. To house their divine deliberations and to afford well-intentioned Romans the opportunity of propitiating them on the proper occasions, the temple known as the Pantheon had been built. After the earlier structure was destroyed by fire, Hadrian undertook its reconstruction about A.D. 120 (Fig. 3:19). The boldness of its design as well as its masterly execution mark it as one of the marvels of Roman engineering.

Unlike his predecesor, Hadrian was a man of thought rather than of action. He took delight in disputations with philosophers and is known to have prided himself on his architectural acumen. No definite records exist to show what role he played in any specific building, but his architects, in deference to their imperial patron, showed their discretion by failing to claim any personal credit for their labors. The most famous architect of Trajan's reign, Apollodorus, is known to have continued his career under Hadrian, and since the Pantheon represents

Fig. 3:20. Pantheon. *Interior.* Diameter 142′, height 140′. Engraving by Piranesi. (Metropolitan Museum of Art, New York)

a kind of culmination of Roman engineering skill, it is generally thought to be mainly his work.

The builders first constructed a cylindrical base the walls of which are 20 feet in thickness. Eight large recesses were left in it, one to allow for the entrance vestibule and the others to provide niches for the largest altars. To furnish support for the massive dome, a system of relieving arches and abutments were embedded in the wall to discharge its great weight. The concrete for the dome was poured in adjoining sections, and as it dried, it became one solid mass of stone, thus justifying description as an artificial monolith. Entrance is made through the octastyle Corinthian portico that measures a little over 100 feet in width. Such a huge structure could easily have been just an overwhelming mass of brick and concrete. Its solid exterior proportions actually do very little to relieve this general impression, but the fact that it was conceived primarily as an interior enclosing a definite space (Fig. 3:20), and not as the solid mass which surrounds it, saves the day. The Pantheon's geometry is based on the union of a cylinder and hemisphere, with the interior diameter and the height of the dome both being about 140 feet. The clarity of form achieved by the visible equality of horizontal and vertical dimensions, as well as by the simplicity of its design, is evident even to the casual eye. The satisfying sense of spatial proportion and the harmonious impression of the interior are based on a union of applied scientific skill and aesthetic feeling. In the Pantheon, the Romans advanced architecture to the place where it achieved significant interiors. The inner surface of the dome is characterized by *coffers*, indented panels which served the dual purpose of diminishing the weight of the dome and furnishing the basis for its decoration. In the center of each coffer was a gilded bronze star, a motif that related the dome symbolically to the sky. The sole source of light is the single, 29-foot-round opening in the middle of the dome. This *oculus*, or eye, as it was called, most likely was interpreted as an allusion to the all-seeing eye of heaven. The shaft of light that streamed downward was sufficient to illuminate the whole interior clearly and uniformly. The general effect is one of brightness and clarity with no hint as yet of medieval mystery.

As seen today, the Pantheon is stripped of its former rich and colorful covering. The bronze plates of the portico ceiling, the gilded bronze tiles that covered the entire exterior of both the drum and the dome, the polychrome marbles that faced the interior walls, and the monumental statues of the gods have all disappeared in the course of time. Despite mutilations, the Pantheon is the best-preserved single building that survives from the ancient world and the oldest structure of large proportions with its original roof intact. It holds its own as one of the world's most impressive domed buildings in spite of such outstanding competition as Hagia Sophia in Constantinople (Fig. 4:20), the Cathedral of Florence (Fig. 9:1), St. Peter's in Rome (Fig. 10:21), and St. Paul's in London (Fig. 15:3). Its descendants are legion—the Villa Rotunda (Fig. 11:6), Thomas Jefferson's home at Monticello, the rotunda he designed for the University of Virginia, the Pantheon in Paris, certain features of the Capitol rotunda in Washington, D. C., and the Low Memorial Library at Columbia University in New York, to name but a few.

The Roman Architectural Contribution

The Roman contribution to architecture was fourfold: (1) building for use, (2) emphasis on verticality, (3) design of significant interiors, and (4) development of the arch and vault as a building principle. In the first case, Roman architecture is marked by a shift in emphasis from religious buildings to the civil-engineering projects that had such an important bearing on the solution of the practical problems of the day. This does not mean that the Romans neglected their shrines and temples or that they lacked religious feeling. As in the 19th and 20th centuries, however, the main architectural expression is to be found in secular rather than religious structures. In this category come the basilicas, aqueducts, roads, bridges, even the sewer systems, which so admirably served the utilitarian purposes of the Romans.

Second, by their technical advances they were able to increase the height of their buildings in proportion to the growing size of their large structures. The six-story mercantile buildings of Trajan's Forum are an impressive demonstration of the practical advantages of such verticality, which allowed the combination of many small shops into a single structure in a crowded city location. The multi-family apartment houses in Ostia and Rome are also cases in point. The trend is seen in the additional height that imparts such pleasing spatial proportions to the halls in the Baths of Trajan and Caracalla as well as the Pantheon—all made possible by cross vaulting and the dome.

Third, the enclosing of large units of interior space was made necessary by the expansion of the city's population. The direction of architectural thought in meeting this need can easily be seen by contrasting a Greek agora with the Forum of Trajan, a Hellenistic theater with the Colosseum, or the Parthenon with the Pantheon. Special attention to space composition and the problems of lighting are in evidence in the planning of such interiors as those of the Basilica Ulpia, the Pantheon, and the halls of the great baths. In all instances, the increasing Roman awareness of the value, tangibility, and reality of the spatial medium is discernible.

Last—and perhaps most important of all—was the Roman exploitation of the possibilities inherent in the arch as a building principle to implement the above objectives. The construction of a true arch by means of the wedge-shaped blocks known as *voussoirs* can be seen more easily in Figure 3:21 than explained in words. When such arches are placed side by side in a series, the resulting

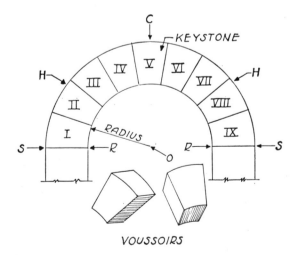

Fig. 3:21. *True Arch.* Drawing by W. D. Richmond

arcade can be used for such structures as aqueducts and bridges, as seen in the Pont du Gard (Fig. 3:16). When placed in a series, from front to back, the result is a barrel vault (also called a tunnel vault), which can be seen in the Arch of Trajan at Benevento (Fig. 3:1) and which was useful for roofing interiors. When two such half-cylindrical vaults intersect each other at right angles, as seen in Figure 3:12, the result is referred to as a cross vault (or groined vault). This is the principle that is used so advantageously in the central halls of the Baths of Trajan and Caracalla. When a series of arches span a given space by intersecting each other around a central axis, the result is a dome, as exemplified in the Pantheon (Fig. 3:20). In greatly oversimplified form, these constitute the technical principles that underlie the Roman architectural achievement.

SCULPTURE

Spiral Frieze of Trajan's Column

To commemorate Trajan's victories in the two campaigns against the Dacian people of the lower Danube region, a monumental column was erected in his Forum by the Senate and people of Rome. It was placed in a small court opening off the Basilica Ulpia between the two libraries. Its base was originally surrounded by a colonnade (Fig. 3:8) that supported an upper gallery from which better views of the sculptures could be obtained. The diameter of the column varies from 12 feet at the base of its shaft to 10 feet at the top. As a whole it rose to a full height of 128 feet, including the 18-foot base, the 97-foot shaft, and a 13-foot colossal statue of Trajan that originally stood at the top. The latter has long since disappeared and has been replaced by one of St. Peter. Inside the column is a circular staircase that winds upward to the top and is lighted by small windowlike slits cut into the frieze. According to tradition, Trajan chose the monument as his burial place, and his ashes were placed somewhere beneath it. The column itself is of the Doric order and is constructed in several sections of white marble. Its surface is entirely covered by a spiral band, carved in low relief, which winds from bottom to top in 23 revolutions. Reading from left to right, the story of the two Dacian campaigns unfolds in a continuous strip about a yard wide and 218 yards long in which more than 2500 human figures make their appearance, in addition to horses, boats, vehicles, and equipment of all kinds.

The hero of the story is, of course, the soldierly Trajan, who is shown fulfilling his imperial mission as the defender of Rome against the encroachments of the barbarians. The Empire was always willing to include any people who accepted the values of Mediterranean civilization, but it could tolerate no challenge. When an important kingdom was founded in Dacia, Trajan regarded it as a threat and set out forthwith to bring it under Roman control. While it took two campaigns to do the job, the lasting result of this Romanizing process is reflected in the name of one of the nations of the region—Rumania. Trajan's brilliance as a commander was well known, and on this and other similar monuments his reputation certainly did not suffer for lack of advertisement. In the frieze, he invariably is present and consistently is portrayed as a resolute figure in complete command of the situation at all times. Sharing top billing with their general is the Roman army; and their opposite numbers are Trajan's antagonist, the Dacian king Decebalus and his barbarian hordes.

The beginning of the campaign is placed on the banks of the Danube in a Roman encampment guarded by sentries and supplied by boats (Fig. 3:22). As the Romans set forth across a pontoon bridge, a river god personifying the Danube rises from a grotto and lends his support by holding up the bridge. From this point onward the action moves with singular directness toward the inevitable climax: the triumph of Roman arms. The ensuing scenes show Trajan holding a council of war; clad in a toga pouring a libation to the gods; and standing on a tribunal as he addresses his troops (Fig. 3:23). The army is shown

Fig. 3:22. *Trajan's Column*. Detail of frieze, *Trajan's Campaign against the Dacians*. Column 97' high. Spiral frieze 656' long. Marble. A.D. 106–113. Rome (Alinari)

Trajan's Column. Details of frieze.

Fig. 3:23 (*right*). *Trajan Haranguing Troops.* (Vatican Photographic Archive)

Fig. 3:24 (*below*). *Trajan Accepting Surrender of Decebalus* (Vatican Photographic Archive)

pitching a camp on enemy soil; burning a Dacian village; and in the midst of battle. At the psychological moment Jupiter appears in the sky, throwing bolts of lightning at the enemy to disperse them in all directions. The aftermath is then shown with the soldiers crowding around the emperor and holding up the decapitated heads of the enemy for his approval; surgeons are seen caring for the wounded; and Winged Victory makes her appearance.

At the making of peace Trajan is shown seated in judgment on the left, while the still-defiant Decebalus stands on the far right in front of the wall of the Roman camp. Between them are the representatives of the vanquished people prostrating themselves before their conqueror and imploring his mercy. Here the protagonist and antagonist of the drama confront each other directly in a single scene in the middle of the frieze (Fig. 3:24), which serves as an interim summary of the action up to this point. On this occasion Trajan made a lenient peace, which gave the king of the Dacians his chance to regather his forces, thus making a second campaign inevitable. At the conclusion of the story near the top of the column, Decebalus is shown falling on his sword; his head is brought to Trajan as a trophy; the barbarians take refuge across a river; and finally a personification of Night is seen hovering over a desolate landscape.

The scenes are designed to promote the continuous flow of action as smoothly as possible. For reasons of clarity the scenes have to be differentiated, and the artist does this through some 90 separate appearances of Trajan, which always signal a new activity. Other devices employed are an occasional tree, to set off one scene from another, and new backgrounds that are indicated in some places by a mountain, in others by a group of buildings, and so on. The comparison of this type of spiral relief has aptly been made with the form of the unfolding papyrus and parchment scrolls that the educated Romans were accustomed to read. Trajan is known to have written an account of his Dacian campaigns, much as Julius Caesar had done in the case of his Gallic wars, but the document is lost. Since commentaries on this bit of history are so fragmentary, the column has become one of the principal sources of information about it. The impression the viewer receives is so vivid that he feels almost as if he had experienced the campaign with Trajan.

The reliefs have a definite affinity to literature in their manner of telling a story by the process of visual narration. The methods that the Romans used in such cases have been distinguished as "the simultaneous" and "the continuous." The first is the same as that used by the Greeks in the east pediment and frieze of the Parthenon, for instance, where all the action takes place at a given moment that is frozen into sculptural form. The simultaneous or isolating method thus observes the classical unities of time, place, and action. The continuous, or cyclic, method was developed by the Romans for just such a series of scenes as Trajan's wars. The unity of action is obtained by the telling of a life story, or it can be broadened to include a couple of military campaigns, as in this instance. The unities of time and place are sacrificed as far as the whole composition is concerned but are preserved in the separate scenes. While the origin of this continuous style is still a matter of scholarly dispute, none has challenged the effective use the Romans made of it. Its spirit is close to their keen interest in historical and current events, and its value for the purposes of state propaganda is obvious.

Despite the direct narrative content, the style is not realistic. For his effects, the artist depended upon as carefully a worked out set of symbols as the writers of epics have done in the case of words. The use of a series of undulating lines, for example, indicates the sea; a jagged outline on the horizon stands for a mountain; a giant rising up out of the water represents a river; a wall can mean either a city or a camp; and a female figure whose draperies are folded in the shape of a crescent moon informs the observer that it is night. In such symbolism, liberties with perspective inevitably occur, and it is quite usual to find a man taller than a wall and an important figure, such as that of the Emperor, much greater in size than those around him. This technique does not preclude such clearly recognizable things as the banners of certain Roman legions as well as the details of their shields and armor. But there is a sharp stylistic differentiation between the approach in this case and the obvious realism of the relief on the Arch of Titus (Fig. 3:3). The Trajan frieze points unmistakably in the direction of the pictorial symbolism employed later by early Christian and medieval artists, who doubtless were influenced by it.

Much of the work will seem crude if placed beside the sculptures of Hellenistic artists who were still active in Rome (see Fig. 3:27 as an example). But this relief is clearly and intentionally an example of Roman popular art, and as such it was addressed to that large segment of the populace that was not accustomed to getting its information and enjoyment from books. Its location between two libraries also indicates a recognition that history could come from pictorial sources as well as from Greek and Latin scrolls. The elegant and placid forms of Greek gods were not apt to arouse the emotions of those Romans who sought amusement in the gladiatorial contests held in the Colosseum. While the educated minority could admire the virtues of dignity and restraint in their sculpture, the vast majority had to be aroused by just such an energetic direct-action story as this, and one that involved people like themselves. Viewed in this light, the work is fresh, original, and astonishingly alive.

The artist who designed the frieze was clearly a master of his medium, who was able to depict with ease in extremely low relief whole armies, pitched battles, and the surrounding land and seascapes. The care in execution is consistently carried out, and, even though the reliefs at the top were almost completely out of view, the workmanship remains the same. Standing in its prominent location from Trajan's time to the present, this column and the similar one of Marcus Aurelius have had incalculable influence on later art. The continuous mode of visual narration was taken over directly into the catacomb paintings of the early Christians; was continued in illuminated manuscripts, religious sculptures, and the stained glass of the medieval period; and can still be found going strong in the comic strips of daily newspapers. Even the motion picture owes a certain debt to the technique worked out here in the 2d century A.D. In this book, examples of the direct influence of this narrative mode include the mosaics relating the story of Christ in the church of Sant' Apollinare Nuovo in Ravenna (Figs. 4:7 and 4:8); the Bayeux Tapestry, which tells the story of the Norman conquest of England (Figs. 6:3–6:5); Giotto's frescoes on the life of St. Francis of Assisi (Figs. 8:4, 8:5, and 8:15); Michelangelo's Sistine Chapel ceiling murals (Figs. 10:12–10:19); and the studious duplication of it made under Napoleon for the Place Vendôme in Paris (Fig. 17:5).

LITERATURE AND MUSIC

While the time of Trajan could boast of no writers of the caliber of Cicero, Lucretius, Vergil, or Horace, it could at least point with pride to some of its eminent men of letters. Quintilian, author of the famous textbook known as the *Institutes of Oratory*, had influenced directly or indirectly a group of writers including Pliny the Younger, a persuasive orator and graceful letter writer; Tacitus, the historian; Juvenal, the satirist; and Suetonius, who was responsible for the gossipy but informative *Lives of the Twelve Caesars*. Plutarch, though a Greek, must also be listed among the major writers of the period, especially for his perceptive series of biographies of Greek and Roman statesmen, the *Parallel Lives*.

A very vivid picture of the life of a Roman of the patrician class is found in the correspondence of Pliny the Younger. As a senator and holder of important offices under Trajan, he enjoyed a wide acquaintance with many men of affairs. As a man of means he was able to enjoy all the refinements of a style of living that was highly luxurious even by modern standards. His civic duties required him to pass much of his time in Rome, but, like so many others of his class, he preferred to live in more rural surroundings. His country estates extended from one end of the Italian peninsula to the other, and he took special pride in the beautiful villas he built on them. Two that he especially liked were located on Lake Como. One he called Tragedy, because it commanded a grand view from its lofty situation; the other he named Comedy, because it was more intimately built on the lakeshore and more conducive to sport. "You may fish yourself," he wrote to a friend, "and throw your line out of your room, and almost from your bed, as from a boat."

Pliny's descriptions of his villa near Florence and another near Ostia are so detailed that architects have been able to reconstruct them with considerable exactness. The pleasures available at his Tuscan estate included hunting, supervising the farming, strolling about in gardens, exercising and playing games in the gymnasium, banqueting, and swimming, for which there were no less than three pools, including a warm one in the sun and a cool one in the shade. Pliny was not one to neglect the pleasures of the mind, which in his case included reading in his extensive library, conversing and corresponding with stimulating friends, and collecting objects of art that took his fancy. His enthusiasm for the latter pursuit is expressed in one of his letters. "I have lately purchased with a legacy that was left me, a statue of Corinthian bronze," he informed a friend. "It represents an old man in a standing posture. The bones, the muscles, the veins, and wrinkles are so strongly expressed, that you would imagine the figure to be animated."

Because of the Ciceronian eloquence he had developed as a pupil of Quintilian, Pliny was chosen by the Senate to make the welcoming speech on the occasion of Trajan's first arrival in Rome after his accession as emperor. The *Panegyric* he delivered was a veritable triumphal arch of flowery oratory. His later correspondence with Trajan, when he served as governor of the distant province of Bithynia, is as businesslike and direct as the speech to the Senate was ornate and devious. Pliny wrote to his superior with a proper note of deference, and Trajan's replies were always terse and to the point. In a typical exchange Pliny asked whether it would be advisable to rebuild the baths in one of the towns under his jurisdiction. The complete text of Trajan's reply was as follows: "If the erecting a public bath will not be too great a charge upon the Prusenses, we may comply with their request; provided, however, that no new tax be levied for this purpose, nor any of those taken off which are appropriated to necessary purposes."

The practice of poetry and music enjoyed higher favor among the educated Roman amateurs than dabbling in the visual arts. Suggesting a plan for a building or some of the details of its decorative design was all right for a patrician, but from there on it was the architect's and carpenter's business. With sculpture and painting, a wealthy man could make an imposing impression as a collector, but the actual chiseling and daubing was something for artisans and slaves. When it came to the writing of verse or singing to the accompaniment of the lyre, however, amateurs abounded in the highest ranks of society right up to the emperors themselves. While Trajan's recreations seem to have been as strenuous as some of his military activities, those of his immediate successors included literary and musical pursuits. Hadrian wrote poetry in both Greek and Latin, but it remained for the last of the Antonines, Marcus Aurelius, to make an enduring reputation as a writer and philosopher. Hadrian, Antoninus Pius, and Caracalla were pro-

Fig. 3:25. *Gladiatorial Contest*, showing Orchestra with Hydraulic Organ, Trumpet, and Horn Players. Mosaic from Zliten, North Africa. A.D. *c.*70

ficient on the cithara and hydraulic organ. Their musical prowess, however, was not destined to put that of their famous predecessor Nero into the shade.

While much is known about Roman literature, no actual examples of Roman music survive. All knowledge about it must be gleaned from occasional literary references, from sculptures, mosaics, and wall paintings that show music-making situations, and from some of the musical instruments themselves. From these sources, it is clear that the Romans heard much music and that no occasion, public or private, was complete without it.

A mosaic showing a small Roman instrumental ensemble performing in an amphitheater during a gladiatorial contest has been found in recent excavation in North Africa (Fig. 3:25). One musician is shown playing the long, straight brass instrument known as the *tuba*, or trumpet; two others are playing the circular *cornu*, or horn; while still another is seated at the *hydraulus*, or water organ. Equipped with a rudimentary keyboard and stops, this highly ingenious instrument worked on the principle of forcing air compressed by two water tanks through a set of bronze pipes. Some of these instruments were 10 feet high, and they were used mainly in open-air arenas where their tone must have resembled that of the calliopes, once so popular in old-fashioned circus parades. Other Roman instruments can be seen in Figure 3:26. The woman at the left is playing the *tibia*, a version of the Greek aulos, or reed pipe; the central figure is clapping together the metal plates known as cymbals; and a player of the drum is seen at the right.

In keeping with the Roman idea of grandeur, the size of their musical instruments was greatly increased. Marcellinus described a performance in which hundreds of players took part, some of whom were said to have performed on "lyres as big as chariots." Owing to their usefulness in warfare, an ever-increasing volume of sound was demanded of wind instruments. Battle signals were relayed by means of trumpet calls, and the larger the legions, the bigger and brassier became the sound. This is borne out by Quintilian, who asks a typical rhetorical question, then proceeds to answer it with a characteristic flourish: "And what else is the function of the horns and trumpets attached to our legions? The louder the concert of their notes, the greater is the glorious supremacy of our arms over all the nations of the earth." The large audiences accustomed to gather in amphitheaters also played a part in the stepping up of the volume of individual instruments and in the development of sizable vocal and instrumental ensembles. Writing in the 1st century A.D., Seneca notes that the size of the vocal and instrumental ensembles was such that sometimes the singers and players in the arena outnumbered the audience. Soloists would obviously be lost in such vast surroundings, and it is not unusual to come across descriptions of large groups of singers accompanied by wind instruments of various kinds and the hydraulic organ.

Quintilian also points out some of the practical applications of music to the art of oratory. He particularly emphasizes the development of the voice because "it is by raising, lowering, or inflexion of the voice that the orator stirs the emotions of his hearers." He then cites the example of one of the great speakers of the past who had a musician standing behind him while making his speeches, "whose duty it was to give him the tones in which his voice was to be pitched. Such was the attention which he paid to this point even in the midst of his most turbulent speeches, when he was terrifying the patrician party."

Literary sources point to a high degree of musical activity in Rome during the 2d century A.D. From the number of Greek-trained singers, instrumentalists, and mimes who were active, clearly the Greek tradition was still very much alive. In its more austere forms, however, Greek art could have appealed only to the aristocratic minority. Hence, like so many other Greek artistic practices, music was adapted to the needs and uses of a large cosmopolitan center that embraced a great variety of tastes. Pliny casually mentions what the entertainment in a cultivated household would have been like, when he chides a friend for not appearing at a dinner to which he had been invited. After describing the menu he had missed, Pliny tells him that he was to have been "entertained either with an interlude, the rehearsal of a poem, or a piece of music," whichever he would have preferred. Music was also a part of every theatrical performance, and, while the Roman drama omitted the chorus that the Greeks had stressed, its dialogue was interspersed with songs accompanied by the tibia. Such musical portions,

Fig. 3:26. Dioskourides of Samos. *Street Musicians.* Mosaic from Herculaneum. *c.*100 B.C. National Museum, Naples (German Archeological Institute)

however, were not composed by the dramatists, as they had been in the Athenian tradition, but were delegated to specialists in this field. The importance of choruses and bands for military morale was not overlooked, and a functional type of military music existed in addition to the trumpet calls to battle. Popular ensembles played music at games and contests, and strolling street musicians (Fig. 3:26) were part of the everyday scene.

The fact that not a single note of any of this music exists today testifies that Roman music was primarily a performing art. While the practicing musicians may very well have composed their own songs and pieces or made variations on traditional tunes, none seems to have been concerned with committing them to paper—and if one had done so, the later church fathers would very likely have seen to it that these pagan melodies were committed to the flames. So, like the folk music that existed only in oral tradition until the advent of modern notation and recording devices, the art died with the people who practiced it.

IDEAS

As a part of the main stream of classical culture, Roman civilization shared many of the basic ideas that produced the Hellenic and Hellenistic styles. Significantly, the Romans widened the scope of the arts to include not only works that were aimed at the connoisseur level but also those that carried broad mass appeal. The two ideas that differentiate the Roman from earlier aspects of the classical styles and dominate the Roman expression in the arts are the genius for organization and the frank spirit of utilitarianism, evidenced in a conception of the arts as a means to popular enjoyment and the solution of practical problems.

Organization

The Roman ability to organize is shown in a consistent application to the building up of a systematic world order, which embraced a unified religion, a unified body of laws, and a unified civilization. Military conquest was, to be sure, one of the means employed; but the allowance of a maximum of self-government to subject peoples, a wide latitude to local customs, even to tribal and cult religions, is proof of the Romans' psychological realism and toleration. Their desire for external unity did not imply internal uniformity, and their frank recognition of this fact was at the root of their success as administrators. With this ability to organize their religious, legal, social, and governmental institutions, their greatest contribution in the arts clearly would lie in the direction of architecture. This organizational spirit, moreover, is revealed most decisively in their undertaking of large public-works projects, such as the building of roads, ports, aqueducts, and the like. It is also seen in their manner of grouping buildings on a common axis, as in the Forum of Trajan, which was so directly in contrast to the Hellenic idea of isolated perfection; in the organization of business activities in common centers, and the various forms of recreation in the baths; in the technical application and development of all the possibilities of construction by means of the arch and vault; in the combination of the Ionic and Corinthian capitals to form the Composite order, their only distinctive contribution to the classical orders; in the combination of three orders on the exterior of the same building, as in the Colosseum where Tuscan-Doric columns are found on the first story, Ionic on the second, and Corinthian on the third; in the development of the multifamily apartment house; in the attention given to the efficient assembling and dispersing of large numbers of people in such buildings as the Colosseum; in the invention of a supermarket, such as the six-storied example in Trajan's Forum; and finally, in the erection of a supertemple for the principal gods, as in the Pantheon.

The same organizational spirit is reflected in the expansion of interior space, as in the Basilica Ulpia, the Pantheon, and the great halls of the baths, in order to accommodate ever larger numbers of people. The Greek idea had been to define space in planes, and the exteriors of their temples were designed as backdrops for processions and religious ceremonies. Those who worshiped Athena at the Parthenon were concerned primarily with its external colonnade, not the interior. Space in this sense was defined but not organized, but in the Pantheon interior space was enveloped and made real. To the Greeks, space always remained a formless void, but the Romans recognized the possibilities of molding three-dimensional space, enclosing it and endowing it with significant form. Among the many ways they sought to enhance this spatial feeling are a sensitivity to scale; a tendency to design buildings in related structural units; an exploitation of color by the use of polychrome marbles, which livened interiors and which added to the perception of depth; a use of illusionistic wall paintings to suggest the third dimension; and an increased attention given to lighting problems. All this the Romans accomplished without sacrificing the classical clarity of form. The same feeling, furthermore, is carried over into sculpture where the tangibility of the spatial environment is reflected in the backgrounds of reliefs by means of buildings and landscapes that suggest depth, whereas the 5th-century B.C. Grecian style consciously omitted any such frame of reference. In addition to this, the organization of time into a temporal continuum, as in the cyclical series presented on the Column of Trajan, shows a new concept of sequential order translated into the pictorial medium.

Still another facet of this Roman organizational ability is found in the allowance for a wide range of taste in the arts. There were styles that appealed to the educated few and those that held the attention of the untutored populace of the middle and lower classes. In one case it was directed to the eye and ear of the connoisseur, and in the other it was frankly popular in its appeal. The conservative tastes of the first group harkened back to the tried-and-true values of Greek art; hence they either collected antique statuary and paintings, or they commissioned new works to be executed in the older style. Exquisite Greek craftsmanship held little interest for the majority, who needed something more like a large bronze equestrian statue or a monumental triumphal arch to capture their attention. In Trajan's Forum, due allowance was made for this variety of taste, with the Greek and Latin libraries placed on either side of a court and a column in between, where the story of Trajan's campaigns was related in a carefully worked out popular language of symbols designed to awaken the curiosity of the multitude.

The disdain of the conservative group for popular art was well stated by Athenaeus, a Greek scholar and teacher who resided in Rome about A.D. 200. He championed the virtues of the older cultural tradition and frequently made unflattering comparisons between the higher standards of the past and those that prevailed in his day. "In early times," he wrote, "popularity with the masses was a sign of bad art; hence, when a certain aulos-player once received loud applause, Asopodorus of Phlius, who was himself still waiting in the wings, said 'What's this? Something awful must have happened!' The player evidently could not have won approval with the crowds otherwise. . . . And yet the musicians of our day set as the goal of their art success with their audiences." Just as in the case of architecture, sculpture, and painting, the Romans were heirs to the Greek musical tradition. The ancient theories survived in philosophical speculation, and Greek music teachers were employed by preference in the homes of the wealthy. The only musical compositions to survive from this period, for instance, are three hymns by Mesomedes, a Greek musician attached to Hadrian's court. Those who cultivated this more austere style still felt that music was meant to educate and elevate the mind, but the popular taste lay in quite another direction.

The music-making that Athenaeus and his conservative group scorned was obviously the very kind that the majority of Romans enjoyed at their public festivals, military parades, games, sporting contests, races, and to some extent the theater. The modern parallel would be the cleavage that exists between audiences interested in chamber music, symphony concerts, and the opera, and those attracted by bands at football games, Broadway musicals, and jazz festivals. What the Romans accomplished here was to broaden the base of the appeal of the arts and gear them to a number of different types of audience. They thus succeeded in providing for the entertainment of a large city population, just as their buildings and civil-engineering projects took care of their physical needs.

Utilitarianism

In referring to the administrations of the last two Antonine emperors, Gibbon declared that "their united reigns are possibly the only period of history in which the happiness of a great people was the sole object of government. The basis of this claim is to be found in the way the Romans managed to steer a middle course between the Scylla of Greek theoretical abstractions about the nature of an ideal state and the Charybdis of religious speculation on the joys of the world to come, which was to characterize the subsequent Christian phases of the Empire. Speculation on the eternal verities could edify the mind, but the understanding of human behavior was rewarded by more immediate advantages. In the late Antonine Age, Rome had reached an equilibrium based on an acceptance of the Stoic doctrine of "live and let live," and the Epicurean idea of pleasure as an index to the highest good. The transfer of these individualistic doctrines to the forms and policies of a government meant a high degree of tolerance and a recognition that the standard of excellence in either a law or a work of art was whether it would bring the greatest good to the greatest number. The construction of elegantly proportioned temples was therefore not so important as the building of new aqueducts. Maintaining a luxurious private palace was secondary to providing people's palaces, such as the public baths and theaters. A private collection of sculpture was subordinate to public exhibitions in city squares and galleries where the statues could be seen and enjoyed by many. A play, poem, or piece of music that awakened only the sensibilities of the cultured minority did not rank so high on this scale as those that were applauded by the multitude. In short, the practical arts were favored over the decorative arts; material goods superseded more remote spiritual blessings; and utility was in the ascendance over abstract beauty (though it must be remembered that the two are by no means mutually exclusive).

Fig. 3:27. *Ara Pacis Augustae* (see p. 95). Detail of frieze, *"Tellus Panel,"* with Earth (in center), Air (at left), Water (at right). Marble. *c.*63″ high. 13–9 B.C. Rome (Gabinetto Fotografico Nazionale)

Since the Romans were little concerned with ideal forms, it was not an accident that their greatest successes were in the arts of government rather than in the fine arts. As Vergil said in the *Aeneid:* "Let others melt and mold the breathing bronze to forms more fair . . . or trace with pointed wand the cycled heaven, and hail the constellations as they rise; But thou, Oh Roman, learn with sovereign sway to rule the nations." As might be expected, the art which was most congenial to Roman aspirations was that of architecture, especially in its utilitarian aspects as found in the field of civil engineering. Building a 200-mile highway over the mountains, moving part of a hill over 100 feet high to make way for a forum, providing a sewer system for a city of over one million inhabitants, bridging the Danube at its widest point, perfecting such new building materials as brick and concrete—all these were taken in stride.

When it came to sculpture, the Romans saw that subject matter served the purposes of the state by extolling the virtues and deeds of the emperors. Such epic poems as the *Aeneid* performed a similar service in the literary medium; and, as Quintilian said, the loud sounds of the brass instruments proclaimed the glory of Roman arms. Other applications of this utilitarianism are found in the brilliant exploitation of such technical devices as the arch and vault. Their success in solving practical problems like bringing water from great distances is proved by the number of roads and bridges that are still serving their purpose today. In sculpture the application of the continuous-narrative method to the telling of a story was progressive, in that it promoted the sense of continuity in the temporal dimension and anticipated later Christian and secular pictorial forms. The development of such a practical form of verbal communication into the art of letter-writing, beginning with Cicero and continuing with the younger Pliny, was the literary facet of the same idea. Finally, when Quintilian pointed out how the art of melody could be applied to oratory by the use of a pitch pipe to give the speaker a more persuasive tone, the cycle was complete.

Effective as this utilitarianism was, it was purchased at the price of a conflict between structure and decoration, extrinsic and intrinsic values, and the purposive and nonpurposive aspects of art. The Romans built and decorated well, but the two activities somehow failed to achieve a harmonious coexistence. This is well illustrated by the somewhat hollow claim of Augustus, who proudly boasted that he found Rome a city of brick and left it a city of marble. Actually, Rome was still a city of brick and concrete under an Augustan marble veneer. Neither material needs a disguise, or even an apology, as proved by the rhythmical grace of the functional arches of the Pont du Gard. Hence Augustus had no need to imply that Roman structures were solid marble like the Parthenon. As a whole, then, Roman architecture was at its best when it stuck to its frank utilitarianism, undertook vast engineering projects, and successfully solved the practical problems of construction.

CONCLUSION

Older cultural centers, such as Athens and Pergamon, were so far off the beaten track that not until the archeological discoveries of the 18th and 19th centuries did their more restrained classical purity exert any appreciable influence on the forms of Western art. All intervening phases of classicism were, in effect, revivals of the Roman style. With the establishment of the Roman building methods, Western architecture was firmly set on its course, and it steered in substantially the same direction until the technological discoveries of the 19th and 20th centuries. Consequently, it must be emphasized once more that Rome was the gateway through which all the styles, forms, and ideas of Mediterranean civilization passed in review. After being transformed by the process of selectivity, and with flashes of genuine originality, into a uniquely Roman configuration, they proceeded onward through the arch into medieval culture by way of the new Roman Empire capitals of Byzantium in the east and Ravenna in the west. When Rome declined as the center of world empire, it still remained the capital of Christendom. As the object of pilgrimages, its architectural, sculptural, and literary monuments were bound to exert a massive influence on the rulers, people, and artists who gravitated at one time or another toward the city. Because of this enduring pre-eminence throughout all subsequent phases of Western culture, no important city exists without a bit of Rome in it. It is therefore with full justification that Rome has been and still continues to be called the Eternal City.

(*Opposite*). Master Matteo. *Pórtico de la Gloria*, Cathedral of Santiago de Compostela, Spain. 31′ 2″ high. 1168–1188. (Ksado)

Part 2
THE MEDIEVAL
PERIOD

CHRONOLOGY:
Ravenna, Late 5th and Early 6th Centuries

General Events

284–305	Diocletian, emperor
306–337	Constantine, emperor
313	Edict of Milan legalized Christianity
323	Old St. Peter's basilica begun on Vatican Hill, Rome; later the other "imperial basilicas" built (San Paolo fuori le Mure, San Giovanni in Laterano, Santa Maria Maggiore)
324	Constantinople built as capital of East Roman Empire
325	First Council of Nicaea
329–379	St. Basil, bishop of Caesarea, liturgist of Eastern Orthodox Church
c.340–397	St. Ambrose, bishop of Milan
340–420	St. Jerome; translator of Latin Vulgate Bible
c.345–407	St. John Chrysostom, patriarch of Constantinople, liturgist of Eastern Orthodox Church
354–430	St. Augustine; baptized by St. Ambrose, bishop of Hippo (North Africa), author of *Confessions* (397), *City of God* (426)
402–476	Ravenna seat of West Roman Empire
410	Rome sacked by Visigoths
c.440	Mausoleum of Galla Placidia built
445	Rome sacked by Vandals
c.450	"Neonian" Baptistry for Roman Christians built

476	Odoacer sacked Rome, conquered Ravenna; end of West Roman Empire
476–540	Ravenna was capital of Gothic kingdoms
476–493	Odoacer, king
493–526	Theodoric the Great, king Church of Sant' Apollinare Nuovo built Arian Baptistry built Theodoric's Palace built Theodoric's tomb built Boethius (c.475–524) was Theodoric's minister; translator of Greek treatises; author *Consolations of Philosophy* Cassiodorus (c.480–575) Theodoric's minister; after 540 founded monastery at Vivarium (Italy)
527–565	Justinian, East Roman Emperor
532–537	Church of Hagia Sophia built by architects Anthemius of Tralles and Isidorus of Miletus
533	*Digest of Laws*
534–540	Justinian's general Belisarius conquered Italy
535–549	Church of Sant' Apollinare in Classe built
540	Belisarius entered Ravenna End of Theodoric's Ostrogothic kingdom
546	Maximian appointed Archbishop of Ravenna and Byzantine Exarch
547	Church of San Vitale, Ravenna, completed
556	Archbishop Maximian died
590–604	Gregory the Great, pope Liturgy of Roman Catholic Church codified; Gregorian chant established

4

THE EARLY
ROMAN CHRISTIAN AND
BYZANTINE STYLES

RAVENNA, LATE 5TH AND EARLY 6TH CENTURIES

Many an old Roman coin bears the inscription *Ravenna Felix*, Happy Ravenna.
By a felicitous stroke of fate, this previously unimportant little town on Italy's
Adriatic coast became the stage on which the great political, religious, and artistic
dramas of a century and a half of world history were enacted. Ravenna was, in
turn, the seat of the last Roman emperors of the West, the capital of a barbarian
Ostrogothic kingdom, and the western center of the East Roman Empire. A
more unprepossessing site could hardly be imagined. To the east lay the Adriatic
Sea, to the north and south wide deltas of the River Po, and the only land
approach was through marshes and swamps. Yet when the barbarian hordes had
Rome under constant harassment, it was this very isolation that led Emperor
Honorius to abandon Rome in A.D. 402 and seek in Ravenna a fortress where his
hard-pressed legions could be supplied by the East Roman Empire through the
nearby port of Classe. But with all its natural advantages, Ravenna could hold
out against the barbarians only until the year 476, when Odoacer succeeded in
entering the all-but-impregnable city and putting an end to the West Roman

135

Empire. The Ostrogothic kingdom of Theodoric, Odoacer's successor, was even more short-lived, and Ravenna fell once more in 540, when Justinian's armies of the East Roman Empire conquered the Italian peninsula and for a brief time reunited the old empire.

Diverse historical traditions as well as wide geographical distances separated Rome in the West, Byzantium in the East, and the nomadic Ostrogoths in the North. Early in the 4th century, after he had made Christianity an official state religion, Emperor Constantine had moved his court to Byzantium, christening the city the "new Rome." Later, this second capital was called Constantinople in his honor, and soon the East and West Roman empires were going their separate courses. With the encroachments of the northern barbarians, a three-way struggle for power began among the conservative theocratic Byzantine monarchy under Emperor Justinian, the liberal but insecure Ostrogothic kingdom of Theodoric, and the increasingly influential Roman papacy.

More than the sea stretched between Ravenna and Constantinople, higher mountains than the Alps stood between it and the restive northern barbarians, and greater obstacles than the Apennines separated it from Rome. Metaphysical barriers, in fact, proved more impassable than seas or mountains, for this was the age that was laying the foundations of basic religious beliefs, and in some respects the controversies in Ravenna foreshadowed the later separations of Christianity into Eastern Orthodox and Roman Catholic and Catholic and Protestant denominations. At this time, the main doctrinal battle centered on the nature of the Trinity, and especially Christ's role as the second person in the Trinity. The Ostrogoths, having been converted by Arius of Alexandria (c. 256–336), believed that since Jesus was created by God the Father, He was subordinate and not of one substance with God. In spite of this denial of the Trinity, the Arians revered Christ as the noblest of created beings, but as human rather than divine. In Byzantium, it was held that Christ as the Incarnated Word was of one single substance with the Father and hence of divine nature only. The Roman papacy found a middle ground between the two extremes and took the position that since the Word was made flesh, Christ possessed both divine and human natures and was a full member of the Trinity. Today, such theological controversies seem remote, but in the early centuries of Christianity they were of sufficient intensity to shake empires, depose kings, and cause decades of war.

Paralleling the political and religious controversy, a conflict of art styles took place within Ravenna as successive rulers built and embellished the city. In the 6th century, Ostrogothic Arian heretics, Byzantine patriarchs, and members of the Roman hierarchy, together with the schools of artists each patronized, had different cultural heritages, different aesthetic goals, and different ways of looking at the world. During the days when the Roman empire was united, cultural influences came from all parts of the Mediterranean world, and, with due allowance for regional diversity, Roman art achieved a recognizable unity. But with the disintegration of Roman power, the adoption of Christianity as an official religion, and the separation of the empire into eastern and western centers, a reorientation in the arts took place. Though there were many overlapping elements, owing to a common heritage, two distinct styles began to emerge. Hence, when reference is to all the art of this period, the designation will be "early Christian"; the term "Early Roman Christian" will be used to distinguish the western style from the declining old pagan Roman arts, on the one hand, and from the subsequent Romanesque and Gothic styles of the later medieval period on the other; and "Byzantine" will designate the parallel eastern style.

ARCHITECTURE AND MOSAICS

Ravenna's replacement of Rome as a capital city demanded a building program that would transform it from a minor town into a major metropolis. No ruler could afford to be outdone by his predecessors. The West Roman emperors and Empress Galla Placidia, whose tomb is seen in Figure 4:1, erected significant secular and religious structures. The barbarian king Theodoric, after he came to power, sought to be more Roman than the Romans. As he wrote to an official in Rome, he wished his age to "match the preceding ones in the beauty of its buildings." And the great Justinian, after the Byzantine conquest, made architectural contributions commensurate with his imperial dignity.

As a capital city with a cosmopolitan population, Ravenna received diplomatic representatives from every part of the Mediterranean world. Each embassy

Fig. 4:1. Tomb of Galla Placidia. Interior 39' x 33'. c.440. Ravenna (Anderson)

Fig. 4:2 (*above*). Sant' Apollinare Nuovo. *Nave Wall*. *c*.493–526. Ravenna (Anderson)

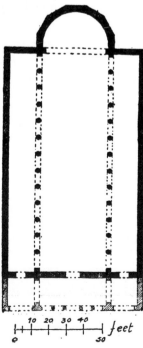

Fig. 4:3. Sant' Apollinare Nuovo. *Plan*.

had to build not only a residence for its delegation but also a church so that its specific form of worship would have an appropriate setting. As a result, there were dozens of churches for the many Christian sects—for the separate Byzantine rites of such eastern cities as Constantinople, Antioch, and Alexandria; for the various Roman, Gallic, and Spanish liturgies of the West—and there was also a synagogue for the Jews. Had all these building survived, Ravenna today would be a complete museum of 5th- and 6th-century Mediterranean architecture. Unfortunately, all but a few fragments of the secular buildings have perished with the passage of time, but the remaining religious structures—churches, baptistries, memorial chapels, and tombs—reveal the rich artistic fruits born of a synthesis of Roman and Byzantine forces. In this proud heritage, the city can still be called happy Ravenna.

The buildings at Ravenna, together with their decorative detail, are an excellent index to the art forms of this important transitional period between the classical and medieval worlds. Two main structural plans were taken over from pagan Rome and adapted to Christian worship: the oblong basilica (see Basilica Ulpia, Fig. 3:7) and the domed central structure (see Pantheon, Fig. 3:19). The two oblong basilicas at Ravenna—Sant' Apollinare Nuovo (Fig. 4:2 and 4:3) and Sant' Apollinare in Classe (Fig. 4:30)—are less elaborate versions of the so-called "imperial basilicas" built in Rome under Constantine—Old St. Peter's (Figs. 4:4 and 4:5), San Paolo fuori le Mure (St. Paul's outside the Walls), San Giovanni in Laterano (St. John Lateran), and Santa Maria Maggiore (St. Mary Major). The five domed central structures reveal a greater variation in respect to origin and purpose. The miniature mausoleum of Galla Placidia (Fig. 4:1) is the earliest surviving example of a chapel built in the form of the equal-winged Greek cross with a dome over the crossing. The octagonal Neonian Baptistry for the Roman Christians also dates from Roman imperial times. The Arian Baptistry (Fig. 4:13) and the tomb of Theodoric (Fig. 4:14), both of which were built under the Ostrogothic kingdom, were derived from older Roman building types. Justinian's domed octagonal Church of San Vitale (Fig. 4:11), modeled on Byzantine lines, completes the list of extant domed buildings. Over the centuries, the oblong-basilican plan with evolving stylistic variants became the standard for churches of Western Christendom, while the central-type plan was favored by the Eastern Orthodox Church.

Sant' Apollinare Nuovo and the Oblong Basilica

Theodoric's building program included a church for his own Arian sect. Originally dedicated by him to "Our Lord Jesus Christ," it now bears the name of Sant' Apollinare Nuovo, honoring Apollinarus, patron saint of the city and by tradition the disciple and friend of St. Peter. The floor plan (Fig. 4:3) is a

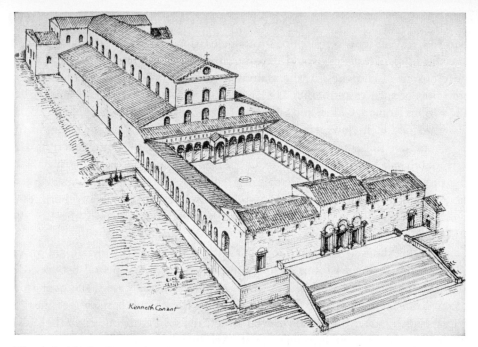

Fig. 4:4. Old St. Peter's Basilica. Grand axis c.835' long, transept 295' wide. Begun 323–326. Rome. Restoration study by Kenneth J. Conant

simplified version of Old St. Peter's (Fig. 4:5) and shows the division of space into a vestibule entrance known as the *narthex*; a central area for the congregation to assemble known as the *nave*, separated by twin rows of columns from the side aisles; and terminating in a semicircular *apse*, which framed the altar and provided seats for the clergy. Older pagan temples, owing to their small dark interiors, were unsuitable for a religion that had to house large congregations. Ancient Greek ceremonies took place around an outdoor altar with the temple as a backdrop. The principal architectural and decorative elements of these temples —colonnades, frieze, and pediments—all faced outward. The Christian basilica turned the Greek temple outside in, leaving the exterior severely plain and concentrating attention on the interior colonnades and the fresco or mosaic decoration of the nave walls and apse.

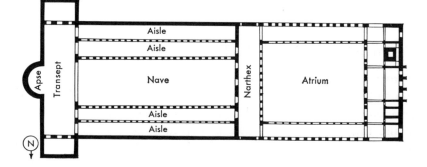

Fig. 4:5. Old St. Peter's. *Plan*

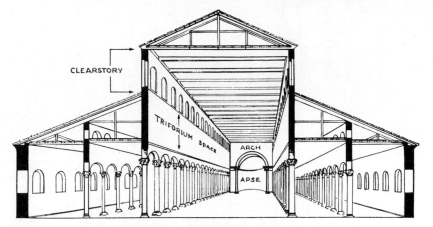

CLEARSTORY

TRIFORIUM SPACE

ARCH

APSE

Fig. 4:6. *Typical Early Roman Christian Basilica.* Drawing by Dorothy Shea

The most complete of these early basilicas was Old St. Peter's (Fig. 4:4), so called because it was razed in the 16th century to make way for the present basilica of Bramante, Michelangelo, and Maderno (Fig. 10:21). As the see of Rome, dating from the year 326 when it was dedicated by Constantine, built over the presumed tomb of the Apostle, and as the largest church of the period, Old St. Peter's, until its demolition, ranked as the key monument of Western Christendom. To provide for all Christian activities, it brought together elements of Roman domestic, civic, and temple architecture into a new harmonious composition. Approached by a flight of steps, entrance to the *atrium* was made through an arched gateway. This open courtyard, derived from old Roman country villas, was surrounded by roofed arcades supported by columns; it provided space for congregations to gather, facilities for the instruction of converts, and offices for church officials. In its center was a fountain for the ceremonial washing of hands. The side of the atrium toward the church becomes the narthex, the vestibulelike corridor that serves as a frontispiece to the church proper. Through the portals of the narthex, entrance was made to the nave and side aisles. This spacious, 80-foot-wide nave resembling the rectangular law-court halls of Roman public basilicas, was flanked on either side by two 30-foot-wide aisles and a procession of columns that led the eye along its 295-foot length to the *triumphal arch* (so called because of its derivation from similar Roman imperial structures) into the wide *transept,* the "arms" set at right angles to the nave that give basilican churches their T-shaped or cruciform ground plans, and an area that functions as a second nave, and beyond to the semicircular apse. From beginning to end, the design sweeps along a horizontal axis of 835 feet, and opening out at its widest point in the 295-foot transept. Vertically, the building (Fig. 4:6) rises above the nave colonnades through an intermediate area called

Fig. 4:7. Sant' Apollinare Nuovo. *Good Shepherd Separating the Sheep from the Goats.* Mosaic. *c.*520 (Soprintendenza)

the *triforium* that extends to the level of the roofing over the side aisles, above which is the clearstory with its rows of windows that light the interior and its masonry that supports the timbered trusses of the shed roof. In keeping with the sheltered and inward orientation of these early basilicas, no windows gave view on the outside world; those at the clearstory were too high and too deeply set to allow even a glimpse of the sky. It was inner radiance of the spirit rather than natural light that was sought.

Various parts of the basilica form acquired symbolic meanings in keeping with the teachings of the Christian faith. The entire building, for instance, was literally oriented so that the congregation would face the rising sun—to commemorate the Eastertide resurrection of Christ. With the long nave terminating in the apse and intersected by the extending wings of the transept, the ground plan of the basilica formed a Latin cross. The nave, its name deriving from the Latin *navis* (ship), symbolically transported the believers as they passed in the communion procession through the arch of triumph to the haven, or heaven, of salvation, which is reflected in the semidome of the apse and which was customarily decorated with stars and a celestial vision of Christ in Glory (Fig. 5:19).

Sant' Apollinare Nuovo, unlike Old St. Peter's which had to accommodate a standing congregation of 40,000 or more, was designed as the private chapel of Theodoric's palace. Only the nave remains intact, all other parts being restorations or later additions. As such, its modest architecture would attract only pass-

Fig. 4:8. Sant' Apollinare Nuovo. *Last Supper*. Mosaic. *c.*520 (Soprintendenza)

ing attention, but the magnificent mosaics that decorate the nave wall are of major importance in art history. But while presenting a harmonious design, they actually represent two different periods and styles.

The mosaics of the earlier period were commissioned by Theodoric and are of Early Roman Christian craftsmanship. "Send us from your city," Theodoric had written through his secretary Cassiodorus to an official in Rome, "some of your most skilled marble-workers, who may join together those pieces which have been exquisitely divided, and, connecting together their different veins of color, may admirably represent the natural appearance." After Justinian's conquest, the church was rededicated and all references to Arian beliefs or Theodoric's reign were removed. Part of the frieze above the nave arcade was replaced half a century later by mosaics in the Byzantine style.

Completely covering both walls of the nave, the mosaic work is divided into three bands (see Fig. 4:2). Above the nave arcade and below the clearstory windows, a wide and continuous mosaic strip runs the entire length of the nave in the manner of a frieze. It depicts two long files of saints (the Byzantine part) moving in a majestic procession from representations of Ravenna on one side and Classe on the other (the Early Roman Christian part). The second band fills the space on either side of the clearstory windows with a series of standing toga-clad figures. At the top level, panels depicting incidents in the life of Christ alternate with simulated canopylike niches over the figures standing below. Both

Fig. 4:9. Sant' Apollinare Nuovo. *Theodoric's Palace*. Mosaic. *c*.520 (Soprintendenza)

the middle and upper bands are of Roman workmanship, and the scenes in the upper band constitute the most complete representation of the life of Christ in early Christian art. On one side, the story of the parables and miracles is told, among them the *Good Shepherd Separating the Sheep from the Goats* (Fig. 4:7), an allusion to the Last Judgment. In this and other scenes Christ appears youthful, unbearded, with blue eyes and brown hair. On the opposite side, scenes of the passion and resurrection are presented. In the *Last Supper* (Fig. 4:8) showing Christ and the Disciples reclining in the manner of a Roman banquet, He is seen as a more mature and bearded figure. In all instances He has the cruciform halo with a jewel on each arm of the cross to distinguish Him from the attending saints and angels. His dignified demeanor and purple cloak also tend to show Him in the light of royal majesty. Standing like statues on their pedestals, the figures in the middle band are modeled three-dimensionally in light and shade and cast diagonal shadows. They apparently were once identified by inscriptions over their heads, and the removal of their names suggests they may have been prophets and saints revered by the Arian Christians.

The great mosaic frieze above the nave arcade starts on the left and right of the entrance with representations of the port of Classe and Ravenna, respectively. In the crescent-shaped harbor with three Roman galleys riding at anchor, Classe is seen between two lighthouses. Above the city walls some of the ancient buildings are discernible, and from the gate issues the procession of virgin martyrs. On the opposite side is Ravenna with Theodoric's Palace (Fig. 4:9) in the foreground. Under the word *Palatium* is the central arch where once was an eques-

Fig. 4:10. Sant' Apollinare Nuovo. *Procession of Virgin Martyrs.* Mosaic. *c.*560 (Soprintendenza)

trian portrait of Theodoric. Under the other arches, outlines and vestiges of heads and hands indicate that members of his court were also portrayed, and Theodoric was again depicted in the city gate at the right. But when the Ostrogothic kingdom came to its abrupt end, these personages were replaced by simulated Byzantine textile curtains. Above the palace are several of Theodoric's buildings with the Church of Sant' Apollinare Nuovo itself on the left and the domed Arian Baptistry on the right. The rest of the frieze apparently pictured events of Theodoric's reign that were obliterated after the Byzantine occupation and replaced with the files of saints issuing from the gates of the two cities. As with the cella frieze of the Parthenon, this procession reflects the ritual that regularly took place in the church. According to the early custom, the congregation gathered in the side aisles, with women on one side and men on the other. At the offertory they went forward through the nave to the altar carrying with them their gifts of bread and wine for the consecration. In a stylized way, the procession frieze re-enacts this part of the service on a heavenly level. On the left, 22 virgins (Fig. 4:10) are led forward by the Three Wise Men to the throne of the Virgin Mary, who holds the Christ Child on her lap. Arrayed in white tunics with richly bejeweled mantles, the virgins carry their crowns of martyrdom in their hands as offerings. In a similar manner, 25 male martyrs are escorted by St. Martin of Tours into the presence of Christ, who is seated on a lyre-backed throne. The eye is led along by the upward folds and curves of their costumes as they tread a flowered path lined with date palms that symbolize both Paradise and their martyrdom. All is ineffably serene and no trace of their earthly suffering is seen. Their heads, though tilted differently to vary the design somewhat, are all on the same level in keeping with the Byzantine convention of isocephaly. Only

St. Agnes is accompanied by her attribute, the lamb; otherwise the faces reveal so little individuality they could not be identified were it not for the inscriptions above.

A completely different artistic feeling is revealed when these Byzantine figures are compared with the earlier Roman work in the bands above. The unshaded lines of the Byzantine design form a frankly two-dimensional pattern, while the garments of the Roman personages fall in natural folds that model the forms they cover in three-dimensional fashion. All the figures in the upper two bands wear simple unadorned Roman togas, while the saints below are clad in luxurious, ornate Byzantine textiles decorated with rare gems. The Roman figures appear against such natural, three-dimensional backgrounds as the green Sea of Galilee, hills, or a blue sky. The Byzantine virgins and martyrs, however, are set against a shimmering gold backdrop with uniformly spaced stylized palms. The candor, directness, and simplicity with which the Roman scenes are depicted likewise contrasts strikingly with the impersonal, aloof, and symbolic Byzantine treatment of the nave frieze. Differences of theological as well as stylistic viewpoints are involved, since the Arian-Roman panels accent the Redeemer's worldly life and human suffering, and the Byzantine frieze accents His divinity and remoteness from mundane matters.

The art of *mosaic*, in general, depends for its effectiveness on directing the flow of light from a myriad of tiny reflectors. After the placement of the panels, the design, and the colors have been determined, the mosaicist must take into account both the natural source of light from windows and artificial sources from lamps or candles. Accordingly, he fits each *tessura*, or small cube made of glass, marble, shell, or ceramic, onto the cement surface, tilting some this way, others that, so that a shimmering luminous effect is obtained. Fresco painting had been widely used for wall decorations of underground chapels in the catacombs and in Early Roman Christian churches even before Christianity became an accepted religion of the Roman Empire. But when Christianity acquired the prestige and wealth to employ the foremost architects, mosaics were preferred to fresco. Unlike fresco painting or stained glass, mosaics are especially well adapted to dimly lit interiors. Capable of catching even the faintest ray of candlelight, they can convey the impression of radiance emanating from within the church rather than from without. In an age accustomed to look beyond the world of reality, the mosaic medium was ideal for conjuring up other-worldly visions and directing thoughts toward the invisible world of the spirit. Mosaics are even more closely allied with architecture than either sculptures or paintings. While the latter, except in the case of frescoes, are detachable, a mosaic is actually the surface of a wall or a floor. Black-and-white photographs convey only a faint impression of the true beauty and emotional appeal of mosaics. Their shimmering, kaleidoscopic color changes must be seen in their original settings to be fully appreciated.

San Vitale and Central-type Structures

Little more than a year's time elapsed between the death of Theodoric and the accession of Justinian as emperor in Constantinople. Almost immediately, Justinian undertook in absentia the laying of the foundation stone of San Vitale at Ravenna (Fig. 4:11). In the statecraft of that day, the building of a church that would surpass anything undertaken by Theodoric served as an assertion of Justinian's authority in Italy and evidence of the weakened power of Theodoric's Ostrogothic successors. At first, Justinian's position in the capital of the West Roman Empire was anything but certain, and the project languished. Eventually, the use of force was needed to assert his Italian claims, and his armies entered the city in the year 540. Thereafter, construction of San Vitale proceeded apace, and seven years later the church was ready for its dedication by Archbishop Maximian. Its plain red Roman brick exterior is proof that as little attention was paid to the outside of San Vitale as to that of any other church of the period. But with its rich polychromed marble walls, carved alabaster columns, pierced marble screens and other delicate details, and, above all, its sanctuary mosaics, San Vitale is a veritable jewel box.

Architecturally, San Vitale is a highly developed example of the central-type church, differing radically from Sant' Apollinare Nuovo. Yet, as the ground plan (Fig. 4:12) will show, it has all the usual features of the basilica, including a narthex entrance, nave, surrounding side aisles, and a triumphal arch leading into a sanctuary with an apse and two side chambers. The striking difference, however, between an oblong basilica and a centralized church is the direction of the axis. In the former, the axis runs horizontally through the center of the building dividing the church lengthwise into equal halves, the eye being led toward the apse; in the central-type building the axis is vertical, leading the eye upward from the central floor space to the dome. Were it not for the addition of the oblong narthex on the west and the apse on the east, San Vitale would be a complete octagon. The two side chambers of the apse are usually associated with Eastern Orthodox churches, and their presence here points to the fact that San Vitale was designed as a theater for the Byzantine liturgy. The northern chamber was designated the *prothesis*, to indicate its use as the place where the communion bread and wine were prepared for the altar. In Eastern usage, the sacrificial aspect of the mass assumed a dramatic character, and the sacramental bread was "wounded, killed, and buried" on the table of the prothesis before it appeared on the altar where it symbolized the resurrection of the body. The southern chamber is called the *diakonikon* and served as the vestry and as a place to store the sacred objects used in the orthodox service.

In order to understand San Vitale and central-type churches, one must look at similar buildings at Ravenna and elsewhere. While the ancestors of the oblong

Fig. 4:11. San Vitale. *Exterior of Apse.* c.526–547. Ravenna (German Archeological Institute)

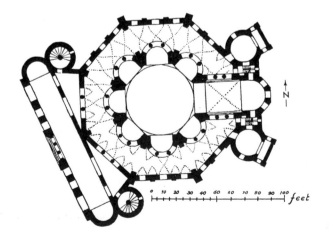

Fig. 4:12. San Vitale. *Plan*

Fig. 4:13. Arian Baptistry, Dome Mosaic. *Baptism of Christ and Procession of Twelve Apostles. c.520.* Ravenna (Soprintendenza)

basilica were Roman domestic and public buildings, the centralized church derives from Roman baths, tombs, and temples. At Ravenna, the other surviving examples of this centralized type are the two baptistries and Theodoric's mausoleum.

The eight-sided Christian baptistry was taken over directly from the octagonal bathhouses found in ancient Roman villas. There the pool was usually octagonal and the structure around it assumed that shape. Early Christian baptisms involved total immersion, and the transition from bathhouse to baptistry was easy and natural. Since baptism is a personal and family affair, not calling for the presence of a congregation, the small size of the baptistries is appropriate. The Arian Baptistry was built in Theodoric's time in the same style as the earlier "Neonian" Baptistry for the Roman Christians. Both are domed structures with the chief interest centered on the fine interior mosaics. Both have similar representations of the baptism of Christ on the interior surfaces of their cupolas. That of the Arian Baptistry (Fig. 4:13) shows the ceremony being performed by St. John the Baptist, while the River Jordan is personified as an old man in the manner of the ancient pagan fluvial gods. Around this central scene are the 12 Apostles who move processionally toward the throne of Christ. Just as the virgins and martyrs re-enacted the offertory procession above the nave arcade of Sant' Apol-

Fig. 4:14. Theodoric's Tomb. Base 45′ in diameter, dome 35 in diameter. c.520. Ravenna (Italian State Tourist Office)

linare Nuovo, the Apostles here mirror the baptismal rites on a more transcendental level. They group themselves around the center above where Christ is being baptized, just as the clergy, family, and sponsors gathered about the font below for the baptism of some Ravenna Christian. Here is yet another example of the *iconography*—the story being told—of the decorative scheme reflecting the liturgical activity that took place within the walls of the building.

Besides the baptistries, Ravenna provides another example of the early centralized structure in Theodoric's tomb (Fig. 4:14), which dates from about 520. Built with blocks of hewn stone, the lower story is a 10-sided crypt, while the upper part is a circular chapel. The whole is surmounted by a shallow dome, a huge monolith 107 feet in circumference, carved from a single piece of Istrian marble. The ancient preference for the circular form of mausoleum can be explained partly by its symbolism. Immortality was frequently expressed by the image of a serpent biting its tail—that is, a living creature whose end was joined to its beginning. A fine example of the Hellenistic type of round mausoleum, known as a *tholos*, is to be seen in Greece at Epidaurus. Another prototype is provided by Hadrian's colossal tomb on the banks of the Tiber in Rome, and an Early Roman Christian example is the small circular Church of Santa Costanza (Fig. 4:31) where the daughter of Constantine was buried.

Fig. 4:15 (*left*). *Pendentives*. Fig. 4:16 (*right*). *Arched Squinch*. Drawings by W. D. Richmond

The idea of a church built in the form of a tomb is by no means as somber as it might seem. In the Christian sense, a church symbolized the Easter sepulchre, reminding all of the resurrection of Christ. In His memory, churches were dedicated to martyrs and saints who were believed to be partaking of the heavenly life with Him, just as the faithful hoped that they themselves would one day be doing. The ancient Orphic cult had stressed the idea of the body being the tomb of the spirit. Hence, death and resurrection were aspects of one and the same idea, and the martyr's death was his mystical union with Christ. Indeed, the altar itself was a tomb or repository for the sacred relics of the saint to whom the church was dedicated. Early altars in the catacombs actually were sarcophagi that served also as communion tables. Thus, in the rites of the church, not only was the earthly past of Christ, His Apostles, saints, and martyrs commemorated, but, at the same time, the glorious heavenly future was anticipated.

Balancing domes over square or octagonal supporting structures was a preoccupation of 6th-century architects. The Romans had found one solution in the case of the Pantheon—resting the dome on supporting cylindrical walls—but in Ravenna later builders found two other solutions. The exquisite little mausoleum of Galla Placidia (Fig. 4:1), which dates from about A.D. 440, was built in the form of a Greek cross. Its dome rests on *pendentives* (Fig. 4:15)—that is, on four concave spherical triangles of masonry rising from the square corners and bending inward to form the circular base of the dome. The role of the pendentives is to encircle the square understructure and make the transition to the domed superstructure. The Ravenna baptistries exemplify the same pendentive solution, but in their cases the domes rest on octagonal understructures. Another solution stemming from the same early period is found in a baptistry in Naples in which a dome rests on an octagonal base by means of squinches (Fig. 4:16)—that is, a series of small apsidal vaults placed across the angles of the octagonal walls. This was the method used for the doming of San Vitale. The eight piers of the arcaded central room below rise upward and culminate in an octagonal drum on which, by means of squinches, the dome rests. In order to keep the load as light as possible, the builders of San Vitale devised a most ingenious method of embedding hollow earthenware pots in the masonry. Above the nave arcade and beneath the dome, the builders included a vaulted triforium gallery running around the church and opening into the nave (see Fig. 4:17). This gallery, which was called the *matroneum*, was for the use of women, who were more strictly segregated in the Byzantine than in the Roman rites.

The more immediate precedents for San Vitale are found in Constantinople in Justinian's church Hagia Sophia (Fig. 4:18) and the octagonal SS. Sergius and Bacchus (known as Little Hagia Sophia), both of which were finished about a decade earlier. Hagia Sophia (Santa Sophia, or Holy Wisdom) is and always will remain the foremost monument of the Byzantine style. As a combination of great art and daring engineering it has never been surpassed. Externally, as the floor plan and view (Figs. 4:19 and 4:20) show, it is square with bulging buttresses and swelling half domes mounting to a full dome on top. From the narthex entrance on the west, the space opens into a large nave, and the eye is led horizontally to the apse in the east. While the most ambitious Gothic cathedral nave never spanned a width of more than 50 feet, the architects of Hagia Sophia achieved here an open space 100 feet wide and 200 feet long.

Rising laterally on either side are colonnades that divide the nave from the side aisles and support a wide triforium matroneum. The forces then gather toward the four massive central piers from which spring powerful arches and tunnel vaults on two sides and two huge half domes on the others that soar to the base of the great dome itself. Four pendentives, the concave spherical triangles originally decorated with mosaic images of winged seraphs, mediate between the square understructure and circular domed superstructure. Under the dome is a crown of 40 windows that combine with those of the vaults below to bathe the interior with light, resulting in such ethereal effect that Justinian's historian Procopius was moved to say that the dome does not appear to rest on the masonry but to be suspended by a golden chain from heaven itself. The atmospheric effect of later medieval cathedrals relies on the mystery of darkness and dim light

Fig. 4:18. Anthemius of Tralles and Isidorus of Miletus. Hagia Sophia. *Interior*. Dome 183′ 8″ high. 532–537. Istanbul (Constantinople) (Hirmer)

Fig. 4:17. San Vitale. *Interior*. Outer octagon 115′, inner octagon 54′ 9″. 526–547.
Ravenna (Anderson)

Fig. 4:19 (*above*). Anthemius of Tralles and Isidorus of Miletus. Hagia Sophia. *Exterior*. 256′ 4″ x 235′ 6″. 532–537. Istanbul (Constantinople)

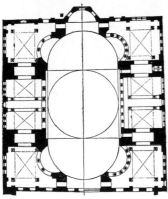

Fig. 4:20 (*left*). Hagia Sophia. *Plan*

filtered through varicolored stained-glass windows. But at Hagia Sophia, it is the mystery of direct light through the many windows and that reflected with suffused radiance from the gold mosaic surfaces which line the interior. This light, as Procopius remarks, makes it seem that the church is "not merely illuminated from without by the sun, but that the radiance springs also from within it." Such spiritual illumination admirably realized the intent of the dedication, which is to Holy Wisdom and Christ as the Creative Word of God.

From this discussion it should be obvious that the dome of the central-type structure unifies the separate structural members, and that the eye perceives this unity at a glance. In the interior of San Vitale (Fig. 4:17) the dome and its supports are clearly visible and the structure is therefore self-explanatory. Psychologically, this equilibrium is important for it produces a restful effect, which is in

Fig. 4:21. San Vitale. *Emperor Justinian and Courtiers*. Mosaic. *c*.547 (Alinari)

direct contrast with the restless interiors of later Gothic cathedrals. There the dynamic urge depends partly on the fact that the exterior buttressing is not apparent. Indeed, the dome of San Vitale is an interior fact only, because on the outside the octagonal base on which it rests has been continued upward and roofed over.

But centralized plans have always conflicted with the liturgy. With the structural accent converging on the axial center beneath the dome, the logical spot for the altar is there, but Christian tradition frowns upon the congregation being placed behind the altar. Consequently, at San Vitale, as well as at Hagia Sophia, an apse was appended in the east for the altar, thus, in effect, dividing the architectural and liturgical climaxes of the edifice.

In the apse of San Vitale, facing the altar from opposite sides, are two panels in mosaic that portray the leading figures of the early Byzantine rule in Ravenna.

Fig. 4:22. San Vitale. *Empress Theodora and Retinue. Mosaic. c.547* (Alinari)

On one, Emperor Justinian appears in the midst of his courtiers (Fig. 4:21) and on the other, facing him as an equal, is Empress Theodora in all her sovereign splendor (Fig. 4:22). It is significant that the finest extant portrait of the great Emperor should be in mosaic rather than in the form of a sculptured bust, a bronze effigy on horseback, or a colossal statue. It is just this medium that could best capture the unique spirit of his life and times. Concerned as he was with the codification of Roman law, presiding at religious councils, and reconciling divergent political points of view, Justinian based his rule on the manipulation of legal and theological formulas as well as on naked military might. He is therefore represented as a symbol of unity between the spiritual force of the church on one hand and the temporal power of the state on the other.

Preceding Justinian in the procession are the clergymen, among whom only Archbishop Maximian is specifically identified by name. His pectoral cross is held up as an assertion of his power as the spiritual and temporal lord of Ravenna. On the Emperor's other side are his courtiers and honor guard holding their jeweled swords aloft. The shield with its Chrismon insignia points to the status of the soldiers as defenders of the faith. The Chrismon was a widely used monogram of the time, made up of the Greek letters Chi (X) and Rho (P), which together form the abbreviation of Christ. Somewhat more allegorically, the letters become a combination of the Cross and the shepherd's crook, which symbolize the Savior's death and pastoral mission. In the center stands Justinian, clothed in all his magnificence and crowned with the imperial diadem. The observer knows immediately that he is in the presence of no ordinary royal personage but rather one who could sign his name augustly to the preface of his *Digest of Laws* as the Emperor Caesar Flavius, Justinianus, Alamannicus, Francicus, Germanicus, Anticus, Alanicus, Vandalicus, Africanus, Pious, Happy, Renowned, Conqueror and Triumpher, ever Augustus.

On her side, the Empress Theodora, richly bejeweled and clad in the imperial purple, is seen as she is about to make her entry into the church from the narthex. Possibly because of her humble origin as the daughter of the feeder of the bears at the circus of Constantinople, Theodora appears more royal than the king. Her offering recalls another remark by Procopius, who said that she fed the geese of the devil while on the stage and the sheep of Christ when she sat on the throne. On the hem of her robe the offertory motif is carried out by the embroidered figures of the Three Wise Men, the first bearers of gifts to Christ. Since they also were from the East, this may have been a subtle attempt to gain the good graces of the people of Ravenna for their Oriental rulers.

These two mosaic portraits are especially precious because they are among the few surviving visual representations of the vanished glories of Byzantine courtly ceremonials. The regal pair appear as if participating in the offertory procession at the dedication of the church, which took place in the year 547, though neither was actually present on that occasion. Such ceremonial entries were a part of the elaborate Byzantine liturgy, and both the Emperor and Empress are shown as the bearers of gifts. On his side, Justinian is carrying the gold paten, which was used to hold the communion bread at the altar, while Theodora is presenting the chalice which contains the wine. Since their munificence was responsible for the building, decoration, and endowment of San Vitale, the allusion is to gifts of gold as well.

In keeping with the rigid conventions of Byzantine art, all the heads appear in one plane. Those of Justinian and Theodora are distinguished by their halos, which in this case allude not only to their awesome power but to a carry-over of the semidivine status assumed by the earlier Roman emperors. Even though they are moving in a procession, they are portrayed frontally in the manner of imperial personages accustomed to receiving the homage of their subjects. In spite of

Fig. 4:23 (*left*). San Vitale. *Byzantine Capital. c.547.* Ravenna (German Archeological Institute). Fig. 4:24 (*right*). Hagia Sophia. *Byzantine Capitals. c.537.* Istanbul (Constantinople)

Fig. 4:25. Capella Palatina (Charlemagne's Chapel). 792–805. Aachen (Aix-la-Chapelle) (Deutscher Kunstverlag)

the stylized medium, the eye can follow the solemn train as it moves in dignified cadence by means of the linear pattern made by the folds of the garments. The elegant costumes and other draperies add generally to the richness of the scene, emphasizing by their designs the lavish luxury of their Oriental origin.

In addition to the mosaics, the decorative design of San Vitale includes carved alabaster columns, polychrome marble wall panels, and many sculptural details. The capitals of the columns are carved with a profusion of intricate patterns, such as the one seen in Figure 4:23, similar to the "basket-woven" capitals of Hagia Sophia (Fig. 4:24). The influence of San Vitale on subsequent western European architecture dates from the time of Charlemagne's conquest. So impressed was he with this church that he not only carried off at least half of its original marble and mosaic decorations but also adopted its plan for his imperial chapel at Aachen (Fig. 4:25). When the harmonious proportions of the building as a whole are compounded with the rich optical effects of the mosaics, polychrome marble, and ornamental sculptures, San Vitale, as the counterpart of Hagia Sophia, is the high point of Byzantine art in the West.

SCULPTURE

From its status as a major art in Greco-Roman times, sculpture declined to a relatively modest place in the hierarchy of early Christian arts. Instead of constituting a free and independent medium, it became primarily an adjunct to the architectural and liturgical forms of the church. Even its classical three-dimensionality was in eclipse, and the art tended to become increasingly pictorial and symbolic in early Christian usage. When sculpture moved indoors, it underwent a radical change in relation to light and shade. A statue in the round, for instance, was either placed against a wall or stood in a niche, which precluded its being seen from all sides. The close proximity in time and place to the pagan religions also served to channel Christian visual expression in other directions, and with the influence of such dictums as the First Commandment that forbade the making of "graven images," it is remarkable that the art survived as well as it did. A rare surviving example of three-dimensional Early Roman Christian sculpture survives in the *Good Shepherd* (Fig. 4:26). Figures of peasants carrying calves or sheep to market are frequently found in ancient Greek and Roman genre sculpture. In the Christian interpretation, however, the shepherd is Christ, the sheep the congregation of the faithful, and, when a jug of milk is included, the whole refers to the Eucharist.

Sculpture, in general, proved adaptable to the new demands and purposes. In the new frame of reference, architectural sculpture—capitals of columns, decorative relief panels, carved wooden doors, and, to some extent, statues in niches —continued with appropriate modifications. The principal emphasis, however,

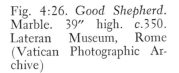

Fig. 4:26. *Good Shepherd.* Marble. 39″ high. *c.*350. Lateran Museum, Rome (Vatican Photographic Archive)

shifted toward objects associated with the new form of worship, such as altars, pulpits, pierced marble screens, carved ivory reliefs, and jeweled book covers. Smaller items, such as precious metal boxes for relics, lamps, incense pots, communion chalices, and patens, all with delicately wrought designs, began to ally the former grand classical art more closely with that of the jeweler.

One of the strongest influences on early Christian design was the new orientation of thought in the direction of symbolism. As long as the religions of Greece and Rome were anthropomorphic, the sculptor could represent the gods as idealized human forms. But in Christian terms, how could he represent in concrete form such abstractions as the Trinity, the Holy Ghost, the salvation of the soul, or the idea of redemption through participation in the Eucharistic sacrifice? The solution could come only through use of parables and symbols. Thus the Christian idea of immortality could be rendered through Biblical scenes of deliverance—Noah from the flood, Moses from the land of Egypt, Job from his sufferings, Daniel from the lion's den, the children from the fiery furnace, and Lazarus from his tomb. One of the most often encountered was the story of Jonah. Jesus had said: "For as Jonas was three days and three nights in the whale's belly; so shall the son of man be three days and three nights in the heart of the earth" (Matthew 12:40). Since a whale was beyond his ken, the sculptor

used the classical sea monster known as the hippogriff to illustrate this old Hebrew legend, which by now had become the symbol of the resurrection of Christ
and frequently was carved on Christian sarcophagi. This is a typical example of
the adaptation of ancient pictorial forms and ideas into new symbols.

In early Christian relief panels, flora and fauna were not represented natu-
ralistically but conveyed symbolic meaning. The dove, for instance, represented
the Holy Spirit, the peacock stood for Paradise, and so on. The Cross is seldom
found in the early Christian art, since it recalled a punishment used for the lowest type of criminal. Instead, the Chrismon symbol already seen on the shield of
Justinian's soldiers was used. A fish, or the Greek word for it, *Icthys*, is often
found as a reference to Jesus making his disciples fishers of men. The letters of
the word also constituted an abbreviation for Jesus Christ Son of God, Savior.
Such symbols and lettered inscriptions caused sculpture to assume the aspect of
engraved designs on stone surfaces, which carried special meaning and mystical
significance to the initiated.

Capitals of columns departed from the unity and regularity of the classical
orders and began to show all sorts of variations. This tendency had begun with
the early phases of Christian art, when materials for new churches had to be
assembled from the parts of ancient buildings that had fallen into disrepair or
disuse. Sant' Apollinare in Classe has a variation of the Corinthian order in its
so-called "wind-blown acanthus" capitals, while still another variety is found at
Sant' Apollinare Nuovo. Far greater complexity and variety appear, however, in
the capitals of San Vitale and Hagia Sophia (Figs. 4:23 and 4:24). These are
more distinctly Byzantine in style and have intricate arabesque designs.

One of the chief forms of Early Roman Christian sculpture is that of carved
stone sarcophagi. The custom of burial above ground was carried over from late
Roman times, and a special Christian impetus came from the desire for inter-
ment within the sacred precincts of the church. The relics of saints reposed in
the altar; tombs of bishops and other dignitaries were housed in the church; while
the sarcophagi of laymen were usually placed outside in the atrium. Survivals of
this latter custom continue well into modern times with burials taking place in
churchyards. A fine example is provided by the sarcophagus of Archbishop Theodore (Fig. 4:27). The center shows the combination of the Chrismon symbol
with that of the first and last letters of the Greek alphabet, Alpha and Omega,
also a reference to Christ taken from his statement that He was both the beginning and the end. Their inclusion here on a tomb indicates the end of earthly
life and the beginning of the heavenly one. Flanking the symbols are two peacocks symbolizing Paradise, while behind them on either side a graceful vine pattern is found, in which the small birds feeding on grapes refer symbolically to
communion. The inscription reads in translation, "Here rests in peace Archbishop Theodore." Above this are repetitions of the same monogram as below,

Fig. 4:27. *Sarcophagus of Archbishop Theodore*. Marble. 39½" x 81". 6th century. Sant' Apollinare in Classe, Ravenna (Gabinetto Fotografico Nazionale)

which are surrounded here by the conventional laurel wreaths symbolizing immortality. The lower end panel symbolized the Trinity, with the urn from which springs the tree of life indicating the Father, the cross the Son, and the descending dove the Holy Spirit.

By far the most impressive single example of sculpture from this period is the chair which is thought to be that of Archbishop Maximian (Figs. 4:28 and 4:29), Justinian's viceroy who is portrayed beside him in the mosaic panel in San Vitale (Fig. 4:21). Such an archepiscopal throne is technically called a *cathedra*, and the church in which it is housed is called a *cathedral*. When the bishop addresses his congregation from it, he is said to be speaking *ex cathedra*. It is also referred to by the Latin word for seat, *sedes*, from which is derived the term *see*, meaning seat of a bishop. Originally it meant a chair denoting high position. Roman senators used such chairs on public occasions, and modern politicians still campaign for a "seat" in the senate or legislature. Both Jewish rabbis and Greek philosophers taught from a seated position; hence the reference in modern colleges to a "chair" of philosophy or history.

Maximian's cathedra is a wooden frame that originally was covered entirely with ivory panels. Since the sides and back are as elaborately covered as the front, the chair was meant to be seen from all angles. During the service, the bishop was seated in the presbyterium either at the side or behind the altar. His words, however, would have been inaudible from this location, and his chair was

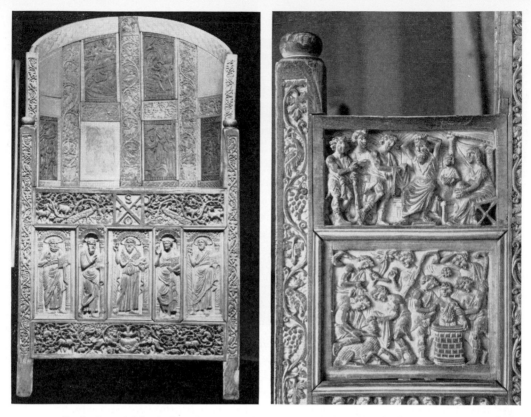

Cathedra of Maximian. Ivory panels on wood frame. 59″ high, 23⅝″ wide. *c.*546–556. Archepiscopal Museum, Ravenna. Fig. 4:28 (*left*). Front view (Hirmer). Fig. 4:29 (*right*). Side view (Gabinetto Fotografico Nazionale)

brought forward at the proper time to a place where he could conveniently be both seen and heard.

The work here consists of a composition made up of ivory plaques, carefully joined together and delicately carved. Originally, there were 39 different pictorial panels, some of which told the Old Testament story of Joseph and his brethren, and the others, the story of Jesus. The chair is thought to have been presented to Maximian by Justinian, and the different techniques employed in the various panels indicate collaboration of craftsmen from Anatolia, Syria, and Alexandria. On the front panel, below Maximian's monogram, is a representation of St. John the Baptist flanked on either side by the Evangelists (Fig. 4:28). The Baptist holds a medallion on which a lamb is carved in relief, while the Evangelists hold their traditional books. One of the side panels that tells the story of Joseph is seen in Figure 4:29. When the two are compared, the workmanship reveals certain inconsistencies. In order to tell his story with compelling force, the carver of the Joseph panel lapses into some crudities of execution. But in both cases the decorative borders with their complex foliated designs are carved with great skill, inventiveness, and high technical competence. While sculpture is not the outstanding Byzantine art, such intricate tracery and arabesque patterns become its unique feature. Since ivory does not make monumentality either possible or desirable, such details, when handled with a jeweler's precision, are perhaps more satisfying than the work as a whole.

At this formative phase, the western and eastern styles are not so separate and distinct as they tend to become in the later medieval period. The situation is also complicated by the fact that Roman artists could be summoned to work in Constantinople just as easily as Byzantine artists could be called to Rome or Ravenna. In general, however, one can conclude that the trend in the west was toward the oblong basilica, while the east developed the central-type structure. In mosaics and sculpture, the Early Roman Christian style stays closer to the heritage of classical naturalism with figures modeled three-dimensionally and appearing against landscape backgrounds, and shows a preference for simpler designs employing recognizable floral and faunal motifs. The Byzantine style, on the other hand, moved more in the direction of flat two-dimensional surfaces, gold backgrounds, nonrepresentational designs, abstract geometrical forms, and luxurious arabesque patterns.

MUSIC

From the writings of Theodoric's learned ministers Boethius and Cassiodorus, some knowledge about the status of musical thought in the Ravenna of the 6th century can be gained. Like the writings of the church fathers and other men of letters of the time, however, these reveal much about the theory of the art and little about its practice. Boethius was an indefatigable translator of Greek philosophical and scientific treatises into Latin, among which were no less than 30 books by Aristotle alone. When he fell from favor and was imprisoned, he wrote his *Consolations of Philosophy*, which became one of the most influential medieval books. Called by Gibbon "a golden volume not unworthy of the leisure of Plato or Tully," the *Consolations* later found its way into English via translations by Alfred the Great and Chaucer. Boethius' was a universal mind, capable of discoursing on anything from the mechanical principles of water clocks to astronomy.

Boethius' treatise on music became the common source of most medieval tracts on the subject, and thus, in transmitting the best of ancient Greek musical theory, it became the foundation stone of Western musical thinking. Like the ancients before him, Boethius believed that "all music is reasoning and speculation," and hence more closely allied with mathematics than with the auditory art that music today is considered to be. He divided music into three classes, the first of which was the "music of the universe," by which he meant the unheard astronomical "music" of planetary motion. The second was "human music," which referred to the attunement of the mind and body, or the rational and irrational elements of the human constitution, in the manner of a Greek harmony of opposites. The third was instrumental music and song, of which he had the philosopher's usual low opinion, considering only the theoretical aspects of the art as pursuits worthy of a gentleman and scholar. The only true "musician" in his opinion was one "who possesses the faculty of judging, according to speculation or reason, appropriate and suitable to music, of modes and rhythms and of the classes of melodies and their mixtures . . . and of the songs of the poets."

Cassiodorus also wrote in a similarly learned vein after he had retired from public life to the haven of his monastery at Vivarium. But while he was still embroiled in the affairs of Theodoric's kingdom, he was constantly called upon to solve every conceivable administrative problem. Among these was a request from Clovis, king of the Franks, for a *citharoedus*—that is, a singer who accompanied himself on the stringed instrument of the classical lyre type known as the cithara. In his search for such a musician, Cassiodorus turned to his fellow senator Boethius, who was in Rome at the time. His letter first launches into a flowery discourse on the nature of music, which he describes as the "Queen of the senses." It continues with interminable discussions about its curative powers, how David cast out the evil spirit from Saul, the nature of the modes, the structure of the Greek scale system, and the history of the art. Then he comes to the lyre, which he calls "the loom of the Muses," and after going off on a few more tangents, he finally gets to the point. "We have indulged ourselves in a pleasant digression," he says, making the understatement of the millennium, "because it is always agreeable to talk of learning with the learned; but be sure to get us that *Citharoedus*, who will go forth like another Orpheus to charm the beast-like hearts of the Barbarians. You will thus obey us and render yourself famous."

This rare document is the only source on the state of secular music in the Ravenna of the 6th century, and it tells little about the capacities and duties of such a musician. It is clear, however, that this type of bardic poet-singer still existed at that time, though apparently so scarce that Cassiodorus had to send to Rome and seek the advice of the most eminent musical authority of the time. It is to be inferred also that such professional poet-musicians were active at Theodoric's court, otherwise the request from Clovis would not have been addressed there. It is also known that Theodoric's exploits, together with those of the other heroes of the migration period, found their way into the fables and songs of the Gothic peoples, undoubtedly through the medium of just such poet-musicians.

Knowledge about the church music of Ravenna at this time is also conjectural and must be gathered from a variety of sources. From the writings of the church fathers, great importance evidently was attached to music in connection with divine worship. The problem was how to separate a proper body of church music from the rude folk musical idioms on one hand, and from the highly developed but pagan art music of Rome on the other. From St. Paul and Pliny the Younger, in the 1st and 2d centuries respectively, it is known that the earliest Christian music sounded very much like the ancient Jewish singing of psalms. A fragment of an early Christian hymn from the latter part of the 3d century was recently found at Oxyrhynchos in North Africa. From the Greek text and ancient musical notation, it is possible to establish its stylistic connection with the late Hellenistic musical tradition. Hebrew, Greek, and Latin sources thus provided the basis for early Christian music just as they had done in the cases of theology and the visual arts. Out of these diverse elements and with original ideas of their own, the Christians of the eastern and western churches over the centuries gradually worked out a synthesis that resulted in a musical art of great power and beauty. The 6th century witnessed the culmination of many early experimental phases; and at its close, the western form of the art found official codification in the body of music known as Gregorian Chant. In its various transmutations and restorations, as well as in its theoretical aspects, this system has remained the official basis of Roman church music up to the present time. Closely related forms are still in use throughout Christendom, where free adaptations of its melodies have enriched the hymn books of nearly every denomination.

Knowledge about the Arian liturgy, such as that which was practiced at Sant' Apollinare Nuovo during Theodoric's reign, is very obscure, because all sources were destroyed when the orthodox Christians gained the upper hand and stamped out the Arian heresy. From a few derogatory comments, however, it is known that hymn and psalm singing by the congregation as a whole were among the practices. Arius, the founder of the sect, was accused of insinuating his religious ideas into the minds of his followers by means of hymns that were sung to melodies derived from drinking songs and theatrical tunes. Such hymns were frowned upon in orthodox circles because they were too closely allied with popular music. Furthermore, the Arian way of singing them was described as loud and raucous, indicating that they must have grated on the ears of the more civilized Roman Christians.

The popularity of these musical practices, however, was such that the Arians were making too many converts. So in the spirit of fighting fire with fire, St. Ambrose, bishop of Milan where the Arians were strong, compromised by introducing hymn and psalm singing into the Milanese church service. A first-hand account of it is contained in a passage from St. Augustine's *Confessions*. In the 4th century, when Bishop Ambrose was engaged in one of his doctrinal disputes with the Byzantine Empress Justina, he and his followers at one point had to barricade themselves in a church for protection. "The pious people kept guard in the church, prepared to die with their bishop," wrote St. Augustine. "At the same time," he continues, "was it here first instituted after the manner of the eastern churches, that hymns and psalms should be sung, lest the people should wax faint through the tediousness of sorrow: which custom being retained from that day to this, is still imitated by divers, yea, almost by all thy congregations throughout other parts of the world." The practice spread widely and was incorporated into the Roman liturgy in the following century. Since Ravenna was the neighboring see to that of Milan, the musical practices there must have been similar.

Aeterne rerum conditor   Hymn of St. Ambrose (After Dreves)

Ae-ter- ne re-rum Con-di-tor, No-ctem di-em-que qui_re-gis,

Et tem-po-rum das tem-po-ra, Ut al-le-ves fa-sti-di-um...

Some half-dozen hymns have been attributed to the authorship of St. Ambrose. Whether he also composed the melodies is not so certain, but they at least date from his time. From the example of *Aeterne rerum Conditor* (above), it can be seen that the extreme simplicity and metrical regularity of these vigorous Ambrosian hymns made them especially suitable for congregational singing. The mosaics of Sant' Apollinare Nuovo show files of male and female saints on opposite sides of the nave arcade. Below them, the men of the congregation were grouped on one side, while the women and children gathered on the other, thus forming two choirs. The psalms were sung in two ways: antiphonally and responsorially. When the two choruses sang alternate verses, then joined together in a refrain on the word *alleluia* after each verse, the practice is referred to as *antiphonal psalmody*. When the celebrant chants one verse as a solo, and the choirs perform the next in unison, it is called *responsorial psalmody*. Both were widespread practices in the western church, including Ravenna.

Since Sant' Apollinare Nuovo and San Vitale were designed for different purposes, it follows that their music must also have differed. As a part of the Byzantine liturgy, the music heard at San Vitale would have been like that of the cathedral in Constantinople. As in the west, congregational singing was included there at first, but, with the abandonment of the offertory procession, congregational singing was gradually replaced by that of a professional choir. Music for congregational singing must always be kept relatively simple, and only with a truly professional group can all the rich potentialities of the art be explored and developed.

Since San Vitale, like Hagia Sophia, was also under the direct patronage of the emperor, and since both constituted a part of Justinian's grand design, the matter of providing for a group capable of performing the music of the Byzantine liturgy could hardly have been overlooked. The principal difference between the music of the eastern and western churches is that between a contemplative and an active attitude. The contemplative aspect of the eastern liturgy is illustrated by a remark of St. John Chrysostom, who said that "one may also sing without voice, the mind resounding inwardly, for we sing not to men, but to God, who can hear our hearts and enter into the silences of the mind." This attitude contrasts strongly with that of St. Ambrose, who said in connection with the participation of the congregation in song: "If you praise the Lord and do not sing, you do not utter a hymn. . . . A hymn, therefore, has these three things: song and praise and the Lord."

Alleluia. Ambrosian chant of Byzantine origin   (After Wellesz)

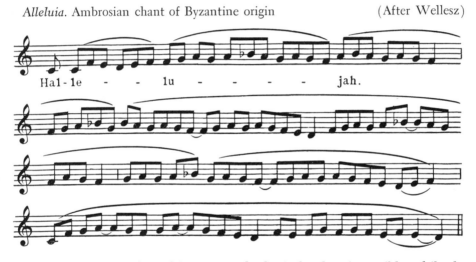

In a static form of worship, greater rhythmic freedom is possible, while the chant that accompanies a procession must have more metrical regularity. The singing of a virtuoso professional choir, furthermore, implies an elaborate and highly developed art, while the practice of congregational singing means the avoidance of technical difficulties. The difference, then, is the difference between the sturdy Ambrosian syllabic hymn (p. 168)—that is, with a syllable allotted to each note—and the melismatic alleluia of Byzantine origin (above)—that is, with single syllables prolonged melismatically over many notes in the manner of a cadenza. Such Byzantine music had a distinctive style of its own, comparable in this respect to that of the visual arts. The elaborate melismas of the latter example would have been heard at San Vitale and at other Byzantine churches at the end of the 6th century. It was precisely such excessively florid alleluias that were ruled out by the Gregorian reform.

IDEAS

Since all the surviving monuments of early Christian art are religiously oriented, it follows that the various sources of patronage, geographical locations, and liturgical purposes will be the qualifying factors in the forms of architecture, the iconography of mosaics, the designs of sculpture, and the performing practices of music. The Early Roman Christian and Byzantine styles were both Christian, and each of the arts lived, moved, and had its being within the all-embracing arms of Mother Church. But her western and eastern arms pointed in different stylistic directions. The disintegrating Roman power in the west led to decentralization of authority and allowed for a wide latitude in local and regional styles, while the Byzantine emperors kept a tight autocratic control of all phases of secular and religious life. Early Roman Christian art, on the one hand, was more an expression of the people; it involved all social levels, its craftsmanship varied from crudity to excellence, and it was more simple and direct in its approach. Byzantine art, on the other hand, was under the personal patronage of a prosperous emperor who ruled both as a Caesar and a religious patriarch. Only the finest artists were employed; and the arts, like the vertical axis of a centralized church, directed attention to the highest level, and tended to become more removed from the people and more purely symbolic. As the arts of both west and east pass by in review, two ideas seem to be the clue to their understanding: authoritarianism and mysticism.

Authoritarianism

Ravenna in the 6th century was the scene of a three-way struggle among a barbarian king, who was a champion of Roman culture; a Byzantine emperor, who claimed the prerogatives of the past golden age; and a Roman pontiff, who had little military might but a powerful influence based on the apostolic succession. As the conflict shaped up, it was among an enlightened secular liberalism, a theocratic traditionalism, and a new spiritual institution with a genius for compromise. In the course of the century, the Ostrogothic kingdom was vanquished by the Byzantine Empire. However, after a brief period of domination, Byzantine power in the west crumbled and the political and military weakness that followed became the soil which nurtured the growth of the new Rome. By the end of the century, Gregory the Great had succeeded in establishing the papacy as the authority that eventually was to dominate the medieval period in the west, while the eastern empire continued in its traditional Byzantine forms of organization.

The principal of authority was by no means foreign to Christianity, which grew to maturity in the later days of the Roman Empire. As an official state religion under the protection of the emperors, Christian organization more and more reflected the authoritarian character of the imperial government. Roman Christian philosophers, such as Boethius and Cassiodorus, cited the authority of Plato and Aristotle on all matters. Theologians accepted the authority of the Scriptures and the commentaries on them by the early church fathers. The thought of the period was expressed in constant quotations and requotations, interpretations and reinterpretations of ancient Hebrew, Greek, Latin, and early Christian authors. No one was willing or able to assume complete authority in his own right; on all issues, each had to cite ancient precedents for his position. The intellectual climate produced by this patristic type of thinking paved the way for the mighty struggle for political and spiritual authority. The only remaining question was what form the authority was to assume, and who would exercise it.

Justinian, who claimed the authority and semidivine status of the old Roman emperors, lived in an atmosphere so static and conservative that the words *originality* and *innovation* were used at his court only as terms of reproach. In paying such a high price for unity, Byzantine civilization purchased only a blanket uniformity. The principal creative energies of Byzantine man, however, were channeled into aesthetic expression, largely because there was no other direction in which to move. Only in art was any variety and freedom to be found. Here again, however, the art of both church and state were under the sole patronage of the emperor. It was then all the more remarkable that such a flowering as that which produced Hagia Sophia in Constantinople and San Vitale in Ravenna could have taken place. In both instances, the methods of construction were experimental, and the solution of the architectural and decorative problems were remarkably uninhibited and daring.

The Byzantine concept of authority was embodied in the architectural and decorative plans of both Hagia Sophia and San Vitale. The central-type church, with its sharp hierarchical divisions that set aside a place for men and women, clergy and laity, aristocrat and commoner, was admirably suited to convey the principle of imperial authority. The vertical axis culminated in a dome that overwhelmed Byzantine man by reminding him, when he was in the presence of the Supreme Authority, of his humble place in the scheme of things. The august imperial portraits in the sanctuary showed him that outside the clergy, only the emperor and empress and those who occupied the top rungs of the social ladder might approach the altar of God. He might not even presume to bring forward his gifts to the altar in the offertory procession. Since all material things came within the province of Caesar, the exalted duty of making the offering was his alone. Byzantine man, furthermore, was not even allowed to raise his voice with those of his fellow men in God's praise, as it was also the emperor's prerogative to provide a chorus of qualified professional musicians whose privilege this was. The attitude of reverence was not only to God alone but also to His viceroys on earth. The imperial portraits left no doubt about that. The majesty of God was felt through the infinite power of government. Through the solemn rituals of sacred and courtly ceremonies, both spiritual and secular authority were imposed on Byzantine man from above. His place in this world was inexorably determined; and his human dignity was in proportion to the blandness of his acceptance of the unified ideal of one Christian empire with one church, one emperor, and one body of laws.

Sant' Apollinare Nuovo as the typical western form of the basilica, on the other hand, indicated a contrasting conception of both God and man. As the twin rows of columns on either side of the nave march forward, they carry the eyes and footsteps of the faithful with them. The approach to the sacred precincts is encouraged rather than forbidden, and even the gift of the widow's mite is acknowledged in one of the mosaic panels above. Just as the congregation had gone forth from the doors of their homes to the house of the Lord, the processions of saints in the mosaics likewise moved out of the gates of the twin cities of Classe and Ravenna. The rites they attended were not so incomprehensible and fearsome that they had, as in the Byzantine liturgy, to be enacted behind curtains and choir screens. In the west they took place in the open, and one enjoyed the privilege of ministering to the Lord. The spatial divisions of the oblong basilica, to be sure, still allowed for differences of status, such as that of men and women, choir and clergy. The allowance for all to participate in the sacred service, however, modified the authoritative concept, so that there was some religious freedom.

By exercising his power to offer gifts and by maintaining his active participation, western man kept the concept of authority on a spiritual level, and he thus retained a certain individual freedom which Byzantine man had surrendered to his rulers. Sant' Apollinare Nuovo and San Vitale thus are reflections of two contrasting images of man. The oblong basilica was designed for active spatial and temporal movement, while the domed central-type church indicated Byzantine man's passive acceptance of the role of spectator. In one case, the horizontal axis, by inviting forward movement, placed man in a progressive relation to space; in the other, the vertical axis, by pointing upward, tended to check physical movement and divert the energies toward stationary contemplation. The mosaics of Sant' Apollinare Nuovo, in addition to the processions, depict the life story of Christ in narrative form, while those in San Vitale are confined to individual representations of separate scenes without any sequential arrangement and are designed to dazzle by their splendor. The music of Sant' Apollinare Nuovo and other churches in the west was intended for congregational participation and had a metrical regularity conducive to marching, while that of San Vitale was highly complex, melismatic, and had an asymetrical cadence that minimized bodily motion.

Fig. 4:30. Sant' Apollinare in Classe. *Apse Mosaics. c.*530 (Soprintendenza)

Mysticism

The art of the 6th century in Ravenna, like that of such other important centers as Constantinople and Rome, crossed the bridge from the classical Greco-Roman into the medieval world. While some of the ancient grandeur remained, the accent on symbolism laid the foundation for the coming medieval styles. The physical was replaced by the psychical, the rational road to knowledge by intuitive revelation. Many of the older art forms were carried over and reinterpreted in a new light. The Roman bathhouse became the Christian baptistry where the soul was cleansed of original sin, and the public basilica was redesigned for church mysteries. Mosaics, which were used for Hellenistic and Roman pavements, became the mural medium for mystical visions. The shepherd of classical genre sculpture became symbolically the Good Shepherd. Classical bird and animal motifs became symbols for the soul and spiritual realm. Music became a reflection of the divine unity of God and man; and the classical lyre, because of its stretched strings on a wooden frame, was reinterpreted by St. Augustine as a symbol of the crucified flesh of Christ. Orpheus, by means of its sounds, had descended into the underworld and overcome death. Christ is therefore frequently represented as playing on the lyre, and at Sant' Apollinare Nuovo he is seated on a lyre-backed throne.

The concept of space turned from the limited classical three-dimensional representation of the natural world to an infinite Christian two-dimensional symbolic world. Invisible things rose in importance above those that could be seen with the eyes. While classical man had regarded his world objectively from without, early Christian man contemplated his subjectively from within. Socrates once asked an artist whether he could represent the soul. The reply was: "How can it be imitated, since it has neither shape nor colour . . . and is not visible at all?" St. Augustine, however, observed that "beauty cannot be beheld in any bodily matter." Such mystical visions could be perceived only through symbolism. While natural science had been the foundation stone of ancient philosophy, symbolic theology became the Christian philosophical viewpoint. Whereas Greek drama (which was a form of religious experience) had reached its climax step by step with remorseless logic, the Christian drama (as expressed in the liturgy) kindled the fires of faith and arrived at its mystical climax by intuitive means. The denial of the flesh and the conviction that only the soul can be beautiful doomed classical bodiliness and exalted abstract bodilessness. Instead of capturing and clothing the godlike image with flesh and blood, the new concern was with releasing the spirit from the bondage of the flesh.

What sometimes seems to be a crude technique in early Christian art, in contrast to the high quality of classical craftsmanship, is partly the result of the new orientation in which artists are no longer attempting to convey a natural image of the world. Elegance of linguistic as well as pictorial expression was considered too close to pagan aberrations for comfort. Civilized Roman men of letters, for instance, chafed at the comparative roughness of the Hebrew Scriptures. St. Jerome, when he went into the wilderness to translate the Bible, took along with him a copy of his beloved Cicero. Such weakness, however, he attributed to his sinful nature. St. Augustine, as a grammarian, loved the noble Latin of Vergil and the beautiful classical melodies, but such "moral lapses" caused him bitter self-recrimination. The fervent congregational singing of the untutored faithful, no matter how unrefined it sounded, was morally preferable to the higher virtuosity of pagan musical sophistication. The church fathers, who were among the highly educated few, had the difficult task of adapting the older theological, philosophical, artistic, and musical forms to the needs of their congregations, whose ranks included former slaves, artisans, and unlettered barbarians. The result was a technical decline from the high standards of classical craftsmanship in the arts and letters owing to a lowering in the relative literacy of those to whom the new visual and verbal vocabularies were addressed. This was an age of transition from one cultural frame of reference to another. The fact that all the arts were adapted to the new religious orientation and acquired in the process an astonishing new vitality is all-important.

Fig. 4:31. Santa Costanza. *Interior*. Center 40′ in diameter. Early 4th century. Rome
(Vatican Photographic Archive)

The great creation and the all-inclusive medium shaped during this period to convey this other-worldly vision was the liturgy. The thought, action, and sequence of the rites of Constantinople, Ravenna, Rome, and other centers determined to a large extent the architectural plans, the symbolism of the mosaics, and the forms of the sculpture and music. At this time, the fruits of generations of contemplative and active lives gradually ripened into mature structures. The content of centuries of theoretical speculation united with the practical efforts of countless generations of writers, builders, decorators, and musicians to produce the Byzantine liturgy in the east and the synthesis of Gregory the Great in the west. Removed from its primary religious association and seen in a more detached aesthetic light, the liturgy as a work of art embodies a profound and dramatic insight into the deepest longings and highest aspirations of the human spirit.

During the 6th century the controversy still raged as to whether Christ's nature was essentially human or divine. The more the eastern view emphasized Christ's divinity, the more remote He became. One of the prayers of St. John Chrysostom, for instance, begins: "O Lord, our God, Whose power is inconceivable and glory incomprehensible, Whose mercy is immeasurable and tenderness to man unspeakable . . .". Such a conception makes highly presumptuous any attempt to comprehend the divine essence by reason or direct representation. Hence the mosaics of San Vitale weave such abstract symbols as that of the Chrismon into a rich arabesque of florid designs. Strict symmetry and other means are employed to raise the representations out of the plane of reality and thus to widen the immeasurable gulf between divinity and humanity. The dim lighting, the golden glow of the mosaics, the mysterious symbols whose meaning it was the privilege of Christians to contemplate—all helped conjure up this unfathomable and invisible divinity. The most sacred rites took place behind carved alabaster screens; the choirs sang softly back of embroidered curtains. The words addressed from Maximian's carved ivory chair took on a superhuman impressiveness. All these in concert conveyed the mystical idea and awakened the vision of eternity in the minds of the beholders.

The western position was eventually settled by a compromise upholding Christ's dual nature as both human and divine, but western thought continued to accent His role as the sufferer and Savior of humanity. The more this aspect was accented, the more approachable and comprehensible the figure of Christ became. This is the side that finds expression in the mosaics of Sant' Apollinare Nuovo, especially in those that recount the parables and miracles as well as the passion, death, and resurrection of the historical Christ.

The Early Roman Christian and Byzantine styles were the responses to the need for new verbal, visual, and auditory modes of expression. In both cases, there was a shift from the forms designed to represent this world to those capable of conjuring up other-worldly visions. Through the poetry of language, the choreographic patterns of step and gesture, and the exalted melodies of the chant, the gripping drama of humanity embodied in the liturgy was enacted in sublime theaters that were furnished with a full panoply of stage settings, decor, costumes, and props created by the inspired hands of the finest craftsmen and artists of the time. The liturgy is, moreover, a continuous pageant lasting not only for a few hours but unfolding with constant variation during the continuous sequence of solemn and joyful feasts through the weeks, months, and seasons of the calendar year, the decades, centuries, and millennia.

CHRONOLOGY:

Cluny, Late 11th and Early 12th Centuries

General Events

c.529		St. Benedict (died c.547) built monastery at Monte Cassino, Italy
768–	814	Charlemagne ruled at Aix-la-Chapelle (Aachen); crowned Holy Roman emperor by pope, 800
		Carolingian Period
		c.792–800 Centula monastery built
		c.796–804 Palatine Chapel at Aix-la-Chapelle built
c.800		St. Gall (Switzerland) monastery begun
	910	Abbey of Cluny at Burgundy, France, founded
927–	942	Odo, abbot of Cluny, reputed author of musical treatises
	962	Otto the Great (936–973) crowned Holy Roman emperor
994–	1049	Odilo, abbot of Cluny
c.995–c.1050		Guido of Arezzo, author of musical treatises, inventor of staff notation
1000–	1150	Romanesque Period at height
1049–	1109	Hugh of Semur, abbot of Cluny
	1050	Holy Roman Empire at height; ascendancy of papal power
	1063	Pisa Cathedral begun
	1066	William, Duke of Normandy, conquered England; reigned as king of England, 1066–1087
1071–	1112	Pilgrimage church at Santiago de Compostela, Spain, built
	1072	St. Peter Damian died

1073–	1085	Gregory VII (Hildebrande), pope
	1077	Emperor Henry IV bowed to Pope Gregory VII at Canossa; Abbot Hugh of Cluny was intermediary
c.1080		Church of Sant' Ambrogio begun at Milan
c.1080–1160		Church of St. Sernin built at Toulouse, France
1088–	1099	Urban II, Cluniac pope
1088–	1130	Great third church at Cluny built
		1088 Third church begun under Hugh of Semur
		1095 Apse dedicated by Pope Urban II
		1120 Church finished
		1125 Nave vaults partially collapsed
		1131 Church dedicated by Pope Innocent X
	1095	Urban II preached the First Crusade
1096–	1120	Abbey church of La Madeleine at Vézelay built
		1096 Abbey church begun
		1104 Original Romanesque choir and transept dedicated
		1110 Nave finished
		1120 Narthex begun and nave revaulted after fire
		1130 Approximate date of the tympanum over the central portal of narthex
		1132 Narthex dedicated
	1098	Cistercian order founded; opposed Cluniac order; St. Bernard of Clairvaux was its principal spokesman
	1109	Pontius became abbot of Cluny
	1122	Peter the Venerable became abbot of Cluny

THE MONASTIC
ROMANESQUE STYLE

THE MONASTERY AT CLUNY, LATE 11TH AND EARLY 12TH CENTURIES

The most typical expression of the Romanesque period was the monastery. The life of ancient Athens and Pergamon had culminated in the constellations of their acropolis buildings, that of Rome had been realized in its forums and civil-engineering projects, and Constantinople and Ravenna had evolved the basilica and palace as the church and state sides of a theocratic social order. In the Gothic period that succeeded the Romanesque it was to be the cathedral. As Christianity had spread northward after the fall of the West Roman Empire, southern classical forms had met and merged with those of the northern barbarian peoples. This union of the older settled Roman civilization, with its ideals of reason, restraint, and repose, and the newly awakened spirit of the north, with its restless energy and brooding imagination, resulted in the Romanesque, a style that reached its maturity between the years 1000 and 1150. Lacking the security of strong central governments, without the advantages of flourishing cities and towns, Romanesque man sought peace of mind in the monastery as a haven from the storm-tossed seas of his anarchic social surroundings. Here in these centers off the beaten path he built a miniature world that contained a cross section of Romanesque life. Besides serving as a religious shrine where pilgrims could gather

179

to revere sacred relics, the monastery was the manufacturing and agricultural center of its region as well as a seat of learning where the only libraries, schools, and
hospitals of the time were found.

The largest and grandest of all Romanesque monasteries was the French
abbey at Cluny, and in Figure 5:1 Kenneth J. Conant reconstructs its plan at
the pinnacle of its power and fame. Within its walls, men of contemplation were
to be found beside men of action; those who were world-weary dwelled side by
side with those who knew little of life beyond the cloister; saints brushed shoulders with criminals who sought refuge from the prosecution of secular authorities.
Those who were drawn to the vocation of monk were firm believers in the seeming paradox in Christ's words: "For whosoever will save his life shall lose it: but
whosoever will lose his life for my sake, the same shall save it" (Luke 9:24). By
taking the triple vows of poverty, chastity, and obedience, the monk automatically renounced such worldly pursuits as individual material rewards, the pleasures of the senses, the personal satisfactions of family life, and even the exercise
of his own free will. According to the Rule of St. Benedict, the founder of European monasticism, a monk "should have absolutely not anything; neither a book,
nor tablets, nor a pen—nothing at all. For indeed it is not allowed to the monks
to have their own bodies or wills in their power." Through this renunciation of
all worldly desires, the monk sought a higher life in the realm of the spirit, which
can be summed up most completely in the words of St. Paul: "I live; yet not I,
but Christ liveth in me" (Gal. 2:20). In order to realize such other-worldly aims,
segregation from the secular world had to be effected, and a special way of life
found.

The value of hard work was stressed in the Benedictine Rule, which prescribed an average of six or seven hours a day of manual labor. At first this meant
literally toiling in the fields and tending the flocks, but with the growth in ranks
and the accumulation of land and treasure, the monastic communities initiated
something like a division of labor. At Cluny, the singing of psalms, reciting of
prayers, the reading and copying of manuscripts were construed as the proper
"work" of a monk, and the actual agricultural pursuits were delegated to peasants
and serfs who worked under the direction of lay brothers. Consequently, when
Cluniac life had to be defended from the criticism of the stricter Cistercian order,
Peter the Venerable, abbot of Cluny during the first part of the 12th century,
wrote: "It is more noble to set one's hand to the pen than to the plow, to trace
divine letters upon the page than furrows upon the fields. Sow on the page the
seed of the word of God, and when the harvest is ripe, when your books are
finished, the hungry readers shall be satisfied by an abundant harvest."

In order to provide such a life, a monastery had to be planned so that the
monks would have all that was necessary for both their bodily subsistence and
their spiritual sustenance. The objective was to be as independent of Caesar as

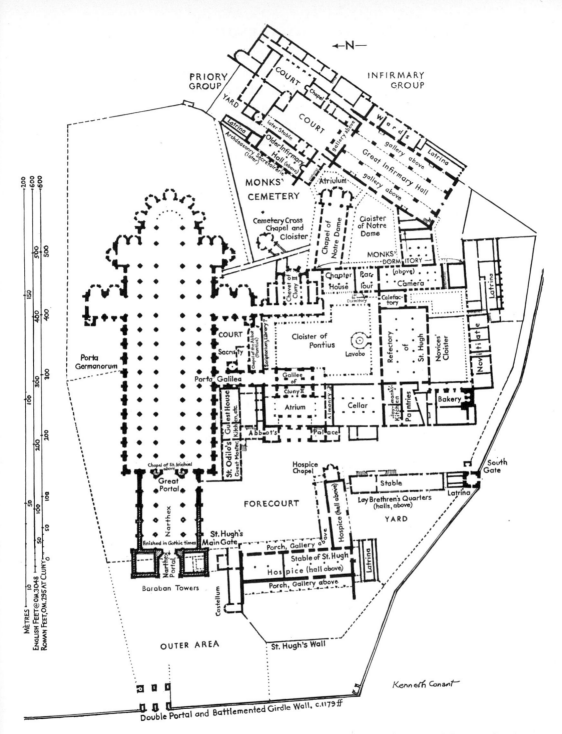

Fig. 5:1. Abbey of Cluny. *Plan. c.*1157. By Kenneth J. Conant (Courtesy Mediaeval Academy of America)

possible, so as to render their all unto God. The Benedictine Rule did not pre-scribe the exact form that a monastic building should take, and each abbey nominally was independent to solve its problems according to its needs, the con-tours of its site, and the extent of its resources. But tradition often operated as rigidly as rules, and with local variations most monasteries adhered to a common pattern. Allowing for its exceptional size and complexities because it was the mother house of a great order, the plan of Cluny was fairly typical.

Since the life of a Cluniac monk was one of almost constant religious ob-servances alternating with periods set aside for contemplation, the soul of the monastery was in its abbey church and its heart was in its cloister. The church served primarily as the scene of the constant devotional activities of the monks day and night throughout the year, and only secondarily as a shrine for the pilgrimages that were made to revere the relics of a saint that were exhibited there at certain seasons. The monk's day was punctuated by the sequence of the Regular Hours that were sung in the abbey church. These holy offices consisted of prayers and canticles appropriate to each time of day and night together with the singing of entire psalms. Matins took place before dawn, with Prime coming just after sunrise and Tierce two hours later. Solemn high mass was celebrated after both Prime and Tierce, the latter being in commemoration of the dead and the mass that all brothers except those who were ill were expected to attend. Sext and None followed after Tierce at approximately three-hour intervals; Vespers came after sundown; Compline at nightfall; and both Nocturn and Vigils, in the course of the night. Since so much of the daily ritual took place at night or early in the morning in the unheated church, the monk had to dress in warm woolen robes, and in the winter he was provided with fur-lined boots. The Cluniac habit had a leather belt, heavy sleeves that could serve as hand muffs, a cowl that could become a hood, and a cape for extra warmth and pro-tection from the elements.

Next in importance to facilities for the church services was the provision for the contemplative life that centered on the cloister. In the plan (Fig. 5:1), the cloister is found, typically, in the center of the abbey and south of the nave of the church, with the other monastic buildings clustering around it. The usual cloister was an open quadrangular garden plot, called the *garth*, which was en-closed by a covered arcade on all four sides. The somewhat irregular shape of the cloister at Cluny in the 12th century was owed to the ambitious building pro-gram necessitated by the rapid growth of the monastery. While the old 11th-century cloister of Abbot Odilo, next to the refectory, had been retained, once the abbey's great new third church was ready, the cloister was enlarged by demolishing the nave of the older second church. (The choir and narthex of this church can be seen in the plan on the east and west sides of the cloister garth.) It was here in this extended cloister that the monks found the creative

Fig. 5:2. Abbey of St. Trophîme. *Cloister c.*1100. Arles

solitude they needed for the inward life as they walked to and fro in all kinds of weather, reading the Scriptures and other books from the adjacent library, pondering on the meaning of the symbolic sculptured capitals of the arcade, or carrying on their silent meditations. The rule of silence was rigidly maintained except for two periods of about half an hour each, one in the morning after the chapter was held, and the other after Sext when the monks were allowed to attend to their personal and domestic duties. The form of the cloister was undoubtedly derived from the atrium that stood before an Early Roman Christian basilica; and, like it, the cloister usually contained a fountain for ceremonial ablutions before entering the church. In the Cluny plan, a font labeled *Lavabo* can be seen before the entrance to the refectory, which was located typically on the south side of the cloister. Since this renowned marble-columned cloister no longer exists, the one of St. Trophime at Arles (Fig. 5:2) will serve as an example. The columns and their outstanding Romanesque capitals date from the year 1100 when the abbey was one of the dependencies of Cluny.

At mealtimes, after washing their hands at the lavabo, the brethren entered the refectory where they ate in common. Here the silence was broken only by the lector who read aloud from the lives of the saints and the writings of the church

Fig. 5:3. Abbey of Vézelay. *Entrance to Chapter Room. c.1170*

fathers. The refectory shown in the plan is the one Hugh rebuilt to accommodate the ever-growing population of resident monks, which in his time numbered around 200, in contrast with the 70-odd during the abbacy of his predecessor. The refectory measured 112 feet in length and 67 feet in width, with a row of six pillars on either side. Besides the rows of tables for the monks, there were two tables on a raised platform, one for the grand prior of the order and one for the claustral prior. Fresco paintings of scenes from the Old and New Testaments decorated its walls, and a large picture of Christ in Majesty as at the Last Judgment was found at one end. Adjacent to the refectory were the kitchens, bakeries, and pantries; and opening out from the monks' kitchen and running along the west side of the cloister were the storerooms for food with cellars below. One of the rooms led into an outside court where alms were distributed to the poor.

Like the chapter house at Vézelay (see entrance in Fig. 5:3), that at Cluny opened off the east walk of the cloister. Here the monks gathered each morning following church service and breakfast. After a prayer and the reading of a chapter from the Rule of St. Benedict, the abbot from his throne presided over the meeting. At this time, the monks were given necessary information, received instruction, and participated in any business that properly might come before them. This might include anything from the admission of novices to the expulsion of an unworthy monk, from matters connected with the sale, purchase, or leasing of property to the acceptance of gifts. The most solemn business, however, came when the abbot himself was chosen from among their numbers on the death of his predecessor.

Except for the church, cloister, refectory, chapter house, and the quarters for distinguished guests, the other monastic buildings were almost entirely utilitarian in character, as the elevation by Professor Conant will show (Fig. 5:4). Above the chapter house and the other large rooms adjoining it was the monks' dormitory. Since services were held during the night as well as by day, it had to be located near one of the entrances to the church. As seen in the plan, the monks at Cluny could go downstairs, move along the eastern walk of the cloister, and enter the church through the end of the greater transept. The dormitory itself, the large barnlike building at the left in Figure 5:4, was a long hall with tall narrow windows between which, on either side of a central aisle, were beds for the monks.

Besides these main centers of monastic activity, a complete abbey had to provide for many other functions and contingencies. Beyond the dormitory on the east was a chapel and small cloister where the aged or infirm monks could worship and meditate. Farther on, beyond the monks' cemetery, was the infirmary hall, which had rows of beds in separate cubicles, with small rooms set aside for the laundry and servants' quarters. Another section, amounting to a miniature monastery, had to be set aside for the training of novices who as yet had not been fully admitted to the order. Complete with its own cloister, this unit can be found on the extreme southern side. Near by were workshops for such craftsmen as blacksmiths, carpenters, cobblers, and tailors. Their location near the novices' quarters and outside the inner precincts of the abbey indicates that they were primarily intended for lay workers rather than for monks. These workers could thus come and go without interfering with the routine of the monastery itself.

Along the western confines were the stables for dairy cattle and other domestic animals, with sleeping quarters for lay brethren above. Hospices for poor pilgrims were also located here, while across the court was the building where distinguished guests were housed. The old guesthouse at Cluny was a spacious room heated by a large ornate fireplace. Above it were separate dormitories for 40 men and 30 women with a common refectory in between. The abbot often entertained hundreds of guests, many of whom were of the princely class who traveled with large retinues. Since donations for the new church and support for the monastery came in part from such visitors, it was imperative that they gain

Fig. 5:4. Abbey of Cluny. *Bird's-eye View from southeast.* c.1157. Reconstruction study by Kenneth J. Conant (Courtesy Mediaeval Academy of America)

the best possible impression. Surrounding the monastery on all sides were thick walls to protect it from marauders, thieves, and armed bands in time of invasion. Outside the walls lay the gardens, groves, and farmlands under its control, which produced the necessities of life. As on the domain of a feudal lord, the soil was tilled by bound serfs working under the supervision of the lay brothers, and sometimes by free peasants who rented land from the monks on a crop-sharing basis. The buildings in this area included only such necessary structures as barns, granaries, and mills.

The plan of Cluny was thus a coherent system of adjoining quadrangles that embraced courts and cloisters of a size and importance which varied with the differing activities they were designed to accommodate. Altogether it was a highly complex and at the same time logical plan for a complete community, taking into account the ideals, aspirations, practices, and everyday activities of a group that gathered to work physically and spiritually toward a common end.

ARCHITECTURE

Hugh of Semur, greatest of the Cluniac abbots, succeeded Odilo in the year 1049. Under him, Cluny was destined to attain a period of such resplendence that it could be described by an enthusiastic chronicler as "shining on the earth like a second sun." Taking as his model the accepted feudal structure of society, by which smaller and more dependent landowners swore allegiance to the larger and more powerful landlords in return for protection, Hugh became the organizer who brought the traditionally independent Benedictine monasteries into the Cluniac orbit. With the express approval of the popes, Hugh gradually concentrated the power of the whole order into his hands and transformed Cluny into a vast monastic empire over which he ruled benignly for 60 years. In the church hierarchy he was outranked only by the pope, and in the secular world he was the peer of kings. He figured prominently in most of the historical events of his day, even to the extent of acting as intermediary between an emperor and a pope on the famous occasion at Canossa, when Henry IV came on bended knee to beseech Gregory VII for forgiveness. Hugh's greatest moment, however, came when Pope Urban II, who had received training as a monk and prior at Cluny under his personal guidance, was present to dedicate the high altar of his great new abbey church. Honor after honor was bestowed upon the monastery by this Cluniac pope, who was also the preacher of the First Crusade. On his deathbed he wrote to Hugh, his former master, saying that he "committed to him the care of his mother the Church, as Christ His mother to the beloved apostle."

In a period when cities were in eclipse, the influence of bishops and their ability to undertake new buildings decreased. Likewise, when they were constantly moving their courts from one city to another, kings had little time or inclination to do any important building. However, with the consolidation of monastic life into a centralized system, and with the increasing concentration of wealth into the collective hands of these stable and growing institutions, one need not wonder that monasteries were the scene of the most significant architectural and artistic developments of the time. Furthermore, the rise of the Cluniac star under the indomitable will of its great organizing genius and builder made Cluny itself the place where the most important and progressive developments occurred. As the influence of the mother house gradually permeated the entire order, a characteristic touch became discernible, and a Cluniac style emerged that, in turn, became synonymous with the highest development of Romanesque art.

Hugh had begun by undertaking many new monastic buildings to accommodate Cluny's ever-growing number of resident monks. Eventually the older second church also proved inadequate for the mother house of a great order, especially when delegations of monks from the priories far and wide assembled there for the chapters general. (Records show that on such an occasion in the year 1132, over 1200 monks were in the processional line.) The growing importance of Cluny as a center for pilgrimages also added to the need for greater space in the abbey church. For these practical reasons, as well as his desire to crown his many achievements with a monument that would rival the legendary temple of Solomon, the great new third abbey church was begun. Even with all his power and influence, however, Hugh did not attempt it before the dominant position of Cluny in the scheme of things was completely consolidated, and before he was certain of generous financial support. The far-flung priories of the order, numbering at this time well over 1000 and extending as far as Scotland in the north, Portugal in the west, and Jerusalem in the east, could all be counted on for contributions. In addition, offerings were received from people of all classes, from bishops to the humblest of their parishioners and from great lords down to the poorest pilgrims, who came to worship at the shrine. Thus in 1088, when he was past 65 and in his 40th year as abbot, Hugh of Semur began the monumental abbey church that in its magnitude and glory eclipsed all other churches in western Christendom. Gilon, one of his earliest biographers, said that Hugh "began and erected such a church within twenty years that if an emperor had built it within so short a time, it would have been considered marvelous."

The Great Third Abbey Church at Cluny

Hugh's great church was dominated on the exterior by its imposing tower forms, one of which is still to be seen atop its single surviving transept (Fig. 5:5). The ground plan (Fig. 5:1) shows its unusual double transepts, the many apsidal chapels radiating outward from the choir, and its massive proportions. It was usual for large abbey churches to have an impressive lantern tower over the crossing of the nave and the transept. At Cluny, as with St. Sernin at Toulouse (Fig. 5:6), the immense size dominated the silhouette of the whole exterior. The twin octagonal towers astride the transept wings, however, were less common. The minor transept also had its central tower, thus making four on the east end, which, added to the two on either side of the narthex entrance, brought the total to six. Unlike later Gothic cathedrals, the exterior was unadorned by sculpture, all such embellishments being concentrated in the interior. Even the western façade was bare, since it was designed for an introspective cloistered community and consequently had no need to extend sculptured invitations to the world outside as did a city church. Rich façades as entrances to the nave did exist in abbey churches elsewhere, but they were masked by the narthex and hence essentially a part of the interior.

Fig. 5:5. Third Abbey Church of Cluny. *Surviving Transept*. 1088–1130

Fig. 5:6. Church of St. Sernin, Toulouse. *Apse. c.*1080 (Archives Photographiques)

While on everyday occasions the monks entered the church from the cloister, high holidays, such as Easter, Pentecost, and the Feast of SS. Peter and Paul to whom the church was dedicated, called for a ceremonial entrance from the west end. Here the double portal between the towers led into a spacious three-aisled narthex, which was called the *minor nave*. In most churches, it was referred to symbolically as "the Galilee," because the celebrant (usually the abbot) who headed the procession going into the nave was likened to Jesus leading his disciples into the city of Galilee. At Cluny, however, the monks had their own Galilee portal, which can be found in the plan about halfway down the nave. The narthex, besides serving as the place where the grand procession could be marshaled, took care of the overflow of laymen who gathered at Cluny during the pilgrimage season. At Vézelay, for instance, the narthex was actually called the *ecclesia peregrinorum*, or church of the pilgrims. When such an entrance was made at Cluny, it was through three carved portals, the central one of which was 21 feet in height. Over the lintel and enclosed by the arch was an immense semicircular *tympanum*, containing a sculptured relief representing Christ in Glory surrounded by a heavenly host, the four symbolic evangelical beasts, and various Apostles and elders.

On entering the nave (Fig. 5:7), the mighty proportions of the huge basilica loomed up. From the entrance portal to the end of the apse, it extended a distance of 415 feet, while the entire horizontal axis from front to back, including the narthex, reached an over-all length of 615 feet. The nave itself had 11 bays that stretched forward a distance of 260 feet. Each bay was separated by a group of columns clustered around the supporting piers, which, as the architectural counterpart of the monks, marched in solemn procession toward the climax of the building at the high altar. In width, the nave spread outward 118 feet and was divided into five aisles. This division was owing in part to the need to provide extra space for altars when it became the custom for the priests to say mass every day. The outside aisles, extending all the way around the church and choir, gave pilgrims access to these numerous altars and, more especially, to the smaller chapels in the choir without disturbing the monastic liturgy. It also provided more room for the grand processionals that distinguished the Cluniac liturgy and that demanded ever more impressive and spacious settings. It can be seen in Figure 5:7 that a screen reached into the nave and closed off a space set aside for the monks' choir. The great height of the church was such that the unified impression of the whole was not broken by the screen, and the eye was drawn aloft to the tall columns around the high altar and above them, in turn, to the lofty figure of Christ, painted in fresco on the interior of the half dome of the apse, that gazed downward as if in a vision.

Whereas the Early Roman Christian basilicas were horizontally oriented, the Romanesque examples, because of the northern influence, raised the levels of the nave upward vertically. This gradually resulted in more and more accent being placed on the parts of the building above the nave arcade. At Cluny, a double row of windows was found, the lower of which was filled in with masonry, while the upper was left open and served as the clearstory. Though it had numerous windows, the church was criticized by later Gothic builders as being too dark. Its thick walls and massive proportions allowed little direct sunlight to penetrate into the church itself. This was not of great importance since so much of the monastic liturgy took place at night when the interior was illuminated by candlelight. Churches designed for city people who worshiped by day naturally had to pay more attention to lighting problems.

As at Santiago de Compostela (Fig. 5:8), the nave at Cluny was spanned by ribbed barrel vaulting, 32 feet in the clear, supported by slightly pointed transverse arches. Rising a full 98 feet above the pavement, the vaults were the highest achieved up to this time. But the emotional exuberance of attaining such height outran the engineering knowledge needed to maintain it, and a part of the Cluny vaulting soon collapsed. Out of this accident came the discovery of the flying buttress (see Fig. 7:7), and when the vaults were rebuilt a range of rudimentary supports with open round arches was placed outside the aisle roofs. Cluny thus achieved the distinction of being the first church to have external buttresses supporting its nave vaults, and, with its pointed arches, high vaulting, and primitive flying buttresses, Cluny combined for the first time in one structure three of the necessary features of the future Gothic style.

The Romanesque basilica differs little from its Early Roman Christian counterpart except in size, vertical accents, and development of the transept and the parts beyond it. Monastic churches all gravitated toward the eastern end (Fig. 5:9) where the choir assembled after the procession, and especially toward the high altar where the solemn rites were performed. In a city church, the nave had to provide space for a congregation, but in a monastic church the clergy, including the monks, numbered into the hundreds, and the congregation often was nonexistent. Logically, then, the space around the altar had to be extended so that all the monks who formed the choir could be seated. The enlarged apse and double transepts at Cluny were clearly developed to give the monks a sense of surrounding the high altar and to produce a spacious and resonant setting for the almost ceaseless chanting.

The high altar itself was set off from the surrounding ambulatory by eight columns of surpassing slenderness and beauty. Crowning them were skillfully carved capitals (one of which is shown in Figs. 5:20–5:23), all that remains of the apse today. That these were as impressive in Romanesque times as they are now is attested to by Hildebert, bishop of Le Mans, who after a visit wrote: "If it were possible for those who dwell in heaven to take pleasure in a house made by hands, the ambulatory of Cluny would be a place where angels walked."

(*Opposite*) Fig. 5:7. Third Abbey Church of Cluny. 1088–1130. Reconstruction Study of Nave by Kenneth J. Conant (Courtesy Mediaeval Academy of America). Fig. 5:8 (*above*). Cathedral of Santiago de Compostela. *Nave Interior from west.* Nave *c.*164′ long, 65′ wide, 79′ high. *c.*1075–1150. Spain (Ksado)

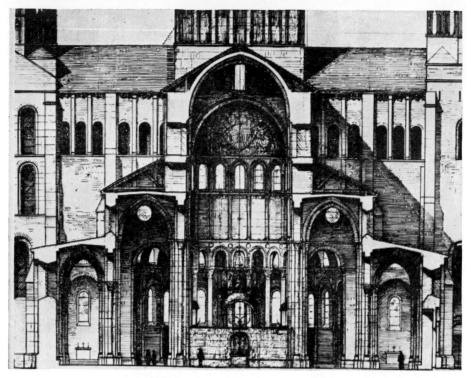

Fig. 5:9. Third Abbey Church of Cluny. *Transverse Section at Transept.* Drawing by
Kenneth J. Conant (Courtesy Mediaeval Academy of America)

The decorative plan of the church was carried out on a scale comparable in
quality to the grandeur of its spatial dimensions. Over 1200 sculptured capitals
surmounted the columns of the structure, while carved moldings outlined the
graceful pointed arches of the nave arcade. Most of the sculpture was painted in
rich colors that gave an added glow to the splendor of the interior, and the whole
church was paved with mosaic floors inlaid with images of saints and angels or
with abstract designs.

All this magnificence did not go unchallenged. The redoubtable opponent
of the Cluniac order, St. Bernard, disapproved violently of such extravagances.
In doing so in writing, however, he unwittingly left a first-hand account of the
glory of Hugh's church soon after it was finished. In a letter to one of the Cluniac
abbots he commented on "the vast height of your churches, their immoderate
length, their superfluous breadth, the costly polishings, the curious carvings and
paintings which attract the worshiper's gaze and hinder his attentions." His feeling was that "at the very sight of these costly yet marvelous vanities men are
more kindled to offer gifts than to pray. . . . Hence the church is adorned with
gemmed crowns of light—nay, with lustres like cart-wheels, girt all round with

lamps, but no less brilliant with precious stones that stud them. Moreover we see candelabra standing like trees of massive bronze, fashioned with marvelous subtlety of art, and glistening no less brightly with gems than with the lights they carry. What, think you, is the purpose of all this? The compunction of penitents, or the admiration of beholders?"

In spite of Bernard's diatribe, this third church became a model for all subsequent Cluniac abbey churches and spread the fame of the Burgundian building art—and the taste for its pointed arches and other features that eventually were incorporated into Gothic cathedrals. As the most representative of all Romanesque churches, embodying as it did the most highly developed forms of the time, Hugh's church became the greatest single factor in the crystallization of the Romanesque style. Furthermore, it was destined to remain the largest and most magnificent edifice of its kind for a full five centuries—specifically until the new basilica of St. Peter was undertaken in Rome in the 16th century.

It stood proudly until the year 1798 when a wave of Revolutionary reaction in France caused it to be sacked and its very stones carried away. Before the romantic interest in things medieval had developed, and before the tourist traffic—that modern counterpart of the medieval pilgrimages—could intervene, Cluny was blown up by dynamite and the rubble sold as common building stone. All that now remains is a single transept with its tower still in place (Fig. 5:5), the capitals of the ambulatory (Figs. 5:20–5:23), and a number of odd fragments of its architectural sculptures. And so it is that the other priories of Hugh's time must be cited for clues about Cluny's architecture and sculpture. The great increase in the power and prestige of the order was reflected not only in the growth of the mother abbey but in the numbers who were attracted as monks and pilgrims to its priories and dependencies. At the same time that Hugh was engaged in his great building program, abbey churches were in the process of construction in more than a dozen other monasteries in France alone, including those of Moissac, Beaulieu, La Charité-sur-Loire, and Vézelay. Each in some way reflected directly the influence of Hugh's great basilica.

SCULPTURE

Fragments of the great period of Cluny's sculptural grandeur today are scattered among its various extant abbeys, priories, and dependencies as well as museums. Some of the finest Cluniac sculpture still to be seen is in the abbey church of La Madeleine at Vézelay. The nave (Fig. 5:10) and narthex (Fig. 5:11) date from the time of Hugh's church at Cluny, and the intelligent restoration in the 19th century by the French medieval archeologist Viollet-le-Duc accounts for their present good condition. While its proportions are considerably smaller than the great basilica at Cluny, La Madeleine is now the largest Romanesque abbey

Fig. 5:10. Abbey Church of La Madeleine, Vézelay. *Nave Interior from East.* 1104–1132 (Archives Photographiques)

church in France. Rich in historical associations, it derived its principal fame in medieval times as the repository of the relics of St. Mary Magdalene. On the eve of her feast in the year 1120, after the completion of the nave, a fire destroyed the wooden portions of the roof, and burning timbers fell on the assembled pilgrims. After the fire, the revaulting of the nave was undertaken, and, for the first time in France, the new principle of the groin vault was used. This type of vaulting can be described roughly as the result of the intersection at right angles of two barrel vaults of an equivalent span and height. The resulting diagonal lines seen from underneath are referred to as the *groins*. The principle used at Vézelay is illustrated in Figure 3:12, and it can be contrasted with the simpler type of half-cylinder barrel vaulting used at Cluny, as shown in Figure 5:7. As at Cluny, strong transverse arches span the nave, but here the alternation of their lighter pink and darker grayish-brown stone results in an interesting color effect. While photographs tend to exaggerate the contrast, the irregularity of the cut-stone voussoirs is pictured accurately.

The principal interest at Vézelay, however, is the seemingly inexhaustible wealth of sculptured capitals and, above all, the relief compositions over its three portals leading from the narthex into the nave and side aisles. For the first time since antiquity, monumental sculpture appears in Romanesque churches in the tympanums over the portals, the largest and most intricate sculpture being used in the tympanum over the central doorway. While only a few fragments of the great tympanum of Cluny have survived, at Moissac there is a fine example that shows a crowned figure of Christ enclosed by the four symbolic beasts representing the Evangelists, and the 24 elders with their lutes and phials who gaze upward as in the apocalyptical vision of St. John. At Beaulieu, the portal tympanum is again dominated by the figure of Christ, this time with his hands outstretched as on the Cross and surrounded by the Apostles. Christ is depicted as at the Last Judgment, and the dead are being called up from their graves by the trumpet blast of the angels. At nearby La Charité-sur-Loire, the tympanum composition depicts the transfiguration of Christ, who is shown between Moses and Elias.

The splendid tympanum over the central portal at Vézelay (Fig. 5:11) stems from the first quarter of the 12th century. In its iconography and workmanship, it is by far the most complex Romanesque tympanum, yet the logical division of space keeps the composition from seeming cluttered or confused. Here, as well as in the other places, the transcendental scene owed its origin to the drawings and miniature paintings that illustrated the texts of the Scriptures in monastic libraries. Such illuminated manuscripts provided convenient models that the monks could show the sculptors who were to carry out the project. The robe of Christ at Vézelay, as well as those of the Apostles, reveals a pattern of clear sharp swirling lines, which stems from the pen drawings in manuscripts of the time.

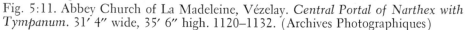

Fig. 5:11. Abbey Church of La Madeleine, Vézelay. *Central Portal of Narthex with Tympanum.* 31′ 4″ wide, 35′ 6″ high. 1120–1132. (Archives Photographiques)

The interpretation most often suggested is the commission of the Apostles as found in the last chapter of Luke's Gospel, and the description of the Pentecost scene in the second chapter of the Acts of the Apostles. A more likely source, however, is the final vision of St. John from the last part of the Book of Revelation. Whether a single scene is intended or two or even three scenes are combined in a subtle Cluniac synthesis is a subject for scholarly speculation. If it is a single scene, the most convincing source is the first two verses of chapter 22 of the Book of Revelation: "And he shewed me a pure river of water of life, clear as crystal, proceeding out of the throne of God and of the Lamb. In the midst of the street of it, and on either side of the river, was there the tree of life, which bare twelve manner of fruits, and yielded her fruit every month: and the leaves of the tree were for the healing of nations."

Here again the figure of Christ dominates the composition, seated, as St. John says, on "a great white throne," but not so much to judge mankind as to redeem it. While the figure is supremely majestic, Christ is not crowned. The streams emanating from his fingers descend upon the barefooted Apostles, the archetypes of the clergy, who bring spiritual understanding through the books they hold in their hands and physical healing through the divine mercy which they transmit to mankind. On one side of Christ's head, the water referred to in the quotation flows forth, while on the other are the branches of the tree. The 12 fruits, one for each month, are found among the 29 medallions in the middle band of *archivolts*—the series of arches that frame the tympanum. A figure treading grapes, for example, represents September; October is symbolized by a man gathering acorns for his pigs. The months themselves, besides being connected with these labors, are also symbolized by the signs of the zodiac that, in turn, remind man of the limited time he has in which to attain his salvation. A few of the other medallions picture strange exotic beasts taken from the *bestiaries*, those curious books of the time that recounted the lore about animals actual and fabulous. A survival from antiquity can be noted in the fourth medallion from the lower right that depicts a centaur.

The inner band of the archivolt is divided into eight irregular compartments that contain figures representing the nations which the leaves of the tree of life are intended to heal. The one on the top left, next to the head of Christ, contains two dog-headed men, called in Isidore's *Etymologies* the Cynocephaloi, a tribe supposed to have inhabited India. The corresponding compartment on the right side shows the crippled and bent figure of a man and that of a blind woman taking a few halting steps as she is led forward. In the others, the lame on crutches are found along with lepers pointing to their sores.

Along the lintel below, a parade of the nations converges toward the center. While the compartments above picture those in physical distress, here are the pagans and heathens of the earth who need spiritual aid. Among these strange peoples who populate the remote regions of the earth are a man and woman (in the far right corner) with enormous ears and feathered bodies. Next to them is a group of dwarfs or pygmies, so small they have to mount a horse by means of a ladder. On the far left, half-naked savages are hunting with bows and arrows, while toward the left center some heathens are shown leading a bull to sacrifice. In the center stands St. John the Baptist holding a medallion with the image of the lamb on it. This is doubtless intended to convey the explanation that the "river of the water of life" is none other than baptism, which is the road to salvation that all must take if they want to enter into eternal life. It is a logical symbol with which to adorn the portal leading into the nave of the church, the interior of which with its glowing colors and jeweled decorations was often likened to the heavenly city, the new Jerusalem, which is so eloquently de-

Fig. 5:12 (*left*) Narthex Capital, *Judgment Angel*. Fig. 5:13 (*center*). Nave Capital, *Angel of Death Killing the Eldest Son of Pharoah*. Fig. 5:14 (*right*). Nave Capital, *Mystic Mill: Moses and St. Paul Grinding Corn*. *c*.1130 (Archives Photographiques)

Fig. 5:15 (*left*). Nave Capital, Vézelay, *Demon*. (Archives Photographiques). Fig. 5:16 (*center*) Nave Capital, Santiago de Compostela, *Demons Hanging Victim* (Ksado). Fig. 5:17 (*right*). Nave Capital, Vézelay, *Combat of Two Demons* (Archives Photographiques).

scribed by St. John: "And the gates of it shall not be shut at all by day: for there shall be no night there. And they shall bring the glory and honour of the nations into it" (Rev. 21:25–26). The open books of the Apostles seated next to St. Peter on the left recall the following verse that states that all who enter it are the ones "which are written in the Lamb's book of life" (Rev. 21:27). Futhermore, in a monastic church especially, the monks would have been conscious of the final reference to these gates: "Blessed are they that do his commandments, that they may have the right to the tree of life, and may enter in through the gates into the city" (Rev. 22:14). The awakened interest in foreign countries and peoples was doubtless owing to the influence of the early crusades, which were then being preached.

The imaginative scope displayed in the profusion of sculptured capitals at Vézelay is breath-taking. Biblical scenes, incidents from the lives of the saints, allegorical commentaries, and the play of pure fantasy are found throughout the narthex and the nave. One of the narthex capitals depicts the flight of the Angel Gabriel with his trumpet ready to sound the call to the Last Judgment (Fig. 5:12). Another in the nave shows the angel of death striking down the eldest son of Pharaoh (Fig. 5:13), and still another shows a bearded figure pouring grain into a handmill that a barefooted man is turning (Fig. 5:14). The real meaning of this scene would be lost were it not for a chance remark in the writings of Suger, the abbot of St. Denis. He noted that the corn is the old law which is poured into the mystic mill by an ancient Hebrew prophet, probably Moses, and is being ground into the meal of the new law by St. Paul. Frequently depicted in the capitals are incidents from the lives of the two favorite Cluniac saints, Anthony and Paul, both hermits in the Egyptian desert. In one of the fearful temptations of St. Anthony, a demon symbolizing luxury (Fig. 5:15) appears in the guise of a ferocious monster, whose hair leaps upward like sulfurous flames and whose grimacing mouth opens to reveal his fangs. Other demons are seen combating for the souls of the unwary (Figs. 5:16 and 5:17).

Unlike the statuary of antiquity that was made of marble or bronze, these Romanesque capitals are of the soft sandstone and limestone found in such abundance in France. Their purpose was mainly to decorate interiors that did not have to resist the elements. The soft material, furthermore, was better adapted to the pictorial forms of Romanesque sculpture, and its plasticity responded more quickly to the imaginative demands made on it than a harder stone could have done.

While the examples discussed have been stone carvings, the general category of Romanesque sculpture in this period should be broadened to include works in metal. Only a few examples of this kind have survived, owing to the fact that they were made of such precious materials as gold, silver, and copper, adorned with enamel work and studded with precious gems. Cluny, according to an early inventory, had a golden statue of the Virgin seated on a silver throne and wearing a jeweled crown. Churches also needed chalices, plates, and pitchers for the sacred services. On important feast days, books with ivory or metal covers encrusted with jewels were used on the high altar. Reliquaries fashioned to contain the relics of saints also reposed there; while candelabras, incense burners, and metal choir screens added their beauty to the sacred precincts.

Romanesque sculpture always remained an integral part of the complete architectural design and is inseparable from the whole picture. The walls, ceiling, portals, columns, and capitals were not merely mute structural necessities; they were the space for the decorative devices that brought to the structural members a communicative value all their own, which spoke to monk and pilgrim alike in the eloquent visual language of form, line, and color.

PAINTING AND OTHER MONASTIC CRAFTS

Miniatures of modest proportions on the parchment pages of books and monumental murals in the apses of abbey churches were the two extremes of the art of painting in the Romanesque period. The one craft known definitely to have been consistently practiced by the monks themselves was the copying, illustrating, and binding of books, activities that took place in a large communal room called the *scriptorium*. This tradition, which dates from the time of Cassiodorus, was followed by all Benedictine houses, and those in the Cluniac order fostered it with both diligence and enthusiasm. While the Cluniac copyists were known for the beauty of their lettering and the accuracy of their texts, a monk skilled in his craft would certainly not have been content merely to copy letters all his life. Blank places in the manuscript provided him with both the space and the challenge to fill them in. At first, these spaces were filled with nothing more than fanciful little pen drawings or an elaborate initial letter at the beginning of a paragraph. Gradually, the drawings grew into miniature paintings, and the initial letters became highly complex designs. The luxurious development of this art of illuminating manuscripts seems to have been one compensation for the austerity of Benedictine life. As the practice became more widely accepted, specialists in the various phases began to be designated. A painter of small illuminated scenes, for instance, was called a *miniator*, while one who did initial letters was known as a *rubricator*.

Cluniac manuscripts were done with the utmost delicacy. Miniatures were painted in many colors, and halos of saints or crowns of kings were made with thin gold leaf. The letter Q (Fig. 5:18) in an Evangeliary from the abbey of St. Omer is an intricate example of the illuminator's art.

Such flourishes of the pen made by expert copyists on their parchment pages, and the gradual refinement of the painstaking miniature art of illumination, had

Fig. 5:18. *Initial Q*. Illuminated Manuscript from an Evangeliary of the Abbey of St. Omer. *c*.1000. Pierpont Morgan Library, New York.

effects far beyond the medium for which either was intended originally. They became the models for the large murals that decorated the walls and apses of churches and for the sculpture that embellished the spaces above portals and columns; later, they were the prototypes of designs for stained glass windows in Gothic cathedrals. The greater freedom provided by the pen and brush on the parchment page had to be developed before more monumental designs in stone and glass could be undertaken. Thus these miniature examples of the medieval painter's art were far more important than their size would indicate. Not only do they provide the few surviving examples of pictorial art in western Europe from the 7th through the 10th centuries, but they were the source that gradually swelled into the flood of monumental sculpture, mural painting, and stained glass of the centuries to come.

Contrasting with the diminutive art of illuminating manuscripts were the huge frescoes painted on the surfaces of barrel-vaulted ceilings, arches, and semi-domed apses of churches of the Romanesque period. Here again, the most notable examples were found at Cluny and its satellite monasteries. The narthex at Vézelay still has one of these frescoes, showing Christ surrounded by the four evangelical beasts, though it is now so faded as to be barely visible. A monk visiting Cluny in 1063 sang the praises of the wall paintings in the great refectory. The most notable of all, however, was the colossal painting of Christ in Glory in the apse of Hugh's great church. From a study of the fragments that have been recovered, its style and technique are known to have been similar to that of an excellently preserved apsidal mural in the little chapel at Berzé-la-ville, less than ten miles from Cluny (Fig. 5:19). This small residence and chapel was built between the years 1100 and 1103 as a retreat for Hugh in the last years of his life. So close is the resemblance of the painting there to that in his great church at Cluny, that it may have been done by the same artist.

In the Berzé-la-ville painting, the seated figure of Christ is enclosed in a many-hued mandorla, a form familiar from the relief sculptures over the portals of the churches. Here Christ is clothed in a robe of white over which is draped a red mantle. While blessing the 16 surrounding Apostles and saints with his right hand, he gives St. Peter a scroll containing the law with his left. The heavenly setting is suggested by the dark-blue background of the mandorla, which is studded with golden stars, and by the hand of God the Father, which hovers above Christ holding a crown. The term *fresco* is not used in the ordinary sense when it refers to this style of painting. A true fresco technique requires that color pigments mixed with water be applied directly to fresh plaster. The lime in the plaster then binds the pigments to the wall by chemical action, and a permanent though somewhat opaque surface is the result. This process seems to have been used only for the red ocher undercoats in the examples at Cluny and Berzé-la-ville. The undersurface was then coated with several layers of

Fig. 5:19. Cluniac Chapel at Berzé-la-ville. Apse Mural, *Christ in Glory*. Fresco *c*.13′ high. *c*.1103 (Archives Photographiques)

tempera—that is, pigments mixed with milk, egg, or glue—and finally glazed with wax overpainting to achieve the brighter and more transparent effect needed for the dark interiors. While their range was small, those colors the painters did develop had an extraordinary intensity well suited to the expressive needs of the style. In the desire for brilliant color and strongly articulated outlines, these murals were undoubtedly influenced to some extent by Byzantine mosaics, especially by those of Ravenna (see Figs. 4:10, 4:21, and 4:22).

Besides the arts of building, stone carving, and painting, many crafts were practiced in the workshops of Cluny and the other monasteries. These included embroidering altar cloths and vestments, weaving, ceramics, goldsmithing and other metal crafts, leather tooling, and the casting of bells. The constant experimentation and research carried on in these centers resulted in a continuous improvement in the methods employed, including better ways of manufacturing glass and the invention of chemical formulas for stained glass. Just how extensively the monks themselves took part in the actual production of such handicrafts at Cluny or elsewhere is not definitely known. There is no evidence, for instance, that a monk ever worked as a sculptor in stone. The capitals and relief sculpture were executed for the most part by journeymen carvers, who went from place to place in groups wherever building activity was in progress. Likewise, similar work in other media was probably performed by itinerant craftsmen or by lay workers from the region. The iconographic schemes, however, were always done under the direct supervision of the monks, some of whom may have possessed the necessary skills so that they could train the craftsmen working under them. The variety and subtle character of the work, therefore, often is as much the monks' as if they had taken the chisel or other tools into their own hands. Wherever a name has survived in connection with sculpture, painting, or other work, it is usually that of a monk who is said to have "made" it. But "made" could mean anything from donating the material, or suggesting the subject to supervising the work in progress or even doing the carving or painting itself.

The monastic attitude toward decorating a church is well summed up by Theophilus, a writer on the various crafts of this time, who addressed his fellow monks, saying: ". . . you have confidently approached the house of God, have decorated with utmost beauty ceilings or walls with various work, and, showing forth with different colours a likeness of the paradise of God, glowing with various flowers, and verdant with herbs and leaves, and cherishing the lives of the saints with crowns of various merit, you have, after a fashion, shown the beholders everything in creation praising God, its creator, and have caused them to proclaim him admirable in all his works. Nor is the eye of man even able to decide upon which work it may first fix its glance; if it beholds the ceilings, they glow like draperies; if it regards the walls, there is the appearance of paradise; if it marks the abundance of light from the windows, it admires the inestimable beauty of the glass and the variety of the costly work. . . ."

MUSIC

Odo of Cluny, abbot from 927 to 942, brought the monastery its earliest musical distinction through his active fostering of choral music. Documents tell of more than 100 psalms being sung there daily in his time; and on his tours of inspection to other monasteries, he devoted much of his energies to the instruction of choirs. His great success made it necessary for his teaching methods to be written down, and from this fortunate circumstance something about the early status of music at Cluny can be ascertained.

Odo's great accomplishments include the arranging of the tones of the scale into an orderly progression from A to G; and by thus assigning to them a system of letters, he was responsible for the earliest effective system of Western musical notation. His method also included the mathematical measurement of spaces on the monochord, which made it possible to determine accurately the pitches and intervals of each of the Gregorian modes. Before Odo's time, the chants used in the sacred service had laboriously to be learned by rote; and if any degree of authenticity was to be achieved, they had to be taught by a graduate of Gregory the Great's Schola Cantorum established in Rome. By teaching the singers to read notes, the treatise declares that soon they "were singing at first sight and extempore and without a fault anything written in music, something which until now ordinary singers had never been able to do, many continuing to practice and study for fifty years without profit."

Further refinements on Odo's method were made in the 11th century by another monk, Guido of Arezzo. His treatise, which was in the library of Cluny, made it clear that he embraced the Cluniac musical reforms. He also freely acknowledged his debt to the work of his great predecessor, the Abbot Odo, "from whose example," he said, "I have departed only in the forms of the notes." This slight departure by Guido was actually the invention of the basis for modern musical notation on a staff of lines. As he explained it: "The sounds, then, are so arranged that each sound, however often it may be repeated in a melody, is always found in its own row. And in order that you may better distinguish these rows, lines are drawn close together, and some rows of sounds occur on the lines themselves, others in the intervening intervals or spaces. Then the sounds on one line or in one space all sound alike." Odo's work also led to Guido's system of *solmization*, which assigned certain syllables, derived from the following hymn to St. John, to each degree of the scale:

> *Ut* queant laxis
> *Re*sonare fibris,
> *Mi*ra gestorum
> *Fa*muli tuorum,
> *Sol*ve polluti
> *La*bii reatum,
> Sancte Ioannes.

Later the syllable *si*, compounded from the first two letters of the Latin form of St. John (Sancte Ioannes), was added as the seventh scale degree. In France, these syllables are still used just as in Guido's time; in Italy and elsewhere, the first note *ut* is replaced by the more singable *do*.

The most remarkable fact about Odo's and Guido's treatises is that both champion music as an art designed to be performed in the praise of the Creator and to enhance the beauty and meaning of prayer. Previously, Boethius, along with most early writers on music, had considered music a branch of mathematics that could reveal the secrets of the universe. Guido, however, made a point of stating that the writings of Boethius were "useful to philosophers, but not to singers," and both Odo and he intentionally omitted heavenly speculations. Cluny, therefore, emerged as a center of practical music-making rather than as a place where theoreticians pondered on music as an abstruse science.

The story of music at Cluny was also told visually with compelling beauty in two sculptured capitals that survive from the apse of Hugh's great church. In the sanctuary, the architectural climax of the whole edifice, was a series of columns grouped in a semicircle around the high altar, and the capitals of these pillars (Figs. 5:20–5:23) constituted the apogee of late 11th-century sculptural skill. Here, capital by capital, were to be seen symbolic expressions of the highest ideals of the monk's life. One capital, for example, presented on its four faces the theological virtues; another, the cardinal virtues. On a third were pictured the cycles and labors of the monk's year in terms of the four seasons; and his hopes for the hereafter were portrayed by the four rivers and trees of Paradise. Finally, his praise for the Creator was expressed in a double quaternity with figures to symbolize the eight tones of sacred psalmody. This inclusion of music in the sacred precinct, next to the symbols of the highest human virtues and heavenly beauties, was further evidence of the high esteem in which the tonal art was held by the monks of Cluny.

On the first of the eight faces of these twin capitals (Fig. 5:20) is inscribed: "The tone is the first in the order of musical intonations," and the figure is that of a solemn-faced youth playing on a lute. Here the symbolism of the stringed instrument stems from the belief in the power of music to banish evil, as David had cast out Saul's evil spirit when he played to him. The second tone (Fig. 5:21) is represented by the figure of a young woman dancing and beating a small drum, the inscription reading "There follows the tone which by number and law is second." Such percussion instruments are known to have been used to accompany medieval processions on joyful feast days in the manner described in the 68th Psalm: "The singers went before, the players on instruments followed after; among them were damsels playing with timbrels." The next inscription (Fig. 5:22) says: "The third strikes, and represents the resurrection of Christ." The instrument here is of the lyre type with a sounding board added, which is one of the 11th-century forms of the psaltery, the legendary instrument with which David accompanied himself as he sang the psalms. This instrument with

Third Abbey Church of Cluny, Ambulatory Capital. Fig. 5:20 (*above left*). *First Tone of Plainsong*. Fig. 5:21 (*above right*). *Second Tone*. Fig. 5:22 (*below left*). Third Tone. Fig. 5:23 (*below right*). Fourth Tone. 1088–1095. Ochier Museum, Cluny

its gut strings stretched over the wooden frame roughly resembles a cross and was used as a symbolic reference to Christ stretched on the Cross for the redemption of the world. The fourth figure (Fig. 5:23) is that of a young man playing a set of chime bells, and the accompanying inscription reads: "The fourth follows representing a lament in song." The Latin word *planctus* denotes a funeral dirge, and the practice of ringing bells at burials is pictured in the contemporary representation of the burial procession of Edward the Confessor (Fig. 6:3), where the figures accompanying the bier have small bells in their hands.

As a series, the eight inscriptions and symbolic figures reveal much about Cluniac musical practice. For example, in the second, fourth, fifth, and seventh tones, the figures are moving or standing, which seems to point to the processional chants; in the others, they are seated in a manner appropriate to the stationary chants. In those that have to do with action, the instruments are a small hand drum or cymbals, bells, and a horn of some type; all the seated figures play stringed instruments. This symbolism apparently points to some of the rhythmic and melodic differences in the two types of chant—the processional and the stationary—which, in turn, reflect the two aspects of life—the active and the contemplative.

The skillful chorus of Cluny was undoubtedly in the musical vanguard of that day, just as the third abbey church headed architecture and sculpture. Odo's teaching methods clearly indicated that a high degree of vocal culture was expected of his monastic choirs; and, since they sang most of the time, they got plenty of practice. They were thus able to perform chants of considerable complexity, and music was well on its way to becoming a highly developed art. While Gregorian plainsong was a purely melodic style and continued to be practiced as such, during the Romanesque period the choral responses began to show variations in the direction of singing in several parts. The 9th, 10th, and 11th centuries thus saw the tentative beginnings of the *polyphonic*, or many-voiced, style that was to flourish in the Gothic period and in the Renaissance.

Unfortunately, the polyphonic practice of the pre-Gothic period is known only through theoretical treatises. From the rules they give for the addition of voices to the traditional chant, however, some idea of the early forms of polyphony can be determined. As might be expected, the influence of mathematics and Pythagorean number theory was woven into the musical usages of the time. The perfect intervals of the octave, fifth, and fourth were preferred over all others, since their mathematical ratios indicated a closer correspondence with the divine order of the universe. In a treatise dating from the beginning of the 10th century, some years before Odo's time, the type of choral response known as *parallel organum* is discussed. The original Gregorian melody was maintained intact; and, as a variant in two parts, the principal voice was paralleled by an organal voice at the fifth below, so that there was a strict melodic and rhythmic concordance between the two parts. When sung in three parts, the organum was doubled at the octave above, so that the principal voice was embellished by the movement of parallel voices a fifth below and a fourth above. With the addition of the fourth part, both the principal and organal voices were doubled in octaves, thus making a composite intervalic texture that included the parallel movement of the three perfect intervals: the fourth, fifth, and octave.

Parallel Organum (10th century)   From the *Scholia enchiriadus*

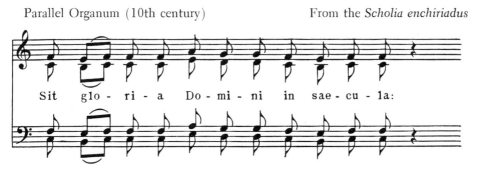

the picture as a whole. The important part of planning a choir section of a monastic church, for instance,

Parallel organum, in effect, built a mighty fortress of choral sound around the traditional Gregorian line of plainsong. By thus enclosing it within the stark and gaunt but strong perfect intervals, a massive and solid style was achieved that was in the spirit of the other Romanesque arts.

The music of this time was yet another expression of the praise of God; and, when related to the great buildings, the richly carved sculpture, the illuminated manuscripts and painted murals, it fits into the picture as a whole. The important part of planning a choir section of a monastic church, for instance, was to provide a resonant setting for the perpetual chant. Hugh's great church was especially renowned for its acoustics. The curved ceiling vaults and the great variety of angles in the wall surfaces of the broad transepts and cavernous nave gave the chant there a characteristic tone color that can be reproduced only in a similar setting. The effect of a monastic choir of several hundred voices performing jubilations with all its heart and soul must have been overwhelmingly impressive.

The sculptured capitals depicting the tones of plainsong represent an obvious synthesis of the arts of sculpture, music, and literature into an appropriate architectural setting. Their expressive intensity, moreover, bespeaks both the motion and emotion typical of the Romanesque style in general. As such, they are representative products of a people capable of the long and arduous pilgrimages and the fantastic effort associated with the organization of the First Crusade. These sculptures reveal something of that indomitable energy, and especially of a vigorous attitude toward the act of worship, that must have been channeled into a performance style which was emphatic in rhythm. They are, in fact, the embodiment of the spirit expressed by St. Augustine to "Sing with your voices, and with your hearts, and with all your moral convictions, sing the new songs, not only with your tongue but with your life." One of the other capitals suggests the representation of athletes with such figures as a boxer, a swimmer, and a tumbler. The whole Cluniac approach was aptly summed up by a friend of St. Hugh's, St. Peter Damian, who referred to Cluny as a "spiritual gymnasium."

IDEAS

The key to the understanding of the Romanesque as a living and active art lies in a knowledge of the opposing forces that created it. As the Roman Christian influence spread northward, it encountered the restless surging energies of the former barbarian tribes. In effect, a veneration for tradition, which tended in the direction of a static order, met an urge for action and experimentation and resulted in the creation of many innovations. When the horizontal Early Roman Christian basilica, for example, was combined with the northern spire, the first step toward Romanesque architecture was taken. The further development of the style was the direct result of this union of southern horizontality and northern verticality, reflecting as it did the broad spirit of the late Roman humanism and the soaring northern aspirations. The musical counterpart is found in the joining together of southern monophony and northern polyphony, which occurred when the Mediterranean tradition of unison melody met the northern custom of singing in parts. The result was the experimentation with primitive forms of counterpoint and harmony that characterized the music of the Romanesque period. This meeting of Roman unity with northern variety, and its slow maturation over the centuries, was thus responsible for the first truly European art style: the Romanesque. The ideas that underlie the monastic aspect of the style are an outgrowth of those that motivated the earlier period in Ravenna. The mysticism of the previous period moved into an other-worldly ascetic phase; and early Christian authoritarianism resulted in the rigid stratification of society into strict hierarchies. The two basic ideas, then, crystallize as asceticism and hierarchism.

Asceticism

The monastic way of life demanded the seclusion of the country as an escape from the distractions of the world. Since the monk conceived his life as a steppingstone to that beyond, living had to be reduced to the barest essentials. Ordinarily such rural isolation would have been exceedingly barren soil for the growth of an important art movement, but the very absence of all external luxury led to the development of a rich inner life. Such virtues as poverty, chastity, and humility were the result of moral rather than aesthetic impulses. The very severity of the monastery, however, acted as a stimulus to imaginative experience, and individual self-denial released a flood of communal energies. The attitude of turning away from the world found its architectural expression in the plain exteriors and rich interiors of monastic churches. Thus the net effect of asceticism was to increase the fervor of the spirit and to express it with great intensity. Two favorite Cluniac saints were the John and Anthony who went the farthest into the forbidding African desert; it was they who had the most fantastic visions and the most horrendous temptations. The diffusion of social centers into widely scattered monastic communities likewise lent a peculiar intensity and a wide variety to the expressive forms of the Romanesque. The arts, consequently, were not intended to mirror the natural world or to decorate the dwelling place of an earthly ruler but, rather, to conjure up other-worldly visions of divine majesty. Thus all the arts find a common ground in their desire to depict the various aspects of the world beyond.

The monks developed an art of elaborate symbolism addressed to an educated cloistered community versed in sophisticated allegories. Such a symbolic language—whether in architecture, sculpture, painting, or music—could only have been fostered by an abbot like Hugh, whose learning was so universal that he succeeded in adding "philosophy to ornament and a meaning to beauty." By contrast, the later Gothic arts were directed toward the humble of the world and the unlettered people beyond the cloister. While the sculpture and stained glass of the Gothic cathedral were destined to become the Bible in stone and glass for the poor, the comparable forms in a monastic church were always aloof and aristocratic and at times intentionally subtle and enigmatic. This does not mean that Romanesque art was overly intellectualized and remote from the experience of those to whom it was addressed. On the contrary, it was very directly related to the intensity of the inner life and the visionary other-worldly focus of the religious communities that developed it.

Greco-Roman sculpture was successful in its way precisely because classical man had conceived his gods in human form, and as such they could be rendered so well in marble. When godhood was conceived as an abstract principle, a realistic representation of it became essentially impossible. Rational proportions were of no help to Romanesque man, who considered it impossible to understand God intellectually. He had to be felt through faith rather than comprehended by the mind. Only through the intuitive eye of faith could His essence be grasped. Hence He had to be portrayed symbolically, since a symbol could stand for something intangible rather than a literal representation. Visible physical substance was secondary, and soul stuff was primary; but the latter could be depicted only in the world of the imagination.

Fig. 5:24. Church of Notre Dame, Souillac. *Isaiah*. Early 12th century. (Archives Photographiques)

A life so metaphysically oriented and one motivated by such deep religious convictions could never have found its models in the natural world. The fantastic proportions of Romanesque architecture, the eccentric treatment and distortions of the human body in its sculpture, the unnecessarily elaborated initials in the manuscript illuminations, and the florid melismas added to the syllables of the chant were all evidence of a rejection of the natural order of things and its replacement by the supernatural. The book of the Bible most admired was Revelation, containing as it did the apocalyptical visions of St. John. The pictorial element in sculpture and painting in both large and small forms reflected Romanesque man's convictions with such intensity that the human figures seem to be consumed by the inner fires of their faith. Calm reason would seek to persuade by placid or serene attitudes, but such an animated figure as that of the Prophet Isaiah at Souillac (Fig. 5:24) seems to be performing spiritual dances in which his slender form stretches to unnatural lengths and his gestures are more convulsive than graceful.

Romanesque man thus dwelt in a dream world where the trees that grew in Paradise, the angels who populated the heavens, and the demons of hell were more real than anything or anybody he beheld in everyday life. Even though he had never seen a one of these creatures, he never doubted their existence. Indeed, the monsters whose fearsome characteristics were described in the bestiaries, and which were represented in the manuscripts and sculptures, had a moral and symbolic function far more real to him than any animals of mere physical existence. All these imaginary creatures existed together in a kind of jungle of the imagination where the abnormal was the normal and the fabulous became the commonplace.

Hierarchism

A strict hierarchical structure of society prevailed throughout the Romanesque period, which was as rigid in its way inside the monastery as was the feudalism outside the cloistered walls. The thought of the time was based on the assumption of a divinely established order of the universe, and the authority to interpret it was vested in the church. The majestic figure of Christ in Glory carved over the entrance portals of the Cluniac abbey churches, and echoed in the mural compositions painted on the interior of their half-domed apses, proclaimed this concept to the world at large. Christ was no longer the Good Shepherd of early Christian times but a mighty king, crowned and enthroned in the midst of His heavenly courtiers, sitting in judgment on the entire world. The keys to His heavenly kingdom, as seen in the Vézelay tympanum (Fig. 5:10) and the apse painting at Berzé-la-ville (Fig. 5:19), rest firmly in the grasp of St. Peter, the first of the popes according to the Roman tradition. As if to lend additional emphasis to this doctrine, St. Peter at Berzé-la-ville is seen receiving a scroll containing the divine statutes from the hands of Christ. The papacy of medieval days always found its most powerful support in the Cluniac order, and through such aid succeeded in establishing an all-powerful theocracy based on this mandate from on high.

The authority of the church is nowhere better expressed than in these monumental sculptural and mural compositions that from their place of eminence warned those who entered that they were walking a road either to salvation or damnation. The milestones that marked the path were placed there by the church, whose clergy alone could interpret them and assure the suppliant that he was on his way to the streets of gold instead of the caldrons of fire. The frequency with which the apocalyptic vision of St. John is represented, with Apostles and elders surrounding the throne of Christ, is evidence of the veneration of the protective-father image in the form of the bearded patriarch. Like the clergy, these are the authorities who show the way by their willingness to offer their crowns to God, to praise Him by means of the musical instruments they hold in their hands, and to petition Him by means of the cups which contain their prayers.

In such a divine order, nothing could be left to chance; and all life had to be brought into an organizational plan that would conform to this cosmic scheme of things. The stream of authority, descending from Christ through St. Peter to his papal successors, flowed out from Rome in three main directions. The Holy Roman emperor received his crown from the hands of the Roman pontiff, and, in turn, all the kings of the Western world owed him homage, and on downward from the great lords to the humblest serf, all of whom had a preordained place in this great cosmic plan. Next, the archbishops and bishops received their mitres in Rome, and all the so-called "secular" clergy, from the parish priest to the deacon, owed their allegiance to the superiors from whom they received their orders. Finally, the monastic communities under their abbots also owed their allegiance to the pope; and through their loyal support of the papacy, the Cluniac order grew so strong that its abbot was the most powerful churchman in Christendom with the sole exception of the pope himself.

Beginning as a small independent monastery, Cluny was from the first exempted from tribute to any power save that of the pope alone. But instead of remaining an independent unit like other Benedictine abbeys, Cluny adopted the feudal principle by expanding and absorbing other monasteries until it dominated the monastic movement. As the head of a monarchical system, the order was the most powerful unifying force of the time, not only in religious and political affairs but in architectural, artistic, and musical thought as well. Through this adherence to the feudal system, it became a great landowning institution, and in an economy where land was the sole source of wealth, the monasteries became the principal commissioners of works of art. In a world where faith triumphed over reason and where the sole road to salvation was through the church, the Cluniac order acted as the mainstay of the Roman tradition and helped to spread its authority, its doctrines, and its liturgy all over Christendom.

The ranks of the monks were drawn mainly from the aristocratic class, whose members were among the few who were free to choose their own way of life. All the higher church offices were held principally by men from noble families, often by younger sons not eligible under the law of primogeniture to inherit the feudal estates. The vow of poverty applied only to individual ownership, and collectively a monastic community resembled a feudal manor. It was only in later times that the mendicant orders of monks attempted to interpret the vow of poverty more literally. Hence, Romanesque art was also an aristocratic art, and it remained so throughout the period with the means of patronage concentrated in the hands of its abbots and bishops.

The Romanesque abbey church was organized according to a rigid hierarchical plan that mirrored the strict order of precedence in the processionals of the liturgy for which it was the setting. By its insistence on visible proportions, it bespoke the invisible plan of a divinely ordered world. The regularity of the monastic buildings that surrounded it likewise was designed to enclose those who expressed their willingness to conform to such a cosmic regularity of life, and thus to constitute a human reflection of the divinely established plan for the salvation of mankind. The very spaciousness of the abbey church was far in excess of anything that was needed to accommodate the few hundreds who normally worshiped there. It was, however, the monument that mirrored the unshakable religious convictions of Romanesque man; and, as the house of the Lord and Ruler of the universe, it became a palace surpassing the dreams of glory of any king on the face of the earth. In the insecurity of the feudalistic world, Romanesque man built a fortress for his faith and for his God, which was designed to withstand the onslaughts of heretics and heathens as well as to survive the more elemental forces of wind, weather, and fire. Furthermore, the abbey church was the place where the heavenly monarch held court, and where His subjects could pay Him their never-ceasing homage in the divine services that went on day and night, year in and year out.

This hierarchical principle, moreover, applied not only to the social and ecclesiastical stratifications but to the basic thought processes as well. Authority for all things rested firmly on the Scriptures and the interpretations of them by the early church fathers. Rightness and fitness was determined by how ancient the tradition was, and scholarship consisted not so much in treading new intellectual paths as in the elucidations of the traditional sources. To the educated, this process took the form of learned commentaries; to the unlettered, it was expressed in the cult of relics. Thousands took to the dusty pilgrimage roads and traveled across France and Spain to touch the legendary tomb of the Apostle James at Compostela. In the arts, this veneration of the past made mandatory the continuance of such traditional forms as the Early Roman Christian basilica and the music of the Gregorian chant.

Yet this traditionalism, curiously enough, never led to stagnation or uniformity. In making learned commentaries on the Scriptures, the writers unconsciously, and sometimes quite consciously, interpreted them in the light of contemporary views. And as the untutored populace traveled about Europe on pilgrimages and later went to the Near East on the crusades, it absorbed new ideas that eventually were to jar the provincialism of feudal times into a more dynamic social structure.

All the arts, however, exhibited an extraordinary inventiveness and such a rich variety as to make the Romanesque one of the most spontaneous and

Fig. 5:25. Church of Sant' Ambrogio, Milan. View from the west. 128′ long, 44′ wide, 62′ high. c.1181. (Soprintendenza)

original periods in history. Diversity rather than unity was the rule of Romanesque architecture. Regional building traditions and the availability of craftsmen and materials contributed to the varied pattern. At St. Mark's in Venice (Fig. 11:2) and St. Front at Perigeux in southern France, the Romanesque combined the multidomed Byzantine style with Greek-cross ground plans. In Sicily at Cephalu and Monreale, it revealed a mixture of stark Norman spired forms, Saracenic pointed arches, and rich Byzantine mosaic interiors. In Spain, the Moorish influence is felt; in northern Italy, Sant' Ambrogio at Milan (Fig. 5:25) has the rich red brickwork and square belfry towers typical of Lombardy; while in central Italy, it is characterized by zebra-striped exteriors composed of alternating strips of dark-green and cream-colored marbles, as at the Baptistry of Florence (Fig. 9:1) and the Cathedral of Pisa (Fig. 5:26).

Romanesque forms never crystallized in the manner of the structural systems of Greek temples, Byzantine churches, and the later Gothic cathedrals. Through constant experimentation, the Romanesque architects found the key to new structural principles, such as their vaulting techniques; and, by gradually achieving complete command of their medium, they were able to have their buildings grow from heavy fortresslike structures into ones of considerable elegance. Meanwhile, the decorators groped their way toward the revival of monumental sculpture and mural painting. The need for bigger and better choirs likewise led to the invention of notational systems, and the emotional exuber-

Fig. 5:26. Pisa Cathedral. 312′ x 106′. Begun 1063 (Brogi)

ance in religious worship made many modifications of the traditional chant, which eventually culminated in the art of counterpoint. All in all, the creative vitality exhibited in each art medium is a constant source of astonishment.

Within the formal framework provided by the abbey church, architectural detail, sculpture and other decorative arts, music and liturgy combined as integral parts of the complete architectonic design. The vast nave and transepts of a church were designed as a resonant hall for the chant, just as the tympanum over the entrance portal and the halfdomed interior of the apse were the settings for sculptural and painted mural embellishments. The sculptural representations of plainsong on the ambulatory capitals in the abbey church at Cluny show a union of music and sculpture, while their inscriptions add a literary third dimension. All the arts converge into the unified structure of the liturgy, since all were created in the monastic concept for service in the glorification of God.

Thus the Cluny of Hugh of Semur was the gathering place for the most outstanding artists of the time. Under his benign influence, the great builder Hezelo worked out plans for the abbey church. While it was being erected, the chisels of Burgundian sculptors were resounding through its walls as capitals were carved to crown its columns. Great mural painters were mixing their pigments, while skillful choristers were carrying out the precepts of Odo of Cluny and Guido of Arezzo by adding their voices in broad choral cadences to this paean of Romanesque art.

CHRONOLOGY:

Feudal Romanesque Period in Normandy, Late 11th Century

800 Charlemagne crowned Holy Roman emperor in Rome

805 Charlemagne's Chapel at Aix-la-Chapelle (Aachen) built in the style of San Vitale in Ravenna

841 Vikings invaded northern France and colonized French territory

911 Dukedom of Normandy ceded by King Charles the Simple of France to Northmen

c.1000 Leif Eriksen, Viking navigator, believed to have reached coast of North America

1000 Minstrels convened during Lenten season at Fécamp in Normandy

1035 William succeeded his father Robert as Duke of Normandy after the latter's death on pilgrimage to Jerusalem

1040 Abbey of Jumiège rebuilt in Norman style

1043 Imperial palace of Holy Roman emperors built near Goslar (Germany)

1053 Duke William married Matilda, daughter of Duke of Flanders

1056 Westminster Abbey (Church of Peter the Apostle), in Norman style, dedicated by Edward the Confessor in London

c.1064 Church of St. Étienne (Abbaye-aux-hommes) begun at Caen under patronage of William

Church of Ste. Trinité (Abbaye-aux-dames) begun at Caen under patronage of Matilda

1066 Death of Edward the Confessor, King of England

Coronation of Harold as his successor

Invasion of England by William the Conqueror

Battle of Hastings: English forces defeated; Harold killed

William crowned king of England

1078 Tower of London begun by William the Conqueror

1085 Domesday Survey, census and land survey of England, ordered by William as basis for taxation

c.1088 Bayeux Tapestry completed in an English embroidery workshop (probably)

c.1237–c.1288 Adam de la Halle, author and composer of *Le Jeu de Robin et Marion* (c.1280), a pastoral play with music containing only authentic example of a *chanson de geste* melody

6

THE FEUDAL
ROMANESQUE STYLE

THE NORMAN CONQUEST AND THE BAYEUX TAPESTRY

Surviving examples of secular art from the Romanesque period are so rare that each is practically unique. The treasures of a monastery or cathedral were under the watchful eye of the clergy, and religious restraints against raiding church property usually were strong enough to prevent wanton destruction. The same cannot be said for secular property. Feudal castles constantly were subject to siege, and those that survived frequently were remodeled in later centuries with the changing fortunes of their successive owners. Among the best preserved of these Romanesque residences are the Imperial Palace at Goslar, Germany, (Fig. 6:1), and Wartburg Castle, where Tannhäuser's famous songfest took place. Towns did grow up in the protective shadows of a castle, a monastery, or a cathedral, but only a few urban dwellings remain, such as those at Cluny (Fig. 6:2). Their arched doorways facing the street sometimes were decorated by sculptured hunting scenes or representations of an artisan's trade—a cobbler bending over his workbench, for example, or a merchant showing cloth to a client. Of the interior decorations—mural paintings, wall hangings, furniture, and the like—almost nothing is left. And, since poetry and music were intended to be heard rather than read by these feudal people, little of either was written down.

221

History, however, is filled with accidents, and by coincidence a single large-scale example of secular pictorial art survives because it was designed for a church instead of a castle. The only French epic poem before the crusades owes its present existence to the hand of some monastic scribe who happened to write it down either for some minstrel with a poor memory or because he wanted to preserve it after it had ceased to be sung. The one authentic melody to which such poetry was chanted is extant because it was included as a jest in a 13th-century musical play. And the keep, or tower, that William the Conqueror constructed in London is still intact partly because of its usefulness as a prison and possibly because it housed an important chapel.

The single large-scale example of pictorial art is the so-called Bayeux tapestry, one of the most eloquent documents of this or any other time. Here, in visual form, is the story of the conquest of England by William the Conqueror recounted from the Norman point of view, in the course of which we have a vivid picture of the life and attitudes of feudal man. The term *tapestry* is largely a misnomer, justified only because of its function as a wall hanging. Since the design is applied in woolen yarn to a coarse linen surface rather than woven into the cloth itself, it is more accurately described an an embroidery. Such cloth decorations were used to cover the bare stone walls of castles, but in this case the extraordinary dimensions—20 inches wide and 231 feet long—and its possession over the centuries by the Bayeux Cathedral indicate that this tapestry or embroidery was intended to cover the plain strip of masonry over the nave arcade of that building. It was probably the product of one of the renowned English embroidery workshops and was apparently completed about 20 years after the great battle it describes. The central figure is, of course, William the Conqueror, who indelibly stamped his powerful personality on the north European scene throughout the latter half of the 11th century. The span of time is from the closing months of the reign of Edward the Confessor to that fateful day in 1066 when the Conqueror made good his claim to the throne by putting the English forces to rout at the Battle of Hastings.

The Bayeux Tapestry, in complete presentations, is divided into 79 panels, or scenes. The first part (panels 1–34) is concerned with William's reception of Harold, an English duke, whose mission to Normandy ostensibly was to tell William that he was to succeed Edward the Confessor as king of England. In one of these scenes, William and Harold are seen at Bayeux, *where Harold took an oath to Duke William.* (The italics here and later are literal translations of the Latin inscriptions that run along the top of the Tapestry above the scenes they describe.) Placing his hands on the reliquaries that repose on the two altars, Harold apparently swears to uphold William's claim, although the exact nature of the oath is left vague. This is, however, the episode that later became the justification for the English campaign—because Harold, false to his sworn word,

Fig. 6:1. Imperial Palace at Goslar, Germany. Begun 1043, rebuilt 1132. (*left*) Chapel of St. Ulrich. 11th century (Deutscher Kunstverlag)

Fig. 6:2. Romanesque House, Cluny. *c.*1159. (Archives Photographiques)

Fig. 6:3. Bayeux Tapestry. Detail, *Death and Burial of Edward the Confessor*. Wool

had had himself crowned king. In these early panels, in the upper and lower borders, a running commentary on the action continues a tradition begun in manuscript illuminations. The commentary here is in the form of animal figures that were familiar to the people of the time from bestiaries and sculpture and the allusion is to certain fables of Aesop. The choice of the fox and crow, the wolf and stork, and the ewe, goat, and cow in the presence of the lion all have to do with treachery and violence and serve to point out the perfidious character of Harold.

William is seated serenely on his ducal throne, foreshadowing his future dignity as king. The scene, furthermore, actually is taking place in Bayeux Cathedral, the exterior of which is shown in the curious representation in back of the seated William. Its bishop was none other than Odo, William's half brother, who in all probability commissioned the Tapestry. If this visual evidence is taken literally, Odo's part in subsequent events was considerable. Besides his implied presence on this occasion, Odo invariably turns up in every important scene—giving William advice on the building of his fleet, blessing the meal after the landing in England, sitting in on the council of war, and exhorting the troops to greater deeds in the thick of battle. This is not at all improbable, since as a feudal bishop Odo was not only the master of manors and forests but the liege lord of more than a hundred knights. As if this were not enough, Odo is shown riding into battle swinging a huge mace, bearing out the medieval saying, "The bloodier the hand, the better the bishop." According to the curious convention of the time, however, his ecclesiastical position forbade his spilling the blood of the enemy with such worldly weapons as the sword and the spear.

HIC EADWARDVS:REX
INLECTO:ALLOQVIT:EIDE JES:
HIC DEDERVNT:HAROLDO:
IAM:SCI
APLI
CORO NA: REGIS
ET HI C: DEFVNCTVS
EST

embroidery on linen. 20″ wide, whole 231′ long. c.1073–1088. Town Hall, Bayeux

On this occasion, he seemed determined to keep pace with Archbishop Turpin in the *Song of Roland*, who delivered in the battle described in this literary epic "more than one thousand blows." Odo intended that the Tapestry be exhibited each year on the anniversary of William's conquest, and thus forever to commemorate the glory of that occasion—and, of course, the bravery of the bishop and builder of the church.

The main course of the action in the Tapestry moves like the words on a printed page—that is, from left to right. At times, however, it was necessary to represent a pertinent episode apart from the principal action, whereupon the pictorial narrator simply reversed the usual order and moved his scene from right to left, thus, in effect, achieving a kind of visual parenthesis and avoiding any confusion with the flow of the main story. Such a reversal is employed in the scene depicting the death and burial of the Confessor (Fig. 6:3). In the upper right corner is *King Edward in his bed* as he *addresses his faithful retainers*. On one side of him is a priest; Harold is on the other; while the queen and her lady-in-waiting are mourning at the foot of the bed. Below, under the words *here he has died*, the body is being prepared for the last rites. Moving toward the left, the funeral procession approaches *the church* of St. Peter the Apostle, the Romanesque predecessor of Westminster Abbey, which Edward had built and dedicated but ten years before, while the hand of God descends in blessing. The procession includes a group of tonsured monks reading prayers and two acolytes ringing the funeral bells.

When William received word that Harold had been crowned, he immediately determined on invasion, and the second part of the Tapestry (panels 35–

Fig. 6:4. Bayeux Tapestry. Detail, *Norman Ships Sailing toward English Coast.*

53) is concerned with the preparations for his revenge up to the eve of the battle. After all was in readiness, he set sail *and crossed the sea* (Fig. 6:4). The ships seen in the Tapestry are similar to those in which William's restless Viking ancestors invaded the French coast two centuries before, and it was in just such ships that Leif Eriksen and his fellow mariners apparently reached the eastern coast of North America earlier in the same century.

After the landing, the grand finale begins with the assembling of forces for the great battle (panels 54–79). The Norman side has both archers on foot and knights on horseback, while the English fight in a solid phalanx with immense battle-axes, small spears, and clubs with stone heads. The Normans move in from left to right and the English from the opposite direction. The climax of the battle is reached in a wild scene at a ravine (Fig. 6:5), where men and horses are tumbling about while the *English and French fall together in battle.* Shortly after, Harold is killed, and the fighting concludes with the *English turned in flight.* The lower border in these scenes spares none of the horrors of warfare; dismembered limbs are strewn about, scavengers strip the bodies of the fallen of their coats of mail, and naked corpses are left on the field.

The design of the Bayeux Tapestry is dominantly linear and, like the illuminated manuscripts of the time, two dimensional with no suggestion of spatial depth. The eight shades of woolen yarn—three blues, light and dark green, red, buff yellow, and gray—contribute a vivid feeling of color, which is not used for natural representation but to enliven the design. Some men have blue, others green hair, and horses often have two blue and two red legs. Faces are merely outlined, though some attempt at portraiture is made in the various likenesses of William. Details, such as costumes, armor, mode of combat, and the deploy-

Fig. 6:5. Bayeux Tapestry. Detail, *Climax of Battle of Hastings* (Archives Photographiques)

ment of troops in battle, however, are done with great accuracy. For this reason, the Tapestry is a never-ending source of amazement and one of the most important historical documents on the manner of life in the 11th century—so much so that its historical value is often allowed to overshadow its quality as a work of art. Admittedly crude and at times naïve, the Bayeux Tapestry does not elaborate details, for it is more concerned with telling its story, and the sweeping effect of the whole takes precedence over any one of its parts. As Hamlet advised his actors, the play is the thing—not the gesticulations, the declamation, or the ranting and roaring. It is a work addressed to men of action in a century in which deeds were admired more than words.

From the aesthetic viewpoint there is much that commands comment. In the handling of the narration, the designer after a slow beginning with frequent digressions and episodes went on to the rather feverish preparations of the middle panels that culminated in the breathless climax of the battle. In both tempo and organization, the Tapestry can stand comparison with the best works in narrative form, visual or verbal. The details, whether in the main panels or in the upper or lower borders, are handled so imaginatively that they not only embellish the design but add visual accents, comment on the action, and further the flow of the plot. Scenes are separated one from another by buildings that figure in the story and by such devices as the stylized trees that are mere conventions. So skillfully are these arranged that the continuity of the whole is never impeded, and the observer is hardly aware of their presence. All in all, a successful work of art designed for such a long and narrow space is a feat of visual virtuosity of no small order, and it leaves no doubt that it is the work of a master designer.

SONG OF ROLAND

A *chanson de geste* is a song of deeds, an action story in poetic form sung by a minstrel to the accompaniment of a viol or lyre, an epic poem in Old French, the medieval vernacular language of France, rather than in Latin. The *Chanson de Roland*, or *Song of Roland*, is narrated in an abrupt, direct manner, and transitions between episodes are sudden and unprepared. A martial atmosphere surrounds all the characters, including the fighting Archbishop Turpin as well as the Archangels Gabriel and Michael who, like the Valkyries in the German epic *Song of the Nibelungs*, swoop down on the battlefield to bear the souls of fallen warriors to heaven. Though nominally set in bygone times, the *Song of Roland* is, both in form and spirit, the product of the warlike feudalistic 11th century, and various chroniclers mention it in connection with the Battle of Hastings. Guy of Amiens, one of William and Matilda's courtiers, who died only ten years after the battle, was the author of a Latin poem about a jongleur by the name of Taillefer. This "minstrel whom a very brave heart ennobled," Guy relates, led William's forces into the battle throwing his sword in the air, catching it again, and singing a Song of Roland. William of Malmesbury, writing about 50 years after the battle, tells that William on that day started the *Song of Roland*, "in order that the warlike example of that hero might stimulate the soldiers." And one of the canons of the Bayeux Cathedral, who was the author of a history of the dukes of Normandy called the *Roman de Rou*, includes a verse which goes:

> Taillefer who was famed for song,
> Mounted on a charger strong,
> Rode on before the Duke, and sang
> Of Roland and of Charlemagne,
> Oliver and the vassals all
> Who fell in fight at Roncevals.

Taillefer, in the age-old tradition of minstrelsy, was a mime and singing actor, and his rendition of the epic was undoubtedly accompanied by skillful vocal declamation as well as with appropriate gestures and action.

The *Song of Roland* is thus a direct-action story, set in the time of Charlemagne and relating some incidents from the campaign in northern Spain where the Emperor had been battling the pagan Saracens for seven long years. Roland, Charlemagne's favorite nephew, and the twelve peers, flower of French knighthood, had been left in charge of the rear guard, while Charles and the main body of the army were crossing the Pyrenees back into France. Betrayed by a false kinsman, strongly paralleling the episode of William and Harold in the Bayeux Tapestry, Roland is attacked near Roncevals by overwhelming pagan forces. The rear guard is cut to pieces, and Roland, before dying a hero's death, sounds his ivory horn summoning his uncle and his army from a great distance.

The third part of the poem has to do with the vengeance of Charlemagne, just as the corresponding section of the Bayeux Tapestry related that of William. All is action and heroism, with swords flashing, helmets gleaming, drums beating, horns blowing, banners snapping, and steeds prancing. The battle unfolds in what amounts to a blow-by-blow account, echoing frequently with such phrases as "wondrous and fierce is the battle." (The quotations and subsequent page references are from Isabel Butler's translation, published by Houghton Mifflin, 1904 edition.) First one hears of the preparations in the camp of Charles. The poet, using a cumulative technique, describes the ten battalions one by one. Knight is added to knight, battle group to battle group, weapon to weapon, in order to build up the full monumentality of the occasion in the listeners' minds and imaginations. All the forces of Western Christendom are eventually drawn up on Charlemagne's side—the French, Normans, Bavarians, Germans, Bretons, and so on. The virtues of the men invariably are those of bravery, valiance, and hardiness; they have no fear of death; never do they flee the battlefield; and their horses are swift and good.

Then quite suddenly and without any transition we are in the midst of the pagan hordes. Ten Saracen battalions are described, and in order to show how the Christians were outnumbered, still another ten is added. The fearsomeness of the enemy, however, is not owed to numbers alone but to their ferocious character. The only admirable quality allowed them is that of being good fighters; otherwise they are hideous to behold, fierce and cruel, and love evil. Yet in spite of this they "ride on like goodly warriors" (p. 116). The physical appearance of the people from these strange parts is fantastically exaggerated. The men of Milciani, for instance, "have huge heads, and along the spine of their backs grow bristles like those of a wild boar" (p. 115). Of the warriors from the desert of Occiant, it is said that "their skins are hard like iron, wherefore they have no need of hauberks or helms [coats of mail and helmets]" (p. 116). Later, during the battle, these same men of Occiant "bray and neigh, and the men of Arguille yelp like dogs" (p. 125). Their religious life is just as much misunderstood as their appearance. The pagans are represented as polytheists who worship as strange an assortment of gods as was ever assembled—Apollo, Tervagant, and Mohamet. When things are not going well from their point of view, they upbraid these gods, take the statue of Apollo and "trod him under their feet" (p. 94); Tervagant is robbed of his carbuncle; and Mohamet is cast "into a ditch, for the dogs and the pigs to worry and gnaw" (p. 94). Later, when Marsila, the king of Spain, dies, the listener hears that "eager devils seize upon his soul" (p. 128). Such descriptions could not have been written after the Crusades had brought western warriors into contact with Moslem culture, and so, like the foreigners depicted on the Vézelay tympanum (Fig. 5:11), the imagery is filled with naïve wonder.

With the lines of battle thus drawn, the setting is described in a single line: "Vast is the plain and wide the fields." Then as the conflict begins, battalion falls on battalion, hewing and hacking away, Christian knights hurtle against pagan knights the whole day long until finally the battle is reduced to a personal encounter between Charlemagne and his opposite number, Baligant the Amiral (admiral). All the formidable fighting qualities of friend and foe are concentrated in these two contestants. Both are described as being older than the hills, and their beards are whiter than snow. The patriarchal image of society is consistently emphasized, just as it is in the representations of the elders of the Apocalypse found so frequently in Romanesque sculpture. Charles is called sometimes "the Emperor with the hoary beard" (p. 95), and at others "Charles the Old." Since all takes place in the present tense, he is by this time well on into his third century. But his adversary is not to be outdone in this respect, and Baligant is so old that he has actually outlived Vergil and Homer. Charlemagne, of course, is the epitome of Christian virtue, but his opponent generously is allowed to be wise "according to his law, and in battle he is fierce and mighty" (p. 113). The combat of the centenarians is on, and in their initial clash their spears shiver against one another, their coats of mail are rent, the blows bring them both to the ground, and the battle continues on foot with bare swords. Each tries to convert the other between blows; and just when all seems blackest, with Charles sorely wounded, the Angel Gabriel appears beside him, and his strength miraculously returns. "He smites the Amiral with the sword of France, shatters the helmet which shines with precious stones, carves through the skull that the brains run out, and through the face even to the white beard, that the Amiral falls dead beyond all help" (pp. 117–128). After this, the pagans flee and the day is won.

The lines of the original Old French proceed according to a rhyming scheme of crude assonance in which the final syllables of each line correspond roughly in sound. The last words of each line of one of the strophes will suffice to illustrate this principle of assonance: *magne, Espaigne, altaigne, remaigne, fraindre, muntaigne, m'enaimet, reclaimet, ataignet*. Much of the direct character and rugged strength of the poem is attributable to rigid avoidance of embellishment. This is observable in such minute details as the forward motion within such single lines as: *So sent Rollanz de tun tens ni ad plus*. Nothing is allowed to impede the progress of these sturdy military monosyllables. So consistently is this carried out all along the line that it even extends to the delineation of the characters themselves. Each is the embodiment of a single ideal and human type: Ganelon is all treachery and hatred; Roland, bravery to the point of rashness; Oliver, reason and caution; and Charles, pre-eminent in his solitary grandeur, represents the majesty of church and state. Through each one of these devices separately and through all of them cumulatively, the poem as a whole rises to the heights of epic art. Its language, style, and form thus well become the brave deeds of the heroic men with which it is concerned.

THE ART OF MINSTRELSY

"A verse without music is a mill without water," said Folquet of Marseilles, the troubadour whom Dante immortalized in his *Paradise*. Poetry in medieval times was a popular art form in which verses were chanted by a *jongleur*, or minstrel, to the accompaniment of a viol or lyre. No festive occasion was complete without a minstrel who sang *chansons de geste*, lays, and romances, told tales and fables, played on a variety of musical instruments, performed dances, and astonished with juggling and sleight-of-hand tricks.

Records of these jongleurs go back many centuries. It is known that jongleurs convened at Fécamp in Normandy in the year 1000 and that similar meets took place regularly during the slack season of Lent when the church banned their performances. They took this opportunity to get together, learn one another's tricks and techniques, and increase their repertories with new tales and songs. A lively account of their place in medieval society is contained in a description of a wedding feast in Provence, which says: "Then the *joglars* stood up, each one anxious to make himself heard; then you could hear instruments resounding in many a key. . . . One played the Lay of the Honeysuckle, another that of Tintagel, another that of the Faithful Lovers, another the lay that Ivan made. . . . Everyone performed at his best and the noise of the instrumentalists and the voices of the narrators made a considerable uproar in the hall."

The jongleurs of the 11th century were not of noble birth as were most of the later troubadours and trouvères, but they were welcomed in every castle and abbey. Their importance in the creation of a secular literature in the vernacular languages of medieval times can hardly be overestimated. The feudal society of the 11th century was groping its way toward distinctive art forms of its own, as seen in the *chanson de geste*. The musical part of these epics was far more primitive than the poetry, but, crude as it was, it marked the beginning of secular art music, separated in style both from the church models and the lost folk music of that time. Under the patronage of the feudal nobility, this music was to bloom in the 12th and 13th centuries into the full-fledged art of the troubadours, trouvères, and minnesingers.

Since the 11th-century forms were just emerging, the models and prototypes undoubtedly were derived from certain forms of church music. The simple repetitive melodies of the *chansons de geste*, together with the assonated verses and insistent rhythms of the poetry, had much in common with the litany—though, of course, the subject matter differed radically. It is greatly to be regretted that the musical setting of the *Song of Roland* has not been preserved. While jongleurs could refresh their memories of longer epics from the manuscripts they carried in the leather pouches that they wore, these manuscripts included no musical parts. Hence it is safe to assume that the melodies were so simple there was no need to write them down.

The music of the *chansons de geste*, according to medieval sources, consisted of a short melody with one note to a syllable, repeated over and over for each verse in the manner of a litany or folk song. At the end of each strophe, or group of lines, was a melodic appendage, which served as a refrain much like the alleluias between the verses of psalms and hymns. In the manuscript of the *Chanson de Roland* the enigmatic letters AOI appear after each of the 321 strophes, while in the songs of troubadours and minnesingers the letters are EUOUAE or some variant. EUOUAE is an abbreviation of the last two words of the lesser Doxology, *saeculorum amen*, and thus is a link between the troubadour's refrain and a Gregorian melody. The AOI in the *Song of Roland* manuscript possibly refers to some similar liturgical cadence formula now lost. If so, either it refers to a repeated vocal cadenza at the end of each strophe, a kind of punctuation mark for the ear to relieve the audience's attention momentarily from the words (as with the "Fa la la's" of the later Renaissance madrigals), or it might indicate a place where a short instrumental interlude was performed on the viol or lyre. In any case, the focus of attention in these epics was on the words of the poem itself, and the musical element was subordinate. In the closing formula, however, the purely musical element could have come to the fore with whatever special effects the jongleur had at his command.

Chanson de geste Melody (11th century)   Adam de la Halle
                                                                          (After Gennrich)

Au-di-gier, dit Raim-ber - ge,   bou-se vous di.

The single authentic example of a *chanson de geste* melody that survives is found in a little pastoral play from the 13th century by Adam de la Halle, where it is quoted humorously by one of the characters. The two halves of this melody are repeated once for each line of the strophe, following which there would have been a short cadenza or refrain for either the voice or an instrument. The operation of this refrain principle is found in a song from *Aucassin et Nicolette*, a French *chante-fable*. Written about a century later, it is similar in style to that of the *chanson de geste*. The melody of the first eight measures is sung for each line of the strophe, each time to different words. The refrain in the final three bars is then either sung or played between each of the verses and again at the end. The extreme simplicity of these melodies indicates that the music alone would not have held the attention of an audience. The dominant interest was obviously epic poetry, and the minstrel's performance of it with appropriate action, gestures, and vocal inflection.

Aucassin et Nicolette. Strophe, or *Laisse* (13th century)   (After Gennrich)

NORMAN ARCHITECTURE

The architecture of the Normans was sufficiently important to give one aspect of the Romanesque style the name of Norman. The building done in 11th-century Normandy not only had a lasting effect on that region of France but reached a logical conclusion in the keeps, castles, abbeys, and cathedrals that the Normans later built in England. Since the Romanesque style in England dates from the time of the conquest, it is still referred to there as the Norman style. As did so many other aspects of their culture, Norman architecture resulted from the union of the rugged pagan spirit of the Vikings and the Gallic Christian remnants of the disintegrated Carolingian Empire. As a representative product of these people, it reflects their blunt strength and forthright character. Both the Carolingian and Viking societies were nomadic. Charlemagne and his successors as well as the dukes of Normandy down to William's time frequently shifted their residences, and the insecurity of the times discouraged building in general. But as the feudal system reached its mature stage, a more settled order became possible, and so the Norman conquerors turned to the assimilation and development of the vast new lands they had acquired instead of seeking further conquests. William's policy thus shifted from offensive to defensive. Earlier he had discouraged the construction of castles and sanctioned only monasteries; now he proposed to impress his new subjects with solid and impregnable fortresses as well as feats of sword on the field of battle.

Tower of London. 1078–1090. Fig. 6:6 (*above*). Air View. Fig. 6:7 (*below*). *Plan*

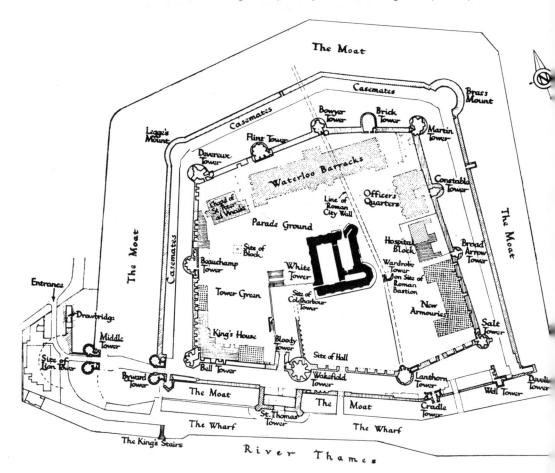

Fig. 6:8. Tower of London. St. John's Chapel. 1078–1097

The so-called Tower of London (Fig. 6:6) was begun by the Conqueror about 1078 and finished by his successor in order to defend and dominate the town. Its form was that of a Norman keep, and as such it was something new to England. The Tower is simply a massive, square, compact stone building, divided into four stories which rise 92 feet with a turret at each corner. A glance at the ground plan (Fig. 6:7) will show some of its many irregularities. Its four sides, for instance, are unequal in length, and its corners are therefore not right angles; three of its turrets are square, while one is round; the one on the west rises 107 feet, while that on the south is 118 feet high; the walls vary from 11 to 15 feet in thickness; and the interior is divided from top to bottom in two unequal parts by a wall running from north to south.

The barrenness of its exterior was well suited to the Tower's function as a fortress, but the austerity of the interior was a commentary on the bleakness and general lack of physical comforts of medieval life. The Tower was divided into several stories by means of wooden floors, and its darkness was relieved only by narrow, slitted glassless windows, which were more important as launching sites for arrows against an enemy than as sources of light and ventilation. After Norman times, other buildings were added until the whole became a concentric system of fortifications with the old Norman keep as its heart. From William's time to the present, the Tower has been in continuous use as a fortress, palace, and prison.

From the plan, it will be seen that the main floor has three divisions: a large council chamber, which also doubled as a banqueting hall, a smaller presence chamber, and the well-preserved St. John's Chapel (Fig. 6:8). Like a miniature church, this chapel has a barrel-vaulted nave of four bays, with aisles on either side that command interest because of their early use of cross vaulting. The columns of the nave arcade are thick and stubby, and the cushionlike capitals have only the most rudimentary scalloped carving by way of decoration. Above is a triforium gallery used by the queen and her ladies, and on either side are slitlike windows that serve as a clearstory.

At Caen in Normandy, two buildings were under the personal protection of William and Queen Matilda and designated as their respective burial places— St. Étienne (Abbaye-aux-hommes) and Ste. Trinité (Abbaye-aux-dames). Since both are abbey churches, they fall more properly into the monastic Romanesque, but here they serve to complete the picture of the Norman style. Begun just prior to the conquest, St. Étienne has a well-proportioned façade (Fig. 6:9). Four prominent buttresses divide the section below the towers into three parts that correspond to the central nave and two side aisles in the interior. Vertically, the façade rises in three stories, with the portals matching the level of the nave arcade inside, while the two rows of windows above are at the triforium and clearstory levels respectively. The windows are mere openings and in themselves are quite undistinguished. But the functional honesty in this correspondence of exterior design and interior plan was a Norman innovation that came into general use in the Gothic period.

The twin towers belong to the original design, but their spires are later additions. As in the usual Norman church, the towers are square and in three stories, thus repeating on a higher level the triple division of the façade below. The first story is of solid masonry; the second has alternate blind and open arches; while the greater open space of the third facilitates its function as a belfry and relieves the general heaviness. Otherwise the austerity and ponderousness of the façade in general is a fitting prelude to the gloomy grandeur of the interior. The church as a whole is as thoroughly rugged and masculine in character as the

Fig. 6:9. St. Étienne (Abbaye-aux-hommes). *Façade*. Nave 157½′ x 32′ 10″, towers 295′ high. *c*.1064–1135 (Clarence Ward)

personality of its founder and typifies the spirit of the Norman people and their forceful leader.

When the barren façade of St. Étienne is compared to the exterior of the Tower of London, it becomes apparent that the lack of decoration was a conscious part of the design. One façade impresses by its bold outlines, sturdiness, and straightforward honesty, and the other by its sheer strength and bluntness. The Norman accent on structure rather than embellishment did, however, lead to advances in the art of building, though it was to be replaced soon after the crusades by Saracenic innovations. In their churches, the Normans achieved more adequate lighting than heretofore by increasing the space allotted to the clearstory, and more unified interiors by connecting the three levels of the nave arcade, triforium, and clearstory by single vertical shafts between the bays that ran from floor to ceiling. Both these features, as well as the harmonious spatial divisions of such a façade as that of St. Étienne, later were incorporated into the Gothic style. In spite of this, however, when the work of the Normans is placed alongside that of their more skillful Burgundian contemporaries, it seems crude by comparison. The Normans were as blunt and brash as the Cluniacs were ingenious and subtle. The difference, in short, is that between men of action and men of contemplation.

FEUDALISM

The relationship of such representative examples of the Romanesque style as the Bayeux Tapestry, the poetry and music of the *Song of Roland*, and the architecture of the Tower of London and the abbey of St. Étienne at Caen is reinforced by the knowledge that each is a high point of Norman culture, falling between the dates of the Battle of Hastings in 1066 and the First Crusade in 1096. The Tapestry was designed soon after the battle whose tale it tells; the *Song of Roland* was sung at the battle; and both evidence the same form and spirit. The building of the Tower and abbey coincides with the zenith of William's success and prosperity after the conquest. The relationship in time, place, and content comes at the climax of feudalism, and it is under this single all-embracing concept that the individual works find their unity.

All the separate concepts of the Norman world were contained in the overpowering central idea of feudalism. Like the concentric rings of inner and outer fortifications of the Tower of London (Fig. 6:6) or the later Gothic castle at Carcassonne (Fig. 6:10), individuals in such a society were but tiny circles in an expanding cosmic scheme of things that determined their relations to their superiors, their peers, and their inferiors. It was a social system modeled on that of an army; and the ethic that bound the whole together was fealty, a kind of

Fig. 6:10. Carcassonne Castle. Gothic Period, mainly 12th and 13 centuries. Walls restored by Viollet-le-duc 1855–1879 (Pan American Airways)

blind loyalty, in which right and wrong were fixed by physical force rather than by reason and principle. The feudal system provided a proper place for every man in a strict hierarchy, with barons holding their power from their overlords, ecclesiastical or secular; dukes holding their realms from their king; and the king, emperor, and pope holding the earth as a fief from God. In the *Song of Roland*, for example, Charlemagne and his 12 peers were considered to be the secular counterparts of Christ and his 12 Apostles, the Apostles being vassals of Christ and Christ himself a vassal of God the Father.

The feudal virtues were faith, courage, and blind loyalty to peer and superior; any departure from this code was treachery and was dealt with by isolation and defeat. Defection had to be decided on the field of battle, with God awarding victory to the righteous cause. Enemies, however, provided their lineage was in order and their family trees properly pruned, were accorded the distinctions of honor and bravery; otherwise it would have been socially impossible to do battle with them. In the poem and in the Bayeux Tapestry, no one below the rank of baron figures with any degree of prominence; likewise, the abbeys of

William and Matilda were intended primarily for persons of rank, and by their foundation the royal pair pledged their feudal oath to God.

In their subject matter, the *Song of Roland* and the Bayeux Tapestry have many points in common. As the song opens: "Charles the King . . . has conquered all the high land down to the sea; not a castle holds out against him, not a wall or city is left unshattered, save Saragossa, which stands on a high mountain. King Marsila holds it, who loves not God, but serves Mahound, and worships Apollon; ill hap must in sooth befall him." If the simple substitution of William for Charles, England for Saragossa in Spain, the barrier of the sea for that of the mountain, and Harold for Marsila is made, the situation becomes the contemporary one that the Tapestry so vividly portrays. Later, at the battle of Roncevals the dominant trio is Roland, Oliver, and the fighting Archbishop Turpin, in whom it is not difficult to recognize their parallels at Hastings: William and his half brothers Robert of Mortain and the irrepressible Bishop Odo.

In both Song and Tapestry, the cause for war ostensibly was religious. In one, it was Christianity *versus* paganism; in the other, the breaking of a sacred oath when Harold became king—and both causes were sanctioned by the pope. Again, in both, the enemy in the best feudal tradition was a worthy adversary, noble and brave but religiously misguided. In the *Song of Roland*, Marsila was crafty but at all times observed the rules of feudal warfare. The glory of Charlemagne's major pagan adversary, with his bright silks from Alexandria, gold of Arabia, carbuncle-studded sword, and bright gonfalons, is glowingly described in poetic language, just as Harold's knightly qualities are pictured repeatedly in visual form. In both, religious symbols figure prominently. Durendal, Roland's sword, is his most sacred possession, having within it a tooth of St. Peter, blood of St. Basil, hair of St. Denis, and a fragment of the Virgin's robe, all souvenirs of his pilgrimage to the Holy Land. The importance of such relics at this time was overwhelming. In the Tapestry, Harold's seizure of the kingly power was treacherous mainly because the oath had been sworn on the reliquaries in Bayeux Cathedral. Harold's perjury and breaking of a vow sworn under such sacrosanct conditions was sufficient cause for invasion.

Religion conviction is absolute in both Song and Tapestry. Such a sweeping statement as "Wrong the pagans, right the Christians are" leaves no room for lingering philosophical or theological doubts on the validity of the cause. In each, the importance and glorification of sheer strength and prowess at arms are apparent from the descriptive details of costume, armor, and weapons, which are dwelt upon with obvious pride. Both Tapestry and poem are set in a man's world based on clear-cut loyalties and moral and physical certainties. The chivalry in each is based on the ways of fighting men. The code of Roland and Oliver, and of William and Odo, was clearly that of "My soul to God, my life to the king, and honor for myself." It remained for a later period to add: "My heart to the ladies." Roland's dying thoughts, for instance, are occupied with his family and lineage; his king, the great Charles; his country, the fair land of France; and his sword, Durendal. Significantly, he makes no mention of his betrothed, the Lady Aude. Earlier, the exasperated Oliver had reproached Roland for his rashness in not summoning aid sooner, and at that time he swore: "By this my beard, and I again see my sister, Aude the Fair, never shalt thou lie in her arms." No true or courtly love is this, only the feudal baron bestowing his female relations like his land and goods on those whose faith and courage he has cause to admire. Later, after Charles returns to France, the poor lady inquires about the fate of her fiancé. The king tells her of his death and as a consolation prize offers her the hand of his son Louis, whereupon the lady expires at his feet. Whether she dies of grief for Roland or from the indelicacy of Charlemagne's suggestion is left open to conjecture. Since scarcely more than a dozen of the 4000-odd lines of the poem are devoted to her, Henry Adams was well justified in his observation: "Never after the first crusade did any great poem rise to such heroism as to sustain itself without a heroine." Curiously enough, on the Saracen side Marsila's queen is shown taking an important part in the affairs of state on the incapacitation of her husband, while nowhere is a woman accorded anything like a similar status on the Christian side. And in the Bayeux Tapestry, the only place where a woman is mentioned by name is the enigmatic inscription *Where a cleric and Aelfgyva*, apparently introduced to give a motive for the minor episode describing an invasion of Brittany. While a few female figures are found in the borders and in attendance at the death of the Confessor, none figures with any prominence. Both works are thus as bold and direct as the poetry and art of the coming Gothic period was delicate and subtle. Roland and his counterparts in the Tapestry fought the good fight for king and country, while the knightly heroes of the later period entered the lists for a loving glance from a pair of blue eyes, the fleeting smile on fair lips, or the fragrant petals of a rose tossed from a lady's bower.

Formal considerations of both Song and Tapestry are in keeping with their rugged character. The emphasis everywhere is on the concrete rather than the abstract, content rather than form, and narrative sequence over structure. The telling of the tale in both cases is almost completely unencumbered with either visual or literary flourishes. Just as deeds take precedence over poetic form in the *Chanson*, the narrative element in the Bayeux Tapestry is more important than the decorative detail. Every part of the Tapestry has some direct bearing on the story, and the action in the poem is so direct that it contains hardly a single figure of speech. In both, the attributes are fixed. In the Tapestry, the English always have moustaches and the Normans are clean shaven. In the poem, kings are always mighty no matter what side they may be on, and knights are invariably brave whatever their allegiance may be. Similarly, in the sculpture of the period, kings always have crowns on their heads, even if they are in bed, Apostles always have bare feet, and so on. The curiously stylized trees in the Tapestry come directly from manuscript drawings rather than from nature, and they function either as an indication that the action is taking place out of doors or as formal devices to divide one scene from another. In the epic, Roland always rests under a pine tree because he is French, while his enemies pause under olive trees because they are Saracens.

Symmetry seldom is considered. The lines of the poem, for example, are rough-hewn but heroic pentameters, which group themselves into irregular strophes averaging 14 lines in length. Similarly, the space given to individual scenes in the Bayeux Tapestry, like the size of the compartments in the archivolt of the Vézelay tympanum (Fig. 5:11) and the unequal height of the arches in a Romanesque cathedral wall such as at Pisa (Fig. 5:26), are disproportionate and asymmetrical.

Details in the *Chanson*, the Tapestry, St. Étienne, and the Tower of London thus remain crude and unpolished. This was an era of forming, building, experimenting, and reaching out toward new modes of expression rather than a time of crystallization, polished expression, and ultimate arrival. In architecture, the process of building was more important than what was built. The emphasis given in the Tapestry to representations of castles, fortifications, and specific buildings, such as Westminster Abbey and Mont-St.-Michel, suggest the image of a builder's world and a century of architectural activity and progress. The forthright and direct narration of deeds in the Song and Tapestry finds its architectural counterpart in the functional honesty of the style of the Tower and William's church at Caen. Just as the direct-action story of the *Chanson* and Tapestry takes precedence over literary form and decorative flourish, so the structural honesty of the building process, as exemplified in the Tower and St. Étienne, becomes the leading characteristic. The process of lengthening balladic poetry into the epic form of the *chanson de geste* capable of sustaining attention through the long Norman winter evenings or of extending a few pictorial panels into the heroic completeness of a tapestry depicting a major historical episode in its entirety was essentially the same as the process of piling up tall towers capable of piercing the gloomy northern skies.

The image of the Norman world as it thus builds up through the various arts is not essentially a complex one. There was little of the mystical about these clear-headed Viking adventurers. They caught on with alacrity to any progressive development of the time, whether it was the discarding of their rather inflexible mother tongue in favor of the more supple French or the adopting of many of the Cluniac moral and architectural reforms. A good example of their forthrightness is seen in the Tapestry, which shows exactly who a figure is and what he is doing, documented with name and place. Whatever they did, they did always with their characteristic determination and energy. Thus the rugged man of action in William unites with the military monosyllables of the *Chanson*, the frank, almost comic-strip directness of the Bayeux Tapestry, and the rough-hewn stones of the Tower and Caen abbey to make a single structure. Each was concerned with forms of action, and whether in picture, word, or stone, the epical spirit is present. Deed on deed, syllable on syllable, stitch on stitch, image on image, stone on stone—each builds up into the great personality, heroic epic, impressive Tapestry, or gaunt Tower, and in the process reveals a Norman feudal structure of truly monumental proportions.

Fig. 6:11. *The German Minnesinger Heinrich Frauenlob [died 1318] Directing a Performance by Minstrels.* Manesse Manuscript. 14th century. Heidelberg

CHRONOLOGY:
Île-de-France, 12th and 13th Centuries

1096– 1291 Crusades: European Christians fought Moslems and Saracens; extended Christianity as well as opened up trade routes

1137 Louis VII began reign as king of France; married Eleanor of Aquitaine

1140 Abbey church of St. Denis, prototype of Gothic cathedrals, begun by Abbot Suger

1142 Abelard, master of School of Notre Dame in Paris, died at Cluny

1163– 1235 Cathedral of Notre Dame in Paris built

1180 Philip Augustus crowned king of France; enclosed Paris with walls; promoted Paris as his capital city

1194 Chartres Cathedral begun after fire destroyed earlier structure

    1006 Fulbert appointed bishop of Chartres

    1020–1028 Romanesque cathedral built by Fulbert

    1134 Fulbert's cathedral destroyed by fire

    1145 Romanesque cathedral again rebuilt

    1194 Fire destroyed Romanesque cathedral with exception of narthex, west portals, two towers, three stained glass windows

1210 Rheims Cathedral rebuilt

1215 Magna Charta signed in England

1220 Amiens and Rouen cathedrals begun

1223 Louis VIII crowned king of France

1225 Beauvais Cathedral begun; choir finished in 1272

1226 Louis IX became king of France under regency of his mother, Blanche of Castile

1233 Chartres added to Crown territory of France

1236 Regency of Blanche of Castile ended

1240 Ste. Chapelle, royal chapel of French kings, begun in Paris

1250 University of Paris founded, with Albertus Magnus as one of its teachers

1260 Cathedral of Chartres dedicated by Louis IX

1274 Scholastic philosophy at height

    St. Bonaventura and St. Thomas Aquinas died

Philosophers
1079– 1142 Abelard
c.1193– 1280 Albertus Magnus
1221– 1274 Bonaventura
c.1225– 1274 Thomas Aquinas

Musicians
c.1122– 1192 Adam of St. Victor, joint author of hymns with St. Bernard of Clairvaux

c.1150 Leonin active at Cathedral of Notre Dame in Paris

c.1183 Perotin active at Cathedral of Notre Dame in Paris

c.1237–c.1288 Adam de la Halle, author and composer of Le Jeu de Robin et Marion, a pastoral play with music

c.1240 "Sumer is icumen in," oldest surviving piece of secular polyphony, written

c.1260 Franco of Cologne, musical theorist, active

7

THE GOTHIC STYLE

ÎLE-DE-FRANCE, LATE 12TH AND 13TH CENTURIES

In contrast to the shores of the Mediterranean, where such resplendent centers of culture as Athens, Alexandria, Antioch, Constantinople, and Rome flourished for centuries, northern Europe had been little more than a rural region with a few Roman provincial outposts and, later, a scattering of castles, monasteries, and villages. Before the 13th century, in fact, not one center north of the Alps could properly have been described as a city. Toward the end of the 12th century, however, Philip Augustus as king of France was promoting the destiny of Paris as his capital, enclosing it with walls and paving some of its streets with stone. The work was continued under his successors, and by the end of the 13th century Paris was the capital of a kingdom of growing importance. With its splendid Cathedral of Notre Dame, its university famed for the teaching of Abelard, Albertus Magnus, Thomas Aquinas, and Bonaventura, and with its flourishing mercantile trade capable of supporting about 150,000 inhabitants, Paris could well claim the status of a capital city. When it is remembered, however, that Constantinople was the hub of the rich East Roman Empire and had been a city of over a million since Justinian's time, the status of this first trans-alpine urban center is seen in proper perspective.

The growth of Paris, while more rapid than other northern centers, was far from an isolated instance. For a full century, the town as a social unit had been gaining ascendancy over the manorial estate, and the literature of the time mentions Ghent with its turreted houses, Lille and its cloth, Tours and its grain, and how all were carrying on commerce with distant lands. With the exception of such occasional references, however, the life of medieval French towns would have remained a closed book had it not been for the visual record preserved in the castles of their feudal lords, in the monasteries, and, above all, in their cathedrals.

The prototype of the Gothic cathedral has been recognized in the abbey church of St. Denis just outside Paris. This monastery was under the direct patronage of the French kings and was their traditional burial place. Around the middle of the 12th century its abbot was Suger, a man whose talents were as remarkable as his origin was obscure. The trusted confidant of two kings, he ruled France as regent while Louis VII was away on a crusade, and when he undertook the rebuilding of his abbey church, his great personal prestige, as well as its importance as the royal monastery, enabled him to call together the most expert craftsmen from all parts of the kingdom. Suger's church thus became a synthesis of all the ideas that had been tried and found successful by the best Romanesque builders. Posterity has had reason to rejoice that the abbot's enthusiasm for his project caused him to write extensively about it, and his book is an invaluable source of information about the architectural thought of the time. In 1130, for instance, when St. Denis was in the planning stage, he made a prolonged visit to Cluny to learn from first-hand observation about its recently completed church. His commentary on the iconography of St. Denis' windows and sculpture suggests that he took a personal hand in this part of the project, but of the architect who carried out the building no mention is made. St. Denis is notable not so much for its innovations as for its successful combining into a working relationship of such late Romanesque devices as the pointed arch, ribbed groin vault, and flying buttress. Many late Cluniac Romanesque churches had used these features separately, but not before Suger's church had they been grouped into a coherent structural system, and the abbot's position at the French court, as well as the proximity of his church to Paris, assured the widest possible currency of his ideas. Hence, St. Denis became the model for many of the Gothic cathedrals that were built in the region shortly afterward.

The Île-de-France, a flexible area encircling Paris, was the setting in which the Gothic style originated and where, over a period extending approximately from 1150 to 1300, it reached the climax of its development. The name of this region referred to the royal domain, or territory, under the direct control of the French king, when the rest of what is now France was still under the dominion of various feudal lords. By heredity, marriage, conquest, and purchase, the Île-de-France gradually had grown over the years into the nucleus of the future French nation, and, like a wheel with Paris as its hub, it radiated outward about 100 miles, with spokes extending toward Amiens, Rheims, Bourges, and Chartres, cathedral towns all. The loftiest expression of the medieval period is seen in these miracles of soaring stone—the crystalized expressions of community effort, religious exaltation, and emotional and intellectual forces of the people who created them.

Unlike an abbey church, a cathedral is located in a populated area where it comes under the jurisdiction of a bishop, whose official seat it is. A cathedral cannot rise from a plain like a monastic church; it needs the setting of a town where it can soar above the roofs and gables of the buildings that cluster around it. The barren exterior of an abbey forbids, while the intricate carving on the outside of a cathedral awakens curiosity and invites entrance. As the center of a cloistered life, a monastic church is richest in its dim interior, while the most elaborate decoration of a cathedral points toward the dwellings of the people. The tall towers of a Gothic cathedral need space from which to spring and room to cast their shadows. Their spires beckon the distant traveler to the shrine beneath and direct the weary steps of the toiling peasant homeward after a day in the fields, and the bells they enclose peal out to regulate the life of a whole town and its surrounding countryside. They tell of weddings and funerals and of the time for work and rest and prayer.

Always the cathedral was, of course, primarily a religious center, but in a time when spiritual and worldly affairs were so interwoven, the line of demarcation was difficult to draw. A cathedral nave was not only the place for religious services but, on occasion, a town hall where the entire populace could gather for a meeting. The rich decorations that clothe the body of the cathedral told not only the story of Christianity but also the history of the town and of the activities of its people. The cathedral was thus a municipal museum on whose walls the living record of the town was carved. The iconography of a cathedral dedicated to Notre Dame was by no means concerned only with religious subjects. Since the Virgin Mary was also the patroness of the liberal arts, her cathedral was often a visual encyclopedia whose subjects ranged over the entire field of human knowledge. The pulpit was not only the place from which sermons were preached but also a podium for lectures and instruction. The sanctuary was the theater in which the constantly changing sequence of the religious drama was enacted; but outside, the deep-set portals served as the stage sets for the mystery plays appropriate to the season, and the porches became platforms from which minstrels and jugglers could entertain their audiences. The stone statues and stained glass were useful not only as illustrations for sermons but as picture galleries to stimulate the imagination. The choir was not only the setting for liturgical song but a concert hall or opera house, where intricate polyphonic motets were performed and the melodies of the religious dramas were chanted.

Chartres (Fig. 7:1), unlike Paris, was never a center of commerce but a small bishopric in the midst of a rural district well off the beaten path. Its greatest

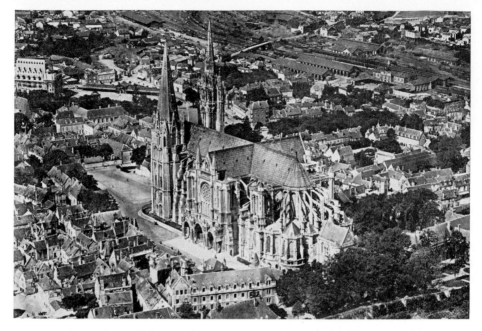

Fig. 7:1. Chartres Cathedral, Air View

distinction came from its shrine of the Virgin Mary where annually thousands congregated from far and wide to celebrate the Feast of the Virgin that was the grand climax of the usual sequence of church festivals. Here, as elsewhere, the cathedral was not only the spiritual center of the lives of the townsfolk but the geographical center of the medieval town as well. Towering over all, its great shadow fell upon the clustering church buildings that included the bishop's palace, the cathedral school, a cloister, a hospice, and an almshouse. Its west façade constituted one side of the marketplace, and from the cathedral square radiated the narrow streets on which were located the houses and shops of the townspeople. Here were the streets of the butchers, the bakers, and the candlestickmakers, for all who practiced the same craft lived on the same street. As members of guilds, or associations, the townsmen had contributed their labor and products to the cathedral when it was being built, and as guilds they had donated windows and statuary. They also undertook to fill such continuous needs as candles for the altars and bread for the communion service.

The cathedral itself, toward which all eyes and steps were drawn, represented a composite effort of the stone cutters, masons, carpenters, and metal workers, all of whom gave of their time, skill, and treasure to build it. It thus was the greatest single product a town and its craftsmen could produce. As a great civic monument, it was the pride of the community, and the ambitions and aspirations of its citizens determined its character and contours. The importance of a town was measured by the size and height of its cathedral as well as by the significance of the religious relics its cathedral housed. Consequently, civic rivalry was involved when the vaulting of Chartres rose 122 feet above the ground. Next came Amiens, which rose 147 feet, and then Beauvais, which added 10 feet more to top them all—going beyond the limits of skill and safety so that its walls collapsed. At this time, the growth of town and cathedral were indistinguishable, and in the broader sense the cathedral with the buildings and dwellings that grouped themselves around it formed a single unit.

The extraordinary religious enthusiasm that prompted the undertaking and construction of these immense projects is well brought out in the accounts of several medieval writers. "Who has ever heard tell, in times past," wrote Abbot Haimon of Normandy (after visiting Chartres) to his brother monks in Tutbury, England, "that powerful princes of the world, that men brought up in honor and wealth, that nobles, men and women, have bent their proud and haughty necks to the harness of carts, and that, like beasts of burden, they have dragged to the abode of Christ these waggons, loaded with wines, grains, oil, stone, wood, and all that is necessary for the wants of life, or for the construction of the church? . . . When they have reached the church, they arrange the waggons about it like a spiritual camp, and during the whole night they celebrate the watch by hymns and canticles. On each waggon they light tapers and lamps; they place there the infirm and sick, and bring them the precious relics of the Saints for their relief."

ARCHITECTURE OF CHARTRES CATHEDRAL

When the harmonious proportions of the west façade of the Cathedral of Notre Dame at Chartres (Fig. 7:2) are first observed, everything seems as right as an immutable truth. Yet what seem so certain, so solid, so monumental is actually the end result of fire salvage, a long process of growth, and a goodly amount of improvisation. Four centuries, in fact, separate the earliest parts from the latest, and the interval between saw rapid construction in time of prosperity, lag in time of poverty, work inspired with religious ardor, and cruel destruction by fire.

The triple portal and lancet windows above first stood a full 40 feet back of the twin towers; together they were all that remained of the previous Romanesque church after the conflagration of 1194. In the rebuilding, they were moved forward flush with the front towers. The large rose window was designed to fill the intervening space, and above it the arcade of kings and a gable were added to mask the apex of the wooden roof that protects the vaulting of the nave.

The stylistic difference between the two unsymmetrical spires is one of the most striking features of the Chartres façade. The supporting towers, as a part

Fig. 7:2. Chartres Cathedral, *Façade*. 157′ wide. South tower (right) 344′ high, North tower (left) 377′ high. Façade *c*.1194–1260 (Portals and lancet windows *c*.1145), South tower *c*.1180, North spire 1507–1513

of the previous church, are approximately contemporary. The upper part and the spire of the one on the right, however, date from the time the later parts of the abbey church at Cluny were being finished; their counterparts on the left are contemporary with the laying of the foundations for St. Peter's basilica in Rome in the early 16th century. Close scrutiny will reveal such minor flaws as the discrepancy between the proportions of the portals and the scale of the façade as a whole, the rose window being set slightly more to the right side, and the awkward joining of the gallery and arcade of kings above it with the tower on the left. In spite of these disparities the façade bears out the initial impression of unity surprisingly well, and its space is so logically divided as to become an external promise of the interior plan. Horizontally, the three entrance portals lead into the nave while the flanking towers face the aisles. Vertically, the portals correspond to the nave arcade within, the lancets to the triforium gallery, and the rose window to the clearstory level. By this means, its composition maintains an integral relationship between the inner and outer aspects of the structure.

Rising above the twin towers are the tall tapering spires that seem such a logical and necessary continuation of the vertical lines of the supporting buttresses below as well as a fitting expression of the Gothic spirit of aspiration generally. The façade of Chartres, however, is almost unique in having a pair of spires. In Paris, Rouen, Amiens, and elsewhere, spires were projected but never completed; and at Strasbourg, one tower has a spire while the other does not. The two at Chartres make an interesting contrast between the attitudes of the early and late architects. In the older one on the south, the builder felt that the junction between tower and spire should be made as smoothly as possible and did so by adding a story between the three levels of the tower below and the single shaft of the spire above. Here the eight dormerlike windows are each

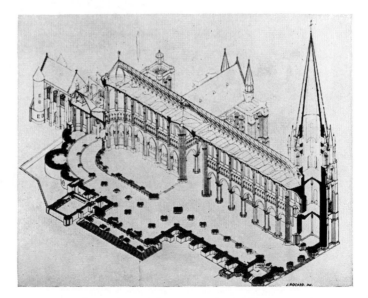

Fig. 7:3. Chartres Cathedral, *Plan*

Fig. 7:4. Chartres Cathedral, *Nave Interior. c.*130′ long, 53′ wide, 122′ high. *c.*1194–1260 (Marburg)

surmounted by alternating higher and lower miniature spire forms of their own that, in turn, overlap the base of the larger spire, break the line, and add to the rhythm of the vertical movement. The transition from the square supporting tower to the octagonal form of the spire, and the continuation of the straight lines rising from ground level to the receding sloping lines of the spire, which culminate 350 feet above, is accomplished with finesse. The later Gothic architect, whose task was to replace the old wooden spire that had burned, was more concerned with intricacy of design and with sending his slimmer and more elegant spire 27 feet higher than its neighbor. While both excel in terms of their separate stylistic frames of reference, it is the old south tower, still sound after seven centuries and almost as many fires, that connoisseurs admire.

When one enters Chartres through the central portal, the broad nave (Fig. 7:4) spreads out to a width of 53 feet, making it one of the most spacious of all Gothic naves. On either side are amply proportioned aisles with their stained-glass windows that allow a rich flood of light to enter. A look at the plan (Fig. 7:3) will show that, in comparison with the abbey church at Cluny (Fig. 5:1), the Gothic architect has practically dispensed with walls. Instead of running parallel to the nave, the supporting piers are now at right angles to it, and the area between is bridged over with vaults, thus allowing open space for glass to light the interior at both the ground and clearstory levels. Since the eye is naturally drawn to light, the interior gives the impression of being all windows. The walls, therefore, instead of serving to bear the weight of the superstructure, now exist mainly to enclose the interior and as a framework for the glass. Through the language of form and color, the wall space could now communicate with the worshipers through representations of religious subjects; and on a sunny day the beams of filtered light transform the floor into a constantly changing mosaic of color. Together with the clearstory windows, the shafts of mysterious light serve also to accent the structural system of arches, piers, and vaults in such a way as to contribute to the illusion of infinite size and height.

Returning to the center of the nave, the attention is next drawn to the arcade of seven bays marching majestically toward the crossing of the transept (Fig. 7:5) and on to the choir beyond. The immense piers consist of a strong central column with four attached colonettes of more slender proportions clustered around them. As Figure 7:4 plainly shows, piers with cylindrical cores and engaged octagonal colonettes alternate with piers with octagonal cores and attached cylindrical colonettes. An interesting rhythm of procession and recession is set up, and a further variation is provided by the play of light on the alternating round and angular surfaces.

The space above the graceful pointed arches of the nave arcade is filled by a series of smaller open arches that span the space between the bays. Behind them runs the triforium gallery, a passage utilizing the space above the internal

Fig. 7:5. Chartres Cathedral, *Interior at Crossing*. c.1194–1260 (Clarence Ward)

roofing over the aisles and under the slanting external roof that extends outward from the base of the clearstory. Above the triforium runs the clearstory level, which now fully accomplishes its purpose. The triple pattern of two lancet windows below and a circular one above, allots a maximum of space to the glass and a minimum to the masonry.

Covering the span of the nave is the triumph of the Gothic builders, the broad quadripartite vaulting (Fig. 7:6), which at Chartres rises 122 feet above the ground level. It is this principle of vaulting that underlies all Gothic thinking and, in turn, explains all the supporting facts of shafts, colonettes, clustered columns, piers, and pointed arches—all of which come into play to direct the descending weight of the intersecting ribs of the vaults toward the ground as efficiently as possible. The heavier transverse ribbing is carried past the clearstory and triforium levels by the large central shaft, while the smaller cross ribs are borne by the groups of slender colonettes that extend downward and cluster

Fig. 7:6. Chartres Cathedral, *Apse Vaulting.* c.1194–1260 (Archives Photographiques)

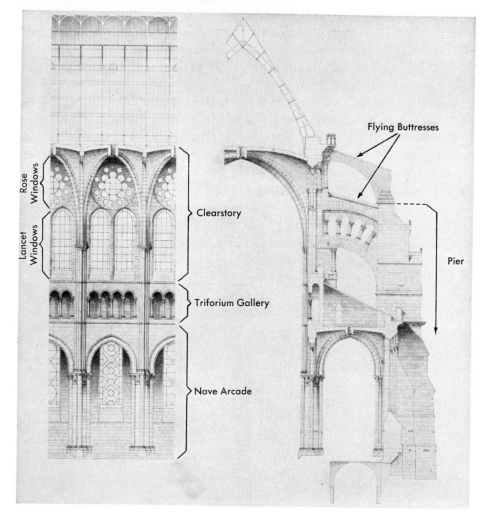

Rose Windows

Lancet Windows

Flying Buttresses

Clearstory

Triforium Gallery

Nave Arcade

Pier

Fig. 7:7 (*above*). Chartres Cathedral, *Transverse Section of Nave* (left) and *Diagram of Vaulting* (right). Drawing by Goubert

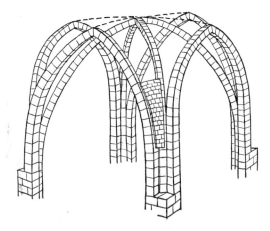

Fig. 7:8 (*right*). *Gothic Vault.*
Drawing by W. D. Richmond

Fig. 7:9. Chartres Cathedral, *Nave Exterior from South.* c.1194–1260 (Archives Photographiques)

around the massive central piers of the nave arcade below. Chartres is about midway in the cumulative trial-and-error process by which the Gothic system was eventually perfected. The central piers of the nave arcade are still somewhat bulky, as though the architect could not entirely trust his own daring. Greater slenderness was achieved at Rheims and Amiens, and the tendency toward slimness and height continued until its limit was passed at Beauvais.

Externally, there is an opposite number to each of these interior members (Fig. 7:7). The function of the flying buttress is to carry the thrust of the vaulting at specific points outward over the aisles to the piers that are set at right angles to the length of the nave. The function of flying buttress, pinnacle, and pier are now clarified. From the observer's point of view, just as in the interior the eye is drawn irresistibly upward by the rising vertical lines, so on the outside it follows the rising vertical piers to the pinnacles, along the rhythmic procession of the flying buttresses toward the gabled roof of the transepts, and on to the infinitude of space beyond.

The purpose of the pointed arch now also becomes clear. The Romanesque architects of Burgundy had used it at Cluny and Vézelay mainly as a decorative motif to promote a feeling of height and elegance. Gothic architects, however, pointed their arches to raise the crowns of the intersecting ribs of the vaulting to a uniform height so as to achieve greater structural stability (see Fig. 7:8). By the ever-increasing skill with which they used this device, they were able to achieve a constantly increasing height, which, in turn, led to loftier vaults and more ethereal effects.

When all these various devices came together in a working relationship, Gothic architects were able to bring the inert masses of masonry into an active equilibrium of weights and balances. Gothic architecture is thus a complex system of opposing thrusts and counterthrusts (see Fig. 7:9) in which all parts exist in a logical relation to the whole. The weight and position of each stone had to be considered in terms of what was above and below it, so that its force could be properly transmitted along the various levels until that force eventually was grounded. If any part should give way, the entire structure would be endangered. It is all the more remarkable when one remembers that Gothic builders used mortar and concrete in the joinings only as reinforcement and as a kind

Fig. 7:10. Chartres Cathedral, *Cross Vaults*. Drawing by Paul Durand after wooden roof burned in 1836

Fig. 7:11. Chartres Cathedral, *South Porch*. 13th century

of structural insurance. Even if no mortar were used, the 122-foot arches would still stand simply by the calculated accuracy of the formula of stone upon stone.

This logic of interior and exterior supports could not always take into account the irregularity of the site. Over the years the ground might settle at certain points, or some of the piers and buttresses might be undermined by floods, thus putting the whole structure in danger. It also was impossible to make the vaults at such high levels heavy enough to withstand wind and weather. At Chartres and elsewhere, the thin-webbed masonry had to be protected by the addition of wooden roofs, which at Chartres actually burned several times without, however, destroying the vaults underneath (see Fig. 7:10). The builder of Chartres achieved such stability that his structure has never had to be reinforced, and it stands today substantially as it did seven centuries ago. Its sister church at Rheims has fared equally well by surviving the centuries, two fires, and an artillery bombardment in World War I. Gothic cathedrals, in fact, have so far borne out the hopes of people who desired to raise buildings that "have nothing to fear from fire till the day of judgment."

At Chartres, the wings of the transepts terminate in triple portals (Fig. 7:11) that surpass in size and magnificence those of the western façade. This section survived from the previous church and resembles the flat Romanesque portals.

Fig. 7:12. *Blanche of Castile and St. Louis.* Illuminated Manuscript. *c.*1226–1234. Pierpont Morgan Library, New York

The portals in the 13th-century style, however, are enframed by row upon row of richly sculptured receding archivolts that bring a maximum of light and shadow into play. Here also the plan will reveal that Gothic builders were not bound by the laws of symmetry, since the north and south porches are of different size and proportion. The shape of such sections was partly determined by the tastes of individual donors. The north transept with its portals, porch, and stained glass was the gift of the royal family of France, especially of Blanche of Castile and her son St. Louis (Fig. 7:12), while its southern counterpart was donated by their arch-rival, the Duke of Brittany. When the cathedral was dedicated in the year 1260, Louis himself was present with such an assembly of bishops, canons, princes, and peasants as had rarely been seen.

Beyond the transepts extend the spacious choir and sanctuary, which are surrounded by a double-aisled ambulatory that gives easy access to the apse and its crown of radiating chapels. The increasingly ornate Gothic liturgy demanded the participation of more and more clergymen, and the cavernous recesses of the huge structure were needed to accommodate an ever-growing number of choristers. The apsidal chapels are also a distinctive feature of a developed Gothic plan, so that pilgrims could have access to the various altars where the venerated relics of saints were kept. The Cathedral of Notre Dame at Chartres, as well as earlier churches that stood on the same site, was closely associated with the cult of the Virgin Mary. Its most renowned relic was the legendary veil of the Virgin which, by tradition, had been presented to Charlemagne by the Byzantine Empress Irene. Another chapel enshrined the skull of Saint Anne, the Virgin's mother, which was brought back by crusaders and given to the church in 1205. This relic explains the many representations of Saint Anne in the statuary and stained glass, and the pilgrimages in her honor were second only to those of the Virgin. The most important chapel in Gothic cathedrals was the Notre Dame, or Lady chapel, devoted to Mary. It was usually placed in the center of the apse on the main axis of the nave, with chapels of other saints grouped on either side. All these considerations caused the parts beyond the transepts to expand to unprecedented proportions.

Gothic interiors need little more decorative detail than the vertical lines of the structural members, the variety of representations in stained glass, and, above all, the flow of light. At Chartres, the lighting is so organized as to achieve a gradual crescendo from the dark violet and blue lancets and rose window in the west through the brighter tones of the aisle and clearstory windows of the nave, past the flaming reds of the transept rose windows to the high intensity of the five red and orange lancets in the apse, which soar above the altar and capture the rays of the morning sun. Romanesque churches were lighted mainly from within by lamps and candles, while Gothic interiors are illuminated by sunlight transformed through stained glass into a myriad of mysterious prismatic colors. The interior masses and voids become activated and etherealized by the directional flow of light, and material and immaterial elements fuse into a glowing harmonious whole.

SCULPTURE OF CHARTRES CATHEDRAL

As important to the medieval mind as the structure itself was the choice and location of the sculptural and pictorial representations that were to give the church its significance and meaning. In a Romanesque monastic church, these were found in the carved tympanums over the narthex portals, on the capitals of the columns throughout the interior, and in wall paintings, especially in the apsidal end. Since such representations were designed for those leading cloistered lives, they gravitated toward the interior, and the variety and subtlety of their subjects make it clear they were meant to be pondered upon and carefully studied. Gothic sculpture was more popularly oriented and faced the outside world where it clustered around and over the porches and entrance portals. Inside, the columns rose too high to make specific subjects distinguishable. The shafts with their colonettes made the surfaces of the capitals too irregular to permit unified pictorial designs, and the eye would have been distracted when viewing them against the complex lines of the vaulting. Hence, the interior capitals at Chartres and in other Gothic cathedrals are decorated mainly with generalized patterns of leaves, fruits, and flowers. Instead of fanciful Romanesque trees of Paradise, they came closer to patterns in nature. When one Gothic bishop was called upon to explain their symbolism, he could come up with nothing better than that they represented "the fruits of good works that grow from the works of virtue." So to dismiss the hundreds of Gothic capitals shows they conveyed little meaning. Except for these foliated capitals, the only other interior sculpture at Chartres was a series of relief panels on the choir screen that separated the sanctuary from the ambulatory.

The intention of Gothic builders was to concentrate sculptural interest on the exterior where it was made an integral part of the architectural design. Both the proliferation of figures and the quality of their execution testify to the importance of sculpture in the art of the period. The exterior of Chartres has, in fact, well over 2000 carved figures, which are about evenly distributed between the west façade and the north and south porches of the transepts. Gothic sculpture, like the Romanesque, was done by journeymen craftsmen who gathered wherever a church was abuilding. From the enormous productivity of the period, it seems clear that the ranks of these craftsmen must have been numerous, and that the strokes of the sculptor's chisel on stone must have been a familiar sound. The Gothic sculptor has the advantage over his predecessors in having excellent stone models to follow rather than having to translate the lines of an illuminated manuscript into the stone medium. While the Romanesque sculpture tends to be more linear, as in the drapery of the tympanum figures at Vézelay (Fig. 5:11), the Gothic is more concerned with carving in depth; and the placement of the sculpture out of doors also made the play of light and shade more important. While the technique of the Gothic sculptor was undoubtedly superior, the standardization of the iconography in his time did not allow him quite so much imaginative freedom as his predecessor had enjoyed. Both periods, however, shared the inevitable ups and downs of school sculpture where the skill of some craftsmen far exceeds that of others.

The profusion of sculpture in a Gothic cathedral might lead to considerable confusion were it not for the close relationship of the sculptured forms to the architectural framework. The Gothic structure was so complete, so overwhelming, that no amount of decorative license would have been able to overshadow it; but the Gothic carvers had no intentions of going their separate ways, and their work was always conceived and executed in terms of the architectural frame or reference. Even so, the enormous number of examples would be bewildering were it not for some attempt to unify the iconography. Since it is a people's church, the cathedral cannot follow so consistent a system as that of an abbey, which was designed for a small group of people following a common ideal of life. Instead of single unified compositions, therefore, the Gothic cathedral went in for greater variety in order to provide something for every level of taste. At Chartres, most of the sculpture as well as the structure dates from the first half of the 13th century, and it is possible from the traditions and thought of that period to arrive at something of a general plan.

A Gothic cathedral, with the all-embracing activities it housed and the all-encompassing subject matter of its sculpture and stained glass, has often been likened to the comprehensive compendiums of law, philosophy, and theology written by medieval scholars. Cathedrals have also been described as the Bible in stone and glass, or the books of the illiterate; but they should not be overlooked as visual encyclopedias for the educated as well. The key to the iconography of Chartres is the encyclopedic character of medieval thought as found in the *Speculum Majus* of Vincent of Beauvais, who divided all learning into Mirrors of Nature, Instruction, History, and Morality. The Mirror of Nature is seen in the flora and fauna that are represented in comprehensive fashion; Instruction in the personifications of the seven liberal arts and the branches of learning taught in the universities; History in the story of mankind from Adam and Eve to the Last Judgment; and Morality in the figures depicting virtue and vice, the wise and foolish virgins, the saved and the damned in the Last Judgment, and in the hovering saints and angels and fleeing gargoyles and devils. There is also a recognizable sequence of presentation with a beginning on the west façade, where the story of Christ from his ancestors to the ascension is told; a middle on the north porch, where the history of Mary is traced along Old Testament lines from the creation of man to her death and heavenly coronation; and an end on the south porch, which takes up the drama of redemption from the New Testament, through the work of the church, its saints, popes, abbots, and bishops, to the climax of the final day of the universe at the Last Judgment. Each of the three porches has some 700-odd carved figures clustered in the three tympanums over the portals, the archivolts that enframe them, and the columns below and galleries above. In addition to the Scriptural scenes and lives of the saints, the designers found a place for ancient lore and contemporary history, for prophecy and fact, for fabulous animals and beasts of burden, for old wives' tales and the latest scientific knowledge, for portraits of princes and those of tradesmen, for beautiful angels and grotesque gargoyles (some of which function as water spouts to drain the roof, others as decorative motifs symbolizing demons fleeing from the sacred precincts of the church).

The iconography at Chartres stems from three principal sources: the dedication of the cathedral to Our Lady, a church privilege that was shared with such other Notre Dame cathedrals as those at Paris, Rheims, Rouen, and Amiens; its cathedral school, an important center of learning, for Mary was also the patroness of the liberal arts; and the preferences of such patrons as the royal family, lesser nobility, and local guilds who donated miscellaneous representations.

As the court of Mary, Queen of Heaven, her cathedral had to surpass in magnificence the grandeur that surrounded any mere earthly queen. Gothic chivalry and courtliness were rapidly replacing the might-makes-right code of Romanesque feudalism. And just as the clergy sang the praises of Notre Dame, so the knights of the castles lauded their ladies in particular and Our Lady in general. The high place of womanhood in secular circles is thus the courtly parallel of the religious cult of the Virgin. In poetry of the time, a knight's lady love is always the paragon of feminine virtue and charm. To woo and win her, he who aspired to her favor had to storm the fortress of her heart by techniques far more intricate and subtle than those needed to take a castle. When successful, he became the vassal of his mistress and she his liege lady to command him as she would. The concept of romantic love originated here in the Gothic period and came to full flower in the complex code of chivalry. With its exaltation of the position of women and its concern with the defense of the weak against the strong, it established the Western code of manners that is valid to this day.

The favorite reading in aristocratic circles ranged from Ovid's *Art of Love* of ancient Roman days to the contemporary *Romance of the Rose*. Included also were such stories as Tristan and Iseult, Aucassin and Nicolette, and the legends of King Arthur's court. Since such works were addressed mainly to the knightly class, they usually began with extended lists of the ancestors of the hero and heroine, and at Chartres their visual counterpart is found in such Biblical genealogies as those showing the kings and queens of Judah as the ancestors of Mary and Jesus. A law of precedence as rigid as any courtly etiquette was observed in the order of presentation and the location of these figures. Because the Old Testa-

Fig. 7:13. Chartres Cathedral, *West Portals*. 20′ 6″ high. *c*.1145–1170 (Archives Photographiques)

ment prophets, for instance, lived before the Christian era, they were placed in the shadows of the north porch, while the Apostles and personalities of the New Testament are in the sunlit south porch. Christ and Mary, as King and Queen of Heaven, are found over the central portals, while lesser figures range outward from them according to their importance. Such a vast amount of statuary would take volumes to describe, and the discussion here is limited to parts of the 12th-century Virgin portal on the west façade and its 13th-century counterpart on the north porch.

The central portal of the west façade (Fig. 7:13) is traditionally called the Royal Portal, and its tympanum encloses the figure of Christ in Majesty surrounded by the four symbolic beasts of the Evangelists and the 24 elders of the Apocalypse. The tympanum over the left portal depicts the close of Christ's days on earth and ascension, while on the right is the tympanum of the Virgin Portal (Fig. 7:14), depicting the beginning of His earthly life. The story is told in the simplest possible terms in three rising panels. Beginning in the lower left is the Annunciation, with just the figures of the Angel Gabriel and Mary; the next pair shows the Visitation; the Nativity is in the center; and the shepherds in the midst of their sheep (Fig. 7:15) are coming from the right for the Adoration, just as their successors came in from the fields near Chartres to worship at Mary's shrine. The middle band depicts the presentation of the young Jesus in the temple. His position on the altar foreshadows His later sacrifice. Friends approach from both sides bearing gifts. In the space above, the Virgin sits crowned and enthroned, holding her Divine Son and attended by a pair of archangels. She is shown frontally as a queen accepting the homage of the humble, who bow their heads as they enter her court through the portal below.

Of great interest are the figures symbolizing her attributes in the archivolts that frame the tympanum. Mary, like Athena of old, was the patroness of the arts and sciences. Albertus Magnus in his *Mariale* declared that the Virgin was perfect in the arts; and in his *Summa*, Thomas Aquinas includes among his propositions the question of "Whether the Blessed Virgin Mary possessed perfectly the seven liberal arts"—which, of course, was triumphantly affirmed. These representations are also reminders that this was an age which produced great scholars, and that intellectual understanding as well as faith was now one of the paths to salvation. The fact that Chartres was the location of one of the great cathedral schools is also brought out; and before the founding of the University of Paris, it shared with Rheims the distinction of being the best-known center of learning in Europe.

The curriculum of the cathedral school was, of course, the seven liberal arts, which were divided into the Trivium, which dealt with the science of words in the three subjects of Grammar, Rhetoric, and Dialectic; and the higher faculty of the Quadrivium, which was concerned with the science of numbers through the

Fig. 7:14 (*above*). Chartres Cathedral. West Façade, *Tympanum of Virgin Portal.* 1145–1170. (Fig. 7:15 (*right*). Detail, *Shepherds Led by Angel* (Houvet)

study of Arithmetic, Geometry, Astronomy, and Music. These seven arts are symbolized abstractly by female figures somewhat akin to the ancient muses, while below them are found their most renowned human exponents. Beginning with the lower left corner of the outside archivolt, Aristotle is seen dipping his pen into the inkwell. Above him is a thoughtful figure representing Dialectic. In one hand she holds a dragon-headed serpent symbolizing subtlety of thought, and in the other the torch of knowledge. Then comes Cicero as the great orator and over him the figure of Rhetoric making a characteristic oratorical gesture. The next pair are Euclid and Geometry, both of whom are deep in their calculations. In the same band, moving now from the top downward are Arithmetic and probably Boethius. Below them is the star-gazing figure of Astronomy, who holds a

Chartres Cathedral. West Façade, *Tympanum of Virgin Portal*, Details. 1145–1170. Fig. 7:16 (*left*). *Grammar*. Fig. 7:17 (*right*). *Pythagoras* (Houvet)

Fig. 7:18 (*left*). *Music* (Houvet)

bushel basket which signifies the relationship of her science to the calendar, so important in a farming district like Chartres. Ptolemy, to whom the medievalists ascribed the invention of the calendar and clock, is her human representative.

The figures on the lowest level are Grammar and Donatus, the ancient Roman grammarian. Grammar (Fig. 7:16) holds an open book in one hand and the disciplinary switch in the other over the heads of two young pupils, one of whom is laughing and pulling the other's hair. The last pair in the series of seven are adjacent to those in the inner archivolt. Below is Pythagoras (Fig. 7:17) the reputed founder of music theory, who is shown writing in medieval fashion with a desk over his knees, while on the wall behind him is a shelf holding a supply of pens and sponges for erasures. Above him is the figure of Music surrounded by instruments (Fig. 7:18). At her back is a monochord, used to calculate the intervals and for accuracy of pitch; on her lap is a psaltery; on the wall hangs a three-stringed viol; and she is striking the set of three chime bells, an allusion to the Pythagorean discovery of the mathematical ratios of the perfect intervals—the octave, the fifth, and the fourth. Both Gerbert of Rheims and his pupil Bishop Fulbert of Chartres are known to have taken an active interest not only in the theory of music but in its performance, and the two figures, showing Pythagoras as the thinker and Music as the performer, symbolize that Chartres was an important center for both the theoretical as well as the practical aspects of music.

A comparison of these figures representing the liberal arts with those on the north porch show how far intellectual inquiry had extended a century later. While the universities had absorbed the humanistic tradition of the arts as taught in the cathedral schools, they also included the study of theology, law, and medicine. So on the north porch are personifications of Philosophy (also by Aristotle); of Geometry, now coupled with Architecture and with Archimedes as their exponent; and of Medicine, represented by Hippocrates. In addition, there are some nonuniversity pursuits, such as Painting, personified by Apelles, Metalcrafts by Tubal-cain, and Agriculture by a group made up of Adam, Abel, and Cain.

Far more elaborate in scope and less restrained in decorative detail than the west façade is the incomparable north porch, which, with its three portals, stretches out to a width of 120 feet, thus spanning the transept completely. A gift of the royal family of France, its construction and decoration extended from the reign of Louis VIII and the regency of his queen, Blanche of Castile, through that of their son St. Louis, or roughly the first three quarters of the 13th century. It is dedicated to the Virgin and expands the theme of the Virgin Portal on the west façade to encyclopedic proportions. Her history from the annunciation and nativity through the childhood of Jesus is found on the left portal, while the scenes of her death and assumption are depicted on the lintel over the central door, and that of her enthronement and coronation in the tympanum above. Her

Chartres Cathedral. *North Porch*, Details. Fig. 7:19 (*left*). *Contemplative Life.* Fig. 7:20 (*right*). Trumeau of central portal, *St. Anne with Virgin. c.*1250 (Houvet)

attributes are revealed in the archivolts through series after series of cyclical representations, such as those of the 14 heavenly beatitudes and 12 feminine personifications of the active and contemplative life, one of the latter of which is seen in Figure 7:19. Especially fine is the single figure of her mother, St. Anne, holding the infant Mary in her arms, which adorns the trumeau of the central doorway (Fig. 7:20). From the harmonious lines of the folds of her drapery to the dignified and matronly face, the work is one of the most satisfying realizations of the mature Gothic sculptural style.

It will be noted from the contours of the south porch (Fig. 7:11) that the arches of the portals are now more highly pointed, and their enclosure by triangular gables further emphasizes their verticality. The deep recession of the porch allows for a much greater play of light and shade in the statuary that covers every available space from the bases of the columns to the peak of the gable. The figures on both the north and south porches, in comparison with the earlier ones on the west façade, have bodies more naturally proportioned; their postures show greater variety and informality; and their facial expressions have far more mobility. The representations of plants and animals are considerably closer to nature; and in comparison with the impersonality of those on the west front, many of the human figures are so individualized that they seem like portraits of living persons. In the change of style, however, they have forfeited something of the previous monumentality as well as the closer union with the architecture.

THE STAINED GLASS OF CHARTRES

Time has taken its inevitable toll of Chartres' exterior sculptures. The flow of carved lines remains, and the varied play of light and shade relieves the present monochrome gray. But only traces of polychrome and gilt are left to remind the observer that here was a feast of color with an effect that now has to be imagined. In the interior, however, where the stained glass remains undimmed, the full color of medieval pageantry still exists. The wealth of pure color in the 175 surviving glass panels hypnotizes the senses, and through the medium of polychromatic light something of the emotional exaltation that inspired medieval man to create such a temple to the Queen of Heaven can still be felt.

Here, as elsewhere, the structural and decorative elements are closely tied together, and, just as with the sculpture, the glass does not exist separately but only as an integral part of the whole. The designer was always aware of the size, proportion, and placement of his window in relation to the architectural setting. Glass is not usually thought of in the structural sense before the 19th and 20th centuries, but in medieval times and later it did have to fill a large architectural void while taking into account the pressure of wind and weather. This the designer accomplished mainly by dividing the space geometrically into smaller parts by the use of stone tracery as in the mullions, by parallel iron bars across the open expanse, and more minutely by the fine strips of lead that held the small pieces of glass in place. While Chartres must divide its architectural and sculptural honors with its neighboring cities, the town was especially renowned as the center of glassmaking, and the highest achievement of its glaziers, as exemplified in their own cathedral, made it in this respect incomparable.

All the visual arts must come to terms in their separate ways with the problem of light. Architectural exteriors must take sunlight into account; sculpture, whether in relief or in the round, demands an expressive use of light and shade; and painting, whether on a fresco or easel, must be done with an eye toward the reflection of light. In each case, however, the observer receives his impression by means of light refracted from an opaque surface. Only in the case of stained glass is the direct ray the primary concern of the artist. In this medium, he transforms his light prismatically through his colored glass and thus achieves a greater variety and intensity than is possible in any other medium, which accounts for the immediate appeal of his art to connoisseur and layman alike. The use of stained glass as wall panels allies it to the earlier use of mosaics, fresco paintings, embroidered wall hangings and tapestries. While the glazier's art was developed in Romanesque times, not until the earliest Gothic structure was built by Abbot Suger did stained glass receive a place in the iconography on a par with that of sculpture and painting. With the virtual disappearance of the walls and the great height of the vaulting in Gothic buildings, mural and ceiling painting was out of the question. Pictorial decoration, however, was needed more than ever before, if the stony logic of the piers and vaults were not entirely to dominate the gaunt interior. The window space consequently became the only available space for such decoration, and much of the expressive impact of Gothic art depended on the effectiveness of these luminous and translucent tapestries.

The great variety of jewellike color was achieved chemically by the addition of certain minerals to the glass while it was in a molten state. When cool, the sheets were cut into smaller sections, and the designer fitted them into his previously prepared outline. Pieces of various sizes next were joined together by lead strips. Details, such as the features in the faces, were then applied in the form of metal oxides and made permanent by firing in a kiln. Finally, the individual panels making up the pattern of the whole window were fastened to the iron bars already imbedded in the masonry. When seen against the light the glass appears translucent, while the lead and iron become opaque black lines that serve to outline the figures as well as to separate the colors and prevent blurring when viewed at a distance. Black and white reproductions can convey only the faintest idea of the brilliantly colored originals, and it should be noted especially that the black lines of the iron and lead become overaccented. It is nevertheless possible to observe from photographs the care with which the formal design and the details were executed.

The stained-glass artists shared with mosaicists and manuscript illuminators a distinct preference for two-dimensional designs. The dignified formality of their figures and the abstract patterns of the borders blended their work admirably into the architectural setting. By thus avoiding any hint of naturalistic effects, such as landscape backgrounds, and by concentrating on patterns of pure color and geometrical forms, they helped to promote the illusion of infinite space.

The iconographical plan of the glass at Chartres, like the exterior sculptures, is held together mainly by the dedication of the church as a shrine of the Virgin Mary. There is never any doubt on the part of those who enter that they are in the presence of the Queen of Heaven, who sits enthroned in majesty in the central panel of the apse over the high altar. Grouped around her in neighboring panels are the archangels, saints, and prophets, portraits of the noble donors, and symbols of the craftsmen and tradespeople, almost 4000 figures in all, who honor her and make up her court. Below, on her feast days, were the crowds of living pilgrims who gathered in the nave and chapels at her feet, and who aspired to come into her eternal presence one day as they had come into her shrine.

An interesting commentary on the changing social conditions of the 13th century can be read in the records of the donors of the windows. In the lowest part of each one is a "signature" indicating the individual, family, or group

Chartres Cathedral. Stained Glass Windows, Details. *c.*1250. Fig. 7:21 (*left*). *Bakers.* Fig. 7:22 (*right*). Furriers (Houvet)

Fig. 7:23 (*right*). *Wheelwrights and Barrel-makers* (Houvet)

who defrayed the great expense of the glass. Only a royal purse was equal to a large rose window, while the lancets of the nave and choir were within the means of members of the aristocracy and the church hierarchy, such as bishops and canons. The status and prosperity of the medieval guilds of craftsmen and merchants, however, was such that the vast majority of the windows was donated by them. While the royal family of France and the Duke of Brittany were content with the wings of the transepts, the most prominent windows of all, the 47-foot-high center lancets of the apse, were given by the guilds; and the one over the high altar toward which all eyes were drawn was the gift of the bakers. Each guild had a patron saint, and a window under a guild's patronage was concerned with the life and miracles of its special saint. In the case of the nobility, the family coat of arms was sufficient to identify the donor, but with a guild the "signature" took the form of a craftsman engaged in some typical phase of his work. Some 19 different confraternities are represented in the windows at Chartres, including the bakers (Fig. 7:21), the furriers (Fig. 7:22), and wheelwrights and barrel-makers (Fig. 7:23).

The great rose window of the west façade dates from the early 13th century and thus is contemporary with the majority of examples in the rest of the church. The three lancets below it, however, like the portals under them on the exterior, originally were part of the previous church. Besides being the earliest of all the windows, they are, by common agreement of the experts, also the best. Their origin has been traced to the school that did the windows for Suger's church at St. Denis, and their work was on the whole much finer grained and more jewellike, with infinite care lavished on the geometrical and arabesque patterns in the borders. They are dominated by their vibrant blue backgrounds, while the figures and abstract patterns are done in several shades of red, emerald green, yellow, sapphire, and white.

The great rose window of the north transept (Fig. 7:24), like the sculpture on the porch outside, glorifies the Virgin Mary. Together with its five lancets, the composition shares with the other glass of the 13th century a preference for red backgrounds instead of the earlier blue; the individual panes are larger; the borders are more conventionalized; and its greatest effect comes from the large splashes of warm color that contrast with the cool tones of the lancets of the west façade.

The art of stained glass thus replaced the mosaics and mural paintings of the early Christian and Romanesque churches, and is the ultimate stage in the etherealization of interior space. By giving form and meaning to light, the art of the glazier is perhaps better adapted to the expression of transcendental concepts than any other medium. By the transformation of raw sunlight into a spectrum of brilliant prismatic color, the architect gained complete control over his interior lighting, which he could cause to flow in any manner he willed. This material

Fig. 7:24. Chartres Cathedral. *North Rose Window*. Diameter 44′. 1223–1226
(Archives Photographiques)

control over an immaterial medium could then be placed at the disposal of the architects and iconographers to shape light to their structural, pictorial, and expressive needs. Something of the ecstasy felt by medieval man in the contemplation of the precious stones that adorned the altar and the jeweled glass of the windows is expressed in the following passage by Abbot Suger: "When the house of God, many colored as the radiance of precious jewels, called me from the cares of this world, then holy meditation led my mind to thoughts of piety, exalting my soul from the material to the immaterial, and I seemed to find myself, as it were, in some strange part of the universe which was neither wholly of the baseness of the earth, nor wholly of the serenity of heaven, but by the grace of God I seemed lifted in a mystic manner from this lower toward the upper sphere."

GOTHIC MUSIC

Massive and magnificent as the Gothic cathedral is, it can be conceived as the highest achievement of Gothic man only if associated with the various activities it was designed to house. Most important, of course, is the liturgy. As the space of the enclosed area increased, the cathedral grew into a vast auditorium that hummed with collective voices at communal prayer, resounded with readings and the spoken word from the pulpit, and reverberated with the chanting of solo and choral song from the choir.

Since no direct performance tradition links Gothic music with that of the present, it must be reconstructed from the meager signs on manuscript pages and from literary descriptions and visual representations of the period. Gothic music, therefore, is today something like a frame without a picture. Its approximate melodic and rhythmic structure are known; but since music comes to life only when performed, the melodic freedom, rhythmic flexibility, dynamic accentuation, as well as the parts known to have been improvised, must remain subjects of conjecture. One also has to take into consideration that, just as a statue or painting loses much of its significance when removed from its original architectural setting to a museum, so also does music suffer when transferred from the resonant spaces of the cathedral to a modern concert hall or recording studio. When heard in such settings, the stark intervals of the fifth and octave seem barren and hollow, and the dissonances somewhat harsh. The same works performed in a cathedral are alive and colorful. The long drawn-out tones reverberate against the irregular surfaces of the piers and vaults, resound through the cavernous vertical and horizontal expanses, and awaken the chants into a vibrant life all their own. In this way, Gothic music takes its place alongside the structural system, sculptural embellishments, and stained glass.

The Ile-de-France, site of the most significant developments in architecture of the 12th and 13th centuries, was also the scene of the most important musical innovations of the Gothic period. Specifically, this was the development of *poly-phonic*, or many-voiced, music and its union with the still universally practiced monophonic, or unison, art of Gregorian chant. Singing in parts was of northern origin in contrast to the prevailing Mediterranean style of singing in unison, and part singing in folk music apparently predates its incorporation into church music by several centuries. Just as the Gothic cathedral was the culmination in the long process of reconciling the northern urge for verticality with the southern horizontal basilica form, so Gothic music was the union of the northern tradition of many-voiced singing with the southern one-voice tradition.

The role of Chartres in these developments is obscure. John of Salisbury, the master of the cathedral school when the beautiful figure of Music was done for the west façade (Fig. 7:18), is known to have approved the theoretical study of music as a part of of the Quadrivium as heartily as he disapproved of certain innovations in the music performed by the choir there. Scholarly discussions about the mathematical ratios of musical intervals had been going on ever since antiquity, and such abstract problems as how the music of the spheres or an angelic choir would sound had been on the academic agenda ever since Boethius' time. It is therefore probable that at this time the greater progress was being made in the field of practical music which John so despised. According to William of Malmesbury, who died about 1142, Chartres was celebrated for its "many musical modulations," and one of the greatest 13th-century musical theorists, Franco of Cologne, is supposed to have been educated at Chartres. From actual documents and the surviving manuscripts, however, it is evident that the greatest forward strides were being made in the Cathedral School of Paris, known after 1163 as the School of Notre Dame.

School of Notre Dame in Paris

It has already been noted that, in the construction of the first Gothic church, the builder of St. Denis brought together many principles that had been developed separately elsewhere and for the first time used them in a systematic whole. The same was true of music, and Paris as the growing capital of the French kingdom was the logical place for the pieces to be fitted into a whole. The contrapuntal forms and textures developed in such monasteries as Cluny and in such cathedral schools as Rheims and Chartres, as well as the tradition of folk singing in several parts, were for the first time systematically organized in the School of Notre Dame in Paris. Again, as in the case of architecture, the man and the time can be fixed with certainty. The first great monument of Gothic music was the *Magnus Liber Organi* by Leonin, dating from *c.*1163 and which, as its name implies, was a great book bringing together a collection of music in two parts, arranged cyclically so as to spread over the entire calendar year.

In the traditional rendering of the Gregorian chant, some parts were sung by a soloist and answered responsorially by a chorus singing in unison. In the Gothic period, the choir still chanted in the way it had done for centuries, but the solo parts began to be performed simultaneously by two or more individual singers. The Paris cathedral, for example, employed four such singers. The distinction between solo voice and choir was hence replaced by the opposition of a group of individual singers and a massed chorus. With several skilled soloists available, the way was open for an art of much greater complexity than heretofore. Since the music, however, was still intended for church performance, it was mandatory that one of the traditional sacred melodies be used; and a special part called the *tenor*, a term derived from the Latin *tenere*, meaning to hold, was reserved for it. This melody was also known as the *cantus firmus*, or fixed song, implying that it could not be changed. The development of Gothic music was that of taking this *cantus firmus* as an established basis, and adding one by one the voices called in ascending order, the *duplum, triplum,* and *quadruplum.* Since these voices were superimposed one above the other, a definite verticality of concept is implied, which contrasted strongly with the horizontal succession of tones that characterized the older monophonic chant.

The earliest forms of Gothic polyphony are almost as rigid in their way as the old parallel organum of the Romanesque period, but they are based on the new principle of *punctus contra punctum,* literally note against note, or point counter point. *Mira Lege* (below) illustrates one of the strictest applications of this idea. The Gregorian melody is in the lower part, while the counterpoint above moves as much in opposition to it as possible. While parallel movement is not against the rule, and from time to time does occur, contrary motion is preferred. A treatise written at the beginning of the 12th century declares: "If the main voice is ascending, the accompanying part should descend, and vice versa." The name given to this newly created melodic line was the *discantus,* or discant, referring to the practice of singing against the established melody, a practice that has continued in religious and secular music ever since.

Mira lege (12th-century Discant)   (After Coussemaker)

Mi - ra le - ge, mi - ro mo - do, De - us for - mat ho - mi-nem

In addition to such examples, Leonin's *Magnus Liber* contains another type of counterpoint known as *organum duplum*. The Gregorian *cantus firmus* is found in the lower part, but the individual tones are stretched out to extraordinary lengths. The discanting, or duplum voice, moves now in free counterpoint consisting of florid melismas over what has in effect become a relatively fixed base.

Duplum (*c.*1175)   In Leonin's style

The greater melodic and rhythmic freedom that the discant now assumed called for expert solo singers, and much of the discanting of Gothic times is known to have been improvised. The practice of such a freely flowing melodic line over a relatively fixed bass points to a possible origin in one of the old types of folk singing. Survivals are found in the instrumental music of the Scottish bagpipers, where such a tune as "The Campbells Are Coming" is heard over a droning bass note. In performance, the slowly moving tenor, or *cantus firmus*, may have been sung by the choir, while the soloist sang his freely moving duplum part over it; or the tenor may have been played on the organ, as the instrument is known to have been in use at this time. The organ keyboard was a 13th-century Gothic innovation, and the numerous pictures from the period point to the wide usage of organs. The term "organ point," furthermore, is still used to refer to a musical passage in which the bass tone remains static, while the other parts move freely over it.

The next most significant development was the addition of a third part above the other two, which was known as the *triplum*, and from which the term treble is derived. This step is associated with the name of the first practicing musician in history to have the attribution of greatness attached to his name. He was Magister Perotinus Magnus, or Perotin the Great, active in Paris in the late 12th and probably the early 13th century. In his revision of the work of his predecessor Leonin, Perotin moved away from polyphonic improvisational practices toward an art based on stricter melodic control and clearer rhythmic articulation. By thus achieving a surer command of his materials, and evolving a logical technique for manipulating them, he was able to add the third voice to the original two, and in two known instances even a fourth. The three-part motet, like its predecessors, still had its *cantus firmus* in the tenor, which was the lowest part and held the *mot*, or word, from which the term *motet* is probably derived. Over it the contrapuntal voices wove a web of two different strands, singing their independent melodic lines. In the hands of Perotin the three-part motet became the most favored and characteristic style of Gothic music, and the form dominating 13th-century musical developments.

Triplum (13th century)

In Perotin's style
(After Yvonne Rokseth)

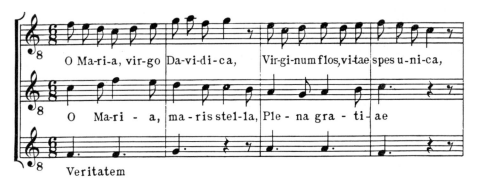

Besides achieving ever greater melodic independence, the two contrapuntal voices even had their own separate texts. A three-part motet thus had three distinct sets of words—the tenor, with its traditional line, and usually two contemporary hymnlike verses over and above it—which were sung simultaneously. Intended as they were for church performance, the words customarily were sung in Latin. However, around the middle of the 13th century, it was not uncommon for one of the contrapuntal voices to have its verses in French. With the entrance of the vernacular language came also popular melodies, so that above the stately tenor, it was possible to have a hymn to the Virgin in Latin and a secular love song in French all going on at the same time. By the simple expedient of replacing the sacred melodies by secular tunes, a fully developed musical art independent of the church was not only possible but by the end of the 13th century was an accomplished fact.

Gothic music exists in such close unity with other manifestations of the Gothic style that it can scarcely be understood as a thing apart. The subjects of the new hymns, especially those with the words of St. Bernard and the melodies of Adam of St. Victor, were mainly praise of the Virgin, just as were the dedications of the cathedrals and the iconography of the sculpture and stained glass. Instead of a monolithic choir chanting in unison or in parallel organum, the Gothic listener now heard a small group of professional singers. In the case of a three-part motet, he could choose, according to his temperament or mood, to follow either the solemn traditional tenor melody, the Latin commentary above it, or the French triplum in his own everyday mode of speech. This allowance for diversity of musical taste is a part of the general shift from the homogeneity of monastic life in the abbey to the heterogeneity of city life, of which the cathedral is the expression. The new melodic, rhythmic, and textual variety implies a congregation made up of people from all walks of life, just as had been the case with the diversified imagery of the sculpture and stained glass.

Since the individual voices were superimposed one above the other, a concept of verticality, similar to the architectural developments, is realized. The ear, like the eye, needs fixed points to measure rises and falls. In the *Mira Lege* example, the intervals of the lower part established the point over which the discant moved in contrary motion. In the case of the *organum duplum*, it was the long sustained tone in the tenor against which the soaring upward and plunging downward movement of the melody could be heard. In addition to this linear impulse, all types of counterpoint achieve a sense of rhythmical progress by having a relatively static point against which the more rapid mobility of the other voices can be measured. Together with the several opposing melodies, the clash of dissonant intervals, the simultaneous declamation of separate texts, as well as the progress of several independent rhythms, Gothic music was able to build up a sense of mounting tension that set it apart as a distinctive new style.

IDEAS

In the century between the dedication of the great Romanesque abbey church at Cluny (1095) and the beginning of Chartres cathedral (1194), much more than a change in artistic styles had occurred. A mighty shift in social and political institutions and in basic modes of thought had taken place, and the resulting changes in church, secular, and artistic life brought into the open sharp divisions of opinion. Old conflicts, long damped by the power of the medieval theocracy, now burst into flames, and new ones broke out, fanned by the breaths of new voices clamoring to be heard. Intellectual disputes grew hot and acrid as emotional tensions deepened. In this critical situation, the rational processes of scholasticism were brought to bear on these divisive forces, and the Gothic is best understood as a clashing and dissonant style in which opposite elements were maintained momentarily in a state of uneasy equilibrium. With the eventual dissolution of the scholastic synthesis in the following century, the basic oppositions became so irreconcilable that they led in some cases to the battlefield, in others to schisms within the church, and generally to growing philosophical and artistic clashes.

Gothic Dualism

Politically, the age-old struggle of church and state, evidenced in Romanesque times by the interminable quarrels between popes and Holy Roman emperors, now shaped up as the conflict between traditional ecclesiastical authority and the growing power of northern European kingdoms, especially France and England. Simultaneously came the beginning of a split between the internationalism of the church and Holy Roman Empire and rising nationalistic consciousness that produced centuries of rivalry between the south and north for the domination of Europe.

The prevailing monastic and feudal organizations of Romanesque times had tended to separate society into widely scattered units of cloister and manor, thereby isolating many of the causes of social strains. But as the towns began to grow into cities, the disparate elements were brought together in a common center where problems became more acute. Tensions mounted between the landed aristocrats on the one hand and the volatile urban groups on the other, between the monastic orders and the growing secular clergy. And towns witnessed at close range the bitter rivalries between abbot and bishop, lord and burgher, clergy and laity. For the common people there were always the contrast between the squalor in which they existed and the luxury of their lords, bishops, and abbots; the poverty of their daily lives and glowing promises of heavenly glory in the beyond; between the strife of their world and the visions of serenity and peace in the next. The arts were torn between expressing the aspirations of this world and those of the next, and the artist, between accepting a relatively anonymous status in the service of God and competing actively with his fellows in search of worldly recognition. Instead of the comparative unity of artistic patronage in the aristocratically oriented Romanesque period, patronage in the city was now divided between the social groups of aristocrats and clergy on the one hand and the increasingly important bourgeoisie and guilds on the other.

In architecture, be it the interior or exterior of the Gothic cathedral, one has an awareness of the opposition between the masses and voids, the interplay of thrust and counterthrust, and of the principle of attraction and repulsion that awaken dead weights into dynamic forces. In sculpture, the conflict of the particular and universal is seen in the remarkable feeling for human individuality in some of the separate figures and the iconographic necessity of molding them into the dignified impersonality required of a row of prophets and saints. In literature, the opposition between Latin and the vernacular languages becomes as evident as the growing distinction between the sacred and secular musical styles. Within the province of the tonal art are found such external disparities as the fruitless academic discussions about the hypothetical nature of the music of the spheres and the increasing importance of the actual sounds heard in the choirs of the churches; the abstract study of theoretical acoustics in the universities and the practical art of writing and making music. Here too are found the awareness of such internal differences as the singing of monophonic choruses alternately with groups singing polyphonically, the contrast between voices and instruments, the flow of horizontally moving melodic lines versus their simultaneous vertical aspects, the juxtaposition of consonance and dissonance, the rhythmical opposition between the independent voices within a polyphonic motet, line against line, *cantus* versus *discantus*—in short all the inherent oppositions of an art based on the principle of point counter point.

The Scholastic Synthesis

In the face of so many disparities, it seems only a step short of the miraculous that the Gothic style was able to effect a synthesis at all. Such dualities, however, generated the need for some sort of *modus vivendi*, and that this was achieved is yet another proof of the remarkable intellectual ingenuity and creative vitality of this period. The method for achieving this coexistence was that devised by scholasticism, a kind of pro-and-con dialogue followed by a resolution. Its results shaped up in the form of the Gothic monarchy, university, encyclopedia, *summa*, and cathedral.

On entering Chartres cathedral through the Virgin Portal, the worshiper was reminded by the personification of the seven liberal arts that faith needed to be enlightened by reason and knowledge. Architecture had to be a kind of logic in stone; sculpture and glass had to be encyclopedic in scope; and music, a form of mathematics in sound. All experience, in fact, had to be interpreted intellectually in contrast to the more intuitive and emotional orientation of the Romanesque. To the scholastic philosopher, God was primarily a rational force, Creator of a world based on principles of reason, and approachable through the power of the mind. Hence the key to the understanding of the universe was in the exercise of man's rational faculties. Philosophical truth or artistic value was determined by how logically it fitted a rationally ordered system.

Abelard's *Sic et Non* (*Pro and Con*) was an early manifesto of Gothic dualistic thinking. With unprecedented audacity, he posed one pertinent question after another, lined up unimpeachable authorities from the Scriptures and church fathers for and against the propositions. His purpose was to bring out into the open some of the wide cleavages of thought among sanctioned authorities, and he made no attempt at reconciliation. His scholastic successors debated whether ultimate truth was to be found through faith or reason, blind acceptance of hallowed authorities or evidence of the senses, universals or particulars, causes or effects, theses or antitheses, determinism or freedom of the will, intuition or reason. Thomas Aquinas and his fellow scholastics found the answer in the dialectical method; and Aquinas' synthesis, as found in his *Summa Theologiae* (*Summation of Theology*), was a comprehensive attempt to bring the entire Christian articles of faith together in a rational system. Abelard's pros and cons, and the divergent views of the previous 1000 years of speculation, were reconciled by a subtlety of intellect that has never been surpassed. Such a *Summa* was as intricately constructed as a Gothic cathedral and had to embrace the totality of a subject, systematically divided into propositions and subpropositions, with inclusions deduced from major and minor premises. Every logical syllogism was fitted exactly into place like each stone in a Gothic vault; and if one of the premises were disproved, the whole structure would fall like an arch without its keystone. Thomas Aquinas' *Summa* mounts the heights of philosophical grandeur, just as the vaults of the cathedrals reached the summit of engineering skill.

From this highly rationalistic viewpoint followed the scholastic definition of beauty, which, according to Thomas, rested on the criteria of completeness, proportion, harmony, and clarity—because, he said, the mind needed order and demanded unity above all other considerations. Mathematical calculation and symbolism therefore played an important part in the thought of the time, though it was sometimes more closely allied with the sort of Pythagorean number-magic now associated with numerology than with the purely logical processes of mathematics in the modern sense. The number 3 was especially favored because of its association with the Trinity; 4, to a lesser extent because it signified the material elements of fire, air, earth, and water; 7, as the sum of the two, indicated man, since his dual nature was composed of both spirit and matter; and their product pointed to such groups as the 12 Apostles, 12 lesser prophets, and so on. Since the sacred number was 3, it was used by most of the over-all formal divisions, with the encyclopedias and the *Summas* each having three divisions; the syllogism, in three parts; the façades of cathedrals, three portals and the sculptural tympanums above, three rising bands. Naves have a main and two side aisles; vertically, they ascend in the triple division of nave arcade, triforium gallery, and clearstory; and in the clearstory, each bay at Chartres had two lancets and one rose window, and so on. The triple rhyming plan of the Latin poetry as in the *Dies Irae* (Ch. 8, p. 311) and in the *terza rima* will serve as literary examples. In music, the favorite Gothic form was the three-part motet, and the prevailing rhythm was ternary, which was called *tempus perfectum* because of its Trinity symbolism, while binary rhythms were ruled out because they were considered too worldly.

In the cathedral schools and later in the universities, music was studied mainly as a branch of mathematics. Bishop Fulbert of Chartres emphasized theory in the training of singers, saying that without it "the songs are worthless." His view was generally held throughout the Gothic period, and as one theorist put it, a singer who is ignorant of theory is like "a drunkard who, while he is able to find his home, is completely ignorant of the way that took him home." Mathematical considerations, in fact, led composers to emphasize the perfect intervals of the octave, fifth, and fourth for theoretical reasons more than for the agreeableness of sound. The whole tendency was to suppress sensuous beauty of tone and emphasize the mathematical, theoretical, and symbolic aspects of the art.

The rise of the monarchies in France and England and the accompanying centralization of civil authority was an attempt to overcome the diversification of feudal power with its inevitable provinciality. A political resolution between king and nobles, and between nobles and commoners, was made in the English Magna Charta that established the basis for parliamentary government, and in France the establishment of a working relationship between the king and the urban middle classes accomplished approximately the same purpose. Louis IX of France even found a way of maintaining cordial relations with the papacy in so successful a manner as to bring him posthumously the crown of sainthood. The undertaking of the fantastic crusades was found to be a way of uniting many opposing European factions in a cause against a common enemy. The code of chivalry was a definite attempt to reconcile the opposition between idealistic love and the gratification of the senses and, more broadly, to establish a standard of behavior between strong and weak, lord and peasant, oppressor and the oppressed. Externally the university was set up as an institution to bring together all the diverse disciplines and controversial personalities and to fit all the various intellectual activities into a single universal framework. Internally, scholasticism became the common mode of thought, and its dialectic, the method of solving intellectual problems. In the cities, the guild system of apprentice-ships and examinations maintained a high standard of quality and craftsman-ship. The structural uniformity of Gothic vaulting and buttressing was, in effect, the Gothic builder's answer to Romanesque experimentalism. Ample allowance for urban heterogeneity was made in the iconography of the individual cathedral and in the differences of cathedrals from town to town, where each had distinc-tive character. Both internally and externally, Gothic architecture tried to syn-thesize the building with the space surrounding it. Externally, the eye follows the multiplicity of rising vertical lines to the spires and pinnacles and then to the sky. Inside, the experience is similar; the vertical lines rise to the window levels and thence through the glass to the space beyond. In contrast to the monastic church that was based on the notion of excluding the outside world, the Gothic cathedral attempted an architectural union of the inner and outer world as the exterior and interior flowed together through the glass-curtained walls. The thrust and counterthrust of the interior vaulting was paralleled on the outside by that of pier and flying buttress; the sculptural embellishments of the exterior were

Fig. 7:25. Gothic Half-timbered House. 15th century. Rouen

repeated in the iconography of the glass in the interior. Through the medium of stained glass, the iconographers endowed light with meaning and transformed physical light into metaphysical.

The various European languages and dialects found a place for themselves in secular literature, but Latin was championed by the church and universities as the universal language of scholarship. In music, the Latin and vernacular were reconciled in the polytextual motet; and when one language was used, the same form provided a highly ingenious method by which an authoritative text was declaimed, while at the same time one or more running commentaries upon it were presented. Gothic music also represented a synthesis of theory and practice functioning together as equals. Through all these separate manifestations the Gothic spirit was revealed, whether in the systematic logic of St. Thomas, in the heightened sense of time and movement achieved by the musicians, or the visual aspirations and linear tensions of the builders.

No one of these resolutions was in any sense final, and the Gothic style must, in the last analysis, be viewed as a dynamic process rather than an end result. By contrast, a Greek temple or even a Romanesque abbey is a completed whole, and the observer's eye in both cases can eventually come to rest. The appeal of the Gothic lies in the very restlessness that prevents this sense of completion. The observer is caught and swept up in the general stream of movement, and from the initial impulse, he gets the desire to continue it. The completion, however, can only be in the imagination. There were, in fact, no finished cathedrals; each lacked something, from a set of spires in some cases to a nave as at Beauvais. Vincent's encyclopedia and St. Thomas' *Summa* were likewise never completed.

Gothic unity is therefore to be found mainly in such methods and procedures as its dialectic in philosophy, structural principles in architecture, and techniques of writing in literature and music. No more effective processes could have been devised to deal with the specific incongruities with which the Gothic mind had to contend. They were, in fact, the only ways to reconcile the seemingly irreconcilable, to arrive at the irrational by ingenious rational arguments, and to achieve the utmost in immateriality through material manifestations. The object of Gothic thought was thus to work out a method for comprehending the incomprehensible, for pondering on the imponderables, for dividing the indivisible. Gothic art as a whole was designed to bridge the impossible gap between matter and spirit, mass and void, natural and supernatural, inspiration and aspiration, the finite and the infinite.

(*Opposite*). Benozzo Gozzoli. *Journey of the Magi*, Detail. Fresco. c.1459–1463. Medici-Riccardi Palace Chapel, Florence (Soprintendenza)

Part 3
THE RENAISSANCE

CHRONOLOGY:
Italian Panorama, Late 13th and 14th Centuries

General Events

1140	Guelph and Ghibelline wars began
1182– 1226	St. Francis of Assisi
	1210 founded Franciscan order (confirmed by pope, 1223)
	1225 wrote *Canticle of the Sun*
	1228 St. Francis canonized
	1229 Thomas of Celano's first *Life of St. Francis*
	1247 Thomas of Celano's second *Life of St. Francis*
	1262 St. Bonaventura's *Life of St. Francis*
	1322 *Little Flowers of St. Francis*
1198– 1216	Innocent III, pope; church reached pinnacle of power
1228– 1253	Basilica of St. Francis built at Assisi
1252– 1273	Great Interregnum
c.1260	Pulpit in Pisa Baptistry finished by N. Pisano
1278– 1283	Campo Santo at Pisa built by G. Pisano
c.1296– 1300	Giotto painted frescoes on life of St. Francis at Assisi
c.1305– 1309	Giotto painted frescoes on history of the Virgin at Padua
1309– 1376	Popes resided at Avignon
1310	First *Compagnie dei Laudesi* founded in Florence
1314– 1321	*Divine Comedy* written by Dante Alighieri
1316	*Ars Nova*, musical treatise, by Philippe de Vitry
c.1320	Giotto painted Bardi Chapel frescoes in Santa Croce, Florence
1330– 1339	Bronze doors of Baptistry at Florence cast by Andrea Pisano
c.1334	Andrea Pisano and Giotto collaborated on sculpture for Florence Campanile
1348	Black Death swept Europe
1348– 1352	*Decameron* written by Boccaccio
c.1350	*Triumph of Death* painted in Campo Santo at Pisa by Traini
c.1354	*Triumph of Death* written by Petrarch
1378– 1417	Great Schism between rival popes

Philosophers

c.1214– 1294	Roger Bacon, Franciscan monk and scientist
c.1225– 1274	Thomas Aquinas, scholastic philosopher
c.1270– 1347	William of Occam, Franciscan monk and nominalist philosopher

Painters

1240–c.1302	Cimabue
c.1255– 1319	Duccio, leader of the Siennese School
c.1266–c.1336	Giotto
c.1285– 1344	Simone Martini of Siena
1305– 1348	Pietro Lorenzetti active
1323– 1348	Ambrogio Lorenzetti active
1321– 1363	Francesco Traini active

Sculptors

c.1205– 1278	Niccolo (d'Apulia) Pisano
c.1250–c.1317	Giovanni Pisano
c.1270– 1349	Andrea Pisano

Writers

1265– 1321	Dante Alighieri
1304– 1374	Petrarch
1312– 1353	Boccaccio

Musicians

c.1200–c.1255	Thomas of Celano
1306	Jacopone da Todi died
1291– 1361	Philippe de Vitry
1325– 1397	Francesco Landini, organist-composer at Florence

8

THE EARLY ITALIAN RENAISSANCE STYLE

ITALIAN PANORAMA, 14TH CENTURY

The opposing forces that the Gothic 13th century had managed to maintain in a state of uneasy equilibrium by the application of scholastic logic and strict structurality broke out in the 14th century into open conflict. Like a stormy landscape, Italy was alternately chilled by the winds of a waning medieval winter and warmed by the first breaths of a waxing Renaissance spring. Gothic cathedrals were still being built in the north, while the dormant beauty of classical art was being revived in the south. Thunderous threats of fire and brimstone and fear of the Lord were hurled from church pulpits one day, to be followed by comforting Franciscan parables and assurance of divine love and mercy the next. Professors in universities still argued with the icy logic of scholastic philosophy, while the followers of St. Francis were persuading people with simple human truths. Some painters designed images of doomsday filled with warring angels and demons, while others portrayed Biblical stories as seen through the eyes of simple folk. And people wondered whether the world they lived in was a moral trap set by the devil to ensnare the unwary or a pleasant place a benign Creator meant them to enjoy.

For a drama of such sweeping scope, no single city or center could serve as the stage. All Europe, in fact, was the theater for this many-faceted performance in which men and their arts were in a state of creative ferment. The old Ghibelline and Guelph wars, which had started as a struggle between the forces loyal to the Holy Roman Empire and the partisans of the popes, assumed a new shape in the 14th century. People were moving from the country to the towns, where the entrenched landowning aristocrats rallied around the Ghibelline banner, and the growing ranks of city merchants and guilds of craftsmen raised the Guelph flag.

The new Franciscan and Dominican orders rarely kept to their cloisters but took to the highways and byways as preachers to all who would gather and listen. Internal church dissensions were such that even the popes had fled their hereditary see in Rome to hold court in widely scattered residences, most notably at Avignon in southern France. Writers, such as Dante and Petrarch, became exiles from their native cities, and their words were written during extended sojourns in half a dozen centers. Like them, the great painters were journeymen, traveling to wherever their commissions called them. Giotto, the leader of the Florentine school, did fresco cycles that occupied him several years each in Rome, Assisi, and Padua as well as in his home city. Simone Martini painted a chapel of St. Francis' church in Assisi and another in the papal palace at Avignon. The great sculptors of Pisa worked also in Siena, Florence, Padua, and Arezzo. Musicians likewise sought their fortunes at various courts, and French influences and musical forms came to dominate the Italian musical scene. Artistic idioms in general showed wide variation, with local styles springing up in such centers as Venice, Pisa, Siena, and Florence, while an international style took shape at Avignon where the papal court attracted the best talents from every country.

In this state of flux a large center like Rome was less representative than the little village of Assisi in the Umbrian hills of central Italy. No artist could have survived indefinitely in this provincial location, and a town of such small size would have been too insignificant to support a major art movement had Assisi not been the birthplace of one of the most beloved of medieval saints. But after the completion of the great pilgrimage basilica in the mid-13th century, many of the outstanding artists of the age gathered there as journeymen to decorate its walls.

The town of Assisi was built upon a rocky hill in the midst of a countryside more austere than lush. A more mountainous terrain might have nurtured a rugged spirit capable of bringing down some new commandments from above, but instead, the gentle rolling green hills brought forth the most humble of

Christian saints. A larger city might have produced a great organizer of men, capable of moving the minds of the many with his clever speech to bring about a new social order. Francis of Assisi, however, recognized the dangers of bombastic oratory and the transient nature of all forms of social organization, and he accomplished his mission with the sweet persuasion of simple parables and the eloquence of his own exemplary life.

While the mature life of St. Francis fell within the 13th century, the collection of tales that made him a living legend, as well as the full development of the Franciscan movement, belongs to the 14th. The clergy who received their training in the universities and the scholarly orders of monks had never reached a broad segment of society. The Franciscans, however, found a way into the hearts and minds of the multitudes by preaching to them in their own vernacular and in the simplest terms, and Franciscan voices were heard more often in village squares than in the pulpits of the churches. The essence of the Franciscan idea is contained in the mystical marriage of the saint to Lady Poverty, the subject of one of Giotto's frescoes. When a young man approached Christ and asked what he should do in order to have eternal life, the answer

Fig. 8:1. Franciscan Monastery and Town of Assisi, Air View (Alinari)

came, ". . . go and sell that thou hast, and give to the poor, and thou shalt have treasure in heaven: and come and follow me" (Matt. 19:21). St. Francis took this commandment quite literally, and in his last will and testament described his early life and that of his first followers. "They contented themselves," he wrote, "with a tunic, patched within and without, with the cord and breeches, and we desired to have nothing more. . . . We loved to live in poor and abandoned churches, and we were ignorant and submissive to all." He then asked his followers to "appropriate nothing to themselves, neither a house, nor a place, nor anything; but as pilgrims and strangers in this world, in poverty and humility serving God, they shall confidently go seeking for alms."

THE BASILICA OF ST. FRANCIS AT ASSISI

Had St. Francis' precept of complete poverty been followed closely, no great art movement could have developed at Assisi, since a building program involves the accumulation and expenditure of large sums. But immediately after his death, dissension on this point arose among those who had been closest to him. Brother Elias wanted to build a great church as a fitting monument to his friend and master, while others felt that Francis should be honored by following his simple life pattern as strictly as possible. Such a monument as Brother Elias had in mind would take a vast treasure to erect, and the majority of his fellow friars were shocked when he set up a porphyry vase to collect offerings from pilgrims who came to Assisi to honor the saint. Yet only two years after his death, at the very time when he was being canonized, a great basilica and monastery (Fig. 8:1) were begun on the crest of the hill where St. Francis had wished to be buried. Taking advantage of the contours of the natural site, the architects designed a structure that included two churches, a large one above for the pilgrims (Fig. 8:2) and a smaller one below for the Franciscan monks themselves. The twin churches seem to grow out of the hillside, the upper church resting like a crown on its brow, and it is this striking location rather than any great architectural distinction that gives the basilica its particular quality.

In spite of their comparatively large size, both churches are without side aisles, having just central naves terminating beyond transepts in polygonal apses. The large interior areas are spanned by spacious quadripartite groin vaults in the Lombard manner, which are partially supported by rows of columns set against the walls. Italian Gothic, contrary to the northern style, did not accent well-lighted interiors in which the walls were almost completely replaced with stained-glass windows. The southern sun made shade more welcome, and the interiors took on the character of cool retreats from the burning brightness of

Fig. 8:2. Upper Church of St. Francis. 1228–1523. Assisi

the world outside. The absence of a nave arcade and aisles, and the small number of stained-glass windows, allowed ample wall space in both churches for the brightly colored fresco paintings that cover them. Lighted principally by the clearstory, the walls of the upper church glow in the dim interior with a mild inner light all their own, illuminated as they are by scenes from the life of St. Francis. More than anything else, it is these murals that bring the twin churches their most special distinction, and the names of the artists who worked on them read like a roster of the great painters of the period: Cimabue and Giotto of the Florentine school and Simone Martini and Pietro Lorenzetti of the Siennese school.

GIOTTO'S FRESCOES

On entering the nave of the upper church at Assisi (Fig. 8:3), the observer encounters on its walls the series of frescoes on the life of St. Francis that tradition attributes to Giotto. The date generally assigned to the work is the four-year span just before the jubilee year of 1300. Knowing that pilgrims in unprecedented numbers would be traveling to Rome for the celebrations, the artists at Assisi made every effort to cover the bare walls in time. The frescoes for the friar's own Lower Church had to wait until the mid-14th century for completion.

Giotto, like other master artists of his period, had learned to work in a variety of techniques. In addition to his frescoes, he did mosaics, painted altarpieces in tempera on wood, and was also a sculptor. Several years before his death, he was named the chief architect of Florence, and it was in this capacity that he designed the bell tower of the cathedral (Fig. 9:1), still popularly called Giotto's Tower. Some of the sculptured reliefs on the ground-floor level of this campanile may have been his, and others were presumably carried out from his designs by Andrea Pisano. Giotto's greatest fame, however, rests most securely on the three fresco cycles in Assisi, Padua, and Florence.

The fresco medium calls for the rapid and deft strokes of a sure hand and for designs that harmonize with the architectural scheme and awaken the walls into a vibrant and colorful life. The artist first must make a charcoal drawing on the wall. Then, taking an area he can finish in a single day, he spreads a thin coat of wet plaster over the dry wall and retraces the charcoal lines underneath. Earth pigments are then mixed with water, combined with white of egg as a binder, and applied directly to the fresh plaster—hence the term *fresco*. The pigments and wet plaster combine chemically to produce a surface as permanent as that of any medium in painting. Artists sometimes paint over the surface after it is dry, but this repainting usually flakes off in time. If corrections are necessary, the whole surface must be scraped off and the section redone. Fresco, then, is a medium that does not encourage overly subtle types of expression; and it is best adapted to a certain boldness of design and simplicity of composition. The emotional depth, the communicative value, and the masterly execution of Giotto's cycles rank them among the highest achievements in world art.

The first two panels of the series at Assisi seem to have been painted by Giotto himself, but since Giotto worked with a corps of assistants, it is impossible to be completely certain these are actually his work. On the right, after one passes through the entrance portals, is the *Miracle of the Spring* (Fig. 8:4), while on the left is the well-known *Sermon to the Birds* (Fig. 8:15). The order of the scenes is psychological rather than chronological; and Giotto, it would seem, placed this pair nearest the entrance in order to impress pilgrims at the outset with the most popular Franciscan legends—those showing the saint ministering to the poor and humble on one side, and his kinship with all God's creatures, including his brothers the birds, on the other.

Fig. 8:3. Upper Church of St. Francis, *Interior*. Assisi (Gabinetto Fotografico Nazionale)

Giotto's literary source for the *Miracle of the Spring* is in the *Legend of the Three Companions*, which tells of the Saint's journey to the monastery of Monte La Verna. A fellow friar, a peasant, and his donkey accompanied him, but the way was steep and the day hot. Overcome by thirst, the peasant cried out for water. Kneeling in prayer, St. Francis turned to him saying: "Hasten to that rock and thou shalt find a living water which in pity Christ has sent thee from the stone to drink." Pilgrims entering the church, like the peasant, were athirst for spiritual refreshment, and the placement of Giotto's picture assured them that they had arrived at a spiritual spring.

Giotto's composition is as simple as it is masterly. St. Francis is the focal center of two crisscrossing diagonal lines like the letter X. The descending light from the rocky peak in the upper right reveals the contours of the mountain in a series of planes and reaches its greatest intensity in its union with St. Francis' halo, diminishing in his shadow where his two companions and the donkey stand. The dark mountain at the upper left moves downward toward the shadowy figure of the drinking peasant at the lower right, as if to say he is still in spiritual darkness. But since St. Francis is also on this diagonal line, the way to enlightenment is suggested. Giotto's inimitable mountains are found in such other of his major compositions as *Joachim Returning to the Sheepfold*, the *Flight into Egypt*, and the great *Pietà* (Fig. 8:16), all in the Arena Chapel at Padua. Structurally, the mountains advance and recede to form niches for his figures, and their hardness and heaviness is complementary to the compassion and expressiveness of his human beings. The mountains, or architectural backgrounds, do not exist in their own right but become volumes and masses in Giotto's pictorial designs as well as inanimate extensions of human nature. Giotto's spatial proportions, furthermore, are psychologically rather than actually correct. Human beings, in keeping with their greater expressive importance, loom large against their mountain backgrounds; and his scattered trees are more spatial accents than natural trees.

The *Sermon to the Birds* (Fig. 8:15) on the other side of the entrance is less dramatic and more lyrical. The incident, taken from St. Bonaventura's life of St. Francis, is the one in which the birds hovered around the Saint or perched in the bushes, inclining their heads as he spoke to them: "My brothers, the birds, much ought ye to praise your Creator, who hath clothed you with feathers and given you wings to fly, and hath made over unto you the pure air and careth for you without your taking thought of yourselves." The masterly touch is seen in the utter economy of means. Balanced by the massive stylized tree on the right, the two human figures contrast interestingly with each other. While St. Francis himself is intent on the birds, and his hands are raised in a gesture of blessing, those of his less-inspired companion are lifted as if he wished to shoo these little feathered brothers right out of the picture.

Fig. 8:4. Giotto. *Miracle of the Spring*. Fresco. *c*.1296–1300. Upper Church of St. Francis, Assisi (Alinari)

Fig. 8:5. Giotto. *St. Francis Renouncing His Father*. Fresco. *c*.1296–1300. Upper Church of St. Francis, Assisi (Gabinetto Fotografico Nazionale)

Perhaps the most dramatic of the series is *St. Francis Renouncing His Father* (Fig. 8:5) after a controversy involving worldly goods. In his haste to abandon the material world, Francis casts off his garments and stands naked before the townspeople saying: "Until this hour I have called thee my father upon earth; from henceforth, I may say confidently, my Father who art in Heaven, in whose hands I have laid up all my treasure, all my trust, and all my hope." The bishop then covers Francis with his own cloak and receives him into the church. The expressions of the various figures as revealed in their gestures and facial expressions make this fresco an interesting study of human attitudes. The angry father has to be physically restrained from violence by a fellow townsman, yet his face shows the puzzled concern of a parent who cannot understand his son's actions. His counterpart on the other side is the bishop, who becomes the new father of the Saint in the church. Disliking such a scene, his glance shows both embarrassment and sympathy. These opposing figures are supported respectively by the group of townspeople and the apartment house and the clergymen and church buildings. Here Giotto uses an interesting pictorial geometry to unify his picture and resolve the tension. The two opposing groups, symbolizing material pursuits and spiritual aspirations, become the base of a triangle; between them the hand of St. Francis points upward toward the apex where the hand of God is coming through the clouds.

A notable example of Giotto's late style is found in the *Death of St. Francis* (Fig. 8:6), the climax of a series of seven he did 20 years later for the Church of Santa Croce in Florence. The static horizontal lines of the recumbent body are relieved by the varied gestures of the surrounding groups, and with one exception all eyes concentrate on the head of St. Francis. The architectural framework echoes the disposition of the figures, with the horizontal line of the wall paralleling the body of St. Francis and the vertical lines, those of the standing figures. Within this setting a sense of depth is conveyed by color. The ermine collar and red robe of the kneeling figure at the Saint's right hand project him into the foreground; the neutral grays and browns of the habits of the monks back of the bier place them in the middle ground; and the deep blue sky recedes into the background. Here again Giotto uses a triangular pattern in telling his story. According to St. Bonaventura's biography, at the moment of Francis' death one of the brothers beheld a vision of the Saint's "soul under the likeness of a star exceeding bright borne on a dazzling cloudlet over many waters mounting in a straight curve unto Heaven. . . ." In the fresco, the sides of the triangle are the line carried upward from the Saint's head by the gesture of the disciple who sees the vision and the line formed by the inclining crucifix that meet at the apex where the heavenward journey is seen. Giotto thus ties the story content, emotional situation, and dramatic tension into a tight whole in his pictorial structure.

Fig. 8:6. Giotto. *Death of St. Francis*. Fresco. c.1318–1320. Bardi Chapel, Church of Santa Croce, Florence (Soprintendenza)

BEFORE AND AFTER THE BLACK DEATH

All went well in Italy during the first third of the 14th century. Townspeople prospered, life was good, the arts flourished. Beginning in 1340, however, a series of disasters befell the peninsula, starting with local crop failures and continuing with the miseries of famine and pestilence. The climax came in a fearful outbreak of bubonic plague in the catastrophic year of 1348. In this so-called "Black Death," more than half the populations of such cities as Florence, Siena, and Pisa perished. A chronicler of Siena, after burying five of his children with his own hands, said quite simply: "No one wept for the dead, because everyone expected death himself."

An event so cataclysmic, and one that spread over the entire continent, was bound to have a deep effect upon social and cultural trends. Many survivors found themselves suddenly impoverished or, through unexpected inheritances, vastly enriched. Thousands of residents in the relatively immune countryside flocked into the cities to take the place of those who had died. The psychological effect on the individual lives of the people was to quicken their normal instincts. For some, it was the "eat, drink, and be merry" philosophy, exemplified in Boccaccio's *Decameron*; for others, it was the moral recrimination and repentance, as seen in the purgatorial vision of the same author's later *Corbaccio*. Driven by fear and a sense of guilt, people felt that something had gone disastrously wrong and that the Black Death, like the Biblical plagues of old, must have been sent by an angry God to chastise mankind and turn him from his wicked ways. Both Boccaccio and Petrarch among the literary men turned to this view after their earlier more worldly writings, and what was true of literature was true also of painting.

The attitude before and after the Black Death is well illustrated at Pisa and Siena where important architectural, sculptural, and pictorial developments took place in the late 13th and early 14th centuries. The Cathedral of Pisa and its campanile (Fig. 5:26), the famous leaning tower, both date from Romanesque times. The Baptistry and Campo Santo, which complete the group, stem from the late 13th century. The Campo Santo (Fig. 8:7) a churchyard for burials, was designed and built by Giovanni Pisano in the form of a Gothic cloister. The garth, or open courtyard, derived much fame at the time because its soil had been taken from Mt. Calvary and transported to Pisa by the shipload.

In addition to his architectural activities, Giovanni Pisano and his father, Niccolo, were the two outstanding sculptors of their time. Niccolo Pisano, also known as Nicola D' Apulia because of his southern Italian origin, designed a handsome pulpit with six religious panels for the Baptistry at Pisa, while Giovanni some years later did one for the Cathedral. Both depict scenes from the New Testament. The differing attitudes of the father's generation and that of the son's are revealed when panels dealing with the same subject are placed side by side; together, their work represents the trend of sculpture before the Black Death.

Niccolo's panel of the *Annunciation and Nativity* (Fig. 8:8) is clearly influenced by the ancient sarcophagi the sculptor knew from his formative years spent near Rome. The Virgin appears as a dignified Roman matron reclining in a characteristic classical pose, while the angel at the left in the Annunciation section is seen against a classical temple and is dressed in a Roman toga as are many of the other figures. Niccolo employs the old simultaneous mode of narration, with the Virgin making three appearances on the same panel, and the relief as a whole is permeated by a monumental calm. Giovanni's work, as evidenced by his *Nativity and Annunciation to the Shepherds* (Fig. 8:9), moved away from his father's classicism into the French Gothic orbit. His figures are smaller in scale and more naturally proportioned to their surrounding space. Greater animation and agitation of line replace the serene repose of his father's style. The work of both father and son, however, has a sense of human warmth that closely resembles the spirit of Giotto's frescoes.

Nearby Siena, prior to the Black Death, was also enjoying a period of prosperity. Unlike its rival city Florence, which was a Guelph stronghold where power was held by the guilds and rich merchants, Siena was a staunch Ghibelline

Fig. 8:7. Giovanni Pisano. Campo Santo. 1278–1283. Pisa

Fig. 8:8 (*above*). Niccolo Pisano. *Annunciation and Nativity*. 1259–1260. Detail of Marble Pulpit, Baptistry, Pisa (Soprintendenza). Fig. 8:9 (*below*). Giovanni Pisano. *Nativity and Annunciation to Shepherds*. 1302–1310. Detail of Marble Pulpit, Pisa Cathedral (Alinari)

Fig. 8:10. Duccio. Maestà Altarpiece, Detail, *Madonna Enthroned*. Tempera on wood. Whole altarpiece 6′ 11″ x 13′ 10″. 1308–1311. Cathedral Museum, Siena (Gabinetto Fotografico Nazionale)

town dominated by landed aristocrats. These opposite dispositions led Florence in a more progressive direction and kept Siena as a bastion of tradition. Although contemporaries, the Florentine Giotto pointed toward the Renaissance, while the Siennese school—Duccio and his successors Simone Martini and the Lorenzetti brothers—continued in the Byzantine tradition that had been introduced into Italy through such centers as Ravenna and Venice many centuries earlier. Despite this conservatism, the Sienese school poured enough late-Gothic wine into the old medieval wineskins to bring about a brilliant, albeit final, flowering of Italo-Byzantine painting. In his *Maestà*, or *Madonna in Majesty* (Fig. 8:10), Duccio reveals himself as a master of graceful, elegant line. Seated on her marble throne and clothed in her gown of ultramarine blue (a costly pigment made of ground lapis lazuli), arranged in delicate folds that form a graceful linear pattern, the Madonna is seen against a gold-leaf background. The same aristocratic

Fig. 8:11. Simone Martini. *Annunciation*. Tempera on wood. 8′ 8″ x 10′. 1333 (Saints in side panels by Lippo Memmi) Uffizi, Florence (Soprintendenza)

aloofness is continued in Simone Martini's *Annunciation* (Fig. 8:11), but here the more active lines tell the story.

Ambrogio Lorenzetti's *Good Government* is one of two large-scale murals that decorate a room in the Palazzo Pubblico (Town Hall) at Siena. The subject is an allegory in which a noble king is enthroned amid such virtues as Justice, Wisdom, Concord, and Peace. In the detail (Fig. 8:12), one sees Siena where a wedding party is in progress (lower center), peasants are bringing produce to market (lower right), and the winding streets lead the eye above where workmen are completing the roof of a building. Borrowing much from Giotto but without his sense of drama, Ambrogio Lorenzetti's crowded scenes are more spacious than earlier Gothic paintings, but his whole composition still retains the gaily colored decorative quality of Gothic tapestries.

When Ambrogio and Pietro Lorenzetti perished in the Black Death of 1348, Siennese art entered a period of decline. The reaction to the great plague is well illustrated in the series of frescoes on the inner walls of the Campo Santo at Pisa. The theme is the Last Judgment, and Traini's *Triumph of Death* (Fig.

Fig. 8:12. Ambrogio Lorenzetti. *Good Government*, Detail. Fresco. 1338–1340. Palazza Pubblico, Siena (Anderson)

8:13) took its name from a poem by Petrarch. While no cause-and-effect relationship between picture and poem can be proved, both were reactions to the plague, both shared common attitudes of the time, and both were based on a similar theme.

The *Triumph of Death* is a grandiose utterance, with so much detail crowded into every square inch of space that something in it was bound to appeal to everybody. Like the sermons of the time, each part warned of the imminence of death, the terrors of hell if the soul were claimed by the devil, or the bliss of being carried off by the angels. The latter process, however, seems anything but peaceful, since the devils contend furiously with the angels for the spirits of the dead that appear as nude forms. The tug of war over the soul of the paunchy monk on the right side above the scene in the pleasure garden is a typical example. When the demons win, they cast their victims into the flames of the open volcano at the top. What happens to the souls saved by the angels is left to the imagination.

Death is beheld in the hideous guise of a blonde woman flying on enormous bat's wings and carrying a scythe like Father Time. She passes over the miserable creatures in the lower center who cry out to be relieved of their intolerable sufferings. Instead she is about to swoop down on the group of ten figures in the prime of their lives, who are reading, conversing, and enjoying the delights of the world. Everything dies in her wake, as seen in the piles of corpses beneath her; and the next two victims are being pointed out by the black-winged angels of

Fig. 8:13. Traini. *Triumph of Death*. Fresco. *c*.1350.

death who hover above the pair on the left of the group. One is a youth holding a falcon and the other a maiden fondling a dog in her lap. In Petrarch's poem, Death is also represented by a feminine form and the scene is similar.

> A lady clothed in black, whose stern looks were
> With horror fill'd, and did like hell appear,
> Advanced, and said, "You who are proud to be
> So fair and young, yet have no eyes to see
> How near you are your end; behold, I am
> She whom they fierce and blind and cruel name,
> Who meet untimely deaths; . . .

The likeness of the group in the pleasure garden to that in Boccaccio's *Decameron* seems too close to be a coincidence. The book tells of ten well-to-do

Destroyed 1944. Campo Santo, Pisa (Alinari)

young Florentines who escape from the plague, which is ravaging their city, to a country villa where they entertain themselves with lively tales, music, and dancing. As in the *Decameron*, the group in the fresco is composed of seven women and three men; all are animated by a vivacious spirit; and, as the description in Boccaccio's introduction goes: "Breakfast done, the tables were removed, and the queen bade fetch instruments of music; for all, ladies and young men alike, knew how to tread a measure, and some of them played and sang with great skill. So, at her command, Dioneo having taken a lute, and Fiametta a viol, they struck up a dance in sweet concert; . . ." The similarity of the group, even to those on the far right who are playing the musical instruments, indicates that the painter may well have had the *Decameron* in mind when he designed his fresco.

In the lower left, a group of mounted nobles are equipped for the chase, but instead of the quarry they are pursuing, they find only the prey of death. Inside the three open coffins serpents are consuming the corpses of the onetime great of the earth. Petrarch also speaks of death as the great leveler when he asks: "the Popes, Emperors, nor Kings, no ensigns wore of their past hight but naked show'd and poor. Where be their riches, where their precious gems? Their miters, scepters, robes and diadems?" Hard by is a bearded Anchorite monk unfolding a prophetic scroll that warns them to repent before it is too late. The only relief from this scene of horror and desolation is found in the upper left where some monks are gathered around a chapel busying themselves with the usual monastic duties. Apparently only those who renounce the world can find respite from its general turmoil and the terror of death.

The space allotted to the tortures of hell by Giotto in his *Last Judgment* at Padua is minimal, while in Traini's mural and in other doomsday pictures done after the Black Death, the stark horror is relieved only by such occasional tranquil scenes as the monastery chapel. The attitude is the reverse of the milder, more humanistic spirit of Giotto. Traini's designs, furthermore, are as complex and burdened with detail as Giotto's are simple. Traini also included allegories that go beyond the pictorial medium. The two angels behind the figure of Death, for example, unfold a scroll; the miserable ones petition Death in writing as well as in gesture; and the monk warning the hunting party does so with an inscription. Such details weigh down the picture with a heaviness quite foreign to Giotto's buoyant work and are apt to obscure the picture's meaning.

MUSIC AND LITERATURE

The *Dies Irae* and the *Canticle of the Sun*

The contrast between the dour, threatening medieval church worldview and the benign, joyful Franciscan spirit is illustrated by two 13th-century hymns. The facts of their composition alone are sufficient to point out the ideational cleavage of the period. The *Dies Irae*, which so admirably reflects the prevailing medieval spirit, was written by the great Latin stylist Thomas of Celano a few years before he met St. Francis and became one of his friars. The second, the *Canticle of the Sun*, is by St. Francis himself. Thomas of Celano entered the Franciscan order about the year 1215, enjoyed the friendship of St. Francis for several years, and was entrusted by Pope Gregory IX with the official biography that was written shortly after the Saint's canonization in 1228.

In the triple stanzas and 51 lines of the *Dies Irae*, the medieval Latin poetic style reaches its highest point. Its content invokes the vision of the final dissolution of the universe, the sounding of the angelic trumpets calling the dead forth from their tombs, and the overwhelming majesty of the coming of Christ as king to judge the quick and the dead. The grandeur of its language and the perfection of its poetic form are in every way equal to this solemn and awesome theme. The images and moods run a gamut from anger and terror to hope and bliss before coming to a close with a final supplication for eternal rest. Sir Walter Scott incorporated a part of the *Dies Irae* in his *Lay of the Last Minstrel*, but since his poem was based on a different metrical and rhyming scheme, he sacrificed the form of the original while preserving its content:

> That day of wrath, that dreadful day,
> When heaven and earth shall pass away,
> What power shall be the sinner's stay?
> How shall he meet that dreadful day?
>
> When, shrivelling like a parched scroll,
> The flaming heavens together roll;
> When louder yet, and yet more dread,
> Swells the high trump that wakes the dead,
>
> Oh! on that day, that wrathful day,
> When man to judgment wakes from clay,
> Be THOU the trembling sinner's stay,
> Though heaven and earth shall pass away. (Canto VI, xxxi)

Although the colorful alliterations and verbal rhythms of the Latin original have a music all their own, the *Dies Irae* is inseparable from a melodic setting in the mixed Dorian mode. While the melody cannot with certainty be attributed to Thomas of Celano himself, the close correspondence of tone and word makes it definite that they were at least from the same time. Both the poem and its melody found their way into the liturgy as a sequence that is still an indispensable part of the requiem mass for the dead. Sequences are so

Dies irae (Sequence, early 13th century)   Thomas of Celano

named because they follow the gradual and alleluia in the part of the mass between the reading of the epistle and the gospel. They attained wide popularity during this period and usually were sung by both congregation and choir.

The most characteristic Franciscan contribution to poetry and music is found in a body of informal spontaneous hymns called *laudi spirituali*—songs of praise, or simply lauds—traceable directly to St. Francis and his immediate circle. The practice of spontaneous hymn-singing continued from his time onward and in the 14th century was firmly established as the most popular form of religious music. Singing societies known as *Compagnie dei Laudesi*, companies of laudists, have existed up to the present time, mainly in Italy. Besides Provençal French, Francis had learned the songs of Provence from his mother, who was of an old family of that region, and the biography known as the *Legend of the Three Companions* recounts how he sang aloud the lauds and canticles while praying and how during his travels "the holy man sang praises in French with a voice loud and clear." Since this was the great period of the troubadours, when many of the best known of these lyric poets visited Italy, St. Francis certainly was well acquainted with their lyrics and music. By his knowledge of the forms of these Provençal poets and by his practice of bursting into rhapsodic verse in his own vernacular Umbrian Italian, he played a leading role in the new poetic movement. Significantly, he called himself and his companions who sang the lauds with him *jongleurs de dieu*, minstrels of God, thus identifying himself with the performing musicians of the people rather than the aristocratic writers of amorous verse.

In music, as in his religious work, St. Francis drew together the sacred, courtly, and popular traditions. The lauds were thus a poetic bridge between the traditional music of the church, the music of the castle, and the music of the streets. The words always had a religious theme; often they were mere paraphrases of psalms and litanies sung to popular airs, but, above all, they were music and poetry that the people could both sing and feel with their hearts. Contrapuntal choral music, whether it was in the form of a church motet or a secular madrigal, was a sophisticated musical medium that needed the voices of skilled professionals. By contrast, the lauds were folklike in spirit, simple and direct in their appeal, and sung either as solos or jointly with others in unison. Just as the highly trained monastic choir was characteristic of the Cluniac movement and the contrapuntal chorus the musical counterpart of the northern Gothic spirit, the lauds were the special expression of the Franciscans.

The *Canticle of the Sun*, known definitely to be by St. Francis himself, is at once the most sublime of all the lauds as well as the most original. The legend goes that when St. Francis was recovering from an illness in a hut outside the convent of St. Clare, the nuns heard from his lips this rapturous new song. The informality, even casualness, of its composition and its rambling rhythms and rhymes make it as simple and unaffected in its form as the Umbrian dialect in which it is written. It is thus characteristically opposed to the canons of scholarly Latin on one hand and to the erotic courtly utterances of the troubadours on the other. Sincerity and deep human feeling dominate its unequal strophes rather than any attempt at learned communication or poetic elegance.

> Altissimu, onnipotente, bon signore, tue so' le laude la gloria
> e l'onore, et onne benedizione a te solu, altissimu, se konfanno
> a nullu homo ene dignu to mentovare!

> O most high, almighty, good Lord God, to Thee belong praise, glory,
> honor, and all blessing!

> Praised be my Lord God with all his creatures, and especially our
> brother the sun, who brings us the day and who brings us the
> light; fair is he and shines with very great splendor; O Lord,
> he signifies to us Thee!

> Praised be my Lord for our sister the moon, and for the stars, the
> which He has set clear and lovely in heaven.

> Praised be my Lord for our sister water, who is very serviceable
> unto us and humble and precious and clean.

> Praised be my Lord for our brother fire, through whom thou givest
> us light in the darkness; and he is bright and pleasant and
> very mighty and strong.

> Praised be my Lord for our mother the earth, the which doth sustain us
> and keep us, and bringeth forth divers fruits and flowers of
> many colors, and grass.

The Assisi manuscript that contains the words of the *Canticle of the Sun* in its purest form also has space provided for musical notation, which is, alas, blank. While the original melody seems to have been lost forever, countless lauds do survive, some of which date back to shortly after St. Francis' time. A Franciscan monk by the name of Jacopone da Todi, who died in 1306, was one of the most prolific producers of lauds. His most famous hymn is the *Stabat Mater Dolorosa*, which, along with the *Dies Irae*, was one of the four sequences to be retained in the official liturgy after the reforms of the Council of Trent in the 16th century. In both cases, retention was based not only on their inherent beauty but also on the deep hold the two hymns had on the people. This remarkable man, like St. Francis before him, was of Umbrian origin; and, after a succession of such diverse careers as lawyer, hermit, and Franciscan preacher, he turned poet and composer. His hymns readily found their way into the texts of the early miracle plays, and his music became the foundation of the laudistic tradition. The following example is a part of one of his lauds, which continues in the form of a dialogue. Its emotional intensity, as well as its stylistic character, marks it as typical of the early Franciscan movement.

Lauda (late 13th century)   Jacopone da Todi
                                                             (After F. Liuzzi)

O Chri-sto' ni-po - ten - te, Do- ve sie-te — in-vi - a - to, Che

si po-ve - ra - men - te ____ Gi - te_pel-le - gri - na - to?

Dante's *Divine Comedy*

In the early years of the 14th century, a synthesis of divergent philosophical, political, and religious worldviews was achieved by Dante Alighieri in his *Divine Comedy*—at once the greatest book of the medieval past and a prophecy of Renaissance things to come. In one stroke, he established vernacular Italian as a modern literary language and endowed his country with its most enduring literary masterpiece. The *Divine Comedy* is not only a synthesis of scholastic and Franciscan philosophies but of the whole thought of the medieval period and of Greco-Roman antiquity as its author knew it. Classical figures, such as Aristotle, Vergil, Ovid, and Cicero, rub shoulders across its pages with Boethius, St. Thomas Aquinas, and St. Francis.

The form of the poem is laden with medieval mathematical symbolism, the mystical number 3 serving as a kind of trinitarian motif. Each stanza has three verses; the rhyming scheme is the melodious *terza rima*—*aba, bcb*, etc.; one time after another, Dante is terrified by three animals; in each case he is saved by the mediation of three holy women; he is piloted on his travels by three guides. The whole poem is divided into three parts—Hell, Purgatory, and Heaven; each section contains 33 cantos, the number of Christ's years on earth; and, finally, the introductory canto, added to the three times 33 others, brings the total to an even 100, that number having the quality of wholeness or completion.

In spite of the heavy burden of number theory and other scholastic baggage —discourses on the laws of planetary motion, civil and canon law, medieval science, dialectical argumentation, and allegorical meanings, such as that of Vergil representing reason and Beatrice inspiration—Dante is far from an orthodox scholastic thinker. If he were, he would have written a treatise in the learned Latin instead of a poem in Tuscan Italian. No scholarly discourse ever began with the announcement: "the style is careless and humble, because it is in the vulgar tongue, in which even housewives hold converse." The revolutionary nature of this linguistic departure is almost impossible for the modern reader to understand, for in Dante's time literature was a possession of the learned few who possessed an adequate knowledge of Latin. All those who read poetry, philosophy, or history in effect had to do so in a foreign language. But even to an Italian, Dante's progress through the Inferno, Purgatory, and Paradise is not an easy one to follow. The path is hard and rough, and its obscurity comes from the doubts and conflicts that clouded the time. Since lecturers in Italian universities offered commentaries on it soon after the poet's death, the *Divine Comedy* must also have been difficult for those close to Dante's own time.

For all its carefully worked-out form, and in spite of its inclusion of a cross section of the medieval scientific knowledge, the *Divine Comedy* is neither learned, elegant, nor aristocratic. It is obscure, unpolished, and abrupt. It is also so complex that no one key, whether that of theology, metaphysics, philosophy, or politics, will open the door to understanding. In contrast to the philosophical writings of that day, it mixes its subjects at times to the point of confusion. References to local politics are found side by side with glimpses into the beauty of Paradise; names of unremembered inhabitants of the towns Dante visited are placed beside those of the immortals; crude gossip and old wives' tales keep company with the scientific knowledge of the period. Hell and Heaven, faith and reason, events of the past and present, history and prophecy, paganism and Christianity, and the Greco-Roman and medieval worlds are all present in its pages. The mass of detail is kept from marring the greatness of the poem only by the vast conception of the whole and by the tight formal framework which tend to throw the multiplicity of its parts into proper perspective. Compensation for the confusion is found in the incomparable beauty of its language, so much of which is lost in translation. Dante, like Giotto, possessed the gift of making his characters live by just a few deft strokes. Like St. Francis', his allegories are not mere riddles for the learned doctors but lively tales for the untutored.

Dante has a true musician's ear for sound, and his verses have a music all their own. He also has the expert painter's eye for the minute details of appearances, and his images are a feast for the inner eye of the imagination as well. One instance of this imagery is his sensitivity to the medium of light. Primarily it is a spiritual light that concerns him, but he conjures up its vision in familiar everyday impressions filtered through the mind's eye of a great poet. He sings of sunlight, firelight, starlight; the sparkle of precious stones; the gleaming rays of a lamp in the darkness; the translucent effects of light filtered through water, glass, and jewels; rainbows and the colored reflections from clouds; the ruddy glow of infernal flames and the pure unearthly radiance of Paradise; the light of the human eye and that of the haloes surrounding the heads of the saints; and finally each one of the three sections of the poem closes on the word "stars."

In spite of the preponderance of so many medieval elements, Dante achieves much that is associated with the Renaissance viewpoint. For all its mathematical structure, the *Divine Comedy* is full of violent human storms, passionate outbursts on the unnecessary wickedness of those in high places, and a general reassertion of the role of emotion in human affairs. For all his austerity, remoteness, and unapproachability, Dante does not pronounce a stern and final judgment. The very title would preclude this, because in his conception, "Comedy, indeed, beginneth with some adverse circumstances, but its theme hath a happy termination. . . ." Dante further specifically states that the didactic purpose of his poem is "to remove those living in this life from a state of misery and to guide them to a state of happiness." He writes with an unbounded faith in humanity, and when he relates the punishments meted out to those who suffer in his Inferno, he does so with the practical moral purpose of correcting such worldly evils as simony, usury, and avarice that he saw being practiced in the world as he knew it. It is important to point out that Dante did not write only the Inferno—a general impression derived from the romantic 19th-century writers who practically took this part to be the whole. His Purgatory and his Heaven, line for line, are equal in space with his Hell.

While the *Divine Comedy* is subtitled the "Vision of Dante Alighieri," and the scene is laid in Hell, Purgatory, and Paradise, Dante's vision was not concerned only with life after death. By inference, he is describing the spiritual course of human life from birth in original sin through the purgation process of experience to a knowledge of ideal goodness. This dynamic spiritual journey is full of quite unmedieval emotions. After plunging with Dante into the bowels of the earth, the reader makes an upward ascent through the infernal regions on the back of Satan to the mountain of Purgatory, and, finally, into the metaphysical stratosphere of the various stages of Heaven. Civilization likewise, as Dante saw it, had struggled upward from the pagan world of Greece and Rome to the theocratic foundations of the medieval world, which had rested on an all-powerful church and its secular counterpart, the Holy Roman Empire. It is a vertical and dynamic concept representing the ascent of humanity from the depths to the heights, from darkness into the light.

IDEAS

The 14th century in Italy had one foot in the Middle Ages and the other in the Renaissance. The opposing worldviews are reflected in the great church schism; the social struggle between the old landed aristocracy and the growing cities; the incompatibility of Gothic architecture and the sunny landscape of Italy; the presence of medieval devils and genuine human types in Giotto's frescoes; the opposing visions of the Inferno and Paradise in the *Divine Comedy*; the attitudes expressed in poetry and painting before and after the Black Death.

The backward and forward directions are illustrated also in the struggle within the minds and consciences of individual men. The life of St. Francis, to cite an example, combined an other-worldly self-denial with an obvious this-worldly love of natural beauty. Fire for him was not created so much for the purpose of roasting the souls of sinners in Hell as it was to give light in the darkness and warmth on a cold night. The Romanesque St. Peter Damian had said: "The world is so filthy with vices the holy mind is befouled by even thinking of it." In contrast, the Gothic encyclopedist Vincent of Beauvais exclaimed: "How great is even the humblest beauty of this world!" St. Francis in his *Canticle of the Sun* found evidence of God's goodness everywhere—in the radiance of the sun, in the eternal miracle of springtime. He saw all nature as a revelation of divinity and, seeing thus, foreshadowed a departure from the divisive medieval dualism based on opposition of flesh and spirit. After a lifetime of self-mortification, he humbly begged pardon of his brother the body.

The two great Italian writers of the 14th century—Petrarch and Boccaccio—reveal a similar inner conflict. Boccaccio, in his youth, wrote the worldly and joyous *Decameron* and reveled in the rediscovery of classical Greco-Roman literature. In his old age, however, he recanted by disavowing the *Decameron* and disposing of his library because it contained so many pagan books. Petrarch's poetry was a curious blend of Gothic chivalry and revival of ancient Roman forms; he wondered whether it was better to write in classical Latin or in vernacular Italian; and his early sensuous sonnets to Laura contrast strongly with his later *Secret*, a moralistic dialogue with the ghost of St. Augustine.

The 14th century thus straddles the medieval and the Renaissance worlds. Looking backward, it represents a culmination of certain aspects of later medievalism; looking forward, it anticipates many of the ideas of the Renaissance. The breakdown of medieval symbolism is seen in the growth of naturalism in painting, and the shift from an other-worldly focus to a this-worldly approach is apparent in the rise of humanitarianism. It is most important, however, to distinguish between the 14th-century naturalism, which is largely an outgrowth of late Gothic ideas, and its more scientific equivalent in the 15th century and between Franciscan humanitarianism and the more classically oriented humanism of the later Renaissance.

Late Medieval Naturalism

The abstractions of the scholastic mind found a new challenge in the concretions of the philosophers who called themselves nominalists. Late scholasticism had, in fact, become more and more a strained exercise in logical gymnastics, and its forms all too often disregarded the real world and the facts necessary to give substance to thought. The nominalists simply turned the scholastic processes of thought completely upside down. They insisted that generalities are built up from the grouping of individual objects, whereas scholastics, by beginning with a hypothetical proposition or eternal Platonic idea, derived the facts of the phenomenal world from their proposition. To use the language of the schoolmen themselves, the scholastics reasoned *a priori*, while the nominalists did so *a posteriori*; one started from premises *ante rem*, and the other from propositions *in re*; or, to put it more simply, one reasoned *before* and the other *after* the fact. These systems approximate the difference between deductive and inductive thought, the latter leading to the experimental method of modern science.

The nominalist viewpoint, as it gained foothold, weakened medieval authoritarianism, in which the world of Aristotle and the church fathers was accepted without question, and initiated the modern practice of finding facts from first-hand observation. Particular things became more important than universal forms. A plant, now, was a vegetable or flower that grew in a garden, rather than the manifestation of an *a priori* universal idea of a plant existing in the mind of God. The result of this new mental orientation was a renewed interest in a tangible reality that was to have as important consequences in art as it did in the realm of scientific inquiry. In the next century, it was to lead to the representation of figures amid natural surroundings, the rendering of the body with anatomical accuracy of bone and muscle, the modeling of figures three-dimensionally by means of light and shadow, and the working out of laws of linear perspective for foreground and background effects.

While opposing systems of logic were being argued in the universities, the friars of St. Francis were bringing his message to town and country folk. With them, religious devotion became a voluntary, spontaneous relationship between man and God rather than an imposed obligation, an act based on love rather than on fear. The Franciscans also sought to establish a common bond between a man, whatever his station in life, and his fellow men—an important shift from the vertical feudal organization of society, in which men were related to those above and below them by a hierarchical authority, to a horizontally oriented ethical relationship that bound man to his fellow men. St. Francis everywhere saw evidence of God's love in everything, from the fruits and flowers of the earth to the winds and the clouds in the sky—a concept that was to have great consequences for the course of art. The birds to which St. Francis preached (see Fig. 8:15), for instance, were the birds that were heard chirping and singing every day, not the symbolic dove of the Holy Ghost or the apocalyptical eagle of St. John. While this tendency toward naturalism was already noticeable in the 13th-century sculpture of Chartres and elsewhere, it became widespread in the 14th century. As this view of the natural world gained ascendance over the supernatural, based as it was on concrete observation rather than on metaphysical speculation, it released the visual arts from the perplexing problems of how to represent the unseen. The love of St. Francis for his fellow men and for such simple things as grass and trees, which could be represented as seen in nature, opened up new vistas for artists to explore.

St. Francis' message was taught in parables and simple images of life that all could understand, and Giotto succeeded in translating these into pictorial form. In this favorable naturalistic climate, he found his balance between the abstract and the concrete, between divine essence and human reality. By refraining from placing his accent on symbolism, Giotto moved away from medieval mysticism and in his pictures portrayed understandable human situations. To him, the saints were not remote transcendental spirits but human beings, who felt all the usual emotions from joy to despair just as did the people in the Italian towns he knew so well. Now that he no longer had to be concerned mainly with allegories but could reproduce the world of objects and actions as he saw it, a new pathway was opened. Even his contemporaries could see that Giotto was blazing new trails. Yet when they extolled him for his faithfulness to nature, their praise must be measured by the art that had preceded his time rather than by 15th-century or later standards. While he undoubtedly showed a love of nature as such, he never accented it to the point where it might weaken his primary human emphasis. His interest was less in nature for its own sake than in its meaning in the lives of his subjects.

In viewing a Giotto picture, one does well to begin with his people and be concerned only secondarily with their natural surroundings, because his pictures are in psychological rather than in linear perspective. His subjects seem to create their own environment by their expressive attitudes and dramatic deployment. While his work shows an increasing preoccupation with problems of natural space, this space remains subordinate to his expressive intentions, and his use of color and shading gives his human figures the sense of depth and volume that brings them to life. In this way, both human nature and nature as such attain an intimate identity in his pictorial conceptions.

Franciscan Humanitarianism

Long before, Cluny had changed the character of monasticism by uniting cloistered life with feudalism. Now the new orientation of the Franciscan Order was no less revolutionary. St. Francis did not confine his monks in cloisters but sent them forth as fishers of men. The idea of evangelical poverty, humility, and love for mankind expressed through living and working with simple people resulted in a union with, rather than a withdrawal from, society. The Franciscans did not shun the world so much as they shunned worldly pursuits, and, as G. K. Chesterton has remarked, what St. Benedict had stored, St. Francis scattered. The Cluniacs were, in the proper sense of the word, an order—that is, a strict hierarchical organization. The Franciscans by contrast were, in every sense of the word, a movement.

The icy intellectualism of the medieval universities was bound to thaw in the warmth of Franciscan emotionalism. Asceticism and self-denial held little appeal for an increasingly prosperous urban middle class. The mathematical elegance of Gothic structurality began to yield to more informal types of buildings. The logical linear patterns of the surviving Byzantine pictorial style gave way to the expressive warmth of Giotto's figures, and the vacuous stylized faces of Byzantine saints pale in the light of the human tenderness found in a smiling mouth or tearful eye in a Giotto picture. The formal architectural sculpture and abstract patterns of Gothic stained glass were replaced by the colorful informality of mural paintings in fresco. St. Francis in his music, as in his religious work, drew the sacred and popular traditions closer together, and in the lauds he encouraged people to sing; he gave them a music that they could feel in their hearts without having to understand with their brains.

St. Francis, son of a village merchant, was not an aristocratic saint. Although his company and counsel were sought by bishops, popes, and King Louis IX of France, he ministered primarily to the poor and humble of town and country alike. The painter Simone Martini of Siena, unlike St. Francis and Giotto, was a member of the knightly class. Martini's fresco in the lower church at Assisi, *St. Martin before Emperor Julian* (Fig. 8:14), shows a preoccupation with social stratification in his concern with protocol and his emphasis on such details as the emperor's orb and scepter and the elegant costuming. Martini's painting harks back to the courtly Gothic tradition, while in the same basilica the work of Giotto, a commoner, appears by comparison strikingly modern. Giotto's art was frankly addressed toward the new middle class, and his figures are simply human beings in all their warmth, frailty, and dignity. In such a picture as the *Sermon to the Birds* (Fig. 8:15), Giotto's work attains something of St. Francis' humanitarian spirit. St. Francis and his successors preferred the simple folk songs of the jongleurs to the more aristocratic troubadour music or the more

Fig. 8:14. Simone Martini. *St. Martin before Emperor Julian*. Fresco. c.1326. Lower Church of St. Francis, Assisi (Alinari)

formal Gothic counterpoint. Since his mission was preaching to the common people as they paused from their labors in the fields or marketplace, he communicated with them in simple, unsophisticated language.

When Dante declared that Giotto's fame outshone that of Cimabue, and when Boccaccio proclaimed that Giotto revived painting after it had "been in the grave" for centuries, his contemporaries were recognizing in Giotto's art the presence of a new spirit and style. These are also apparent in the *Decameron*, where the ten city dwellers satirize the manners and foibles of Gothic knights, abbots, and monks and the outmoded feudal ideal to which they clung. And they were also apparent in music. In France, Philippe de Vitry published a musical treatise c.1316 with the title *Ars Nova*, or new art, which he opposed to the *ars antiqua*, or old art, of the Gothic 13th century. The new movement of which he was the spokesman, especially in its ardent championship of the new secular rhythms, was deemed sufficiently important to warrant censure in a vigorous bull issued by Pope John XXII at Avignon in 1325.

Fig. 8:15. Giotto. *Sermon to the Birds*. Fresco. *c.*1296–1300. Upper Church of St. Francis, Assisi (Anderson)

Fig. 8:16. Giotto. *Pietà (Lamentation)*. Fresco. 1305–1306. Arena Chapel, Padua (Alinari)

A new spirit of freedom was in the air, a freedom from tradition. St. Francis earlier had struck out in a new religious direction, and Giotto, by translating the Saint's life into pictures, avoided the traditional Biblical subjects and their traditional stylized treatment. Actually he was working on an almost-contemporary subject as well as rendering it in a new manner. Subjects that came within the iconographical tradition, such as the *Pietà*, or *Lamentation* (Fig. 8:16), were done far more dramatically than previously. In general, his figures moved about in the space Giotto created for them with greater suppleness than heretofore. His world was marked by a new and intelligible relationship between man and his fellow men, between man and nature, and between man and God.

Representations of Christ as an infant in arms began to replace the mature image in divine majesty of the Gothic period, and along with the growing interest in the cycle of Christ's infancy, legends of Mary's life became more and more prominent. The emotional element in the Passion was largely conveyed through compassion for the Virgin as the mother of sorrows. This was as true for Giotto's cycle in Padua as it was for Jacopone da Todi's *Stabat Mater Dolorosa*. The adoption of the vernacular tongue in literature, the informal treatment of fresco painting, and the folk spirit in the music— all make it apparent that the works of art were being addressed to a new group of patrons. Furthermore, one of Giotto's recorded sayings reveals the artist's new conception of himself. Each man, he said, "should save his soul as best he can. As for me, I intend to serve painting in my own way and only so far as it serves me, for the sake of the lovely moments it gives at the price of an agreeable fatigue." Even the Black Death had some beneficial effects for the artists after Giotto's time, since the younger masters could assert their independence and develop new ideas and techniques with fewer restrictions from their conservative guilds.

What appears to be a renewed interest in classical antiquity began to be seen, heard, and read in the works of the artists and writers of the 14th century. The panels of Niccolo Pisano's pulpit show the classical Roman influence of such narrative reliefs as Trajan's Column (Fig. 3:22). His son Giovanni, in spite of the Gothic orientation of his own work, placed ancient Roman sarcophagi alongside contemporary examples in the arcade of the Campo Santo in Pisa. The Roman poet Vergil appears prominently in Dante's *Divine Comedy*. All these phenomena, however, can be explained much more logically as the continuation of a tradition that had, in fact, never really died out. If Niccolo's sculpture is placed chronologically after a group of French Gothic examples, it certainly seems to be closer to the art of ancient Rome. But since Roman sculpture was present everywhere in Italy, any Italian sculptor with his eyes open could not miss seeing it. Simple as it may sound, the explanation is a geographical rather than a chronological or psychological one: central Italy is closer to Rome than to northern France. Since Dante was writing an epic poem, the obvious antecedent was the *Aeneid*, which had never ceased to be read. While a growing consciousness of the classical in the works of Dante and his contemporaries is not to be overlooked, it must be seen from the 14th-century point of view as a continuation of a cultural tradition rather than as a rebirth of classicism. The influence of the classic authors and classical art had never been quite so neglected or dead as many historians have supposed. Vergil and Cicero, as well as certain works of Aristotle, were quite as widely read in medieval times as they were in the 14th and 15th centuries.

This is not to deny the fact that a new spirit of curiosity enlivened the search, instituted by Petrarch and Boccaccio, in monastic libraries for manuscripts by other Greek and Roman authors than those who bore the hallowed approval of church tradition. This also went hand in hand with the discovery in

Rome of some long-buried antique sculpture and with the study of Roman building methods. Even though Petrarch was crowned in Rome amid much classical fanfare with the laurel wreath, that ancient token of immortal fame, and even though he wrote his cycle of Triumphs with the Roman triumphal arch form in mind, it is doubtful that he or Dante or Boccaccio did more than bring the ancient world a little closer to their own time. They certainly had no such admiration for pagan antiquity for its own sake as did the 15th-century Florentines. Even though Giotto spent some time in Rome, the joyous humanistic spirit that permeates his work is much closer to the new Franciscan outlook and the continuous tradition of Roman relief sculpture and fresco painting than to any conscious reappraisal of classical culture as such. It is necessary, then, to dissociate the spontaneous 14th-century Franciscan humanitarianism from the more self-conscious revival of antiquity that characterized developments in 15th-century Florentine and early 16th-century Roman humanism.

This 14th-century conflict of opposing ideas and forward-backward trends is usually designated as the post-Gothic, proto-Renaissance, or pre-Renaissance period. But any period that contains the magic names of St. Francis, Dante, Petrarch, Boccaccio, Giotto, Duccio, and Simone Martini and that exhibits such a high degree of originality and creativity can well stand on its own rather than being a postlude or a prelude to another. In style as well as ideas it is indeed the Early Renaissance.

CHRONOLOGY:
Florence, 15th Century

General Events
1401   Competition for north doors of Baptistry

1403–1424   Ghiberti worked on Baptistry north doors

1406   Pisa under Florentine rule

1421   Giovanni de' Medici elected magistrate

1425–1452   Ghiberti worked on Baptistry east doors

c.1429   Pazzi Chapel begun by Brunelleschi

1434–1444   Pope Eugene IV resided in Florence

  Pro-Medici government elected

  Cosimo de' Medici (1389–1464) began rule

1436   Cathedral dedicated (begun 1298; dome by Brunelleschi)

1439–1442   Council of Florence brought nominal union of eastern and western churches

1444–1459   Medici-Riccardi Palace built by Michelozzo

1447   Parentucelli, Florentine humanist, elected Pope Nicholas V

1464–1469   Piero de' Medici ruled after Cosimo's death

1469–1492   Lorenzo de' Medici ruled

1476   Portinari Altarpiece by van der Goes of Flanders brought to Florence

1478   Pazzi family led unsuccessful revolt against Medici; Giuliano de' Medici assassinated; Lorenzo consolidated political power

c.1480   Heinrich Isaac succeeded Squarcialupi as organist at cathedral; court composer to Lorenzo

1482   Marsilio Ficino's translations of Plato's dialogues printed

c.1485   Alberti's treatise *On Architecture* printed; *On Painting* (1436), *On Sculpture* (1464) also printed c.1485

1489   Savonarola (1452–1498) preached moral reform

  Michelangelo apprenticed to Ghirlandaio

c.1490   Aldine Press founded in Venice; began publishing works of Plato and Aristotle

1492   Lorenzo de' Medici died

1494   Medici exiled from Florence; government dominated by Savonarola

1497   Burning of books, pictures, and all "vanities"

1498   Savonarola burned at stake

Architects
1377–1446   Brunelleschi
1391–1473   Michelozzo
1404–1472   Alberti

Painters
1387–1455   Fra Angelico
1397–1475   Paolo Uccello
c.1400–1461   Domenico Veneziano
1401–1428   Masaccio
c.1406–1469   Filippo Lippi
c.1416–1492   Piero della Francesca
1420–1497   Benozzo Gozzoli
1423–1457   Andrea del Castagna
c.1429–1498   Antonio Pollaiuolo
1444–1510   Botticelli
1449–1494   Ghirlandaio
1452–1519   Leonardo da Vinci
1458–1504   Filippino Lippi

Sculptors
1371–1438   Jacopo della Quercia
1378–1455   Ghiberti
1386–1466   Donatello
1400–1482   Luca della Robbia
c.1429–1498   Antonio Pollaiuolo
1435–1488   Verrocchio
1475–1564   Michelangelo

Musicians
1400–1474   Dufay
1430–1495   Ockeghem
1436–1475   Squarcialupi
c.1450–1517   Heinrich Isaac
1450–1505   Jacob Obrecht
c.1460–1521   Josquin des Prez

Writers and Philosophers
1304–1374   Petrarch
1313–1375   Boccaccio
1433–1499   Marsilio Ficino
1454–1494   Angelo Poliziano
1463–1494   Pico della Mirandola
1469–1527   Machiavelli
1478–1529   Baldassare Castiglione

THE FLORENTINE
RENAISSANCE STYLE

FLORENCE, 15TH CENTURY

Colorful festivals were the delight of all Florentines, but March 25, 1436, was a special occasion that was to linger long in the memory of this prosperous and pleasure-loving people. It was the dedication of their newly completed cathedral (Fig. 9:1) that brought together an unprecedented number of church dignitaries, statesmen, and diplomats, and in their entourages were famous artists, men of letters, and musicians. The white-robed pontiff Eugene IV, crowned with the triple tiara, attended by seven cardinals in bright red and no less than 37 bishops and archbishops in purple vestments, accompanied by city officials and heads of the guilds with their honor guards, made a triumphal progress through the banner-lined streets. Appropriately enough, the cathedral was christened Santa Maria del Fiore (Mary of the Flower), since Florence (derived from *flora*) was indeed the city of flowers. March 25 was also the Feast of the Annunciation, the beginning of new life nine months before Christ's birth, and both the Annunciation and Nativity were favorite subjects of Florentine painting.

The eyes and thoughts of all Florentines that day were directed upward to the mighty cupola that crowned the crossing of their cathedral and gave their

327

city its characteristic profile. Though the building had been begun in the late 13th century, construction had languished because no architect had the necessary knowledge to dome such an enormous, gaping, 140-foot-wide octagonal space. But Filippo Brunelleschi, after studying the Pantheon and other ancient monuments in Rome, had returned and undertaken the gigantic task now at the point of completion. Starting at a level some 180 feet above ground, he sent eight massive ribs soaring skyward from the angles of the supporting octagon to a point almost 100 feet higher where they converged at the base of a smaller lantern tower. Concealing them from external view, he added two minor radial ribs between each major one, 24 in all, to make his inner shell. Reinforcing these by wooden beams and iron clasps at key points, he then had the necessary support for the masonry of his inner and outer shells. The structure is, in effect, an eight-sided Gothic vault. But by concealing the functional elements and shaping a smooth external silhouette, Brunelleschi crossed the bridge into Renaissance architecture.

Opposite the façade of the cathedral is the old Romanesque baptistry (Fig. 9:1, lower right), which was feeling new Renaissance life with Ghiberti's gilded bronze doors. Already in place were the handsome north doors, and the sculptor was well on his way to completing the east doors (Fig. 9:11), which Michelangelo later was to hail as worthy of being the Gates of Paradise. Helping him cast these doors in his workshop at various times were the architect Michelozzo, the sculptor Donatello, and the painters Paolo Uccello and Benozzo Gozzoli. Donatello, at the same time, was working on a series of statues of prophets for niches on the exterior of both the cathedral and the campanile, known as Giotto's Tower.

In Pope Eugene's entourage were some of the leading Florentine humanists, including the artist-scholar Leone Battista Alberti, who had just completed his book *On Painting* and was at work on his influential treatise *On Architecture*. On hand to provide music for the occasion was the papal choir, whose ranks included the foremost musician of his generation, Guillaume Dufay, who composed the commemorative motet for the occasion. Antonio Squarcialupi, regular organist of the cathedral and private master of music in the Medici household, is thought to have composed the solemn high mass. According to an eye witness, the magnificent pontifical procession was preceded by a great band of wind players, "each carrying his instrument in hand, and arrayed in gorgeous cloth of gold garments." After them came the combined choirs that "sang at times with such mighty harmonies that the songs seemed to the listeners to be coming from the angels themselves."

Lining the streets for the grand procession and crowding their way into the vast nave of the cathedral were the colorfully costumed citizens of this

Fig. 9:1. *Florence Cathedral Group.* Cathedral 508′ long, dome 367′ high. Begun by Arnolfo da Cambio in 1296; dome by Brunclleschi, 1420–1436, present façade, 1875–1887. Campanile, "Giotto's Tower," begun 1334 by Giotto; continued by Andrea Pisano, 1336–1348. Baptistry (right) begun *c.*1060

prosperous Tuscan town. In contrast with northern countries, in this region city life by this time had come of age. At a time when many feudal aristocrats still inhabited their dank fortresslike castles, the Florentine patrician families lived in a style that could well have been the envy of kings. The working members of the population belonged to the various guilds and trade organizations, the most important of which were those dealing with the carding, weaving, and dyeing of wool and silk for the famous Florentine textile industry. Metal crafts and stonework followed in importance, and so on down to the butchers and bakers. The masters of the principal guilds were the influential citizens from whose ranks the members of the Signory were chosen and from which the wealthy merchant and banking families emerged.

The most renowned of these was the Medici family, whose head at this time was Cosimo. By a combination of political sagacity and financial acumen in manipulating his large fortune, he dominated the government of the city. Knowing his fellow townsmen's passion for equality, Cosimo never assumed a title or other outward sign of authority but, instead, was the benign political boss, ruling from behind the scenes with the support of the guilds, which knew that a stable government and peaceful relations with their neighbors were the best safeguards of their prosperity. The Medicis were also the papal bankers who received on deposit church funds from England, France, and Flanders; and from their branch offices in London, Lyon, and Antwerp, they lent the money at fantastic rates of interest to foreign heads of state. With the papal revenues, they also bought English wool, shipped it to Florence to be woven into fine fabrics, and exported these at a handsome profit. It was Cosimo who made the florin the soundest unit of currency in Europe. But political power and high finance were not the only pursuits of this ambitious banker.

Cosimo's other accomplishments were unusual for a Renaissance merchant capitalist. As a diligent student of Plato, he became the founder of the Neo-Platonic Academy, an institution that had enormous intellectual influence. From all the parts of Europe where his fortune extended, he commissioned works of art, while at home he gathered a library of rare manuscripts for scholars to study and translate. Through his generosity, a group of Dominican monks had just moved into the monastery of San Marco, which was being rebuilt for them by his personal architect Michelozzo. Among them was Fra Angelico, whom Cosimo encouraged to decorate the monastery walls with his famous frescoes. Although Masaccio, one of the century's most original painters, had been dead for six years, such others as Filippo Lippi, the future teacher of Botticelli, were active and looking to Cosimo for commissions. Cosimo took Donatello's advice, collected antique statuary, and placed it in the cloister gardens of San Marco. By encouraging young sculptors to work there, he founded the first art academy since antiquity. Small wonder, then, that after his death in 1464, the Signory voted him the posthumous title *Pater Patriae*, father of his country.

For such solemn ceremonies as dedications and coronations, it was the custom to perform a motet especially written for the occasion. Dufay, a musician educated in the Burgundian French tradition, had been a member of the papal choir since 1428 and had composed such an occasional motet for the ceremonies at the conclusion of peace between Pope Eugene and the Emperor Sigismund in 1433. The motet, coming as it does outside the normal liturgical music of the mass, lent itself well to the purposes of an occasional piece that could be composed for a specific ceremony to a text which contained topical allusions. The words in this case begin: *Nuper rosarum flores ex dono pontificis*—Flower of roses, gift of the pontiff. The cathedral is referred to as this "most spacious temple," and Brunelleschi's dome is praised as a "mighty artifice," or a "marvel of art." The text appropriately concludes with a supplication to the Virgin Mary on behalf of the people of Florence: "O Virgin, the glory of virgins, thy devoted people of Florence beseech thee that he who prays . . . may deserve to receive thy gracious benefits. . . ." Since such motets were composed for official occasions, their style tended toward traditional practices rather than experimentation. Dufay therefore built his formal structure on the severe isorhythmic principles developed by the 14th-century French composers. Such a method is governed by certain rules of musical logic, and the forms are compounded of sections that are unified by an identity of rhythmic relationships but not necessarily of melodic patterns. Such music was never intended primarily to please the ear or stir the emotions but, rather, to mirror the hidden harmonies of the universe and thus to constitute a worthy offering to its Creator. In Dufay's conception, however, the universe is no longer mere structure but is populated with shapely melodies, warm harmonic colors, and a variety of rhythmic forms.

This dedicatory scene of the cathedral has often been cited, both by those who witnessed it and by later historians, as the beginning of a new era. There was, of course, a new spirit in the air, but at the same time it was never clearer that no sharp break with the medieval past was being made. The cathedral itself was late Gothic in style; Brunelleschi's dome was constructed by Gothic vaulting methods; and Dufay's isorhythmic motet was a late Gothic musical form. The Italian Gothic, however, had never had either the dynamic verticality or the aspiring force of its northern counterpart. Brunelleschi's dome was, to be sure, the first of such magnitude to be constructed since antiquity, but smaller domes over the crossing were not unusual in Tuscany, as a glance at the cathedral of nearby Pisa (Fig. 5:26) will show. But while the construction of Brunelleschi's dome fell within the scope of the Gothic, the new emphasis was on smoother lines and the shapeliness of the external silhouette. Dufay's motet, for its part, showed an increasing secular feeling in church music, since the composer was apparently much less concerned with making a pious setting of his text than he was with making his mathematical proportions fit smoothly into his musical structure. While such mental gymnastics were late Gothic in conception, the Italian sense of melodic contour, the increased emphasis on secular duple time, the softening of the dissonant passing tones, and the pliancy of the contrapuntal texture, all point in the direction of the Renaissance. Dufay's special contribution was in clothing the austere skeletal structure of such a composition with skillful voice leading and a fluency of sound that made it a joy to the ear as well as to the mind.

PAZZI CHAPEL AND MEDICI-RICCARDI PALACE

Impressive as is the immense cupola of the cathedral, the new architectural spirit is more readily grasped in Brunelleschi's smaller Pazzi Chapel (Fig. 9:2). Here, in a building of diminutive proportions, the architect could give his full attention to design without having to be absorbed in complex construction problems. The fruits of his studies of ancient Roman buildings are more in evidence, and the break with the Gothic tradition is complete. The harmonious spacing of the columns of the portico, the treatment of the walls as flat surfaces, and the just balance of horizontal and vertical elements make Brunelleschi's design the prototype of the Renaissance architectural style. The entablature (Fig. 9:3) gives still further evidence of the classical influence. The curved pattern above comes directly from ancient Roman sarcophagi, while the elegant carving of the Corinthian capitals, the Composite pilasters, and other design details reveal Brunelleschi's early training as a silversmith as well as his study of authentic Roman originals.

The interior (Fig. 9:5) fully bears out the initial promise of the façade and shows a Roman classical concern with the logical molding of the interior space. Without a trace of Gothic mystery and indefiniteness, the pilastered walls give a

Brunelleschi. Pazzi Chapel. *c*.1429–
1451. 59′ 9″ x 35′ 8″. Cloister of
Church of Santa Croce, Florence.
Fig. 9:2 (*opposite*). Façade (Alinari).
Fig. 9:3 (*right*) Façade, Detail (Ali-
nari). Fig. 9:4 (*below*). *Plan*

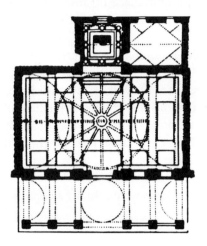

Fig. 9:5 (*below*). Pazzi Chapel, Interior (Alinari)

cool, crisp impression. Frames of dark-colored stone divide the surfaces into geometric forms easily assimilated by the eye. Mystery and infinity have yielded to geometrical clarity. Overhead the rectangular room is covered by transverse barrel vaults, with a low dome on pendentives rising in the center at the point of intersection. Somewhat hesitantly to be sure, this interior indicated a new concept of space without, however, realizing its full implications. The clear-cut simplicity of its design made the Pazzi Chapel a highly influential model throughout the Renaissance, and the unity of its centralized organization under a dome became the point of departure for the church plans of Alberti, Bramante, and Michelangelo.

When Cosimo de' Medici decided to build himself a new house, he is said to have rejected a palatial plan submitted by Brunelleschi, with the observation that envy was a plant that should not be watered. For the Medici-Riccardi Palace (Fig. 9:7) he chose instead a less ostentatious design submitted by Brunelleschi's disciple Michelozzo. (The hyphenated name comes from the fact that the Riccardi family acquired the palace from the Medicis in the middle of the 17th century.) As the design materialized, the building turned out to be an appropriately solid structure, eminently suited to the taste of a man of such considerable substance as Cosimo. As a type, such buildings were actually a continua-

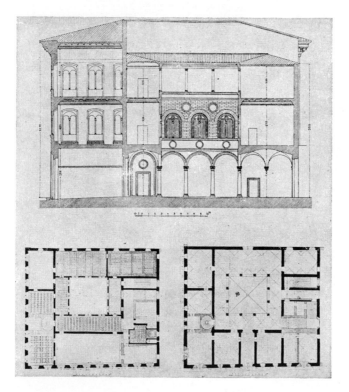

Fig. 9:6. Michelozzo. Medici-Riccardi Palace, *Plan*

Fig. 9:7. Michelozzo. Medici-Riccardi Palace. Façade c.225′ long, 80′ high. 1444–1459. Florence (Soprintendenza)

Fig. 9:8. Michelozzo. Medici-Riccardi Palace, Courtyard. 1444–1459. (Barsotti)

tion, rather than a revival, of the multistoried Roman city apartment house, such as the one at Ostia (Fig. 3:18). Here the dominance of solid mass over the space allotted to the windows, plus the heavily rusticated masonry of the first story (many of the stones stick well over a foot outward) still has something of the forbidding aspect of a medieval fortress. But as the eye moves upward, the second and third floors present an increasingly urbane appearance. The accent on horizontal lines, seen in the molding strips that separate the several stories and in the boldly projecting cornice at the roof level, are quite unmedieval. An allusion to the classical tradition can be seen in the semicircular arches that frame the windows (the pediments over those on the lower story are a somewhat later addition). Details, such as the colonettes of the windows on the second and third floors as well as the egg-and-tongue pattern and the dentil range that appear in the cornice frieze, are definitely Renaissance in style.

In the courtyard (Fig. 9:8) the classical interest is even more apparent. The various rooms are grouped around the court as in a Pompeiian columned interior courtyard, and a staircase connects the various parts of the house as in a Roman atrium. An interesting detail is the use in the frieze of the Medici coat of arms, which is also observable in a corner of the exterior. These are the *palle*, or red balls, on a field of gold. The Medici, with a classical flourish, said the balls represented the golden apples of the Hesperides. The townspeople, however, interpreted them more prosaically—either as the pills (*palle*) of the medicos, or physicians, who were the family founders or as the trademark of the Medici banks, which, then as now, was the same as a pawnbroker's emblem.

Cosimo's sense of austerity stopped with the palace's exterior, and inside the doors everything was on a princely scale. With the fresco murals of Benozzo Gozzoli (see page 289) and Filippo Lippi decorating its second floor chapel, easel paintings by Uccello and Botticelli hanging on salon walls, antique and contemporary bronze and marble statues standing in the courtyard and gardens, collections of ancient and medieval carved gems and coins in its cabinets, and precious metal vessels and figurines standing on its tables, a library with priceless manuscripts including the works of Dante, Petrarch, and Boccaccio, the Medici-Riccardi Palace was, in fact, one of the first and richest museums in Europe.

SCULPTURE

In the year 1401, the Signory of Florence together with the Guild of Merchants had held a competition to determine who should be awarded the contract for the projected north doors of the Baptistry. Like the earlier pair by Andrea Pisano, the material was to be bronze, and the individual panels were to be enclosed in the quatrefoil pattern. The subject, for the purpose of the contest, was to be the Sacrifice of Isaac. Some half dozen sculptors were invited to submit models, among them Brunelleschi and Lorenzo Ghiberti. Both men were in their early twenties; both were skilled workers in metal and members in good standing of the Goldsmiths' Guild. A comparison of their panels (Fig. 9:9 and Fig. 9:10), however, reveals many significant differences of viewpoint and technique. Brunelleschi's composition shows the influence of Gothic verticality in the way it builds up in three rising planes; Ghiberti's composition is almost horizontal, and his two scenes are divided diagonally by a Giotto-like mountain. Brunelleschi's is crowded and his figures spill out over their frame; Ghiberti's is uncluttered, and all his figures and details converge toward a center of interest in the upper right formed by the heads of the principal figures. Brunelleschi accents dramatic tension, with Abraham seizing the screaming Isaac by the neck and the angel staying his hand at the last moment; Ghiberti sacrifices intensity for poise and decorative elegance. Brunelleschi shapes Isaac's awkward body with Gothic angularity; Ghiberti models it with smooth lines and the impersonal grace of a Hellenistic statue. (Ghiberti's *Commentaries* mention the discovery near Flor-

Fig. 9:9. Brunelleschi. *Sacrifice of Isaac*, Competition Panel. Gilt bronze. 21" x 17½" (without molding). 1401. National Museum, Florence (Alinari)

ence of the torso of an ancient classical statue after which he modeled his Isaac.) Finally, Brunelleschi cast his relief in separate sections, mounting these on the bronze background plate; Ghiberti, with greater technical command, cast his in a single mold. The decision in Ghiberti's favor showed the way the aesthetic winds were blowing in 1401. Ghiberti then set to work on the 20 panels of the north doors, which were to occupy the major part of his time for the next 24 years, while Brunelleschi, accompanied by his friend Donatello, went off to Rome to study architecture.

Ghiberti's north doors were no sooner in place than he was commissioned, this time without competition, to execute another set. The famous east doors (Fig. 9:11) on which he worked from 1425 to 1452 tell their own tale. The Gothic quatrefoil frames were now a thing of the past, and, while his north doors were conceived in terms of their architectural function, the east doors served largely as a convenient framework for decoration. They even show some disregard for techniques appropriate to the two-dimensional medium of relief sculpture and in effect became pictures painted in gilded bronze. Ghiberti attempts daring perspectives far in advance of the painting of the period; and some figures, such as those in the center panel of the left door, are in such high relief as to be

Fig. 9:10. Ghiberti. *Sacrifice of Isaac*, Competition Panel. Gilt bronze. 21″ x 17½″ (without molding). 1401. National Museum, Florence (Alinari)

almost completely in the round. In the Adam and Eve panel (Fig. 9:12) at the top of the left door, he uses three receding planes: the high relief in the lower foreground is used to tell the creation of Adam (left) and Eve (center) and of the expulsion (right) in the present tense; the immediate past is seen in the half-relief of the middle ground showing the Garden of Eden; and the low relief in the background is such that the figure of God and his accompanying cloud of angels seem to be dissolving into the thin air of the remote past.

On either side of the pictorial panels, Ghiberti included a series of full-length figurines that alternate with heads which recall Roman portrait busts. Hebrew prophets on the outer sides are set opposite pagan sibyls, all of whom were supposed to have foretold the coming of Christ. The figure beside the second panel from the top on the right door is that of the Biblical strong man Samson, but his stance and musculature are those of a Hellenistic Hercules (see Fig. 2:11). Ghiberti mentions in his *Commentaries* how he sought to imitate nature in the manner of the ancient Greeks when molding the flora and fauna of these door frames. The care and delicate craftsmanship he lavished on these and other details make the east doors a high point in the metal worker's art. Ghiberti, as was said, belonged to the Goldsmiths' Guild, and its influence is

Fig. 9:11. Ghiberti. *East Doors of Baptistry*, Florence. Gilt bronze. 18′ 6″ high. 1425–1452 (Brogi). Fig. 9:12 (*opposite*). *Story of Adam and Eve* detail. Gilt bronze. 31¼″ square. *c.*1435 (Brogi)

obvious in every aspect of Florentine Renaissance art. It is to be seen not only in such door moldings but in pulpits, wall panels, window brackets, columns, pilasters, cornices—all of which were wrought with a wealth of fine detail lovingly dwelt upon.

Donatello's personality and career contrast strongly with Ghiberti's. A man of fiery temperament and bold imagination, he scorned the fussy details that allied Ghiberti's work with that of the jeweler, and his sculpture has a rugged grandeur that makes Ghiberti's appear precious by comparison. While Ghiberti studied local examples and read Vitruvius' treatises, Donatello had gone to Rome with Brunelleschi to see classical statuary first hand. While Ghiberti remained a specialist in bronze, Donatello was at home with all materials—marble, wood, painted terracotta, gilded bronze; in all mediums—relief and in the round, small scale and heroic size, architectural embellishment and independent figure; in all subjects—sacred and secular, historical scene and portraiture. While Ghiberti had a single style, Donatello had many. His power of epical expression, enormous energies, vehemence, and impetuosity make him the representative sculptor of his period and the immediate artistic ancestor of Michelangelo.

Fig. 9:13. Donatello. *Prophet* ("*Lo Zuccone*") from the Campanile. Marble. 77″ high. 1423–1425. Cathedral Museum, Florence (Brogi)

   Lo Zuccone, or the *Baldpate* (Fig. 9:13), was one of a series of marble statues that Donatello was commissioned to do for the Florence cathedral and campanile in 1424. Designed for a third-story niche of the campanile, it was intended to be seen about 55 feet above ground level. The deep-cut drapery and lines of the face consequently took into account this lighting and angle of vision. By the boniness of the huge frame, the powerful musculature of the arms, the convulsive gesture of the right wrist, the tension of the sinews of the neck, and the intensity of the face, Donatello sought to produce a powerfully expressive rather than a handsome figure. Representing an Old Testament prophet (either Habakkuk or Jeremiah), the figure is full of inner fire and fear of the Lord, capable of fasting in the desert, dwelling alone on a mountaintop, or haranguing an unheeding multitude from his niche and exhorting men to penitence. The classical influence is discernible in the drapery, an adaptation of the toga, and in the rugged features and baldness, which recall realistic Roman portraiture. With *Lo Zuccone,* Donatello created a unique figure of strong individuality rather than one of the traditional iconographical types. And the nickname the Florentines gave the statue shows that it was accepted as such.

In his bronze *David* (Fig. 9:14), Donatello works in a more lyrical vein. As a figure meant to be seen from all angles, the *David* is definitely a departure from the Gothic tradition of sculpture in niches and as architectural embellishment; and as the first life-size bronze since antiquity, it marks the revival of classical nude statuary. David stands alone in the confident attitude of the victor over the vanquished, a sword in his right hand, a stone in his left. The serenity of the classical profile and the stance and modeling of the youthful body show

Fig. 9:14 (*left*). Donatello. *David.* Bronze. 62¼" high. *c.*1430–1432. National Museum, Florence (Brogi). Fig. 9:15 (*below*). Antonio Pollaiuolo. *Hercules Strangling Antaeus.* Bronze. 17¾" high. *c.*1475. National Museum, Florence (Alinari)

Fig. 9:16. Donatello. *Equestrian Monument of Gattamelata.* Bronze. *c.*11' long, 13' high. 1443–1453. Padua (Brogi)

Hellenistic influence. A local touch is provided by the Tuscan shepherd's hat, which throws the face into strong shadow and serves to accent the somewhat gawky lines of the adolescent body.

Donatello's *Gattamelata* (Fig. 9:16), an equestrian statue of Erasmo da Narni, condottiere of the Venetian Republic, was the first heroic bronze monument to be executed since the days of the Roman Empire. It stands in Padua where the sculptor worked during the decade 1443–1453. The work was undoubtedly inspired by the equestrian portrait of Marcus Aurelius (Fig. 3:9) which Donatello had observed in Rome, and the horse was possibly modeled after those above the portals of St. Mark's in nearby Venice, which date from the time of Nero. Other classical touches are found in the short-skirted Roman armor worn by the rider and the general poise of the composition. The anatomy of the horse has been well observed, and the contrasting textures of the horse-flesh, saddle leather, and metal armor are handled with assurance and telling effect.

Quite another attitude is revealed in the sculpture of the succeeding generation, of which Antonio Pollaiuolo and Verrocchio are the leading representatives. The work of Pollaiuolo is dominated by scientific curiosity, especially in regard to human anatomy. (He is known to have dissected cadavers in order to study the muscle and bone structure at first hand.) Trained with his brothers in his

Fig. 9:17. Verrocchio. *Equestrian Monument of Bartolommeo Colleoni.* Bronze. c.13' high. 1485–1488. Venice (Böhm)

father's goldsmith shop, he is best known for his small figures in bronze, such as the group of *Hercules Strangling Antaeus* (Fig. 9:15). The legends of the strong man of antiquity were excellent subjects that permitted the sculptor to bring out the musculature of the male figure in action. In this instance, Hercules overcomes his adversary, the Lybian giant, by raising him off the earth that was the source of his strength, while Antaeus struggles desperately to release the stranglehold Hercules has upon him. The sinews in Hercules' legs as they bear the weight of both bodies should be noted. Pollaiuolo also painted a series of pictures on the Labors of Hercules. Like his work in bronze, they are studies of muscular tension, full of athletic energy and quite unrelieved by gracefulness.

Verrocchio, a contemporary of Pollaiuolo's, was the official sculptor of the Medici. For this family he designed everything from tournament trophies and parade paraphernalia to portraits and tombs. Like Donatello, he occasionally worked outside Florence, and at the time of his death in 1481, he was just completing the monument to Bartolommeo Colleoni (Fig. 9:17), a condottiere who left his entire fortune to the Venetian Republic in return for an equestrian statue to stand in the city he had served so long. Verrocchio portrays him as the stern 15th-century man of action he was. With arrogant mien he dominates his mount, just as he would the troops under his command. Donatello's rider and mount are generalized, while Verrocchio's are more individually and literally treated. Bartolommeo's steed, a warhorse capable of bearing the fully armored figure on his back, stands with one foot unsupported, impatient to be off. Details of the saddle and armor definitely belong to the 15th century and are richly wrought with all of Verrocchio's silversmith's skill.

Both Antonio Pollaiuolo and Verrocchio were also painters at a time when sculpture led the field in experiments with perspective, anatomy, and light and shadow. When they painted, however, the sharp outlines and hard contours of their figures reveal them primarily as workers in metal, especially bronze. Unlike the classical orientation of Ghiberti and Donatello, Pollaiuolo and Verrocchio were primarily scientifically minded, and it was in Verrocchio's workshop that Leonardo da Vinci got his training. It was Leonardo who carried on the unquenchable scientific curiosity of his master, while it remained for Michelangelo, under the stimulus of Donatello's art, to carry on the humanistic ideal into the next century.

PAINTING

With Brunelleschi and Donatello, the third member of the triumvirate of early 15th-century innovators, and the only one born within the century, was Masaccio. The importance of his series of frescoes in the Brancacci Chapel of the Church of Santa Maria del Carmine can hardly be overestimated. In the *Expulsion from the Garden* (Fig. 9:18) he chose one of the few subjects in the iconographical tradition in which the nude human body could be portrayed in churches without raising ecclesiastical eyebrows. By visualizing the source of light as coming diagonally from the right and by having Adam and Eve approach it, Masaccio could have his figures cast natural shadows. He thus creates an atmospheric perspective that surrounds his figures, blends them with the space they occupy, and models them in light and shade so revealing that they appear as if seen in the round and with all the weight and volume of living forms. Masaccio, however, was also aware of the drama of the situation. The full force of man's first moral crisis is expressed by the human body alone with almost no reliance on surrounding details. Eve, aware of her nakedness, cries aloud; while Adam, ashamed to face the light, expresses his remorse by covering his face. Even the avenging angel who drives them out reflects the tragedy of the fall of man by an expression of human concern and solicitude. Adam's right leg was apparently drawn so as to show the motion of the expulsion; but the proportions of his arms, and the drawing of Eve's lower hand, are definitely incorrect. Such flaws, however, are minor in comparison with the momentous step in painting that puts man in an entirely new relationship to his spatial environment. Masaccio's premature death at the age of 27 prevented a more complete realization of his

Fig. 9:18. Masaccio. *Expulsion from the Garden.* Fresco. 6′ 6″ x 2′ 9″. c.1425. Brancacci Chapel, Church of Santa Maria del Carmine, Florence (Alinari)

Fig. 9:19. Fra Angelico. *Annunciation.* Fresco. 7′ 6″ x 10′ 5″. c.1445–1450. San Marco, Florence (Anderson)

vision, and it remained for Leonardo da Vinci and Michelangelo to work out its full implications.

Spiritually, Fra Angelico was in many respects a late-Gothic artist, who never painted anything but religious subjects. While he dwelt lovingly on the older forms, he did, however, often treat them within the new frame of reference. The *Annunciation* (Fig. 9:19) he painted for the upper corridor of his own monastery of San Marco is a remarkable blend of these old and new elements. A mystic by temperament, Fra Angelico found angels as real as his fellow human beings. But while he always paints with the deepest religious sentiment, his figures in this case appear within the new conception of space. The perspective and the 15th-century architectural details are so exact that the event could well be taking place in a corner of the San Marco cloister that Michelozzo had recently rebuilt. Furthermore, the native Tuscan flowers seen in the garden are well enough observed to satisfy a botanical expert. The lighting, however, is far from the natural illumination of Masaccio; Fra Angelico manages it so that the figure of Gabriel and the ineffable purity of Mary are beheld as if in a vision.

Unlike the eyes of Fra Angelico, those of his pupil Benozzo Gozzoli were focused firmly on this world. While the subject of his murals that cover three walls of the chapel in the Medici Palace was ostensibly the *Journey of the Magi* (see p. 289), the religious content is in name only. Though painted some 20 years after the event, the mural commemorates one of Cosimo's diplomatic triumphs—the convening at Florence of a general church council in 1439 to discuss the union of the eastern and western churches. The heads of the Eastern Orthodox delegation, Emperor John Paleologos and the patriarch of Constantinople, attended by their retinues of theologians, philosophers, and scholars, appear as two of the kings. It would be expected that Pope Eugene would be the third member of this triumvirate, but instead Benozzo gave this honor to Cosimo's young grandson Lorenzo, later to be known as the Magnificent (see p. 289). Sumptuously attired, he sits astride his splendid white mount. In his wake follow the rest of the Medici, headed by the elderly Cosimo on a gray mule, a blackamoor groom at his side, a diamond ring on his finger, and his motto *Semper* (Always) embroidered on his saddle. Bringing up the rear are figures thought to be portraits of the philosopher Pico della Mirandola, the poet Poliziano, Fra Angelico, and a self-portrait of the painter identifiable by a band around the cap that reads *Opus Benotii*. The fresco continues along the other two walls and approaches the fourth where Fra Filippo Lippi's altarpiece *Virgin Adoring the Child* is found. The picturesque setting, showing the Medicis winding downward from a castle in the Apennines along a road punctuated by tall parasol pines and needle cypresses, is replete with naturalistic detail. The rocky landscape, stylized to some extent, is nevertheless recognizable as part of the countryside surrounding Florence.

Fig. 9:20. Paolo Uccello. *Battle of San Romano*. Tempera on wood. 72" x 125".
*c.*1455. Uffizi, Florence (Soprintendenza)

To decorate one of the salons of the Medici Palace, Cosimo called upon Paolo Uccello. As a student of spatial science, Uccello was trying to solve the problem of *linear perspective*, the art of arranging lines so that they converge at a vanishing point on the horizon to create more natural foreground-background effects and the illusion of recession in depth. One of his three battle scenes depicting the *Rout of San Romano* (Fig. 9:20), a skirmish of 1432 in which the Florentines put the Siennese army to rout, shows his pioneering effort in applying Euclidean geometry to pictorial mechanics. As a scientific experiment, Uccello lays his lances and banners out on the ground as if on a chessboard. He was evidently so absorbed with his lines that his bloodless battle is staged more in the manner of a dress parade than of a clashing conflict. He also apparently forgot about light and shade so that his merry-go-round-like horses remain as flat as cardboard. For all this intellectual effort, the solution of the linear problem eluded him, and in this respect he was always a pupil and never a master.

Present in Florence during the 1440's was Piero della Francesca. As an assistant to Domenico Veneziano, he absorbed the richness of Venetian color; studying Masaccio, he learned about atmospheric perspective and how to model figures in light and shade; and associating with Ghiberti, Brunelleschi, Alberti, and Paolo Uccello, he eventually became a master of linear perspective and later wrote a treatise on the subject. His *Resurrection* (Fig. 9:21), painted for the

Fig. 9:21. Piero della Francesca. *Resurrection*. Fresco. *c*.1460. Town Hall, Borgo San Sepolcro (Brogi)

chapel of the town hall of his native Umbrian town of Borgo San Sepulchro, is one of his most sophisticated works. His geometrical clarity of design is seen at once in the compact pyramidal composition that builds up from the sleeping soldiers (the second from the left is generally thought to be a self-portrait) and sarcophagus to the figure of Christ modeled like a classical statue and holding the triumphant banner. Color contrasts as well as light and shade play appointed roles both in the pictorial mechanics and in the symbolism. The somber tones of the soldiers' costumes are offset by the diaphanous pink of Christ's robe. Furthermore, the dark-clad soldiers are paralleled by the shadowy earth to set up an alternating rhythm with the glowing figure of Christ against the Easter dawn. The barren earth on the left yields to the springtime regeneration of the fields on the right; and the effect of the brightening sky above, together with the radiant spirit of Christ with His piercing, almost hypnotic gaze, is reflected in the disturbed soldiers below who, though still asleep, are yet dimly aware of the dawn.

Botticelli's role as painter for the Medici is revealed in his *Adoration of the Magi* (Fig. 9:22). Among the admirably arranged figures, one finds the elderly

Fig. 9:22. Botticelli. *Adoration of the Magi.* Tempera on wood. 43½″ x 52¾″. *c.*1475. Uffizi, Florence (Soprintendenza)

Cosimo kneeling at the feet of the Christ Child; also kneeling are his two sons Piero and Giovanni; behind them, standing against the ruined wall, is the profiled figure of Giuliano, who was the handsome grandson of Cosimo and the younger brother of Lorenzo the Magnificent, who is to be found in the extreme left foreground. His opposite number at the right is usually identified as Botticelli himself. Though the coloring is bright—ranging as it does from the cool azure of the Virgin's robe and the dark-green and gold embroidery of Cosimo's costume to the ermine-lined crimson cloak of the kneeling Piero and the bright orange of Botticelli's mantle—it falls into a harmonious pattern. Attention should also be called to the classical touch provided by the ancient Roman ruin in the left background.

Botticelli was not a popular painter of pageants like Benozzo Gozzoli and his contemporary Ghirlandaio but a member of the sophisticated group of humanists who gathered around his patron, Lorenzo. In this circle, which included the poet Angelo Poliziano and the philosophers Marsilio Ficino and Pico della Mirandola, classical myths were constantly discussed and interpreted.

Fig. 9:23. Botticelli. *Venus and Mars*. Oil on wood. 26¾" x 67¾". *c.*1485. National Gallery, London (Anderson)

The dialogues of Plato, the *Enneads* of Plotinus, and Greek musical theory were all thoroughly explored. With the Florentine interest in the pictorial arts, the ancient references to sculpture and painting were not neglected. This neopagan atmosphere is reflected directly in many of Botticelli's paintings.

In his *Venus and Mars* (Fig. 9:23), Botticelli is concerned with the intellectual phases of Florentine life. The painting is an allegory relating to the tournament given by Giuliano de' Medici in honor of Simonetta Vespucci on January 28, 1475. Simonetta Cattaneo was the wife of Marco Vespucci and hence a cousin by marriage of Amerigo Vespucci, the Florentine geographer who modestly gave his name to the new world that Columbus discovered. The blonde Simonetta was celebrated for her beauty as well as her docile disposition; and, as a member of the exclusive Florentine Neo-Platonic set, she could not have been entirely devoid of intellectual accomplishments. Known as the *gentilissima*, she was not only the object of Giuliano's most ardent affections but the subject of sonnets by Lorenzo the Magnificent, verses by Poliziano, and the pictures of Botticelli. To each, though in a different way, she represented the ideal Platonic type of beauty and goodness and was enshrined by them in a poetic niche, much as Beatrice was by Dante and Laura by Petrarch. In spite of the presence of the playful young satyrs, the picture is tinged with a certain melancholy, since Simonetta was in 1476 destined for an early death, and Giuliano was killed in the Pazzi conspiracy two years later. Both events apparently occurred before Botticelli finished the picture, which possibly explains why the shape of the wooden panel on which it is painted recalls that of a sarcophagus. Giuliano won the tournament that day in 1475 and received the trophy of victory from the hands of Simonetta. He is depicted here as Mars dreaming after the battle of the ideal beauty of Venus who appears to him in the form of the fair Simonetta.

Fig. 9:24. Botticelli. *Birth of Venus*. Tempera on canvas. 79″ x 110″. *c*.1480. Uffizi, Florence (Soprintendenza)

The *Birth of Venus* (Fig. 9:24) is likewise filled with the mythological and allegorical allusions of the Neo-Platonic circle. In Poliziano's poem *La Giostra* (The Joust, or Tournament), the birth of the goddess of love is vividly described as she floats across the sea on a pink shell gently blown by Zephyrs. On the shore waiting to clothe her in a flowery mantle is one of the Horae, or Hours. In one verse there is an allusion to the ancient picture of Venus Anadyomene by Apelles, painter to Alexander the Great, which was known only through literary references and some relief sculptures it was thought to have inspired. The legendary place where Venus is supposed to have landed on Italian shores is Portovenere, which, by coincidence, was also the birthplace of Simonetta. The head of the goddess accordingly bears the features of Simonetta, while the pose of the body is that of the *Venus de Medici,* an antique marble statue belonging to that family and now in the Uffizi Gallery. The coloring of the picture is as cool as called for by such a classical subject. The fluttering drapery of the side figures imparts a sense of lightness and movement and leads the eye toward the head of Venus, which is surrounded by an aura of golden bronze hair. The features of the face have an individuality notably lacking in the more impersonal antique statuary, while the incisiveness of outline recalls the technique of relief sculpture. The chief expressive interest, however, is in the balletlike choreography of dancing lines and the skillful pattern of the varied linear rhythms.

Fig. 9:25. Botticelli. *"Calumny" of Apelles.* Tempera on wood. 24" x 35⅜". c.1485–1490. Uffizi, Florence (Soprintendenza)

Botticelli's penchant for intellectualized interpretations of antiquity reaches record proportions in his later picture called *Calumny* (Fig. 9:25). This is yet another attempt to reconstruct a lost painting by Apelles. A literary description by the Roman author Lucian was known to Botticelli in a translation by Alberti, and the subject was undoubtedly discussed at length by the group of scholars around Lorenzo. Moving from right to left in this elaborate allegory on justice, the observer notes that the seat of judgment is occupied by a wicked prince. On either side of him are his advisers, Ignorance and Superstition, who whisper evil counsel into his long donkeylike ears. Before him in tattered clothing stands the plaintiff, Envy, who is leading Calumny, the holder of the flaming torch, before the judge. She, in turn, is dragging by the hair the innocent victim, who raises his hands in a gesture of supplication. Treachery and Deceit, personified by two feminine figures, are entwining Calumny's hair with precious ornaments. The dark-hooded figure in mourning garments to their left is Remorse, whose hands point to the accused and whose face is turned toward the naked Truth, who, in turn, raises her hand to high heaven.

In spite of the heavy allegorical burden it has to carry, the picture is a success. The painting has a smooth surface finish, and the colors, even after the passage of more than 470 years, are still of enamellike clarity and brilliance. The placement of the figures in relation to the architectural setting makes pictorial as well as allegorical sense. The movement of the draperies expresses extreme agitation, but the turbulence of the human drama is kept within bounds by Botticelli's mastery of composition. The finely proportioned and spacious building, though it was intended to represent a Roman basilica, is completely in the Florentine Renaissance style. Even the relief sculptures and statuary in niches, in spite of their classical intentions, are far more Florentine in feeling than they are antique.

With Lorenzo's death in 1492, just about the time *Calumny* was finished, Botticelli's career and the arts generally underwent a period of eclipse. Under the influence of the monk Savonarola, a fiery preacher and prophet of doom, all sorts of apocalyptical visions were conjured up. His maledictions and deprecations gathered all the anti-Medici factions around him which succeeded in driving the ruling family out of Florence only two years after the death of the Magnificent. Botticelli, always an introspective personality, repented of his paganism, reputedly burned as many of his pictures of nude subjects as he could lay his hands on, and became a follower of Savonarola. His late work reflects this religious preoccupation. The beautiful pagan dream of Lorenzo's time, however, had burst like a bubble, and with it Botticelli's inspiration which he never succeeded in recapturing.

Medici patronage reached out beyond Florence to all the European centers where the family had branch banks—Milan, Venice, Lyon, London, and especially Bruges, where two Medici representatives figured prominently in Flemish painting. *Giovanni Arnolfini and His Wife* (Fig. 9:26) by Jan van Eyck is a masterly portrait of the shrewd calculating Medici banker and his wife, who is about to become a mother. Light suffuses the entire space and illuminates every object evenly and naturally. Each detail is described with the keenest observation from the more subdued tones and textures of the wooden floor and shoes, the furry dog, and the cloth of costumes and bed to the higher gloss of the metal chandelier and the mirror, itself a picture in miniature.

In the latter half of the 15th century, Tommaso Portinari, another Medici representative in Bruges, commissioned an altarpiece (Fig. 9:27) for the hospital of Santa Maria Nuova in Florence. Hugo van der Goes, the artistic heir of van Eyck, paints the donor, his wife and children, and their patron saints Thomas and Margaret in the folding wide wings of the triptych. In the central panel, depicting the Adoration of the Shepherds, one sees the same close observation of naturalistic detail as van Eyck's—from the weather-beaten faces of the shepherds to the brocaded cloth of the angel's robes. But van der Goes is also concerned with symbolism—the harp in the tympanum of the background building indicates that Mary and the Child stem from the house of David; the sheaf of wheat signifies Bethlehem; and the flowers, the future sorrows of Mary. The artist also makes use of some spatial distortion to achieve expressive effect—the floor tipped

Fig. 9:26. Jan van Eyck. *Giovanni Arnolfini and His Wife.* Oil on wood. 33" x 22½". 1434. National Gallery, London (Anderson)

Fig. 9:27. Hugo van der Goes. *Portinari Altarpiece,* Center Panel. Oil on wood. Center panel 8' x 9' 2½", entire triptych 9' 2½" x 20' 20½". c.1476. Uffizi, Florence (Soprintendenza)

slightly upward to project the figures forward, and the relative sizes of the figures in relation to the picture frame, Joseph, Mary, and the shepherds in the middle ground looming larger than the angels in the foreground.

The arrival of this triptych in Florence in 1476 created a sensation, for it provided the first opportunity local painters had to observe a large-scale product of one of their northern contemporaries. Clearly it influenced Ghirlandaio, Pollaiuolo, and Botticelli. Their special interest was in the new oil medium perfected by Jan van Eyck. In Italy, such panels traditionally were done with water-soluble pigments in the process known as tempera. The Flemish painters, however, were now using oil to suspend pigments. The boards on which they painted were first built up with a fine white cementlike substance called gesso, and on this a cartoon of the picture was drawn with ink and modeled in light and shade. After the painting had been made in opaque oil colors, a translucent glaze with varnishlike brightness was then applied. This glaze, also in an oil medium, could be worked with the brush to give iridescent effects, so that the colors seemed to glow from within the picture. Gradually, the deeper colors and brilliant enamellike finish of this oil medium supplanted the brighter colored but duller surfaces of Italian tempera painting.

POETRY AND MUSIC

Lorenzo de' Medici's title *Il Magnifico*, in retrospect, seems fitting recognition of his activities as poet, humanist, philosopher, discoverer of genius, patron of the arts and sciences, and adviser to writers, sculptors, painters, and musicians. From the terracotta bust from Verrocchio's workshop (Fig. 9:28), his contemporaries apparently saw a different side of the man, that of the forceful statesman, the victor in the Pazzi family conspiracy, the averter of war with Naples, the holder of the political balance in Italy, the sponsor of lavish civic celebrations—in short, the personification of the Machiavellian prince. There is

Fig. 9:28. Verrocchio's Workshop. *Lorenzo de' Medici.* Painted terracotta. 25⅞" high. c.1480. National Gallery, Washington, D. C.

little in Verrocchio's portrait to suggest that behind the impassive face of the shrewd professional diplomat, which shows so well a will to power, was the soul of a poet, the contemplative mind of a philospher, and a heart and spirit capable of the warmest human understanding. For a portrait of this other side of a complex personality, we must turn to his creative interests that led a contemporary historian to conclude in 1530 that Florence could not have had a better or more delightful tyrant.

Under the wise guidance of his grandfather Cosimo, *Pater Patriae*, Lorenzo had been educated by Pico della Mirandola and other Latin and Greek scholars of the highest repute to be the type of philosopher-ruler that Plato had expounded upon in his *Republic*. Social conditions, however, had changed considerably since Cosimo's time, and while his grandfather had been a banker with intellectual and artistic tastes, Lorenzo became a prince whose power rested on philosophical prestige and leadership in matters of taste as well as on his banking fortune. Lorenzo maintained embassies at all the principal courts to which he made loans, but while he was willing to finance foreign conflicts, provided he saw a substantial profit for himself, he preferred to fight his own wars with words. By having the services of the greatest humanists under his command, he never ran out of ammunition in the form of elegantly turned phrases, apt epithets, veiled threats, and invectives. Changes in the status of the arts had also come about as the century progressed. In the early decades Ghiberti had been employed by the Signory, and his work was intended for public view. Later the major commissions came from a few families, and under Lorenzo the arts took on more of a courtly character, and the audiences grew correspondingly more restricted. Some painters —Ghirlandaio, for instance—were able to remain outside the charmed circle and to make careers painting social scenes of births and marriages for an upper middle-class clientele. Botticelli's pictures, however, were done mainly for the group of humanistic connoisseurs.

Lorenzo himself, though the leader of this exclusive group, had the instincts of a popular ruler and did not neglect the common touch. He participated actively in the gay Florentine festivals by composing new verses for the traditional folk tunes, by encouraging others in his circle to do the same, and by holding competitions among composers for better musical settings of the songs. Lorenzo thus gave new impetus to popular literature in the vernacular. In a commentary on four of his own sonnets, he went to considerable lengths to defend the expressive possibilities of Tuscan Italian; and, after comparing it with Hebrew, Greek, and Latin, he found that its harmoniousness and sweetness outdid all the others. While he continued to write sophisticated sonnets, Lorenzo also wrote popular verses that have, in addition to their beauty and literary polish, all the spontaneous freshness, humor, and charm of folk poetry. In some of his pastoral poems he even uses the rustic dialogue of true country folk. Few poets could rival the lyricism of his *canti carnascialeschi,* or carnival songs, one of which contains the oft-quoted lines:

Quanto è bella giovinezza,	Fair is youth and free of sorrow,
Che si fugge tuttavia!	Yet how soon its joys we bury!
Chi vuol esser lieto, sia:	Let who would be, now be merry:
Di doman non c' è certezza.	Sure is no one of tomorrow.

In order to flourish, popular poetry of this kind needed appropriate musical settings. As a young man of 18, Lorenzo was in search of a composer to set his lyrics, and a letter he wrote at that time (1467) requests the "venerable Gugliemo Dufay," who by this time was approaching 70, to compose music for his verses. This was the same Guillaume Dufay who some 30 years earlier had composed the dedicatory motet for the cathedral. Popular songs and traditional church music were, of course, poles apart.

Popular music-making in Florence and other Italian cities was as much a part of the good life as any of the other arts. But it was mainly an art of performance, and little music was ever written down. The Franciscan tradition of singing lauds during Advent, Lent, and especially Holy Week continued throughout the 15th century, and both Lorenzo and his mother wrote lauds for performance by members of their family and households. Antonio Squarcialupi, music master to the Medici, enjoyed a high reputation for his skill on the organ and lute, but as a composer he was a minor figure in comparison with his great contemporaries from Burgundy or the Netherlands—Dufay, Ockeghem, Obrecht, and Agricola —each of whom was active in Florence at one time or another. When the time came to appoint a successor to Squarcialupi after his death in 1475, Lorenzo's choice fell on Heinrich Isaac, a native of Flanders and a rapid and prolific composer. Florence immediately became a second home to this truly cosmopolitan figure, and native Italian idioms soon were combined with those of his own background and training.

Isaac's duties included those of organist and choirmaster at the Florence cathedral as well as at the Medici palace, where Lorenzo is known to have had no less than five organs. Together with the poet Angelo Poliziano, he was also the teacher of Lorenzo's sons, one of whom was destined to be the music and art-loving Pope Leo X. But most important, Isaac collaborated with Lorenzo on the songs written for popular festivals. He thus became co-creator of one of the popular genres of secular choral music that eventually led to the madrigal. Dufay's settings of Lorenzo's verses are now lost, but many by Isaac are extant. In one of these, he shows the tendency away from complex counterpoint and toward simple harmonic, or chordal, texture. Its style is that of a Florentine *frottola,* a carnival song for dancing as well as singing, and its lilting rhythm freely shifts its meter, as in the fourth bar:

Un dì lieto   Lorenzo de' Medici and Heinrich Isaac

A-mor a tal fol-li - a M'in - dus-se al-lor_ ch'-i' rup-pi

As the setting stands, it could be performed for three-part chorus; as a solo song with the two lower parts taken by the lute or two viols; or as a vocal duet with the soprano and any one of the two other voices. The collaboration of Lorenzo and Isaac thus resulted both in a meeting of minds and a merging of poetic and musical forms. Lorenzo's verses were a union of the courtly *ballata* and popular poetry; while Isaac succeeded in Italianizing the Burgundian *chanson*, or song. Italianizing in this case means simplifying, omitting all artificiality, and enlivening a rather stiff form with the graceful Florentine folk melodies and rhythms. It can be seen that such a movement worked both ways by raising the level of popular poetry on the one hand, and at the same time rejuvenating the more sophisticated poetic and musical forms by contact with popular idioms.

IDEAS

The dominating ideas of the Florentine 15th century cluster around three concepts—classical humanism, scientific naturalism, and Renaissance individualism. In their broadest meaning, humanism, naturalism, and individualism were far from new. Humanism in the humanitarian Franciscan sense was a carryover from the 14th and 15th centuries; naturalism stemmed from late Gothic times; and some form of individualism is always present in any period. The term *Renaissance*, implying as it does a rebirth, is a source of some confusion. To the early 16th-century historians, it meant an awakening to the values of ancient classical arts and letters after the long medieval night. But just what, if anything, was *reborn* has never been satisfactorily explained. Since all the principal ideas were present in the Gothic period, one might do better to speak of a maturation of certain tendencies present in late medieval times. Yet there was a specific drive that gave an extraordinary impetus and color to the creative life and thought of this small Tuscan city-state in the 15th century. It is important, therefore, to discover just what it was, and what it was not, that gave Florence its special flavor.

That the Renaissance meant a secularization of life as opposed to the predominantly religious outlook of the medieval period has often been asserted. The secular spirit may indeed have been stronger during the Renaissance, but in medieval times there was a secular tradition in the architecture of castles, guild halls, and market buildings, in such pictorial works as the Bayeux Tapestry, in such epics as the *Chanson de Roland*, in Goliardic folk verse, in the aristocratic poetry of the troubadours, and in the music of the minstrels. The fact that so little of this has survived has led too often to the conclusion that secular works did not exist. And a look at the record of the 15th century will reveal that more than 90 percent of the statuary, paintings, and music were religious works intended for placement or performance in churches. Such works as Antonio Pollaiuolo's Hercules series, Botticelli's mythological pictures, and Isaac's and Lorenzo's carnival songs were conspicuous exceptions rather than the rule. On the other hand, the 15th century did have Dufay's dedicatory motet *Nuper Rosarum* and Benozzo Gozzoli's *Journey of the Magi*, which, though nominally religious, are actually records of contemporary events. Lorenzo's sacred drama *San Giovanni e Paolo*, with music by Isaac, was a family affair performed at the Medici Palace, and Botticelli's *Adoration of the Magi* is in reality a family portrait. Although the pure piety of Fra Angelico was becoming increasingly rare, there is no reason to assume that the 15th century in Florence was antireligious or even irreligious. Religious motivation was still a powerful force, as the career of Savonarola proved, but its expression simply assumed another form.

Though Florentine humanism evolved from the Franciscan spirit, it did take on a consciously classical coloration. Here again, however, a word of caution is necessary when speaking of a "rebirth" of the spirit of antiquity. In Italy, much more than in northern Europe, the classical tradition had been more-or-less continuous. Roman remains were everywhere in evidence. Many arches, aqueducts, bridges, and roads were still in use, while fragments of ancient buildings, such as columns, were used and reused over and over again as building materials. In the late 13th century, Niccolo Pisano's sculptural models were the Roman remains he saw all around him, and the same influence is seen in the work of Ghiberti. Aristotle was still the official philosopher of the church, and ancient musical theory was still studied. What was new to Florence was the study of the Greek language, the setting up of Ciceronian rather than medieval Latin as a standard, and a passionate interest in Plato. In spite of a certain antiquarianism, however, the net result was less a revival of things past than a step forward. It was—as such movements usually are—a search for past precedents to justify present practices.

Much has been said also about the pagan aspect of this interest in antiquity. Here again it was less anti-Christian than appears on the surface. Florentine Neo-Platonism was certainly antischolastic, but it was mainly a substitution of the authority of Plato for that of Aristotle. Marsilio Ficino, as the high priest of the movement, in his interpretation of the *Republic* and *Laws*, speaks of Plato as the Attic "Moses." He is also known to have added "Saint" Socrates to the litany and to have burned a candle before the bust of Plato. In this light, his thought appears more as a reinterpretation of Christianity in Platonic terms than paganism as such. There was also a certain amount of anticlericalism in Florence, just as there was in other places at this time. Lorenzo, however, as the papal banker and as a father who chose the church for his son Giovanni's career, was not so much a religious skeptic as he was a political realist. It is important to keep in mind that the Florentine humanists were a small band of learned men, whose Platonic disputations have made much more noise in history books than they did in their own time. Actually, they never had, nor did they seek, a large audience. In the first quarter of the following century, however, the humanists had the international forum of Rome. The artistic expression of Neo-Platonism came to its climax in the works of Michelangelo, and the full discussion of the movement—which must also include the art of Botticelli and Raphael, the patronage of Julius II and the Medici popes Leo X and Clement VII, as well as the Neo-Platonic philosophers—will be discussed in the next chapter.

Naturalism, in the sense of fidelity to nature, appears in a well-developed form both in the northern Gothic sculpture and in the poetry of St. Francis, who had died as long before as 1226. By the 14th century, representations of man and nature alike had pretty well lost their value as other-worldly symbols. But rather than remaining a generalized interest in this world, Florentine 15th-century naturalism took a noticeably scientific turn. Careful observation of natural phenomena and the will to reproduce objects as the eye sees them was evidence of an empirical attitude; dissection of cadavers in order to see the structure of the human body revealed a spirit of free inquiry; and the study of mathematics so as to put objects into proper perspective involved a new concept of space. Thus, while Fra Angelico's religious and Botticelli's pagan dreams are ample evidence that the visionary element was still present, clearly a new scientific spirit had entered the picture.

While individualism as such is practically universal, the distinctive feature of its Florentine expression was that conditions in this small city-state were almost ideal for artists to come into immediate and fruitful contact with their patrons and audience. Competition was keen; desire for personal fame was intense; and a high regard for personality is seen in the portraiture, biographies, and autobiographies.

It should therefore be clear that the Florentine Renaissance was characterized by no sharp cleavage with the past, and that the special savor of this period lies in the quality of its humanism, in the tendency of its naturalism, and in its particular regard for individualism.

Scientific Naturalism

The two basic directions taken by the naturalism of the 15th century led to a new experimental attitude and a new concept of space. A close partnership between art and science developed, with architects becoming mathematicians, sculptors anatomists, painters geometricians, and musicians acousticians. The spirit of free inquiry was by no means confined to the arts alone. It permeated all the progressive aspects of the life of the time from a re-examination of the forms of secular government to Machiavelli's observations on how men behave in a certain given set of political circumstances. This searching curiosity reached its full fruition in the early years of the next century in Machiavelli's political handbook *The Prince*; in the same author's attempt to apply the Thucydidean method of rational historical analysis in his *History of Florence*; and in the scientific observations in Leonardo's notebooks, which cover everything from hydraulics to astronomy. Well within the 15th century, however, the same spirit manifested itself. Ghiberti's *Commentaries* took up the mathematical proportions of the human body as the basis of its beauty, and he wrote the first treatise in Italian on optics. Brunelleschi, as a diligent student of Vitruvius, was concerned with the mathematical proportions of his buildings. Alberti, in his books on painting, sculpture, and architecture, stressed the study of mathematics as the underlying principle of all the arts.

The sculptors and painters who followed the leadership of Antonio Pollaiuolo and Verrocchio were animated by the desire to express the structural forms of the body beneath its external appearance, and their anatomical studies opened the way to the modeling of the movements and gestures of the human body, ranging from Verrocchio's realization of incipient muscular movement to Pollaiuolo's energetic athleticism. The result was the reaffirmation of the expressive power of the nude. In painting, naturalism meant a more faithful representation of the world of appearances and one based on detailed and accurate observation. Even Fra Angelico showed an interest in the exact reproduction of Tuscan botanical specimens in the garden of his *Annunciation*; and Botticelli, under the influence of Pollaiuolo and Verrocchio, combined objective techniques with his highly imaginative subject matter. The culmination of this line of thought was reached in Verrocchio's pupil Leonardo da Vinci, who considered painting a science and sculpture a mechanical art. In music there was a continued interest in Greek theory, coupled, however, with attempts to experiment with acoustical problems. The compositions of Dufay and others of the northern school were characterized by extreme erudition; and mathematical laws were strictly applied to such aspects of composition as rhythmical progressions, formal proportions, and the development of elaborate technical devices.

Highly dramatic was the conquest of geographical space beginning with the voyages of Columbus, leading to the development of trade routes and commerce and the tapping of new and distant sources of wealth. In architecture, this breakthrough in space is reflected in the raising of Brunelleschi's cupola almost 400 feet into the air. In painting, it is seen in the placing of figures in more normal relationship to the space they occupy, and in landscape settings; in Masaccio's development of atmospheric perspective, in which figures are modeled in light and shade; in working out the rules of linear perspective whereby the illusion of space is created by converging lines and the illusion of proper size achieved by *foreshortening*—the diminishing of size of objects in direct ratio to their distance from the picture plane.

Since the subject matter of medieval art was drawn from the other world, it was outside the scope of naturalistic representation and had to be rendered symbolically. Art now entered a new phase of self-awareness as Renaissance artists began to think less in terms of allegory, symbolism, and moral lessons and more in terms of aesthetic problems, modes of presentation, and pictorial mechanics. In medieval music, the emphasis had been on perfect intervals and mathematical rhythmic ratios in order to please the ear of God. Renaissance musicians now reversed the process by concentrating on sounds that would delight the human ear. The new spirit was also heard in the extension of the range of musical instruments in both higher and lower registers, to broaden the scope of tonal space. Thus the development of pleasant harmonic textures, the softening of dissonant passing tones, and the writing of singable melodies and danceable rhythms are all related phenomena.

In this trend toward scientific naturalism, the arts of painting and sculpture became firmly allied with geometrical and scientific laws, a union that lasted until 20th-century expressionism. The 15th-century Florentine artists literally reveled in the perspective, optical, and anatomical discoveries of their day. And when all the basic research, experiments, and discoveries had been made, it was left for their successors—Leonardo da Vinci, Michelangelo, and Raphael—to explore their full expressive possibilities.

Renaissance Individualism

Whether one considers the Renaissance patrons' reasons for commissioning artists, the forms and techniques employed in the various arts, the regard for human personality seen in portraiture, the desire for personal prestige through art, or the social status of the artist, one finds evidence everywhere of a special attitude of Renaissance man toward himself, his fellow men, and his place in the world. The religious nature of the vast majority of the works of art has already been pointed out, but personal patronage was in the ascendancy. Brunelleschi built the Pazzi Chapel, Masolino and Masaccio decorated the Brancacci Chapel, and Benozzo Gozzoli and Filippo Lippi did the paintings for the Medici Chapel on commission from private donors as memorials to themselves and their families. San Lorenzo, the parish church of the Medici, was rebuilt and redecorated by Brunelleschi and Donatello—but the money came from Cosimo and not from the church. Fra Angelico decorated the corridors of the monastery of San Marco, which was under the protection of the Medici family, and Squarialupi and Isaac were on the payroll of the Medici when they played the organ in the cathedral, in a church, or in the family palace. Piousness and the desire for spiritual salvation were not the only motives for such munificence; a knowledge that the donor's present and posthumous fame depended on his building of monuments and his choice of artists to decorate them was also present.

In addition to the circumstances of patronage, certain technical considerations within the arts themselves point in the same individualistic direction. The development of perspective drawing, for instance, implied that the subject in the picture—whether a Madonna, a saint, or an angel—was definitely placed in this world rather than symbolically in the next, and hence was more on a par with the observer. The unification of space by having all the lines converge at one point on the horizon tended to flatter the spectator. By such clear organization of lines and planes, central perspective presupposes that everything is seen from a single optical vantage point. While it is actually that of the artist, he makes it seem as if it were also that of the observer. By closing his form, the artist further implies that nothing of importance lies outside, and the whole of the picture can then be taken in at a glance. Since nothing, then, is beyond the grasp of the viewer, and all can be comprehended with relatively little effort, the eye and mind of the onlooker are reassured. The central-type church that Alberti, Bramante, and later Michelangelo and Palladio preferred to design, in which the space is unified under a dome, is the architectural expression of the same idea. The Gothic cathedral purposely led the eye and imagination outward into the transcendental beyond, while the central-type church revolves around man himself. Standing under the cupola, the observer is aware that the axis of the building is not objectively outside or transcendentally beyond, but subjectively in himself. He is, for the moment at least, the center of the architectural space; and the center of the universe is not therefore at some remote point beyond the horizon but within man himself.

Human figures, whether intended as prophets or portraits, tended to become more personal and individual. Each statue by Donatello, be it *Lo Zuccone*, the *David*, or the *Gattamelata*, was a human individuality who made a powerful and unique impression. Even Fra Angelico's Madonna was a personality more than an abstraction, and his figure of the Angel Gabriel possessed genuine human dignity. Whether the medium was marble, terracotta, paint, words, or tones, there was evidence of the new value placed on human individuality. Whether the picture was a disguised family group, as Botticelli's *Adoration of the Magi,* or a personal portrait, as Verrocchio's bust of Lorenzo, the figures were authentic personages rather than stylized abstractions; even though Lorenzo de' Medici was the most powerful political figure of Florence, Verrocchio saw him as a man, not as an institution.

The higher social status accorded Florentine artists was evidenced by the inclusion of such self-portraits in paintings as that of Benozzo Gozzoli in his *Journey of the Magi* and the prominent position Botticelli accorded himself in his *Adoration of the Magi.* Ghiberti's personal reminiscences in his *Commentaries* were probably the first autobiography of an artist in history; his inclusion of the lives and legends of his famous 14th-century predecessors were the first biographies of individual artists. Signatures of artists on their works became the rule, not the exception; and the culmination came when Michelangelo realized that his work was so highly individual that he no longer needed to sign them. The desire for personal fame grew to such an extent that Benvenuto Cellini no longer was content to let his works speak for him but wrote a voluminous autobiography filled with self-praise. The painter Giorgio Vasari likewise took up the pen to record the lives of the artists he knew personally and by reputation. More broadly, such works as Pico della Mirandola's essay on the *Dignity of Man,* Machiavelli's *The Prince,* and Castiglione's *The Courtier* were written to enhance the intellectual, political, and social status of man in general and the scholar, politician, courtier, and artist in particular.

In late medieval and early Renaissance times, artists were content with their status as craftsmen. They were trained as apprentices to grind pigments, carve wooden chests, make engravings, and prepare wall surfaces for frescoes as well as to carve marble reliefs and paint pictures. In the late 15th and early 16th centuries, however, it was not enough for an artist to create works of art. He had to know the theory of art and the place of art in the intellectual atmosphere of his period. The trait most admired in Renaissance man was *virtù* (the word comes closer in the modern sense to *virtuoso* than *virtuous*). *Virtù* revealed itself in the boundless vitality and extraordinary ability that led to the achievements of a Lorenzo the Magnificent or the breathtaking conceptions of a Michelangelo. With *virtù*, the Renaissance artist could no longer confine himself to a single specialty but sought to become the *uomo universale,* the universal man. Brunelleschi was a goldsmith, sculptor, engineer, mathematician, and student of ancient languages as well as one of the leading lights of Renaissance architecture. Alberti was an athlete, horseman, brilliant wit, Latin stylist, mathematician, architect, musician, and playwright as well as the founder of Renaissance theory of art. For

Leonardo da Vinci, it is more difficult to find a field in which he was not profi-
cient than one in which he excelled.

From Lorenzo's time through the early 16th century, the greatest artists were
intellectuals. Alberti was a scholar-architect who wrote books on the subject,
designed buildings on paper, and left the actual construction to a master mason.
Botticelli associated with men of letters and worked elaborate allegories into his
pictures. Leonardo da Vinci disdained sculpture because of the physical labor
involved, and in his later years devoted himself more to science than to painting.
Bramante and Raphael were to be artist-scholars as well as architects and painters.
Michelangelo hated the workshop, even though the realization of his grandiose
designs depended on the work of many hands. He was to become the ideal of the
modern individualistic artist, consciously an intellectual, dealing with popes and
princes as equals, insisting that he painted with his brains not with his hands, and
rejecting all offers of noble titles. When people began calling him "the divine,"
the cycle was complete.

CHRONOLOGY:
Rome, Early 16th Century

General Events

1471–1527	Roman Renaissance art and humanism reached climax
1471–1484	Sixtus IV (della Rovere), pope
1473–1480	Sistine Chapel built
1481–1482	Sistine Chapel side-wall frescoes painted by Rosselli, Ghirlandaio, Botticelli, Perugino, Signorelli, Pinturicchio, Piero di Cosimo
1484–1492	Innocent VIII (Cibò), pope
1486–1492	Josquin des Prez in Sistine Chapel Choir
1492–1503	Alexander VI (Borgia), pope
1493–1506	Excavations uncovered ancient Roman frescoes and statues: *Apollo Belvedere*, *Laocoön Group*
1496–1501	Michelangelo in Rome, working on *Bacchus* and *Pietà*
1503–1513	Julius II (della Rovere), pope
1505	Michelangelo began Julius II's tomb
1506	New Basilica of St. Peter begun by Bramante; Old St. Peter's razed
1508–1512	Michelangelo painted Sistine Chapel ceiling
	Raphael painted frescoes in Vatican Palace
1512	Capella Giulia Choir founded
1513–1516	Leonardo da Vinci in Rome
1513–1521	Leo X (de' Medici), pope
1515	Ariosto wrote *Orlando Furioso* (*Madness of Roland*)
1517	Protestant Reformation began in Germany with Luther's 95 Theses
1521	Luther excommunicated
1523–1534	Clement VII (de' Medici), pope
1523	Michelangelo worked on Medici tombs in Florence
1527	Rome sacked by Emperor Charles V; Clement VII imprisoned
1528	Castiglione's *The Courtier* published
1532	Machiavelli's *The Prince* published
1534–1549	Paul III (Farnese), pope
1534	Church of England separated from Rome
	Reaction to Renaissance humanism began
1535–1541	Michelangelo painted *Last Judgment* in Sistine Chapel
1542	Michelangelo painted frescoes in Pauline Chapel
1547	Michelangelo named architect of St. Peter's
1550	Vasari's *Lives of Most Eminent Painters, Sculptors, and Architects* published
c.1550	Philippe de Monte in Rome; published first book of madrigals 1554
1551	Orlando Lassus in Rome
1564	Michelangelo died

Architects

c.1444–1514	Bramante
1475–1564	Michelangelo
1556–1629	Carlo Maderno

Sculptors

1460–1529	Andrea Sansovino
1475–1564	Michelangelo
1500–1571	Benvenuto Cellini
c.1524–1608	Giovanni da Bologna

Painters

1452–1519	Leonardo da Vinci
1454–1513	Pinturicchio
1475–1564	Michelangelo
1483–1520	Raphael

Writers

1474–1533	Ludovico Ariosto
1478–1529	Baldassare Castiglione
1483–1531	Martin Luther
1511–1574	Vasari
1544–1595	Torquato Tasso
1548–1600	Giordano Bruno

Musicians

c.1445–1521	Josquin des Prez
c.1521–1603	Philippe de Monte
1525–1594	Giovanni da Palestrina
c.1532–1594	Orlando Lassus

THE ROMAN

RENAISSANCE STYLE

ROME, EARLY 16TH CENTURY

On April 18, 1506, when the foundation stone of the new basilica of St. Peter (Fig. 10:21) was laid, Rome was well on its way to becoming the undisputed artistic and intellectual capital of the Western world. Pope Julius II was gathering about him the foremost living artists in all fields, and together they continued the transformation of the Eternal City from the darkness of its medieval past into the resplendent Rome of today. Donato Bramante, originally from Umbria but educated in Lombardy, was the architect at work on the plans for the central church of Christendom. Michelangelo Buonarroti from Florence was collecting the marble for a monumental papal tomb and was about to begin the painting of the Sistine Chapel ceiling. Raffaelo Sanzio from Umbria was soon to be summoned from Florence to decorate the walls of the Vatican Palace. The Florentine Andrea Sansovino was carving a cardinal's tomb in one of Julius II's favorite Roman churches, Santa Maria del Popolo, where the Umbrian Pituricchio was covering its choir vaults with a series of murals in fresco. Conspicuously absent from the scene were Leonardo da Vinci, who had left Rome to continue his peregrinations elsewhere, and the singer-composer Josquin des Prez, who had been a member of the papal choir for eight years but had left to become choirmaster to the king of France.

369

The flight of the Medici from Florence had signaled a general exodus of artists. Many had found temporary havens in the ducal courts of Italy, but the magnet of attraction had been the papal court at Rome. Hence, during the days of the two great Renaissance popes, Julius II (della Rovere) and Leo X (de' Medici), the cultural capital shifted from Florence to Rome. And, since Leonardo, Andrea Sansovino, Michelangelo, and Pope Leo were from Florence, and since Bramante and Raphael had absorbed the Florentine style and ideas in extended sojourns there, the cultural continuity was unbroken. It was, in fact, like a smooth transplantation from the confines of a nursery to an open field—a move that gave artists the opportunity to branch out from local styles in the universal air of Rome. Such projects as the building of the world's largest church, the construction of Julius II's tomb, the painting of the Sistine ceiling, and the Vatican Palace murals could be found only in Rome. Nowhere else were monuments of such proportions or commissions of such magnitudes possible. In Rome also were the cardinals in residence, who maintained palaces and princely retinues that rivaled the brilliance of the papal court.

The Eternal City, though it was the artistic heir of all the ages, curiously enough lacked an indigenous Renaissance style of its own. It had, in fact, no native artists of any stature; and during the 15th century, architects, sculptors, painters, and musicians had been imported from various European centers. When their projects were completed, they departed. The plans of the 16th-century popes, however, were on such a colossal scale that they were able to absorb the major creative energies of the giants of their age. Furthermore, the popes were determined to regenerate the authority and glory of the Holy See—as well as to insure their own immortality—through their patronage of the arts. While Lorenzo de' Medici, for instance, had remained more or less a local Florentine figure, his son Leo X became a *magnifico* on an international scale that made his pontificate a golden age for the arts.

The interest in antiquity had animated many other Italian Renaissance centers, but when the movement got under way in Rome, it was, so to speak, on home soil. When antique statues were excavated elsewhere, they caused a considerable stir. In Rome, however, many of the ancient monuments were still standing, and when the archeological shovels probed the proper places, a veritable treasure trove was waiting. One by one the *Apollo Belvedere*, the *Venus of the Vatican*, and the *Laocoön Group* (Fig. 2:21) came to light to give new impetus to the work of Michelangelo and other sculptors. The frescoes from Nero's Domus Aureus and the Baths of Titus provided the first important specimens of ancient painting. While the art of working in tempera on fresh plaster had never died out, these ancient Roman fragments gave fresco painting a new respectability in the Renaissance vocabulary. But for their powerful challenge, Michelangelo might otherwise never have been persuaded to try his hand at the art.

Fig. 10:1. Raphael. *Portrait of Julius II*. Oil on wood. 39″ x 32″. 1512. Uffizi, Florence (Soprintendenza)

Julius II had received most of his training in diplomacy and statecraft from his uncle Pope Sixtus IV and, fortunately, a passionate love of the arts was included in this education. It was Sixtus who had built the chapel that has subsequently borne his name, and who had installed there the group of papal singers that have ever since been known as the *Cappella Sixtina*, or the Sistine Chapel Choir. It remained for Julius to establish a chorus to perform in St. Peter's—one that still bears his name, the *Cappella Giulia*, or Julian Choir. This latter group corresponded to the ancient Schola Cantorum and prepared the singers for the Sistine Choir. Both have always received strong pontifical support, and both are still flourishing institutions.

Essentially a man of action, Julius II was an expert wielder of the sword as well as the crozier. He met his age on its own terms, and the spectacle of *il papa terribile* riding a fiery steed into the smoke of battle had a remarkably demoralizing effect on his enemies. As one of the principal architects of the modern papacy, he also saw the need of a setting in keeping with the magnificence of the Apostolic church and made it a matter of policy to command artists as well as soldiers. At the end of his career, his volcanic energies spent, Julius II became the subject of one of Raphael's most penetrating portraits (Fig. 10:1).

When Leo X ascended the papal throne, one of the eulogies ran: "Venus has had her day, and Mars his, now comes the turn of Minerva." Venus symbolized the reign of the Borgia pope, Alexander VI; Mars, of course, referred to

Fig. 10:2. Raphael. *Portrait of Leo X with Two Cardinals*. Oil on wood. 50″ x 47″. *c*.1518. Uffizi, Florence (Soprintendenza)

Julius II; and Minerva, the Roman equivalent of Athena, was Leo who, as the son of Lorenzo the Magnificent, brought with him to Rome the spirit of Florence, that latter-day Athens. Michelangelo, whom Leo had known since his childhood at the Medici palace, was unfortunately bound by the terms of his contract to serve the heirs of Pope Julius, but the suave and worldly Raphael was available —and more congenial to the personal taste of Pope Leo than the gruff titan. Once again Raphael served as papal portraitist in the unusually fine study of *Pope Leo X with Two Cardinals* (Fig. 10:2).

Heinrich Isaac, Leo's old music teacher, wrote the six-part motet that commemorated his accession, and Isaac's pupil became one of the most liberal of all Renaissance patrons of music. Other princes of Europe had difficulty in keeping their musicians, because the pope's love of the tonal art was so well known. Leo collected lute and viol players, organists, and the finest singers; chamber music was avidly cultivated at the pontifical palace; and a wind ensemble performed at papal dinners. Leo's encouragement of music to the point of putting it on a par with literary pursuits caused considerable murmurings among men of letters. As a competent composer in his own right, he knew the art from the inside as few patrons have ever known it. As a philosopher, writer, connoisseur, and collector, his patronage, like that of his father, was accompanied by an active participation in many of the pursuits that he sponsored.

The luster of the papal court is recorded in the *Horatian Epistles* by Ludovico Ariosto, a friend from Leo's university days. Ariosto, author of the great Italian epic poem *Orlando Furioso* (*Madness of Roland*), described some of the distinguished artistic events he witnessed, among which were the presentation of his *Suppositi*. This poetic comedy called for a solo singer, a chorus, and an orchestra of fifes, viols, cornets, bagpipes, lute, and organ. The scenery was painted by Raphael, and a later English adaptation with the title *Taming of the Shrew* led to Shakespeare's play of that name.

As one of the leading representatives of Renaissance humanism, Leo X brought a lofty intellectual tone to Rome. Even more than his father, Leo aspired to be a Platonic philosopher-king. He envisaged the papacy as a great civilizing force, and under him the visual arts, letters, music, and the theater entered a period of rare florescence. Other aspects of his pontificate appear, by comparison, somewhat less lustrous. Ominous rumblings of the Protestant Reformation reverbated across the Alps, and the papal treasury approached bankruptcy. But rarely has Athena been served so well, and Leo's reign might indeed be called a carnival of culture. The Renaissance historian Jacob Burkhardt put it well when he wrote that Rome "possessed in the unique court of Leo X a society to which the history of the world offers no parallel."

SCULPTURE

In spite of his many masterpieces in other media, Michelangelo always thought of himself first and foremost as a sculptor. Other projects were undertaken reluctantly, and on the contract for the painting of the Sistine Chapel ceiling he pointedly signed Michelangelo *scultore*—Michelangelo the sculptor—as a protest. His first visit to Rome at the age of 21 coincided with the discovery of some ancient statuary, including the *Apollo Belvedere*, that proved a powerful stimulant to his own productivity. His most important statues from this early period are a *Bacchus* and a *Pietà*, which illustrate the conflicting pagan and Christian ideals that were to affect his aesthetic thought throughout his long career.

The *Pietà* (Fig. 10:3), now in St. Peter's, was commissioned in 1498 by Cardinal Villiers, the French ambassador to the Holy See. Its beauty of execution, delicacy of detail, and poignancy of expression reveal that Michelangelo was still under the spell of the Florentine Renaissance. In its pyramidal composition, a type worked out by Piero della Francesca (Fig. 9:21) and by Leonardo da Vinci, as exemplified in his drawing for *Madonna and Child with St. Anne* (Fig. 10:4), Michelangelo uses the voluminous folds of the Madonna's drapery as the base and her head as the apex. The figure of Christ is cast in the perfect form of a Greek god, while the Madonna, though overwhelmed by grief, maintains a

Fig. 10:3. Michelangelo. *Pietà*. Marble. 69″ high. 1498–1499. St. Peter's, Rome (Vatican Photographic Archive)

Fig. 10:4. Leonardo da Vinci. *Study for the painting Madonna and Child with St. Anne.* Charcoal and white chalk on paper. 54¾″ x 39¾″. 1498–1500. National Gallery, London

classical composure. No tears, no outcry, no gesture mars this conception of Mary as the matronly mother of sorrows. Yet Michelangelo allows himself many liberties with the proportions of his figures in order to heighten their expressive effect and enhance the harmony of his design. The excessive drapery exists to provide a multiplication of folds and sweeping lines. The horizontal body of Christ is far shorter than the vertical Madonna, but the disproportion serves to make the composition more compact. The triangular shape, as a self-sufficient form, holds the attention within the composition and obviates the necessity for such external considerations as niches or architectural backgrounds. As such, the *Pietà* is a kind of sculptural declaration of independence, and it bears the unique distinction of being the only work Michelangelo ever signed.

After finishing the *Pietà*, Michelangelo went home to Florence, where he worked on the *Bruges Madonna* and the *David*. In 1505, however, he was summoned back to Rome by the imperious Julius to discuss a project for a colossal tomb. In the inception of this gigantic composition, the artist's imagination for once met its match in his patron's ambitions. Julius' monument was conceived as a small temple within the great new temple—St. Peter's—that was abuilding. It was to rise pyramidally from a massive quadrangular base visible from all four sides (Fig. 10:5), and it was to include well over 40 statues. Consequently, the entire marble quarries of Carrara had to be placed at Michelangelo's disposal. But, like all such challenges to the gods, fate proved stronger than human will power. Floods on the Tiber prevented the marble from reaching Rome; wars and rumors of wars distracted the attention of the pontiff; and the monumental dream soon turned into a nightmare. In exasperation, Michelangelo defied papal authority and temporarily fled from the Eternal City. "If I were to remain in Rome," he wrote to a friend, "my own tomb would be prepared before that of the Pope. This is the reason for my sudden departure."

When Julius died in 1513, only a few parts of the project had been finished and a new contract with his heirs had to be negotiated. Further revisions were made later, each reducing the proportions of the project and eliminating more of the unfinished statues. In its final form of 1545, the magnificent temple had shrunk to the relatively modest wall tomb now to be seen in the aisle of the Church of San Pietro in Vincoli. Thus it is that Michelangelo's biographers have referred to this unfinished chapter in his life as the "Tragedy of the Tomb." As with all great art, however, the grandeur and idealism of the original conception outweigh the later compromises and ultimate realization.

Tombs of the popes, like the triple tiaras with which they are crowned, were traditionally in three rising zones, symbolizing earthly existence, death, and salvation. For the original project, Michelangelo translated these divisions into Neo-Platonic terms representing the successive stages of the liberation of the soul from its bodily prison. For the final project, the monument lapsed into more traditional stratifications. In the original scheme, the lowest level was to have figures symbolizing those who are crushed by the burden of life and those who rise above the bonds of matter. This idea was retained in some of the later revisions, and some six of the so-called "slaves" or "captives" and one victory survive in various stages of completion.

Heroic figures of the leaders of mankind were to have been placed on the second level of the original project. Here were the individuals who pointed the way toward the divine goal of humanity—reunion with God. Moses and St. Paul were to represent the old and new law, while Rachel and Leah were to personify the active and contemplative ways of life. Of these, only the Moses was finished by Michelangelo. The figures of Rachel and Leah, begun by the master but finished by assistants, now stand on either side of Moses in the finished tomb, though whether they are in the form intended for the initial project is questionable. The third and highest level was to have represented the gates of heaven with angels receiving the soul of Pope Julius. None of these was completed or even begun by Michelangelo.

The three figures that date from the years 1513 to 1516, when Leo X was pope, are the two "slaves" now in the Louvre and the *Moses*. The *Bound Slave* (Fig. 10:6) is the more nearly finished of the two, and seems to represent a sleeping adolescent tormented by a dream rather than a "dying captive" as it is sometimes called. The imprisoned soul, tortured by the memory of its divine origin, has found momentary respite in sleep. The cloth bands by which the figure is bound are only symbolic, since Michelangelo is not concerned with the external aspect of captivity but rather with the internal torment. Its companion piece, the so-called *Rebellious Slave* (Fig. 10:7), represents the violent though vain struggle of a wide-awake, enormously muscular figure. The implied power of the strong bodies in both figures only emphasizes their ineffectiveness and makes their attempts at escape seem all the more futile. In both is the same grappling with fate; in both, the battle is hopeless. It is the tragedy of man, limited by time but troubled by the knowledge of eternity; mortal but with a vision of immortality; bound by the weight of his own body yet dreaming of a boundless freedom. This tragedy of the tomb was understood only too well by Michelangelo himself, who had the conception of his great project in mind but was doomed to see only a few fragments of his dream completed. Figures, such as the "slaves" and "victory" that Michelangelo envisaged, were associated with the triumphal arches as well as with the mausoleums and sarcophagi of ancient Rome. Models for the "slaves" can be traced to the Hellenistic Marsyas figures (Fig. 2:18), and the similarity between the *Bound Slave* (Fig. 10:6) and the younger son in the *Laocoön Group* (Fig. 2:21) has aptly been pointed out.

The Platonic idea of man's soul confined in the bonds of the flesh was continued in a later version of the tomb. The four so-called *"Boboli Captives,"* two of which are seen in Figures 10:8 and 10:9, were part of the revised plan of 1532, but they were eventually given by Michelangelo to Duke Cosimo de' Medici, who placed them in a grotto of the Boboli gardens in Florence. Here in these figures the imprisonment by matter is all but complete. Unconscious, locked in their stone wombs, they struggle and writhe to be born out of their material medium. Their unfinished state gives an interesting glimpse into Michelangelo's methods, which were similar to that of relief sculpture. In one of his sonnets Michelangelo addressed his friend Vittoria Colonna: "Lady, it is the taking off that puts into the rough hard stone a living figure, grown most great just where the stone has grown most small." The statue, therefore, to Michelangelo was a potential form hidden in the block of marble awaiting the hand of the master sculptor to be born. The Neo-Platonic implication is that the soul of man is still entombed in the body and can only be perfected into pure being by the hand of a higher creative power.

Moses (Fig. 10:10) is the only statue completed entirely by Michelangelo's hand to find its place in the completed tomb. Both Julius II and Michelangelo

Fig. 10:5. Michelangelo. Projected Tomb of Julius II. Drawing. Uffizi, Florence (Alinari)

(*Opposite, above*). Michelangelo. Figures for the Tomb of Julius II. Fig. 10:6 (*left*). "Bound Slave." Marble. 89″ high. 1513–1516. Louvre, Paris (Archives Photographiques). Fig. 10:7 (*right*). "Rebellious Slave." Marble 82½″ high. 1513–1516. Louvre, Paris (Archives Photographiques).

(*Opposite, below*). Michelangelo. Unfinished Figures for the Revised Tomb of Julius II. Fig. 10:8 (*left*) and Fig. 10:9 (*right*). "Boboli Captive." Marble. 90½″ high. c.1530–1534. Academy, Florence (Soprintendenza)

Fig. 10:10. Michelangelo. *Moses*. Marble. 8′ 4″ high. *c.*1513–1515. San Pietro in Vincoli, Rome (Vatican Photographic Archive)

himself possessed the quality of *terribilità* that is incarnated in this figure. Julius was known as *il papa terribile,* meaning the forceful or powerful pope, imbued with the fear of the Lord. Michelangelo conceives his *Moses* as the personification of a powerful will, and partially as an idealized portrait of the indomitable Julius who, as the codifier of canon law, had something in common with the ancient Hebrew lawgiver. Moses is further portrayed as the personification of the elemental forces—the human volcano about to erupt with righteous wrath, the calm before a storm of moral indignation, the dead center of a hurricane of emotional fury, the author of those thunderous Thou Shalt Nots of the Ten Commandments, the man capable of ascending Mt. Sinai to discourse with God and coming back down to review all humanity from the seat of judgment.

Medieval rather than classical precedents are to be cited here, with Moses' immediate ancestors found in Donatello's seated *St. John the Evangelist.* Details, such as the stone tablets of the law and the long beard, are according to the iconographical tradition. The horns are also traditional for Moses, although they stemmed from a medieval mistranslation of the Bible. (After Moses descended from Mt. Sinai where he had heard the voice of the Lord, the children of Israel beheld two *rays* of light [not horns] issuing from his head.) Rodin once made the observation that the statue could be rolled down hill without any essential part being broken off. This compactness reinforces its expressive power by holding it in check. The smoldering agitation revealed through the drapery, the powerful musculature of the arms, the dominating intellectuality of the face, the fiery mood, and the torsions of the body as it twists in the act of rising are characteristic of Michelangelo's style. An interesting detail is the carved irises of the eyes, also done earlier in his *David*, which Michelangelo did to express a look of fixed determination. When he wanted to convey the qualities of dreaminess, gentleness, and resignation, as in his Madonnas, he left the eyes untouched.

From 1521 to 1534, Michelangelo again worked in Florence on various sculptural projects, the most outstanding of these being the Medici tombs (Fig. 10:11). Thereafter he was in Rome, occupied with fresco painting and architectural projects. Only in the spare moments of the last 30 years of his long life, and without specific commissions, did he work on several Pietàs. One of them (Fig. 11:27), at long last, was intended for his own tomb; like all the others, it was unfinished when he died.

Fig. 10:11. Michelangelo. Tomb of Giuliano de' Medici, Duke of Nemours. Marble. *c.*20′ high. Central figure, 5′ 11″ high. 1524–1534. New Sacristy, San Lorenzo, Florence (Soprintendenza)

Michelangelo's work coincided with a time when many of the most out-standing examples of antique statuary were being unearthed and admired. In-evitably this led to critical comparisons. Michelangelo, like the Greco-Roman artists, saw man as the lord of creation, but nature itself was always a matter of indifference to him. His early art especially was an affirmation of man's supreme place in the universal scheme of things. That world was populated by godlike beings at the peak of their physical power, full of vitality, creatively active, and buoyantly self-confident. As his art matured, his men and women were beset with quite unclassical tensions, doubts, and conflicts. Unlike the statutes of antiquity, his figures, when they come to grips with fate, are armed with mental and moral powers that imply the hope of ultimate victory. Having thus excelled the art of the ancients as well as that of his own time, not only by his technical mastery but by his expressive power, he came to be regarded by his contemporaries with awe. Vasari, his pupil and biographer, wrote: "The man who bears the palm of all ages, transcending and eclipsing all the rest, is the divine M. Buonarroti, who is supreme not in one art only but in all three at once." History has had no reason to reverse this judgment.

THE SISTINE CHAPEL CEILING

When Michelangelo fled from Rome because of accumulated frustrations with plans for Julius II's tomb, the pope resorted to every means from force to diplo-macy to get him to return. Knowing he had a genius on his hands, Julius con-ceived two interim projects to keep Michelangelo busy until all the problems with his tomb were solved. The first was a colossal bronze statue of himself, sword in hand, for the newly conquered city of Bologna; the statue was de-stroyed after the pontifical army was routed a few years later. The second was the painting of the ceiling of the Sistine Chapel. The building itself, the roof of which can be seen paralleling the nave on the right of St. Peter's in Figure 10:21, was built by and named for Julius' uncle, Sixtus IV, as the private chapel of the popes. The interior consists of a single rectangular room 44 by 132 feet. Around the walls were frescoes painted by the foremost 15th-century artists, including the Florentines Ghirlandaio, who was one of Michelangelo's teachers, Botticelli, and Perugino, teacher of Raphael. Above them were six windows high up on either side and a barrel-vaulted ceiling 68 feet above the floor with 700 square yards of surface stretching before Michelangelo.

All Julius apparently had in mind was a series showing the Twelve Apostles, but, according to a letter of 1523, Michelangelo was given a free hand. "Then he [Pope Julius]," wrote the sculptor, "gave me a new commission to make what I wanted, whatever pleased me." The design and details of the iconography evolved slowly from the mind of the artist as he worked. As the time for this "interim project" dragged on from months into years, the pope's impatience increased correspondingly. On his periodic visits of inspection, the scenes between them mounted in violence with threats being hurled from below and above the scaffolding. Julius knew Michelangelo's temperament as only one volcano can know another, and his eruptions alternated with periods of quiescence and generosity, with the result that the job finally got done—though it took four years to do it.

The entire Sistine ceiling (Fig. 10:12) was conceived as an organic composition motivated by a single unifying philosophical as well as artistic design, as has so convincingly been pointed out by Charles de Tolnay in the second volume of his monumental monographs on Michelangelo. As with the initial project for the Julius tomb and in the later Medici tombs, the iconography is a fusion of the traditional Hebrew-Christian theology and the Neo-Platonic philosophy that Michelangelo knew from his days in the Medici household, where he came into daily conversation with Lorenzo himself, Poliziano, Marsilio Ficino, and Pico della Mirandola. His space is divided into geometrical forms, such as the triangle, circle, and square, which were regarded in Plato's philosophy as the eternal forms that furnish clues to the true nature of the universe. Next is a three-way division into zones in which the varying intensity of the lighting plays a part. The lowest and darkest comprises that of the eight triangular spandrels and the four corner pendentive-shaped spandrels. The second is the intermediate zone that includes all the space outside the spandrels except that allotted to the nine center panels, which in turn constitute the third and brightest zone.

Symbolically these divisions correspond to the three Platonic stages—the world of matter, the world of becoming, and the world of being. Analogies to such triple divisions run as an undercurrent through all aspects of Plato's thought. He divided society, for instance, into three classes: workers, free men, and philosophers, which he symbolized by the metals brass, silver, and gold. Each stratum had its characteristic goal: the love of gain, the development of ambition, and the pursuit of truth. Learning was similarly broken down into the three stages of ignorance, opinion, and knowledge. Plato's theory of the human soul was also tripartite in nature, consisting of the appetitive, emotional, and rational faculties, located in the abdomen, breast, and head, respectively. Of these only the rational or intellective part could aspire to immortality. Man, by reason of his intellect, said Plato at the end of his *Timaeus*, "is like a tree with its root not in the earth but in the sky." It is then the rational element of the soul which "raises us from earth to our kindred who are in heaven."

Michelangelo's image of man agreed in all essentials with that of Pico della Mirandola, who considered man "the intermediary between creatures." In his address on *The Dignity of Man*, Pico declared that it was possible for man "to descend among lower forms of beings, which are brute beasts," or be "reborn out

Fig. 10:12. Michelangelo. *Sistine Chapel Ceiling*. Frescoes.

of the judgment of your own soul into the higher beings which are divine." Michelangelo thus places uninspired man on the low level of the spandrels. In the intermediate area are the inspired Old Testament prophets and pagan sibyls who have knowledge of the divine and mediate between man and God. In the central section are the panels that tell the story of man in his direct relationship to God, and they are seen through the architectural divisions as if taking place beyond on a more cosmic plane. In Michelangelo's time, the chapel was separated into two parts by a screen with the section near the altar reserved for the clergy and the other for laymen. The central space of the ceiling is divided lengthwise into nine panels, with the part over the lay section telling the story of man and that over the altar, the story of God. Instead of starting at the beginning and proceeding chronologically as in the Book of Genesis, Michelangelo conceives the story of creation in reverse order, or as the Platonic ascent of man from his lowest estate back to his divine origin. In this return to God, the soul in its bodily prison gradually becomes aware of God and moves from finiteness to infinity, from material bondage to spiritual freedom. Immortality in this sense is not the reward for a passive and pious existence but the ultimate achievement of a tremendous effort

384

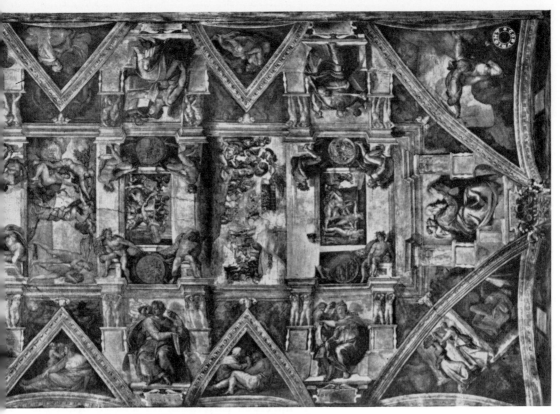

44' x 128'. 1508–1512. Vatican, Rome (Anderson)

of the soul as it struggles out of the darkness of ignorance into the blinding light of truth.

The eight spandrels, one of which is seen in Figure 10:14, tell the dismal tale of humanity without vision—"and Ezekias begat Manasses; and Manasses begat Amon; and Amon begat Josias." So reads the genealogy of the ancestors of Christ at the beginning of St. Matthew's Gospel. Endless generations of humdrum humanity, whose sole purpose is to reproduce themselves and hand the spark of life down to their children; as St. Luke says, they "sit in darkness and in the shadow of death," awaiting the light that will come when the Savior is born. In Gothic iconography, the ancestors were the kings of Judah starting with Jesse, David, and Solomon. Here in this spandrel, the child is the future King Josias, but Michelangelo represents him and all the others as a succession of common people dwelling in darkness. The mixture of good and evil is implied by the beauty of the mother on the child's right and the unenlightened form of his father Amon, who adored idols, on his left. The families huddled within these triangular prisons are but dimly aware of the words of the prophets above them and are quite unconscious of the divine happenings in the ideal region. In the

385

four corner spandrels are the heroic men and women whose active deeds secured temporal deliverance for their people. David's slaying of Goliath, Judith's decapitation of Holophernes, and Haman's punishment through Esther—all have to do with the victory of the weak over the strong with the aid of God. A note of prophecy and ultimate hope is sounded by the episode of Moses and the brazen serpent, an incident in the delivery of the children of Israel from their Egyptian bondage. The allusion comes from the Gospel of St. John: "And as Moses lifted up the serpent in the wilderness, even so must the Son of man be lifted up: that whosoever believeth in him should not perish, but have eternal life" (3:14–15).

This serves as an introduction to the representations of the seven Hebrew prophets, who alternate with five pagan sibyls like a chorus prophesying salvation. These are the inspired men and women who, through the exercise of their minds and imaginations, become the mediators between the human and divine spheres. They are consequently placed outside the confines of the dark spandrels and in a zone where the lighting approaches that of the central panels.

The *Delphic Sibyl* (Fig. 10:13) is the first of the series. In the Greek tradition and in Plato, she was the priestess of Apollo at Delphi. In Vergil's *Aeneid*, Book VI, she is described as a young woman possessed by the spirit of prophecy. In the grip of divine fury, she turns her head toward the voice of her inspiration. Though clothed in Greek garments, her beauty is similar to that of Michelangelo's early Madonnas. On either side of her throne are pairs of caryatidlike figures that are a part of the painted architectural pattern. In the shadow below the tablet, the head of a figure that symbolizes her corporeal nature can be seen. Diagonally behind her are a pair of nude figures that symbolize her inspiration. According to Plato, the soul, when concerned with the truth, is borne aloft on two wings. Ficino interpreted these as the mind and will; and Landino, a fellow Neo-Platonist, as the active and contemplative aspects of life, both of which are necessary for salvation. Above each of the prophets and sibyls and enframing the central panels are *ignudi*, or nude youths, as seen in Figure 10:19. In the Christian tradition, these figures would have been represented as angels, but in the Platonic theory, they personify the rational faculties of the sibyls and prophets by which man rises to the contemplation of divine truth, and by which he is able to bridge the gap between the physical and spiritual, or earthly and heavenly regions. Thus all the prophets and sibyls have a single figure below to denote the body, a pair of nudes behind them to signify the will, and a heroic *ignudo* to personify the immortal soul. These three levels correspond to Plato's tripartite conception of the soul—the appetitive, the emotional, and the intellective. These symbolic figures also play an aesthetic part in the softening of the harsh

(*Opposite.*) Michelangelo. Sistine Chapel Ceiling, Details. Fig. 10:13 (*above*) *Delphic Sibyl*. Fig. 10:14 (*below*). *Ancestor of Christ* (*Josias*). 1509 (Anderson)

DELPHICA

Michelangelo. Sistine Chapel Ceiling, Details. Fig. 10:15 (*above*). *Drunkenness of Noah*. 1508–1509. (Anderson). Fig. 10:16 (*below*). *Fall of Man and Expulsion from Paradise*. 1509–1510. (Alinari)

Michelangelo. Sistine Chapel Ceiling, Details. Fig. 10:17 (*above*). *Creation of Adam.* 1511. (Anderson). Fig. 10:18 (*below*). *Creation of Sun and Moon.* 1511. (Anderson)

contours of the architectural design. The nude adolescents function ostensibly as the bearers of the garland that runs around the central panels and from which the painted bronze medallions are suspended. By covering the corners of the frames, and by their postures, they contribute a needed diagonal accent and bring a welcome variety to the design as a whole.

The first of the histories in the central group is the *Drunkenness of Noah* (Fig. 10:15). As in the "slave" figures of the Julius monument, the picture of Noah shows man in his most abysmal condition as the victim of his own bodily appetites. His servitude is symbolized at the left, where he is seen tilling the parched soil. Though still strong physically, his spirit is overwhelmed by the flesh. His sons, young adolescents in their physical prime, do not seem to be discovering their father's nakedness, as related in the Bible, but the tragic fate of man himself, who must work, grow old, and die. Noah's reclining posture recalls that of the ancient Roman river gods, and in this case the head has sunk forward on his chest in what seems to be a premonition of death. After this picture of Noah as the prisoner of his own baser nature, the next panel pictures the Deluge, which shows the plight of man when beset by the elemental forces of nature beyond his control. In the third panel, *Noah's Sacrifice*, man's dependence on God is first implied.

Fall of Man and Expulsion from Paradise (Fig. 10:16) follows next. Temptation here is no mere passive affair but a willful greedy act of man. Adam eagerly reaches out for the fruit—again the victim of his appetites but with the power of making decisions. Eve, contrary to the Biblical story, is seen as the more passive of the two. Adam's hulking body is almost subhuman, while that of Eve is soft and sensuous. The motif of her uplifted arm is repeated by the branch springing out of the tree trunk in the background. The serpent with the torso of a woman recalls that of the ancient sirens or maenads. The pairing of the serpent and the avenging angel on the expulsion side probably implies that sin and retribution, like cause and effect, are the twin aspects of evil. Masaccio's fresco in the Brancacci Chapel (Fig. 9:18) was clearly the model for Michelangelo's Adam and Eve on this side. Adam's body, however, has undergone a significant change from the temptation side, and he now appears morally aware of his action, while Eve cringes and attempts to hide in his shadow. On one side, the concern was with blind desire; on the other, it is a matter of knowledge and remorse.

The last five panels are concerned with the various aspects of God's nature. In the *Creation of Eve*, He appears as a patriarchal figure closed within the folds of His mantle, His head bent forward as if in deep thought. As in the Gospel according to St. John: "In the beginning was the Word, and the Word was with God, and the Word was God." The implication in Michelangelo's Neo-Platonic conception is that the creative process is a rational one. In the *Creation of Adam* (Fig. 10:17), God appears in the skies, His mantle surrounding Him like a cloud, as He moves toward the earth and the inert body of Adam. The creative force is here the divine fire that flashes like lightning from the cloud to the earth. Adam's body is one with the rock on which he lies, not unlike the unfinished "slaves" of the Julius tomb. In keeping with the Platonic idea of life as a burden and imprisonment, Adam is awakening to life reluctantly rather than eagerly. With His other arm, God embraces Eve, who again resembles Michelangelo's Madonna types, and who looks with fear and awe on this act of creation; His fingers point to the coming Christ Child, while behind Him are the heads of unborn generations of mankind.

In the *Creation of the Sun and the Moon* (Fig. 10:18), the representation of God becomes a personification of the creative principle. Like one of the celestial bodies, He moves in an orbit throwing off stars and planets, which continue in the courses He sets for them. This flight through the firmament implies the omnipresent aspect of God. The progressive minimizing of the subject matter as the story unfolds shows that Michelangelo was concentrating progressively on God's creative power rather than on the things created.

In *God Dividing the Light from Darkness* (Fig. 10:19), the final panel of the series, the climax and the realm of pure being are attained. Here is clarity coming out of chaos, order from the void, existence from nothingness, the idea from unconsciousness. You shall know the truth and the truth shall make you free, according to the Scriptures; or know thyself, as the Delphic oracle told Socrates. The conception of God has progressed from the patriarchal human figure of the *Creation of Eve* to that of a cosmic spirit in the intervening panels, and now He is seen as a swirling abstraction in the realm of pure being. The Neo-Platonic objective of the union of the soul with God has been achieved by the gradual progress from the bondage of the spandrels, through the prophetic visions of the seers, and, finally, by ascending the ladder of the histories into the pure light of knowledge, to the point of dissolution into the freedom of infinity. In the words of Pico della Mirandola, man "withdraws into the center of his own oneness, his spirit made one with God."

The weight of expression, story content, and philosophical meaning is carried entirely by Michelangelo's disposition and treatment of the 300-odd human figures in a seemingly infinite variety of postures. His method of work commands considerable interest. The cartoon of the whole was first drawn on paper, next cut up into sections of a size corresponding to each day's work, and then transferred to the ceiling surface. A section of moistened lime wash of the same proportions was prepared, and the painting was then done in the technique known as *fresco-buono*. The departures Michelangelo made from the cartoons show that there was an element of improvisation as he went along. The colors are limited by the medium, and as the work progressed his preference was more and more in the direction of shades of gray, which accented the three-dimensional, sculptur-

Fig. 10:19. Michelangelo. Sistine Chapel Ceiling, Detail. *God Dividing Light from Darkness*. 1511. (Anderson)

esque quality of the figures. Such large projects are almost always school jobs, but from the internal evidence of the frescoes, as well as from documentary sources, Michelangelo appears to have done all the painting himself, with assistants doing the preparatory work only.

Owing to the extremely awkward nature of ceiling painting, Michelangelo had to lie on his back most of the time—a fact that gave rise to one of his most eloquent sonnets, which goes in part:

> My beard turns up to heaven; my nape falls in,
> Fixed on my spine: my breast-bone visibly
> Grows like a harp: a rich embroidery
> Bedews my face from brush-drops thick and thin.

Though he later returned to the Sistine Chapel to paint the *Last Judgment* (Fig. 12:1) and worked on another group for the Pauline Chapel in the Vatican, Michelangelo never recaptured the buoyant optimism and creative force of the earlier series. The impact of the Sistine Chapel ceiling today, as it was on Michelangelo's contemporaries, is like a revelation of one of the eternal verities. Coming as this stupendous work did at the height of the artist's creative powers, the composition as a whole is among the highest peaks in the mountain range of Western art.

At the same time that Michelangelo was painting the Sistine ceiling, Raphael, a younger contemporary, was at work on the murals of the Vatican Palace. In the *School of Athens* (Fig. 10:20), Raphael presents such a complete visual philosophy that it places him, along with Michelangelo, in the rarified ranks of artist-scholars. Raphael's fresco is full of intellectual as well as pictorial complexities. Yet by the expanding space of the setting, and the skillful deployment of the figures, as well as their relationships to each other and the architecture, it is clear and uncluttered. As members of a philosophical circle intent on reconciling the views of Plato and Aristotle, Raphael and his friends held that any point in Plato could be translated into a proposition of Aristotle and vice versa—the principal difference being that Plato wrote in poetic images, while Aristotle used the language of rational analysis. The two philosophers, "who agree in substance while they disagree in words," are placed on either side of the central axis of the fresco with the vanishing point between them. The book Plato holds in his hands is his *Timaeus*, and he points skyward to indicate his idealistic world view; Aristotle carries a copy of his *Ethics* and indicates by his earthward gesture his greater concern with the real and practical world.

In the spacious hall, which recalls the Roman poet Lucretius' remark on "temples raised by philosophy," the various schools of thought argue or ponder on the ideas propounded by the two central figures. On Plato's side a niche contains a statue of Apollo, patron of poetry; on Aristotle's is one of Athena, goddess

Fig. 10:20. Raphael. *School of Athens*. Fresco. c.26′ x 18′. 1509–1510. Stanza della Segnatura, Vatican, Rome. (For a detail, see frontispiece of this book.) (Vatican Photographic Archive)

of reason. This division of the central figures equates the entire picture, with the metaphysical philosophers ranked on Plato's side and the physical scientists pursuing their various researches on Aristotle's. Spreading outward are groups corresponding to the divergent schools of thought within the two major divisions, and who carry the various arguments to their logical conclusion. The figure of Plato is thought to be an idealized portrait of the aged Leonardo da Vinci, and in the group at the lower right (see frontispiece) Raphael portrayed his architect friend Bramante as Euclid bending over his slate to demonstrate a geometrical proposition. At the extreme right, Raphael paints a self-portrait in profile next to his friend and collaborator, the painter Sodoma. In the *School of Athens* as a whole, Raphael captured the intellectual atmosphere and the zest with which Renaissance ideas were argued. By his grouping and placement of figures, and by their attitudes, attributes, and gestures, he provides a far clearer commentary on the complex thought of his time than did the more tortuous philosophical treatises of the period. To paint such metaphysical abstractions at all, and clothe them with plastic form, is a triumph of clear thinking and logical organization; and posterity is fortunate to have this summation of Renaissance humanism as seen through the eyes of such a profound artist.

THE DOME OF ST. PETER'S

The religious and intellectual atmosphere of Rome was a far cry from what it had been in the days of Julius II and Leo X when in the 1540's Michelangelo completed his series of frescoes on SS. Peter and Paul in the Pauline Chapel of the Vatican. The Protestant Reformation was an established fact, and the Council of Trent was beginning the deliberations that set the forces of the Counter-Reformation in motion. Ignatius Loyola had already been in Rome, and the Jesuit order had received papal approval. The Congregation of the Inquisition and the censorship of printed matter promised restrictions on the expression of ideas. Artists no longer were given a free hand with their pictures but had to accept the advice of ecclesiastical authorities. And Michelangelo, now in his 70's, was under attack for the nudes and pagan elements of his *Last Judgment* mural completed several years earlier in the Sistine Chapel.

These and other considerations weighed heavily on Michelangelo's mind and to a certain extent influenced his decision to devote himself mainly to architecture during the remainder of his life. Consequently, it was not difficult for his friend Pope Paul III, for whom he had painted the Pauline Chapel frescoes, to persuade Michelangelo to finish the Farnese Palace in 1546 and then to become chief architect of St. Peter's (Fig. 10:21), the project that absorbed most of his energies thereafter.

While the foundations of the new St. Peter's had been laid as early as 1506, when Michelangelo was starting plans for Pope Julius' tomb, comparatively little progress had been made in the tempestuous years that followed, in spite of the succession of brilliant architects. Michelangelo favored the centralized church plans of Brunelleschi and Alberti just as his predecessor Bramante had done. The latter's design, however, was to have culminated in a low dome, modeled after that of the Pantheon but with a peristyle base and a lantern on top. Michelangelo accepted Bramante's Greek-cross ground plan with a few alterations of his own (Fig. 10:22), but he envisaged a loftier canopy rising over the legendary site of St. Peter's tomb. This dome was to be of such monumental proportions that it would unify not only the interior spaces and exterior masses of the building but would serve also as the climax of the liturgical, religious, and artistic forces of the Catholic world and as a symbol of the center of Christendom.

Michelangelo's first problem was an engineering one—to see whether the masonry was strong enough to support such a dome. It was not, and he had to reinforce the four main piers until they were a massive 60 feet square. Pendentives became the means by which the square understructure was encircled, and then the drum was ready to rise. Meanwhile he made a large model of the dome itself, so that it could be built by others if necessary. All the preparatory work was thus completed, and Michelangelo lived just long enough to see the drum

Fig. 10:21. St. Peter's Basilica and the Vatican, Rome. Apse and dome by Michelangelo, 1547–1564, dome completed by Giacomo della Porta, 1588–1592; nave and façade by Carlo Maderno, 1606–1626 (façade 147′ high, 374′ wide); colonnades by Gianlorenzo Bernini, 1656–1663 (Alinari)

Fig. 10:22 (*below*). St. Peter's, Rome. Bramante's, Michelangelo's, and Present *Plans*

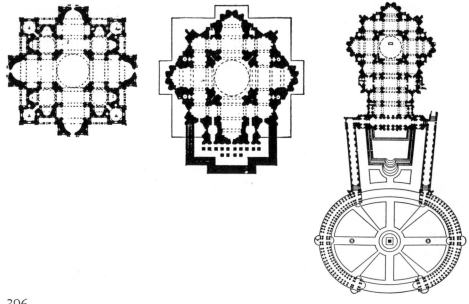

Fig. 10:23 (*above*). Michelangelo. St. Peter's, *Apse and Dome*. 452′ high. Begun 1547. (Vatican Photographic Archive). Fig. 10:24 (*below*). Michelangelo and Maderno. St. Peter's, *Interior beneath Dome*. (Vatican Photographic Archive)

finished. The dome was completed after his death by two of his associates without substantial alterations. But for the aftermath of the Council of Trent and the Counter-Reformation, Michelangelo's centralized church might also have been finished. The new spirit of orthodoxy, however, frowned on anything that might be considered a pagan form, and a reactionary wave was started in favor of a return to the traditional Latin-cross plan. In the early 17th century, Carlo Maderno undertook the lengthening of the nave (Fig. 10:22). Liturgically, the new nave provided more space for the grandiose processions; practically, it provided room for larger congregations; historically, it absorbed all the area formerly occupied by Constantine's basilica, which had been demolished to make way for the new structure; but, aesthetically, the proportions suffered, and the climactic effect of the great dome was diminished. The scale of the interior (Fig. 10:24), however, was already set by Michelangelo's huge piers beneath the dome, and Maderno had to continue the same proportions. The vaulting thus rises a little over 150 feet above the pavement, while the enormous interior covers more than 25,000 square yards in area.

The exterior of the church Michelangelo planned can best be seen from the apse, and the interior from beneath the dome where it appears as the compact unified structure he wanted. From the apse of the completed church (Fig. 10:23), where the lengthened nave does not detract, the effect is still substantially as Michelangelo intended it to be. From this vantage point the building itself appears as a great podium for the support of the vast superstructure; and from the ground level to the base of the dome there is a rise of about 250 feet. The cupola then continues upward to the top of the lantern, where an ultimate height of 452 feet above the ground level is attained. Until the advent of the Eiffel Tower and the 20th-century skyscrapers, St. Peter's was at once the world's tallest and largest building. Coming as it did with the spread of the Counter-Reformation and the commercial exploitation and colonization of the New World, the church and its great dome had an enormous influence on future church architecture (see Figs. 12:12, 15:3, 16:4) and on such secular structures as the national capitol in Washington, D.C., and numerous state capitols.

JOSQUIN DES PREZ AND THE SISTINE CHAPEL CHOIR

"I am well aware that in his day Ockeghem was as it were the first to rediscover music, then as good as dead, just as Donatello discovered sculpture in his; and that of Josquin, Ockeghem's pupil, one might say that he was a natural prodigy in music, just as our own Michelangelo Buonarroti has been in architecture, painting, and sculpture; for just as Josquin has still to be surpassed in his compositions, so Michelangelo stands alone and without a peer among all who have practiced his arts; and the one and the other have opened the eyes of all who delight in these arts, now and in the future." So wrote a Florentine literary historian in a book on Dante published in 1567. Josquin des Prez, to whom he referred, was thus still regarded almost half a century after his death as a figure comparable to that of Michelangelo. A Florentine could bestow no higher praise. The same opinion, moreover, was held by musicians. The distinguished theorist Glareanus wrote that the work of Josquin was "the perfect art to which nothing can be added, after which nothing but decline can be expected."

The so-called *ars perfecta*, or perfect art, rested on the typical Renaissance historical assumption of the great development of the arts in antiquity, which had been lost in medieval days and subsequently rediscovered in the then-modern times. The quotations above are a critical application of this doctrine of perfection regained to the art of music. Italians, whether at home or abroad, took the greatest pride in the achievements of their own architects, sculptors, and painters, but universally they acknowledged the supremacy of the northern composers. The spread of the northern polyphonic art dated from the time the popes had become acquainted with it at Avignon. Later, it led to the establishment of the *Cappella Sixtina* in 1473, which was dominated by Flemish, Burgundian, and French musicians, whose influence from there spread over the entire Christian world. From this time forward, their mastery of contrapuntal writing became the standard of perfection.

Under Pope Sixtus IV, church music had moved from its status as the modest handmaiden of the liturgy to a position of major importance. The grandeur of the Roman liturgical displays called for music of comparable magnificence. Owing to the prevailing taste of the time, musicians from the great singing centers of Antwerp, Liège, and Cambrai flocked to Rome to seek their fortunes. The highest honor of all was an appointment to the Sistine Choir, whose privilege it was to perform on the occasions at which the pope himself officiated. Membership was highly selective, totaling from 16 to 24 singers except during the time of the musical Leo X when it was increased to 36. These singers were divided into four parts: boy sopranos, male altos, tenors, and basses; normally they sang *a cappella*—that is, without instrumental accompaniment—a practice that was exceptional rather than usual at the time. The quality of the choir can be deduced from the roster of distinguished men who made their reputations in its ranks. Dufay, the first composer to view the Mass as an organic work of art, entered the choir in 1428. In its archives are numerous masses, motets, and psalm settings by Josquin des Prez, who served from 1486 to 1494. Palestrina, who learned contrapuntal fluency from Josquin, first became a member in 1551 and later brought the organization to a pinnacle of technical perfection.

Josquin's attitude on the dignity of the art of composition is most revealing. When the Duke of Ferrara needed a composer, he hesitated between Isaac and Josquin. He was advised in a letter from a friend who knew them both to choose

Isaac, "because he is able to get along with his colleagues and composes new pieces quicker. It is true, Josquin composes better, but he does it only when it suits him and not when he is requested. More than this Josquin asks 200 ducats while Isaac is pleased with 120." Like Michelangelo, then, Josquin behaved very much as the modern independent artist with high standards of proficiency, rather than as a craftsman who produced works on order regardless of quality.

In Josquin's compositions, the stark barren intervals of Gothic polyphony and all traces of harshness in the voice leading are eliminated. He allows dissonances to occur only on weak beats or as suspensions on the stronger ones. His rhythms and forms are based on strict symmetry and mathematically regular proportions. His writing is characterized by the usual northern fondness for canonic imitations and other complicated contrapuntal constructions. Such devices, however, are managed with complete mastery, and his tremendous technique in composition never intrudes upon his expressive design. He was at home in all Renaissance musical forms, excelling perhaps in his motets and in his solo and choral chansons. In Rome, where his unique abilities were combined with the warmth and fluidity of Italian lyricism, his art mellowed into a style of incomparable beauty, formal clarity, and the purest expressivity.

Ave Maria. 4-Part Motet   Josquin des Prez

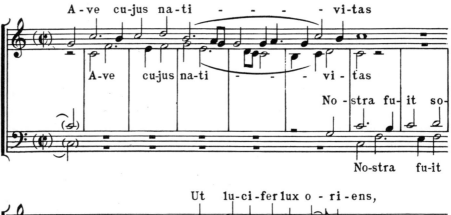

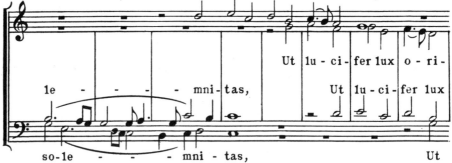

Josquin's four-part motet *Ave Maria* will serve as an admirable illustration of his art. Like Michelangelo's early *Pietà*, it is in a perfectly self-contained form, emotionally restrained, and full of luxuriantly flowing lines. Even such a short excerpt as this shows his penchant for canonic imitation between the voices and the smoothness of contour that comes with stepwise melodic motion. He treats all four voices with balanced impartiality but prefers to group them in pairs, as in this instance, in order to achieve a transparency of texture and an ineffable purity of sound. Darker sides of Josquin's emotional spectrum can be found in his Requiem Masses and in his setting of the psalm De Profundis.

Later periods saw in Michelangelo both a summing up of the Renaissance and the beginning of the baroque style. Josquin's place was more limited; and while he was universally acknowledged as the greatest musical mind of the early 16th century, the very perfection of his art implied that it was on the verge of becoming archaic. His mantle was inherited by a number of composers in the succeeding generation, who carried his art to its logical conclusion. Palestrina's music has been held to be better adapted to religious purposes, though he remains Josquin's inferior in invention, inspiration, and depth of expression. Victoria carried the style to Spain, William Byrd to England; and through Philippe de Monte and Orlando Lassus, it spread throughout France and Germany. In the 17th century, though the art was still studied, it became known as the "antique style" in contrast to the baroque music, which was called the "modern style." Within its limitations the art has never been surpassed. Even today it is considered the ideal for church music, and no conservatory curriculum is complete without a course in 16th-century counterpoint.

HUMANISM

Florentine humanism and its Roman aftermath were motivated by a reappraisal of the values of Greco-Roman antiquity, by an attempt to reconcile pagan forms with Christian practices, by a desire to reinstate the philosophy of Plato and reinterpret that of Aristotle, and, above all, by a rediscovery of the world and man. The Renaissance humanist was not primarily religious- or scientific-minded. He tended to substitute the authority of respected classical writers for that of the Bible and church dogma. In looking forward, he found more convenient and convincing precedents in the civilizations of Greece and Rome than in the immediate medieval past. Lorenzo de' Medici, for instance, found a new orientation for secular government in Plato's *Republic*, Machiavelli a new method for writing history in Thucydides.

The humanists preferred purer versions of classical art forms to the adaptations that had been made in the 1000-year period between the fall of Rome and their own time. The members of the Florentine humanistic circle learned to read

Fig. 10:25. Leonardo da Vinci. *Last Supper*. Fresco. 14′ 5″ x 28′ ¼″. *c.*1495–1498.
Santa Maria delle Grazie, Milan (Soprintendenza)

and speak ancient Greek under native tutors. Ficino translated the dialogues of
Plato, while Poliziano translated Homer from the original Greek into Italian and
wrote treatises in Latin on Greek poetic and musical theory. Other scholars catalogued and edited books for the Medici library, while Squarcialupi compiled the
musical compositions of the preceding century. The interest in cataloguing,
editing, translating, and commenting was pursued with such enthusiasm that it
all but blotted out the production of live literature. The Latin of Renaissance
scholars was Ciceronian rather than medieval Latin, which they considered corrupt. The architects read Vitruvius and preferred central-type churches modeled
on the Pantheon to the oblong-basilica form that had been evolved over the centuries. They revived the classical orders and architectural proportions in a more
authentic form. Decorative motifs were derived directly from ancient sarcophagi,
reliefs, and carved gems. Sculptors reaffirmed the expressive possibilities of the
nude, and with Michelangelo it became the chief expressive vehicle of his art.
Painters, lacking tangible survivals, used mythological subjects and the literary
descriptions of ancient masterpieces.

Musicians reinterpreted Greek musical thought, and some made concrete
attempts to put into practice the theories expounded in Euclid's musical treatise.
The Greek assertion that art imitates nature was universally acknowledged, but
in architecture and music it had to be applied in the general sense of nature as
an orderly and regular system conforming to mathematical proportions and laws.
Josquin des Prez was hailed as a modern Orpheus who had regained the lost

perfect art of the ancients—though the Greeks would have been bewildered by his musical style. Josquin's less-enthusiastic admirers pointed out that the trees and stones still showed some reluctance to follow him as they had not in the case of the original Orpheus. His art, however, like that of Michelangelo, was thought by the humanists to be a path back to a lost classical paradise.

Both Botticelli and Michelangelo set out to produce works in the Neo-Platonic spirit. The literary ancestry of Botticelli's *Allegory of Spring, Birth of Venus* (Fig. 9:24), and *Venus and Mars* (Fig. 9:23) has been traced back to the Roman poets Lucretius and Horace through the poetry of his contemporary, Poliziano. Its philosophical forebear, however, is the Plato of the *Symposium*, which deals with the nature of love and beauty. Man, according to Plato's theory, has drunk of the waters of oblivion and forgotten his divine origin. Falling in love with a beautiful person reminds him of his natural affinity for beauty. From physical attraction and ephemeral loveliness, he is led to thoughts of the lasting beauty of truth and, finally, to the contemplation of the eternal verities of absolute beauty, truth, and goodness. Venus was, of course, the image of this transcendent beauty, and the way to approach it is through love. The eternal feminine, as Goethe said in the closing lines of *Faust*, draws us ever onward. Michelangelo's Plato, however, was the Plato of the *Timaeus*, which discourses on the creation of the world by the Demiurge, the metaphysical na-

Fig. 10:26. Bramante. Tempietto. Marble. *c.*15′ diameter. 1502. San Pietro in Montorio, Rome (Soprintendenza)

ture of the human soul, and the return to God. Unlike Botticelli's fragile dream of beauty, Michelangelo had a virile vision of the creative process itself. When Botticelli came under the influence of the fiery Savonarola with his resurgence of medievalism, he repented of his paganism and turned exclusively to religious pictures. He never tried to combine his paganism and Christianity as did Michelangelo, and for him they remained in separate compartments and on an either/or basis. Michelangelo, however, had the mind to assimilate Platonic abstractions, the overwhelming urge to express his ideas, and the technical equipment to translate them into dramatic visual form. But the voice of Savonarola spoke loudly to him, and in his rugged mind he was destined to wrestle with the two essentially irreconcilable philosophies for the rest of his life. Leonardo da Vinci, contrariwise, kept the religious themes of his paintings (see Fig. 10:25) and his scientific inquiries in separate intellectual compartments.

To Michelangelo, a work of art always had to participate in the world of ideas, and all his works are philosophical as well as aesthetic creations. In his early *Bacchus* he wholeheartedly embraced paganism, a fact that made the *Pietà* that followed it no less a sincere declaration of religious faith. Then came the synthesis of the Sistine Ceiling, in which pagan sibyls sit side by side with Hebrew prophets, and the Platonic theory of the return to God is reconciled with the Christian doctrine of salvation. Even in the apocalyptical fury of the *Last Judgment*, mythological characters are juxtaposed with those from the Old and New Testaments. In his late years, he entered a passionate religious phase, but his sonnets written at the same time show him still true to the Platonic ideas of his youth. His Madonnas reveal the unity between bodily beauty and eternal beauty; his *Moses* links human moral power and eternal goodness; and his organic compositions connect temporal with eternal truth. His triple divisions symbolizing the stages of the soul as it progresses from its bodily tomb to its liberation and reunion with God are a constantly recurring preoccupation. Even in his abstract architectural forms of St. Peter's, the pilasters are the "slaves" imprisoned by the weight of the material burden they must carry, while overhead soars the lofty dome in the geometrical perfection of the circular form, symbolizing the paradise that man has lost and that he must somehow regain. The whole building is thus conceived as an organic system of pressures and tensions leading upward and culminating in a cupola that ascends toward the divine realm and finally dissolves into the freedom of infinity.

Borromini. Church of Sant'Ivo della Sapienza. *Façade from Courtyard*. 1642–1650. Rome (Gabinetto Fotografico Nazionale)

Part 4

THE BAROQUE PERIOD

CHRONOLOGY:

Venice, 16th Century

General Events

1453	Fall of Constantinople to Turks; Venetian commerce challenged
1492	Geographical discoveries by Spanish and Portuguese navigators began to weaken Venetian maritime trade
1495	Aldine Press began publishing inexpensive editions of Greek and Roman classics
1501	*Odhecaton*, anthology of vocal and instrumental works by Josquin des Prez, Obrecht, Isaac, and others printed in Venice by Petrucci
1517	Protestant Reformation began
1527– 1562	Willaert choirmaster of St. Mark's
1536	Library of St. Mark built by J. Sansovino
1545– 1563	Council of Trent initiated the Counter-Reformation
1570	Palladio published *Four Books of Architecture*
1571	Naval Battle of Lepanto; Venice and Spain defeated Turks
1573	Veronese called before Inquisition
1576	Palladio's Church *Il Redentore* dedicated
1585– 1612	Giovanni Gabrieli choirmaster of St. Mark's
1589	Olympic Theater at Vicenza finished; performance of Sophocles *Oedipus* (music by A. Gabrieli)
1613– 1643	Monteverdi choirmaster of St. Mark's
1631	Santa Maria della Salute begun by Longhena

Architects

1477–	1570	Jacopo Sansovino
1508–	1580	Palladio
1552–	1616	Scamozzi
1604–	1675	Longhena

Painters

1429–	1507	Gentile Bellini
c.1430–	1516	Giovanni Bellini
c.1455–c.1526		Carpaccio
1477–	1576	Titian
1478–	1510	Giorgione
1510–	1592	Jacopo Bassano
1518–	1594	Tintoretto
1528–	1588	Veronese

Musicians

c.1480–	1562	Willaert
1510–	1586	Andrea Gabrieli
1516–	1565	Cipriano de Rore
1517–	1590	Zarlino
1557–	1612	Giovanni Gabrieli
1567–	1643	Monteverdi
1602–	1676	Cavalli

Italian and International Mannerists

c.1492–	1546	Giulio Romano
1494–	1540	Rosso Fiorentino
1494–	1556	Pontormo
1500–	1571	Benvenuto Cellini
1503–	1540	Parmagianino
1503–	1575	Bronzino
1511–	1574	Vasari
1529–	1600	Giovanni da Bologna
1555–	1619	Ludovico Carracci
1560–	1609	Annibale Carracci

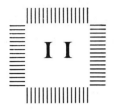

I I

VENETIAN MANNERISM
AND EARLY BAROQUE

VENICE, 16TH CENTURY

Through the eyes of the painter Gentile Bellini, one can catch a glimpse of
Venice as it was at the threshold of the 16th century. Gentile's faithful report-
ing—so accurate that architectural historians can make reconstructions of buildings long since razed; that researchers can study the mosaics and sculptures of
St. Mark's basilica as they were before later restorations; that historians of liturgy,
musical performance, and costume find it prime source material—belongs to
Renaissance naturalism. When compared with the forthcoming flights of mannerist and early baroque imaginations, its stateliness and stability are all the more
striking. The subject matter of the *Procession in St. Mark's Square* (Fig. 11:1),
its story content, mode of representation, formal organization, and circumstances
of its commission reveal much about the life of Venice and the unique developments in the arts during this transitional period.

Surrounding the spacious piazza are the buildings from many periods and in
the several styles that reflect the history of the city, and the façade of St. Mark's
itself at once proclaims that Venice was a meeting place of Occident and Orient.
Begun in the 10th century, St. Mark's is the product of centuries of community
effort, and indeed an early law required every Venetian ship to bring back

materials for the construction or decoration of the church. As a result, fragments from every Mediterranean country can be found somewhere in its fabric—from the four Roman bronze horses of the first century A.D. that stand over the central portal, the Alexandrian polychrome marble columns and Greek alabaster windows, to the present-day additions and alterations. The plan is that of a Greek cross with domes covering each of the four wings and a 42-foot cupola in the center (Fig. 11:2).

Above the narthex entrance, stretching the full width of the façade, is an open gallery on which, in Bellini's picture, several figures can be seen. Above the gallery is a row of five 13th-century Gothic ogee gables that frame the upper tier of mosaics. On the crest of the central gable is the winged lion of St. Mark, one of the four beasts that symbolize the Evangelists, placed here to honor him as the city's patron saint. To the right is a corner of the Doge's Palace where the ruler and his guests are seated on the second-story arcade. This bizarre variation of a Gothic town hall rises in two stories of open pointed arches surmounted by a third story notable for its diamond-shaped design in bright pink marble. On the extreme left is the old library from which many spectators are watching the activities in the square below. The building resembles a Renaissance palace in some respects, but the castellated roof and odd-shaped chimney pots give it a character that defies exact classification. More remarkable than its architecture, however, is the institution of the library itself. In lieu of outstanding literary figures, Venice treasured the collections of books left to her by such donors as the poet Petrarch and the Greek scholar Cardinal Bessarion because they would be less in danger of fire in this watery city than elsewhere. In addition, the library housed all the specimens of the city's elegant printing and book-making industry, which included the fine but inexpensive editions of classics published here for the first time by the famous Aldine Press, and which gave such great momentum to the spread of learning throughout the educated world. In the 16th century, these collections were transferred to the handsome building across the square designed by Sansovino especially to house them (Fig. 11:3). In Bellini's painting, after the ceremony the procession files out of the basilica through a passageway between St. Mark's and the Doge's Palace in the right background and moves around the square to the opposite side where all the separate groups gather.

Since it was commissioned by the organization known as the *Gran Scuola di San Giovanni Evangelista* as a mural for its chapter house, and since it is a collective portrait of the *Scuola's* membership, Bellini's painting is technically a *corporation picture*. Aristocrats and commoners, priests and laymen, men and women—all in all about two thirds of Venice's population—were members of some 200-odd *scuole*. These fraternal bodies combined the activities of a social club, lodge, professional society, charitable institution, and insurance company

Fig. 11:1. Gentile Bellini. *Procession in St. Mark's Square*. Oil on canvas. 10′ high. 1496. Academy, Venice (Böhm)

Fig. 11:2. Venice, Air View. Doge's Palace (center, below); St. Mark's (center, above); Library of St. Mark (left, below); Campanile and St. Mark's Square (left, above)

as well as the patronage of the arts. On the annual feast days of their patron saint, they sponsored grand public ceremonies such as that depicted.

While Bellini's picture narrates an event in the history of the school, one has to look hard to find the main character in the kneeling figure of a visitor from Brescia. That morning he had heard that his son had been injured in a hunting accident, and he drops to his knees imploring divine aid as the reliquary containing a splinter of the true Cross passes by. Later he learns that his son was restored to health at that very moment. The miraculous incident is obviously subordinated by Bellini to the construction of a large picture in skillful perspective, to the portraiture of members of the *scuola* in their ceremonial robes, and to the splendor of the colorful pageant. Such detachment foreshadows the break from the tyranny of subject matter that is to come in the pastoral themes and elusive moods of Giorgione and Titian, and the establishment of formal controls that is to result from the academic approach of Palladio and Veronese. Bellini's picture also stands in direct opposition to the turbulent treatment and feverish illusionism a similar scene is to receive at the hands of such free mannerist and early baroque figures as Tintoretto and El Greco.

A feeling of open public life and freedom of social movement can be sensed in the participants as well as the bystanders in this processional scene. The independence of Venice as well as the prosperity of her citizenry was owing in many respects to her unusual situation. Built on a group of island lagoons at the head of the Adriatic, Venice was truly what a Florentine poet described as "a city in the water without walls." Secure from attack by land and by sea by possession of the largest navy then in existence, Venice carried on an active commerce between Orient and Occident that afforded her citizens a manner of life unrivaled in its time for comfort and luxury. Lacking the ups and downs of other medieval and Renaissance cities, such as Pisa and Siena with their brief periods of florescence, Venice developed slowly and consistently from the glow of its Byzantine dawn, through a Renaissance high noon and a brief thunderstorm of mannerism, to its magnificent florid baroque sunset.

Here lived no literary giant such as Dante, no magnifico with the vision of a Lorenzo, no political philosopher of the caliber of Machiavelli, no thundering religious reformer like Savonarola. In fact, without great men of letters, without outstanding individual art patrons, without inspired religious leaders—in short, without experiencing the heights and depths of the human spirit known in Florence or Rome—Venice nevertheless built up in its architecture, painting, and music a culture uniquely its own.

Though the Venetian government was dominated by a coalition of wealthy merchant families, a measure of political freedom was maintained under the doges, who were elected rather than hereditary rulers. Some religious freedom was also achieved by isolation from Rome and by such strategic devices as designating immense St. Mark's as the "private chapel of the doges," since heads of state could always control the appointment of clergy, choirmasters, and singers in their personal establishments. But while this island city-state in Bellini's time could still justify its chosen title of Most Serene Republic, storm clouds were gathering on the horizon.

The fall of Constantinople to the Turks and the rising power of the Ottoman Empire spelled competition for Venice's commercial empire, and sporadic warfare had already begun. While Venice had given birth to one great explorer, Marco Polo, the voyages of the 16-century Spanish, Portuguese, Dutch, and English navigators were being exploited to enrich rival countries, thereby upsetting the traditional economy in which Venice had flourished. Italy was soon to become a battleground in the European power struggle between the Holy Roman Empire and France. Charles V, Titian's great patron, became emperor in 1519, and in addition to Spain his dominions included the Low Countries, Germany, and Austria. Francis I of France, feeling his country caught in a giant pincers, tried to fortify his position by invading Italy. But one by one each Italian kingdom, principality, dukedom, and republic fell to Charles V. Finally, by sacking and pillaging Rome itself with his ruthless mercenaries and imprisoning Pope Clement VII, Charles achieved the surrender of the papacy itself. The religious crisis brought on by opposing forces of the Reformation and Counter-Reformation likewise unsettled Venice's trade and cultural relations with northern Europe. Though the Universal Inquisition was felt more mildly in Venice than elsewhere, Roman Catholic censorship of printed matter and assertion of the clergy's control of art proved more than a threat to Venice's publishing industry and artistic freedom. Venetians, to be sure, were no strangers to insecurity as fabulous fortunes were made overnight when their ships came in, and financial ruin and debtor's prison followed shipwrecks, seizure by pirates, or sinkings in naval battles. This Pandora's box of troubles pointed to a decline of Venice's commercial position and a crisis in its art. One road out of the crisis was to lead to a freezing of classical order, formal logic, and balanced symmetry in a type of conservative academic *mannerism*—art "in the manner" of the great painters of the past; the other was to lead to the capricious eccentricities, unresolved tensions, and restless imbalances of free mannerism, and eventually to the new synthesis of the baroque.

ARCHITECTURE

As did all the other arts, Venetian architecture reached out toward new forms. Although begun as early as 1536 and still within the Renaissance tradition, the Library of St. Mark (Fig. 11:3) by Jacopo Sansovino already has enough new ideas to qualify it as a transition to the coming baroque style. Standing out boldly

Fig. 11:3. Jacopo Sanso-
vine. Library of St. Mark.
c.290′ long, 60′ high. Begun 1536. Venice (Ander-
son)

from the façade are the rich decorative details the Venetians loved. Instead of
the solid, flat surfaces of Renaissance façades with their heavily rusticated ground
floors (see Fig. 9:6), Sansovino has an open arcade, paralleled above by the row
of deeply indented windows. This projection in depth makes for an effective
play of light and shadow, an element hitherto associated more with sculpture and
painting than with architecture. It seems, moreover, far from accidental that the
origins of baroque architecture can be traced to Michelangelo, Sansovino, and
Palladio, who were first trained as sculptors. This transfer of sculptural thought to
architecture is also responsible for the ascendancy of embellishment over architectural function that characterizes the baroque. In this instance, however,
Sansovino's design can hardly be characterized as florid. The dignified arcade of
the lower story serves as a base for the increasingly rich adornment of the upper
parts. The deeply arched windows of the second floor are unified by the regularity of the Ionic columns, while the poses of the sculptured nudes in the spandrels
provide variety. Above runs a frieze of cherubs in high relief holding garlands
that alternate with small, deep-set windows. Over this rises a balustrade that

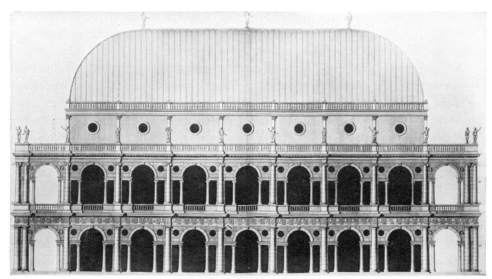

Palladio. Basilica at Vicenza. Fig. 11:4 (*above*). *c*.1550. Architectural drawing

Fig. 11:5 (*right*) Detail.
c.1550. Vicenza (Böhm)

goes all the way around the roof and supports a row of statues silhouetted against the skyline. The proportion of the upper entablature is noteworthy in that it is over one third the height of the supporting order itself.

Sansovino's designs influenced Andrea Palladio, the greatest architect associated with the Venetian style. As the author of the highly influential *Four Books of Architecture*, first published in Venice in 1570, Palladio has left a detailed exposition of his philosophy. In his Preface he pays eloquent tribute to his ancient Roman mentor Vitruvius, whose writings stimulated his study of the classical buildings in Rome. "Finding that they deserved a much more diligent Observation than I thought at first Sight," he noted, "I began with the utmost Accuracy to measure every minutest part by itself." Palladio's ideas are thus based on a thorough grounding in traditional design. He likewise pays tribute to his immediate predecessor Sansovino, whose Library is praised as "perhaps the most sumptuous and the most beautiful Edifice that has been erected since the time of the Ancients."

Palladio's architecture can be studied more fully in Vicenza than in Venice itself. The winged lion of St. Mark is as prominent a feature there as it is in the corresponding main square in Venice some 42 miles away, since the city was at this time a part of the Venetian Republic's extensive holdings on the mainland of Italy. The most imposing building of the central piazza at Vicenza is Palladio's Basilica (Figs. 11:4 and 11:5). Explaining his intentions, he states: "As the Ancients made their *Basilicas* after such a manner, that in the Spring and Summer People might come together there, to treat of their affairs, and to carry on their Law-suits; so in our times every City, both in *Italy* and out of it, do erect certain spacious publick Halls, which may deservedly be term'd *Basilicas*." While the nucleus of his building was an old Gothic public hall, the surrounding porticos, arcades, and galleries are his own. Like Sansovino, Palladio uses the Doric order on the ground floor with the Ionic above. In both cases, balustrades separated the stories, while another is found above outlining the roof and supporting a row of statues. But Palladio goes a step farther than his predecessor by including spacious galleries on both floors, by using more slender supporting piers with open spaces on either side, and by piercing the spandrels on each level with the round portholelike openings to promote a sense of deep space and achieve a greater surface play of light and shade.

Just outside Vicenza is the Villa Rotonda (Fig. 11:6), which Palladio built for his own retirement. It is a country villa in the grand style and the prototype of many later buildings. Geometrically, it is a cube enclosing a cylindrical core and topped by a low saucer dome. The villa rests on a hill from which it dominates the surrounding countryside. Facing the four points of the compass, grand flights of steps lead up to Ionic porticos that project 14 feet forward and spread 40 feet outward. The pediments are in the manner of a classical temple

Fig. 11:6. Palladio. Villa Rotonda. 80′ x 80′. Dome 70′ high. Begun 1552. Near Vicenza (Fondazione Cini)

with statues placed on either side and above. Each portico provides entrance to the imposing reception room that gives the villa the name *rotonda*. This central salon is as high as the house itself and culminates in the cupola above. Alcoves left over from the parts between the round central hall and the square sides of the building allow space for four winding staircases and for no less than 32 rooms in the adjoining corners—all excellently lighted both from the outside and from the eight round windows at the base of the cupola. At the corners of the main floor are four large reception rooms, each 20 by 30 feet, and four smaller ones—eight in all on this floor alone. Below, a basement includes storerooms, servants' quarters, and kitchens. Palladio's achievement here is a house that is spacious but simple in plan. Such villas were built for a formal style of living, and Palladio observes that when an architect "builds for Persons of Quality, and more especially for those that are in publick Employment, he must build their Palaces with Portico's, Galleries, and large stately Halls richly adorn'd: that those who come for business, or to pay their respects to the Owner, may be received commodiously, and delighted and amused whilst they wait for him."

When advancing years curtailed Sansovino's activities, Palladio was called to Venice to construct several buildings, among them the churches of San Giorgio

Palladio. Church of Il Redentore (The Redeemer). 1576–1592. Venice. Fig. 11:7 (*left*). *Exterior.* (Fondazione Cini) Fig. 11:8 (*below*). *Interior.* (Böhm).

(*opposite*). Fig. 11:9. Palladio. Olympic Theater. 1580–1584. Vicenza (Fondazione Cini)

Maggiore and Il Redentore (Fig. 11:7). Palladio set himself the problem of reconciling the Greco-Roman temple with the traditional oblong Christian basilica plan. Since a classical temple is of uniform height with a simple shed roof, and a Christian basilica has a Latin-cross groundplan with a central nave rising high above two side aisles, his solution shows great ingenuity. The central part of the façade of Il Redentore becomes the portico of a classical temple complete with columns and pediment to face the high central nave within, while the acute angles of a fragmentary second pediment face the side aisles. The pediment idea is repeated in the small triangle above the entrance and in the side angles at the roof level to make in all two complete and two incomplete pediments. This broken-pediment motif was later incorporated into the baroque vocabulary. To create the feeling of deep space, Palladio alternated square pilasters with round attached columns and arranged the pediments in a complex intersecting design. The interior (Fig. 11:8) is a model of geometrical clarity; and in order to create a feeling of spatial depth, he eliminated the traditional walled apse that closes the space around the altar and replaced it by a semicircular open colonnade against clear glass windows so that the eye is led past the altar into the distance.

The last building Palladio undertook was the Olympic Theater at Vicenza (Fig. 11:9). It was begun the year of his death and finished later from his designs by Scamozzi. An ingenious device to create the feeling of deep space is seen

through the central arch from which actors made their entrances—a rising ramp flanked by building façades that recedes only about 50 feet but creates the illusion of a long avenue leading to an open city square in the distance. Clearly inspired by ancient Roman amphitheaters, the Olympic has, in turn, been the inspiration for many later theaters, such as the Palladium in London.

A notable contrast in the work of Sansovino and Palladio that deserves mention is the materials that they used. Sansovino, as architect of large public edifices, had his choice of rare marbles and the finest stone; Palladio, working so frequently on private dwellings and buildings in the more provincial and less wealthy Vicenza, had to content himself largely with brick, stucco, and terracotta. Palladio comments many times on the importance of design over materials, and his achievement of richness and monumentality with baser materials proves that architectural grandeur lies more in conception of form than in content. Reasoned proportion of the whole and logical disposition of the parts are two prime characteristics of his art. His love of symmetry and his systematic use of the five architectural orders—the Tuscan, Doric, Ionic, Corinthian, and Composite—were transmitted to the succeeding age. His skillful use of the principle of dualism and opposition—both in the winged organization of his palace façades and in his allowance for the reflection of façades in the water (as at San Giorgio Maggiore and other Venetian buildings)—is also noteworthy. The use of water as an element of architecture was absorbed into the later baroque vocabulary. But, whereas the ripple of water was natural to Venice, artificial reflecting pools had to be designed to set off the façades of buildings in other locations (see Figs. 12:11 and 13:4).

Scamozzi, the younger collaborator of both Sansovino and Palladio, was commissioned in 1584 to add a wing to Sansovino's library on the side toward St. Mark's Square (Fig. 11:10). His design shows the usual Palladian angularity but adds a touch of mannerist caprice in the precariously perched nudes atop the third-story window brackets. Here again, architecture is borrowing the materials of sculpture, for the figures are variations of those on Michelangelo's Medici Tombs (Fig. 10:11). But at their height, Scamozzi's nudes seem even more in danger of slipping down the sloping sides than do those on Michelangelo's sarcophagi. Similar mannerist shock techniques are seen in the Palazzo del Tè (Tea Palace, Fig. 11:11) that Giulio Romano built for the ruling family of the neighboring duchy of Mantua. To enclose this small pleasure garden, he used heavily rusticated masonry, much too massive for its function, and Doric columns far larger than necessary to support the frieze. This dramatic overstatement, however, pales in comparison with the startling effect of the frieze itself in which every third triglyph slips downward a notch.

It remained for Longhena in the early years of the 17th century to make the break from the brittle rectilinear style of Palladio and Scamozzi and carry Vene-

Fig. 11:10 (*right*). Scamozzi. Procuratie Nuove, Façade detail. 1584. Venice (Alinari)
Fig. 11:11 (*below*). Romano. Palazzo del Tè, Courtyard detail. 1525–1535. Mantua (Gabinetto Fotografico Nazionale)

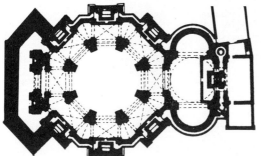

Longhena. Church of Santa Maria della Salute. 1631–1656. Venice. Fig. 11:12 (*above*). *Exterior.* Fig. 11:13 (*left*). *Plan*

tian architecture over into the exuberant baroque spirit with his church of Santa Maria della Salute (Figs. 11:12 and 11:13). From the octagonal base, each side of which is treated like a Roman triumphal arch and surmounted by a triangular pediment and pierced by a Palladian "porthole," the structure culminates in the high-pitched main dome and the smaller echoing one at the rear. Buttressing the cupola and mediating between it and the octagonal mass below are the striking ornamental scrolls. The elaborately decorated exterior is held together by the good composition of the design as a whole. This building was far more to the taste of the Venetians than the more restrained and academic Palladian style, and it is one of the finest examples of the early baroque.

Palladio, however, emerges as the most influential architect of his period. Throughout the succeeding century, the classical temple façade is accepted as a norm for Roman Catholic church buildings, but with later architects it becomes structurally weaker and increasingly the basis for the elaborate ornamentation characteristic of the florid baroque (see Fig. 12:13). To counteract this tendency Palladio's academicism is also carried over into the new style, and his objectivity and exactness operates as a balance to the more exuberant tendencies of the new style. One of his remarks that must have been frequently pondered by later generations was: "But as for what concerns the ornaments, that is, the Bases, Columns, Capitels, Cornishes, and such like things, I have intermix'd nothing of my own; but they were measur'd by me with the utmost care and exactness, from divers fragments found in the very places where stood the Temples themselves." And finally his thought as expressed in his *Four Books of Architecture* with their sketches and drawings had an even wider influence in France, England, Ireland, and America than did his buildings. The English translation, published with notes by his disciple Inigo Jones, did much to establish the Georgian tradition both in England and in America, where it was carried on by Thomas Jefferson. The latter's staunch Palladianism is seen in his designs for his residence at Monticello and the library of the University of Virginia, both of which are adaptations of the Villa Rotonda. Jefferson also wanted to build the White House at Washington, D. C., on the same plan but was overruled at the last moment. However, even in its present form the White House has Palladio's winged design on either side of a classical temple portico.

PAINTING

Venetian painting in the course of the 16th century ran a gamut of styles from the transitional late-Renaissance work of Giorgione and Titian with its partial emancipation from traditional subject matter and story content to the mannerist and early baroque pictures of Tintoretto and Veronese with their illusionism and flights of imagination. Technically, Venetian painting is marked by the refine-

Fig. 11:14. Giorgione. *Pastoral Concert*. Oil on canvas. 43¼″ x 54⅜″. *c.*1510. Louvre, Paris (Archives Photographiques)

ment and perfection of painting with oil on canvas, since the methods of tempera on wood panels and fresco were unsuited to the damp Venetian climate. Venetian painters also developed rich color palettes and used high intensities of light by which the principal figures are dramatically spotlighted and subordinate ones thrown into various degrees of shadow.

Giorgione's *Pastoral Concert* (Fig. 11:14) impresses with its spaciousness and its distribution of interest from foreground to background. The eye first is arrested by the four figures of the picture plane, then is led leisurely toward the middleground where the shepherd is tending his flock, and finally comes to rest on the gleaming water of the distant horizon. This pastoral idyll is enlivened by such oppositions as the clothed male figures and feminine nudes; the pairing of the urbane courtier and stately lady at the left with the rustic shepherd and shepherdess on the right; the attitudes of the two women—one intent upon her lover, the other turning away; and the lute symbolizing lyric poetry, and the flute pastoral poetry. Giorgione's so-called *Tempest* (Fig. 11:15) is even less concerned with literary allusions and more with pictorial mechanics. The sunny foreground and human figures define the picture plane, while the eye is led in receding

Fig. 11:15. Giorgione. *Tempest*. Oil on canvas. 32¼" x 28¾". Academy, Venice (Soprintendenza)

planes to deep space and the threatening sky in the distance. Stability is maintained by judicious balance of vertical (the standing figure, broken columns, trees, and buildings) and horizontal lines (the unfinished parapet and bridge). In both the *Pastoral Concert* and the *Tempest*, Giorgione creates a mood rather than tells a story, builds a picture rather than communicates concrete meaning. A puzzle to his contemporaries who were accustomed to the usual iconographical subjects, he is understandable to the modern observer accustomed to separate subject matter from pictorial form and see a picture as a composition complete within itself rather than an illustration of a religious or literary theme.

A similar reconciliation of opposites is found in Titian's *Venus and the Organ Player* (Fig. 11:16), one of the many versions of a theme the artist did in his later years. The young man at the organ seems torn between the sacred pursuits symbolized by that instrument and the sensual pleasures implied by Venus. In addition to this major one, several minor contrasts are present, such as the foreground interior against the receding landscape, the clothed organist and the undraped Venus, the immature Cupid beside the mature Venus, and the tactile quality of the nude flesh against the velvet couch cover. These oppositions are harmonized by the warm colors and brilliance of surface treatment.

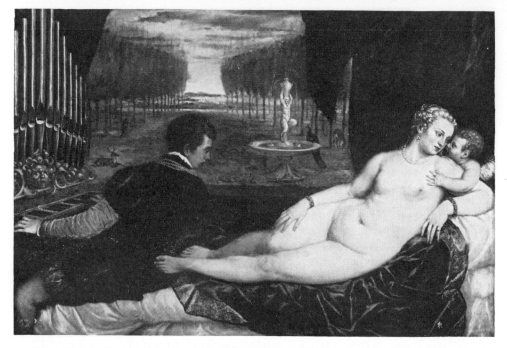

Fig. 11:16. Titian. *Venice and Organ Player*. Oil on canvas. 54″ x 90″. Prado, Madrid (Anderson)

A more complex handling of this idea is found in Titian's *Sacred and Pro-fane Love* (Fig. 11:17), the title of which is not Titian's but one of many advanced to solve the riddle of its interpretation. It will be enough here to call attention to the facial resemblance of the clothed (profane or worldly love) and unclothed (ideal or sacred love) figures—close enough to make them alter egos—and to the secluded setting at dawn with the awakening life of a new day—the rabbits and butterflies on the meadow, the shepherd tending his flock, and the hunters going forth to the chase. The attitudes of the two women set a contemplative mood, while the playful Cupid swishing the water of the fountain suggests that their thoughts have turned to love. This is supported by the resemblance of the nude figure to Renaissance Venus types. The first rays of the sun come from the goddess' side and have just touched the tower on the left, and the opposition of divinity and mortality is reinforced by the light-bathed open landscape behind Venus and the shadowy confined space between the clothed figure and the castled hill behind her. The warmth of the right side is further supported by the red mantle of Venus, while the shadows of the left are supported by the cool steel-gray costume of her counterpart. The dimension of time is suggested by the wreath of flowers in the hand of the clothed figure and the rose petals strewn on the edge of the fountain, which like her beauty will fade. Under her arm is a

Fig. 11:17. Titian. *Sacred and Profane Love.* Oil on canvas. 8′ 7″ x 3′ 6″. *c.*1514. Borghese Gallery, Rome (Anderson)

brazier, filled with the dying embers of coals, which Venetian ladies customarily carried with them for warmth. On the other side, one sees the timeless beauty of the goddess holding in her hand the brightly burning lamp that points to the sky. For continuity, the eye is quietly led from the darkness at the lower left by the lines of the drapery and the inclining attitude of the clothed figure past the playful Cupid diagonally to the nude figure and upward by her extended arm to the eternal sea and sky at the right. This quiet and dignified action fits well with the Platonic theory of earthly love as the means by which the thoughts of time-bound mortals are led to the contemplation of the eternal aspects of things, or from physical beauty to the ideal form of divine beauty. The Platonic concept of time is also present in the contrast of the changing world of appearances, and the unchangeable world of forms beyond. These were frequently the subjects for the Neo-Platonic dialogues of the Renaissance and seem to fit the intent of this picture better than any of the other interpretations.

An entirely different pictorial organization is found in Titian's altarpiece *Assumption of the Virgin* (Fig. 11:18). In this dramatic composition, heavenly and earthly spheres converge momentarily. Below in deep shadow are the Apostles, whose uplifted arms point to the intermediate zone and the ascending Madonna, whose gesture, in turn, raises the eye to the dazzling brightness above. The upward motion is then arrested by the descending figure of God the Father surrounded by His seraphs. Linear movement and gradations of light, as well as transitions of color from somber shades to light pastel hues, are skillfully adapted by Titian to carry out his theme of the soaring human spirit triumphant over the gravitational pull of material considerations. Titian herewith created a new pictorial type that was to have profound influence on El Greco (see Fig. 12:15), Bernini, and the whole of Counter-Reformation baroque art. In spite of such in-

Fig. 11:18. Titian. *Assumption of Virgin.* Oil on canvas. 22′ 6″ x 11′ 8″. 1516–1518.
Frari, Venice (Anderson)

novations, Titian's art as a whole remains within the scope of the late Renaissance. The painting of his younger colleague Tintoretto, however, crosses the stylistic bridge and probes the expressive possibilities of free mannerism.

"The drawing of Michelangelo and the color of Titian" was the motto Tintoretto is supposed to have written on the walls of his workshop. His violent contrasts of light and dark; his off-center diagonal directions; his interplay of the natural and supernatural, earthly and unearthly light, human and divine figures; and his placement of principal figures on the periphery of the action, from whence he created lines that lead the eye in several different directions, all combine to strain mannerism to the breaking point. His *Finding St. Mark's Body* (Fig. 11:19), one of a series he painted for the *Scuola di San Marco*, tells the tale of the Venetian search in Alexandria for the body of their patron saint. Because the men do not know which of the several corpses is the correct one, St. Mark (left foreground) appears to stay the hands of those in the upper right and confirm that the body in the lower right is his. The gesticulating figures in the foreground set up a complex series of criss-crossing diagonals, while the eye is led along the spiraling lines of the vaulting with its phosphorescent lighting into the deep space of the background. Even here the eye does not come to rest, for through the strange half-open wall, the space continues into the mysterious distance. Lacking a natural source, light apparently can come only from the apparition of St. Mark, but it emanates from no single source and falls capriciously on the several figures.

Fig. 11:19. Tintoretto. *Finding St. Mark's Body*. Oil on canvas. 13′ 3½″ square. *c.*1562. Brera Gallery, Milan (Soprintendenza)

Fig. 11:20. Tintoretto. *Last Supper*. Oil on canvas. 12′ x 18′ 8″. 1592–1594. San Giorgio Maggiore, Venice (Böhm)

In his *Last Supper* (Fig. 11:20), Tintoretto represents the miraculous moment when Jesus changes the bread and wine into his body and blood, then gives it to his disciples. This is a departure from the traditional scene when Christ has just said: "Verily I say unto you that one of you shall betray me." And each of the Apostles asks: "Lord, is it I?" (Matt. 26:21–22) To illuminate this unfathomable mystery of faith and reveal the hovering angelic host, Tintoretto bathes his canvas in a supernatural luminosity that emanates partly from the figure of Christ and partly from the lamp. The drastic diagonals of the floor are paralleled by those of the table; but instead of directing the eye to the head of Christ, they lead to an indefinite point in the upper right and to space beyond the picture.

Of all subjects, the most congenial to Veronese's art was festivity. Painted with the primary object of delighting the eye, his canvases nevertheless captured an important aspect of Venetian life—the conviviality of large social gatherings and the love of sumptuous surroundings embellished with fruits, flowers, animals, furniture, draperies, and jesters in bizarre costumes. Veronese seems never to have refused a commission to do a feast, and a note on the back of one of his drawings, believed to be in his own handwriting, bears this out. "If I ever have time," he wrote, "I want to represent a sumptuous banquet in a superb hall, at which will be present the Virgin, the Saviour, and St. Joseph. They will be served by the most brilliant retinue of angels which one can imagine, busied in offering them the daintiest viands and an abundance of splendid fruit in dishes of silver and gold. Other angels will hand them precious wines in transparent crystal glasses and gilded goblets, in order to show with what zeal blessed spirits serve the Lord."

It is in his consummate rendering of the world of appearances that Veronese most completely realizes himself, and in so doing, despite the foreign origin implied in his name, he succeeds in being more Venetian than the Venetians. In his *Marriage at Cana* (Fig. 11:21), the scene, except for the recognizable central figures of Jesus and the Virgin Mary, is that of a rich wedding feast in Venice, compounded from his own observations and imagination. The black-bearded groom, dressed in purple and gold and seated at the extreme left, is Alfonso d'Avalos, a contemporary Spanish grandee. Seated next to him as the bride is Eleanor of Austria, sister of Charles V and in real life the wife of Francis I of France. Other royal portraits in the scene include those of Francis I, Charles V,

Fig. 11:21. Veronese. *Marriage at Cana*. Oil on canvas. 21′ 10″ x 32′ 5″. c.1560. Louvre, Paris (Archives Photographiques)

Suleiman I, the sultan of Turkey, and Queen Mary of England. Monks, cardinals, and the artist's personal friends are portrayed as other wedding guests. The major interest in portraiture is concentrated in the center foreground where the orchestra (Fig. 11:22) is made up of the leading Venetian painters of that day— Veronese is the striking, bald, black-bearded seated figure in the yellow cloak; the elderly Titian, in a red damask robe, stands opposite, playing the bass viol; Tintoretto, holding another viol, whispers in Veronese's ear; and the seated flute player is Jacopo Bassano. To the right, in the large canvas, the figure holding the cup in his left hand is the artist's brother Benedetto Cagliari, who collaborated with him by adding architectural backgrounds to this and other of Veronese's large paintings. Less important figures are everywhere. Over Christ's head behind the balustrade, a butcher chops meat with a cleaver, while bustling servants prepare food or rush to and fro to serve it on smoking gold and silver platters.

For unity in composition, the picture relies principally on the horizontal and vertical linear patterns beginning with the table, back through the balustrade and the rich Corinthian columns on either side, to the Sansovinian-Palladian architecture against the bright sky. The rigidity of such a plan is softened by the series of intricate curves that carry the eye to the head of Christ. A fine balance is contained in the opposition of the crowded scene below to the serene architectural order and the spaciousness of the open sky above.

Another of Veronese's colossal canvases is the *Feast in the House of Levi* (Fig. 11:23), originally painted as a *Last Supper* for the monastery of SS. Giovanni and Paolo. The spacious design is appropriate to its huge size, and origi-

Fig. 11:22. Veronese. Marriage at Cana, *Detail*. Portraits of Veronese (left foreground), Tintoretto (whispering to Veronese), Jacopo Bassano (playing flute), Titian (right foreground) (Alinari)

Fig. 11:23. Veronese. *Feast in House of Levi*. Oil on canvas. 18′ 2″ x 42′. 1573. Academy, Venice (Böhm)

nally it covered the entire wall of the refectory where its architectural background and open sky seen through the three arches gave the cloistered monks the illusion of the out-of-doors. Questions were soon raised, however, about the propriety of its content, because by tradition a *Last Supper* portrayed only Christ and the 12 Apostles. Veronese, however, included some 50 figures, and this departure from tradition brought the artist before the Inquisition.

In one of the most remarkable documents in the history of painting—a summary of the painter's actual testimony—much about this picture in particular and about Veronese's conception of art in general is revealed. The inquisitors were disturbed not only by the 50-odd figures but by the presence of a dog and cat, which Veronese had painted in the foreground. Even more disquieting was the inclusion of German soldiers, sitting on the staircase at the extreme right, at the very time when the church was having such trouble in Germany with the Lutheran Reformation.

Question. Did anyone commission you to paint Germans, buffoons, and similar things in that picture?
Answer. No, milords, but I received the commission to decorate the picture as I saw fit. It is large and, it seemed to me, it could hold many figures.
Q. Are not the decorations which you painters are accustomed to add to paintings or pictures supposed to be suitable and proper to the subject and the principal figures or are they just for pleasure—simply what comes to your imagination without any discretion or judiciousness?
A. I paint pictures as I see fit and as well as my talent permits.

Q. Does it seem fitting at the Last Supper of the Lord to paint buffoons, drunkards, Germans, dwarfs and similar vulgarities?

A. No, milords.

Q. Do you not know that in Germany and in other places infected with heresy it is customary with various pictures full of scurrilousness and similar inventions to mock, vituperate, and scorn the things of the Holy Catholic Church in order to teach bad doctrines to foolish and ignorant people?

A. Yes, that is wrong; but I return to what I have said, that I am obliged to follow what my superiors have done.

Q. What have your superiors done? Have they perhaps done similar things?

A. Michelangelo in Rome in the Pontifical Chapel painted Our Lord, Jesus Christ, His Mother, St. John, St. Peter, and the Heavenly Host. These are all represented in the nude—even the Virgin Mary—and in poses with little reverence.

Those figures that are seated with Jesus at the damask-covered table should be the 12 Apostles, but only two could be specifically identified by the artist—St. Peter, on His right, in robes of rose and gray, who according to the painter is "carving the lamb in order to pass it to the other end of the table"; and St. John, on His left. When questioned about the other figures, Veronese was evasive and pled that he could not recall them as he had "painted the picture some months ago." Since but ten months had passed, a faulty memory was his convenient way of avoiding explanation of the portraits of Titian and Michelangelo seated at the table directly under the left and right arches, respectively.

The verdict required Veronese to make certain changes in the picture. Instead, he simply changed its title from the *Last Supper* to *Feast in the House of Levi*, a subject outside iconographical tradition. So that there would be no future misunderstanding, he took the unusual step of painting the title on the stair railing at the left, while on the staircase railing at the right he cites chapter and verse —Luke 5:29–31. This passage reads in part: "And Levi made him a great feast in his house: and there was a great company of publicans and of others that sat down with them. But their scribes and Pharisees murmured against his disciples, saying, Why do ye eat and drink with publicans and sinners? And Jesus answering said unto them, They that are whole need not a physician; but they that are sick." Thus there was a place here even for the German halberdiers. The buffoon seated below the host, a dwarf with a bird on his wrist being teased by a young Negro, and the dog intently eyeing the cat under the table all remained in the picture. This altercation with the Inquisition is a landmark in art history. By defending his artistic code and seeing that his picture remained intact, Veronese raises a monument to the ascendancy of aesthetic and formal considerations over the traditional religious viewpoint. The picture also proclaims that laws of space, color, form, and composition are more important than subject-matter considerations.

Fig. 11:24. Veronese. *Triumph of Venice*. Oil on canvas. *c.*1585. Ceiling mural, Doge's Palace, Venice (Soprintendenza)

Veronese also departs from the Renaissance pictorial tradition and reveals some traits of mannerism in the *Feast in the House of Levi*. His triple archway, for instance, automatically centers his composition with Christ as the central figure. But instead of drawing all the lines so that the focus is on the head of Christ, as Leonardo da Vinci had done in his famous *Last Supper* (Fig. 10:25), Veronese sets up several different converging points. The floor tiles run slightly to the oblique; the lines of the architectural background meet not at one but several points in the sky above; and the prominent diagonals of the stairs lead the eye not to Jesus but to the self-portrait of Veronese greeting the guests on the left and to the corresponding figure of the steward supervising the feast on the right. The cavalier treatment of the iconographic tradition, the strict academic control of pictorial structure, the liberties with linear perspective, the disregard for normal diminution in the size of figures in relation to their distance from the picture plane are distortions that make for manneristic restlessness rather than Renaissance repose. In his ceiling paintings for various villas, and in the *Triumph of Venice* (Fig. 11:24) for the Doge's Palace, Veronese goes a step farther and produces surprising illusions by his bold foreshortening effects. Such manneristic devices, as well as the grandiose size of his pictures, were to become part of the baroque vocabulary.

MUSIC

The frequent representation of musical subjects in Venetian painting is evidence of the importance of music in the life of the city. Angelic choirs with complex orchestras were often represented in Venetian Renaissance paintings, and keyboard instruments were included in 16th-century canvases at the time when the organists of St. Mark's were among the most progressive composers on the European scene. Critics frequently have turned to musical analogies when discussing Venetian painting. When referring to the composition of a painting, one 17th-century writer used such terms as *orchestrale* and *concertare*; and a present-day historian still speaks of Giorgione's plastic *orchestration*. Significantly, Giorgione, Titian, Tintoretto, and Veronese actually played musical instruments, frequently employed small house orchestras to perform while they were painting, and took a lively interest in the city's musical life.

The high peak of Renaissance musical development was the polyphonic style of the Netherland composers, and the general admiration for this art at the beginning of the 16th century is reflected in a remark of the Venetian ambassador to the court of Burgundy. In effect, he said that three things were of the highest excellence: first, the finest, most exquisite linen of Holland; second, the tapestries of Brabant, most beautiful in design; and third, the music, which certainly can be said to be perfect. With such sentiments being expressed in official circles,

The text of *In ecclesiis* is as follows:

1. In ecclesiis benedicite Domino,
   Alleluia, alleluia, alleluia.

2. In omni loco dominationis benedic,
   anima mea, Dominum.
   Alleluia, alleluia, alleluia.

3. In Deo, salutari meo et gloria mea.
   Deus auxilium meum et spes mea
   in Deo est.
   Alleluia, alleluia, alleluia.

4. Deus, te invocamus, te adoramus,
   Libera nos, salva nos, vivifica nos.
   Alleluia, alleluia, alleluia.

5. Deus, Deus, adjutor noster aeternam.
   Alleluia, alleluia, alleluia.

1. Praise the Lord in the congregation,
   Alleluia, alleluia, alleluia.

2. In every place of worship praise the
   Lord, O my soul.
   Alleluia, alleluia, alleluia.

3. In God, who is my salvation and
   glory, my help, and my hope
   is in God.
   Alleluia, alleluia, alleluia.

4. O God, we invoke thee, we adore
   thee,
   Deliver us, save us, enliven us.
   Alleluia, alleluia, alleluia.

5. O God, my God, our eternal judge.
   Alleluia, alleluia, alleluia.

The structure of Gabrieli's motet is based on the recurring word *alleluia*, which functions as a refrain and acts as a divider between the verses. The alleluias also are set in the more static triple meter suggesting a pause in the procession, while the stanzas have the more active beat of march time. The work opens with the sopranos of Chorus I singing the first verse with organ accompaniment. The first Alleluia refrain (measures 6–12) is taken by the sopranos of Chorus I, all of Chorus II, and the organ (the numbering of the bars follows the edition published by G. Schirmer, Inc., New York). The tenors of Chorus I then sing the second verse with organ accompaniment (measures 13–31), while the Alleluia following this verse is the same as at first. Now come the blazing chords of the instrumental Sinfonia (32–43) with their strange almost barbaric dissonances. The third verse is sung in two-part counterpoint by the altos and tenors of Chorus I supported now by the six-part instrumental group without organ. The Alleluia after this verse (93–99) is taken by the same two voices of Chorus I, with the full Chorus II and organ but without the brass ensemble. The fifth verse is for full double choir, instruments, and organ, making a total of 14 independent parts. The gradual build-up of volume can be heard in the sequence of sopranos and full chorus; tenors and full chorus; the instrumental Sinfonia first alone, then in combination with tenors and altos; and the instrumental color against the chorus with organ support. The cumulative climax is then brought about by the final grandiose union of all vocal and instrumental forces, ending in a solid cadence radiating with color and producing the huge sonority necessary to bring the mighty work to its close. The brassy magnificence of these massive sounds seems determined to fill the out-of-doors, just as they had filled the vast interior of St. Mark's. Giovanni Gabrieli's music foreshadows the baroque by setting up such oppositions as chorus against chorus, solo and choir, voices versus instruments, strings alternating with wind ensembles; the interplay of harmonic and contra-puntal textures; diatonic and chromatic harmony; the polarities of soprano and bass lines, loud and soft dynamics; and the distinction of sacred and secular styles.

While Gabrieli's vast tonal murals became the precedent for the later "colos-sal baroque," it remained for his great successor Claudio Monteverdi to divine the inner spirit of the new style; and like Longhena in architecture, with Monte-verdi the transition to the baroque is complete. Appointed master of music of the Most Serene Republic in 1613 after serving as court composer at Mantua for 23 years, Monteverdi achieved a working synthesis of Renaissance counterpoint and all the experimental techniques of his own time. The new emotional orientation is stated in the Foreword to his *Eighth Book of Madrigals* (1638): "I have reflected that the principal passions or affections of our mind are three, namely, anger, moderation, and humility or supplication; so the best philosophers declare, and the very nature of our voice indicates this in having high, low, and middle registers. The art of music also points clearly to these three in its terms 'agitated,' 'soft,' and 'moderate' [*concitato, molle*, and *temperato*]." The collection has the significant subtitle "Madrigals of War and Love," and Monteverdi says he in-tends to depict anger, warfare, entreaty, and death as well as the accents of brave men engaged in battle. According to Monteverdi, vocal music of this type should be "a simulation of the passions of the words." Descriptive melodies in this *repre-sentative style* reflected the imagery of the text, with rising and falling lines for "mountains and valleys" and undulating figures for waves"; and appropriate rhythms were chosen for dancing, marching, or warlike situations (pp. 560, 561).

A striking instance of Monteverdi's "agitated" style occurs in his short theater piece *The Combat of Tancred and Clorinda*, the text of which comes from the 12th canto of *Jerusalem Delivered* by the Italian baroque poet Torquato Tasso. In his Preface, Monteverdi requests the singers and instrumentalists to play their parts "'in imitation of the passions of the words." The score includes a rhythmic figure representing the galloping of horses and a *tremolando* on the strings to simulate trembling or shuddering. At Mantua, Monteverdi had already written his *Orfeo* (1607), the first full-length and complete opera in music history. At Venice, where the first public opera house was established in 1637, he continued with a series of lyrical dramas of which only the last two survive: *Return of Ulysses* (1641) and the *Coronation of Poppea* (1642).

VENICE, MANNERISM, AND ROADS TO THE BAROQUE

Certain themes, attitudes, qualities, shapes, and ideas recur frequently enough in Venetian architecture, painting, and music to establish not only a local Venetian style but a style of sufficient breadth to include a significant phase of mannerism and to mark the beginning of the baroque.

Venetian space is never in repose but is restless and teeming with action. Sansovino's and Palladio's buildings with their open loggias, recessed portals and windows, and pierced deep-cut masonry invite entrance; and inside, their capacious interiors alllow for freedom of movement. Action is also felt in the lively contrasts of structural elements and decorative details, rectangularity juxtaposed with rotundity, and complete and broken intersecting pediments. Palladio's churches, with their open semicircular colonnades around the altar and windows in the apse, allow the eye to continue into deep space beyond. The reflection of façades in the rippling waters of the canals and the use of mirrored interior walls serve to activate the static masses of masonry and to increase the perception of light and space.

The compositional decentralization of Venetian painting is a similar manifestation in two dimensions. Dynamic space is felt in the winged balance of opposites on the picture plane, as in Titian's *Venus and the Organ Player*; the receding planes of a composition in depth that let the eye travel from fore- to middle- and background with points of interest in each succeeding plane, as in Giorgione's *Pastoral Concert* and *Tempest*; in the rising planes of a vertical organization, as in Titian's *Assumption*; in the giddy heights reached by Veronese in his *Triumph of Venice*; and in the wheellike rotary movement Tintoretto sets up in his *Bacchus and Ariadne* (Fig. 11:27). The diagonal accent is found both in the gentle movement from lower left to upper right in Titian's *Sacred and Profane Love* and in the slashing zigzag lines of Tintoretto's *Finding of St. Mark's Body*. Breaking up the unity of central perspective in the pictures of Tintoretto and Veronese produces a fragmentation that leads the eye simultaneously in several directions.

A similar expression is heard in music. In Gabrieli's "broken" choirs, parts of one group are contrasted with the full sound of a whole chorus, and the sequence of contrasting sonorities progressively builds up ever-larger volumes until the climax is reached in the union of them all. The tossing back and forth of contrasting or unequal sound masses in the concerting style, the alternation of loud and soft dynamic levels of opposing groups as well as in the Venetian echo nuance, and the polarization of high and low parts, are all devices to intensify the motional and emotional effects of music.

Fig. 11:27. Tintoretto. *Marriage of Bacchus and Ariadne*. Oil on canvas. 57″ x 65″. 1577–1588. Doge's Palace, Venice (Soprintendenza)

Each of the Venetian arts also shows an affinity for the reconciliation of opposites with the notion of heightening the sense of drama and involving the observer and listener on as many levels as possible. Especially is this evident in the case of textures—with architects contrasting smooth with rough or rusticated materials, painters placing clothed next to undraped figures or metal and glass objects against rustling silks and satins, and composers alternating voices and instruments, large and small ensembles.

The increased dimension in all the arts is also striking. Palladio's interiors are designed for large gatherings and to impress visitors by their spaciousness so necessary to the grand manner of living to which his clients aspired. His preference for central plans in such private dwellings as the Villa Rotonda and for church buildings as well is, as he says, because "none is more capacious than the round." The growth in the size of paintings by Titian, Veronese, and Tintoretto is a phenomenon in itself. The dimensions alone predispose them to the monumental. The grandeur of sound produced by the vast musical resources Gabrieli marshaled for his polychoral motets also exceeded anything before their time. The Venetian ideal of the human figure is likewise large and ample. Womanhood, draped and undraped, approaches the monumentality of the spacious façades, the large canvases, and the huge sonorities of polychoruses. All point in the direction of the grandiose.

While mannerism had its inception in Florence early in the 16th century and subsequently flourished elsewhere, it was the Venetian adaptation of the style that was most readily assimilated into the baroque.

Living in the shadow of such universal masters of the immediate past as Leonardo da Vinci, Michelangelo, and Raphael created a dilemma for the younger generation of painters. Quite aware that a golden age had preceded them, and that there was no possibility of improving on the craftsmanship of their illustrious forebears, these young artists found themselves at a crossroads. Following the old paths would mean selecting certain ideas and techniques of their predecessors and reducing them to workable formulas. Striking out in new directions would imply taking for granted such perfected technical achievements as linear and atmospheric perspective, mathematical principles of foreshortening, and correct rendering of anatomy and then deliberately breaking the rules with daring and telling effect.

The first course meant working "in the manner" of the giants of the past, and academies sprang up to transmit the traditional techniques to young artists. The second led to bold dramatic departures from past precedents. It was this revolutionary aspect that partisans of the Renaissance saw as the dissolution of an ideal order and the adoption of an "affected manner" by highly individual artists. Either course eventually led in new directions, and some present-day historians separate the period from about 1520 to 1600 from the dying Renaissance and the baroque that was aborning. To encompass and characterize much of the art of these years, they propose (and at present it is still only a hypothesis) a period and style called *mannerism*. Since mannerism was born of crisis, it is a style facing in two different directions. The more conservative artists linked themselves with the past and consequently can be classified as academic mannerists; the more liberal group can be termed free mannerists.

Academic Mannerism

When Vasari, the disciple of Michelangelo, used the term *de maniera*, he meant working in the manner of Leonardo, Michelangelo, and Raphael. By reducing their art to a system of rules, he could work fast and efficiently; and his boast was that before his time it took a Michelangelo six years to finish one work, while he had made it possible to do six works in one year. The experimental stage was over; the era of fulfillment was at hand. No more eccentric geniuses and soul-searching prophets, only competent craftsmen. Such was the course taken by Vasari, Palladio, Scamozzi, and Veronese. Vasari, in Florence, was instrumental in founding an Academy of Design in 1561. Some 36 distinguished artists were selected as members; and while it was not a teaching organization in the modern sense, its members bore the title of professor and were expected to advise younger artists. At Bologna in 1585, the Caracci family also established an institute with the significant word *academy* in its name, and there courses in the theory and practice of art were offered.

Such academic mannerist artists did not go to nature as Leonardo had done but studied masterpieces with the thought of assimilating systematically the vocabularies of the late Renaissance giants. Art, in other words, did not hold up a mirror to nature but to art. At the lowest level, this implied well-schooled craftsmen and a style based on stereotypes; an eclectic borrowing and reassembling without the birthpangs of the original creative synthesis. At its highest, this approach could lead to virtuosity of execution, and in no way did it rule out inspiration—that intangible essence that could be caught but not taught.

With Palladio, academic mannerism came to terms with the classical orders of his ancient Roman mentor Vitruvius. By adapting Roman architectural forms to contemporary needs, he contained the Venetian love of lavishness and curbed the excesses of overdecoration. Veronese, by the symmetry of his compositions, closed forms, and organizing function of his architectural backgrounds, was able to handle large crowds and bustling movement without impairing his pictorial unity. And while Gabrieli's music broke up the unity of the Renaissance choir—encompassing and increasing the scope of musical space—his adherence to the traditional Renaissance polyphonic methods kept his work under strict academic control.

Free Mannerism

Mannerism also includes the "mannered" art of highly individual artists who, in their revolt against Renaissance ideals, cultivated eccentricity and reveled in inner conflicts. This generation of painters could no longer be thrilled by the mathematics of linear perspective or by finding the proper relation of figures to their surrounding space. Instead, they found excitement in breaking established rules with dash and daring and in violating Renaissance assumptions for the sheer shock effect. Under such capricious conditions, naturalism gave way to the free play of the imagination; classical composure yielded to nervous movement; clear definition of space became a jumble of picture planes; symmetry and focus on the central figure were replaced by off-balance diagonals that made it difficult to find the protagonist of the drama amid the multiplicity of directional lines; backgrounds no longer contained the picture but were nebulous or nonexistent; the canon of body proportion was distorted by the unnatural elongation of figures; chiaroscuro served no more to model figures but to create optical illusions and theatrical lighting effects; and strong deep color and rich costumes faded to pas-

Fig. 11:28. Michelangelo. *Pietà (Deposition)*. Marble. 88⅞" high, base 48" wide. *c.*1547–1555. (Figure of Joseph of Arimathea is a self-portrait. Front side of Mary Magdalene [left] was finished by Tiberio Calcogni.) Cathedral, Florence (Soprintendenza)

tel hues and gauzy fluttering drapery. In short, the Renaissance dream of clarity and order became the mannerist nightmare of haunted space.

Some of these tendencies were already present in the late Renaissance. Giorgione's enigmatic pictures that broke with the iconographical tradition puzzled his contemporaries. In Leonardo's *Madonna and Child with St. Anne* (Fig. 10:4), the figures are uncomfortably superimposed on each other; how St. Anne supports the weight of the Madonna and what they are sitting on is left to the imagination. The unstable figures of Day and Night in Michelangelo's Medici tombs (Fig. 10:11) seem to be sliding down the sides of the sarcophagus. His late *Pietà* (Fig. 11:28) no longer has the serenity of the earlier period (Fig. 10:3), and the gaunt figures bear no relation to classical bodily forms. In the black terror and bleak despair of his *Last Judgment* (Fig. 12:1), clarity of space no longer exists—there are crowded parts and bare spaces; the size of figures is disproportionate; and one cannot even be sure who are the saved and the damned.

The exception in the late Renaissance, however, became the rule under mannerism, which quickly, albeit briefly, became an international style. Such Florentine mannerists as Rosso Fiorentino and Benvenuto Cellini were summoned to Paris to become court artists of Francis I, and Raphael's pupil Giulio Romano was the official architect of the Duke of Mantua. In spite of their desire to dazzle and their capriciously contrived tricks, these men had no intention to deceive, since this art was addressed to the sophisticated few. Only those well aware of the rules could enjoy the witty turns and startling twists by which they were broken. This courtly phase of the mannerist style, however, was too restricted to a single class and too refined and self-conscious in its aestheticism to endure long. In the more cosmopolitan, middle-class atmosphere of Venice, however, where the group patronage of the *scuole* broadened its base, mannerism gained vitality and virility. It was these aspects that were transmitted almost intact to the baroque.

Roads to the Baroque

From Venice, as well as from Rome and the centers where international mannerism flourished, the roads to the baroque fanned out in all directions. The thriving printing industry assured currency for Venetian ideas in every civilized country. The writings of Palladio, for instance, as translated into English with commentary by Inigo Jones, led to the architecture of Christopher Wren and the Georgian styles and thence to the colonial and federal styles in America. The printing of musical scores likewise assured Venetian composers of general prominence. Venetian diplomacy, by avoiding commitments to either extreme, paved the way for the acceptance of certain aspects of the Venetian style in both Reformation and Counter-Reformation countries. Venetian innovations in architecture and painting were eagerly adopted in church and court circles of Spain and France. Both the church hierarchy and the aristocracy needed the impressive splendor of the arts to enhance their exalted positions. The more monumental the buildings, the more lavish the decorations, the more grandiose the musical entertainments, the better the arts served their purpose. Hence it was natural for both to seek out the richest expression of this ideal, which was to be found in Venice.

El Greco, after studying in Titian's workshop and absorbing Tintoretto's mannerism, found his way to church and court circles in Spain where his art left an indelible impression. Rubens spent eight years in Italy, much of the time making copies of Titian's pictures, then took the Venetian techniques with him to the Low Countries and France. His pupil Van Dyck, in turn, transmitted them to England, and eventually they reached America. In the Counter-Reformation countries, church music remained more constant to the Roman tradition, but Venetian music was readily accepted in secular circles. However, for the Reformation centers—Holland, Scandinavia, and particularly northern Germany— the greater liturgical freedom of Venetian musical forms proved more adaptable to Protestant church purposes precisely because of their deviation from orthodox Roman models. Sweelinck, who studied in Venice with Andrea Gabrieli and Zarlino, carried the Venetian keyboard style to Amsterdam, where his great reputation brought him organ students from Germany who later taught the generation of Pachelbel and Buxtehude, both major influences on the style of Bach and Handel. Cavalli, Monteverdi's successor at the Venetian opera, was called to Paris to write the music for the wedding festivities of Louis XIV. Heinrich Schütz, the greatest German composer before Bach and Handel and another force in determining their art, was a pupil of both Giovanni Gabrieli and Monteverdi. In sum, the Venetian style became a part of the basic vocabulary of the larger baroque language.

CHRONOLOGY:
16th and Early 17th Centuries

General Events: Rome

1527	Charles V and mercenaries sacked Rome
	Protestant Reformation in progress under Luther in Germany, Zwingli and Calvin in Switzerland
	Reaction to Renaissance humanism began
1534	Counter-Reformation began
1540	Society of Jesus (Jesuit order) founded by Ignatius Loyola
1542	Universal Inquisition established
1543	Copernicus' *De Revolutionibus Orbium Coelestorum* published
	Censorship of printed matter began
1545	Council of Trent (1545–1563) undertook reform within church; reaffirmed dogma
1547	Michelangelo named architect of St. Peter's
1555	Volterra ordered to paint drapery on "offending" nudes in Michelangelo's *Last Judgment*
c.1562	Teresa of Avila and John of Cross reformed Carmelite orders
1575	Congregation of Oratory (founded by Philip Neri) approved
1616	Galileo enjoined by pope not to "teach or defend" researches confirming Copernican theory; called before Inquisition in 1633
1622	Canonization of Ignatius Loyola, Teresa of Avila, Philip Neri, Francis Xavier

Musicians

c.1500–1553	Morales
c.1500–1566	Antonio de Cabezón
1524–1594	Palestrina
c.1548–1611	Victoria

General Events: Spain

1474–1516	Ferdinand and Isabella reigned; West Indies discovered by Columbus (1492); South America (1498); expulsion of Moors and Jews from Spain
1516–1556	Charles I, King of Spain; became Holy Roman Emperor Charles V in 1519
1556–1598	Philip II, King of Spain; Spanish empire reached greatest extent
1561	Madrid chosen as capital
1563–1584	Escorial Palace built
1588	Spanish Armada sunk by English navy
1598–1621	Philip III, King of Spain; decline of Spanish power
1604	Cervantes' *Don Quixote*, Part I, published in Madrid (Part II, 1615)
1621–1665	Philip IV, King of Spain
1623	Velásquez appointed court painter
1648	Treaty of Westphalia; Spanish power in Europe checked

Architects

? –1567	Juan Bautista de Toledo
1507–1573	Giacomo Vignola
1530–1597	Juan de Herrera
c.1540–1604	Giacomo della Porta
1556–1629	Carlo Maderno
c.1580–1648	Gomez de Mora
1598–1680	Gianlorenzo Bernini
1599–1667	Francesco Borromini
1650–1723	José de Churriguera

Painters

c.1541–1614	El Greco
1573–1610	Caravaggio
1599–1660	Velásquez
1617–1682	Murillo
1642–1709	Pozzo

Writers

1491–1556	Ignatius Loyola
1515–1582	Teresa of Avila
1538–1584	Charles Borromeo
1542–1591	John of Cross
1547–1616	Cervantes
1562–1635	Lope da Vega
1600–1681	Calderón

12

THE COUNTER-REFORMATION BAROQUE STYLE

ROME, LATE 16TH AND EARLY 17TH CENTURIES

The cataclysmic events that convulsed Rome and all Europe in the course of the 16th century awakened the eternal city from its Renaissance dream of harmony and confronted it with the stark reality of contradiction and conflict. Subsequently, every aspect of life—religious, scientific, political, social, economic, and aesthetic—was destined to undergo re-examination and radical change. A succession of disturbing visitors proved to be harbingers of developments to come. Martin Luther had been in Rome at the turn of the century, and his observations had added fuel to the fire of his moral indignation. The reform movement he initiated, along with Zwingli and John Calvin, was destined to sever the unity of the universal church and divide Europe into Reformation and Counter-Reformation camps.

The next visitor, the Holy Roman Emperor Charles V, was even less welcome. Previously, the voyages of the great navigators and the exploits of the conquistadors who followed in their wake had brought most of North, Central, and South America under the Spanish crown. With the monopoly of the spice trade

449

of the Orient and with the gold and silver mines of the New World pouring fabulous riches into its treasury, Spain was rapidly becoming the most powerful country in the world. By a combination of heredity, marriage, and high finance, Charles I of Spain had become Charles V of the Holy Roman Empire. With the Low Countries, the Germanies, and Austria firmly in his grasp, the ambitious emperor turned his attention next to Italy, and, one by one, the formerly independent duchies and city-states came under his domination. Opposition from any quarter proved intolerable, and in 1527 His Catholic Majesty and his mercenaries marched on Rome, sacking and plundering. Eight days later the great city was a smoking ruin, the Vatican a barracks, St. Peter's a stable, and Pope Clement VII a prisoner at Castel Sant' Angelo. Thereafter, the papacy had no choice but to acquiesce in Spanish policy, a Spanish viceroy ruled in Naples, and a Spanish government was installed in Milan. Through the Gonzagas in Mantua, the Estes in Ferrara, the Medici in Florence, the Spaniards controlled all important centers; and with Spanish rule came Spanish austerity and religiosity, etiquette and elegance.

With the Holy Roman emperor destroying the center of Christendom and threatening the life of the pope, with the universal church split asunder by reformers, with once-proud independent states reduced to puppet regimes, with rampant inflation and speculation bringing sudden wealth to some and total ruin to others, with the shift of economic power from old centers to new ones depriving Italy of her primary position in commerce and banking, a general sense of crisis prevailed throughout Europe.

Another visitor was the astronomer Copernicus, whose book on the *Revolution of the Planets in their Orbits* was destined to change the conception of the cosmos from an earth-centered to a sun-centered world. A shock reaction followed as baroque man began to realize he inhabited a minor planet whirling through space, and that he was no longer at the center of creation. Later, when his observations tended to prove the Copernican theory, Galileo was tried for heresy, sentenced to prison, and released only when he recanted. The cumulative effect of these and other scientific discoveries began to weaken the belief in miracles and divine intervention in human affairs.

Then came the theologians, during the sessions of the Council of Trent which undertook the reform of the church from within. When the test came, bold humanistic thinking was transformed to violent reaction; Neo-Platonic philosophy was succeeded by a reversion to Aristotelean scholasticism; the distant but seductive voices of pagan antiquity were drowned out by the roar of rekindled medieval fire and brimstone; the reveling in sensuous beauty was followed by bitter self-reproach; promises of liberal religious attitudes were inundated by a return to strict orthodoxy; new access to literature and knowledge through the printing press and scientific discoveries was suppressed through the Universal

Fig. 12:1. Michelangelo. *Last Judgment*, Detail. Fresco. 48′ x 44′. 1535–1541. (Self-portrait in lower left). Sistine Chapel, Vatican, Rome (Anderson)

Inquisition and the censorship of the *Index Expurgatorius*; God appeared not as the Loving Father but as a terrifying Judge, Christ not as the Good Shepherd but as the Great Avenger.

The founders of the new Counter-Reformation religious orders, which were to shape the course of Roman Catholicism in the 17th century, were in Rome at various times. Philip Neri brought together laymen of all classes, from aristocrats to street urchins, in his Congregation of the Oratory for informal meetings and encouraged them to pray or preach as the spirit moved them. By dramatizing and setting to music familiar Biblical stories and parables (prototypes of the baroque oratorios), he generated a cheerful devotional spirit that stirred the hearts of the poor and humble. Ignatius Loyola came from Spain to obtain papal sanction for his Society of Jesus, a militant order dedicated to foreign missionary work, education, and active participation in worldly affairs. There were also the mystics

Teresa of Avila and John of the Cross, whose abilities to combine the contemplative and active ways of life resulted in a significant literary expression of the period and in the reorganization and redirection of the Carmelite orders; and there was Carlo Borromeo, the young energetic archbishop of Milan, who wrote manuals for artists as well as for the students and teachers in the many seminaries he founded. At a single grand ceremony in the newly completed Basilica of St. Peter on the 22nd of May 1622 Ignatius Loyola, Francis Xavier, Teresa of Avila, and Philip Neri were canonized and admitted to the honors of the altar. Thereupon the architects Giacomo Vignola, Giacomo della Porta, Carlo Maderno, Gianlorenzo Bernini, and Francesco Borromini were called upon to build churches and chapels dedicated to them.

In this floodtide of reform, the classical harmony, stability, and poise of Renaissance art were not hardy enough to survive, nor could the overrefined, overly dramatic art of mannerism adapt itself to the new religious climate. Gaiety gave way to sobriety, Venuses reverted to Virgins, Bacchuses and Apollos to bearded Christs. The organic form and unity of Michelangelo's Sistine ceiling was succeeded by the calculated shapelessness of his fearful *Last Judgment* (Fig. 12:1). Palestrina was conscience-stricken for having written madrigals and henceforth wrote only masses. Under the rulings of the Council of Trent, church art was firmly realigned with religion, and the clergy had to assume responsibility for the way artists rendered religious subjects.

The lives and attitudes of Counter-Reformation artists were profoundly affected by the new religious climate. Michelangelo's *Last Judgment* was censured because his Apollo-type Christ was unbearded and because such classical details as Charon, the sepulchral boatman, rowing souls across the river Styx had been included. Drapery was ordered to cover his "offending nudes," and only the timely intervention of a group of artists saved the *Last Judgment* from complete obliteration. The great man became a recluse in his last years, gave up figurative art for the abstractions of architecture, and devoted himself to the building of St. Peter's, a project for which he would accept no fee. In the privacy of his own studio, he worked intermittently at sculpture and brooded over his last Pietàs, one of them intended for his own tomb (Fig. 11:28). Palestrina was banished from his post as leader of the Sistine choir because he refused to take the priestly vow of celibacy and give up his wife. Later he was reinstated and entrusted with the reforms of church music.

Gianlorenzo Bernini, busiest and most successful sculptor-architect of the Counter-Reformation baroque, was closely associated with the Jesuits and annually interrupted his career to practice St. Ignatius' *Spiritual Exercises*. Andrea Pozzo, who painted the illusionistic ceiling of the Church of San Ignazio, was himself a member of the Jesuit Order. El Greco, Spain's greatest representative of Counter-Reformation art, was a religious mystic in whose last visionary canvases physical matter practically ceases to exist, his figures more spirit than flesh, his settings more heavenly than earthly.

As matters shaped up, the Counter-Reformation baroque style had its inception in Rome where it reached its apogee in the 50-year period from about 1620 to 1670; its reverberations were felt simultaneously in Spain, the strong secular arm of the church militant. Thereafter the impetus spread throughout the Roman Catholic countries of Europe and traveled with the missionary orders to the Americas and the far-flung colonies of Spain and Portugal.

ROMAN COUNTER-REFORMATION ART

Architecture

As the central monument of the Jesuit Order, the Church of Il Gésu in Rome became the prototype for many Counter-Reformation churches. Indeed, so many different versions and variants have since appeared that with justification it has been called the most influential church design of the past four centuries. Begun in 1564, Il Gésu combines classical motifs from the Renaissance heritage with some of the new elements that were to identify Counter-Reformation architecture. The nucleus of the structure—the domed crossing of the nave and the short

Fig. 12:2. Giacomo Vignola and Giacomo della Porta. Il Gesù, *Façade*. 105′ high, 115′ wide. *c.*1575–1584. Rome (Gabinetto Fotografico Nazionale)

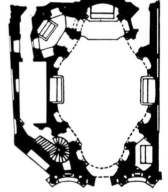

Borromini. San Carlo alle Quattro Fontane. Begun 1635. Rome. Fig. 12:3. (*left*). *Façade*, 1667. (Vatican Photographic Archive)

Fig. 12:4 (*right*). *Plan*

transepts—are derived from Michelangelo's and Palladio's centralized plans. But the longitudinal nave reaching outward from the façade repeats the compromise reached in St. Peter's when Bramante's and Michelangelo's plans were combined with the appendage of Carlo Maderno's long nave. Giacomo Vignola's façade design (12:2), somewhat revised after his death by his successor Giacomo della Porta, recalls a Roman triumphal arch on the ground floor, but the lean-to roofing of the side aisles is covered with graceful scrolls that swirl upward toward the triangular templelike pediment.

The full force of the baroque power to mold space into astonishing new forms was not felt until the 17th century was well under way. By that time, Counter-Reformation churches had become theaters where a concert of all the

Fig. 12:5. *Interior of Dome. c.*1638. Rome (Alinari)

arts was played. Painting of the tunnel-vaulted naves and inner surfaces of domes produced the visionary illusions of souls being wafted heavenward on wings of seraphic choirs; sculptured saints and angels floated aloft on marble or stucco clouds; Biblical stories were dramatized in miracle plays; and earthly choirs were echoed by unseen angelic voices of choristers concealed around the domes.

Borromini's San Carlo alle Quattro Fontane (Fig. 12:3) is one of the most ingenious expressions of the period. Turning to full advantage the small site at the intersection of two streets with fountains at each corner, the architect devised a plan embracing a complex interplay of geometrical shapes. The ground plan (Fig. 12:4) is based on the intersection of two equilateral triangles to form a six-pointed star; and the outer shell suggests a rhomboid. The undulating walls rise upward like a rippling stage curtain toward an oval dome (Fig. 12:5), the inner surface of which is encrusted with coffering of hexagonal, octagonal, and cross-shaped forms. Partially concealed openings allow light to filter in and give the honeycomblike pattern a gleaming brightness. The façade (Fig. 12:3) is set into swaying motion by the alternating concave and convex walls and the flow of curvilinear forms, which allow a maximum play of light and shade over the irregular surface.

12:6. Caravaggio. *Calling of St. Matthew*. Oil on canvas. 11′ 5″ x 11′ 1″. *c.*1797–1798. Contarelli Chapel, San Luigi dei Francese, Rome (Alinari)

Painting and Sculpture

Caravaggio, who painted in Rome from about 1590 to 1606, scorned Renaissance decorum, dignity, and elegance and set out to depict religious subjects in a vivid, down-to-earth way. His *Calling of St. Matthew* (Fig. 12:6) shows the future Evangelist among a group at a public tavern. A significant darkness hovers over the table where money is being counted; and as Jesus enters, a shaft of light illuminates the bearded face of St. Matthew and those of the young men in the center. As the light strikes each figure and object with varying degrees of intensity, it becomes the means by which Caravaggio penetrates the surface of things and reveals the inner spirit of the subjects he depicts.

In the *Conversion of St. Paul* (Fig. 12:7), he creates a blinding, lightning-like flash to highlight the Saint's inner illumination. "And suddenly there shined

Fig. 12:7. Caravaggio. *Conversion of St. Paul.* Oil on canvas. 90½" x 69". 1601–1602. Cerasi Chapel, Santa Maria del Popolo, Rome (Soprintendenza)

round about him a light from heaven" reads the New Testament passage, "and he fell to the earth, and heard a voice saying unto him, Saul, Saul, why persecutest thou me?" (Acts 9:4–5). As the observer beholds St. Paul's prone body from an extremely foreshortened angle, with his arms flung out as if to embrace the new light that has dawned, he is caught up in the event and shares the wonderment and concern of the attendant and the huge horse.

Caravaggio's efforts to create a truly popular religious art as seen through the eyes of the common man met with a mixed reception, and paradoxically, it was only the sophisticated few who grasped its originality and significance. The *Calling of St. Matthew* was refused by the clergy of the church for which it had been painted because it showed the Saint in a too-worldly situation, even though the story is told by the Evangelist himself. Other untraditional pictures, such as those showing the Apostles as peasants with dirty feet, were rejected by the priests and public who preferred more conventional elegance and illusionism and found the works of Pozzo and Bernini more congenial to their taste.

Andrea Pozzo succeeded in capturing the new spirit in his extraordinary painting on the barrel-vaulted ceiling at St. Ignazio (Fig. 12:8), a church dedicated to the founder of the Jesuit Order. Above the clearstory windows, the walls

Fig. 12:8. Pozzo. *St. Ignatius in Glory*. Fresco on ceiling of nave. *c.*1691. Sant' Ignazio, Rome (Alinari)

of the building seem to soar upward so that the vaulting of the nave becomes that of heaven itself. With astonishing foreshortening effects, St. Ignatius is borne aloft by a heavenly host, ascending in ever-winding spirals toward figures symbolizing the Trinity. Here all the lines converge and beams of light radiate outward to illuminate the four corners of the world—personified by allegorical representations of Europe, Asia, Africa, and America—where the missionary work of the order was carried on. Pozzo was also the author of a definitive book on perspective, in which he advised artists "to draw all points thereof to that true point, the Glory of God."

In Gianlorenzo Bernini, the impetuous and versatile architect-sculptor-painter, the Roman Counter-Reformation baroque found its most representative and prolific exponent. Designer of the piazza of St. Peter's (Fig. 10:21) that begins with the trapezoidal *piazza obliqua* in front of the façade and opens out into the mighty elliptical area enframed by massive four-fold Doric colonnades; sculptor of the gigantic bronze canopy over the high altar (Fig. 10:24) whose four spiraling columns soar 100 feet upward toward Michelangelo's great dome; sculptor of many of the basilica's key chapels, notably the one in the apse with the chair of St. Peter; designer of such monuments as the Fountain of Four Rivers at Piazza Navona in which allegorical river gods and rock and shell forms join with the lively movement of gushing springs to form a revolutionary design —Bernini, even more than Michelangelo, is responsible for lifting the face of modern Rome.

Of all his many works, the Cornaro chapel dedicated to the *Mistica Dottora* St. Teresa is most typical of this phase of the baroque. In the central group over the altar (Fig. 12:9), Bernini portrays the Saint in a state of ecstasy, his source being one of Teresa's poems in which she graphically describes her mystical union with God:

When that sweet Huntsman from above	The dart wherewith He wounded me
First wounded me and left me prone,	Was all embarbed round with love,
Into the very arms of Love	And thus my spirit came to be
My stricken soul forthwith was thrown.	One with its Maker, God above.
Since then my life's no more my own . . .	No love but this I need to prove:
And all my lot so changed is	My life to God surrender'd is
That my Beloved One is mine	And my Beloved One is mine
And I at last am surely His.	And I at last am surely His.

St. Teresa, as revealed by the undulating folds of her deep-cut drapery, seems to be rising and falling in voluptuous ecstasy, and the angel (closely resembling Cupid with his dart) is about to pierce her heart. The polished white-marble group is framed by dark marble columns and set in a niche of varicolored marbles of agate, red, pink, green, and amber hues. Gleaming gilded-bronze rays descend from above, and the whole is lighted magically by a concealed window

Fig. 12:9. Bernini. *St. Teresa in Ecstasy*. Lifesize. 1645–1652. Cornaro Chapel, Santa Maria della Vittoria, Rome (Gabinetto Fotografico Nazionale)

glazed with yellow glass. On either side are groups in relief portraying members of the Cornaro family, donors of the chapel, who are watching the miraculous proceedings as if from stage boxes at the theater.

The chapel begs the question—"Is it architecture, sculpture, painting, stage design? Is it sculpture in the round, in relief?" The answers in each case must be "yes"—but combined not separated, in fusion not isolation. The sculptured center group is surrounded by actual and simulated architecture; the painted sky above and the theatrical lighting effects are all part of a single conception in which the real and visionary elements are blended into one; in which metal, marble and pigments, forms, colors and light are harmonized into a concert of the arts.

SPANISH COUNTER-REFORMATION ART

The personal tastes of that morose monarch Philip II, who succeeded his father Charles V, were austere to the point of severity. His worldly position and ambitions, however, made it mandatory that he surround himself with the necessary magnificence to command awe and respect. To unify his kingdom, wrest local authority from his feudal lords, and vest himself with all the power of an absolute monarch, Philip selected as his capital the then-obscure but centrally located town of Madrid. Consequently, an enormous building program had to be undertaken in order to house the court and provide city palaces for the aristocracy.

With the riches of the Old World and the unlimited resources of the New at his command, Philip summoned the leading artists of Europe to help build and embellish his chosen capital, and his ambassadors were under instruction to buy any available masterpiece of painting and sculpture. While they remained in their native cities, Titian and other Italian artists continued to paint for Philip as they had for his father, but Domenicos Theotocopoulos, a young Greek painter who had studied in Venice and Rome, settled in Spain, where he became known as the foreigner El Greco (the Greek). The Spanish composer Victoria, though he was fully established in Rome, dedicated a book of masses to Philip in the hope of receiving a court commission. Attracted by the glitter of Spanish gold, artists from all parts of Europe, known and unknown, flocked to Madrid in search of fame and fortune. Thus, while Spain's power and prestige was to decline in the 17th century, the precedent set by Charles V and Philip II as patrons of the arts continued through the reigns of Philip III and Philip IV to round out a full century of brilliant artistic activity.

Architecture

Bound by the terms of his father's will to build Charles V a tomb, bound by his own solemn oath to found a monastery dedicated to the Spanish martyr St. Lawrence, on whose day he gained his great military victory over the French, and bound also by his intense religious fervor and his consciousness of his royal prerogatives, Philip II envisioned a vast architectural project that would coordinate these diverse objectives and resolve some of his own inner conflicts. As the plan matured in his mind, this monument was to be at once a temple to God, a mausoleum for his ancestors and descendants, a national archive of arts and letters, a dwelling place for the Hieronomite monks, a college and seminary, a place of pilgrimage with a hospice for the reception of strangers, a royal residence, and, in general, a symbol of the glory of the Spanish monarchy.

A site in the barren foothills of the Guadarrama Mountains about 30 miles from Madrid was chosen for the undertaking, which took its name from the

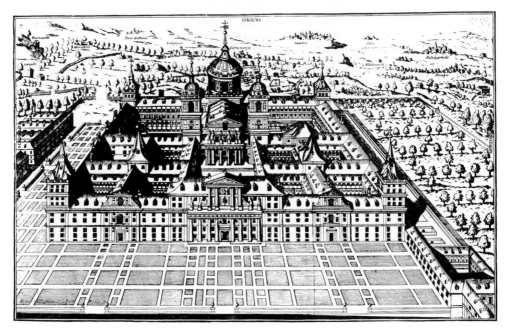

Fig. 12:10. J. B. de Toledo and Juan de Herrera. Escorial Palace. 675′ x 685′. Towers 200′ high, dome 312′ high. 1563–1584. Near Madrid. Engraving after an elevation by Herrera. (*opposite*). Fig. 12:11. *Sideview* (Anderson)

near-by village of Escorial. The original plans were drawn up by Juan Bautista de Toledo, who had studied with Jacopo Sansovino and Palladio and worked on St. Peter's in Rome under the direction of Michelangelo, and were completed by his collaborator Juan de Herrera.

According to Philip's instructions, the monument had to embody the ideals of "nobility without arrogance, majesty without ostentation." Both Philip and his father, as pillars of the church and as international rulers, were conscious of the reincarnation of Roman power in their empire and kingdoms. The Roman classical style, as formulated by Palladio and others, seemed best to symbolize their international position and prestige. The simplicity and severity of the Escorial were therefore in keeping with Philip's personal taste; and the hard unyielding yellow granite of which it was built exercised a still further restraining influence on the architects and decorators. As it stands, the Escorial is a vast quadrangle of almost 500,000 square feet, which is subdivided into a symmetrical system of courts and cloisters (Fig. 12:10). The form symbolically refers to the gridiron of St. Lawrence on which he met his martyrdom. The corner towers can be said to represent the legs of the iron grill, while the palace, which projects from the east end, forms its handle. Elsewhere in the building the grill idea is widely used as a decorative motif.

The sides (Fig. 12:11) present a long expanse of wall, entirely devoid of decoration, their monotony broken only by the endless rows of seriate windows. The principal entrance, found on the west front (Fig. 12:10), is carried out in the strict Doric order with only the royal coat of arms and a colossal statue of St. Lawrence holding his gridiron to relieve the general austerity. The portal leads into the Patio of the Kings, which is named from the statues of David, Solomon, and the other kings of Israel that stand over the entrance to the imposing church, which is located on the central axis. The plan of the church, as well as many of the interior and exterior details, was adapted from Michelángelo's original design for St. Peter's (Fig. 10:23). It is a centralized structure, following the form of a Greek cross and culminating in a dome that rises more than 300 feet above the floor. The main body is conceived in the strong and dignified Doric style, relieved by a series of chapels, numerous altars with painted altarpieces, and ornate organ lofts. Below the high altar is the burial crypt known as the Royal Chapel of the Pantheon, which was finished during the reign of Philip IV, in which the kings and queens of Spain repose in baroque coffins arranged in strict hierarchical order.

Fig. 12:12. Herrera. Escorial, *Court of Evangelists*. 210′ x 207′. 1563–1584

Much of the Escorial's area is devoted to the monastery and seminary of the order of St. Jerome. The heart of this section is the handsomely designed double-decked cloister known as the Court of the Evangelists (Fig. 12:12), which faces one wing of the church. The enclosed walk below is again in the Doric order with its simple frieze punctuated by the rhythmical triglyphs. Still more space for monastic meditations is provided by the Ionic gallery, which, in turn, is surmounted by a balustrade in the Palladian manner. In the center of the garth is a small structure of polychrome marble that functions as an echo of the great dome of the church that soars above it. Statues by Monegro of each of the four Evangelists look outward from their niches toward their respective pools, which are watered from spouts in the forms of the symbolic evangelical beasts.

In the palace section are the reception halls, the impressive galleries, and the state dining rooms that go with the grandeur of the proud Spanish monarchy. The only departure from the prevailing air of splendor is the monastic severity of Philip's own apartment. Elsewhere there are the quarters of the major-domos, the secretaries of state, the lords of the bedchamber, lodgings for ambassadors, and apartments for members of the royal family. Some galleries have mural and ceiling decorations devoted to the great battles of Spanish history; others are hung with rich Flemish tapestries depicting Biblical, mythological, and literary subjects. The picture galleries contain a vast number of the paintings that were purchased so liberally over the centuries by the Spanish kings. The Escorial still houses many of Philip's own collection of the Venetian masters he so much admired. Other Italian schools, as well as Flemish and native Spanish artists, are also represented with outstanding examples. Of interest also is the library, a barrel-vaulted structure with its east and west windows arranged according to the maxims of Vitruvius. Drawings for its decoration with detailed notes of instruction to the artists show that Herrera kept a firm hand on every aspect of the design of his building. Many rare medieval manuscripts and codices are housed in this library as well as the royal collection of medals, coins, and bronzes. Among its treasures are the manuscripts of the books of St. Teresa of Avila, that pillar of the Counter Reformation who was once Philip's guest at the Escorial. Works of the great Arabic and Jewish authors are placed in a special enclosure where they can be seen but not read or touched.

So vast is the whole Escorial that it has been estimated one would walk ten miles to visit every room. On it Philip lavished the energies of nearly 40 years of his leisure, and it was his fondest wish to see it completed during his lifetime. Most of the work actually was done before his death, but the Pantheon and many details of the complex structure remained for his successors to carry to completion. The fact that the building was conceived and built mainly under one patron in less than half a century gives it a closer unity than palaces such as

Fig. 12:13. Gomez de Mora. La Clérica, Façade. 1617. Casa de las Conchas (House of Shells). 1514. Salamanca

the Vatican and the Louvre, which evolved over many centuries and constantly were changing with the varying tastes and fortunes of their proprietors. For this reason too, the Escorial appears to be dominated by the restless melancholy spirit of its founder, which seems to have crystallized here into the rigidity and majesty of death. The Escorial nevertheless remains unique among the buildings of the world, combining as it does in a single structure the functions of a royal residence, military fortress, colossal church, national art gallery, state archives and library, monastery, theological college, pantheon of Spanish kings, and sepulchre of princes.

The Escorial Palace, by reaching out to bring all the functions of an absolute monarch within a single structure, is baroque in the grandeur of its conception. However, the restraint of Philip's taste, as well as the discipline of his architects, kept decorative exuberance well within academic bounds. Exercising the prerogatives of an absolute monarch, Philip insisted on the right to pass on the suitability and style of every public building that was undertaken during his reign. Herrera, as the court architect, was commissioned to inspect all such plans and, as a consequence, became an artistic dictator who enforced the restricted preferences of his royal master on the nation. Not until after Philip's death was Spain free to develop the florid style that is now such a prominent feature of the face of its large cities. And some of the florid baroque's emotional exuberance and excesses came as a direct reaction to the austere formalism of Philip's time. Daring designs, fantastic forms, curved lines, the spiral twist of corkscrew columns rapidly replaced the severe façades and traditional classical orders enforced by Herrera.

Two buildings in Salamanca (Fig. 12:13) dating about a century apart will serve as illustrations. The Casa de las Conchas, or House of the Shells, is a Renaissance structure built in 1514, well before Philip's time. It nevertheless shows the tendency toward applied decoration that was popularly known as the *plateresque style*, a name derived from the Spanish word *platero* (silversmith). Across the street is the church of the Jesuit college of La Clérica, which was begun after the period of Philip and Herrera. The lower part dates from the early 17th century and was designed by Juan Gomez de Mora. Even though it still adheres nominally to the classical orders, the decorative urge is clearly seen in the attached Composite columns and in the baroque triglyphs above them, as well as in many of the other details. The towers and gable belong to the latter part of the 17th century and were executed by Churriguera, whose name is associated with the more florid aspects of the Spanish baroque, the *Churrigueresque* style.

Painting

While the Escorial Palace was still abuilding, Philip II commissioned El Greco to paint an altarpiece for the chapel of St. Maurice. The subject of El Greco's early masterpiece, the *Martyrdom of St. Maurice* (Fig. 12:14), is typical of the Counter Reformation in that it has to do with the dilemma of the individual who is caught between conflicting loyalties. St. Maurice, the figure in the right foreground, was the commander of the Theban Legion, a unit of Christians serving in the Roman imperial army. An order has just arrived commanding all members of the unit to acknowledge the orthodox Roman deities or be put to death. In the expressive gestures of their hands, St. Maurice and his staff officers reveal their positions in this matter. Christ, it is true, has sanctioned by his own example the rendering unto Caesar the material things that are Caesar's, but the worship of false idols is another matter. The line is thus clearly drawn, and a choice has to be made between duty to the state and duty to the church, between the city of man and the city of God. For St. Maurice there is but one possible decision, and his hand points upward.

El Greco's spiral composition is well adapted to convey the tension between the material and spiritual realms, the natural and supernatural, the terrestrial and celestial. It can be sensed in the twitching muscles, flamelike fingers, taut faces, and swirling upward motion of the composition itself. In serpentine fashion, it winds around to the left middleground where St. Maurice is seen again, this time giving comfort to the men as they await their turn for decapitation. The tempo is accelerated toward the background where the nude figures of the army seem already to have parted company with corporeality and are drawn into the spiritual vortex that bears them aloft on a Dantesque whirlwind. The eye is led upward by the constantly increasing light and the transition of color from the darker hues below to the vaporous pink and white clouds above. There a visionary vista in the heavens is beheld, where some of the floating angelic figures hover and hold crowns for those who suffer and die below, while others produce the strains of celestial harmony.

In spite of the grimness of the subject, the light transparent-color palette El Greco uses gives the work an almost festive air, with the rose-colored banners and steel-blue and yellow costumes set against a background of silvery gray. The originality of the work, with its daring color dissonances and the lavish use of costly ultramarine blue, forfeited for El Greco the favor of King Philip, whose tastes ran to the more conservative Italian style. He made only one other attempt to interest the royal patron: a study for a picture later called the *Dream of Philip II*. The commission for its execution on a large scale, however, was not forthcoming.

Fig. 12:14. El Greco. *Martyrdom of St. Maurice and Theban Legion*. Oil on canvas.
174″ x 118″. 1581–1584. Escorial (Anderson)

Fig. 12:15. El Greco. *Assumption of Virgin*. Oil on canvas. 13′ 2″ x 7′ 6″.
c.1577. Art Institute, Chicago

If the doors to the Escorial were closed, the gates to Toledo, see of the archbishop primate, always remained open to El Greco. His reputation there had been securely established by the series of paintings he had done for the Church of San Domingo el Antiguo. Most renowned of these was the *Assumption of the Virgin* (Fig. 12:15) for the high altar. El Greco's model was the picture Titian had painted on the same subject some 60 years earlier (Fig. 11:18). El Greco's version, however, reveals the baroque preference for open space, while Titian contains all action within his picture. By dividing his composition into three planes, Titian starts a vertical ascending motion in the lower two but arrests it by the descending figure of God above. By combining the acute receding diagonal lines of the sarcophagus with the circular groupings of the Apostles, El Greco in his *Assumption* forms a conelike base from which the Madonna soars aloft in a spiraling movement that leads the eye upward out of the picture into the open space above.

The *Expulsion from the Temple* (Fig. 12:16) was a religious subject hitherto outside the iconographical tradition. The fact that El Greco painted no less than six versions of it shows that the theme had become important in the Counter-Reformation period. The driving out of the money changers from the temple is the only incident in the Gospels where Christ is seen in an attitude of righteous anger, and the only time He resorted to physical action and corporeal punishment. The church, after the Council of Trent, was in the throes of a rigid

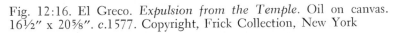

Fig. 12:16. El Greco. *Expulsion from the Temple.* Oil on canvas. 16½" x 20⅝". *c.*1577. Copyright, Frick Collection, New York

Fig. 12:17. El Greco. *Cardinal de Guevara*. Oil on canvas. 67¼" x 42½". *c*.1596–1601. Metropolitan Museum of Art, New York

self-purification, and the image of Christ as a reformer was therefore the predominant one of Him. Since this was the period of the church militant as well as that of the Inquisition, churches that ordered the picture probably intended to revive the incident as a justification of their course of action.

Christ appears here in the role of the refining fire as prophesied by Isaiah, and His mood of fiery anger is reflected in El Greco's clashing colors of crimson red, pink, orange, and greenish yellow. While Christ's gesture bespeaks violence, His face is serene in the knowledge that what He does is for the good of those whom He chastises. The atmosphere recalls that of a *Last Judgment* with the figure of Christ separating the two groups. The side toward which His lash is directed is full of turbulence and confusion as the traders cringe under the accusing eye, yet try to save their wares. On the other side, all is calm as the Disciples ponder the meaning of the event. The contrast is carried out also in the reliefs painted between the columns in the upper part of the picture: at the left Adam and Eve are driven from the garden by the sword of the avenging angel, while, opposite, the messenger of the Lord stays the sword of Abraham as he is about to sacrifice his son Isaac.

In his penetrating portrait of Cardinal Don Fernando Niño de Guevara (Fig. 12:17), El Greco has produced a personification of the spirit of the Counter Reformation. At the time it was painted, the cardinal was about to leave his post as archbishop of Toledo to assume the office of Grand Inquisitor at Seville, a position that gave him the leadership of the dread Inquisition. His bearded face betrays an attitude of uncompromising righteousness. The piercing eyes, magnified by thick lenses, are those of a religious zealot combining fanaticism with pitiless logic. The tense pose of the body is that of a prosecutor and the practitioner of a rigid spiritual discipline. The generally austere impression is relieved only by the obvious delight El Greco took in the brilliant carmine red and the contrasting white lace of the cardinal's robes, which are sumptuously painted.

In an attempt to understand the various aspects of El Greco's style, it is possible to offer some rationalistic arguments. His use of bright colors, for instance, undoubtedly had something to do with the dark Spanish churches for which his pictures were painted. The lengthening of the bodies as well as the hands and heads of his figures are related to the artist's Byzantine background and to the distortions of Italian mannerism. As an expressive device, his verticality and elongations produce the illusion of figures on a higher level, somewhat like statues seen from a kneeling position. But, more important, El Greco's figures are animated by inner fires and are caught up in spiritual whirlwinds as they behold mystical visions. El Greco was concerned with the translation of such miracles into convincing visual terms, reinforced by a heightened emotionalism and an exploration of mystical experience. Within this frame of reference naturalistic and logical explanations simply do not apply; but his inner world does not for this reason lack either coherence or consistency. When El Greco is accepted on his own terms, his world responds to its own laws, and its forms then become communicable patterns of the utmost expressivity.

Less than a decade after El Greco's death, Philip IV appointed Velásquez as his court painter. As such, Velásquez' art comes within the category of the aristocratic baroque that is treated more fully in the next chapter. As a complete contrast to El Greco and as an equally towering figure of the high Spanish period, it is more convenient to discuss him here. While El Greco concerned himself almost exclusively with religious subjects, Velásquez, with few exceptions, painted scenes of courtly life. In contrast to El Greco's personal involvement in his pictorial content, Velásquez sees his world with cool detachment and an objective eye. His work is admirably summed up in his masterpiece *Las Meninas*, or the *Maids of Honor* (Fig. 12:18). In it, the painter combines the formality of a group portrait with the informality of a genre scene in his studio. Attention is about evenly distributed among the various groups. In the foreground, the Infanta Margarita dressed in a gown of white satin is standing in the center. On the left, a maid of honor is offering her a drink of water from a red cup on a gold tray. At the right is a group made up of a second maid of honor and two of the court dwarfs, one of whom is poking the sleepy mastiff with his foot. In the middleground, on the left, is Velásquez himself wearing the

Fig. 12:18. Velásquez. *Las Meninas (Maids of Honor)*. Oil on canvas. 10′ 5¼″ x 9′ ¾″. 1656. Prado, Madrid (Anderson)

cross of the Order of Santiago, which was conferred on him by his friend and patron, the king. He stands before a canvas which, by reason of its large dimensions, seems to be *Las Meninas* itself. He is looking at King Philip IV and Queen Mariana, whose faces are reflected in the mirror at the back of the room. As a balance for his own figure, Velásquez paints the conversing lady-in-waiting and courtier in the right middleground. In the rear of the room, a court attendant stands in the open doorway pulling back a curtain, possibly to adjust the light for the painter.

Velásquez is a virtuoso in the handling of space and light. With the utmost precision, he has organized the picture into a series of receding planes and by so doing gives the figures their spatial relationships. The first plane is in front of the picture itself where the king and queen and, by inference, the observer are standing. Next comes that in which the principal group stands in the light of the window at the right, which again is outside the picture but which provides the brilliant illumination that falls on the blonde hair of the princess. The light here is balanced by that from the door at the rear, which defines the plane in the background. In between is the intermediate plane with the figures of Velásquez and the attendants, who are shown in more subdued light. Otherwise the space is broken up geometrically into a pattern of rectangles, such as the floor, ceiling, the easel, the pictures hanging on the wall, the mirror, and the door at the back.

In such a precise analytical study of space and light, which lacks both the spiritual mysticism of El Greco and the worldly grandiosity of the Venetian painters, the baroque qualities are not immediately apparent. Velásquez, however, is a virtuoso of external rather than internal vision, and therefore his baroque qualities are found in such things as the intricate play of light and shadow, the complex spatial arrangements, the fact that much lies outside the picture space itself, and the subtle relationships of the subjects to each other. Proof of the latter is evidenced by the fact that Velásquez experts still cannot agree on what is actually going on. Is Velásquez painting the king and queen, and have the infanta and her ladies wandered in to look around? Or is Velásquez looking into a mirror as he paints the infanta, and have the king and queen dropped in to watch the proceedings?

Just as Spanish architecture showed a reaction when the restraints of the earlier period were lifted, Spanish painting also moved away from the austerity and intensity of the previous century. No painter could sustain the spiritual insight and emotional power of El Greco. The relaxation into sentimentality is clearly seen in Murillo's *Immaculate Conception* (Fig. 12:19). The subject was one in particular favor with the Spanish church, and Murillo and his workshop are known to have turned out some 20 versions of it. According to the ecclesi-

Fig. 12:19. Murillo. *Immaculate Conception*. Oil on canvas. 81″ x 56⅝″. *c*.1665–1670. Prado, Madrid

astical formula, the Virgin should be shown in all the beauty of her late girlhood, and, like the vision in the 12th chapter of Revelation, be clothed with the sun and with the moon under her feet, and be borne aloft by a cherubic choir. In this instance the cherubs hold the lily, olive branch, and palm leaf—symbols of purity, peace, and martyrdom.

Music

The Roman zeal for reform predisposed church music to look more to the past than the future, to traditional rather than experimental forms. "The Antiphoners, Graduals, and Psalters have been filled to overflowing with barbarisms, obscurities, contrarieties, and superfluities as the result of the clumsiness or negligence or even wickedness of the composers, scribes, and printers," read the papal brief authorizing Giovanni da Palestrina to undertake the reform of church music along lines laid down by the Council of Trent. An ardent advocate of the Flemish contrapuntal style of Josquin des Prez and Heinrich Isaac, Palestrina, together with his great contemporaries Orlando di Lasso and Tomás Luis de Victoria, brought that art to its final fruition. Palestrina's prayers in song achieved a fluidity and transparency of texture, a balance of melody and harmony, a spiritual and organic unity worthy of the closing years of the *ars perfecta,* or perfect art. The music of his younger colleague Victoria, however, has a darker emotional tone, a brooding emotional fervor, and a deeper concern with the dramatic meaning of his texts. After serving 30 years as a chaplain, singer, and composer in the German College in Rome, an institution founded by his fellow Spaniard Ignatius Loyola, Victoria returned to his native country as choirmaster in court circles.

The music at the court of Philip II, like the architecture, painting, and sculpture, was religiously oriented, and the records of the period, as well as the design of the church at the Escorial, testify to the important place accorded the tonal art there. The choir at the Escorial was established even before the whole building was completed and in 1586 numbered in its ranks 150 monks. The choir section of the church is divided into two parts, since Philip's musical preferences were for the Venetian double-choral style he had heard in his youth. Besides the two organs in the choir, there are two others on either side of the nave, both large double-manual concert instruments of Flemish manufacture, 50 feet wide and 40 feet high. The same maker also built three portable organs for processions, which were placed in the galleries, thus making it possible on high feast days to hear seven organs pealing forth.

Since his patron's taste embraced both the traditional counterpoint and the new developments of the Venetian style, Victoria was able to bridge the gap between Renaissance polyphony and the baroque polychoral style. The book of masses he published in 1600 are in the massive Venetian polychoral style with an independent organ part. The vocal demands are of such complexity that it must be assumed these masses were composed for the skilled chorus of the Escorial. Certain idioms recur often enough in Victoria's writing to give clues to his expressive purposes. Among these are the characteristic descent along the line of the minor triad and the use of the dissonant minor second to symbolize sorrow and pain. At times, he also breaks up the normal continuity of contrapuntal lines into a succession of short phrases to produce a sobbing effect.

Victoria's settings of the *Offices for Holy Week* have become an established tradition for performance in the Sistine Chapel. One of these is the four-part motet *O vos omnes,* the text of which comes from Jeremiah and the mood of which is one of lamentation. The passage below shows the characteristic grief motive in the descending tenor voice in measure 4, as well as the dissonance created by the dip of the minor second by the same voice in the 5th measure, both of which intensify the meaning of the word *dolor,* or sorrow.

O vos omnes. 4-Part Motet   Victoria

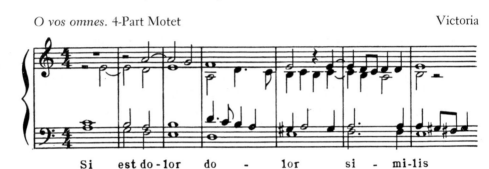

Si   est do - lor   do   -   lor   si - mi-lis

Victoria never wrote a single note of secular music. As he stated in one of his dedications, he was led by some inner impulse to devote himself solely to church music. In his motets and masses, he even avoided the secular *cantus firmus* themes that were customarily employed by his contemporaries. Instead, he chose his motives and melodies from his own religious works or from the traditional plainsong. In his later compositions after his return to Spain, his work took on an even greater fervor and passionate intensity. With its ascetic quality, religious ardor, and devotional spirit, his music rises in its way to the same heights of mystical grandeur as the writings of St. Teresa of Avila, the architecture of Herrera, and the pictures of El Greco.

MILITANT MYSTICISM

The Counter Reformation was accompanied by a vigorous reassertion of the mystical worldview. In keeping with the spirit of the times, however, it was a practical mysticism of this world as well as the next, a realistic blending of the active as well as contemplative life, a religious experience not limited to future saints but broadened to include all those faithful to the church as the mystical body of Christ. The new mysticism was socially oriented to enlist laymen as well as clergy, those active in worldly affairs as well as those behind convent walls.

It was a rekindling of the fires of faith at a time when its foundations were threatened by new scientific discoveries; a call to arms for all those willing to fight for their convictions in a war to the finish against doctrines the church considered heretical; a military mysticism of a church militant on the march.

The enemy was made up of the various Protestant movements, the material-istic world view that went with growing nationalism and colonial expansion, and the forces of rampant rationalism unleashed by free scientific inquiry. The Counter Reformation was just as much a resurgence of spiritual and moral values in the face of growing scientific materialism as it was an anti-Protestant move-ment. The church plainly saw that if the mechanistic image of the world as "matter in motion" were generally accepted, the belief in miracles would be undermined, the notion of divine intervention in worldly affairs would be de-stroyed, and the sense of mystery would be drained out of the cosmos.

The new psychology was not so much concerned with abstract theological speculation as with concrete religious experience through vivid imagery. The mysticism of St. Teresa and St. John of the Cross differed from medieval mysti-cism in its rational control and written documentation of each stage of the soul's ascent from the abyss of sin to the ecstasy of union with the divine. As expressed by St. John of the Cross:

O happy night and blest!
Secretly speeding, screen'd from
    mortal gaze,
Unseeing, on I prest,
Lit by no earthly rays,
Nay, only by heart's inmost fire
    ablaze.

When from the turret's height,
Scattering his locks, the breezes
    play'd around,
With touch serene and light
He dealt me love's sweet wound,
And with the joyful pain thereof I
    swoon'd.

The most typical expression of the church militant, however, was the So-ciety of Jesus, founded by that soldier and man of action St. Ignatius Loyola. His Jesuits helped adapt church doctrine to modern conditions, faced the moral and political realities of the century, and took an active part in education, public af-fairs, and missionary work. Under their director general, a Jesuit enlisted as a "warrior of God under the banner of the Cross" and stood ready to go for the "propagation of the faith to the Turks or other infidels even in India or to heretics, schismatics or some of the faithful." The whole world, for missionary purposes, was divided into Jesuit provinces, and the priestly army of occupation followed in the wake of the navigators and conquistadors.

The spiritual side of the Jesuit military organization is reflected in St. Igna-tius' *Spiritual Exercises*, a precise disciplined exploration of the mysteries of faith through the medium of the senses. As part of the Jesuit system of education, St. Ignatius worked out a four-week series of meditations leading to a purgation and purification of the soul. All faculties are brought into play so that the experience becomes a vividly personal one. Sin is the subject of the first week, and its consequences are felt through each of the senses in turn. In the "Torment of Sight," the student visualizes the terrible words engraved on the gates of Hell—*Ever, Never*—and sees the flames spring up around him. In the "Torment of Sound," he listens to the groans of millions of the damned, the howls of demons, the crackle of flames that devour the victims. With the "Torment of Smell," he is reminded that the bodies of the doomed retain in Hell the corruption of the grave. Their "stink shall come up out of their carcasses," prophesied Isaiah (Is. 34:3). For the "Torment of Taste," the condemned shall suffer hunger like dogs; "they shall eat every man the flesh of his own arm" (Is. 9:20), and their wine shall be the "poison of dragons, and the cruel venom of asps" (Deut. 32:33). And in the "Torment of Touch," the damned will be enveloped in flames that boil the blood in the veins and the marrow in the bones but do not consume the victim. Both flames and flesh are forever renewed so that pain is eternal. In the final phases, the progress leads up to the suffering, resurrection, and ascension of Christ, and it closes with the contemplation of heavenly bliss. By proclaiming that man could influence his own spiritual destiny, Jesuit optimism held a ready appeal for men of action.

Such a strong accent on sense experience as the means to excite religious feeling was bound to have repercussions in the arts. Through architectural, sculptural, pictorial, literary, and musical illusions, miracles and transcendental ideas could be made to seem real to the senses, and the mystical worldview could be reasserted through aesthetic imagery. The increasing complexity of life, the proliferation of new knowledge, the deepening of psychological insights, all shaped the course of baroque art. As religious, social, and economic pressures mounted, people were increasingly inclined to resolve their insecurities by turning to the cults of visionary saints or to the power of the absolute state. Artists were enthusiastically enlisted to enhance the power and glory of both church and state. Counter-Reformation churches were spacious, light, and cheerful; and visual artists, dramatists, and composers joined forces to make them like theaters where a concert of the arts played a prelude in an optimistic tonality to the delights of future heavenly bliss. In Counter-Reformation churches, the arts, which had remained independent media in the Renaissance, became fused into one grand ensemble to make the religious experience as complete as possible. Artists had, of course, to conform to the prevailing interpretation of church dogma; otherwise their imaginative flights could soar without limitation.

Renaissance clarity of definition and the compartmentalization of space into clearly perceived patterns gave way to an intricate baroque geometry that took fluidity of movement into account. Neat Renaissance lines, circles, triangles, and rectangles became the intertwining spirals, parabolas, ovals, elongated lozenge shapes, rhomboids, and irregular polygons of the baroque. With Borromini, horizontal and vertical surfaces were set into waves of rippling rhythms; balance and symmetry yielded to restless, unsettled movement; walls were molded sculpturally; surfaces treated with a rich play of color, light, and shadow. Pictures escaped from their vertical walls and settled upon spherical triangular pendentives and spandrels, concave and convex moldings, and the inner surfaces of ceilings, vaults, and domes. With Pozzo's paintings, solid walls, vaulted ceilings, and domes dissolved into nebulous, illusionistic vistas of the great beyond. With Bernini, marble saints and angels floated freely in space. With El Greco, corporeal being almost ceased to exist, and his figures are more spirit than flesh, his landscape backgrounds more heavenly than earthly. St. Teresa recorded and published her ecstatic visions in sparkling Spanish prose and poetry so that a wide public could experience them vicariously. Palestrina and Victoria illuminated the hymns of the liturgical year with the clarity of their counterpoint, and their moving melodies made them glow with new mystical meaning.

By adopting the baroque style as their own and helping shape the artistic vocabulary of the time, the Jesuits not only brought baroque art down from the exclusive aristocratic level but carried the new idioms with them wherever they went, thus broadening the baroque into an international style. Counter-Reformation baroque churches are found as far afield as Mexico, South America, and the Philippines. The extraordinary vigor of the church militant thus succeeded in tapping new spiritual sources and invigorating Roman Catholicism to such an extent that it emerged once more as a popular religious movement.

CHRONOLOGY:
France, 17th Century

General Events
1598–1610 Henry IV, king of France
1610–1643 Louis XIII, king of France with his mother Maria de' Medici (1573–1642) as regent during his minority
1615–1624 Luxembourg Palace built for Queen Mother by Salomon de Brosse
1621 Rubens commissioned to paint murals in Luxembourg Palace
1624–1642 Cardinal Richelieu (1585–1642), prime minister
1635 French Academy of Language and Literature established
1636 Mersenne's *Traité de l'Harmonie Universelle* (*Treatise on Universal Harmony*) published
1640 Poussin returned from Rome to decorate the Louvre Palace
1643–1715 Louis XIV, king of France
1643–1661 Cardinal Mazarin (1602–1661), prime minister
1648 Treaty of Westphalia concluded Thirty Years' War; Spain and Austria defeated, France became dominant European nation
1661–1715 Louis XIV ruled without a prime minister
1661–1688 Versailles Palace built by Louis Levau and J. Hardouin Mansart; chapel added 1699–1708
1665–1683 Colbert (1619–1683), minister of finance
1665 Bernini came to Paris to rebuild the Louvre Palace
French Academy in Rome established
1666 Academy of Sciences established

1667–1674 East façade of the Louvre Palace built by Perrault
1669 Paris Opera established by Lully
1671 Academy of Architecture established
1674 Alceste, lyrical tragedy by Quinault and Lully, performed at Versailles
Boileau's *L'Art Poétique* (*Art of Poetry*) published
1683 Government and ministries of France installed at Versailles

Architects
1552–1626 Salomon de Brosse
1612–1670 Louis Levau
1613–1688 Claude Perrault
1613–1700 André Le Nôtre
1646–1708 J. Hardouin Mansart

Painters
1577–1640 Peter Paul Rubens
1594–1665 Nicolas Poussin
1600–1682 Claude Lorrain (Gellée)
1619–1690 Charles Lebrun
1659–1743 Hyacinthe Rigaud

Writers and Philosophers
1596–1650 Descartes
1606–1684 Corneille
1621–1695 La Fontaine
1622–1673 Molière
1623–1662 Pascal
1635–1688 Quinault
1636–1711 Boileau
1639–1699 Racine

Sculptors
1598–1680 Lorenzo Bernini
1622–1694 Pierre Puget
1640–1720 Coysevox

Musicians
1602–1676 Cavalli, Venetian opera composer
c.1602–1672 Chambonnières, organist and clavecinist
1632–1687 Jean Baptiste Lully
1668–1733 Couperin le Grand, clavecinist
1683–1764 Jean-Philippe Rameau

13

THE ARISTOCRATIC
BAROQUE STYLE

FRANCE IN THE TIME OF LOUIS XIV

Everything about Louis XIV suggested grandeur. His concept of kingship assured him of the designation of *le grand roi*; his code of etiquette created the
grand manner; he was in every sense the *grand seigneur*; and his reign gave his
century the name of *le grand siècle*. At the time his portrait (Fig. 13:1) was
painted by Hyacinthe Rigaud in 1701, Louis had been king in name for well
over half a century and a king in fact for a full 40 of those years. Dressed in
his courtly ermine-lined coronation robes, with the collar of the Grand Master
of the Order of the Holy Ghost draped about his regal neck, he might actually
be uttering the very words for which he was so famous: *L'état c'est moi*—I am
the state. Since he was in fact the personification of France, his portrait, appropriately enough, was that of an institution; and his figure was as much a pillar
holding up the state as that of the imposing column which supports the building
in the background. Pompous and theatrical though the portrait is, it was part
and parcel of the illusionism of a period that strove to make such transcendental
abstractions as the divine right of kings seem real to the senses.

Absolute monarchy, accompanied by the cult of majesty, did not lack a
rational basis. Louis' favorite image was provided, possibly, by the astronomer

Copernicus, who proclaimed in his famous treatise that "the sun, as if sitting on a royal throne, governs the family of stars which move around it." Louis was indeed the center of a solar system that included among its satellites innumerable ministers and mistresses as well as a slightly more select company of poets and artists. Descartes, in like vein, built his philosophy on the premise that the universe was an orderly system, whose parts were derived from the whole and where all the forces emanated from a single center. The philosopher believed that the things he clearly and distinctly perceived were true, and in this connection often cited the image of sunlight. Political theorists hastened to point out that, since the sun was the center of the solar system and the source of light, the king was the logical center of the state, the apex of the social pyramid, the head of the civil service, the army, the police, and so on. In this frame of reference, Louis' exalted place in the scheme of things was not quite so arbitrary as it appears today, and it would certainly have been impossible even in his own time had it not enjoyed the support of the most astute French politicians of the century, Henry IV, the cardinals Richelieu and Mazarin, and the finance minister Colbert.

The success of this system of centralization is seen in the list of positive accomplishments of a reign in which the feudal power of the provincial nobles was broken; the church became a part of the state instead of the state a part of the church; Paris became the intellectual and artistic capital of the world; and France attained the dominant position among European nations. For the arts, the alliance with absolutism meant that they were of value as instruments of propaganda; factors in the assertion of national power and prestige; and the means of enhancing the glory of the court, impressing visiting dignitaries, and stimulating export trade. All this led, of course, toward the concept of art as an adjunct to the cult of majesty and as the perpetuator of the myth. With the king as principal patron, art inevitably became a department of the government, and Louis was surrounded with a system of cultural satellites each of whom was supreme in his own field. The foundation of the Academy of Language and Literature in 1635, the Royal Academy of Painting and Sculpture in 1648, and the others which followed later, made it possible for Boileau to dominate the field of letters, Lebrun that of the visual arts, and Lully the art of music. Absolutism in this sense meant standardization, since no artist could receive a commission or even employment except through official channels. Louis, however, was quite aware of what he was doing, and in an address to the Academy he once remarked: "Gentlemen, I entrust to you the most precious thing on earth, my fame." Knowing this, he defended his writers and artists, supported them generously, and above all exercised that most noble attribute any patron can possess—good taste.

Fig. 13:1. Rigaud. *Louis XIV*. Oil on canvas. 9′ 1½″ x 6′ 2⅝″. 1701. Louvre, Paris (Archives Photographiques)

The outward and visible sign of this absolutism was to be seen in the dramatization of the personal and social life of this *roi du soleil*, or Sun King. The adoption of the sun as his symbol was natural enough, and such motifs as the sunburst were widely used in the decor of his palaces. As patron of the arts Louis could identify himself freely with Apollo, the sun god, who was also the Olympian protector of the muses. In the morning, when it was time for the Sun King to rise and shine, the *lever du roi* was as dazzling in its way as a second sunrise. This special dawn was accompanied by a cloud of attendants who flocked into the royal bedchamber precisely at 8 A.M. in order to hand the king the various parts of his royal apparel. A similarly colorful ceremony accompanied the *coucher du roi*, when the Sun King in a golden glow of candlelight finally set at 10 P.M. Louis' life was one continuous pageant in which each hour had its appropriate activity, costume, cast, and audience. Less frequent events, such as a christening, a wedding, or a coronation, had their special ceremonies. Even the royal births called for an audience so as to assure the country of the legitimacy of any future sovereign. In the present day of prosaic cabinet officers and drab parliamentary bodies, it is difficult to imagine the overwhelming effect of the formal pomp and circumstance surrounding an absolute monarch's court. If his peers and subjects beheld a sufficiently majestic spectacle or grandiose procession, a ruler apparently could get by with anything.

Throughout a reign of 72 years, Louis XIV played the leading role in this incessant court drama with all the effortless technique and consummate self-discipline of an accomplished actor. His play was a success from the opening night, his press notices invariably extravagant, and the ambition of every aristocrat in the world was to get into the act if possible—or at the very least to receive a ticket to the performance. Such a great actor needed, of course, a great audience; and such a dramatic spectacle demanded an appropriate stage setting. Architects therefore were called upon to plan the endless series of communicating salons as impressive backdrops for the triumphal entries; landscape designers to fashion the grand avenues for the open air processions; painters to decorate the ceilings with pink clouds so that the monarch could descend the long flights of stairs as if from the sky; and musicians to sound the ruffles and flourishes that accompanied the grand entrances. It was therefore no accident that the Louvre and Versailles palaces resembled vast theaters, that the paintings and tapestries of Lebrun seemed like curtains and backdrops, that Bernini's, Puget's and Coysevox' sculptural adornments took on the aspect of stage props, that the most important literary expression should be the tragedies of Racine and the comedies of Molière, and that the characteristic musical forms should be Lully's court ballets and operas.

ARCHITECTURE

In 1665, at the insistence of his minister Colbert, Louis XIV requested the pope to permit his principal architect Lorenzo Bernini to come to Paris to supervise the rebuilding of the Louvre Palace. When he arrived on French soil, Bernini was received with all the honor due him as the ranking artist of his day. The design he made for the Louvre was radical in many ways. It would have necessitated the replacement of the existing parts of the building by a grandiose baroque city palace of the Italian type, and it completely neglected to take certain particular qualities of French life into account, notably the important place accorded to women. His plan got as far as the laying of the cornerstone. Then, after a round of festivities, Bernini returned to Rome; his plan was scrapped; and a French architect, Claude Perrault, was appointed to finish the job. This little episode in cultural history marked the weakening of Italian artistic influence in France, it also indicated that Louis XIV had certain plans of his own.

Fig. 13:2. Perrault. Louvre, *East Façade. c.*600′ long. 1667–1674. Paris (Archives Photographiques)

Perrault's façade (Fig. 13:2) incorporated some parts of Bernini's project, such as the flat roof concealed behind a Palladian balustrade and the long straight front with the wings extending laterally instead of projecting forward to enclose a court in the traditional French manner. Perrault's own contributions can be seen in the solid ground floor, which is relieved only by the seriated windows. This story functions as a platform for the classically proportioned Corinthian colonnade, with its rhythmic row of paired columns marching majestically across the broad expanse of the façade. The space between the colonnade and the wall of the building allows for the rich play of light and shadow that was so much a part of the baroque ideal. The frieze of garlands adds a florid touch, while the central pediment as well as the classical orders of the columns and pilasters act as a restraining influence. Both combine harmoniously with the other details to complete this highly successful design.

Even before Bernini came to Paris and long before the Louvre was completed, Louis XIV had conceived the idea of a royal residence outside Paris where he could escape from the restrictions of the city, take nature into partnership, and design a new way of life. Colbert, who felt that a king's place was in his capital, advised against it, and Louis allowed the Louvre to be completed as a concession to Paris. But his real capital was destined to be Versailles (Fig. 13:3). This project was sufficiently awe-inspiring to serve as a symbol of the supremacy of the young absolute monarch as he asserted his power over rival nations, the landed aristocracy of his own country, the parliament, the provincial governments, the town councils, and the middle-class merchants. Away from Paris there would be a minimum of distraction and a maximum of concentra-

Fig. 13:3. Mansart. Versailles Palace, *Airview.* 1661–1688. Palace 1935′ wide.

Fig. 13:4. Mansart. Versailles Palace, *Garden Façade*, Detail. 1669–1685.

tion on his own person. In a wooded site almost half the size of Paris, which belonged entirely to the crown, everything could be planned from the beginning, nothing need be left to chance, and an entirely new manner of living could be organized.

The grand axis of the Versailles Palace starts in Paris, continues along the boulevard, bisects the palace building itself, and runs along the grand canal toward the horizon where it trails off into infinity. As the avenue enters the palace grounds, the barracks, coach houses, stables, kennels, and orangery are found on either side. The latter building caused an ambassador from a foreign country to remark that Louis XIV must indeed be the most magnificent of beings since he had a palace for his orange trees more beautiful than the residences of other monarchs. The wide avenue narrows progressively with the parade grounds toward the marble court of honor (Fig. 13:19) above which is found the heart of the plan—the state bedroom of Louis XIV (Fig. 13:5). The whole grand design is so logical, so symmetrical, that it becomes a study in absolute space composition and makes Versailles an all-embracing universal structure which encompasses a vast segment of external as well as internal space. No one building or any part of it is a law unto itself, and together they are inconceivable without their natural environment. The gardens, parks, avenues,

489

Mansart. Versailles Palace.

Fig 13:5 (*above*). *Louis XIV's State Bedchamber*

Fig. 13:6 (*left*). *Queen's Bedchamber*

and radiating pathways are just as much an integral part of the whole as the halls, salons, and communicating corridors of the palace itself.

As the king's power expanded, the palace grew like a living organism capable of adapting itself to changing conditions. With the victories over Spain and Franche-Compté, the palace sprouted new wings as if to symbolize the triumphs. For well over a quarter of a century, the place hummed with the activities of architects, sculptors, painters, decorators, woodcarvers, masons, and carpenters. Altogether it has been estimated that more than 30,000 men, including practically all the trained artists and craftsmen in the country, were employed at one time or another in the various building activities. Finally, in 1683, the palace was proclaimed Louis' official residence, and all the ministries of France were installed in the new wing designed for them. Versailles thus became a royal residence, the court with all its attendant social activities, and the administrative center of the French government. The roofed area of the palace covered 17 acres and housed a population of around 10,000 people, including the royal family, the lords and ladies of the court, the priests and clergy, and the military guard of honor, plus the armies of servants, gardeners, and grooms.

Jules Hardouin Mansart was the architect of the two wings that extended the main building to a width of over a quarter of a mile. His design is noteworthy for the horizontal accent attained by the uniform level of the roof line, broken only by that of the chapel, which was added in the early 18th century. The simplicity and elegance of these long straight lines, in contrast to the irregular profile of a medieval building, proclaim the new feeling for space. From every room vistas of the garden are a part of the interior design and tell of a new awareness of nature. A detail of the garden façade (Fig. 13:4) reveals how freely Mansart treated the classical orders, and how the levels become increasingly ornate from the podiumlike base below to the attic and balustrade with the silhouetted statuary above. As a whole the building is a commanding example of baroque exuberance tempered by Palladian restraint.

Some of the interior rooms have been preserved or restored in the style of Louis XIV. All the heavy ornateness of the period can be seen in Louis' state bedroom (Fig. 13:5). Above the bed is a gilded stucco relief depicting France between two figures representing Fame. Elsewhere tapestries, paintings, carved wood, and mirrors cover every available inch of space. On the mantlepiece is a marble bust of the Duchess of Bourgogne by Coysevox. Since comfort was considered a purely private matter, it seems to have been given hardly a thought. In one of the rooms of the queen's apartments (Fig. 13:6), the baroque interior style is again seen in the heavily decorated ceiling, with its painted murals and caryatids perched on the fanciful scroll frames; the large Gobelin tapestries on the walls; and the furnishings of carved wood, bronze, polychrome marble, and rich fabrics.

Fig. 13:7. Mansart and Lebrun. Versailles Palace, *Hall of Mirrors*. 240′ long, 34′ wide, 43′ high. Begun 1676. (Archives Photographiques)

The grandest room of the palace, however, was the famous Hall of Mirrors (Fig. 13:7) stretching across the main axis of the building and looking out toward the spacious gardens. Designed by Mansart and decorated by Lebrun, it was the scene of the most important state ceremonies and a kind of apotheosis of the absolute monarchy. Corinthian pilasters of green marble support the ornate vault that is covered with paintings by Lebrun and inscriptions by Boileau and Racine—all to the greater glorification of the Sun King. The room was originally decorated sumptuously with brocaded damask curtains, chairs of enameled silver, orange trees reposing in silver urns, mirrors framed with chased copper, and chandeliers of crystal and gold. Clear geometrical divisions prevented the elaborate details from getting out of hand yet allowed full scope for the general magnificent effect of the composition.

The gardens, which were laid out by André Le Nôtre, are not just a frame for the buildings but are incorporated into the whole spatial design. Their formality and geometrical organization symbolized the dominance of man over nature, but with the idea of embracing nature rather than keeping it at arm's length. The square pools across the garden side, so liberally populated with goldfish and swans, reflected the contours of the building like an external echo of the mirrored halls within. The statues of river gods and nymphs, which are found at the angles, were executed from sketches by Lebrun and personify the rivers and streams of France. The gardens and park form a logical system of terraces, broad avenues, and pathways radiating outward from clearings. They are liberally embellished by fountains, pools, canals, pavilions, and grottos, all of which are richly decorated with statuary. More than 1200 fountains were installed by skilled engineers of waterworks, and with their jets spouting water into the air in many different patterns, they were marvels of their craft. Each had its name, and each was adorned with an appropriate sculptural group.

The great fetes that took place at Versailles served the purpose of distracting the unemployed nobility and compensating them for the loss of their power. Since royal favors were obtainable only at court and since the entertainment there was on such a lavish scale, the proud nobles were inevitably drawn into Louis' orbit, thus relinquishing their local privileges in exchange for an opportunity to participate in the festivities. This shift of the aristocrats from their country castles to the ultraurbane surroundings of Versailles sometimes necessitated a hasty and hectic education in the social graces for many of the courtiers. Lessons in courtly deportment, dancing, and the elegant use of language were obligatory in a place where one of the worst disasters that could befall a man was to make a *faux pas*, literally a false step, in the minuet. It might even necessitate his withdrawal from courtly life for an indefinite period. The gardens, parks, and canals provided endless opportunities for strolling, picnicking, lovemaking, hunting, fireworks displays, boating, and water pageants. The various salons in the palace provided the setting for card games, gambling, masquerade balls, theatrical entertainments, concerts, ballets, and opera performances.

The Versailles Palace, therefore, was not so much a monument to the vanity of Louis XIV as it was a symbol of the absolute monarchy and the outstanding example of aristocratic baroque architecture. It represented a movement away from a feudal decentralized government toward a modern centralized state. As a vast advertising project it was a highly influential factor in the international diplomacy of the time. By urbanizing the country aristocracy and promoting court activities, Versailles built up for the arts a larger and more discriminating audience. It assured the shift of the artistic center of gravity from Italy to France. The court also functioned as a center of style and dress; and, as a school for the training of skilled craftsmen, it virtually assured the status of France as a continuous center of elegant workmanship and fashion to this day. By combining all the activities of a court in a single structure, Versailles pointed the way toward the concept of architecture as a means of creating a new pattern of life. At Versailles a large housing development the size of a town was constructed so as to encompass rather than escape from nature. Details of Le Nôtre's garden plan, such as the radiating pathways, were the acknowledged basis for the laying

Fig. 13:8. Bernini. *Bust of Louis XIV*. Marble. 33⅛" high. 1665. Versailles Palace (Archives Photographiques)

out of new sections of Paris; and the city plan of Washington, D. C., for instance, was a direct descendant of the parks of Versailles. Modern city planners and housing developers have hailed Versailles as the prototype of the contemporary ideal of placing large residential units in close contact with nature. Finally, by starting with a grand design, Versailles pointed the way to the planning of whole cities from the start without the vicissitudes of haphazard growth and change. In this light Versailles is seen as one of the earliest examples of modern urbanism and city planning on a large scale.

SCULPTURE

While Lorenzo Bernini was working on the Louvre plans, he was besieged by requests from would-be patrons to design everything from fountains for their gardens to tombs for their ancestors. The king as usual came first in such matters, and Bernini received a commission from Louis XIV for a portrait bust (Fig. 13:8). This minor by-product of the artist's Paris sojourn ultimately turned out to be far more successful than his major mission. The recorded conversations of the artist and the accounts of his contemporaries make this portrait one of the most amply documented works in art history.

Dispensing with the usual formal sittings, Bernini made rapid pencil sketches while the king was playing tennis and presiding at cabinet meetings, so that he could observe his subject in action. He was convinced that movement was the

Fig. 13:9. Bernini. *Model for Equestrian Statue of Louis XIV.* Terracotta. 30″ high. 1670. Borghese Gallery, Rome (Gabinetto Fotografico Nazionale)

medium that best defined the personality and brought out the unique characteristics of his subjects, and the informal sketches were made, as he said, "to steep myself in, and imbue myself with, the king's features." After he had captured the individuality he was to portray, his next step was to decide on the general ideas—nobility, majesty, and the optimistic pride of youth. Here all the accessories, such as the costume, drapery, position of the head, and so on, would play their part. After the preliminaries were over and the particular as well as the general aspects were settled, the king sat 13 times, while Bernini, working directly on the marble now, put on the finishing touches.

Bernini's expressed intention was to paint in marble, but the problem was always that of transferring the impression of color to the white material. He said that if a man's hair and face were completely whitened, "even those who see him daily would have difficulty in recognizing him." His solution was in the use of shadow for the features, even if it meant altering them somewhat, and elsewhere making strong contrasts in the textures, such as those of the soft hair, starched lace collar, metallic armor, and silken drapery. To liven the static medium, Bernini thought "the best moment to choose is when the model is about to speak, and I tried to catch that moment." It will be seen that the lips are slightly parted as if about to give a command. The eyes were of great importance to Bernini, who at the sittings marked in the irises with black chalk. Only after many changes was he ready to use the chisel, and the proper look of determination was thus achieved. The complex folds of the deep-cut drapery

Fig. 13:10. Bernini. *Apollo and Daphne*. Marble. Life-size. 1622–1625. Borghese Gallery, Rome (Alinari)

were done with great care to appear as if blown by the wind and so bring a spontaneous movement into the otherwise static form.

Like all the works of the period, the bust had its allegorical allusions. Bernini noted in his conversations the resemblance of the king to Alexander the Great, whose countenance he knew from ancient coins. Courtly flattery was partially responsible, of course; but according to the conventions of the time, if the king were to appear as a military hero, it would be as a Roman emperor on horseback; or, if he were to be the *roi soleil*, it would be in the guise of Apollo. Since Bernini's intention here was to convey grandeur and majesty, Alexander, as the personification of kingly character, was the logical choice.

After his return to Rome, Bernini did one more sculptural work for Versailles—an equestrian statue of Louis XIV in marble. It was so fiery and turbulent and met with so much disfavor that the king ordered its removal to a remote part of the garden where the features were altered and it was renamed for the ancient Roman hero Martius Curtius. Bernini's original conception, however, has been preserved in his clay model (Fig. 13:9).

In addition to such portraits, Bernini's fame as a sculptor rested more broadly on religious statues, such as his *St. Teresa in Ecstasy* (Fig. 12:9), on the many fountains he designed for Rome, and on mythological groups to embellish aristocratic residences, such as his *Apollo and Daphne* (Fig. 13:10). This youthful work is full of motion and tense excitement. According to the myth, Apollo, as the patron of the muses, was in pursuit of ideal beauty, symbolized here by the nymph Daphne. The sculptor chose to make permanent the pregnant moment from which the previous and forthcoming action may be inferred. As Daphne flees from Apollo's ardent embrace, she cries aloud to the gods, who hear her plea and change her into a laurel tree. Though root-bound with the bark already enclosing her limbs, she seems to be in quivering motion. The diagonal line from Apollo's hand to Daphne's leafy fingers leads the eye upward and outward. The complex surfaces are handled so as to give maximum play to light and shadow. The sculptor has carefully delineated the various textures, such as the smooth flesh, flowing drapery, floating hair, the bark, leaves, and branches, in keeping with his objective of painting in marble. But above all Bernini has realized his express intention, which was to achieve emotion and movement at all costs and to make marble seem to float in space.

The Versailles gardens provided French sculptors with an inexhaustible outlet for their wares. Many went to Italy to copy such admired antiques as the *Laocoön* (Fig. 2:21), the *Farnese Hercules* (Fig. 2:11) and *Marsyas and the Slave* (Fig. 2:18). These replicas were then sent back and placed on pedestals along the various walks at Versailles. Other sculptors, like Girardon, made variants of Bernini's fountains and incorporated the movement of the water into their designs as he had done. Most of the statuary at Versailles, however, is effective mainly as part of the general setting, and only a few works have survived the test of time to emerge as individual masterpieces. Puget's *Perseus Delivering Andromeda* and his well-known *Milo of Crotona* (Fig. 13:20) originally stood along the Royal Walk but are now in the Louvre. Coysevox, who lived and worked at Versailles, likewise was influenced by Bernini. Such examples as his oval relief in the Hall of War and his numerous portrait busts were instrumental in establishing the tradition of French academic sculpture.

PAINTING

Peter Paul Rubens (Fig. 13:11), as the ranking painter of his day, had been summoned to Paris by Louis XIII a generation earlier just as Bernini later was called to the court of his son. At that time, the Luxembourg Palace was being completed as the residence of the Queen Mother Maria de' Medici, and her

Fig. 13:11. Rubens. *Self-portrait*. Oil on canvas. 43⅛" x 33½". c.1638–1640. Kunsthistorisches Museum, Vienna

(*opposite*) Fig. 13:12. Rubens. *Henry IV Receiving Portrait of Maria de' Medici*. Oil on canvas. 13' x 9' 8". 1622–1625. Louvre, Paris (Archives Photographiques)

expressed desire was for a painter who could decorate the walls of its Festival Gallery in a manner matching the Italian baroque style of its architecture. Maria's career as Henry IV's queen and as Louis XIII's regent was as lacking in luster as her own mediocre endowments could possibly have made it. Nevertheless, as the direct descendant of Lorenzo the Magnificent, she seemed to sense that the posthumous reputations of princes often depended more on their choice of poets and painters than on their skill in statecraft. The famous Flemish artist was brought to her attention by her sister, the Duchess of Mantua, at whose court Rubens had spent eight of his youthful years. Since then he had achieved a formidable reputation for his accomplishments as a courtier and diplomat as well as for his pictures, which were eagerly sought after by popes, kings, and cardinals.

Rubens' cycle of 21 murals gave the needed imaginary apotheosis to Maria's unimaginative life, and the triumph belonged more truly to the man who painted it than to the lady who lived it. The remarkable thing was how Rubens could exercise so much individual freedom within the confines of courtly officialdom and succeed so well in pleasing both himself and his royal mistress. In his grandiose conception, the ancient gods had deserted the rarified regions of Mt.

Olympus and taken up their abode in the vastly more exhilarating atmosphere of Paris. Even before Maria's birth, Juno and Jupiter had cajoled the Three Fates into spinning a brilliant web of destiny for her. The governess who taught her to read was none other than Minerva, while her music teacher was Apollo himself. Her mythical eloquence came from the lips of Mercury, and every possible feminine fascination was imparted to her by the Three Graces. When this paragon of brilliance and virtue reached the apex of her grace and beauty, the Capitoline Triad themselves presided over the scene where *Henry IV Receives the Portrait of Maria de' Medici* (Fig. 13:12). Minerva, as goddess of peace and war, whispers words of wisdom into the king's ear, while a whimsical

Fig. 13:13. Rubens. *Disembarkation of Queen Maria de' Medici at Marseilles.* Oil on canvas. 13′ x 9′ 8″. 1622–1625. Louvre, Paris (Archives Photographiques)

touch is provided by the cupids who playfully try to lift the heavy helmet and shield of the king's armor. The celestial scene above assures everyone concerned that marriages are indeed made in heaven, where Jupiter with his eagle and Juno with her peacocks are seen bestowing their Olympian blessing.

When the royal marriage was solemnized in Florence, the accompanying festivities included the performance of Peri's *Euridice,* the earliest extant opera. This great event, however, was much too incidental for inclusion in such a cosmic conception, and the observer is next privileged to witness the *Disembarkation of Maria de' Medici at Marseilles* (Fig. 13:13). As she steps ashore, a personification of France makes a low bow of welcome, figures representing Fame sound the triumphal trumpets to announce the arrival. The denizens of the sea are overjoyed at the safe conclusion of the voyage, and Neptune himself issues the commands to moor the galley, while tritons and sea nymphs disport themselves in the rippling rhythms of the water and playfully tug at the ropes. From the accentuated lighting and undulating movement, it is obvious that the painter was most concerned with this part of his picture. Authorities have also established that the voluptuous water nymphs were done by Rubens' own hand. All his love of the robust female form is present in these opulent figures. He was painting large surfaces—in this instance the mural is 13 by almost 10 feet— and his concept of space demanded feminine forms capable of filling both the canvas and the eye.

The demand for Rubens' work was such that he employed about 200 apprentices and assistants. This series was executed in his studio in Antwerp beginning in 1622. As was his custom in such a project, Rubens sketched out the composition of each picture, then delegated the preparatory work to one assistant, an architectural background to another, landscape and animal figures to other specialists, and for himself reserved certain choice parts. When the pic-

Fig. 13:14. Rubens. *Garden of Love*. Oil on canvas. 78″ x 111½″. *c.*1632–1634. Prado, Madrid (Anderson)

tures were installed at the Luxembourg Palace in 1625, Rubens was on hand to put in the finishing touches, while Queen Maria watched him at work and, from reports, took pleasure in his conversation.

The baroque ideal of richness and lavishness is seen once again in a picture from Rubens' later years, the *Garden of Love* (Fig. 13:14). The setting for this allegory was the garden of his palatial home at Antwerp, and the ornate doorway in the background still exists. The bacchanalian theme unfolds in a diagonal line beginning with the chubby cherub in the lower left. Rubens himself is seen urging his second wife Helena Fourment, who appeared in so many of his later pictures, to join the others in the garden of love. The rest of the picture unfolds in a series of spirals mounting upward toward the figure of Venus who, as a part of the fountain, presides over the festivities. The use of large areas of strong primary colors—reds, blues, yellows—enlivens the scene and enhances the pictorial structure.

Rubens succeeded in combining the rich color of Titian and the dramatic tension of Tintoretto with an unbounded energy and physical exuberance of his own. His conceptions have something of the heroic sweep of Michelangelo, though they lack the latter's introspection and restraint. His complex organization of space and freedom of movement recall El Greco, but his figures are as round and robust as the latter's were tall and emaciated. His success in religious pictures, hunting scenes, and landscapes, as well as the mythological paintings that suited his temperament so well, shows the enormous sweep of his pictorial powers. For sheer imaginative invention and bravura with a brush he has rarely, if ever, been equalled.

While Rubens was executing his murals for the Festival Hall, an obscure French painter named Nicolas Poussin, who had been working on minor decorations, left the Luxembourg Palace for the less confining atmosphere of Rome. There he soon built a solid reputation that came to the attention of Cardinal Richelieu, who bought all of Poussin's paintings and became determined to bring the artist back to Paris. In 1640, Poussin did return to decorate the grand gallery of the Louvre—and receive from Louis XIII a shower of favors and the coveted title of First Painter to the King. The inevitable courtly intrigues that followed such marked attention made Poussin so miserable that after two years he returned to Rome. There he acted as the artistic ambassador of France and supervised the French painters sent under government subsidies to study and copy Italian masterpieces for the decoration of the Louvre. There, too, for the rest of his life Poussin had the freedom to pursue his classical studies, the independence to work out his own principles and ideals, and the time to paint pictures ranging from mythological and religious subjects to historical canvases and architectural landscapes.

Fig. 13:15. Poussin. *Rape of Sabine Women*. Oil on canvas. 61″ x 82½″ *c.*1636–1637. Metropolitan Museum of Art, New York

The *Rape of the Sabine Women* (Fig. 13:15) shows how Poussin, in his effort to recreate the classical past, turned to the Roman historians Livy and Plutarch for his subject, to the Roman museums for the models of many of his figures, and to Vitruvius for his architectural setting. In the incident that he depicts, Romulus, the legendary founder of Rome, having been unsuccessful in negotiating marriages for his warriors, has arranged a religious celebration with games and festivities as a stratagem to bring families from the neighboring town of Sabina to the Roman Forum. From his position of prominence on the portico of the temple at the left, Romulus is giving the prearranged signal of unfolding his mantle, whereupon every Roman seizes a Sabine girl and makes off with her. Though his subject is one of passion and violence, Poussin manages to temper his picture by a judicious juxtaposition of opposites. The anger of the outraged victims contrasts with the impassive calm of Romulus and his attendants. As a ruler, Romulus knows that the future of his city rests on the foundation of families, and that in this case the end justifies the means. The turbulent human action is counterbalanced also by the ordered repose of the architectural and landscape background. The smooth marblelike flesh of the women contrasts

Fig. 13:16. Poussin. *Et in Arcadia Ego* (*Shepherds in Arcady*). Oil on canvas. 33½″ x 47⅝″. 1638–1639. Louvres, Paris (Alinari)

with the bulging musculature beneath the bronzed skins of the Romans, and the contours of the figures generally are clearly defined as if they had been chiseled out of stone. Poussin's constant preoccupation with antique sculpture is readily seen when the group in the right foreground is compared with the Hellenistic *Gaul and His Wife* (Fig. 2:4). While such direct derivations are comparatively rare, this group is indicative of the close study the artist made of the antique statuary in the Roman museums. The building at the right, a reconstruction Poussin made from a description of a Roman basilica by Vitruvius, is further evidence of Poussin's desire for accuracy of detail.

Et in Arcadia Ego (Fig. 13:16) shows Poussin in a quieter and more lyrical mood. The rustic figures of the shepherds might well have stepped out of one of Vergil's pastoral poems, while the shepherdess could be the tragic muse in one of Corneille's dramas. As they trace out the letters of the Latin inscription on the sarcophagus, "I Too Once Dwelled in Arcady," their mood becomes pensive. The thought that the shepherd in the tomb once lived and loved as they, casts a spell of gentle melancholy over the group. In this meditative study in spatial composition, the feminine figure parallels the trunk of the tree to define the vertical axis, while the arm of the shepherd on the left rests on the sarcophagus to supply the horizontal balance. Each gesture, each line, follows inevitably from this initial premise with all the cool logic of a geometrical theorem. The subject is obviously a sympathetic one to Poussin, as he had found his own Arcadia in Italy and took a lifelong delight in the monuments of antiquity and the voices from the past that spoke through just such inscriptions. Like the ancients he tried to conduct his own search for truth and beauty in a stately tempo and with a graceful gesture. Like them, too, he sought for the permanent in the transient, the type in the individual, the universal in the particular, and the one in the many.

Claude Lorrain, like his countryman Poussin, also preferred life in Italy to that in his native country. His lifelong interest was landscape, but the convention of the time demanded human beings as well as titles with pictures. He solved the problem by painting his landscapes, letting his assistants put in a few incidental figures, and giving the pictures obscure names, such as *Embarkation of the Queen of Sheba, Landing of Cleopatra, Expulsion of Hagar,* or *David at the Cave of Adullam.* With tongue in cheek, he once remarked that he sold his figures and gave away his landscapes. Scenes like the *Harbor at Sunset*

Fig. 13:17. Claude Lorrain. *Harbor at Sunset.* Oil on canvas. 45″ x 41″. Uffizi, Florence (Soprintendenza)

Fig. 13:18. Lebrun. *Alexander the Great Entering Babylon*. Oil on canvas. 14′ 9″ x 23′. c.1666. Louvre, Paris (Alinari)

(Fig. 13:17) were his special delight. In them, he could concentrate on limitless space and the soft atmospheric effect of sunlight on misty air. His usual procedure was to balance his compositions on either side of the foreground with buildings or trees, which are treated in considerable detail. Then the eye is drawn deeper into the intervening space with long vistas over land or sea toward the indefinite horizon. Formal values dominate, and nothing arbitrary or accidental intrudes to mar their stately quality.

Charles Lebrun was one of the painters who came under Poussin's influence when he was in Rome. Though a friend and ardent admirer of Poussin, he preferred the fuss and feathers of life at Versailles. An opportunist of the first magnitude, he ingratiated himself there by designing the costumes for Louis XIV's pageants, fountains for the parks, and tapestries for the salons. His facile painting technique and his talent for courtly flattery hastened his rapid rise to the position of leader of the Academy, first painter to the king, head of the royal tapestry and furniture studios, and artistic arbiter of the reign. His *Alexander the Great Entering Babylon* (Fig. 13:18), like most of his other pictures, was one of a series of huge canvases designed for the pompous interiors of the Versailles Palace. Since Louis XIV spent much of his time and energy cultivating the art of Mars, and since his courtiers invariably hailed the returning victor as a second Alexander, the significance of the central figure was not likely to be overlooked by anyone. Lebrun left the victorious army discreetly outside his picture, so that Alexander could dominate the scene in lonely triumph from his elephant-drawn chariot. While he thought he was carrying out Poussin's theories, Lebrun's pictures illustrate what happens when an artist allows the letter to crowd out the spirit. In all fairness, however, it must be said that Lebrun was a better decorator than he was a painter; consequently, his pictures usually make better sense in the context of their original surroundings than as separate entities.

The acquisition of paintings by the crown was begun under Colbert on a massive scale. The purchases reveal the gradual veering away from an international toward a national viewpoint. Rubens and the Italian artists were liberally represented, but, on Lebrun's advice, the systematic buying of Poussin's pictures and those by French artists exhibiting in the annual salons was begun. By 1709 the collection of Louis XIV numbered over 2400 pictures including 29 Poussins. While their primary purpose was to decorate the royal galleries, they were available for study to French painters and were the subjects of discussion at sessions of the Academy. The stylistic differences of Rubens and Poussin admirably illustrate the free and academic sides of the baroque coin. Both painters were well versed in the classics, both reflected the spirit of the Counter-Reformation, and both in their way represented the aristocratic tradition. But while Rubens' impetuosity knew no bounds, Poussin remained aloof and reserved; while Rubens cast restraint to the winds and filled his pictures with violent movement, Poussin was austerely pursuing his formal values; while Rubens' figures are soft and fleshy, Poussin's are hard and statuesque; while Rubens sweeps up his spectators in the tidal wave of his volcanic energy, Poussin's pictures are more conducive to quiet meditation. The Academy's championship of Poussin made clear the distinction between academic and free baroque. In the late 17th and 18th centuries, painters were divided into Poussinist and Rubenist camps, and in the 19th century echoes were still to be heard in the classic versus romantic controversy.

MUSIC

The musical and dramatic productions at the court of Louis XIV were as lavish in scale as the other arts, and three groups of musicians were maintained. First came the *chambre* group, which included the famous *Vingt-quatre Violons*, or Twenty-four Viols, the first permanent stringed orchestra in Europe. This was the string ensemble that played for balls, dinners, concerts, and the opera. Lutenists and clavecinists were also found in this category. Next came the *chapelle*, the chorus that sang for religious services, and the organists. The *Grand Écurie* formed the third group, which consisted mainly of the wind ensemble that was available for military processions, outdoor fetes, and hunting parties.

Fig. 13:19. Levau. *Marble Court at Versailles during a Performance of Lully's Opera "Alceste", 1674.* Engraving by Lepautre. Metropolitan Museum of Art, New York

The favored form of entertainment during the early years of Louis XIV's reign was the *ballet de cour,* an elaborate form of the ballet that began with an instrumental overture and in addition to the dancing included a sequence of sung recitatives, choruses, and songs as well as instrumental interludes. Louis XIV himself, who was an excellent dancer, took an active interest in these court ballets and frequently appeared at the climactic moment in the role of Apollo, the sun god. He was serious enough about his acting to rehearse diligently under the supervision of Lully and Molière.

During the years of Louis' minority, the popularity of the court ballet had been challenged by Italian opera, the "spectacle of princes" that Cardinal Mazarin sought to introduce from his native land. In 1660, Cavalli, who had brought the Venetian lyric drama to a high point of development, was invited to Paris to write and produce an opera. It met with a mixed reception, but two years later Cavalli was again on hand to write another, this time for Louis' wedding celebration. Another challenge to the court ballet came from Molière, who united the elements of comedy, music, and the dance into a form he called the *comédie-ballet.* The best known of these is the perennially popular *Le Bourgeois Gentilhomme—The Would-be Gentleman*—which was first performed at the court in 1670. A full decade of these brilliant performances was brought to a close by the death of the great dramatist.

The ever-resourceful Jean Baptiste Lully, however, was biding his time on the sidelines until he could spring some surprises of his own. A Florentine by birth and French by education, he was fiddling away at the early age of 17 as a violinist in the *Vingt-quatre Violons*. When Cavalli produced his two operas, it was Lully who wrote the ballet sequences that, incidentally, proved more popular than the operas themselves. It was Lully again who collaborated with Molière by supplying the musical portions of the *comédie-ballets*. And when the propitious moment arrived, it was Lully who came up with a French form of opera that he called *tragédie lyrique*, or lyrical tragedy. One of the earliest of these was the performance of *Alceste* in the Marble Court at Versailles July 4, 1674 (Fig. 13:19). With a genius for organization, Lully used the *Vingt-quatre Violons* as the nucleus of his orchestra, supplementing them with wind instruments from the *Grand Écurie* for fanfares as well as for the hunting, battle, and climactic transformation scenes. The *chapelle* was also drafted into the operatic service, and the generous dance sequences he included assured the ballet group plenty of activity. Lully could have had the collaboration of the great dramatist Racine for the texts, but he deliberately chose Quinault, a poet of some distinction, who would be more pliable to his demands and who could be counted upon not to claim too much of the credit.

The form of these lyrical tragedies crystallized early and changed relatively little in the following years. Each begins with an instrumental number of the type known as the French Overture. The first part is a ponderous dignified march with dotted notes, massive sonorities, and chains of resolving dissonances as in the Ritornel on page 510. The second half is livelier in tempo and more contrapuntal in texture. Next came the prologue, and that of *Alceste* is quite typical. The setting is the garden of the Tuileries, still the official royal residence at this time, where the Nymph of the Seine is discovered. Declaiming her lines in recitative style, she makes some topical allusions to the current war, couched in flowery mythological terms. Glory now enters to the tune of a triumphal march, and a duet and solo air ensue. The two are joined eventually by a chorus of naiads and pastoral divinities, whose songs and dances give assurance that France will be ever-victorious under the leadership of a great hero, whose identity is never for a moment in doubt. The overture is then repeated, and the five acts of a classical tragedy follow with much the same formal pattern as that of the prologue.

Two excerpts from Act III, Scene V of *Alceste* will illustrate Lully's style. After the death of Alceste, a long instrumental ritornel provides the pompous elegiac strains for the entrance of the mourning chorus. One of the grief-stricken women comes forward, indicating her sorrow by her gestures and facial expressions. Her Air (p. 509) is in the recitative style which J. J. Rousseau considered Lully's chief "title to glory." The composer always insisted that the music

Alceste. Air, Act III, Scene 5   Lully

as well as the other elements of the opera were the servants of drama and poetry, and he always counseled his singers to emulate the noble and expansive intonations of the actors trained by Racine. A Lully air consequently is never so set as an Italian aria, but follows instead the elastic speech rhythms and the natural declamation of French baroque poetry and prose. The mourning chorus takes up where the Air leaves off with a variant of the opening ritornel, and the scene closes with a long cadential passage alternately for orchestra and chorus based on a continuation of the ritornel.

Alceste. Ritornel, Act III, Scene 5   Lully

Since the hero was so closely identified with the monarch, a tragic ending was quite impossible. A *deus ex machina*, therefore, invariably appeared in the fourth act, just when all seemed darkest, and the fifth act always brought the lyrical tragedy to a triumphant and glorious conclusion.

By exploiting the success of his operas and through clever diplomatic strategy, Lully became by royal warrant the founder and head of the *Académie Royale de Musique*. With the substitution of the word *Nationale* for *Royale*, this is still the official title of the Paris grand opera company. With incredible energy, this musical monopolist of the regime produced an opera every year; and in addition to writing the score, he conducted the orchestra, trained the choir, coached the singers and dancers in their parts, and directed the staging. He ruled his musical and dramatic forces with the iron hand of an absolutist, allowing nothing arbitrary or capricious to creep in anywhere. As a consequence Lully developed the best-disciplined group of singers, dancers, and instrumentalists in Europe. Their fame spread far and wide, and from contemporary accounts, his orchestra was especially noted for the purity of its intonation, uniform bowing of the strings, accuracy of tempo and measure, and the elegance of its trills and melodic ornaments that were compared to the "sparkling of precious stones."

Practically singlehanded, Lully unified the ballet and founded French opera. His standardization of the sequence of dances became known as the French suite; his form of the overture, the French overture; and his organization of the opera became standard practice for almost two centuries. Even though Quinault wrote the texts, Lully's operas may be considered the musical reflection of Racine's tragedies. In them is found the same observance of classical proprieties, the same dignified declamation, the same polished correctness. Their limitations were the inevitable outgrowth of the circumstances of their creation. By being addressed so exclusively to a single social group, they neglected to provide the more resonant human sounding board needed for survival in the repertory. Like Poussin they remained aloof, restrained, and aristocratic. Opera, however, by its combination of grandiloquent language, emotional appeal, sonorous splendor, majestic movement, and visual elegance, emerges as one of the most magnificent creations of the baroque era.

IDEAS

The many manifestations of the aristocratic baroque style crystallize mainly around two distinct but interrelated ideas—absolutism and academicism.

Absolutism

The concept of the modern unified state, which first emerged in the Spain of Philip II, was adapted to French political purposes by Cardinal Richelieu and ultimately reached its triumphant consummation under Louis XIV. "It is the respect which absolute power demands, that none should question when a king commands," was the way Corneille stated the doctrine in 1637 in his heroic drama *The Cid*. As the principal exponent of monarchical absolutism and the centralized state, Louis XIV as the Sun King assumed the authority to replace natural and human disorderliness with a reasonable facsimile of cosmic law and order. All human and social activities came under his protectorship, and by taking the arts under his paternal wing, he saw that they served as useful adjuncts to the cult of majesty. Versailles thus became the symbol of his absolutism, the seat of the absolute monarchy, and the personal apotheosis of the king.

Fig. 13:20. Puget. *Milo of Crotona*. Marble. 8' 10" high, 4' 7" wide. 1671–1683. Louvre, Paris (Archives Photographiques)

Just as political absolutism meant the unification of all social and governmental institutions under one head, its aesthetic counterpart implied the bringing together of all the separate arts into a single rational plan. While *le grand siècle* produced some buildings, statuary, paintings, literature, and music that command attention in their own right, they spoke out most impressively in their combined forms. It is impossible to think of Versailles except as a combination of all art forms woven together into a unified pattern and as a reflection of the life and institutions of the absolute monarchy. The parks, gardens, fountains, statuary, buildings, courtyards, halls, murals, tapestries, furnishings, and recreational activities are all parts of a single coordinated design. As such, Versailles accomplished the daring feat of unifying all visible space and all units of time into a spatio-temporal setting for the aristocratic way of life. Indoor and outdoor space are inseparable, even music and the theater went outdoors. Sculpture was an embellishment of the landscape; painting became the handmaiden of interior design; comedy was allied with ballet; and tragedy was absorbed into opera. All the arts, in fact, were mirrored in the operatic form with its literary lyricism, orchestral rhetoric, dramatic declamation, instrumental interludes, statuesque dancing, architectural stage settings, mechanical marvels, and picturesque posturings. In Lully's hands opera became a kind of microcosm of court life, an absolute art form in which all the separate parts existed in the closest possible relation to the whole. None was allowed to dominate, nothing was disproportionate.

The spirit of absolutism was also directly revealed in the drama surrounding the life of the monarch. All the arts took the cue, became theatrical, and sought to surprise and astonish. The purely human element was buried under an avalanche of palatial scenery, pompous wigs, props, and protocol. Only in Molière's satires, La Fontaine's fables, and the secret memoirs of the period is it possible to catch glimpses of a more truthful version of the actualities behind the scenes of courtly life. Otherwise the architecture of Versailles, the statuary of Bernini and Coysevox, the triumphal murals of Lebrun, the tragedies of Racine, and the operas of Lully were all designed to promote the illusion that Louis XIV and his courtiers were beings of heroic stature, powerful will, and grandiose utterance.

Academicism

While the academic movement began formally with the foundation of the first French Academy during the reign of Louis XIII, it was not until later in the century that its implications were completely realized and its force fully mobilized. Both Louis XIV and his minister Colbert believed that art was much too important to be left exclusively in the hands of artists. The various academies, therefore, became branches of the government and the arts a part of the civil service. Boileau as the head of the Academy of Language and Literature, Lebrun of the Academy of Painting and Sculpture, Mansart of the Academy of Architecture, and Lully of the Academy of Music were subject directly to the king and were absolute dictators in their respective fields. As such, they were the principal advisers to the king and his ministers, and, in turn, they were responsible for carrying out the royal will. Complete control of patronage was centered in their hands; theirs was the final word in determining those who would receive commissions, appointments, titles, licenses, degrees, pensions, prizes, entrance to art schools, and the privilege of exhibiting in the annual salons.

The academies were thus the means of transmitting the absolute idea into the aesthetic sphere. Academicism invariably implied a patriarchal principle whereby regularly constituted arbiters of taste placed their stamp of approval on the products in the various art media. These interpreters of the official point of view inevitably tended to become highly conservative. Aristocratic art was the superpersonal expression of a class whose code of behavior was based on etiquette, politeness, and cultivation of good taste. All intimate personal feeling, capriciousness, and eccentricity had to yield to self-discipline, urbanity, correctness, and accepted standards of good form. The academies were therefore charged with the making of aesthetic definitions, artistic codes, and technical formulas valid for their respective fields. They functioned as a kind of board of directors who decided what was best for the stockholders. They had, moreover, the power to enforce their decisions, which meant that academicism could, at best, establish and maintain a high level of creative quality and, at worst, degenerate into conventionalism and downright regimentation, with varying degrees of standardization in between. What artists stood to gain in official recognition was liable to be matched by a corresponding loss of artistic freedom.

One example will show how academicism worked. Under Lebrun, the Academy of Painting and Sculpture favored the restrained style of Poussin over the passionate exuberance of Rubens. It thereby set up an academic subdivision of the baroque style as opposed to the expression of the free baroque. Many reasons for the choice can, of course, be advanced. Poussin's pictorialism, for instance, can more readily and demonstrably be reduced to a system of formal values based on geometrical principles, while Rubens' style was so personal, impetuous, voluptuous, and violently emotional that it always remained a bit beyond the grasp. Academicism in this case was trying to tame baroque exuberance and reduce it to formulas and rules. Nothing eccentric, nothing unpredictable, was allowed to creep in and destroy the general impression of orderliness. The Academy always remained somewhat skeptical of emotion just as it was of color, since neither was subject to scientific laws. The pictorial standards of the Academy were therefore based on formal purity, demonstrable mathematical relationships, logical definition, and rational analysis. These were the qualities that brought academic art the designation of *classic*, a term that was defined at the time as "belonging to the highest class" and hence approved as a model. Since similar standards were generally to be found in Roman antiquity, the two inevitably became associated. The interpretation of such models in the 17th century, however, was quite in the spirit of the time, and hence must not be confused with the archeological exactitude that was set up as the standard for classicism in the late 18th century and the Napoleonic period.

French academicism was from the start an unqualified practical success. Under the academies, the artistic hegemony of Europe passed from Italy to France where it has effectively remained up to the present time. The hundreds of skilled artists and artisans who were trained on the vast projects of Louis XIV became the founders and teachers of a tradition of high technical excellence. French painting alone, to use the most obvious example, has continued its unbroken supremacy from the foundation of the Academy to the present day. In Spain, by way of contrast, the only successor to El Greco, Velásquez, and Murillo was the lonely figure of Goya; in Flanders there were no outstanding followers of Rubens and Van Dyck except Watteau, who to all intents and purposes was French; in Holland there was no one to take up where Rembrandt and Vermeer had left off. In France, however, painting continued on a high level throughout the 18th and 19th centuries; and, by setting high technical standards, academicism was a determining force even in nonacademic circles. The work of Perrault and Mansart in architecture, Boileau in criticism, Molière in comedy, Racine in tragedy, Lully in opera was also absorbed directly into a tradition that succeeded in setting up measuring sticks of symmetry, order, regularity, dignity, reserve, and clarity, which to this day still have a certain validity even if only as a point of departure.

CHRONOLOGY:
Amsterdam, 17th Century

General Events

1517	Protestant Reformation began in Germany
1535	*Institution of Christian Religion* published by John Calvin (1509–1564); Dutch Reformed Church established later along Calvinistic lines
1566	Revolt of Netherlands against Spain began
1575	University of Leyden, first of the Dutch universities, founded by William the Silent, Prince of Orange
1602	Dutch East India Company organized
1609	Low Countries given virtual independence in truce with Spain
1618–1648	Thirty Years' War
1621	Dutch West India Company founded
1629–1648	René Descartes resided in Holland
1630–1687	Limited public art patronage dispensed through Constantijn Huygens
1631	Rembrandt settled in Amsterdam
1637	*Discourse on Method* published in Leyden by Descartes
1642	Dutch explorer Tasman discovered New Zealand
1644	*Principles of Philosophy* published by Descartes in Amsterdam
1648	Independence of Netherlands recognized by Treaty of Westphalia
1652–1674	Anglo-Dutch commercial wars
1670	Spinoza published *Tractatus theologica-politicus*

Painters

c.1580–1666	Frans Hals
1609–1669	Rembrandt van Rijn
c.1617–1681	Gerhardt Terborch
c.1628–1682	Jakob van Ruisdael
c.1629–1679	Jan Steen
c.1629–1683	Pieter de Hooch
1632–1675	Jan Vermeer van Delft
1638–1698	Gerrit Berckheyde

Philosophers and Scientists

1467–1536	Erasmus
1583–1645	Hugo Grotius, founder of international law
1596–1650	Descartes
1629–1695	Christian Huygens
1632–1677	Baruch Spinoza

Writers

1587–1679	Joost van den Vondel, Dutch dramatist and author of *Lucifer*, poem similar to Milton's *Paradise Lost*
1596–1687	Constantijn Huygens, poet, humanist, diplomat

Musicians

1562–1621	Jan Pieterszoon Sweelinck

English School

c.1542–1623	William Byrd
c.1562–1628	John Bull, organist of the Cathedral of Antwerp (1617–1628), friend of Sweelinck
c.1562–1638	Francis Pilkington
c.1576–1643	Henry Peacham, author of *Compleat Gentleman*, teacher and composer
1583–1625	Orlando Gibbons

German School

1587–1654	Samuel Scheidt, pupil of Sweelinck
1596–1663	Heinrich Scheidemann, pupil of Sweelinck
1623–1722	J. A. Reinken, successor of Scheidemann as organist at Hamburg, and influencer of J. S. Bach
1685–1750	Johann Sebastian Bach
1685–1759	George Frederick Handel

14

THE BOURGEOIS
BAROQUE STYLE

AMSTERDAM, 17TH CENTURY

If a visitor to 17th-century Amsterdam—or any of the other sturdy Dutch towns for that matter—looked about for triumphal arches, pretentious palaces, or military monuments, he was doomed to disappointment. In fact, if there was anything grand at all about life in the Low Countries, it was in its complete commonplaceness. After they had achieved their cherished independence by wresting their country town by town and province by province from the grasp of the Spanish despots, the people organized it with a minimum of unity and a maximum of diversity. The Netherlanders had no intention whatsoever of substituting one brand of tyranny for another, much less a domestic variety; and so the land became the United Provinces under a *stadtholder*, or governor. Let their English rivals call them the "united bogs"; although their muddy swamps and marshlands were poor things, at least they were their own. Their wars of independence, geographical isolation, constant struggle against the encroachments of the sea, dour climate, seafaring economy, Calvinistic Protestantism, and individualistic temperaments conspired with all the other circumstances of Dutch life to focus the center of interest in the home. A Dutchman's home was not

517

even his castle; it was just his solid, comfortable, plain, brick house. Instead of the cult of majesty, his was the cult of the home.

When Jakob van Ruisdael painted the *Quay at Amsterdam* (Fig. 14:1), he was painting more than just a view of the old fish market at the end of the broad canal known as the Damrak. In this local variant of the international academic style (compare with Fig. 13:17), he was in fact picturing the bourgeois way of life in a scene where thrifty housewives were gathering up good things for their dinner tables; where a part of the fishing fleet that gave the Dutch a monopoly of the pickled and salted herring industry was moored; where, lying at anchor in the distance, there were some of the merchant vessels that helped the Dutch create an efficient modern commerce by plying the seven seas, trading their clay pipes, glazed tiles, Delft pottery, and cured herrings for Russian furs, West Indian sugar, tobacco, and other raw materials; where the spice trade of the Indies had led to the formation of corporations whose shares were traded on a modern stock exchange—complete with booms, like that in the stock of the Dutch West India Company in 1628 after it had declared a 50-percent dividend, and busts, like that of the tulip crash a decade later when more of the treasured bulbs had been sold than could be delivered. In short, Ruisdael was painting the scene of the active mercantilism that spread the base of prosperity so widely that every industrious citizen could aspire to have at least some share of the good things of life for his home.

In such a scheme of things, some families inevitably accumulated more than others, and by means of the wealth that was concentrated in their hands, they became a ruling oligarchy. These so-called "regent" families were the ones from whose ranks the members of the town councils and mayors were selected. They were, however, an upper-middle-class group rather than an aristocracy, and there was safety in their numbers. Their power, together with that of the professional and mercantile societies known as guilds, depended upon the retention of a maximum of local authority. This decentralization favored the growth of universities—those at Leyden and Utrecht became the most distinguished in Europe —and promoted the careers of such eminent native humanists as Constantijn Huygens, friend and patron of Rembrandt, and Hugo Grotius, founder of the new discipline of international law. The freedom to think and work attracted such foreigners as the French philosopher René Descartes, who resided in Holland for almost 20 years, and the parents of Baruch Spinoza—one of the profoundest human intellects of all time—who found refuge in Amsterdam after the persecution of the Jews had made life intolerable for them in their native Portugal.

The architectural expression of this bourgeois way of life is found in the various town halls, of which that of Amsterdam is a good example (Fig. 14:2);

Fig. 14:1. Ruisdael. *Quay at Amsterdam*. Oil on canvas. 20¾" x 26". *c*.1669, Copyright, Frick Collection, New York

in such mercantile structures as warehouses, counting houses, and the market building, seen on the extreme right in Ruisdael's painting; and, above all, in the long rows of gabled brick houses like those seen on either side of the canal in the same picture. Dating from former times were such ecclesiastical buildings as the Oudekerk, or Old Church, whose Gothic tower is silhouetted against the sky in the right background; originally Roman Catholic, it had been taken over by the Dutch Reformed Church after the Reformation. As organized under the precepts of John Calvin, the Reformed Church held that religious truth was not the monopoly of any individual or any group, and that the word of God was available to all without the mediation of priestly authority. Through the development of the printing press, every family could have its own Bible, and by means of the high degree of literacy that prevailed, almost everyone could read it. As in government, the Dutch people were wary of authority in religion; and as confirmed Protestants, they took rather literally the words of Christ to go into their closets and pray. Thus through family devotions, hymn singing, and Bible

Fig. 14:2. Berckheyde. *Flower Market at Amsterdam*. Oil on canvas. 17¾″ x 24″.
Rijksmuseum Amsterdam

reading, much of the important religious activity took place in the home. According to the teaching of Calvin, the reason for going to church was to hear
a sermon and sing the praises of the Lord. This, of course, discouraged any
distraction from these primary activities, such as architectural embellishments,
statuary, paintings, and professional choirs or orchestras. Since commissions were
no longer forthcoming from church and aristocratic sources, the artist had to
conceive his work more and more in terms of the home.

The prosperous Dutch families fortunately felt the need of an art that
would reflect their healthy materialism and reveal their outlook, their institutions, and their country just as they were—solid, matter-of-fact, and without airs.
In this happy state of affairs, patronage was spread on a broad-enough basis so
that every home had at least a small collection of pictures. In spite of the
turbulent times, Dutch art avoided heroic battle scenes just as it did grandiose
mythological allegories and complex symbolism. Landscape had a strong attraction since the Dutch had fought for every inch of their soil, and paintings of

their fields, mills, and cottages appealed to their sense of proprietorship. Genre scenes were likewise popular, since such casualness and informality harmonized with their domestic surroundings. The severe simplicity of still-life compositions also found favor because quiet arrangements of fruit, flowers, oysters, herrings, ceramics, and textiles were visible evidences of the good life. As men of affairs, they liked corporation pictures where they were depicted among their fellow directors or board members in a group portrait designed to perpetuate their memory on the walls of some guild hall, professional society, officers' club, or charitable trust. Above all, the Dutch burgher wanted family portraits for his living room—commemorative pictures of such family festivals as christenings and weddings; paintings of quiet interiors with his wife or daughter dutifully doing some household chore or, if one of them showed special talent, perhaps playing a musical instrument; and for himself, he liked to be portrayed at his work, surrounded by the distinctions of his worldly position.

Under Calvinistic austerity, the only professional musicians to survive were the church organists; the hired groups of singers and instrumentalists who performed for weddings, banquets, and parades; and the band of music teachers who taught the younger members of the family to sing and to play the lute, viola da gamba, and keyboard instruments, such as the virginals and spinet. Music, therefore, like all the other aspects of Dutch life, was centered in the home. During the Renaissance, the Low Countries had dominated European music with the polyphonic glories of their distinguished composers. Owing to the fact, however, that the artistic and material rewards were so much greater elsewhere, such a lively export trade in musicians developed that it eventually depleted the home ranks. Only one musical genius of universal stature was left in the Amsterdam of the early 17th century: Jan Pieterszoon Sweelinck, whose career brought the radiant chapter of Netherlands music to a brilliant close.

All the arts were thus centered in the home. The simple and unpretentious Dutch domestic architecture with its polished tiled floors, tidy interiors, and window boxes for the tulips was the modest framework for this bourgeois way of life. Unless ceramics are included, there was little sculpture other than a few figurines on the mantlepiece and an occasional statuette, such as that over the doorway in Figure 14:8. The primary aesthetic indulgences of the Dutch were their pictures and domestic music-making, while such things as their Delft pottery jugs, tablecloths, laces, and draperies enriched their world of qualities. The reality of daily life was made up of the routine of the business establishment, the market place, and the household. It was a reality of simple truths in which nothing was too small to be overlooked. All things, even the most insignificant, were considered to be gifts of God; and, as such, they were studied in the Dutch art of the 17th century in the minutest detail.

PAINTING

Towering above all other Dutch painters, because of the breadth of his vision, the power of his characterizations, and the uncompromising integrity of his ideals, stands the figure of Rembrandt van Rijn in lonely eminence. Like his contemporaries, he painted portraits, genre scenes, historical subjects, and landscapes, but unlike them he refused to specialize and succeeded magnificently in all. Furthermore, he brought a new psychological profundity to his portraiture, an unaccustomed animation to his genre scenes, a greater dramatic intensity to his religious pictures, and a broader sweep to his landscapes than had been achieved before in the northern tradition. His discoveries of the power of light, in all its varying degrees, to illuminate character both from without and from within, to define space by the interpenetration of light, and to animate that space by the flowing movement of shadows identify him as one of the prime movers in the establishment of the northern baroque pictorial style. Rembrandt's art as a whole reveals a consistent growth from his early to his late years in the power to penetrate the world of appearances to lay bare the quickening spiritual forces that lie beneath.

Soon after he settled in Amsterdam, the 26-year-old painter received his first important assignment from the local Guild of Surgeons. The result was *Dr. Tulp's Anatomy Lesson* (Fig. 14:3), a typical corporation picture, which went far toward establishing Rembrandt's reputation. The subjects of the group portrait were the heads of the Guild, and their names are duly recorded on the sheet of paper in the hand of the figure next to that of Dr. Tulp. Less typical is Rembrandt's unusual grouping, which imparts a certain freedom and informality to the composition yet allows each of the almost life-sized figures to be seen impartially. By the use of light, he develops the inherent drama of the situation and brings out the expression of each of the faces, which vary from intentness to casual indifference. The fullest light falls on the cadaver, the body of a newly executed criminal, and on the hands and face of Dr. Nicholas Tulp, the professor of anatomy. The large folio volume at the feet of the corpse most probably is the 1555 edition of Vesalius' *Anatomy*, opened to the page that shows the structure of the arm, which the lecturer is demonstrating. The subject is akin to the scientific spirit of the time, and in this case Rembrandt's objective statement is well suited to the intellectual atmosphere. What some historians have referred to as Rembrandt's indecisive treatment of space has had to be revised in this instance, because a recent thorough cleaning sharpened the architectural background and clearly revealed the vaulted contours of the Anatomical Hall of the Amsterdam Athenaeum in which such lectures were held. In the process the somber yellowish and dark brown tints also yielded to a wider color range than had been apparent before.

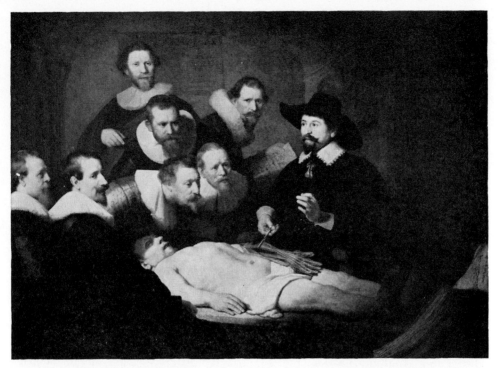

Fig. 14:3. Rembrandt. *Dr. Tulp's Anatomy Lesson*. Oil on canvas. 63¾" x 85¼". 1632. Mauritshuis Museum, The Hague

Exactly a decade elapsed between the *Anatomy Lesson* and the *Sortie of Captain Banning Cocq's Company* (Fig. 14:4), Rembrandt's masterpiece of this type. Group portraits of such military units that fought against the Spaniards were common enough at the time to have the designation of "musketeer pictures." Once their original purpose in the struggle for independence was gone, many of these companies continued as parts of the civic guard and as officers' clubs, available as the occasion warranted for anything from emergency duty to a parade. By 1642, most members had become prosperous shopkeepers, who hugely enjoyed dressing up now and then in their dashing uniforms, polishing their shooting irons, and posing as warriors in processions or civic celebrations. In "musketeer pictures," they were usually shown in convivial situations, such as a gathering around a banquet table, but in order to get some life and movement into his picture, Rembrandt discarded this rather stilted pose and chose to show Captain Cocq's company in action, as if responding to a call to arms. Its members are therefore seen moving out of the city gate before falling into formation.

Fig. 14:4. Rembrandt. *Sortie of Captain Banning Cocq's Company of the Civic Guard*. Oil on canvas. 12′ 2″ x 14′ x 7″. 1642. Rijksmuseum, Amsterdam

For generations, this picture has been known as the "Night Watch." But an expert cleaning job in 1946–1947 revealed to a startled world that the scene occurs in early daylight and that Rembrandt's varnish, which had thickened in the course of time, had been responsible for the general gloom. Now the free flow of light can be seen moving rhythmically throughout the whole composition, pervading every corner with dynamic gradations varying from dark to bright. It is most intense in the center, where the captain is explaining the plans to his lieutenant. The shadow of his hand, which falls across the lieutenant's uniform, helps to define the direction of the light, which in turn relates all the other figures to the central pair by the degree of illumination that falls upon them. Such virtuosity in the handling of light and shadow for dramatic purposes was one of Rembrandt's most unique achievements. Contrary to popular legend, the picture was not a failure, and it was proudly hung in the company's hall.

The etching, *Christ Healing the Sick* (Fig. 14:5), popularly known as the "Hundred Guilder Print," is one of Rembrandt's several hundred examples in this new medium. The relatively modest price of an etching assured a wider distribution of Rembrandt's work at the times when many of his paintings were piling up unsold in his studio. The price in this instance, however, was a record rather than a rule. Technically, the medium gave him the opportunity to explore the qualities of light by means of simple line patterns independent of pigments and colors. By scratching a wax-covered metal plate with a stylus, a linear pattern is formed that is etched or bitten into the metal upon immersion in an acid solution. When the inked impression on the metal plate is transferred to paper, the gradations of light and dark run from such inky blackness as that behind the figure of Christ to the whiteness of the untouched paper as that of the rock in the extreme left.

Rembrandt's true artistic stature is revealed in the way his art scales the heights of moral grandeur within such severe limitations. The expressive power of *Christ Healing the Sick* is as great as the material medium is small. Rembrandt was brought up in a family of Anabaptists who tried to live according to strict Biblical precepts. His religious subjects are seen from a Protestant point of view and, as such, show an intimate personal knowledge of the Scriptures. Since he

Fig. 14:5. Rembrandt. *Christ Healing the Sick*, "Hundred Guilder Print." Etching. 10⅞″ x 15⅜″. c.1649. Metropolitan Museum of Art, New York

Fig. 14:6. Rembrandt. *Self-Portrait*. Oil on canvas. 51⅝" x 40¼". 1658. Copyright, Frick Collection, New York

was not painting for churches, and thus was under no compulsion to conform to the usual iconographical tradition of Madonnas and Child, Crucifixions, and so on, he was free to develop new themes and new points of view. Much of the intimacy and effectiveness of this type of work are owed to the fact that they were not conceived as public showpieces. Rembrandt also loved to explore the Amsterdam ghetto and found stimulation as well as many of the types for his religious pictures among the descendants of the people who created the Old Testament.

Rembrandt painted over 60 self-portraits, surely a record number. The motivation, however, came more from a deep introspective tendency than from personal vanity. In a late *Self-portrait* (Fig. 14:6), done when he was 52, the artist is seen seated in an armchair, tired to the point of exhaustion. With no attempt at self-flattery, he shows himself clad in a shabby yellow smock, with his head enframed by an old black velvet hat with an upturned brim. Most striking are the luminous dark eyes, whose searching gaze seems to be studying the spectator but which are actually focused on himself as he peers into the mirror next to his easel. As an example of his late psychological portraiture, this self-portrait reveals Rembrandt as a man who has endured all the slings and arrows

Fig. 14:7. Hals. *Merry Lute Player*. Oil on canvas. 35½″ x 29½″. *c*.1627. Oscar B. Cintas Collection

of outrageous fortune, but who has been mellowed and ennobled by the experience and emerged with all his human dignity unimpaired. The penetrating look, glowing with an internal light, peers into the depths of his own character and seems to be asking, "Whither now?" From this point onward, Rembrandt realized more and more that his mission was to explore the world of the imagination and leave the world of appearances to others. Consequently, his countenance bespeaks the serenity of a man who has chosen his course and knows there is now no turning back.

Between the polar extremes of the introspective Rembrandt and the objective Vermeer, the emotional range of their contemporaries is illustrated by three pictures—the infectious gaiety of Frans Hals in the *Merry Lute Player* (Fig. 14:7), the quiet domesticity of de Hooch's *Linen Cupboard* (Fig. 14:8), and the brooding melancholy of Ruisdael's *Cemetery* (Fig. 14:9). The *Merry Lute Player* is typical of Frans Hals' most brilliant period. With his tousled hair and black cap cocked at a jaunty angle, the subject might be an entertainer at a public tavern. The way he holds up the glass of sparkling wine defines the source of light, which falls most strongly on one side of his face and on the varnished wooden surface of his instrument. In Hals' pictures, the people of his native

Haarlem—quarreling fishwives, carousing officers, and tipsy merrymakers—live again with all their animal vitality and capacity for life. Hals found his inspiration in the lighter moments of his slightly disreputable fellow townspeople who were without the moral restraints of the more sober Bible-reading burghers. While Rembrandt sought to portray the spirit of the whole man, Frans Hals was content to capture human individuality in a fleeting glance or casual gesture. In his earlier work he was interested more in appearances than essences. Later, when he came under the shadow of Rembrandt, he gave up his vivid colors and light touch for more somber subjects.

Pieter de Hooch's *Linen Cupboard* (Fig. 14:8) is a quiet study of domestic life in a proper household. Like his fellow painters, de Hooch knew that light was the magnet that attracted the eye, and that its vibrations gave such an interior its share of life and movement. But de Hooch works with a subdued light that matches the tranquillity of his subject matter. The highest intensity is reflected from the canal and sunlit wall of the house, which are visible through the open door in the background. The painter shows interest in delineating the contrasting textures of the tiled floor, the carved wood of the walls and oaken cupboard, and the qualities of the linen cloth and the costumes of the mistress, maid, and child. In contrast with Vermeer, de Hooch is more concerned with what his figures are doing, while Vermeer is more interested in what they are. The looseness of de Hooch's pictorial organization is also noticeably different from Vermeer's tight-knit interiors.

Fig. 14:8. De Hooch. *Linen Cupboard*. Oil on canvas. 28¾" x 30¼". 1663. Rijksmuseum, Amsterdam

Fig. 14:9. Ruisdael. *Cemetery*. Oil on canvas. 56" x 74¼". c.1660. Institute of Arts, Detroit

Jakob van Ruisdael's somber study of a *Cemetery* (Fig. 14:9) comes in the category of the landscapes that meant so much to the Dutch people who fought for their country so persistently against the Spanish oppressors. Ruisdael, however, seems to be searching in this instance for deeper values than the usual quiet country scene. The abandoned ruins of the old castle and the skeletonlike trunks of the two trees unite with the white stone slabs of the tombs to permeate the picture with thoughts of death. The inscriptions on the headstones—several of which are still there—remind the viewer that the religious toleration of the Netherlands made the country the haven for the Jewish refugees from the Spanish and Portuguese inquisitions. Under one of them a Dr. Montalto, physician to King Henry IV of France, was buried in 1615. Another grave contains the remains of Chaicham Usiel, head rabbi of Amsterdam, who was a native of Fez in Morocco. Ruisdael projects a depth of feeling as well as of space into this landscape. With the waterfall, gnarled trees groping toward the threatening sky, he captures something of the sublimity of nature that sweeps both man and all his works before it. His eye for the picturesque anticipates in a remarkable way certain aspects of 19th-century romanticism.

In his *View of Delft* (Fig. 14:10), Jan Vermeer paints a typical Dutch town sandwiched cozily between the elements of water and sky. From the canal opposite the town, where some people are gathering in the lower left foreground, the artist draws the attention along the profile of the mercantile buildings and houses behind the city wall on the left, past the stone bridge in the center with the steeple of the church rising in the background, and toward the moored boats and drawbridge on the extreme right. Vermeer's feeling for space is revealed in this horizontal sweep and in the fact that he makes little attempt to treat it as a study in deep perspective. Missing in the photograph, but most important to the effectiveness of the picture, is the subtle treatment of color. As the sunlight filters through the broken clouds, the static light falls unevenly over the landscape, leaving the brick houses in the shadowy foreground a dull red that contrasts with the flame-red and orange tones of those in the sunny background. More than half the area of the picture is allotted to the sky, where patches of blue alternate with the silvery and leaden grays of the clouds that are mirrored below in the placid water.

A *Street in Delft* (Fig. 14:11) again uses the warm red color of brick, tempered by the cool gray tints of a cloudy Dutch sky. A touch of contrast is provided by the brown pavement, the green shutters, and the yellows and blues

Vermeer.

Fig. 14:10 (*opposite*). *View of Delft.* Oil on canvas. 38¾" x 46¼". *c.*1658. Mauritshuis Museum, The Hague

Fig. 14:11 (*right*). *Street in Delft.* Oil on canvas. 21¼" x 17¼". *c.*1658. Rijksmuseum, Amsterdam

of the women's dresses. More important than the color this time, however, is Vermeer's meticulous geometrical organization in which each part is related to the whole. The picture can be broken down into a system of sharply defined rectangular surfaces, such as those of the pavement, open doorways, shuttered and unshuttered windows, and stepped gables of the houses. Highly selective rather than literal, Vermeer has eliminated everything that is not germane to his picture. Nothing extraneous is allowed to clutter up the tidiness of the composition, and each element of texture and surface is worked out to the minutest detail and presented with crystal clarity.

The same meticulousness and economy of means apply to such interior scenes as the *Officer and Laughing Girl* (Fig. 14:12). Here Vermeer's logical organization of rectangles and intersecting surfaces is somewhat softened by the prominence given to the conversing figures. The daring cameralike perspective projects the figure of the officer forward and gives greater size to his large slouch hat and head than to that of the girl. His red coat and sash also contrast noticeably with the cooler colors of the girl's white cap, black and yellow bodice, and blue apron that allow her figure to recede. The map on the wall is painted with the greatest care in relation to the light and angle of the wall. Its Latin title is quite clear, and reads: "New and Accurate Map of all Holland and West Fries-

Vermeer.

Fig. 14:12 (*left*). *Officer and Laughing Girl*. Oil on canvas. 20" x 18". *c*.1656. Copyright, Frick Collection, New York

Fig. 14:13 (*opposite*). *Artist in his Studio*. Oil on canvas. 52" x 44". *c*.1665–1670. Kunsthistorisches Museum, Vienna

land." The warm, rich, natural light that streams in from the open casement window gives both unity and life to the severe division of planes. It bathes every object and pervades every corner of the room, starting with the maximum intensity of the area adjacent to the source and tapering off by degrees into the cool bluish tones of the shadows in the lower right.

Almost always content to let objects and situations speak for themselves, Vermeer, on rare occasions, ventures into the realm of symbolism. *The Artist in his Studio* (Fig. 14:13) is, to be sure, a self-portrait, and the studio is his own. The lady, however, personifies Fame, and the artist starts his picture with her laurel wreath to indicate his pursuit of beauty and immortality. The trumpet, as if to sound a fanfare for a famous person, is one of Fame's attributes; and the book in her arm and the volumes and death mask on the table add a literary and sculptural dimension to this allegory of the arts.

The contrast between Rembrandt's restless searching spirit and Vermeer's sober objective detachment is fully as great as that between El Greco and Velásquez, or Rubens and Poussin. Rembrandt's light is the glow of the burning human spirit, Vermeer's that from the open casement window. Rembrandt tries to penetrate the world of appearances, Vermeer is content with the visual image. With his warm personal quality, Rembrandt embraces humanity as completely as Vermeer's cool impersonality encompasses space. Rembrandt is con-

cerned at all times with moral beauty, Vermeer with physical perfection. Rembrandt's inner dramas need only the monochromatic crescendo of a single color from deep brown to golden yellow or in an etching from black to white, while Vermeer's absence of drama demands the entire chromatic spectrum. Like a philosopher, Rembrandt lays the soul bare in his moving characterizations, while Vermeer, like a jeweler, delights the eye with his unique perception of the quality and texture of things. Thus, in both Spain and France as well as Holland, the 17th century, like a stormy March, had been swept in on the leonine gusts of free baroque flamboyance and had gone out on a gentle lamblike academic breeze.

MUSIC

The one great musician of 17th-century Holland was Jan Pieterszoon Sweelinck, who succeeded his father and was, in turn, succeeded by his son as organist at the Oudekerk, so that the family rounded out a century of music-making there. Under the strict tenets of Calvinism, church music consisted mainly of the congregational singing of psalms and hymns, preferably unaccompanied. As such, the development of music as an art would have been ruled out were it not for the fact that Dutch tradition favored the organ, and the organist was allowed to play preludes and postludes on sacred themes before and after the service. On special occasions, choral settings of the psalms with some degree of elaboration were performed. Sweelinck's viewpoint, like that of the other Dutch composers of the century, was international in scope. He had studied in Venice with Zarlino and Andrea Gabrieli and was a colleague of the famous Giovanni Gabrieli. He had also visited England and was thoroughly familiar with the English keyboard school and choral-composing tradition. His official title was Organist of Amsterdam, and as such his duties included the giving of public concerts. The church, according to contemporary accounts, was always crowded on these occasions, and large audiences consistently took delight in his improvisations and variations on sacred and secular themes; the baroque flourishes of his Venetian toccatas; his fantasies "in the manner of an echo," a keyboard adaptation of the Venetian double-choral style; and the choral preludes and fugues that he built on Protestant hymn tunes.

The other public Dutch music was of the occasional type, given by choral groups and instrumental ensembles that, for a modest price, would furnish anything from the madrigals sung at weddings to the dances played at receptions. All available evidence points to the home as the center of the major part of the musical life of the time. Most of the extant compositions from this period are found in the numerous manuscript copies that were made for home use. Printed scores, however, were obtainable from Venice and London, and early in the century music printing began to flourish in Antwerp, Leyden, and Amsterdam. Holland also became noted as a center for the manufacture of musical instruments. The musical practices of the time can be vividly reconstructed by combining the surviving scores and musical instruments with the rich visual evidence available in the paintings of the period. Vermeer's *The Concert* (Fig. 14:14), for instance, shows a typical musical situation in the home. The trio is made up of the young woman, who reads her song part from the score she holds in her hand; the seated man, who supplies the harmonic background on his theorbo, a species of the lute; and the girl at the spinet, the winged version of the virginals, who plays the keyboard part. A viola da gamba, which corresponds to the modern 'cello, is seen on the floor; and, ordinarily, if a player

Fig. 14:14. Vermeer. *Concert*. Oil on canvas. 28″ x 24¾″. *c*.1660. Isabella Stewart Gardner Museum, Boston

were available, it would be used to duplicate the bass line of the keyboard part in the instrumental combination known as the *continuo*.

The widespread custom of domestic music-making resulted in a large body of literature that was designed for home rather than public performance. Since such music was always on a friendly, sociable basis, it was mainly for two or more participants. Even the solo pieces were written for amateurs and purposely avoided any complexities that might imply showing off. The attitude is well summed up in *The Compleat Gentleman*, published in London in 1622 by the English schoolmaster Henry Peacham. "I desire no more in you," he said, "than to sing your part at first sight; withal to play the same upon your Viol, or the exercise of the Lute, privately to yourself."

An example of the type of music Mr. Peacham's gentlemen or Vermeer's ladies were prepared to perform is Francis Pilkington's "Now Peep, Boe Peep," a number from that composer's *First Booke of Ayres*, published in 1605. The score was arranged and printed so that the participants could be seated comfortably around a table (see Fig. 14:15). On the left side, the words and melody of the Canto, in this case the soprano part, appear above the lute tablature. To their right sits the tenor opposite the alto, with the bass in between. A transcription of the beginning of the piece is given on page 538.

One of the interesting things about such a work is the great number of ways it can be performed. In its complete form, it is a vocal quartet with a lute

Ow peep, boe peep, thrife happie bleft mine eies, For I haue found faire Phillis, for I haue found faire *Phillis* where fhe lies, Vpon her bed, with armes vnfpred, all faft a fleepe, Vnmaskt her face, thrife happie grace, fare-well, fare-well my Sheepe, Looke to your felues, new charge I muft ap-proue, *Phillis* doth fleepe, *Phillis* doth fleepe, And I muft guard my Loue. Looke.

2 Now peep boe peep, mine eyes to fee your blifle,
Phillis clofd eyes atrackts you, hers to kiffe :
Oh may I now performe my vow, loues ioy t'impart,
Affay the while, how to be-guile, farewell faint hart.
Taken fhe is, new ioyes I muft approue,
Phillis doth fleep, and I will kifle my Loue.

3 Now peep, boe peep, be not too bould my hand,
Wake not thy *Phillis*, feare fhee doe with-ftand :
Shee ftirs alas, alas, alas I faint in fpright,
Shee opes her eie, vnhappie I, farewell delight.
Awakt fhee is, new woes I muft approue,
Phillis awakes, and I muft leaue my Loue.

Fig. 14:15. *First Booke of Songs or Ayres of 4 Parts: With Tablature for Lute or Orpherian, with violl de gamba.* Newly composed by Francis Pilkington, . . . London, 1605. Huntington Library, San Marino, California

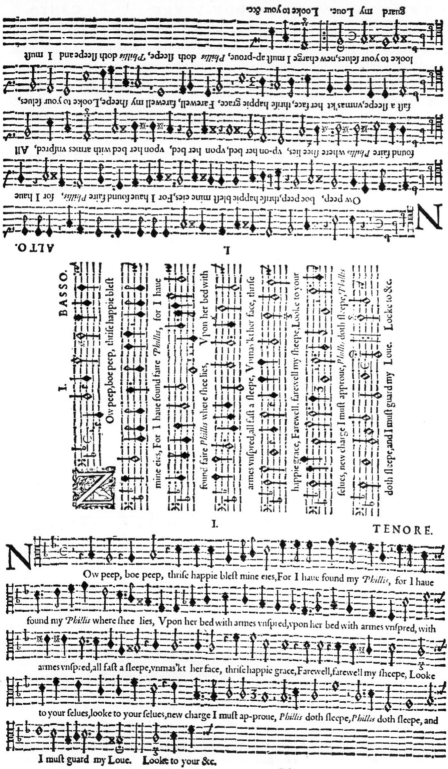

accompaniment that duplicates the three lower parts. It can also be performed as a soprano solo with lute accompaniment, as given on the left half of the page; a cappella—that is, for four voices without the lute; as a duet for soprano and any one of the other voices, as a lute solo; as an instrumental piece with viols instead of voices; as a combination of voices and viols; as an instrumental ensemble with doublings of the parts, or with wind instruments substituting for the voices and viols, and so on practically ad infinitum. Such music had to be adaptable to the size and skill of any group that might gather together for an evening of musical pleasure in the home.

The music of the Netherlands at this time was much more international in scope and character than was Dutch painting. While Italian and French influences were far from negligible in the visual arts, such painters as Frans Hals, Rembrandt, Vermeer, and their contemporaries were identified with a distinct national style. English influences were strong, especially in the keyboard style of music, and, as the century progressed, Italian influences gradually became dominant in the Netherlands just as they did in France and England. In the decade before 1650, Dutch composers were publishing instrumental ensemble pieces called sinfonias for from two- to five-stringed instruments. These corresponded closely to the fantasies for the same combinations that were written in England by such composers as William Byrd and Orlando Gibbons. After the middle of the century, however, Italian trio sonatas for two treble instruments (usually violins or flutes), and continuo began to be heard. Eventually this became the standard form of chamber music here as elsewhere. Such trio sonatas came to be

Now Peep, Boe Peep (1605) Francis Pilkington

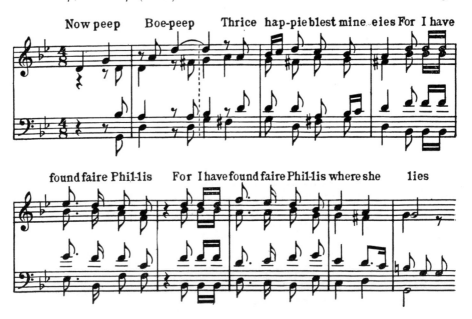

written by French, German, and Dutch composers as well as by Italians, but the form was essentially international in style.

The style that did develop a distinctively northern character was that of the keyboard literature, whether for organ, virginals, spinet, clavichord, or harpsichord. Sweelinck had absorbed both the Venetian and English traditions, and his organ-playing attracted to Amsterdam students from all over northern Europe. Through them his influence was widely extended, especially over the Protestant parts of Germany. His most noted pupil here was Samuel Scheidt of Halle, whose *Tablatura Nova*, which he published in 1624, did much to crystallize the German Protestant organ and choral style. In this book, all the technical procedures he had learned from Sweelinck were brought together and worked out with characteristic Germanic thoroughness. Happily, however, they were coupled with a considerable degree of creative imagination as well as technical invention. In its pages are found compositions intended for home performance, mainly in the form of variations. French and Flemish secular songs as well as dances, like the *allemande, paduan, courant*, and *gaillard*, appear with variants that are full of the complexities which so intrigue the baroque mind. The first two parts also contain fugues, echo fantasies, and chorales, while the third is concerned with harmonizations of Lutheran hymns and Protestant chorales with ornamental commentaries in the form of variations. Scheidt's work became a landmark in organ literature, since it assimilated and systematized the ornate Venetian manner, the English keyboard variation style, and Sweelinck's contrapuntal ingenuity. It brought together for the first time a collection of pieces admirably adapted for Protestant church purposes, and a number of musical models for other composers to emulate. A direct line thus extended from Sweelinck, who coordinated the Venetian and English schools, through his pupils like Scheidt, who transmitted the tradition to northern Germany, down to the time of Johann Sebastian Bach and George Frederick Handel, both of whom were born in this part of Germany in the year 1685.

DOMESTICITY

The various aspects of the bourgeois baroque style find a common undercurrent in the idea of domesticity. Many related ideas, such as mercantilism, Protestantism, anti-authoritarianism, nationalism, and individualism, together with the championship of individual rights and liberties, all impinge on this central concept, but the unity lies in the cult of the home. Bourgeois house comforts, for instance, were never so highly cultivated in the warmer friendlier south where so much recreational activity can take place in the open air, while the northern climate was conducive to the concentration of communal pleasures in the home.

The spirit of commerce led to navigational adventure on the high seas and to the exploration of distant lands. The Dutch conquests, however, were mainly

Fig. 14:16. Rembrandt. *Portrait of Jan Uytenbogaert, Receiver General (The "Gold-Weigher")*. Etching. 1639

those of the businessman; their empire was based on corporate enterprise; and their personal kingdoms were those of the banking houses and holding companies, which were often under the dynastic control of a single family. All was undertaken with the thought of ultimately enriching and enlivening their home and family life. The success of Calvinistic Protestantism was owing in no small part to the sanctioning of business activity and the regarding of success as a sign of divine favor. The Calvinist could charge interest with good conscience and without the fear of bringing down priestly maledictions on the practice of usury. Hard work and industriousness coupled with frugality led to a widespread accumulation of wealth in the hands of the middle class. No riotous living or public displays of luxury were possible when the church allowed no embellishment in its buildings and no musical elaboration in its services. While both the Anglican and Lutheran reform movements preserved much of the beauty of the traditional liturgy in a modified form, the Calvinistic movement was marked by its extreme austerity. A strict interpretation of Calvinism would lead directly to a gloomy form of asceticism, but the innate good sense and honest enjoyment of material pleasures saved the Dutch from the bleaker aspects of this doctrine. But the principal outlet for their prosperity and desire for aesthetic enjoyment was in their homes.

The wealthy burgher, however, did not build a palace—though he certainly had the means to do so. He was content with a comfortable house that was functionally suited to his needs. Fighting the Spanish crown for their independence, and resisting the growing menace of Louis XIV's absolute state, made the Dutch look with disfavor on any form of courtly pomp and ostentation. The Protestant movement also fortified their hostility to authority and intensified their nationalist consciousness. The middle-class merchant particularly resented the draining off of his province's wealth in the direction of Rome, and the resentment was equally strong against the secular arm of the Roman Catholic Church: the Holy Roman Empire. Protestantism thus took root and became identified in the Dutch mind with patriotism. The protection of their national and provincial rights, together with their individual freedoms, further focused their attention on their homes where they were their own lords and masters.

Philosophy, philology, social theory, and the natural sciences flourished in the Dutch universities. Such intellectual pursuits speculated on the existence of an ordered and regulated universe in which everything could be measured and understood. The solid citizen instinctively distrusted the physical and emotional forces that could render his world chaotic and unpredictable. Hence such an ideal universe had considerable appeal for a bourgeoisie whose security and comforts could be perpetuated in such a world order. Descartes' rationalistic cosmology and psychology and Spinoza's mathematically demonstrable ethical system paralleled the concept of art as a form of reasoned organization, though it took a Rembrandt to achieve an emotional spectrum wide enough to infuse it with the warmth of life.

The circumstances of the Dutch state of mind and material prosperity led to the placement of artistic patronage in the hands of a well-to-do middle class. Outside such necessary public buildings as the town halls, churches, and mercantile structures, Dutch architecture was for all intents and purposes domestic architecture. Since the houses were about the same size as middle-class homes today, there was no place in the scheme of things for monumental sculpture. The major domestic aesthetic expressions, therefore, were painting and music, together with all the minor decorative arts that added to the comfort and beauty of the home. Since pictures were destined for living-room walls, their sizes were correspondingly smaller than those painted for palaces and public halls. Easel pictures rather than murals became the norm for Dutch painting. There was a seemingly insatiable demand for pictures and the output was prodigious. The number of professional artists multiplied with the demand and led to a corresponding degree of specialization. In portraiture there were the painters of the decorous *pater familias* types, of the winebibbers in public taverns, and of corpo-

Fig. 14:17. Rembrandt. *The Three Trees.* Etching. 8¼″ x 11″. 1643.

ration pictures. There were landscapists, seascapists, skyscapists, and even those whose specialty was cows. Painters also gravitated to the various social levels, with Jan Steen painting ribald tavern scenes full of roguish humor, Frans Hals finding his subjects among fishwives and fruit pedlars, de Hooch and Vermeer painting scenes of proper middle-class homes, and Terborch delighting in upper-class manners and elegant society portraiture.

The character of music was likewise molded by bourgeois patronage. In free cities, the organist and other municipal musicians were chosen by committees of the town councils, who supervised the musical life of the community as diligently as any of its other aspects. Auditions were held and competition encouraged. Public employment from the musician's point of view meant freedom from the arbitrary whims of a single aristocratic patron, and this was generally preferred because of the security it implied. When the tastes of the many had to be taken into consideration, however, experimentation tended to be suppressed and standardization was often promoted. This was balanced to a considerable extent by the vast opportunities for private music-making in the home, where musical expression took on a distinct domestic coloration.

The home was thus the factor that determined the art forms and imparted to them such an intimate character and quality. Dutch domestic architecture, painting, and music were all designed to be lived with and enjoyed by middle-class people who frankly took delight in their physical comforts and the arts that enriched their lives. Large canvases designed for altarpieces or to cover palace ceilings, colossal choral compositions for cathedrals or operatic performances for palaces were productive of grandiose oratorical utterances but had no place in the home. The more modest dimensions of a painting or an etching designed for a living-room wall, a chamber sonata or solo keyboard piece meant to be played in the same room, were conducive to a more intimate and personal form of communication. The choice of medium is analogous to a composer's selection of the modern symphony orchestra for his epical pronouncements and a chamber music group or a piano sonata for his more confidential statements. The home was the dominant architectural form as well as the place where the pictures were hung, the books read, and the music played. In Holland and the northern countries generally, the baroque style was thus adapted both to Protestantism and to the tastes of the middle class. The bourgeois aspect of baroque art thus finds its unity in the cult of the home, and domesticity is the key to the understanding of the style.

CHRONOLOGY:
London, 17th Century

General Events

1603–1625	James I (Stuart), reigned
1604	*Advancement of Learning* by Francis Bacon
1611	King James authorized English translation of the Bible completed
1619–1621	Banqueting House, Whitehall, built by Inigo Jones
1620	*Novum Organum* by Francis Bacon
1625–1649	Charles I, reigned
1628	*Treatise on Terrestrial Magnetism and Electricity* published by William Gilbert
	Circulation of blood discovered by Harvey
1629–1640	Charles I ruled without calling Parliament
1642–1660	English Civil Wars
1643	Theaters closed by act of Parliament
1649	Execution of Charles I; England proclaimed a commonwealth
1651	*Leviathan; or the Matter, Form, and Power of a Commonwealth, Ecclesiastical and Civil,* published by Hobbes
1653–1658	Oliver Cromwell ruled
1660	Restoration of monarchy
1660–1685	Charles II, reigned
1662	Royal Society of London for Improving Natural Knowledge founded; Christopher Wren and John Dryden charter members
1662	Christopher Wren appointed deputy surveyor-general to king; 1665 in Paris to observe remodeling of Louvre; met Bernini, Perrault, and Mansart
1664–1665	Black Death; bubonic plague swept London
1666	Great Fire of London
1667	Milton's *Paradise Lost* published
1669	Wren appointed surveyor-general to king
1670	John Dryden appointed poet laureate and royal historiographer
1671–1680	St. Mary-le-Bow and other parish churches built by Wren
1675–1710	St. Paul's Cathedral built
1678	Bunyan's *Pilgrim's Progress*, Part I, published (Part II, 1684)
1680	Purcell appointed organist at Westminster Abbey; 1683 composer-in-ordinary to king
1685–1688	James II, reigned
1687	*Philosophiae Naturalis Principia Mathematica* published by Isaac Newton
1688	The Glorious Revolution. Catholic king James II deposed; William of Orange and Mary (Stuart) became parliamentary rulers
1689–1704	William and Mary reigned
c.1689	*Dido and Aeneas*, opera, composed by Purcell
1690	Wing of Hampton Court Palace built by Wren
	Essay Concerning Human Understanding published by John Locke (1632–1704)
1692	Nahum Tate poet laureate
1722–1726	St. Martin-in-the-Fields built by Gibbs

Writers

1564–1616	William Shakespeare
1573–1637	Ben Jonson
1608–1674	John Milton
1628–1688	John Bunyan
1631–1700	John Dryden
1633–1703	Samuel Pepys
1652–1715	Nahum Tate

Architects

1573–1652	Inigo Jones
1632–1723	Christopher Wren
1682–1754	James Gibbs

Painters

1599–1641	Anthony Van Dyck

Musicians

1606–1668	William Davenant
1647–1674	Pelham Humfrey
c.1648–1708	John Blow
1658–1695	Henry Purcell
1685–1759	George Frederick Handel

15

THE BAROQUE
SYNTHESIS

LONDON DURING THE RESTORATION

That day in the year of our Lord 1661, as Charles II made his triumphal progress
to Westminster Abbey for his coronation, the sounds of Mr. Matthew Locke's
march music for the sackbuts and cornets mingled with the cordial cheers of his
subjects. They were the cheers of a people wearied by a generation of civil strife
and the effort of conforming to the rigors of puritanical idealism. They were the
cheers of a people who hoped and prayed that the Restoration would bring them
peace and normalcy. They were the cheers of a people who did not know that
their numbers would be decimated a few years hence by an outbreak of the
dreaded bubonic plague; that their city would be leveled by the Great Fire of
London; and that the Restoration, which was supposed to be bringing back the
old order, was actually ushering in the new.

The picture of a period embellished by a merry monarch, libertine lords,
licentious ladies, and amorous adventurers has been painted all too often. That of
a time which vibrated to the thunder of John Milton's poetry, spoke with the
polished rhetoric of John Dryden, wondered at the mathematical ingenuity of
Isaac Newton's equations, marveled at the majesty of Christopher Wren's architecture, and heard the harmonies of Henry Purcell's music has received much

545

less attention. Even the merry monarch had a serious side, developed through the trials and tribulations of a troubled youth (during which his father's stormy reign had led to Charles I losing his head) and throughout his exile in France where his most formative and impressionable years were spent. Charles II was an amateur astronomer, whose enthusiasm led to the founding of the Greenwich Observatory; a patron of the theater, whose interest played an important role in the development of the Restoration drama; a connoisseur of the arts, whose support of Christopher Wren led to an architectural rebirth in his country; and a music lover, who took pride now and then in lifting his voice in song in what has politely been described as a "plump bass." Thus, in 1661, Charles II's years at Louis XIV's court were about to pay off handsomely, because in addition to some questionable absolutistic political ideas and some doubtful French courtly morals, he had brought back with him a goodly measure of Continental enthusiasm for the arts. During his reign, London was to become as much a cultural suburb of Versailles as the common sense of his subjects would bear.

London had caught a brief glimpse of continental elegance under his father Charles I, who had appointed Anthony Van Dyck, a pupil of Rubens, to paint the family portraits (Figs. 15:1 and 15:2), and when Inigo Jones built the Banqueting House at Whitehall as the first unit of a projected royal palace. This faithful follower of Palladio might have done much more had not other and more pressing matters intervened. Now the gates were about to be flung wide open. Nicholas Laniere was dispatched to Italy to purchase pictures for the royal collection. William Davenant, who had been a guest in Paris of Charles and his mother and had closely observed Lully's musical methods, was summoned to become England's first opera manager. When the French opera composer Robert Cambert was outmaneuvered by the wily Lully, he found a ready welcome at the English court. Pelham Humfrey, a promising young composer of 17 and later the teacher of Purcell, was sent to Paris by Charles to see how Lully managed his orchestra and ballet. Since Louis XIV had his *Vingt-quatre Violons,* Charles II would have his Four-and-twenty Fiddles. When he was looking around for a poet laureate, the choice fell to Dryden, who was most familiar with Boileau and the French baroque drama. When Charles heard that King Louis and Colbert were getting ready to remodel the Louvre, he saw to it that Wren was on the spot to study the plans and to meet Bernini and Perrault.

The stage on which the Restoration scene was to be played, however, had a distinctive character of its own. The City of London was a mercantile center that was not under the domination of either a church or a monarchy. To this day, the London County Council does not have jurisdiction over the City of London, and the British sovereign must—theoretically at least—request the permission of the Lord Mayor to enter its territorial limits. In the 17th century, the City of London, with its population of about 500,000, was London. The aristocracy

Fig. 15:1. Van Dyck. *Charles I of England*. Oil on canvas. 8′ 11″ x 6′ 11″. *c.*1635. Louvre, Paris (Archives Photographiques)

Fig. 15.2. Van Dyck. *Children of Charles I*. Oil on canvas. 64½" x 78½". 1637. Replica of original at Windsor Castle. Metropolitan Museum of Art, New York

maintained their country houses elsewhere, leaving London to the merchants and clerks who worked in their shops and counting houses and lived upstairs. To change anything in this conservative middle-class stronghold took one of those decisive events that are defined legally as acts of God. In 1666 it came in the form of the fire which, according to the diary of Samuel Pepys, destroyed 13,000 houses, 400 streets, and 90 churches, including much of Old St. Paul's Cathedral dating from shortly after the Norman conquest. Before the charred ruins had stopped smoking, Christopher Wren was sketching out a plan for the rebuilding of the entire city. The fire gave him the greatest opportunity ever afforded an English architect; and even though his plan was not to be carried out completely, enough of it was realized to determine the architectural course of late 17th-century London and to give that city its superb skyline.

The collision between this staunch middle-class citizenry and their foreign-bred king brought further tangible proof of the English genius for compromise The Stuarts from the beginning had tried to impose the continental concept of absolutism on their reluctant subjects. The extremes of Charles I and his failure to come to terms with the middle-class merchants and their official body, the House of Commons, had brought about the Cromwellian Commonwealth. The uncompromising Oliver Cromwell on his side had alienated the still-powerful aristocracy. Charles II had some success in trying to find a middle ground. His successor James II, however, again overstepped his prerogatives, and it took still another revolution—this time a bloodless and Glorious one—to bring about the alliance between the sovereign and the middle class under the compromise formula known as the limited monarchy.

Much the same struggle is mirrored in the arts. The French aristocratic baroque, just like the absolute monarchy, was too rich for the English diet. When it came time to build a new cathedral, for instance, Charles and his principal architect, Sir Christopher Wren, thought in terms of the richly embellished classical orders, the splendor and spaciousness of the Louvre and Versailles, and the central-church plans of Palladio and Michelangelo. The clergy and their lay advisors, however, still thought of a cathedral as a tall, imposing Gothic structure. Wren wanted it to be crowned with a dome; the churchmen thought it should have a spire. So Wren built his dome and put a high lantern tower on top of it. Charles wanted Lullian opera, but the theater-goers showed remarkable resistance toward sung recitative. So they got a hybrid form of spoken dialogue interspersed with some songs and punctuated with instrumental interludes.

With political authority divided between the monarch and parliament, literary precedents between the classical and Elizabethan traditions, architectural ideas between the French baroque and English Gothic, and musical expression between the latest continental developments and native preferences, the British genius for compromise effected a synthesis of aristocratic and middle-class institutions, Roman Catholicism and Protestantism, as well as the continental and English traditions. Through the efforts and genius of three men—Wren in architecture, Dryden in literature, and Purcell in music—the continental influences were absorbed, adapted, mingled with native traditions, and finally synthesized into a distinctive Restoration style.

ARCHITECTURE

In the crypt beneath St. Paul's Cathedral in London an inscription on a stone slab reads: "Beneath is laid the builder of this church and city, Christopher Wren, who lived more than ninety years, not for himself but for the good of the state. If you seek a monument, look around you." As the observer studies the structure he will first be struck by the unity of St. Paul's (Fig. 15:3), for this is the only major cathedral in Europe to be built by one architect, by one master mason, and during the episcopate of one bishop. In contrast it took 13 architects, 20 popes, and more than a century to build St. Peter's in Rome (Fig. 10:21). The last stone on the lantern tower above the dome of St. Paul's was put in place by one of Wren's sons in 1710 in the presence of the 78-year-old builder, and for another eight years Wren continued to supervise the completion of the last decorative details.

Fig. 15:3 *(left)*. *Façade* Wren. St. Paul's Cathedral. 1675–1710. London

Fig. 15:4 *(opposite)*. *Apse and Choir*, View from the East.

Even before the Great Fire, Wren was a member of a commission charged with the remodeling of Old St. Paul's. The plan had to be scrapped when a survey after the fire showed the building beyond repair. It was this that gave Wren his great opportunity. Like Bramante and Michelangelo before him, Wren envisaged a centralized area of great spaciousness surrounded radially by subsidiary spatial units. Like his eminent predecessors, he too favored a central-church plan based on the Greek cross to the lengthened form of the Latin cross. In this way, a building of such monumental proportions could have both its exterior mass and interior space dominated by the all-embracing unifying force of a dome. From a practical point of view, Wren was also aware that he was designing a Protestant cathedral that should permit as many people as possible to be within earshot of the pulpit so as to hear the sermon-centered service of the Anglican church of his day.

The conservative members of the clergy, with thoughts of the ancient Catholic processional liturgy in mind, wanted a long nave with aisles on either side. Wren, therefore, without sacrificing the heart of his plan, lengthened the

edifice by adding an apse in the east and a domed vestibule with an extended porch in the west. His model (Fig. 5:5), however, brought further objections from the clergy, necessitating still other revisions. All Wren's diplomacy, versatility, ingenuity, and, above all, patience were called into play to effect a workable compromise that would satisfy his difficult clients and yet save the essence of his cherished conception. He gave the clergy their aisled nave and transepts and their deep choir, but these he grouped around the central plan of his original design. In this way, he could still concentrate great space under the dome. Wren thus was actually building two churches, the clergy's and his own, a procedure that was bound to produce some architectural dissonances but for which he was able to find a satisfactory if somewhat uneasy resolution in the cathedral that was finally completed.

The diplomatic problems disposed of, Wren had then to overcome the many practical difficulties that put to full use his knowledge of science and his inventive turn of mind. Funds for the cathedral were severely limited, and from the outset he was handicapped by a difficult site where solid ground was buried beneath 40 feet of clay and sand. So, in order to avoid excessive weight, he had to lighten the vaulting of the choir, nave, and transepts by constructing them of the thinner masonry demanded by a series of low saucer domes resting on pendentives. Even so, the outward thrust of the superstructure had to be counteracted by a row of flying buttresses. Such medieval details were, in Wren's opinion, crude and unsightly, so, consequently, he concealed them from below by extending the outside walls upward enough to hide them.

Fig. 15:5. Wren. St. Paul's Cathedral, *Perspective View of Great Model Design*. Engraving by Soane. 1726.

Next, he had to abandon his hopes for an unimpeded view and an axial approach to his façade (Fig. 15:3) when it proved impossible to clear the way up Ludgate Hill on which St. Paul's rests. Even before his cathedral was completed, the building was cluttered up by surrounding houses, and it took the German air force in World War II to clear the land around the sides and choir so that St. Paul's would cast a decent shadow (Fig. 15:4). And when no quarry could supply stone of the necessary lengths for the great columns of his original façade (Fig. 15:5), he had to separate the façade into two separate stories of the Corinthian and Composite order, the lower of which is barely discernible in Figure 15:3. His use of paired columns recalls that of Perrault's colonnade on the east front of the Louvre (Fig. 13:2). The side turrets were designed after 1700, and it is interesting to take passing note of the fact that one of them was left hollow except for a circular staircase, so that Wren and his fellow astronomers could use it temporarily for an observatory.

Externally, the proportions of St. Paul's needed a massive dome while, internally, one of lesser size would suffice. With the foundations demanding as little weight as possible, Wren's solution was a double dome with a smaller inner shell of brick ingeniously supporting the outer sheath of lead-coated timber, which rises over 275 feet above the ground. The colonnade around the outer part of the drum functions practically to absorb the lateral thrust of the masonry and decoratively to complete the rhythm of the classical orders that mount upward from below. But the clergy still longed for a lofty spire that would dominate the city's skyline as that of Old St. Paul's had done. Wren therefore added a tall lantern tower that soared upward a full 90 feet above the top of his dome.

The effect of Wren's preferred plan is felt most strongly in the rotunda beneath the dome (Fig. 15:6). Geometrically, the space is bounded by a gigantic octagon, punctuated at the angles by the eight piers on which the cupola rests. These are bridged over by a ring of contiguous Roman triumphal arches, which, in turn, are crowned by the great dome, the culmination of the entire composition. From this central area, the arches open outward into eight spatial subdivisions that give the interior such constant variety and interest. The centralization under the lofty dome, the complex divisions and subdivisions of space, the imaginative design and Roman detail reveal Wren's affinity for the baroque. The restraining influences of the conservative clergy, the lack of unlimited funds, and Wren's rationalistic viewpoint demonstrate his remarkable achievement in making the style palatable to British taste.

Fig. 15:6. Wren. St. Paul's Cathedral, *Rotunda.* Aquatint by Thomas Malton. 1798

Fig. 15:7. Wren. St. Mary-le-Bow. Total height 216′ 1″, steeple 104′ 6″. 1671–1680. London

Wren's plan for the rebuilding of London met with even stiffer resistance than his project for St. Paul's. It included the laying out of a series of new streets that radiated outward starlike from central squares and that took the main traffic routes into consideration. Certain public buildings were to be oriented on an axis involving the new cathedral and the Royal Exchange. The spires of the various parish churches were to punctuate the silhouette at certain points and by degrees lead up to the grand climax of St. Paul's dome. The plan, if it had been carried

Fig. 15:8. Gibbs. St. Martin-in-the-Fields. 1721–1726. London

out, would have gone far beyond Versailles. But Wren's king was not an absolute monarch with the power to condemn property and the money to buy it. Time also ran against Wren, because the shopkeepers were in a hurry to rebuild and start their business concerns again. About all he was able to rescue were the steeples of the parish churches he was called upon to design.

As London's principal architect, Wren was commissioned to build more than 50 of these new parish churches. Consultations with the churchwardens on

Fig. 15:9. Wren. Hampton Court Palace. *Garden Façade*. 1690. Near London

the problems and needs of each church had to be held. Owing to the limited funds at his disposal, the churches of necessity had to be rather modest affairs. Wren, in keeping with the spirit of the time, wanted to build them in the restrained baroque style based on the classical orders. His clients and the Gothic tradition still demanded the spires that not only had the force of symbols but the practical purpose of housing the bell tower, which was still a functional unit of a church. Wren's problem, therefore, was to balance the vertical tendency of the steeple with the horizontality of his classical temple façades—once more, the reconciliation of northern and southern building traditions. Wren's solution, which can be counted among his minor miracles, can only be understood through an actual example.

The steeple of St. Mary-le-Bow (Fig. 15:7), where the famous Bow Bells once rang out, shows the mathematician's obvious delight in a free play of geometrical forms. From a solid square base it moves through several circular phases and terminates finally in an octagonal pyramid. By the judicious use of baroque scrolls and twists at various points, this is achieved without a hint of abruptness. Knowing that the churches themselves were bound to be hidden by the surrounding buildings, Wren lavished most of his skill on their spires. The continuation of the Wren tradition into the next century is seen in James Gibbs' church of St. Martin-in-the-Fields (Fig. 15:8). Wren had always planted his steeples firmly in the ground, so to speak, so that they seemed to grow in an organic relation to the whole composition. Gibbs' spire, by contrast, appears to sprout unexpectedly out of the roof. The memory of these churches and their steeples was carried to the American colonies by the founding fathers; and when they came to build their own churches in the new cities of Boston and Philadelphia, it was to the designs of Wren and Gibbs that they turned for their models.

Among all his other responsibilities, Wren also found the time to design some commodious houses for well-to-do middle-class clients. During the reign of William and Mary, he was also commissioned to build a new wing for the Hampton Court palace. His patron, William of Orange, remembered the good red brick of his native Holland, while Wren recalled the grandeur of the Louvre and Versailles palaces. Another of Wren's famous compromises was effected in his design for the Fountain Court and the garden façade at Hampton Court (Fig. 15:9).

Thus it was that the professor of astronomy at London and Oxford left off probing the mysteries of the heavens with his telescope and equations and became the engineer and architect who penetrated that segment of the sky above London with the majestic spires and domes that gave the city its characteristic profile and skyline.

DRAMA AND MUSIC

On the gala occasion of the formal opening of the King's Theatre in 1674, His Majesty and London's most distinguished audience gathered there for the evening's entertainment. John Dryden, that cold, aristocratic but brilliant author, took advantage of the situation afforded by the Prologue to express his sentiments in some well-chosen words, which went in part:

> 'Twere folly now a stately pile to raise,
> To build a playhouse while you throw down plays;
> Whilst scenes, machines and empty Operas reign,
> And for the Pencil you the Pen disdain;
> While Troops of famished Frenchmen hither drive,
> And laugh at those upon whose Alms they live:
> Our English Authors vanish, and give place
> To these new Conquerors of the Norman race.

Dryden was thus making the valiant effort of an exasperated man of letters to stem the tide toward the foreign forms of opera, which, in his opinion, threatened to engulf reason with rhyme. The course of events, however, was flowing far too strongly; and, to keep from being inundated, he found himself before very long collaborating with one of those fashionable Frenchmen and writing some very fancy "scenes and machines" himself.

With all the adaptability of a thoroughly equipped professional writer, Dryden honestly tried to squeeze some content into those "empty Operas." To help acclimate this exotic form to its new surroundings, he fell back on the tradition of the English court masque, a native equivalent of the French *ballet de cour*, which had set the precedent for the development of opera at the court of Louis XIV. The masque was a hybrid that included poems, songs, dances, spoken dialogue, and scenic spectacle. In the reign of James I, Court Masques were produced on a lavish scale and enlisted the efforts of the foremost talents. In a performance of Ben Jonson's *Masque of Blackness* at Whitehall in 1605, the dancers included the queen and her ladies, and the designer of the scenic spectacles was none other than the famous architect Inigo Jones, who is credited with the invention of modern movable scenery. Ludlow Castle was the setting in 1634 for Milton's *Comus*, with music by Henry Lawes.

When Dryden came to write his *Albion and Albianus*, he had to summon all his tactical skill to balance these opposing elements and try to keep them in proper proportion. In his Preface, he was more than a little apologetic about having to write so as "to please the hearing rather than gratify the understanding"; and, he continued, "it appears, indeed, preposterous at first sight, that rhyme, on any consideration, should take the place of reason." His solution was to use spoken dialogue for the ordinary mortals in the play but to include what he called a "songish part" for such supernatural characters as gods, goddesses, and heroes. Their behavior, he observed, "being extended beyond the limits of human nature, admits of that sort of marvelous and surprising conduct, which is rejected in other plays."

This opera of Dryden contains many remarkable scenes and machines. In one, "Mercury descends in a chariot drawn by ravens"; in another, "the clouds divide, and Juno appears in a Machine drawn by Peacocks; while a Symphony is playing"; in yet another, Venus and Albianus rise out of the sea in a great scallop-shell drawn by dolphins to a symphony of "flutes-doux." The stage directions for the final scene read: "Whilst a Symphony is playing, a very large, and very glorious Machine descends; the figure of it oval, all the clouds shining with gold, abundance of Angels and Cherubins flying about them, and playing in them; in the midst of it sits Apollo on a throne of gold; he comes from the machine to Albion."

Dryden's attempt in this instance, in spite of the gaudy machines, was a failure, possibly because it was not sufficiently distinguished from the court masque to be a true opera, but more probably because the music provided by Monsieur Grabu was too mediocre. Though Henry Purcell was already 26 years old, England had to wait almost a decade before it was to have the collaboration of a poet and musician comparable in stature to Molière and Lully in France.

While awaiting the invitation from Dryden to collaborate on *King Arthur*, England's greatest composer had to content himself with writing incidental music to dozens of undistinguished plays. The best of them were Shakespearean adaptations, such as *The Tempest* and *The Fairy Queen* (from *A Midsummer Night's Dream*), which bear only a remote resemblance to the originals. For his one great opportunity in the operatic field, *Dido and Aeneas*, he had to get along with a book by Nahum Tate, whose stature in English letters is several notches below that of his French counterpart Quinault, who was Lully's chief librettist. But there is not a shred of evidence to show that Purcell was unhappy about the situation. The picture of his career is simply that of a professional composer, diligently active at all times, and technically capable of fulfilling any commission which came his way, whether from church, court, or independent sources.

It was through Josias Priest, a dancing master in one of the London theaters, that Purcell received the invitation to write a short opera to be performed at his boarding school for young gentlewomen at Chelsea. Thus it was that in 1689, Purcell came to write his little operatic masterpiece for a group of schoolgirls. As such it is a true chamber opera, designed for a limited space and restricted to a limited cast of characters. Though it is small in scale, it is large in its emotional scope; and while it falls within the province of amateur performance, it is filled with the utmost musical sophistication. Its immediate antecedent was *Venus and Adonis*, a three-act chamber opera written a few years earlier by his teacher John Blow. This charming intimate work had been performed for the entertainment of Charles II and his court circle shortly before the monarch's death. It was one of the few existing through-composed operas (that is, with the entire text set to music) in English; otherwise there was only the masque tradition and the Dryden-Grabu experiments to guide him. Purcell, however, was conversant with the latest continental developments in the operatic field, and it is the piquant blend of these native and foreign elements that give his work its characteristic color and variety.

Dido and Aeneas opens with a dignified overture in the Lully style, marked by the halting rhythms and harmonic suspensions of its slow beginning, and the fugal imitations of its lively conclusion. All the orchestral sections seem to have been scored only for strings with the usual keyboard support. For his recitatives and airs, he turns to the models developed by Monteverdi and his successor at the Venetian opera, Cavalli. He makes particularly bold use of the so-called "representative style," a type of word-painting, by which the descriptive imagery of the text is reflected in the shape and turn of the melodic line. This prosody of the representative style can be illustrated by the first word in the opera, "Shake" (a), and the menacing movement of the line for "storms" (b). When speaking of Aeneas' parentage, the valor of his father Anchises is characterized by a martial

Dido and Aeneas. Recitative Excerpts

Purcell

rhythm (c); while immediately afterward a modulation to the minor mode and a caressing chromaticism express the voluptuousness of Venus' charms (d); and when Aeneas' entrance is announced, Belinda's words take on the shape of a trumpet fanfare (e).

The airs show a considerable variety as to type. Dido's opening and closing songs are built over a short repeated bass pattern as in the Italian *ostinato aria.* The melody of "Oft She Visits" is written over a continuously flowing bass line in the manner of an Italian *continuo aria*; while the three-part melodic form of "Pursue Thy Conquest, Love," in which the final section is a repetition of the beginning, identifies it as a *da capo aria.*

The emphasis on the choruses and dances is in the English court masque tradition, but these are handled with a highly ingenious blend of native and continental elements. In the palace scenes, the courtiers function as a true Greek chorus by making solemn comments in unison on the action. The final number, "With Drooping Wings," is a typical French mourning chorus straight out of Lullian opera. The witches, however, sing in the English madrigal style with the amusing substitution of some malicious "Ho, ho, ho's" for the jollier "Fa la la's," to signify their sinister purposes. Highly interesting is Purcell's introduction of a Venetian echo chorus in these solemn surroundings. While the witches sing "In Our Deep Vaulted Cell," an off-stage chorus softly echoes "-ed cell." By thus increasing the perception of space, Purcell is able to add the necessary uncanny touch he needs as the witches start to prepare their mysterious charms. The spell is further carried out in the Echo Dance of Furies, in which an offstage instrumental ensemble echoes the principal orchestra with telling effect. The dances show much of the same stylistic mixture as the choruses. Scene I concludes with the courtiers doing a Triumphing Dance, which is a vigorous version of a Lully *chaconne* treated as a set of instrumental variations over a ground bass. During Act III, when Aeneas is preparing to sail away from Carthage, Purcell paints a typical English seaport scene in which the swinging sailors' dances mingle with the salty comments of a chorus of common people. The angularity of such native dance rhythms is a distinct contrast to the more formal *courantes* and *chaconnes* that are danced by the courtiers.

Purcell's logic and fine dramatic perception does not permit him to soften his opera toward the end by allowing a *deus ex machina* to bring it to a happy ending in the manner of the French court style of Lully. The human will when contending with the gods is always doomed, and the plot must move inexorably onward. The tragedy is therefore carried through to its predestined conclusion with growing eloquence and mounting emotion. As a consequence, "Dido's Farewell" (below) becomes one of the most moving moments in all music, combining as it does the most passionate feeling with the dignified restraint demanded of a tragic heroine out of Vergil's *Aeneid*. It is cast in the form of an *ostinato aria* with an obstinately repetitive bass figure, which descends chromatically to the rhythm of the stately *passacaglia*. Dido's inner struggle is expressed by the tension between the free obbligato melodic line that she sings and the inflexible bass, and she contends with this fixed force as with her tragic fate. Vainly she tries to bend it to her will, as seen in some of the assymetrical diagonal shifts of her phrases off their center, but in the end she must resign herself to it while the orchestra carries the aria onward to its tragic conclusion.

Dido and Aeneas. When I Am Laid in Earth   Purcell

my fate, Re-mem-ber me, but ah!___ for-get my_fate!

Within the limitations of this short opera, which takes but little more than an hour to perform, Purcell produced a major work of art. Though it is his only through-composed piece for the lyric stage, it reveals the sure touch of one who knows every aspect of his dramatic business. The extensive emotional range and the variety of technical devices are all the more astonishing in view of the meager resources he had at his disposal. Purcell possesses, first of all, the rare power to delineate and create believable human characters by musical means, a gift he shares with Gluck and Mozart. He is also one of the few composers who know how to convert the dry academic techniques of counterpoint into lively dramatic devices, a quality he shares with Bach and Handel. This is apparent, for instance, in Dido's first air, "Ah, Belinda." Her melody is like a series of descending sighs over a ground bass that, like destiny, is relentless and unyielding. At the words "Peace and I are strangers grown," the parting of the ways is depicted by a canon at the octave; and on the word "strangers," the predominant four-bar pattern begins to wander and is stretched out into five bars. Again, after Aeneas declares he will defy destiny itself in order to remain with Dido, the chorus makes contrapuntal comments that graphically give expression to their disturbed and conflicting emotions. When Purcell wants to depict the hustle and bustle around the departing ships in the scene at the dockside in Act III, the independent lines of the fugal introduction, with their imitative thematic entries and exits, humorously describe the coming and going of the people. When such skillful means as these are combined with his fanciful orchestration, colorful use of chromaticism, and deep poetic feeling, they are sure to lead to significant ends—as indeed, in this case, they did.

One more chance presented itself to Purcell when Dryden, the literary arbiter of Restoration drama, invited him to collaborate on *King Arthur* in 1691. Dryden, in this case, was trying to breathe something of the grandiloquence of the French baroque theater into a patriotic English drama. His Preface shows that he was still groping for a formula to adapt music and poetry to the English lyric stage. His sincere misgivings are apparent when he complains: "I have been obliged to cramp my Verses, and make them rugged to the Reader, that they may be harmonious to the Hearer." Like a good rationalist, he was also worried about writing a play "principally designed for the Ear and Eye" rather than for the mind. He still felt that the human characters should speak and that only the superhuman ones should sing. In this parenthetical way, the music could be made to sound more plausible and thus not seem like an intrusion into the course of the dramatic sequence. Fortunately for Purcell, there were so many superhuman characters that his score assumed very ample proportions. *King Arthur* was a truly distinguished attempt to solve the problem of English opera; and, in its way, it was still another typically English compromise, since it was neither an opera nor a play but a compound of elements drawn from both. If this collaboration had continued, it eventually might have led to a distinctive English form of the music drama. As *King Arthur* stands, it remains a noble but somewhat inconclusive experiment.

In spite of Purcell's sparing but convincing use of the sung recitative, and his efforts to extract the essence out of Monteverdi's representative style by removing some of the Italian bombast in order to render it palatable to London audiences, recitative simply did not take root, and the through-composed opera remained an exotic plant on English soil. As the *Gentlemen's Journal* of January 1692 put it, "Experience hath taught us that our English genius will not rellish that perpetual singing."

A judicious comparison between the three great figures of the Restoration style—Wren, Dryden, and Purcell—can be highly illuminating. Each in his way was trying to bring his country up to date on the latest continental developments, just as each was trying to inject something of the grandeur of the baroque style into English art forms. In order to do it, each was willing to make the necessary compromises so as not to part company with English audiences. When Wren was designing his preferred models on his drawing board, when Dryden was writing solely for his readers, and when Purcell was composing experimentally for amateurs, each could be as free as he chose. But when it came to building a cathedral, mounting a play, and composing music for the theater, many subtle and even drastic adjustments had to be made. Each had sufficient mastery in his field and each was sufficiently versatile and inventive to make those adjustments. Each preferred and developed an aristocratic style but never neglected the common touch. Each, in his turn, had an effect on posterity that lasted well into the next century. Wren's buildings became the backbone of the Georgian style; Dryden's works, the background for 18th-century classicism in English letters; and the fact that many of Purcell's works have until recently been thought to be by Bach and Handel is proof enough that they were absorbed directly into the sacred and secular music of the succeeding generation.

IDEAS

Baroque Rationalism

Stimulated by the explorations of the navigators of the globe, the scanning of the skies by the astronomers, and the ingenuity of the inventors, baroque man came to have a new concept of himself and his place in the universe. Galileo's telescope confirmed and popularized Copernicus' theory of a solar system in which the earth revolved around the sun rather than vice versa. The concept of the static Aristotelean universe thus had to yield to one that was full of whirling motion. Since the earth was no longer considered as a fixed point located at the nerve center of the cosmos, man could hardly be regarded any longer as the sole purpose of creation. It was some consolation, however, to know that this strange new moving universe was at least subject to mechanical and mathematical laws, and therefore to a considerable extent predictable. Copernicus and Kepler as well as the other scientists were convinced of its unity, proportion, and harmony; and the fact that man had the privilege of probing into the secrets of nature, if his intellect proved equal to the task, was a highly exhilarating thought. The rationalism of the 17th century, then, was based on the view that the universe could at last be understood in logical, mathematical, and mechanical terms. As a philosophy and semireligion, this viewpoint had far-reaching consequences by preparing the pathway for the theories of positivism and materialism, the doctrines of deism and atheism, and the mechanical and industrial revolutions.

While Greek rationalism had been based on the perception and measurement of a static world, baroque rationalism had to come to terms with a dynamic universe. Scientific thought was concerned with movement in space and time. The need for a mathematics capable of comprehending a world of matter in motion led Descartes to his analytical geometry, Pascal to a study of cycloid curves, and both Leibniz and Newton to the simultaneous discovery of integral and differential calculus. Baroque invention led to refinements in navigation, improvements in the telescope and microscope for the exploration of distant and minute regions of space, the barometer for the measurement of air pressure, the thermometer for the recording of temperature changes, and the anemometer for the calculation of the force of winds. Astronomers were occupied with the study of planetary motion; William Harvey discovered the circulation of the blood in the human body; and physicists were making speculations in the field of thermodynamics and gravitation.

Newton's preoccupation with mass, force, and momentum, his speculations on the principles of attraction and repulsion, and his calculations on terrestrial and celestial mechanics led him to a monumental synthesis that he presented to the British Royal Society in 1686 and published in London a year later. Newton's *Principia* embraced a complete and systematic view of an orderly world based on mechanical principles, capable of mathematical proof, and demonstrable by accurate prediction. His work was, in fact, a scientific *summa* that established the intellectual architecture of the new view of the universe.

Such a changed world view was bound to have important consequences on the arts, which responded in this case with a ringing reassertion of man's supremacy and a joyous acceptance of this new understanding of the universe. The application of rationalistic principles to aesthetic expression is by no means accidental or casual. Before he became an architect, Christopher Wren was a mechanical inventor, an experimental scientist, and a professor of astronomy at London and Oxford. As one of the founders of the Royal Society, he was in close communication with such men as Robert Boyle and Isaac Newton. The fellows of the Royal Society appointed John Dryden to a committee whose purpose was to study the English language with a view toward linguistic reforms. They recommended that English prose should have both purity and brevity, so that verbal communication could be brought as close to mathematical plainness and precision as possible. Dryden's embarrassment in writing an opera that was designed to please the ear rather than gratify the understanding was therefore quite understandable. Purcell's music likewise was based on a system of intricate contrapuntal principles and tonal logic in which certain given premises, as in a sequence for instance, are followed by predictable conclusions. His music, moreover, is characterized by intellectual discipline, symmetry, clarity, and a sure sense of direction. His forms are models of brevity in which each part has its proper place, no loose ends are left dangling around, and his cadences bring everything to a positive conclusion. Together with Wren's architecture and Dryden's poetic drama, Purcell's music reflects a buoyant self-confidence, an inventive spirit that gave birth to new forms, an exploration of novel optical and acoustical ideas, and a conviction that a work of art should in its way be a reflection of an orderly and lawful universe.

Baroque Synthesis

While the baroque period generally falls within the 17th century, its extreme temporal limits extend all the way from the mid-16th to the mid-18th centuries, from Michelangelo to Johann Sebastian Bach. During this time the concept of the world had moved from a terracentric to a heliocentric universe; philosophical speculation turned from a supernatural to a natural world view; the fundamental processes of thought shifted from the acceptance of authority on faith to scientific experimentation; the unity of Christianity symbolized by one universal church dissolved into a number of Protestant sects; and the theoretical political unity of the Holy Roman Empire gave way to the practical fact of a balance of power distributed among a family of nations. The baroque period was one in which irresistible modern forces met immovable traditional objects. Out of the resulting theological disputations, philosophical discussions, scientific arguments, social tensions, political strife, and warring nations, both the baroque style and the modern age were born.

The baroque world was one in which irreconcilable oppositions had to find a way of coexistence. The rise of rationalism was accompanied by the march of militant mysticism; the aristocratic cult of majesty was echoed by the bourgeois cult of domesticity; the internationalism of Roman Catholicism was in conflict with the nationalism of the Protestant sects; religious orthodoxy had to contend with freedom of thought; the Jesuits brought all the arts into their churches, while Calvin did his utmost to exclude all art; Philip II built a palatial mausoleum and monastery, while Louis XIV erected a pleasure palace and theater; Charles I tried to force an absolute monarchy on England, and Cromwell's answer was a republican commonwealth; the printing press made books available, while suppression by censorship took them away; the boldest scientific speculation took place alongside a reassertion of the belief in miracles and a renewal of religious fundamentalism; Newton's *Principia* and the final part of Bunyan's *Pilgrim's Progress* appeared in London within two years of each other. In Spain, the emotional involvement of El Greco was succeeded by the optical detachment of Velásquez; in France, the spontaneity of Rubens was followed by the academic formalism of Poussin; in Holland, the broad humanity of Rembrandt led to the specialization and precision of Vermeer.

Such oppositions could hardly be expected to resolve themselves into a single uniform style. At best, they could achieve a temporary resolution and a fusion of forms such as that found in a Counter-Reformation church, the Versailles Palace, Rembrandt's visual dramatization of the Bible, or Purcell's operatic synthesis. In them, forceful striving and restless motion are more characteristic than serenity and repose. Baroque art thus emerges from these tensions and speaks in eloquent accents of the expanding range of human activities, grandiose achievements, and a ceaseless search for new and more powerful means of expression.

All this took place within the framework of a tremendously enlarged sense of space. The astronomers told of remote regions populated by an infinite number of stars. Pascal speculated on the mathematical implications of infinity. The gardens and avenues of Versailles were laid out in keeping with this vastly extended conception of space. The vistas led the eye toward the horizon and invited the imagination to continue beyond. The unification of the vast buildings and gardens there placed baroque man wholly within the scope of nature and declared him to be a part of the new measurable universe. Wren's attempt to bring his cathedral, parish churches, and public buildings into one all-embracing scheme was also in keeping with this image of the comprehensive baroque universe. Painters likewise delighted in leading the eye outside their pictures and attempted to convey the impression of infinity through the bold use of light and exaggerated perspective effects. The Dutch landscapists tried to capture atmospheric perspective, and Rembrandt was concerned with the infinite gradations of light. Through use of illusionistic effects ceilings of Counter-Reformation churches tried to promote the feeling of a world without end.

In music there was a corresponding expansion of tonal space. The organs and other keyboard instruments were built to encompass a wider range from bass to soprano. Both the wind as well as the stringed instruments were constructed in families, ranging all the way from what Orlando Gibbons called the "Great

Dooble Base" to the high soprano register of the violin. Louis XIV and Charles II incorporated this string family into ensembles of twenty-four viols, thus increasing both the resonance and volume of sound through the doubling process. The coming into use of chromatic harmony with all the half-tone divisions of the octave was the internal extension of the same idea. Purcell's opposition between his ground basses and soprano melodies emphasized the baroque love of a spacious distribution of sonorities. His adoption of the Venetian double chorus and his dramatic use of the echo effect in *Dido and Aeneas* was still further evidence of the desire to increase the perception of space through sound and to use it for expressive purposes.

Above all, the baroque universe was in ceaseless movement. Whether a rationalist thought of it in terms of whirling particles or a mystic as full of swirling spirits, both saw their world as a vortex of spheres and spirals describing infinitely complex patterns of motion. Kepler's planets revolved in elliptical orbits; Counter-Reformation churches were built over undulating floor plans; their walls rippled like stage curtains; the decorative profusion of their façades further activated the static masses and increased their rhythmic pulsation; under their domes terra-cotta angels flew in parabolas; the unyielding stone of the statuary finally rose off the ground and melted into a myriad of fluid forms; paintings escaped from their flat wall spaces up to the more congenial concave surfaces of the ceilings, where they could soar skyward and where more daring perspective effects were possible. Baroque music also mirrored this moving universe. Its restless forms took on the color of this dynamic age, and its sound patterns floated freely through their tonal spaces unencumbered by gravitational laws. No longer in bondage to religious ritual, to the dance, or to poetry, its emancipation was now complete. Of such ideas and materials was the image of this brave new baroque world constructed.

CHRONOLOGY:
18th-century Panorama

General Events

1715	Louis XIV died
1715–1774	Louis XV, king of France
1726	*Gulliver's Travels* published by Swift
1728	*Beggar's Opera* by John Gay (1685–1732) performed in London
1740–1780	Maria Theresa, empress of Austria
1740–1786	Frederick the Great, king of Prussia
1744	Schönbrunn Palace built in Vienna (begun in 1696 by Fischer von Erlach)
1748	*Spirit of Laws* published Excavations at Pompeii begun
1751–1772	*Encyclopédie, or A Classified Dictionary of Sciences, Arts and Trades* published by Diderot
1752	Pergolesi's *Serva Padrona* performed in Paris *Guerre des Bouffons,* "war" in Paris over serious *versus* comic opera
1759	Voltaire's *Candide* published
1762	*Social Contract* published by J. J. Rousseau Gluck's *Orpheus* performed in Vienna
1762–1796	Catherine the Great, empress of Russia
1774–1792	Louis XVI, king of France
1774	Gluck's *Orpheus* and *Iphigenia in Aulis* performed in Paris
1775	Beaumarchais' *Barber of Seville* presented in Paris
1776	American Declaration of Independence *Sturm und Drang* (Storm and Stress), play by Maximilian Klinger (1752–1831), gave name to art movement
1780–1790	Joseph II, emperor of Austria
1781	Mozart settled in Vienna Kant's *Critique of Pure Reason* published
1784	Beaumarchais' play *Marriage of Figaro* presented; 1786 Mozart's *Marriage of Figaro* performed in Vienna
1787	Mozart's *Don Giovanni* performed in Prague, in Vienna 1788
1789	French Revolution begun
1790	Goethe's *Faust, A Fragment* published in Leipzig
1794	Condorcet, *Progress of the Human Spirit*
1797	*Sense and Sensibility* written by Jane Austen (1775–1817); published in 1811

Architects

1650–1723	Fischer von Erlach
c.1660–1726	Jakob Prandtauer
1668–1745	Lukas von Hildebrandt

Painters

1684–1721	Watteau
1697–1764	Hogarth
1699–1779	Chardin
1703–1770	Boucher
1725–1805	Greuze
1732–1806	Fragonard

Sculptors

1716–1791	Falconet
1738–1814	Clodion
1741–1828	Houdon

Musicians

1683–1764	Rameau
1688–1733	Couperin (Le Grand)
1714–1787	C. W. Gluck
1714–1788	C. P. E. Bach
1732–1809	Joseph Haydn
1756–1791	W. A. Mozart

Writers and Philosophers

1667–1745	Swift
1689–1761	Richardson
1694–1778	Voltaire
1698–1782	Metastasio
1707–1754	Fielding
1712–1778	J. J. Rousseau
1713–1784	Diderot
1724–1804	Kant
1728–1774	Goldsmith
1729–1781	Lessing
1732–1799	Beaumarchais
1744–1803	Herder
1749–1832	Goethe
1749–1838	Da Ponte
1759–1805	Schiller

16

THE 18TH-CENTURY STYLES

THE 18TH-CENTURY PANORAMA

The momentum of the baroque was sufficient to propel that style well into the 18th century. New social dynamics, new springs of ideas, new aesthetic currents came together to bring about, in some cases, a confluence of the main baroque streams and, in others, the formation of new ones. With the death of Louis XIV in 1715, the aristocratic baroque style moved into its final rococo phase. The regent for his young successor closed the majestic Versailles Palace and re-established the royal residence in Paris. Artistic patronage was no longer the monopoly of the court, and the painter Watteau, arriving in Paris the same year the Sun King died, had to look for his patrons among a broad group drawn from the ranks of both the nobility and the middle class. Throughout the century, the operas of Rameau, Gluck, and Mozart were composed for public opera houses where aristocrats rubbed shoulders with the bourgeoisie. The arts, in effect, moved out of the marble halls into the elegant salons where finesse and charm were considered higher aesthetic virtues than impressiveness and grandeur.

The rococo, that latter-day manifestation of the aristocratic baroque style, was by no means confined to Paris. All European courts assumed in some degree the character of cultural suburbs of Versailles. French fashions in architecture, painting, furniture, costume, and manners were echoed in such far-off corners as the courts of Catherine the Great of Russia and of Maria Theresa in Vienna. Whether a prince ruled a province in Poland or a duchy in Denmark, French was spoken in his household more naturally than the language of his native country. In Prussia, Frederick the Great built a rococo palace at Potsdam and called it *Sans-souci*; the king of Saxony commissioned the jewellike Zwinger Palace in Dresden; and the Prince-Bishop erected a handsome residence in Würzburg. Such French authors as Voltaire and Jean Jacques Rousseau found an international reading public; French dances dominated the balls; and French plays the theaters. In southern Germany and Austria, however, Italian influence was still strong. At the court of Vienna an Italian architect finished the Schönbrunn Palace for Maria Theresa; Italian paintings decorated its walls; Metastasio was the poet laureate and opera librettist; and only plays and operas in Italian could be performed in the royal theaters. The missionary zeal of the Jesuits working outward from Rome spread and popularized the ecclesiastical counterpart of the aristocratic style throughout the Counter-Reformation countries.

Baroque rationalism had remained restricted to a relatively few eminent minds. In the 18th century, however, as the scientific knowledge of Newton and the social theories of John Locke became the common property of the educated classes, rationalism broadened into the movement known as the *Enlightenment,* a term—like the *rococo*—that generally refers to the period between 1715 and 1789. In it, the streams of rationalism and academicism converged, and the most characteristic expression of the Enlightenment is the *Encyclopédie,* which was edited by Denis Diderot. In this *Classified Dictionary of the Sciences, Arts, and Trades,* the outstanding intellects of the time collected and made available in clear language all the knowledge that had heretofore existed only in difficult scientific tracts. Trade secrets that for centuries had been the closely guarded property of the guilds and a few master craftsmen now appeared in print. Knowledge that had in the 17th century remained for the most part in the realm of pure science began to be applied to the solution of practical problems. Middle-class manufacturers saw the commercial usefulness of baroque inventiveness and turned it toward the production of new wealth.

While the fruits of rationalism became the common property of the middle class, in the vocabulary of the 18th century, *reason* by no means implied only cold intellectuality. It was considered to be a mental faculty shared by all who chose to cultivate it. Among its implications were common sense, exercise of good judgment, and the development of taste, all of which were accompanied by a healthy involvement in active human pursuits. As applied to the arts, reason meant the search for expressive forms and sentiments of sufficient universality and validity to be accepted by all who subscribed to the principles of good taste and judgment. With the broadening of the bases of wealth and education, the middle class was able to rise and challenge the ancient authority and prerogatives of the aristocracy. Through the power of knowledge released by the Enlightenment, the age-old shackles of superstition, intolerance, and fear began to be thrown off. The ideals of freedom championed by men of reason were eventually written into the American Declaration of Independence and Bill of Rights and became the moving force behind the French Revolution. More and more, it was now the middle class who wrote and read the books, who constructed and lived in the buildings, who painted and bought the pictures, and who composed and listened to the music.

The philosophy of the Enlightenment did not, however, go unchallenged, and undercurrents of irrationalism are found in movements that presaged 19th-century romanticism. Just as the more emotional approaches to religion emphasized revelation, so literature and the other arts came to consider intuition a higher human faculty than reason. In England, such novelists as Fielding told their tales in the first person, a device designed to promote greater subjectivity of feeling on the part of readers and a break with the Enlightenment ideal of viewing events with objective detachment. The opposition of reason and intuition is mirrored in the title and two heroines of Jane Austen's novel *Sense and Sensibility*. Rousseau gave sensibility a deeper emotional tone, and in France generally *sensibilité* meant tugging at the heart strings of readers, observers, and listeners. In sensibility literature, the poor were always nature's noblemen in proud possession of a few paternal acres, living by the honest sweat of their brows, constantly having their peace of mind disturbed by the intrusion of material progress, which usually appeared in the guise of an elegant city slicker. In Germany, emotionalism burst out in the more violent form of the so-called "Storm-and-Stress" movement. This group made a rather personal interpretation of Rousseau's initial statement in his *Social Contract:* "Man is born free, and everywhere he is in chains." Goethe's characterizations of Faust and Prometheus and Mozart's Don Giovanni were independent human beings, who defied the gods of convention and demanded a gamut of inner and outer experience, even if they had to pay the penalty of eternal torment. The truth they sought was one of feeling rather than logic, and their curiosity was insatiable. By bursting the bonds of civilized restraints, they were in full rebellion against hereditary aristocratic privilege as well as stern middle-class morality. Their freedom was far from that of the Age of Reason; it was in fact an anti-rationalistic, anti-universal, powerfully pro-individualistic freedom that bordered on destructiveness and anarchy.

The 18th century as a whole was marked by a quickening of the pulse in human affairs. The flood of material from the printing presses alone made it all but impossible to keep up with the pace set in philosophy, literature, and music. The spread of wealth led to the development of urban centers and widespread building projects. Writers, painters, and musicians no longer aimed their output exclusively at one social group. While it is often called the Age of Reason, the 18th century gave birth to some of the most bizarre and irrational beings, real or imaginary, ever to populate the mind or imagination. The passionate disputes begun in the 17th century continued, but on the surface at least the divisions did not appear to be so sharp. The irreconcilable oppositions of the baroque were softened into sarcastic satires, gentle ironies, witty repartee, and wistful melancholies. What appeared as a period of comparative quiescence, however, was but the calm before the storm, the prelude to a social explosion that brought the aristocratic rococo to a violent revolutionary end, and catapulted the forces of reason and emotion it had generated into the next century.

THE ROCOCO

The name *rococo* apparently was a pun on *barocco*, the Italian word for baroque, and on the French *rocailles* and *coquilles*—rocks and shells—that were so widely used as decorative motifs in the style. As such, the rococo must be considered as a modification or variation of the baroque rather than a style in opposition to

LES JARDINS DE BACHUS

Fig. 16:1. Watteau. *Drawing*, after an engraving by Huquier. 10¼″ x 15″. Cooper Union Museum, New York

Fig. 16:2. Erlach and Pacassi. Schönbrunn Palace. *Salon.* 1760–1780. Vienna

baroque. Its effect is more that of a domesticated baroque, better suited to fashionable town houses than palace halls, though the rococo was used in both. It was mainly an interior style adapted to the small salons where intimate groups could gather tête à tête and match wits in the subtle art of conversation. But the rococo was not confined to the major arts and could apply to any interior feature, from the graceful curves of a table leg to the gilded scroll tracery of a ceiling design. Quite typical of the time is a drawing by Watteau (Fig. 16:1) that makes prominent use of the shell motif. It is seen here as an engraving, but the design could have been used for the paneling of a room, a stage curtain, a wall paper, a terracotta relief finished in white and gold, a tapestry, a mantlepiece, a needlepoint piece for the back of a chair, and so on. When a rococo interior like that in the Schönbrunn Palace in Vienna (Fig. 16:2) is compared with one from the time of Louis XIV (Fig. 13:6), the difference becomes apparent at once. Where the baroque was ponderous, massive, and overwhelming, the rococo is delicate, light, and charming. Monumentality is succeeded by finesse, stateliness by elegance, the pompous purples and golds by modulated pastel shades.

In the Belvedere Palace in Vienna (Fig. 16:3), the decorative impulse can be seen as the rococo bursts out of doors into a lavish exterior design. Details that the French architects had for the most part confined to interiors are found here

Fig. 16:3. Hildebrandt. Belvedere Palace. *Garden Façade*. 1721–1724. Vienna

on the garden façade of a summer palace built in 1713 by Lukas von Hildebrandt for Prince Eugene of Savoy. Palladian academic restraint has been cast to the four winds. On either side of the second-story windows highly ornate Composite pilasters can be found, and over the portal some grotesque caryatid figures are grouped in a balletlike formation. Otherwise the architectural orders as points of reference have all but disappeared. The triangular repose of the temple pediments and window brackets of the academic style has dissolved into a flowing pattern of undulating curves and broken rhythms.

Much the same evolution took place in the Austrian Counter-Reformation churches. Fischer von Erlach, who studied in Rome with Bernini, exercised considerable restraint in his design for the Karlskirche in Vienna (Fig. 16:4). Not only was it dedicated to the same saint, Carlo Borromeo, as the baroque church of San Carlo alle Quattro Fontane in Rome (Fig. 12:3), which was finished in 1667, but Borromini's masterpiece had a direct influence on Erlach's thinking. His façade shows the same tendency to break up a flat surface so as to allow for a sculpturesque play of light and shadow varying with the time of day, and it is in full motion. From side to side there is a swelling of the convex and concave masses—forward and backward from the Corinthian portico to the depth of the elongated oval dome, and upward and downward with the spiral lines of the twin bell towers in the form of Trajanesque columns.

The Counter-Reformation fusion of the arts in order to produce mystical-emotional excitement is well exemplified in the abbey church at Melk in Lower Austria (Fig. 16:5). In its colorful interior, designed by a Viennese theater architect, red marble columns writhe upward in serpentine spirals. All the other decorative details combine to carry out this sense of heightened motion. A climax is reached in the choir loft and ceiling (Fig. 16:6), where the tones of the organ mingle with the concealed chorus and float upward past the terracotta angels perching precariously on stucco clouds to a point where the eye is lost in the vast atmospheric perspective of the ceiling mural.

Fig. 16:4. Erlach. Karlskirche. *Façade*. 1716–1737. Vienna

Fig. 16:5 (*above*). Prandtauer. Abbey Church. 1702–1736. Melk-on-the-Danube. Fig. 16:6 (*below*). *Choir Loft and Organ*

Fig. 16:7. Watteau. *Music Party*. Oil on canvas. 25½″ x 36¼″. *c*.1719. Wallace Collection, London

The rococo painter par excellence was Antoine Watteau. A quick comparison of *The Music Party* (Fig. 16:7), an example of his *fêtes galantes* style, with a bombastic Lebrun canvas (Fig. 13:18) or the sensuous *Garden of Love* by Rubens (Fig. 13:14) will reveal the earmarks of the new idiom. The dimensions of the pictures alone tell their story, since Watteau did small easel paintings for the drawing room rather than murals for a grand gallery. Watteau was both a fellow countryman of Rubens and an ardent admirer of his art. In Watteau's pictures, however, Rubens' massive figures are reduced to lithe and slender proportions. They are animated with movement, but Rubens' bacchanalian furies now dance the graceful minuet. With Watteau the effect is capricious rather than monumental, and the spirit vivacious rather than voluptuous.

In *The Music Party* (Fig. 16:7), a group has gathered on a terrace for a pleasant afternoon of musical instruction. The 'cello has been laid aside, the score is still open, and the lady who has just had her lesson lets her elbow rest on her guitar. The music master is tuning his theorbo before beginning to play, and a gentle melancholy mood settles over the company in anticipation. The music master was an established character in 18th-century life. Bazile in Beaumarchais' *Barber of Seville* was helpful to the young ladies in carrying on their amorous intrigues and always stood by considerately to console them with sweet music

Fig. 16:8. Boucher. *Toilet of Venus*. Oil on canvas. 42⅝" x 33½". 1746. Metropolitan Museum of Art, New York

when things turned out badly. Misty languorous landscapes are very important in conveying Watteau's elusive moods. As in the pastoral novels of the time, elegant ladies and their equally elegant lovers stroll at their leisure through lush gardens in fancied emulation of the life of Arcadian shepherds. Watteau handles such scenes with a characteristic lightness of touch, jewellike color, and a delicacy of nuance that set the tone for the later development of the rococo style.

Boucher, the favorite painter of Mme. Pompadour, worked in a gayer vein than Watteau. The *Toilet of Venus* (Fig. 16:8) shows the 18th-century boudoir ideal of feminine charm in all its artificiality. Love is no longer the robust passion it was with Rubens but a sophisticated flirtation. Voluptuous mature womanhood is replaced by slender girlish forms. Fragonard was Boucher's successor as the leading exponent of the French Rococo. *The Swing* (Fig. 16:9), which was done for a young aristocrat, reveals the pleasure-seeking preoccupation of his class. The artist's fine feeling for color and the masterly draftsmanship with which he handles his diagonal composition saves it from the twin perils of preciousness and triviality. Much the same spirit animates the sculpture of Clodion. The possibility of quick modeling made the terracotta medium well

Fig. 16:9. Fragonard. *The Swing*. Oil on canvas. 32″ x 25½″. *c*.1766–1769. Wallace Collection, London

Fig. 16:10. Clodion. *Monumental Urn*, Detail. Marble. 52⅛" high, 38" wide. 1782. National Gallery of Art, Washington, D. C.

suited to capturing the fleeting rhythms of a Bacchic dance. The relief on a monumental urn (Fig. 16:10) and terracotta figurines, such as the *Nymph and Satyr* (Fig. 16:11), were much franker in their eroticism than the paintings of the period.

THE BOURGEOIS INFLUENCE

While the aristocrats were still powerful as leaders of fashion and arbiters of taste, their influence on the arts was on the wane. Not only did wealth put the means of patronage in the pockets of a rising bourgeoisie, but education was letting its members speak more and more in accents of a cultured class. In France, many of Watteau's pictures were painted for bourgeois walls; and in England, the clientele for Hogarth's drawings and engravings came mostly from middle-class ranks. The vast majority of Voltaire's and Rousseau's readers were members of the middle class, while the novels of Richardson, Fielding, and Goldsmith were aimed at this growing reading public. Lessing's *Miss Sara Sampson* (1755) and Diderot's *The Natural Son* (1757) established the German and French bourgeois drama. The collective patronage of the concert hall replaced that of the restricted court

Fig. 16:11. Clodion. *Nymph and Satyr*. Terracotta. 23¼" high. *c*.1775. Metropolitan Museum of Art, New York

circle. Instead of aiming to please one patron, the composer and virtuoso now tried to win the favor of the many. Mozart, for instance, felt strong enough to break with his tyrannical archbishop and strike out as an independent composer; and it is far from an accident that his great opera *Don Giovanni* was commissioned for the municipality of Prague rather than the royal capital of Vienna.

One of Watteau's most significant pictures was painted for a Paris art dealer by the name of Gersaint, who had suggested that the painter fill a period of inactivity by doing a signboard for his shop (Fig. 16:12). Watteau idealized his sponsor to the extent of showing him as the proprietor of a gallerylike showroom filled with the fashionable élite of Parisian society—though that was not the case at the time. On the right, Gersaint is extolling the virtues of a Watteau-like painting to a lady and gentleman who view it through their lorgnettes; on the left, the packing of pictures after the sale is in progress. (Some time after the middle of the century the painting was cut in half.)

Genre pictures with casual everyday subjects are to be reckoned among 18th-century middle-class reactions to aristocratic posturing just as they had been before in 17th-century Holland. A master of this category was Chardin (Figs. 16:13 and 16:14), whose sensitive painting revealed visual poetry in commonplace people and things. With Greuze, such family scenes had more sentimental than artistic value, but they satisfied Diderot's injunction that art should praise virtue and condemn vice. In the *Father's Curse* and the *Return of the Prodigal*

Fig. 16:12 Watteau. *Gersaint's Signboard*. Oil on canvas. Left half,

Fig. 16:13. Chardin. *Boy Playing Cards*. Oil on canvas. 32″ x 25¾″. Uffizi, Florence (Soprintendenza)

5′ 3⅞″ x 4′ 10⅞″; right half, 5′ 3⅞″ x 5′ ½″. 1720–1721. Charlot-tenburg Palace, Berlin (Archives Photographiques)

Fig. 16:14. Chardin. *Still Life*. Oil on canvas. 17¾″ x 19¾″. c.1758. Copyright, Frick Collection, New York

Fig. 16:15. Hogarth. Scene I from *Marriage à-la-mode, The Marriage Contract*. Oil on canvas. 27" x 35". 1744. Tate Gallery, London

Son, however, this earnestness of Greuze crosses the borderline where moral uplift ends and hypocrisy begins.

The English painter William Hogarth must be reckoned among the distinguished company of 18th-century social satirists. Like Swift's *Gulliver's Travels*, John Gay's *Beggar's Opera*, and Voltaire's *Candide*, Hogarth's series of six pictures entitled *Marriage à-la-Mode* was a merciless exposé of the conditions and customs of his time, tempered by the saving grace of a brilliant wit. As Dickens and Zola, Goya and Daumier were to do in the less-humorous 19th century, Hogarth dramatized the conditions he saw and issued a challenge to society to do something about it. In this case it is the evil of putting human beings on the auction block of marriage. *The Marriage Contract* (Fig. 16:15) introduces the characters as in the first scene of a play. The gouty nobleman points with pride to the family pedigree as he is about to sell his social standing in the person of his son to pay off the mortgage on his ancestral estate. The merchant, who is marrying off his daughter, scrutinizes the settlement through his spectacles just as

Fig. 16:16. Hogarth. Scene IV from *Marriage à-la-mode*, *The Countess' Dressing Room*. Oil on canvas. 27″ x 35″. 1744. Tate Gallery, London

he would any other hard-driven bargain. The pawns in this game—the future bride and groom—sit with their backs to each other, while the lawyer flatters the future Lady Squanderfield and her fiancé consoles himself with a pinch of snuff.

The other five scenes show the unhappy consequences of this loveless union as it progresses from boredom and frivolity to infidelities, a duel, and death. In *The Countess' Dressing Room* (Fig. 16:16), Lady Squanderfield entertains some of her fine-feathered friends as she makes her morning toilet. Counselor Silvertongue, her lover, reads his latest amorous verses, while an Italian barber dresses her hair, a servant passes cups of chocolate, a fencing master snores, a little Moorish slave points gleefully to the horns on his doll, and a grotesquely fat singer and his lean flute-playing accompanist add to the general din. The singer is considered to be Carestini, the famous castrato, who sang the feminine leads in Handel's Italian operas.

This and such other series as the *Harlot's Progress* and the *Rake's Progress* were first made as paintings and then copied in the form of copper engravings.

The prints were widely sold by subscription, and this type of group patronage made them financially successful. Horace Walpole likened them to Molière's plays, and Charles Lamb said: "other pictures we see, Hogarth's we read." The series were indeed managed in the manner of chapters in a novel; and, since they were done for a public whose primary responses were literary, Hogarth knew that his audience expected a picture to have narrative content. Based as they are on an intimate knowledge of London, the stories are told with a zest for life that saves them from cynicism. Every detail in his crowded rooms is a commentary on both the action and the taste of his time. In addition to their biting satire, Hogarth's draftsmanship and sense of composition give his pictures substance in their own right.

As might be expected, bourgeois sculptural expression was primarily in the domain of portraiture. Houdon's fine feeling for individuality assured him pre-eminence in this field, and any number of famous 18th-century personalities sat for him, including George Washington, Benjamin Franklin, Thomas Jefferson, John Paul Jones, and Robert Fulton. His bust of Voltaire (Fig. 16:17) is but one of several portraits he did of the famous French philosopher and dramatist. By the tilt of the head and the humorous gleam of the eye, Houdon captures the bemused look of the philosopher as he ponders and discourses on the foibles and follies of his fellow mortals. To chisel a glance of amiable skepticism in marble is no small feat. By leaving a rough edge in the outline of the pupil of the eye, the artist is able to produce a special glint which gives just the desired effect. By such means Houdon achieved a speaking likeness in which, during a fleeting moment of animated conversation, the philosopher might just have coined one of his famous epigrams.

Fig. 16:17. Houdon. *Bust of Voltaire.* Marble. 20″ high. 1781. Victoria and Albert Museum, London

THE MOZARTIAN SYNTHESIS

Mozart's most mature music was written during the last decade of his life as a resident of Vienna. While he continued to compose chamber music for aristocratic salons, an occasional chamber opera for the Schönbrunn Palace, and German *Singspiele* (comic operas) for the popular musical theater, his art attains its most universal expression in the works he created for the public opera houses and concert halls where noblemen and commoners gathered together for their mutual recreation. It was here that Mozart's musical cosmopolitanism found its widest scope, here that he could explore the endless variety of tragic and comic situations that give his operas their boundless humanity, and here that his dramatic power could make its greatest impact. It is also these qualities that were carried over into the less direct and more abstract form of his symphonies and concertos and that give them their particular dramatic intensity.

As a highly impressionable child, guided by a wise father, Mozart had been piloted around the important musical centers, met the most eminent composers, and absorbed all the current ideas. In London, he came under the sway of Christian Bach, one of the sons of the prolific Johann Sebastian. His generation had reacted to that of J. S. Bach and Handel much as the French painters had to Rubens and Lebrun, and their music spoke in the gentler accents of the gallant style rather than in the more muscular rhythms and massive sonorities of the baroque. In Paris, Mozart was introduced to the rococo keyboard style, that art of the elegant trifle expressed in tinkling bon-bons for the ear. There he also made his first contact with the operas of Gluck, from which he learned his deep regard for dramatic truth and elimination of everything except what was germane to the unfolding of the plot. In Italy, he came to know the full beauty of the human voice and the all-persuasive quality of Latin lyricism. In Mannheim, he heard the finest orchestra in Europe and was struck by the lightning of its dynamic crescendos and diminuendos as well as the brilliance of its wind instruments. In Vienna, he learned from Joseph Haydn how to divine the soul of the orchestra and to explore the full expressive possibilities of the symphonic form. From first-hand contact he had discovered the idioms of the Neapolitan *opera seria*, Pergolesi's *opera buffa*, Rousseau's pastoral opera, and the German *Singspiel*. The spirit of the Enlightenment can be seen in the logical clarity and constructive unity of his forms; his letters show his enthusiasm for Rousseauian naturalness; and from his knowledge of literature, the explosive energy of the Storm-and-Stress movement finds its way into his music. Everything in his epoch was assayed in the laboratory of his brilliant mind, sifted through his creative consciousness and eventually refined into pure musical gold. In opera, however, he found the form in which he could combine all these ideas, idioms, and styles into one grand kaleidoscopic pattern, and for him the lyrical theater was always his most natural medium of expression.

Mozart's power of characterization is akin to that of Shakespeare, though his dramas are made with musical materials. No composer understood better than Mozart that an opera is not a drama *with* music but a drama *in* music, or knew better that a character has no existence apart from the melody he sings; he *is* the melody. As the supreme musical dramatist, Mozart can awaken a character to life by a phrase or a rhythmical pattern, carry him through living situations by the direction of a melodic line, and develop the most complex interactions with the others in a scene by harmonic modulations and contrapuntal intricacies. His emotional range is enormous. Within but a short span of time, Mozart can be both gay and profound, serene and agitated, cheerful and serious, calm and turbulent, ethical and diabolical, yet all takes place within an ordered framework and nothing ever gets out of hand. His *Marriage of Figaro*, an adaptation of Beaumarchais' play, is one vast human panorama in which all the characters, whether master or servant, nobleman or knave, appear as equal partners in the dance of life. Every possible amorous situation is explored with objectivity, deep psychological insight, good humor, and warm understanding. From Cherubino's adolescent awakening to the fascinations of the opposite sex and the mature love of Figaro and Susanna, he moves on to the Count and Countess as the philandering husband and neglected wife, and finally to a pair of scheming blackmailers. The situations meanwhile run a gamut from intrigue, coquetry, and lust to infidelity, forgiveness, and tender reconciliation. Much of Beaumarchais' political satire is missing, but every nuance of human feeling is explored and exploited to the utmost. By contrast, when Mozart had to perform the duties of a court composer and write an opera on a stilted Metastasio libretto in connection with the emperor's coronation, the work was a failure. When, however, the invitation to write a new opera came from the provincial but highly musical city of Prague, he had both the ideas and the audience he needed, and the result was the operatic masterpiece *Don Giovanni*.

Don Giovanni

For *Don Giovanni*, Mozart was fortunate in having the collaboration of Lorenzo da Ponte, a skillful writer and facile adapter with a real theatrical and histrionic flair. On hand at the final rehearsals of this saga of the world's greatest lover, and helping put a few finishing touches on the text was none other than Giacomo Casanova, a man who had done enough research on the subject to qualify him as an authority. The Don Juan story was far from a novelty, and like the Faust legend, it went all the way back to the medieval morality drama. In literature, the earliest known version is by a Spanish playwright, and in Italy, the tale was frequently dramatized in Jesuit churches under the title of *Atheisto Fulminato*, or the *Blaspheming Atheist*. Molière made a prose comedy out of it, in which the satirical element replaced the moralizing tone. Many passages and phrases from Molière's play found their way into Da Ponte's libretto. Donna Elvira, a lady whom Don Juan had kidnapped from a convent and later deserted, as well as the pastoral pair, Zerlina and Masetto, also stem from Molière. An English version called *The Libertine* by Thomas Shadwell, with incidental music by Purcell, was mounted in London in 1676; and as late as 1817 a play called *Don Giovanni, or A Spectre on Horseback*, inspired Byron's poem on the subject. The direct ancestor of Da Ponte's book, however, was an Italian libretto by Bertati, though elements from all the known Italian, French, and German plays made their contribution.

Both the subject matter and Mozart's marvelous music led to the adoption and deification of *Don Giovanni* by the following generation, who saw in it the prototype of the romantic opera. In one of his late conversations, Goethe remarked rather wistfully that Mozart should have composed *Faust*. What the venerable poet overlooked was that Mozart had already done so, since the Faustian concept completely permeates the character of Don Giovanni, who was a Mephistopheles and Faust rolled into one. Stylistically, the opera incorporates the spirit of the storm-and-stress drama and led directly to Spohr's opera *Faust*, E. T. A. Hoffmann's *Undine*, and Weber's *Freischütz*. The 19th century unfortunately burdened *Don Giovanni* with all kinds of interpretations. To the partisans of the French Revolution, Don Giovanni was the dissolute nobleman bent like an arch-criminal on bringing about the destruction of the moral law. If so, he was certainly the most beloved villain in all melodrama, with the sympathies of the audience enlisted for once on the side opposite law and order. The philosopher Kierkegaard regarded him as the incarnation of Desire, which by its very nature can never admit of satisfaction. He thus became a Nietzschean superman, or personification of the Dionysian life force. How then is it that in the opera each love affair either ends in frustration or leaves him in some ridiculous situation? To the classical enthusiasts, Don Giovanni was the mortal who dared to defy the very gods themselves and by so doing brought about his own destruction. To the romantics, he was the towering tragic hero who, like Faust, was the victim of his own insatiable lusts. To others, he was the uncompromising idealist always in pursuit of perfect beauty, and so on.

To find Mozart's real meaning, one must blow off the accumulation of 19th-century moral and philosophical dust and appraise it anew. Is it a tragedy or a comedy? Even today performances tend to emphasize one aspect or the other. Mozart's subtitle *dramma giocosa* suggests a combination of both. In the thematic catalogue of his own works, he also refers to it as an "opera buffa in two acts." Bearing in mind that Mozart was entirely capable of leaving it as a subtle enigma, that his inspired music raises it to the status of a unique masterpiece, and that it was originally composed for a small theater, one may decide that the best approach to it is as a high-spirited 18th-century comedy of manners, in which Molièrian satire is mixed with some storm-and-stress demonic elements.

The pace of the opera is breathtaking. In the first scene alone there is an attempted rape, a challenge and duel, the dying gasps of an outraged father, blasphemy, the escape of the culprits, and oaths of vengeance. In all this the absolute dramatic center is Don Giovanni himself, who bursts the bonds of civilized restraint, defies all social conventions, sweeps aside any barriers in his way, and stands alone against the world. In the *Marriage of Figaro* all the characters interacted with each other; here the figures, like the spokes of a wheel, exist only in their relation to the hub, Don Giovanni. Opposite him are the three feminine leads, each of equal importance—Donna Anna, Donna Elvira, and Zerlina, in the order of their appearance. Chronologically, Donna Elvira comes first, since she has been seduced and deserted before the curtain rises. Hers is the fury of a woman scorned, joined with the desire to forgive and forget and to save Don Giovanni from perdition. Her character is most clearly revealed in Aria No. 8, *"In qual eccessi,"* where she advises the lightheaded young Zerlina of the pitfalls of life with the gay Don. Mozart writes it as a typical Handelian baroque rage aria. By so doing, he implies that Elvira's moral preachments are somewhat archaic, and the dignified form makes it an effective contrast to the prevailing frivolity. The emotional life of Donna Anna, whose screams are heard at the beginning of the opera, is no less complicated. Full of righteous wrath, tempered with filial affection for her murdered father, she swears vengeance on his assassin. She is joined in this resolve by her gentlemanly fiancé, Don Ottavio, and together they constitute the serious couple usual in Italian opera buffa. Since Don Ottavio is the lonely champion of lawful love versus licentiousness, he is bound to appear somewhat pale in these highly charged surroundings. His two tenor arias, *"Dalla sua pace"* and *"Il mio tesoro"* (Nos. 10B and 21), contain lovely lyricism but are parenthetical rather than part of the main action. Donna Anna, on the contrary, rises to truly tragic stature in *"Or sai chi l'onore,"* Aria No. 10; where, outraged by yet attracted to Don Giovanni, she intermingles hatred with passion. Third in this list is the naïve but flirtatious Zerlina, torn between loyalty to her rustic bridegroom and the flattering attentions of the dashing Don. The duet *"La ci darem la mano"* (No. 7) is a subtle piece of musical characterization in which the division of the melody between the voices and the minute melodic variants point up their respective attitudes. The Don is tender, yet always the imperious aristocrat, accustomed to having his own way; Zerlina is very feminine, hesitant, doubtful of his good intentions, but thoroughly enjoying every moment. Later, in a reconciliation scene with her young peasant husband, the aria *"Vedrai carino"* (No. 18) brings out all her maternal impulses toward him.

On the male side, Don Giovanni has no romantic competition, only a very substantial shadow in the form of Leporello, the comic manservant who plays Sancho Panza to his Don Quixote. Leporello is a stock opera-buffa character, who expresses his rather earthy cynicism in some chattering patter songs based on a running series of rapidly repeated syllables and notes. He introduces himself in the first aria of the opera; and in the famous Catalogue Aria (No. 4), he enumerates the list of his master's amorous conquests in what must surely be the most hilarious set of statistics in history.

The two scenes in which all the characters are on stage are the Finales to Acts 1 and 2. In the first, Don Giovanni is entertaining a lively peasant wedding party in the hopes of winning the bride Zerlina for himself. Fine dramatic contrast is provided in Don Giovanni's gay drinking song (No. 11) that sparkles like the wine he is ordering, and the sullen resentment of Masetto when he senses that his bride's head is being turned by this glamorous member of the privileged class. The scene reaches its brilliant climax when the dance music strikes up. There are no less than three ensembles on stage in addition to the main orchestra in the pit. Everyone at the time would have recognized this as a typical Viennese public ballroom scene for which Mozart frequently composed music. So that there would be dances that appealed to everybody, minuets were customarily played in one room, waltzes in another, and so on. Here the three groups also play different dances. The first, consisting of two oboes, two horns, and strings, plays the best

Don Giovanni. Dance Scene, Finale, Act I   Mozart

known of all minuets. On the repetition of the last part, the second stage orchestra, made up of violins and a bass, does a type of square dance known as a contre-danse; while a third band, also of stringed instruments, plays an old-fashioned German waltz. An obvious stratification of social levels is implied, with the masked figures of Donna Anna and Don Ottavio doing the aristocratic minuet; the peasants stamping out the vigorous, laendlerlike meter of the waltz, with strong accentuation on the beats of three and one, while Don Giovanni and Zerlina meet on the middle-class ground of the bourgeois contre-danse. Each social group is thus expressed through a characteristic rhythm. With the stage bands playing against the main orchestra below, all the plots and subplots boiling merrily away, and all the characters conversing and commenting on the action, the resulting rhythmic complexity and dramatic tension make this scene one of the major miracles of musical literature.

In the cemetery scene, which precedes the Finale to the second act, Don Giovanni as a fugitive from justice is confronted with the equestrian statue of the Commendatore whom he has murdered at the beginning of the opera. The stentorian tones of the voice from the tomb reproach him for his wickedness; and Don Giovanni, always the courteous host, responds by inviting the statue to a midnight meal. The final scene opens with the preparations for the banquet, while the trumpets and drums sound the proper note of aristocratic hospitality. Like all noblemen of his time, Don Giovanni has his own liveried house orchestra standing by to play dinner music. This wind ensemble plays snatches from two popular Italian operas by Mozart's rivals; and a delightful bit of humor is introduced when they quote the "Non più andrai" from his own Marriage of Figaro, which happened to be a hit tune of that season, not a classic as now.

Donna Elvira, ever the kill-joy, now enters to play her trump card, which is the announcement that she is returning to her convent where life under the veil will presumably be more peaceful. As she reaches the door, her shriek heralds the arrival of the statue. With ominously heavy footsteps, the monument sings a long melodic line as rigid in its way as rigor mortis itself, reinforced by the sepulchral sounds of the trombones, instruments which were then associated with solemn church festivals and funerals. The contrast between the quick and the dead is brought out by the static pedal point of the statue's melody, around which the other characters react in ways varying from farce to tragedy. When Don Giovanni takes the hand of his marble guest, the horror music that had been foreshadowed in the overture is heard once more. Strings play spine-tingling scale figures upward and downward alternately soft and loud. Claps of thunder are heard, a chorus of demons shouts from below, flames mount upward; and Don Giovanni, unrepentant to the last, goes to his predestined doom singing the descending scale of D major. Breathlessly the other characters arrive too late for the excitement but in the nick of time to sing a quintet to the following words before the curtain falls:

> Sinner, pause, and ponder well,
> Mark the end of Don Juan!
> Are you going to Heaven or Hell?

IDEAS

The 18th-century styles either continued, modified, or departed from some baroque source. The shift of audience from a declining aristocracy to the rising bourgeoisie was accelerated, and the final phase of the aristocratic baroque style is reflected in the rococo; the continuation of 17th-century rationalism is found in the Enlightenment; voices of a classical revival begin to be heard; new emotional outbursts are felt in the emphasis on sensibility and in the storm-and-stress movement. Deferring the discussion of neoclassicism to Chapter 17, the ideas that weave the arts of the 18th-century into a coherent pattern are the rococo, the Enlightenment, and the emotional reaction to them known as the storm and stress.

The Rococo

The rococo is the last Western style that can lay claim to universality and that adhered strictly to the canons of beauty. This comes about because the aristocracy was the last international social group of sufficient persuasion to control artistic patronage. After the French Revolution and the Napoleonic wars, the power of nationalism grew so strong that the arts appeared more and more in local frames of reference. The Renaissance cult of the beautiful likewise finds its terminal point in the rococo, where it comes perilously close to mere prettiness and over-refinement. Fischer von Erlach, Lukas von Hildebrandt, Watteau, Boucher, Fragonard, and Clodion never overstep the boundaries of beauty. Mozart, in spite of his extraordinary emotional power, makes his aesthetic views on this point quite clear in a letter to his father: "Passions, whether violent or not," he wrote, "must never be expressed in such a way as to excite disgust, and as music, even in the most terrible situations, must never offend the ear, but please the hearer, or in other words must never cease to be *music*." Examples of the rococo style are found in all countries where the aristocracy possessed the means to follow the fashionable style, and where the Counter-Reformationists undertook the building of churches. The earmarks of the style are found in the details of the interiors of salons; the paintings of Watteau, Boucher, and Fragonard; the sculptures of Clodion; and in such moments in Mozart as the exquisite aria sung by the Countess at the beginning of Act II of the *Marriage of Figaro*.

The Enlightenment

The Enlightenment is a blanket term under which it is possible to group such tendencies as the inventive spirit, scientific inquiry, the encyclopedic movement, the optimistic world view, and the belief in progress. The impetus that the Enlightenment gave to scientific invention was applied by middle-class manufacturers and businessmen to the production of wealth. Pure science and nature in this case were less important than technology and artifact. The new social order is mirrored most directly in the shift of artistic patronage in the direction of the middle-class audience. For the first time, it is possible to speak of the bourgeois novel and drama. Watteau painted one of his most important pictures for an art dealer; Chardin, Greuze, and Hogarth found their clientele among the same social segment; and making the Count the villain and the servant the hero in Beaumarchais' and Mozart's *Marriage of Figaro* was certainly not calculated to flatter the aristocracy.

The Enlightenment spirit of free scientific inquiry, which grew out of 17th-century rationalism, was so violently anticlerical that it almost developed into a substitute religion. To the deists, God was a kind of cosmic clockmaker who created a mechanical universe, wound it up for all eternity, and let it go. The experimental method of science became the liturgy of this pseudo religion, the encyclopedia its bible, nature its church, and all men of reason the congregation. One of the most productive impulses of this aspect of the Enlightenment resulted in the encyclopedic movement. All the important intellects made their contributions to Diderot's *Encyclopédie*, with Voltaire writing the historical parts, Rousseau the sections on music, and so on. The same intellectual spirit, though in different religious circumstances, is observable in the comprehensive musical output of J. S. Bach. In *The Art of the Fugue* he applied the scientific method to musical composition. By keeping his themes constant, he carefully controlled the variables of form and thus systematized all possible fugal types. His extant cantatas add up to four for each Sunday of the year. His keyboard compositions are conceived encyclopedically and comprise examples in all possible forms. His 48 preludes and fugues, known as the *Well Tempered Clavier*, are written as a double cycle, two for each possible tonality; and his Brandenburg concertos explore every possible instrumental combination. His entire works thus emerge as a comprehensive design consciously planned to survey and sum up all the musical practices known to him.

The Enlightenment image of the cool man of reason inhabiting a world governed by purely rational principles was the object of Voltaire's satirical pen in the novel *Candide*. While maintaining his staunch belief that he lives, in the Leibnizian "best of all possible worlds," the hero experiences every disaster known on the planet, including the great earthquake of Lisbon in 1745. The use of satire as a social weapon takes visual form in Hogarth's *Marriage à-la-Mode*. A certain amount of Voltairean skepticism can also be found in the character of Don Giovanni, who fears neither the supernatural nor the hereafter. When the statue talks in the cemetery scene, the unenlightened Leporello cowers with superstitious fear; but Don Giovanni assumes the role of an art critic, sees that the statue is really nothing more than a typical cemetery monument, and addresses it: "*O vecchio buffonissimo*"—ridiculous old gentleman. The Enlightenment spirit finds an even clearer statement and takes a more constructive form in Mozart's last opera, *The Magic Flute*, an allegory of Freemasonry in which the forces of reason are lined up squarely against those of superstition and fear.

The Enlightenment was accompanied by a spirit of optimism and by a belief in progress and the perfectibility of man. Theologically, the Hebraic and Christian viewpoints were based on the fall of man and the doctrine of original sin dating from the expulsion of Adam and Eve from the Garden of Eden. Philosophically, Plato's theory of knowledge was also founded on a doctrine of prenatal perfection and the subsequent acquisition of knowledge by the process of remembrance. Humanists, such as Gibbon, believed in the intellectual and artistic paradise of ancient Greece and Rome and as a consequence wrote their declines and falls. Without denying the greatness of Greece, the exponents of the Enlightenment were well aware that they had gone far beyond classical science and believed that, if the rational processes could be properly applied, they could eventually surpass the ancients in all fields. Kant, for instance, enthusiastically hailed Rousseau as the Newton of the moral world, and Condorcet in his *Progress of the Human Spirit* enumerated the ten stages by which man had raised himself from savagery to the threshold of perfection. Material progress was certainly an observable fact; and, they thought, since nature held all the secrets that a man needed to know, and reason could unlock them, eventually he could control his environment. If man therefore would only use his mental and moral powers to their fullest extent, the argument ran, he could go in one direction only, onward and upward. The full force of this optimism is felt in the American and French revolutions, and in the painting of David and the music of Beethoven, which will be discussed in the next chapter.

"Storm and Stress"

In the latter half of the 18th century, various irrational tendencies came about as reactions to both the rococo cult of the beautiful and the Enlightenment's emphasis on reason. As early as 1756, Burke's *Essay on the Sublime and the Beautiful* insisted that in literature and art there is an element more important than beauty. This was the Sublime, which transcends mere beauty and can even admit of the ugly. "Whatever is fitted in any sort to excite the ideas of pain and danger," he said, "whatever is in any sort terrible, or conversant about terrible objects, is the source of the Sublime." The free exercise of the emotions and the imagination, even if it meant the painful, the astonishing, the horrible, was therefore legitimate territory for art to explore. This movement led to a renewed interest in Shakespeare; reveled in Rousseau's descriptions of alpine scenery, accompanied as they were by avalanches and storms; and delighted in the Rousseauian revolt against the restraints of civilization. This line of thought also constituted the background of the storm-and-stress movement in Germany. While the Enlightenment was trying to tame nature and bring it under man's control, the *Sturm und Drang* authors were reveling in how nature imposed her obscure and unfathomable will on man. In Goethe's early drama, Faust was the rebel against all accepted forms of wisdom, especially those arrived at through mathematical or scientific formulas. Both Faust and Don Giovanni were engaged in a quest for emotional truth and succeeded in unleashing the infernal forces that eventually consumed them.

Such, in brief, were the social, ideational, and emotional impulses that defined the horizon before which the panorama of the 18th-century arts unfolded.

(*Opposite*). Daumier. *The Uprising*. Oil on canvas. 43⅞" x 133¾". *c.*1860. Phillips Collection, Washington, D. C.

Part 5
THE REVOLUTIONARY PERIOD

CHRONOLOGY:
Paris, Early 19th Century

General Events

1748	Excavations begun at Pompeii and Herculaneum
1762	*Antiquities of Athens* published by Stuart and Revett
1764	*History of Ancient Art* published by Winckelmann (1717–1768)
1766	*Laocoön* published by Lessing (1729–1781)
1785–1820	Federal Style in the United States
1788–1791	Brandenburg Gate in Berlin built by Langhans
1789	French Revolution began
1792–1794	First French Republic
1796	Napoleon's first Italian campaign
1798	Napoleon's campaign in Egypt
	Battle of the Pyramids
1799	Napoleon became First Consul
1802	Napoleon made Consul for life
1803	Napoleonic Code of Laws issued
1804	Napoleon crowned emperor
	Beethoven finished *Eroica* Symphony
1806	Temple of Glory (later La Madeleine) begun by Vignon
	Arc du Carrousel begun by Percier and Fontaine
	Arc du Triomphe de l'Étoile begun by Chalgrin

1814	Napoleon abdicated. Bourbons restored to French throne
1814–1821	Louis XVIII, king of France
1815	Napoleon defeated in Battle of Waterloo
	Elgin Marbles exhibited in London
1816	Elgin Marbles purchased by Parliament, placed in British Museum
1821	Napoleon died
1824–1830	Charles X, king of France
1830	July Revolution
1830–1848	Louis Philippe, king of France; constitutional monarch

Painters

1746–1828	Goya
1748–1825	David
1771–1835	Gros
1780–1867	Ingres
1791–1824	Géricault

Sculptors

1757–1822	Canova
1770–1844	Thorwaldsen

Architects

1739–1811	Chalgrin
1762–1820	Vignon
1762–1853	Fontaine
1764–1838	Percier

Musicians

1714–1787	Gluck
1741–1813	Grétry
1741–1816	Paisiello
1760–1837	Lesueur
1760–1842	Cherubini
1770–1827	Beethoven
1774–1851	Spontini

THE NEOCLASSICAL STYLE

PARIS, EARLY 19TH CENTURY

Some books, some archeological discoveries, and some social upheavals brought to Paris many radical changes in intellectual orientation, in styles of art, and in forms of government during the latter part of the 18th and early part of the 19th century. Stuart and Revett, two Englishmen who had visited Greece, had published in 1762 a volume called *Antiquities of Athens*, which made a clear differentiation between Greek and Roman architecture. Two years later, Winckelmann's *History of Ancient Art*, the equivalent of a best-seller, made the same point for sculpture. "The principal and universal characteristic of the masterpieces of Greek art is a noble simplicity and a quiet grandeur," he declared. "As the depth of the sea remains always at rest, however the surface may be agitated, so the expression in the figures of the Greeks reveals in the midst of passion a great and steadfast soul." These words provided the critics of the courtly rococo style with the needed aesthetic ammunition, and Diderot fired verbal volleys at Boucher and Fragonard because of the frivolous content of their paintings. The function of art, insisted Diderot, was to make "virtue adorable and vice repugnant."

599

The wave of enthusiasm for antiquity that now swept France made that country into a kind of classical phoenix rising from the volcanic ashes of Pompeii and Herculaneum. News of the excavation of these ancient cities was eagerly followed by the French, before whose eyes an image of a widespread high standard of living seemed to be unfolding. Luxury previously had been associated with a decadent aristocracy, and it came as something of a revelation for the French middle class to learn that the ordinary inhabitants of these old Roman resort towns had lived so well. Classicism, which hitherto had meant temples, forums, and great monuments, now could be associated with an unpretentious but luxurious domestic architecture and ideals of comfort that people like themselves could live with and understand. Since the French Revolution, for all its fury, was essentially a bourgeois movement in which the rights of property remained unquestioned, the excavation of these ancient ruins gave the people something worth striving for at precisely the time when they were able to do something about it.

Ancient Rome now became a symbol for the revolutionary protest. In politics, this at first meant a republican instead of a monarchical form of government. In religion, it was associated with a tolerant paganism as opposed to a dogmatic form of Christianity. (For a brief time, in fact, the Cathedral of Notre Dame in Paris was rededicated to the goddess of Reason.) Heroism and self-sacrifice, rugged resolve and Spartan simplicity became manifestations of the revolutionary spirit, and reflections of these qualities were readily found in Roman literature and art. The political writings of Cicero and Seneca were widely read and quoted to confirm the principle that sovereignty resided in the people and that government should be based on a voluntary agreement among citizens. Political pamphlets came to be studded with quotations from Tacitus, Sallust, and Horace, and the oratory of the period was modeled on that of Cicero. The convention hall where the revolutionary legislators met was lined with laurel-crowned statues of Solon, Camillus, and other ancient statesmen, and in their debates the speakers relied on apt phrases from Cicero to clinch important points. They referred to their partisans as Brutuses and Catos and to their opponents as Catalines; their postures and gestures were studied imitations of Roman statues, and their oaths were sworn on the head of Brutus or by the immortal gods. (The painter David even designed a costume for these representatives of the people that combined the ancient tunic with a togalike cape draped over the shoulders, but this at least did not catch on.)

Everyone who could read became biography-conscious and spoke like living characters out of Plutarch's *Parallel Lives*. (On the day she murdered Marat, Charlotte Corday had spent her time reading Plutarch.) Never before had public personalities seemed so obviously to have walked straight out of books. Surely

Oscar Wilde must have had this revolutionary period in mind when he wittily twisted the old Greek aesthetic doctrine by saying that nature, especially human nature, imitates art.

Many of the revolutionary symbols too were borrowed directly from the ancients. The cap of liberty was a copy of the Phrygian cap worn by the liberated slaves in Rome; the *fasces*, or bundle of sticks with the protruding ax tied together with a common bond, as seen in David's *Oath of the Horatii*, was once again the symbol of power; the calendar was reorganized, and the months of the year given Latin names. The rainy month became Pluviose; planting time, Germinal; the month of blossoms, Floreal; midsummer, Thermidor; and harvest time, Fructidor. Façades of houses featured classical columns; rooms were furnished with Roman couches, lighted by bronze lamps, and decorated with replicas of ancient statuary.

Dominating this neoclassical scene was Napoleon Bonaparte, who shared the popular enthusiasm for all that was ancient. His chosen models were Alexander the Great and Julius Caesar, especially the latter since his career and Napoleon's had so many parallels. Napoleon became first a republican consul; later he ruled France through a tribune; and then, after a plebiscite, he became the modern incarnation of a Roman emperor. The *fasces* became his emblem of authority; the eagles of the old Roman legions he made into the insignia of the French battalions; and eventually he was crowned with the laurel wreath, that ancient symbol of immortal fame.

Such a manipulation of the forms and images of ancient glory had a vast appeal to this man of modest birth. Coming to power so soon after the demise of an unpopular monarchy, Napoleon had to emphasize that many of the Roman emperors were of equally plebian backgrounds, and that the imperial toga had not always been hereditary. But his hold on the people was indisputable and his elevation was made with full popular consent. His mission was to bring order to what had been revolutionary chaos and to consolidate the social gains that had been made. His meteoric career was the success story of the 19th century, embodying as it did the ideal of the emancipated individual rising to leadership through his own efforts rather than by an accident of birth. In it, members of the parvenu society of his time could find substance for their fondest materialistic daydreams. The truth was that now, with the reins of power in their hands, the middle class did not know quite how to manage them. Napoleon did.

Napoleon's achievement of these ancient prerogatives of power, however, was not made with antiquated methods, and the highly modern means he employed make a fascinating study in contrasts. Never could Napoleon have risen to power had he not forged a mighty war machine, and this was possible only by the application to industry and agriculture of all the latest technological and scientific knowledge. By being the first modern ruler to employ universal conscription to populate his armies and by his undoubted administrative ability, he was able to regiment all the various parts of his state into efficient cogs in his wheel of victory. Further, he had inherited the popular classical vocabulary, and he proceeded to use it. The ancient symbols that served his state by upholding the ideals of heroism and self-sacrifice and by awakening latent national ambitions were both useful and decorative. Consequently, Napoleon cast himself in varying roles at different times: when he was crossing the Alps, he was Hannibal; on a far-off battlefield, he was Alexander; burdened with administrative affairs at home, he was Caesar. And those around him had their assigned roles also. When David requested a sitting for a portrait, Napoleon dismissed the thought with a wave of his hand, instructing the astonished artist to paint his genius, not his likeness, and asking rhetorically if Alexander had ever posed for Apelles.

Like its Roman prototype, Napoleon's empire was international in scope, and its intellectual and artistic life transcended national boundary lines. What Greece had been to Rome, Italy was now to France. Napoleon brought the Italian sculptor Canova to Paris for various commissions, and his musical preferences were for such composers as Paisiello and Spontini. His proclamation to the Italian people on the eve of his invasion of their country points up this internationalism. "We are the friends of all nations," he protested, perhaps too much, "especially the descendants of Brutus, the Scipios, and of the great men we have chosen for our own model." And he took frequent pains to point out that he was embarking on a cultural as well as a military mission. Here was no barbarian Attila storming the citadel, but a conqueror who came to sack Rome in the company of a group of art experts who were well aware of the value of everything they took. A petition signed by all the important French artists actually had been sent to the Directory in 1796, pointing out how much the Romans had become civilized by confiscating the art of ancient Greece and how France would likewise flourish by bringing original works to Paris to serve as models. While this returning Caesar brought back with him no human captives, his victory celebration was livened by the presence of such distinguished prisoners of war as the *Apollo Belvedere*, the *Discobolus*, the *Venus de' Medici*, the paintings of Raphael, and the rare treasures he had pilfered from the Vatican and other Italian museums.

As an Italian himself, Napoleon knew the value of such pomp and circumstance, and his life was consciously conditioned by these visions of ancient splendor. Inevitably, however, the tables were turned, and he sometimes found that his critics also could find apt parallels from the past. When things began to go from bad to worse, Chateaubriand, his ambassador in Rome, compared him with Nero. Yet even when his cause was hopelessly lost, Napoleon summoned one last bit of Plutarchian grandeur to adorn his letter of surrender. "I throw myself," he wrote, "like Themistocles upon the mercy of the British people."

ARCHITECTURE

With the reorganization of the government, the remaking of the constitution, and the recodification of the laws on the model of his reincarnated Roman Empire, Napoleon was determined that Paris should be replanned as a new Rome. He therefore undertook the ordering and commissioning of buildings with the same incredible vigor that marked his activities in other fields. The heart of the new city was still to be the spacious center designed around the old Place Louis XV, which under the Directory had been renamed the Place de la Concorde (Fig. 17:1). Its axis began on the left bank of the Seine River with the old Palais Bourbon, now the Chamber of Deputies, which was to have its face lifted by a Corinthian colonnade. It was then to continue across the river, by the bridge that had been begun in early revolutionary days, to the center of the Place, where some statuary was to cover the spot where the guillotine had done its grim work. Its termination was to be the unfinished church of La Madeleine at the end of the Rue Royale, which was to be rebuilt in the form of a Roman temple. To complete the scheme, Napoleon commissioned Percier and Fontaine, his favorite architects, to redesign the Rue de Rivoli that intersected the axis at right angles and ran parallel to the Seine. Elsewhere throughout the city, triumphal arches and monumental columns were to proclaim to the world the presence of a new Caesar and Trajan.

Fig. 17:1. Place de la Concorde, Paris

Fig. 17:2. Vignon. Church of La Madeleine. *Façade*. Building 350′ long x 147′ wide.
1762–1829. Paris

Napoleon showed his interest in these projects by frequently conferring with
his architects and engineers, by visiting construction sites, and by dreaming up
new ideas while on distant battlefields. It was in Poland that he signed the de-
cree for the building of his Temple of Glory (La Madeleine, Fig. 17:2). According to his express wish, the unfinished church was to be transformed and bear a
dedicatory inscription: "From the Emperor to the soldiers of the Grande
Armée." The building was not to look like a church but like such a temple as
one would find in Athens or Rome. The interior was to contain marble tablets
that were to be inscribed with the names of all the troops who had participated
in the battles of Ulm, Austerlitz, and Jena; silver panels that would list their
names again according to the Departments of France which had sent their sons
to the grand army; and gold plaques, which would bear the names of those who
had fallen on the field of battle. Around the room were to be bas reliefs of the
regiments with their insignia; statues of the marshals were to occupy niches; and

elsewhere trophies, regalia, banners, and drums were to be displayed. Each year on the anniversaries of the three battles the temple was to be illuminated and a grand concert given. Preceding the music, there were to be odes and eulogies stressing the virtues necessary for a soldier's life; and in a magnanimous mood of self-renunciation, Napoleon expressly forbade any mention of himself in these commemorative poems and orations. The grand council of the Legion of Honor was to be entrusted with the annual ceremonies, choosing the best poetry and music from the works submitted and rewarding the authors with gold medals. The minister of the interior, who was commissioned to carry out the order, promptly issued an artistic call to arms, summoning all the architects, sculptors, and painters to submit designs of a grand and noble character. Napoleon personally selected an architectural plan by Vignon, because it fulfilled his conditions by looking sufficiently ancient and pagan.

The building is indeed a pagan Corinthian temple, and, except for the sculptural details, it was completed according to Vignon's plan. In the Roman manner, it stands on a platform 23 feet high and is approached by a flight of steps in the front. Running completely around the building is a series of Corinthian columns about 63 feet in height, 18 on each side, 8 on each end, and an additional row of 6 in front that supports the cornice. Since its rededication for religious purposes, this pagan temple of glory has had a large sculptural group by Lemaire on its pediment, representing the Last Judgment. In the center stands the figure of Christ, 17 feet high, with the repentant Mary Magdalene at His feet. To His left are allegorical figures representing the sins of Envy, Hypocrisy, and Avarice,

Fig. 17:3. Church of La Madeleine. *Interior.* (Archives Photographiques)

while on His right are an angel of mercy and personifications of the virtues of Faith, Hope, Charity, and Innocence.

The interior cella of an ancient temple was never intended as a gathering place and always remained dark and mysterious. Hence, of necessity, Vignon had to depart from precedent and come up with something new. The surprise that awaits the visitor as he passes through the massive bronze doors is complete, for the interior and exterior actually amount to two different buildings. The aisleless nave (Fig. 17:3) is divided into three long bays and a choir, which are not roofed in timber as in a Greek temple or vaulted in the Roman manner but crowned with three low saucer domes on pendentives in the Byzantine style. The nave terminates in a semicircular apse that is roofed over by a semidome. Chapels are located in the recesses created by the buttresses that support the domes, and two classical orders—the Corinthian and Ionic—form the basis of the decorative scheme. Rich use is made of marble paneling, and the domes are coffered in the manner of the Roman Pantheon. What little light there is in this windowless interior comes from skylights at the tops of the domes, an idea derived from the oculus of the Roman Pantheon. The best that can be said about this method is that it keeps the exterior roof line intact. The exterior, as a study in classical design, has a certain dignity in its archeological faithfulness to such older models as the Maison Carrée (Fig. 3:15), though it excels its prototypes only in its larger proportions. The interior, however, can be said to have a certain originality as an early example of the 19th-century eclectic style.

From its letters of foundation in 1757 to its final dedication in 1845, the building had a checkered history, to say the least. When Louis XV laid its cornerstone in 1764, he proclaimed it a monument to the piety of the French royal family. Work on it ceased during the Revolution, and it served during the days of the Terror as a morgue for the headless victims of the guillotine. The old unfinished pile was cleared off under Napoleon to become a temple to his cult of military glory. The word *glory*, however, began to have a hollow ring even before the end of the Empire, and after Waterloo the building reverted to its status as a church of the Magdalene. Under the Bourbon restoration it was declared to be an expiatory monument to atone for the execution of Louis XVI and his family. This was again changed after the Revolution of 1830; and, after its completion in 1842, it was finally dedicated by Louis Philippe, somewhat anticlimactically, as a simple parish church.

In 1806, after winning military victories in Germany and Austria, Napoleon entrusted to Percier and Fontaine the building of a triumphal arch. Now known as the Arc du Carrousel (Fig. 17:4), it was designed as a gate of honor to the Tuileries Palace. It turned out to be a rather slavish imitation of the Arch of Septimus Severus in Rome, though of more modest proportions, but standing on the platform above it was one of Napoleon's proudest battle trophies—the group

Fig. 17:4. Percier and Fontaine. *Arc de Triomphe du Carrousel*. 1806. Paris

of four bronze horses taken from St. Mark's in Venice. Owing to the shifting fortunes of war, however, Venice got back the horses as a result of a peace treaty, and a triumphal chariot drawn by horses of a considerably later vintage was installed in their place to celebrate, somewhat ironically, the restoration of Louis XVIII. The face of the arch is decorated with rather undistinguished bas reliefs depicting such scenes as the battle of Austerlitz, the surrender of Ulm, the peace of Tilsit, and Napoleon's triumphal entries into Munich and Vienna.

When finished, the result was too meager to measure up to Napoleon's imperial ambitions, and so another and still grander arch was commissioned for the Place de l'Étoile. This familiar Paris landmark was also Roman in inspiration, but Chalgrin, its architect, achieved some life and elasticity in its form by freely adapting rather than copying a known model. For his monumental effect, he relied on bold proportions and a grand scale. Conspicuously omitting the classical orders, he relieved the severity of the general outline by the skillful placement of high-relief sculptures of Cortot and Rude (Figs. 18:8 and 18:9), works on a scale comparable to the immense size of the arch itself.

Still not content, Napoleon ordered a monumental Doric column to be erected in the Place Vendôme (Fig. 17:5). In its size and style of ornamentation, it was a conscious copy of Trajan's column in Rome (Fig. 3:22), the main difference being that its spiral reliefs are done in a strip of bronze cast from the guns and cannons that were captured from the defeated Prussian and Austrian armies. The sculpture recounts the story of the campaign of 1805 in scenes, such as the address of Napoleon to his troops, the capture of Ulm, the meeting of the three emperors, and the conquest of Istria and Dalmatia. The statue at the top

Fig. 17:5. Percier and Fontaine. *Vendôme Column.* Marble with bronze spiral frieze. 1810. Paris

originally was to have been of Charlemagne, but Napoleon yielded to flattery and allowed himself to be portrayed in the manner of a Roman emperor crowned with the laurel wreath and holding an orb surmounted by winged victory. This statue was carried off to England by the British army of occupation that entered Paris in 1814. Louis XVIII replaced it with one of Henry IV, but Louis Philippe again put Napoleon back on top, this time as Citizen Bonaparte. In 1865, Napoleon III thought this statue an affront to his uncle and predecessor, and so Citizen Bonaparte came down and Napoleon in the imperial toga went up again. In 1871, under the Commune, the whole column was pulled down with ropes and pulleys by a group that included the painter Courbet, but under the Third Republic it was reassembled and today stands substantially as it was in the time of Napoleon III.

This wave of enthusiasm for classical architecture was by no means confined to Paris. While, in general, the Roman revival was strongest in the countries identified with the revival of the empire under Napoleon, the Greek revival was accented in the nations of the anti-Napoleonic coalition, notably England and Germany. In England, country houses built by Robert and James Adams and such public buildings as the British Museum were all strongly Greek in character. In Germany, an early example is the Brandenburg Gate in Berlin, modeled after the Athenian Propylaea. Two later buildings in Munich were based on the same model, while a Hall of Fame near Regensburg, called, of all things, Walhalla, is an archeologically exact reproduction of the Parthenon. In the United States, the period corresponded generally to the Federal style, which ran its course from about 1785 to 1820. Buildings that show the Roman influence are the Virginia state capitol, which Thomas Jefferson designed after the Maison Carrée (Fig. 3:15); the University of Virginia campus, which was planned after the rambling style of a large Roman country villa; and the library of the same institution, which was modeled after the Pantheon (Fig. 3:19).

PAINTING

Into this stern world of revolutionary fervor and ancient Roman heroism stepped a painter whose temperament and technique were ideally suited to the spirit of the times. Jacques Louis David was a reformer by nature and a classical enthusiast by nurture. The austerity of his pictures was a conscious reaction to the rococo extravagances exemplified in the work of his grand uncle, Boucher; and by virtue of his studies in Rome, David had absorbed all that was necessary for the exploitation of the classical enthusiasms of the readers of Plutarch's *Parallel Lives* and Winckelmann's *History of Ancient Art*. It was inevitable that the high moral purposes of the French Revolution would be reflected in some kind of didactic art, and David's immediate success can be attributed to the fact that his style extolled the same stalwart ideas that the revolutionists espoused. Bourgeois by birth and upbringing, David frankly addressed his art to the newly established middle-class social order.

Over and beyond his work as a painter and the intrinsic value of his painting, David assumed the role of power politician in the field of art with far-reaching effects. In a period when it was something of a triumph for a man to keep his head on his shoulders, David showed a political shrewdness and sense of timing that would have done credit to a prime minister. After accepting many commissions from Louis XVI and election to the Academy of Painting and Sculpture, established under Louis XIV, he went over to the side of the Revolution at the opportune moment. As a member of the Convention, he not only voted for the execution of his former patron but succeeded in abolishing the Academy and establishing in its stead the École des Beaux Arts, which he reoriented from the traditional baroque and rococo styles toward the study of Roman antiquity. He

Fig. 17:6. David. *Lictors Bringing Back to Brutus the Bodies of His Sons*. Oil on canvas. 128" x 166½". Louvre, Paris

then blandly hitched his wagon to Napoleon's rising star and became by title the First Painter of the Empire, a commanding position that he proceeded to exploit to the fullest. His activities included the organization of official ceremonies, coordination of the system of state museums, and the granting of licenses to the artists who wished to show their works in the annual public exhibitions. More academic than the former academicians, he succeeded in laying the foundations of official art that endured for the rest of the 19th century. While his theories and subject matter are still a matter of controversy, David's craftsmanship was on a par with any of the master painters of the past, and many distinguished painters of the present have not overlooked his style and manner of execution. The technique of Salvador Dali and the 20th-century neoclassicism of Picasso, for instance, owe much to the cool objective draftsmanship of their 19th-century predecessor.

David's picture of the *Lictors Bringing Back to Brutus the Bodies of His Sons* (Fig. 17:6) bears the date of the fateful year of 1789. It is both a reminder that his career had its inception during the latter days of the monarchy and that he was attempting to continue the subject and substance of his earlier spectacular success, *Oath of the Horatii*. In it one finds the same stern spirit of self-sacrifice, the same severity of style that had appealed so much to the eyes that were weary of the fussy rococo, the same somber type of setting, which had interested those who were reading about the archeological discoveries at Pompeii and Her-

Fig. 17:7. David. *Battle of the Romans and Sabines.* Oil on canvas. 12′ 8″ x 17′. 1799. Louvre, Paris (Archives Photographiques)

culaneum. With remarkable boldness, David was able to flaunt the dour, do-or-die virtues of Roman republicanism right under the noses of his aristocratic patrons. These two pictures were not only the manifesto of a new style in art but of a new image of society as well, and their unparalleled success was owed in no small measure to the fact that they appeared at precisely the right moment.

For his subject David chose an incident from the days soon after the founding of the ancient Roman republic. Lucius Junius Brutus, one of the two First Consuls, had discovered that his own sons were involved in a plot to restore the recently overthrown monarchy. After ordering their execution for treason, his isolated figure is discovered in the statuesque shadow of the goddess Roma. Behind him are the lictors bearing the bodies of his sons, while a third group is formed by his wife and daughters who are crying out in their grief. Many who lived through the trying times of the Revolution could see something of themselves in that figure of stoical resolution, torn between his public duty to the state and his private paternal grief.

Equally melodramatic but with more of the violent action of the Revolution was the picture that followed a decade later, *Battle of the Romans and Sabines* (Fig. 17:7). Romulus, the legendary founder of Rome, and his warriors had

Fig. 17:8. David. *Madame Recamier*. Oil on canvas. 68″ x 95¾″. 1800.
Louvre, Paris (Archives Photographiques)

taken the women of the Sabines by violence, as pictured by Poussin (Fig. 13:15).
Here David depicts the sequel when the Sabine fathers and brothers came to
avenge the rape of their womenfolk. By this time, however, the women had become Roman wives and mothers and are shown rushing outward from the city
gates with their children and throwing themselves between the combatants to stop
the bloodshed. Again the subject is one of conflicting loyalties, brought out by the
principal protagonists in the foreground. Romulus is about to throw his spear
at the king of the Sabines, while the king's daughter Hersilia, now the wife of
Romulus, rushes between them, begging them to desist. In keeping with his
aesthetic theory of placing principles above reality, David idealizes his figures and
minimizes detail by showing the men almost nude and the horses without harness.
For all its sound and fury, however, the composition as a whole tends to become
almost as cold and hard as the carved stone relief that inspired it.

In his portraiture, David reveals himself an expert appraiser of personality,
and his viewers find in this genre a certain relief from his more heroic efforts. A
sensitive example is the portrait of *Madame Recamier* (Fig. 17:8), one of the
most fascinating and intelligent women of the period. In her, David found a congenial subject who furnished her salon in the fashionable Pompeiian style he had
done so much to popularize. Here she reclines in the classical manner on an
Empire chaise longue just as she might have done on the days she received her

Fig. 17:9. David. *Bonaparte on Mount St. Bernard*. Oil on canvas. 107½" x 91½". 1800. Versailles (Archives Photographiques)

guests. Her white gown is draped with deep folds reminiscent of antique statuary. The only other pieces of furniture are the footstool and bronze lamp, which were drawn from Pompeiian originals. The clarity with which David handles the outlines of the figure and the silhouette of the head combine with the austere setting to give a general effect of orderliness and elegance.

David did many portraits of Napoleon, mostly in official attitudes, but in his *Bonaparte on Mount St. Bernard* (Fig. 17:9) he captures something of the essence of Napoleon the conqueror. Shortly after the conclusion of the successful Italian campaign, the artist told the First Consul that he wanted to paint him sword in hand on the field of battle. Napoleon is reported to have replied: "No, it is not with the sword that battles are won—paint me calm and serene on a fiery steed." Lest one be swept away by this disarming touch of honesty on Napoleon's part, let him recall that the actual crossing was made on the back of a surefooted mule. In addition to the use of such poetic license, David makes doubly sure that no one will miss the point by providing the observer with a history lesson. Written on the rocks in the foreground are the names of the great former transalpine conquerors, Hannibal and Charlemagne, beside that of Bonaparte.

To commemorate his assumption of the imperial dignity, Napoleon in 1804 commissioned David, his court painter, to execute four grandiose pictures. Since the Empire was destined to last but a decade, David had time to complete only two of them: the *Coronation* or *Le Sacre* (Fig. 17:10) and the *Distribution of the Eagles,* those ancient standards of the Roman imperial legions that Napoleon had adopted as his own. Both were historical canvases in the grand tradition of Poussin and Lebrun, but in these paintings David extended that genre to include contemporary events.

Napoleon's coronation had taken place in the choir of the Cathedral of Notre Dame in Paris, where his decorators, Percier and Fontaine, had designed a special setting for the occasion. The ancient Gothic arches had been camouflaged with the imitation marble pilasters seen in the picture, between which were boxes and galleries for distinguished guests. David originally proposed to paint the moment after Pope Pius VII had blessed the crown and Napoleon had taken it from the altar to place it on his own head. But the Emperor preferred the more gallant pose when he put the crown on the brow of his kneeling empress. Aside from this bit of incidental activity, David's painting amounts to a stately group portrait on a grand scale. As a piece of official art, the placement and attitude of every personage had to be passed on by the master of protocol and ratified by Napoleon himself, even to the inclusion of his mother who happened not to have been present that day. David, however, had been present and had made sketches on the spot. But when he drew Pius VII with hands resting on his knees as the artist had actually observed him, David was told by Napoleon that the successor of St. Peter had not come so far to do nothing. Consequently, David had to revise his drawing to show the pope extending his arms in benediction.

In such circumstances, it is a minor miracle that David was able to get as much elasticity into the composition as he did. His achievement is all the more remarkable when one reflects how easily the whole thing could have become nothing more than a fancy-dress ball, with Napoleon as the middle-class messiah standing in the midst of the members of his family whom he had made kings, princes, cardinals, and so on. But David, by his masterly grouping, commanding postures, and handling of the wealth of detail, preserves the uncluttered spaciousness of the setting and the proportions of the whole. The scene also provided the painter of classical austerity with a chance to exploit the element of color, and David made rich but not lavish use of the medium. In all these ways the versatile David was able to adapt his art to Napoleon's dreams of imperial Roman grandeur.

The immense 20- by 30-foot canvas contains some 150 life-size portraits, and it took several years before each of these individuals had visited the church where David set up his studio to sit for his or her likeness. The assemblage is made up mostly of beplumed marshals of the imperial army, maids of honor to the empress,

Fig. 17:10. David. *Le Sacre* (*Coronation*). Oil on canvas. 20′ x 30′ 6½″. 1805–1808.
Louvre, Paris (Archives Photographiques)

court chamberlains, and members of the diplomatic corps. The United States
ambassador is included, but the English delegation is conspicuous by its absence. Napoleon's mother and other members of his family occupy the center box,
while in the gallery above is a group of artists and intellectuals, including the
composer Grétry. As a signature, David painted himself sitting and sketching,
accompanied by his wife and daughters, favorite pupils, and his teacher Vien.

The symbolism in *Le Sacre* deserves some comment because it underscores
Napoleon's problem of holding a coronation that would not evoke memories of
the hated aristocracy and yet have an aura of legitimacy, of striking a balance between the luxury and elegance of the old regime and the Spartan simplicity of the
revolutionary period. This he had managed to achieve in the form of government when, figuratively speaking, he set ahead the hands of the clock of history
to point to the hour of the prosperous Roman Empire instead of the austere
Roman republic, and it was this image that the pomp and circumstances of the
coronation must confirm. Past coronations had been designed primarily to impress other aristocrats, but Napoleon, as a popular ruler, was concerned with impressing the populace, and in the actual coronation and in David's painting, he
let them savor the taste of glory and quickened their pulses with a sense of
destiny. The crimson coronation robes of the emperor and empress are em-

Fig. 17:11. Goya. *Executions of May Third 1808*. Oil on canvas. 8′ 8″ x 11′ 4″. 1814–1815. Prado, Madrid

broidered all over with golden bees, Napoleon's chosen symbol for the integrated state in which all members had their appointed place and worked for the good of the hive in order to produce the honey of prosperity. Elsewhere in the painting, the sheaves of wheat and cornucopias are symbols of imperial plenty; palm branches and figures of victory symbolize triumph; and Napoleon's laurel-wreath crown is the ancient symbol of literary immortality. The papal coat of arms below the canopy at the left gives a touch of historical continuity so necessary to Napoleon's regime, but the throne that had stood under a triumphal arch festooned with curtains of imperial purple and facing the high altar was omitted from the painting. The supreme symbol on the actual occasion was Napoleon's act of crowning himself to signify the break with the past and his derivation of authority from the people by a plebiscite. By this dramatic touch, Bonaparte also proclaimed the existence of the free individual who recognized no authority superior to himself and the fact that his power was derived through his own efforts and those of the people and not from above. In the painting, this symbolism was transferred to Napoleon's act of crowning Josephine.

No presentation of this revival of the Roman Empire would be complete that showed only the histrionic attitudes of the conqueror. The sufferings of a subjugated people, which invariably follow in the wake of an invading army, find

Fig. 17:12. Ingres. *Apotheosis of Homer*. Oil on canvas. 12′ 8″ x 16′ 10¾″. 1827.
Louvre, Paris (Archives Photographiques)

vivid expression in the scenes painted by Goya after the French campaign in Spain
of 1808. One of these (Fig. 17:11), an execution scene which Goya finished some
years later, accents the obverse side of the Napoleonic coin. Goya saw nothing of
the heroic aspect of warfare, only the desolation of his country and its accompanying bloodshed and carnage. In this picture both the technique as well as the subject matter are quite the opposite of the correct and pompous presentations of
David.

After David, the leading arbiter of the art world was his pupil Ingres. Like his
teacher, Ingres realized the importance of championing the arts in official circles;
eventually he became a senator of France. The Academy had been re-established
after Napoleon's downfall, and the idea of placing the official stamp of approval
on writers and painters finds full expression in *The Apotheosis of Homer* (Fig.
17:12). Commissioned as a ceiling mural in the newly established Charles X
Museum in the Louvre, the painting is well adapted to its museum setting for it is
impressive in content as well as in its large proportions. Ingres treats his subject
as if it were some supreme session of an academy of arts and letters for the immortals. In their midst sits the enthroned Homer, the greatest of them all. Behind
him is the façade of an Ionic temple; winged victory holds the laurel wreath above
his brow; at his feet are the personifications of his brain children, the *Iliad* and the

Odyssey; and about him are his successors who have carried the torch for poetry and art throughout the ages. In this exclusive society, Aeschylus is seen unfolding a scroll listing his tragedies; the poet Pindar holds up his lyre in tribute; Vergil and Dante are present as epic poets; Longinus is standing up for philosophy, Boileau for criticism; at the lower right Racine and Molière, in the courtly wigs of the time of Louis XIV, make an offering of tragic and comic masks; and Raphael, the pro-filed figure on the upper left, represents the pictorial arts. Relegated to the extreme left and almost crowded out of the picture are Dante and Shakespeare, whose heritage of medievalism places them on the periphery of this pantheon of classical authors.

Ingres' source seems to have been a Hellenistic relief now in the British Museum showing a simplified version of the same subject with allegorical representations of the *Iliad* and *Odyssey* as well as personifications of Time and the muses of History, Poetry, Drama, and Mythology. Ingres' virtuosity in drawing is seen in the sharply delineated figures. Like his contemporaries, he accepted the Greek aesthetic of art as a representation of nature, with the reservation that it was the artist's function to endow nature with orderliness through the process of rear-rangement and editorial excision. In this case, he builds his composition by means of precise lines, which he then organizes into a series of receding planes. Color for him, as it was for David, was always secondary.

SCULPTURE

The sculptor Canova, who in his day enjoyed a reputation second to none, was summoned from Rome to Paris by Napoleon to execute statues of the emperor and his family. Through his neoclassical spectacles, the Italian artist saw Napoleon's mother as the matronly Agrippina of old, his sister Pauline—not without some justification—as Venus Victorious, and Napoleon himself, most obligingly, as a Roman emperor (Fig. 17:13). Canova was accompanied to Paris by his brother who recorded the conversations between artist and patron from which we learn that Napoleon had a few qualms about being portrayed, as the saying goes, in the "heroic altogether" and suggested an appropriate costume. To this Canova grandiosely replied: "We, like the poets, have our own language. If a poet intro-duced into a tragedy, phrases and idioms used habitually by the lower classes in the public streets, he would rightly be reprimanded by everybody. In like manner, we sculptors cannot clothe our statues in modern costumes without deserving a similar reproach." The sculptor's arguments prevailed, and, except for the sugges-tion of a toga draped over his shoulder, Napoleon stands there in all his bronze glory, holding in his right hand an orb surmounted by winged victory and in his left, a staff of authority in lieu of a scepter. The head is idealized but recognizable;

Fig. 17:13. Canova. *Napoleon*. Bronze. *c.*11′ 6″
high. 1808. Brera Palace, Milan (Alinari)

the body with the shifting of the weight toward one side points directly to
Praxitelean models as does the inevitable Hellenistic tree trunk.

The reclining statue of *Pauline Bonaparte as Venus* (Fig. 17:14) is another
instance of the use of a Hellenistic prototype, for Canova, like David, had come
under the sway of Winckelmann. While it is almost an exact sculptural counterpart of David's *Madame Recamier* (Fig. 17:8), the statue conveys much less of
the individuality of its subject than does the painting. Both Canova statues show
how much more a sculptor was restricted in his expression than a painter was dur-

Fig. 17:14. Canova. *Pauline Bonaparte as Venus*. Marble. Lifesize. 1808. Borghese Gallery, Rome (Soprintendenza)

ing this wave of classical enthusiasm, simply because of the wealth of antique material available for study. While practically nothing of ancient painting was known to David, museums filled with well-preserved ancient statues were open to Canova. While the one was free to create a new style, the other had to conform quite closely to existing models. Like a good academician, Canova advised his students on a "scrupulous adherence to rules" in order to guard against "arbitrary and capricious errors." Judicious deviation from the "rules" was possible, however, when it could be justified on rational grounds. In Canova's aesthetics, everything was defined by classical canons. Hence when he did a portrait of a contemporary figure, the body, its pose, and the drapery were taken directly from antique models, and the head was idealized just enough to fit the subject. In theory, Canova accepted the Greek idea of art as an imitation of nature, but in practice his art became an imitation of art. For his observations of human nature, he was content to look about the Vatican collections instead of going out on the highways and byways. Furthermore, his constant self-conscious striving to create objects of art too often led to artificial works. In the mind and hands of a greater artist, Canova's aesthetic might possibly have produced more significant results, but in his own case it had a definitely stultifying effect.

Because of the great demand for his work, Canova employed a large number of assistants in his studio. His large output, plus the use of some modern devices and methods that were unknown to Praxiteles, gave his workshop something of the aspect of a factory. Among other things, he used chemical solutions to achieve the extraordinary smoothness of his surface textures, and he employed a pointing machine to make exact copies of ancient sculptures. Despite murmurings from less successful sculptors, nothing in Canova's lifetime diminished his glittering reputation. The many young Americans who were attracted to Rome by his fame returned from their studies to do things like Horatio Greenough's colossal statue of George Washington as Zeus, which outgrew its intended setting in the Capitol and now stands in the Smithsonian Institution. The British Parliament invited him to London to pass on the value of the Parthenon sculptures before it purchased them from Lord Elgin. One would have thought that, after feeling the full force of these originals, Canova might have realized their superiority to his previous models. Instead, he smugly found in them the justification of his own life's work and seized the opportunity to point out how wrong his critics had been. He did show good judgment, however, in refusing to attempt a restoration and in some of his observations on the differences between the real Greek sculpture and the works designed for the Roman market.

MUSIC

"Among all the fine arts, music is the one which exercises the greatest influence upon the passions and is the one which the legislator should most encourage." So wrote Napoleon to the Inspector of the Conservatory soon after he became a Consul. Napoleon's interest in music, or in any of the arts for that matter, was always conditioned by its effect on the people at large and its function in the service of the state. His personal band, for instance, stood in readiness for a parade or a public celebration; and the popular side of the art, especially where military music was concerned, was never neglected. The welfare of composers, opera singers, and orchestra musicians was also a matter of much concern to all the post-revolutionary governments. Since the aristocrats had fled the country, patronage had now to come from another source. Napoleon, therefore, interested himself in the affairs of the Paris opera, insisting that all budgetary matters and commissions for new works be submitted to him even when he was away on his military campaigns. He regularly attended public performances whenever possible and took special pleasure in the popular demonstrations his appearances usually provoked. The beneficial effects of this interest, however, must be equated with a control over all aspects of each stage production that amounted to a strict form of state censorship.

Napoleon's attempts to win over the French artists and those of the conquered countries extended into the field of music. His personal preferences leaned rather strongly to the Italian vocal style, especially that of Paisiello, whose gentle lyricism was congenial to his taste. It was Paisiello who received the commission to compose the *Te Deum* for the national celebration of the condordat with the Vatican, and the appointment as first conductor of the Imperial Chapel Orchestra. Second in charge was the French composer Lesueur, who had written the music for the coronation ceremonies and a successful opera on Macpherson's *Ossian*, one of Napoleon's favorite books. The production that most closely caught the spirit of the new Empire, however, was Spontini's opera *La Vestale*. Appearing as it did in 1807 at the height of Napoleon's military successes, it had the necessary pomp and pageantry to whip public enthusiasm to a pitch of frenzy. It had the requisite Roman setting, and the spectacle of a vestal virgin's struggle between her desire for personal happiness and her vows of service to the state was sufficient to insure more than 100 performances in its first season in Paris. The libretto stressed the gaining of glory on the battlefield, and Spontini supplied the necessary triumphal marches. His music is full of the sounding brass and the trumpet's blare, singing in the grand style, and the declamation of massive choruses. One of his contemporaries wrote: "his *forte* was a hurricane, his *piano* a breath, his *sforzando* enough to wake the dead." It was none other than Berlioz who attributed to him the invention of the "colossal crescendo."

Unknown to Napoleon, however, the essence of the heroic ideal had been distilled in musical form in one of the countries he had conquered. Beethoven's *Third Symphony*, which the composer himself called the *Eroica*, or Heroic, was never heard by the man whose career had suggested it; nor was it played in Paris until 1828, a quarter of a century after it was composed. Yet a French writer of later times, Romain Rolland, could declare with the full weight of history on his side: "Here is an Austerlitz of music, the conquest of an empire. And Beethoven's has endured longer than Napoleon's." The inception of this mighty work apparently took place in 1798 when General Bernadotte, as an emissary of France, visited Vienna. The General was enough interested in music to have the French violinist Rodolphe Kreutzer in his suite, and Beethoven soon came to his attention. It is Bernadotte who is credited with the suggestion that Beethoven write a work honoring Consul Bonaparte, although he probably had in mind little more than a dedication. For four years Beethoven thought about the suggestion, and eventually the *Eroica* bore the desired dedication. But the year that the symphony was completed was the year in which Napoleon accepted the title of emperor. Beethoven, feeling that the erstwhile apostle of liberty had become both a traitor and a new tyrant, erased the name from the title page and inscribed it instead "to the memory of a great man." This memory indeed had stirred Beethoven deeply, and from the days of his youth he had been a lifelong partisan of the ideals of liberty, equality, and fraternity. It was Napoleon's espousal of these principles, his implacable opposition to hereditary privilege, his will and ability to translate these ideals into action, that had moved Beethoven profoundly as it had so many other artists and writers of the time. The symphony is not, and never was, narrowly Napoleonic, but more generally an elaboration of the heroism of one who, for a time at least, rallied the progressive and freedom-loving people of all nations around his standard.

The music Beethoven wrote for the theater was invariably based on themes involving the quest for individual liberty and the cause of popular freedom. His *Prometheus* ballet, for instance, was about two statues that were brought to life by the divine fire of knowledge and human creativity. The overtures and incidental music he wrote for plays had to do, in the case of Collin's *Coriolanus*, with an inner struggle for freedom, and in the case of Goethe's *Egmont* as well as Kotzebue's *Ruins of Athens* and *King Stephen*, with the liberation of an oppressed people. While he admired the music of Mozart's *Marriage of Figaro* and *Don Giovanni*, Beethoven was shocked by the immorality of the plots and some of the characters. In his only opera, he therefore insisted on a libretto that would reflect high moral purpose and steadfast resolve.

In his instrumental compositions, these self-same ideals of liberty, equality, and fraternity attained their most abstract and universal expression in his fluid forms. Beethoven used the power of his art to convey the spirit of these great human declarations, and, by so doing, he illuminated the path of man as he works toward his ultimate destiny of progress and perfectibility. His achievement was all the greater because he was able to do it without programmatic dilutions, thereby strengthening rather than weakening his art. Through the *Eroica*, Beethoven was giving tangible shape to the aspirations of a large segment of mankind during those stirring times. In it he mirrored the titanic struggle between the opposing attitudes of submission and assertion, between passivity and activity, and between acceptance and challenge. Through it he gave flesh to the word of the victory of spirit over matter, will over negation, and the victorious human drive against the forces of suppression. Though the length of the symphony is unprecedented and the orchestra somewhat expanded, Beethoven never fell into the trap that many of the French composers of the revolutionary period did when they equated colossal size with grandeur of utterance. While they wrote their choruses for 1000 voices, accompanied by cannons and three or four combined orchestras, Beethoven added just one horn to his brass section. He clothed his ideas in rich folds of lustrous sound that grow out of the poetic idea itself. Furthermore, by raising the level of musical content and making it commensurate with his instrumental forces, he succeeded in producing an organic work of art where the others failed. While the symphony as a whole can be criticized on formal grounds and for a certain lack of unity in the four separate movements, the fiery spirit of creation in which Beethoven is at the height of his mature powers has never been surpassed. It was as much a revolution in the musical field as the French Revolution was in that of political thought and action.

Each of the four movements is in its way precedent-shattering. The first is distinguished by its restless surging character and its expansion of the first-movement form to encompass a development section of 245 bars. The mobilization of such forces, as well as the transformation of the coda into a terminal development 140 measures in length, caused Romain Rolland to call it a "Grand Army of the soul, that will not stop until it has trampled on the whole earth." A cogent formal analysis of this opening movement by Tovey can be found in the *Encyclopædia Britannica*, 14th Edition, under "Sonata Forms." A Funeral March as the second movement of a symphony was another innovation, though Beethoven had included one in his earlier *Sonata for Piano* Op. 26 which bears the inscription "on the death of a hero." Its heroic proportions here, as well as its poetic conception as an apotheosis of the hero, link it with the first movement. While such an apotheosis is a fairly common idea for a painting, statue, poem, play, or opera, its incorporation into the more abstract symphonic form is unique. The effect is one of a glowing elegy for the heroic among mankind who give up life itself so that the ideals for which they fought may live. It is, in this case, a collective rather than an individualized expression, though it emphasizes that every great advance of mankind is accompanied by personal tragedy. The stately measured rhythms and muffled sonorities also reminded the listener of Beethoven's time that contemporary heroes, as well as such ancient ones as Socrates and Jesus, often suffered martyrdom at the hands of an uncomprehending society. The title Scherzo over the third movement also appears for the first time in a formal symphony, though again it had been used earlier in piano sonatas and chamber music. Beethoven again reveals himself a man of the revolutionary period by the substitution of this robust humor for the traditional minuet, but in such a grand design he hardly had any other alternative. Berlioz has referred to its energetic rhythms as a kind of play, "recalling that which the warriors of the *Iliad* celebrated round the tombs of their chiefs."

For his finale, Beethoven writes such a monumental set of variations that it becomes a veritable musical arch of triumph through which the image of a liberated humanity joyfully passes in review. To comprehend its full meaning, one needs to look both backward and forward to other landmarks in Beethoven's work. The theme itself is taken from the last dance of his ballet music for *Prometheus*. Its frequent appearance in his notebooks, and its existence in two other versions—a set of piano variations and a simple country dance—show that it figured prominently in his musical thought for several years. For him the theme had definite Promethean associations and a certain buoyant optimism. For Beethoven, as for Shelley, the figure of Prometheus represented "the type of the highest perfection of moral and intellectual nature impelled by the purest and truest motives to the best and noblest of ends." It was Prometheus who first defied the gods themselves in order to bring the divine fire of the arts and sciences from the Olympian hearth to animate the spirits of men and release them from the bondage of ignorance. Prometheus thus became a symbol of creative power through which Beethoven was able to convey his conviction of the ultimate perfectibility of mankind. The fiery and precipitous descent of the opening bars had also been heard in the ballet music in a more literal sense. Here it serves as a mighty preparation for the emergence of the skeleton theme.

Symphony No. 3. Finale: Allegro Molto (Bars 76–83)   Beethoven

What is heard at first is simply a structural outline derived from the bass of the Promethean dance, which defines a tonal center together with the upper and lower dominant limits of the tonality. This harmonic vacuum is gradually populated by the addition of a second, third, and fourth voice, while the rhythmic divisions are simultaneously quickened by similar subdivisions. Not until the 76th bar is the Promethean melody joined to its previously heard skeletal bass.

The form of the finale is a series of variations unequal in length and strongly contrasted in style. What had before been but a pleasant little dance tune now assumes the imposing shape of a triumphant melody, which Beethoven, by the piling up of his additive process, is able to build into the cumulative structure he needs for his victory finale. Here the great idea springs fully grown and fully armed from the brain of its creator. The heroic image is later continued in the finales of the *Fifth* and *Ninth Symphonies*, and the amplification in these later works contributes to a more profound understanding of the earlier *Eroica*.

All three finales envision the emergence of a strong and free human society, and all three start with quasi-popular themes. In the *Eroica*, it is a modest little country dance; in the *Fifth*, a simple marching tune; and in the *Ninth*, an unpretentious hymn. One and all, they are built up to epical proportions. By the use of an immense variety of styles, episodic deviations, a wide range of keys, and shifting orchestral color, they become collective rather than individual expressions. Instead of being restricted to one side of life, they embrace a cross section of musical levels and reach out to encompass the entire human panorama. Some variations are aristocratic in sound, while others are rough and ready. Compare, for instance, the elegant sonorities of bars 175–197 in the *Eroica* finale with the boisterous band music heard in bars 211–255. A similar open-air episode to that heard in bars 211–255 occurs in the finale of the *Ninth*, where the composer inserts a popular "Turkish" march, scored in a bizarre manner for bassoons, horns, trombones, cymbals, triangle, and drums. Further contrasts in the *Eroica* finale can be heard in the fugal episodes (bars 117–174, and 266–348), which employ sophisticated contrapuntal devices, such as the inversion of the skeleton theme (277–280) and the rather stolid German chorale (249–364) that begins at the point where the tempo is slackened to a Poco Andante. All this vast variety of forms—dances, songs, fugues, chorales—are arranged sequentially in the manner of a procession that eventually leads up to the rousing triumphant climax heard in bars 381 to 395. At this point, Beethoven throws in all his orchestral forces, including the brasses and drums, to bring about the image of ultimate achievement of the heroic idea. Afterward there remains only the quieter anticlimax (396–430), in which the whole awesome spectacle is contemplated retrospectively, and the whirlwind *presto* that terminates the movement.

THE ARCHEOLOGICAL IDEA AND REVIVALS OF THE PAST

The Napoleonic era was a paradoxical mixture of progressive and retrogressive tendencies. At the very time when the social aspirations of the revolutionary period were about to be realized in democratic forms, Europe was confronted with a militant revival of ancient Roman autocracy. The 18th-century individualism that had led to the struggle for freedom was now engulfed in a 19th-century regimentation disguised as a movement to maintain the social gains that had been made. Revolutionary ideals stood in direct contrast to Napoleonic actualities; the desire for freedom collided with the need for order; the rights of man conflicted with the might of man; and spiritual well-being was pitted against material considerations.

New scientific and technological advances competed for attention with revivals of ancient glories. Napoleon boasted of a new culture, yet he clothed it in a Roman toga. The architecture of La Madeleine's interior was modern by early 19th-century standards, but the exterior was a cold archeological study. Canova, in his portrait sculpture, matched the heads of his clients with bodies copied from antique statues. And painters, trying to express new ideas, ran head on into the strength of established academic tradition. Voltaire, in the previous century, had said that the voice of the people was the voice of God; and Mengs, in his *Thoughts on Beauty* (1765), had said that the beautiful was that which appealed to the majority. Now came David, with strong governmental support, to dictate to the majority what they should enjoy. At a time when emotionalism was rampant, David insisted on a rational system of rules for the pictorial arts. Such a cleavage between feeling and thinking, however, must be seen as a necessary reaction to the excessive passion of revolutionary times.

The 19th century was by no means unique in its revival of a bygone era, for every period in Western art since Greco-Roman days has revived classical ideas and motifs in one manner or another. From the 1000-year span of Greco-Roman civilization, many choices have been made by succeeding centuries. Dramas and operas have been set in Athens, in Sparta, the Alexandrian empire, the Roman republic, and the West and East Roman empires, and their characters have been lofty Olympian deities and rugged Roman heroes. Dramatists have chosen the Roman playwright Seneca as a model, as did Quinault and Racine in the baroque period, and the Athenians Aeschylus and Euripides, as did Shelley and Goethe. Architects in the 17th century, such as Bernini and Perrault, built then-modern palaces that they decorated with classical motifs, while the neoclassicists Vignon, Percier, and Fontaine constructed almost precise models of Greek and Roman temples. In forms of government, likewise, the range of choice has been from the democratic city-state and republic to the autocratic kingdom and empire. Aside from the shape and spirit a revival assumes, it is largely a matter of selectivity.

Each period tends to choose from the past those elements that harmonize with its specific ideals and aspirations. Florentine Renaissance humanists, in their reaction to medieval scholastic thought and the traditional church interpretation of Aristotle, turned to the pagan beauties of antiquity in general and to the philosophy of Plato in particular. The Renaissance revival of classicism, however, was confined to a few intellectuals and artists and was of short duration. Neoclassicism, however, was mirrored in forms of government, became the officially approved art style, and rested on a base of broad popular acceptance. Baroque classical interests reflected an aristocratic image of man and were restricted to courtly circles. Louis XIV and his associates identified themselves with the gods of Mt. Olympus, and their moral standards, like those of the ancient deities, were the ethics of a highly privileged class. Napoleonic neoclassicism, by contrast, was oriented toward the comfortable middle-class, which saw a congenial hedonistic image in the living standards of ancient Pompeii and Herculaneum but tempered luxury with the stricter moral standards of a revolutionary regime. The new interest in classical architecture, sculpture, and painting was also a bourgeois criticism of the artificiality and extravagance of courtly life as mirrored in the 18th-century rococo. Otherwise the choice of conservative classical art forms would have been extremely odd for the revolutionary period.

The principal difference between early 19th-century artists and their predecessors was the former's desire for faithfulness to antique models. Archeological correctness was now possible owing to a more detailed knowledge of the past. Winckelmann and his generation had made classical archeology a science, and the excavations at Pompeii and Herculaneum had provided the material and stimulus for authenticity. For neoclassical success, a building had to be archeologically accurate. The Vendôme Column was planned as a replica of Trajan's Column and the Arc du Carrousel preserved the proportions of the Arch of Septimus Severus, even if reduced somewhat in size. When variations were made, as in the case of the Arc de Triomphe de l'Étoile and La Madeleine, the results were more interesting than slavish copies. The first two resemble a pair of competent academic theses, while the latter pair approximate the livelier style of good historical novels. Archeological correctness meant lifting an ancient building, which had been designed for an antiquated purpose, out of its context, period, and century and putting it down bodily into another period where it had no practical reason for being. This transposition would never have occurred to the rational Enlightenment period. While Palladio, Mansart, and Wren had been concerned with adapting classical principles to the needs of their times, Vignon, Percier, and Fontaine were busy trying to fit activities of the Napoleonic period into ancient molds. The use of a Roman portico over a baroque period doorway was one thing; Napoleon's invention of a cult of glory as an excuse to build a Roman temple was quite another. If such antiquarianism were carried to its logical conclusion and architecture were to become the handmaid of archeology, a city eventually would be turned into a museum. While people occasionally visit museums, they do not necessarily want to live in one—and, fortunately, the Napoleonic period was not that logical.

Likewise, in the neoclassical style, a successful statue had to be accurate. And since such a profusion of antique models existed, the sculptors were limited in their creative freedom. Their desire for exactitude often led them to the point of absurdity. They omitted carving the irises and pupils of the eyes and left them blank, because they did not know that the Greeks had painted in such details. The prevailing whiteness made their works resemble mortuary monuments, since they had overlooked the fact that the ancients had designed their friezes for the strong light and shadow of the open air and not for the dim interiors of museums. While Praxiteles and Michelangelo had turned marble into flesh, Canova and Thorwaldsen converted the living flesh of their models into cold stone.

Enthusiasm for antiquity sometimes led David into similar predicaments. For the heads of figures in his early pictures he used ancient Roman portrait busts instead of live models. In the baroque period, when Poussin and Claude Lorrain painted Rome, they did so usually in terms of picturesque ruins, but David and Ingres painted archeological reconstructions. Madame Recamier was a 19th-century Parisian socialite, but David made her into a fancy-dress reincarnation of a Pompeiian matron. The *Battle of the Romans and Sabines* was inspired by the reproduction of an ancient relief David had come across as an illustration in a book. In this instance, while he did use living models, he said that his desire was to paint the ancient walls and drape his figures with such exactness that if an ancient Roman were to come to life, he would find himself right at home. David's adherence to lines and planes was often so strict that the effect of his paintings was almost as severe as that of relief sculpture. From his preoccupation with the pallid world of museums and Winckelmann's books, David, like Canova, also gained the impression that the Greeks and Romans had lived in a gray-and-white world. As a result, he neglected the element of color. David was saved, however, from the major pitfalls of his architectural and sculptural colleagues because so few examples of ancient painting were known at the time; and, as a consequence, he was forced to divert his considerable talent as a painter in the direction of a new style.

In poetry, a similar motivation can be found in the reforms of André Chénier, which were based on his studies of the Latin and Greek originals. For the forms of his odes and elegies, his pastoral idylls and epics, he drew directly on Homer, Pindar, Vergil, and Horace. "Let us upon new thoughts write antique verses," he had declared; and to a considerable degree his enthusiasm helped him to carry out his announced objective.

In this archeological era, however, the musicians fared the best of all because they had no examples surviving from antiquity to emulate. An opera, to be sure, could get some authenticity into its plot, decor, and costumes; and such productions of 1807 as Persuis' and Lesueur's *Triomphe de Trajan*, their *L'Inauguration du Temple de la Victoire*, and Spontini's *La Vestale* tried to make the grade in this respect. All this, however, was on the surface and could hardly be compared with the type of authenticity represented by the Vendôme Column or the Napoleonic arches of triumph. Since the musicians had to evolve their own style, the music of the period has overshadowed the other contemporary arts and its vitality has given it a lasting general appeal. Just as the fussy rococo had brought about a countermovement in the pre-revolutionary neoclassicism, so a reform in music had been carried out in the 18th century under Gluck. By reducing the number of characters in his operas, omitting complicated subplots, strengthening the role of the chorus, transferring much of the lyrical expression to the orchestra, writing simple unadorned melodies, and avoiding Italianate coloratura cadenzas, he had brought about a musical revolution similar to David's in painting and paved the way for a new style. His ideas were based partially on a reinterpretation of Aristotle's *Poetics,* and in his Preface to *Alceste* (1767) he had stated that his music was designed to allow the drama to proceed "without interrupting the action or stifling it with a useless superfluity of ornaments." Echoing Winckelmann, he added that the great principles of beauty were "simplicity, truth and naturalness."

These principles found their ultimate expression in the sinewy music of Beethoven, who, by impatiently brushing aside ancient precedents, achieved an expressive style that was genuinely heroic and not merely histrionic. Of all the artists of the neoclassical persuasion, Beethoven emerges as the most truly representative, and for this reason, his art was and remains the outstanding expressive accomplishment of his time. People can point to the fact that his idealism had classical overtones; or that his devotion to the cause of freedom echoed the creative genius of ancient Greece; that the dithyrambic finale of the *Eroica* breathes a Promethean spirit; that the elegiac quality of the Funeral March is akin to the Greek tragic form; that by thus paying tribute to past glory, he associates himself with the revival idea; that by raising the image of Napoleon to an archetype of heroism, he is in harmony with Greek aesthetics; and that the clarity of his forms, the economy of his means, and the simplification of his materials are akin to classical methods. If all this is so, it is true only in the general sense in which Shelley spoke in his Preface to *Hellas:* "We are all Greeks. Our laws, our literature, our religion, our arts, have their roots in Greece."

Neoclassicism was the earliest of the 19th-century revivals of the past, and soon the passion for exactitude divided it into separate Greek and Roman revival movements. Through historical novels and romantic imaginations, interest in medieval times was awakened; and as medieval scholars extended their studies, a breakdown into Gothic, Romanesque, and Byzantine revivals occurred as artists delved ever deeper into the Middle Ages. The romantic affinity for medievalism was then expanded into admiration for the Renaissance and baroque styles. The library of St. Geneviève (Fig. 19:15) in Paris and the Boston public library, in their exteriors at least, were revivals of Renaissance architecture, and—shades of the French Revolution—the Paris opera house, begun in 1861, revived Louis XIV's Versailles. Wagner composed the opera *Rienzi* after a novel by Bulwer-Lytton about a ruler of the Roman Renaissance, and Mendelssohn discovered the greatness of Bach's baroque oratorios and in 1829 performed the St. *Matthew Passion* for the first time since the composer's death.

In retrospect, the 19th-century antithesis of classic and romantic has been resolved as both are seen as component parts of the same broader revival idea. The artists who lived on into the post-Napoleonic period drew their inspiration from

Fig. 17:15. Thorwaldsen. *Villa Carlotta*, Salon. *c.*1829–1831. Cadenabbia, Lake Como (Brunner)

Greco-Roman or medieval times with equal facility. John Nash, for instance, built himself a neoclassical town house in London and a romantic Gothic castle in the country; Rude made statues of Roman nymphs and of Joan of Arc; Ingres painted the *Apotheosis of Homer* and later a picture of the Maid of Orleans; Keats wrote "Ode on a Grecian Urn" and also "St. Agnes' Eve"; Victor Hugo included neoclassical odes in the same volume with his medieval ballads. Berlioz admired Vergil quite as intensely as he did Dante and wrote the *Trojans at Carthage*, an opera based on the *Aeneid*, as well as his *Requiem*, based on the medieval hymn *Dies Irae*. After neoclassicism and romanticism had run their courses, the revival idea led, in the later 19th century, to a broad eclecticism, whereby a virtuoso architect could build in any past style, a painter could do a portrait or historical canvas à la Titian or Rubens, a poet could employ any form or metrical organization with facility, and a composer could pull out at will a Renaissance or baroque stop on his organ.

CHRONOLOGY:
Paris, Mid-19th Century

General Events

1814	Fall of Napoleon
	Restoration of the monarchy under Louis XVIII
1821	Napoleon died
1824	Louis XVIII succeeded by Charles X
1830	July Revolution overthrew old line of Bourbons
	Louis Philippe began reign as limited monarch
1837	Commission for the Preservation of Historical Monuments founded by Louis Philippe
1840	Guizot (1787–1874), French historian and statesman, became prime minister
1848	February Revolution overthrew Louis Philippe's government
	Second Republic proclaimed
	Louis Napoleon, nephew of Napoleon I, elected president
1852	Louis Napoleon elected emperor; reigned as Napoleon III
1870	Napoleon III abdicated after unsuccessful conclusion of Franco-Prussian War
	Third Republic proclaimed

Architects

1748–1813	James Wyatt
1752–1835	John Nash
1790–1853	François Christian Gau
1795–1860	Charles Barry
1802–1878	Richard Upjohn
1814–1879	Viollet-le-Duc
1817–1885	Théodore Ballu
1818–1895	James Renwick
1824–1881	George Street

Sculptors

1784–1855	François Rude
1787–1843	Jean Pierre Cortot
1796–1875	Antoine Louis Barye

Painters

1755–1851	Turner
1776–1837	John Constable
1780–1867	Jean Auguste Ingres
1791–1824	Théodore Géricault
1796–1875	Camille Corot
1798–1863	Eugène Delacroix
1808–1879	Honoré Daumier
1814–1875	François Millet

Writers

1717–1797	Horace Walpole
1749–1832	Johann Wolfgang Goethe
1766–1817	Germaine de Staël
1768–1848	Chateaubriand
1771–1832	Walter Scott
1774–1843	Robert Southey
1783–1842	Stendhal
1787–1874	François Guizot
1788–1824	Lord Byron
1788–1860	Arthur Schopenhauer
1792–1822	Percy B. Shelley
1795–1821	John Keats
1797–1856	Heinrich Heine
1799–1850	Honoré Balzac
1802–1870	Alexandre Dumas
1802–1885	Victor Hugo
1803–1870	Prosper Mérimée
1804–1876	George Sand
1811–1872	Théophile Gautier

Musicians

1782–1871	Daniel Auber
1782–1840	Niccolo Paganini
1786–1826	Carl Maria von Weber
1791–1864	Giacomo Meyerbeer
1803–1869	Hector Berlioz
1809–1849	Frederic Chopin
1809–1847	Felix Mendelssohn
1810–1856	Robert Schumann
1811–1886	Franz Liszt
1813–1901	Giuseppe Verdi
1813–1883	Richard Wagner
1818–1893	Charles Gounod
1833–1897	Johannes Brahms
1838–1875	Georges Bizet

18

THE ROMANTIC STYLE

PARIS, 1830

Well before the romantic Revolution of July 1830, new ideas were stirring the minds and imaginations of the intellectuals and artists of Paris. In 1827, as the new movement was gaining momentum, Victor Hugo published his *Cromwell*, a drama with a preface that served as a manifesto of romanticism. Guizot was lecturing at the Sorbonne on the early history of France. François Rude, destined to be the principal sculptor of the period, returned from his Belgian exile. And Delacroix, the painter, wrote in his journal that when he went to the Odéon Theater to see Shakespeare's *Hamlet*, he met the writers Alexandre Dumas and Victor Hugo. The Ophelia in that production was Harriet Smithson, later to become the wife of Hector Berlioz. Gérard de Nerval's translation of Goethe appeared that autumn and inspired the composition of Berlioz' *Eight Scenes from Faust*, later to reach popularity in the revision called the *Damnation of Faust*. Delacroix, who had just exhibited his *Death of Sardanapalus* in the Salon, was already at work on his famous *Faust* lithographs to illustrate an edition of Goethe's drama, which was published in 1828. All in all, the 1820's were an inspiring time, and when Théophile Gautier later came to write his history of romanticism, he looked back on his youthful years with nostalgia. "What a marvelous time," he wrote, "Walter Scott was then in the flower of his success; one was initiated into the mysteries of Goethe's *Faust*, which as Madame de Staël said, contained everything. One dis-

633

covered Shakespeare, and the poems of Lord Byron: the *Corsair*; *Lara*; *The Gaiour*; *Manfred*; *Beppo*; and *Don Juan* took us to the orient, which was not banal then as now. All was young, new, exotically colored, intoxicating, and strongly flavored. It turned our heads; it was as if we had entered into a strange new world." Romanticism was swept in on a wave of political unrest culminating in the July Revolution of 1830, and it was destined to remain the dominant French style until the February Revolution of 1848.

Nowhere is there a better example of the mating of an artistic genius with the spirit of his time than Eugène Delacroix with the events in the Paris of 1830. His *Liberty Leading the People* (Fig. 18:1) brought those glorious July days to incandescent expression. The canvas, in which he distilled the essence of that revolution, is dominated by the fiery allegorical figure of Liberty, here seen as the spirit of the French people whom she leads onward to triumph. No relaxed Mediterranean goddess but a virile, energetic reincarnation of the spirit of 1789, her muscular arms are strong enough to hold with ease both a bayoneted rifle and the tricolored banner of the Republic. Though bare-breasted she betrays no sign of softness or sensuality, and her powerful limbs stride over the street barricades as she leads her followers forward through the oncoming barrage. Though an allegorical figure, she is treated by Delacroix as a living personality, clothed in the garments of a daughter of the French people. Only the Phrygian cap and the almost-classic profile, serene in the face of danger, indicate her symbolic significance. She does not hover over the action on wings as so many other artists depicted her; instead, with her feet on the ground, she is in the midst of action. Her motley followers include both impetuous students and battle-scarred soldiers who have heeded her call rather than that of their reactionary king. The boy on the right is recruited from the Paris streets. Too young to understand the significance of the events, he is there, a pistol in each hand, joining in the general excitement. In the background are the remnants of the old guard from revolutionary days still carrying on the struggle. Two main social classes are represented—in the shadows on the extreme left, the man armed with a saber is an obviously proletarian figure, while in front of him toward the center the more prominent figure in the modish frock coat, top hat, and sideburns is a bourgeois gentleman who has grabbed his musket and joined in the general confusion. It was his class that controlled the fighting and derived the benefits from it by stamping its image on the new monarchy represented in the person of Louis Philippe, the Citizen King. Though the July Revolution was essentially a palace revolt replacing a reactionary Bourbon with his more liberal cousin, no aristocrats are represented as taking part. In the shadow below, the wounded and dying are strewn on the loose cobblestones looking toward Liberty, for she is both their inspiration and their reason for being. Through smoke at the right the towers of the Cathedral of Notre Dame are discernible.

Fig. 18:1. Delacroix. *Liberty Leading the People*, 1830. Oil on canvas. 8′ 6″ x 10′ 10″. Louvre, Paris (Archives Photographiques)

Because of the contemporary frame of reference in which one recognizes the familiar shirts, blouses, trousers, rifles, pistols, and other 19th-century paraphernalia, the picture sometimes has been called realistic. But, since the spirit of the work transcends the event itself, and since the artist has rendered feeling rather than actuality, the picture surely is in the romantic style. By infusing reality with the charge of an electric emotional attitude, Delacroix raises his picture to the level of an idealized though highly personal expression, so that all who see it seem to be experiencing the event for themselves. More eloquent than any page in a history book, the canvas has captured the feeling as well as the facts that make up the incident. It is as if all the noise had awakened the artist from his dreams of the past, and now suddenly wide awake, he has applied his expressive techniques consciously to one of the stirring happenings of his own time.

As always with Delacroix, color plays an important part in the communication of mood. Here, a striking instance of the use of color is seen in the way he takes the red, white, and blue of the banner (the symbol of patriotism) and merges them into the picture as a whole. The white central strip, signifying truth and purity, blends with the purifying smoke of battle; the blue, denoting freedom, matches the parts of the sky visible in the top corners through the smoke; while the red in the flag high above balances the color of the blood of those below who have fallen for the ideal of liberty. Thus the symbolism of the banner blends into the color scheme and both combine with the dramatic lighting to define the emotional range. All these, in turn, expand the patriotic theme into a formal pictorial unity of concentrated intensity. With the purchase of this picture in the name of the state by the new bourgeois king himself at the time it was shown in the Salon of 1831, the seal of official approval was stamped on the romantic style.

PAINTING

It was characteristic of romantic painting that Delacroix, its leading representative, should look to the fantasy of the literary world for the sources of his pictorial visions rather than to the world of appearances. His choice of subjects as well as his treatment of them makes this immediately apparent. The *Death of Sardanapalus, Mazeppa, Giaour and the Pasha,* and the *Shipwreck of Don Juan* all point to their inception in the poetry of Byron. His interest in Shakespeare is shown in his drawings of scenes from *Hamlet* and the witches' scene from *Macbeth* (Fig. 18:2). His *Abduction of Rebecca* steps directly out of Chapter 31 of Scott's *Ivanhoe,* and his illustrations for Goethe's *Faust* (Figs. 18:3–6) won the complete admiration of the author himself, who felt that for clarity and depth of insight they could not be surpassed. Delacroix' imagination had been haunted by this drama since he first saw it in London, and, in a letter to a friend in Paris, he had commented particularly on its diabolical aspect. The lithographs that eventually re-

Fig. 18:2. Delacroix. Illustration for *Macbeth*, Act IV, Scene I. *Witches' Scene.* Lithograph

Delacroix. Illustrations for Goethe's *Faust*, Part I, lines 1709–19 and 2078–89. Fig. 18:3 (*left*). *Mephistopheles in the Air*. Fig. 18:4 (*right*). *Witches' Kitchen* Lithographs. 1828. Metropolitan Museum of Art, New York.

sulted show his mastery of illustration and prove Delacroix as adept in works of small dimensions as in epical pictures. In spite of his close kinship with Byron and Goethe, Delacroix was not always in sympathy with the work of his romantic Parisian contemporaries. In his diary he spoke of Meyerbeer's opera *Le Prophète* as "frightful" and referred to Berlioz and Hugo as those "so-called reformers." "The noise he makes is distracting," he wrote about Berlioz' music, "it is an heroic mess." Of all musicians he admired Mozart the most, and among his contemporaries only Chopin had the requisite polish and craftsmanship to measure up to his standards.

Delacroix. Illustrations for Goethe's *Faust*, Part I, lines 3449–82; 4095–4124. Fig. 18:5 (*left*). *Margaret in Church*. Fig. 18:6 (*right*). *Faust and Mephistopheles Galloping*. Lithographs. 1828. Metropolitan Museum of Art, New York

Fig. 18:7. Delacroix. *Dante and Vergil in Hell*. Oil on canvas. 73½″ x 94½″. 1822. Louvre, Paris (Archives Photographiques)

The technique of Delacroix' art was designed as a means of conveying a highly emotional and turbulent subject matter. For him, color was dominant over design, and as he declared, "gray is the enemy of all painting . . . let us banish from our palette all earth colors . . . the greater the opposition in color, the greater the brilliance." His admitted models in painting were the heroic canvases of Rubens and the dramatic pictures of Rembrandt with their emphasis on the dynamics of light, and among his contemporaries he admired the mellow landscapes and subtle coloring of Constable. His own art was built on an aesthetic of color, light, and emotion rather than on line, drawing, and form. This is nowhere better illustrated than in his early masterpiece, *Dante and Vergil in Hell* (Fig. 18:7), the first of his pictures to attract wide attention when it was exhibited in the Salon of 1822.

Stemming from the predilection for the medieval and macabre, the interest in Dante was one of the main facets of the romantic style. What Homer had been to neoclassicism, the Tuscan poet was to romanticism. Shelley and the Pre-Raphaelites were making England Dante-conscious; and while Schlegel and Schelling were translating and interpreting him for the Germans, Chateaubriand and Sainte-Beuve were doing the same for the French. To realize the extent of the *Divine Comedy's* influence, one needs only to recall such works as Hugo's poem *Après une lecture de Dante* (*After Reading Dante*), which Franz Liszt used as a programme for a piano fantasy of that name and for his *Dante Symphony*.

In his picture, Delacroix enters the realm of pure pathos. The central figure is that of Vergil in the crimson robe of a Florentine crowned with the laurel wreath, standing with impassive monumentality as a symbol of classic calm. On his left is Dante with a red hood on his head, expressively human in contrast to the serenity of his immortal companion and emotionally involved with his grotesque and gruesome surroundings. He looks with terror on the damned who swirl about him in the water below. The wake of the boat is livid with the writhing forms of the condemned, who hope eternally to reach the opposite shore by trying to attach themselves to the bark. One attempts to clamber aboard, the gnashing teeth of another bites into the edge of the boat, but in vain as they are plunged again into the dark waters. Distress and despair are everywhere. On the right is Phlegyas, the sepulchral boatman, seen from the rear as he strains at the rudder to guide the boat across the river Styx to the flaming shores of the city of Dis, visible in the distant background between the clouds of sulfurous fumes. The lurid coloration serves to create the illusion that the picture has been painted in blood, phosphorus, and flame.

When Delacroix was at work on it, he had a young friend read Dante's *Divine Comedy* to him and, as he says in his journal: "The best head in my Dante picture was swept in with the greatest speed and spirit while Pierret was reading me a canto from Dante which I knew already but to which he lent, by his accent, an energy that electrified me. That head is the one of the man behind the boat, facing you and trying to climb aboard, after throwing his arm over the gunwale." The particular passage that inflamed the artist's imagination and on which he built the picture is from the eighth book of the Inferno.

When first exhibited, the picture brought down storms of protest and vituperation on Delacroix' head, which helped immeasurably to bring the young artist to critical attention. One defender of David's academic tradition called it a "splattering of color," and another thought he had "combined all the parts of the work in view of one emotion." While its expressive intensity was novel then, the work now easily falls into place as part of the macabre aspect of the romantic style. Even the nude figures, as muscular as those of Michelangelo and Rubens, function here more as color masses than as three-dimensionally modeled forms. As Delacroix once declared, color *is* painting, and his development of a color palette capable of eliciting specific emotional reactions from his viewers was destined to have a far-reaching effect on impressionistic and postimpressionistic painting.

Fig. 18:8. Cortot. *Apotheosis of Napoleon*. 42′ high. 1838. Left relief on the Arc de Triomphe, Paris (Archives Photographiques)

SCULPTURE

One of the dominating sculptural works of the romantic style is the *Departure of the Volunteers* (Fig. 18:9) by François Rude. It achieved its stature by its vehement expression and sustained heroic mood, and by its prominent location on one side of the Arc de Triomphe in Paris that assured it the largest possible audience. Sculptured in the boldest high relief, the dimensions of the composition alone—rising to a height of almost 42 feet and spreading laterally 26 feet—make it of truly colossal proportions. Its conception and commission date from the wave of patriotic emotion associated with the revolution of July 1830 and the memories that stirred of earlier struggles for freedom. It took Delacroix but a year to get his painting of Liberty before the public, but a sculptural work of these proportions took Rude six years to execute. The scene depicted is that of a band of volunteers rallying to the defense of the newly established French Republic when it was threatened by foreign invasion in 1792. The five resolute figures in the foreground are coming together to meet the common danger and are receiving common inspiration from the figure of Bellona, the Roman goddess of war, who hovers over them, inciting them onward with the singing of *La Marseillaise*. A fine rhythmical mood is established by the compact grouping of the figures, reinforced by the repeated motif of the legs that combine in a neat marchlike manner with the arms

Fig. 18:9. Rude. *Departure of Volunteers of 1792, "La Marseillaise."* c.42′ x 26′. 1836. Right relief on the Arc de Triomphe, Paris (Archives Photographiques)

of the soldier stooping to tie his sandal. This rhythm serves to weld the composition together as a whole in the manner of a lively yet majestic march. These representatives of the humanity so recently liberated by the French Revolution are self-motivated protectors of their newly won liberty, equality, and fraternity. The full manhood of four of the volunteers is balanced by the potential strength of the finely realized nude figure of the impetuous youth and the waning ability of the old man behind him who can only point out the direction to the others and wave them on. The surging power, directed by the common ideals, impels the volunteers onward with irresistible force and momentum.

Because Rude designed the *Departure* for a Napoleonic arch of triumph, his motifs are of Roman derivation. The soldiers are outfitted with Roman helmets and shields, though the coats of mail and weapons in the background recall those of the medieval period. The avoidance in the costumes and symbols of any contemporary reference in this representation of an event that had taken place less than a half-century before links the composition with the tendency to draw on the past for inspiration. Popularly, and quite properly, called the "*Marseillaise* in stone," it represents a most ingenious sculptural use of a musical motif in suggesting the great revolutionary song, which serves here both in unifying the spirit of the group and in reinforcing the patriotic symbolism. The anthem was composed by Rouget de Lisle, a young lieutenant in the revolutionary army, was practically

Fig. 18:10. Rude. Detail of *Departure of Volunteers of 1792, "La Marseillaise,"* 1836. Arc de Triomphe, Paris (Archives Photographiques)

forgotten during the days of Napoleon's empire, and under the Bourbon restoration was, of course, officially banned. Credit for its rediscovery and revival goes to Hector Berlioz. Stirred to patriotic frenzy by the events of July 1830, though avoiding direct participation, this erratic genius contented himself with scoring the song for double chorus and orchestra, characteristically asking "all who have voices, a heart, and blood in their veins" to join in. The final stanza begins dramatically with three unaccompanied voices; then, as Berlioz gradually marshals his vocal and orchestral forces, a big crescendo leads up to the refrain: "To arms, O citizens." This version received many performances, the most notable being a large benefit with the proceeds going to the families of the victims of the July Revolution. Later, the song was officially adopted as the French national anthem, though not with Berlioz' orchestration, and has become one of the world's best-known tunes.

Rude's treatment of the subject, the momentum of his composition, and the impassioned facial expressions, especially of the Goddess of War (Fig. 18:10), make the *Departure* an odd contrast to its companion piece, Cortot's *Apotheosis of Napoleon* (Fig. 18:8), executed at the same time. Rude had made a complete design for the decoration of the arch, but he was commissioned to do only the *Departure of the Volunteers*. Public taste and official circles still leaned toward neoclassicism, and Cortot's group shows a typical academic approach. While the neoclassical style continued throughout the century, the vitality it had shown during Napoleon's heroic days was now definitely waning. With Rude, all is passion and movement, and his composition seems almost to burst its bonds in its dynamic forward tendency. With Cortot, all is balanced and rigidly poised in a static equilibrium centering on the standing figure of Napoleon. Clothed in the toga of

Fig. 18:11. Rude. *Joan of Arc Listening to the Voices*. Marble. Lifesize, 1845. Louvre, Paris (Archives Photographiques)

a Roman emperor, Bonaparte is being crowned by a seminude personification of the spirit of France, looking as if she were the Venus de Milo, with arms happily restored for the occasion, who had just walked over from the Louvre Museum. Other allegorical figures, including one representing History, make up the rest of the group. The best that can be said about it is that it has a certain stateliness and avoids the pitfall of pomposity. These two examples standing opposite each other on the same monument do show, however, the difference between the neoclassical and romantic styles, as well as the continuation of the rather stilted academic tradition and the assertion of the vigorous new romantic treatment with its movement, action, and emotion.

In a later work, *Joan of Arc Listening to the Voices* (Fig. 18:11), Rude combines emotionalism and medieval subject matter. Executed originally in 1845 for the gardens of the Luxembourg Palace, it later found its way into the Louvre. Rude represents the maid of Orleans in peasant costume with a suit of armor at her side, thus indicating both her rural origin and her heroic mission. The mystic element is suggested as she lifts her hand to her ear in order to hear the angelic voices that guide her. By trying to capture the intangible sounds of these heavenly voices as Joan listens quiveringly with upraised head, Rude strains his marble medium to its expressive limits.

Rude, who had grown up in revolutionary times, was always thoroughly in sympathy with the liberal spirit. He accepted exile in Belgium in 1815 rather than live under a Bourbon ruler. Action was his aesthetic watchword. "The great thing for an artist," he once said, "is to *do*." Some critics find his *Departure of the Volunteers* overcrowded, overloaded, and unbalanced. Others feel that this is justified by the subject of a concerted uprising of the masses and that unity is achieved by the direction of its movement. Clearly it shows no will toward classical repose, and its sheer energy makes a clean break with academic tradition. By thus liberating sculpture from many outworn idioms and clichés, Rude revealed himself as a true romanticist.

ARCHITECTURE

Romantic architecture received its initial impetus from the popularity in the late 18th century of the so-called "Gothic" novels. Romances and plays of this type published in England were variously entitled: *The Haunted Priory; The Horrid Mysteries; Banditti*, or *Love in a Labyrinth; Raymond and Agnes*, or *The Bleeding Nun of Lindenberg*, and Horace Walpole's famous *Castle of Otranto* was subtitled *A Gothic Tale*. The settings for these stories were large baronial halls or decayed abbeys, liberally equipped with mysterious trapdoors, sliding panels, creaking postern gates, animated suits of armor, and sepulchral voices emanating from ancient tombs. Such scenes served as backdrops for the injured innocence of fragile and helpless heroines and the intrepid, if somewhat reckless, courage of dashing heroes. These tales played their part in the redefinition of the word *Gothic*—which Voltaire had called a fantastic compound of rudeness and filigree—into something more redolent of the mystical, tinged with weirdness and bordering on the fantastic. These imaginary castles of the novels first took on concrete form in England as the architectural whims of wealthy eccentrics. Walpole, the well-to-do son of a powerful prime minister, had indulged his fancy in a residence that gave its name to one aspect of this style, "Strawberry Hill Gothick." Another wealthy individual, William Beckford, had the architect James Wyatt construct him a residence he called Fonthill Abbey (Fig. 18:12). Its huge central tower rose over a spacious interior hall that was approached by a massive staircase (Fig. 18:13). The rest of the interior was a labyrinth of long drafty corridors that provided the wall space for the proprietor's collections of pictures and tapestries as well as a suitable setting for his melancholy musings. In his frenzy to have it completed, Beckford drove the workers day and night to the point where, in their haste, they neglected to provide an adequate foundation for the tower; and shortly after its completion, the tower of Beckford's dreamcastle fell to the ground. Since ruins were greatly in demand as residences at the time, this catastrophe served only to enhance the abbey's picturesqueness and make it all the more desirable.

Wyatt. Fonthill Abbey. 1796–1814. Wiltshire, England (No longer standing)

Fig. 18:12 (*above*). *Exterior.* Tower 260′ high

Fig. 18:13 (*right*). *Interior.* c.245′ long, 35′ wide

Fig. 18:14. Barry. Houses of Parliament. 940′ long. 1839–1860. London

The Gothic-revival movement in literature and architecture steadily gained momentum, and Jane Austen's *Northanger Abbey*, a delicious satire on the movement, was published just as Sir Walter Scott's historical novels were bringing their author such huge acclaim. Scott's novels were translated into French beginning about 1816, and they, in turn, paved the way for the popular romances of Hugo and Dumas. Among the surviving English architectural expressions of this literary phase are the Houses of Parliament (Fig. 18:14), begun by Sir Charles Barry in 1839, and the New Law Courts by Street, both of which are familiar landmarks in the London of today. In Germany, as early as 1772, the young poet Goethe, under the guidance of his university mentor Gottfried Herder, was writing in praise of the builder of the Strasbourg cathedral, Erwin von Steinbach. The book significantly was entitled *Von Deutscher Baukunst (On German Architecture)*. Later, Goethe placed his drama on the medieval Faust legend in a Gothic setting. In the 19th century, German literary interest in neomedievalism became the background for Richard Wagner's operas *Tannhäuser, Lohengrin,* and *Parsifal.* Wagner's most enthusiastic patron was King Ludwig II of Bavaria, who helped the composer build his opera house at Bayreuth. To stimulate his own Gothic fancies, the king built Castle Neuschwanstein (Fig. 18:15) amid picturesque alpine scenery. Medieval revival architecture is also found on the American scene. In New York the Gothic spires of Trinity Church, designed by Upjohn, rise among lower Broadway's skyscrapers. Two churches by Renwick furnish further examples—Grace Church in the Bowery (1845), and St. Patrick's Cathedral, begun in 1850. Many American colleges and universities, in their zeal to be identified with ancient and honorable causes, were also built in the neomedie-

Fig. 18:15. Castle Neu-schwanstein. Begun 1869. Bavarian Alps (Pan American World Airways)

val style. And scattered throughout the country are half-timbered houses, castle residences, railroad stations, and other public buildings that show the influence of the medieval revival on 19th-century American architecture.

In France, architectural energies at first were diverted toward the preservation of the many medieval monuments still in existence. Less than a year after the July Revolution, Victor Hugo had published his *Notre Dame de Paris* (known to the English-speaking world as the *Hunchback of Notre Dame*). The fact that the real hero of the novel is Paris' Gothic cathedral fanned into flames the popular enthusiasm for the restoration of cathedrals, castles, and abbeys. Support for the reconstruction of Notre Dame was soon forthcoming in official circles from Guizot the historian, who was then prime minister. It was he who founded in 1837 the *Commission pour la Conservation des Monuments Historiques*. In France, as previously in England and Germany, romantic architecture was associated with the resurgence of patriotic and nationalistic sentiment. At last, Gothic architecture had arrived on home soil, channeling French national energies into new flights of the imagination and providing French minds with an escape from recent dreams of Roman imperial glory that had turned into the nightmare of the Napoleonic defeat.

The precise scholarship of the French academic minds found a ready outlet in the establishment of the new science of medieval archeology, which resulted in the reconstruction of such buildings as Ste.-Chapelle and the Cathedral of Notre Dame in Paris; and Viollet-le-Duc's skillful reconstructions of Carcassonne Castle on the Pyrenees border (Fig. 6:10) and the abbey church of La Madeleine at Vézelay (Figs. 5:10 and 5:11). In his essays on medieval architecture, Viollet-le-Duc called attention to the engineering logic of medieval builders and demonstrated the organic unity of Gothic architecture, in which each stone played its part in the structural system, and that in the period of Gothic florescence even the decorative details served useful purposes. That everything was necessary and nothing was used merely for effect, not only revised 19th-century architectural thought but laid one of the bases for the 20th-century return to functional building.

As comparatively latecomers on the medieval revival scene, the French architects were in no hurry to leave their reconstructions and design new buildings. The advantage was theirs when they did so, however, since they could review all the previous experiments and avoid the follies and excesses that characterized the movement elsewhere. Though planned long before, it was not until two decades after the early activities of Victor Hugo, Delacroix, and Berlioz that Paris ground was broken in 1846 for the Church of Ste.-Clotilde (Fig. 18:16). Designed by François Christian Gau, a native of Cologne but a naturalized Frenchman, the project was completed after his death by Théodore Ballu. Although Ste.-Clotilde was built principally of white stone, the use of cast-iron girders in the vaulting to assure strength and durability was a distinctive technical innovation. To be sure, the girders were disguised by blocks of stone, but the fact that a building of medieval design used materials developed by the 19th-century Industrial Revolution was sufficient to arouse great interest among contemporary architects.

Based on Gothic models of the 14th century, the ground plan has the usual features of a nave with side aisles, transept, choir, and apse with radiating chapels. The space of the richly ornamented façade is divided by four buttresses into three parts, each with an entrance portal. Those on the sides have tympanums showing in sculptured relief the martyrdom of St. Valery and the baptism of Clovis. The approaches to the portals have niches containing standing figures of the Merovingian saints who were associated with the earliest history of French nationhood, including Clovis' queen Ste. Clotilde and Ste. Geneviève, patroness of Paris.

The interior is lighted by a clearstory with as many as 60 stained glass windows, which carry out the iconographical scheme promised by the sculptures of the façade. The representations tell the legendary stories of Ste. Clotilde and some of her contemporaries, St. Valery, St. Martin of Tours, St. Remi, and two of her

Fig. 18:16. Gau and Ballu. Church of Ste.-Clotilde. 1846–1857. Paris

children who were canonized, St. Cloud and Ste. Bathilde. The choir is the setting for a large three-manual organ with a case elaborately carved in the Gothic manner. It was here that the distinguished composer César Franck presided from the year 1872 until his death, and here that he made his famous improvisations.

The dedication of a church to a Merovingian saint connected with the early history of Paris was entirely in the spirit of that part of the Gothic-revival movement which appealed so strongly to nationalistic sentiment. While an account of Clotilde's life is to be found in the writings of Gregory of Tours and other medieval chronicles, she was known to the Paris of this time through Guizot's widely read *History of France*, a book based on his lectures of 1827–1830 at the Sorbonne, which told of the country's evolution from the 5th century A.D. With the growing knowledge of the 19th-century historians, the beginnings of French nationhood could be traced to the early conquests of Clovis, who united the remnants of the Roman Empire in Gaul into one kingdom. Furthermore, local civic pride was touched by the fact that, even at this early date, Clovis and Clotilde had considered Paris as their royal seat. The dedication of an important new church to Ste. Clotilde and of the Sorbonne library to Ste. Geneviève (Fig. 19:15) and the awakening interest in St. Joan of Arc point to a growing awareness of France's national medieval glory. The choice of female saints can be linked to the revival of the spirit of chivalry and its medieval expression in the form of numerous Lady churches, such as Notre Dame of Paris, of Chartres, and of Rheims. When the Church of Ste.-Clotilde is compared with these original Gothic monuments, however, it seems studied, overly symmetrical, and academically frigid. But when it is viewed in the context of its times and combined with the reflections of medieval fervor of Victor Hugo, the moving craftsmanship of Rude, the lively chromaticism of Delacroix' painting, and the fantastic imagery of Berlioz' music, it catches some rays of their glowing warmth and becomes at once both their worthy architectural companion and an important incident in the unfolding of the romantic style.

POETRY

Of the three great literary figures who influenced the writings of Victor Hugo at this time, Dante and Shakespeare were out of the past, and only his elder contemporary Goethe came from his own time. These three writers, as he states in the Preface to *Cromwell,* pointed out the sources of the grotesque elements that were to be found everywhere, "in the air, water, earth, fire those myriads of intermediate creatures which we find alive in the popular traditions of the middle ages; it is the grotesque which impels the ghastly antics of the witches revels, which gives Satan his horns, his cloven feet and his bat's wings. It is the grotesque, still the grotesque, which now casts into the Christian hell the frightful faces which the severe genius of Dante and Milton will evoke. . . ." Needless to say his understanding of his great predecessors involved a high degree of selectivity. It was the Inferno section that he extracted out of Dante's *Divine Comedy.* Hugo's poem of 1837—*Après une lecture de Dante*—closely parallels Delacroix's picture of Dante: "When the poet paints the image of hell," he wrote, "he paints that of his own life." The substance of the poem continues. "Beset by shades and specters, the poet must grope blindly through mysterious forests as weird forms bestrew his dark voyage. Lost amidst indecisive fogs, with each step he hears lamentations and the faint sounds of the grinding of white teeth in the black night. All the vices such as vengeance, famine, ambition, pride and avarice darken the scene still more. Farther on, the souls of those who have tasted the poison of cowardice, fear and treason are mingled with the grimacing masks of those whom hatred has consumed. The only light amidst this general gloom is the voice of the eternal artist, Vergil, who calls, 'Continue onward.' "

In Petrarch, it was the Triumph of Death that Hugo admired; in Boccaccio, the vivid descriptions of the black plague; in Shakespeare, the macabre scenes from *Hamlet* and the boiling and bubbling of the witches' caldron in *Macbeth;*

and in Goethe's *Faust*, the descriptions of the Walpurgis-Night. Collectively these constitute a veritable carnival of the macabre, the horrible, and visions of doom. Hugo's transition to this new psychology is apparent as early as 1826 when he brought out a new edition of his *Odes* to which he added 15 *Ballades*, No. 14 of which was entitled "Witches' Sabbath." This new orientation he explains in his introduction. The odes, he wrote, included his purely religious inspirations and personal expressions, which were cast in classical meters. Those bearing the title of ballad have the character of caprice, and include pictorial fantasies, dreams, and legends of superstition. He tells of the latter coming to him under the inspiration of the repertoire of medieval troubadours, especially those Christian rhapsodies of epical nature that were chanted by the minstrels to the accompaniment of their harps as they wandered from one castle to another.

The ballad begins with a description of a Gothic church at midnight; the clock in the belfry tolls 12, and the witching hour begins. Strange lights flash, the holy water begins to boil in the fonts; shrieks and howls are heard, as from all directions come those who answer Satan's call—specters, dragons, vampires, ghouls, monsters, and the souls of the damned from their fresh-emptied tombs. While Satan sings a Black Mass, an imp reads the Gospel, and the whole fantastic congregation performs a wild dance.

> All in unison moving with swift-circling feet
> While satan keeps time with his crozier's beat,
> And their steps shake the arches colossal and high,
> Disturbing the dead in their tombs close by.

The last two lines serve as a refrain and are repeated after each of the ten verses, two of which will suffice as samples.

> Come, he-goats profane,
> Come, lizards and snails,
> Come, serpents with scales,
> So fragile and frail.
> Burst into the fane!
> Let discord take wing,
> With melodious swing,
> Come, enter the ring,
> And repeat the refrain.

> And their steps shake the arches colossal and high,
> Disturbing the dead in their tombs close by.

> From his tomb with sad moans
> Each false monk to his stall
> Glides, concealed in his pall,
> That robe fatal to all,
> Which burns into his bones.

> Now a black priest draws nigh,
> With a flame he doth fly
> On the altar on high
> He the curst fire enthrones.
>
> . . .
>
> The dawn whitens the arches colossal and gray,
> And drives all the devilish revellers away;
> The dead monks retire to their graves 'neath the halls,
> And veil their cold faces behind their dark palls.

For his introduction and refrain Hugo uses a dual rhyming scheme, *aa, bb, cc,* and so on. That of the intervening verses, however, is based on a variant of an old medieval triple-rhyming pattern recalling that of the 13th-century *Dies Irae* (p. 311), which is still an important part of the requiem mass. The first, fifth, and ninth lines rhyme, while two groups of triple rhyme are placed between them to make a pattern of *a, bbb, a, ccc, a.* The *Dies Irae* had made an earlier appearance in the church scene of Goethe's *Faust,* where Margaret, aware of her forthcoming doom, hears the chorus intone the awesome lines (Fig. 18:5). Both the technique and imagery of Hugo's ballad are related to the fantastic sections of *Faust,* while each poem, in turn, has a common ancestor in the witches' scene from Shakespeare's *Macbeth.* The similarity of metrical plan and black-magic imagery is unmistakable. Especially in the Walpurgis-Night scene from *Faust,* one finds the same lilting language that is designed to charm the ear and stimulate the imagination rather than make logical sense. The scene is filled with witches riding he-goats and giant owls; the earth crawls with salamanders and coiling snakes; while bats fly around and glittering fireflies provide the illumination. As Mephistopheles describes the ghostly dance:

> They crowd and jostle, whirl, and flutter!
> They whisper, babble, twirl, and splutter!
> They glimmer, sparkle, stink, and flare—
> A true witch-element! Beware!

The sources of Hugo's inspiration are thus clear, but while he must be counted among the masters of language and the outstanding literary figures, he was never a prime mover or noted for his originality. Highly skilled as a manipulator of symbols and a master of poetic forms, he was able to give articulate expression to the changing voices of his time. In spite of all this verbal virtuosity and the uniform high quality of his output, he never succeeded in producing a poetic masterpiece that stood out above all others. In his work all the ideas of his time are mirrored in his unparalleled rhetoric, and his voice is as typical as any within the framework of this period. The brief but pungent reply of a modern critic pretty well sums it up. When asked whom he considered the greatest French poet of the 19th century, he answered, "Unfortunately, Victor Hugo."

MUSIC

The salons of Paris during these days were populated with poets, playwrights, journalists, critics, architects, painters, sculptors, musicians, and utopian political reformers without number. Henrich Heine, poet and journalist from north Germany, Chopin from Poland, Liszt from Hungary—all mixed freely with the home-grown artists and intellectuals, such as Hugo, Théophile Gautier, Lamartine, Chateaubriand, de Musset, Dumas, George Sand, and others. Social philosophers, such as Lamennais, Proudhon, Auguste Compte, and Saint-Simon, gave a political tinge to the heated aesthetic debates. In this supercharged atmosphere Hector Berlioz must have appeared as an authentic apparition embodying in the flesh the wildest romantic dreams and nightmares. One contemporary described him as a young man trembling with passion, whose large umbrella of hair projected like a movable awning over the beak of a bird of prey. The German composer Robert Schumann saw him as a "shaggy monster with ravenous eyes"; his personality as that of a "raging bacchant"; and spoke of his effect on the society of his times as being "the terror of the Philistines." The suave and polished Felix Mendelssohn, on the other hand, found his French colleague completely exasperating, and he continually reproached Berlioz because, with all his strenuous efforts to go stark raving mad, he never once really succeeded.

In one striking personality, Berlioz combined qualities that made him a great composer, the ranking orchestral conductor of his day, and a brilliant journalist and autobiographer. As a conductor, he was the embodiment of the mad musician of popular imagination. At the first performance of one of his overtures, when the orchestra failed to give him the effect he demanded, he burst into tears, tore his hair, and fell sobbing on the kettledrums. His *Memoirs* are stylistically a literary achievement of the first magnitude and rank with the few top autobiographies of world literature. From this lively source one gathers that Berlioz' development proceeded in a series of emotional shocks that he received from his first contacts with the literature and music of his time. One after the other, the fires of his explosive imagination were ignited by Goethe's *Faust*, which resulted in his oratorio the *Damnation of Faust*; by the poetry of Byron, which became the symphony for viola and orchestra, *Harold in Italy*; and by Dante's *Divine Comedy*, which was sublimated into his great *Requiem*. In music it was first Gluck, then Weber, and he said that he had scarcely recovered from these when he "beheld Beethoven's giant form looming over the horizon. The shock was almost as great as that I had received from Shakespeare, and a new world of music was revealed to me by the musician, just as a new universe of poetry had been opened to me by the poet." It was, of course, the Beethoven of the *Eroica*, *Pastoral*, and *Ninth* symphonies. To a milder extent, the literary figures of Vergil, Walter Scott, and Victor Hugo made up the more distant claps of thunder in his creative brainstorms.

Berlioz even insisted on actually living out his enthusiasms to an alarmingly realistic degree. He fell violently in love with the Irish actress who was playing the feminine leads in the Shakespearean troupe that was so successful in the Paris season of 1827. After a desperate romance leading both to the brink of suicide, he finally married the beautiful feminine package whom he thought of as Juliet and Ophelia wrapped up in one. When his wife turned out to be merely the actress Miss Harriet Smithson, now Mme. H. Berlioz, he wrote with acute anguish to a friend: "She's an ordinary woman." The cold dawn of disillusionment brought years of personal misery, compensated for by some happier results on the musical side. For all his external flightiness, his literary, musical, and human loves were completely enduring; and he carried them with him to the end of his life. There one finds him still musing on the "mild, affable, and accessible" figure of Vergil; on Shakespeare, "that mighty indifferent man, impassable as a mirror"; on Beethoven, "contemptuous and uncouth, yet gifted with such profound sensibility"; and on Gluck, "the superb."

Berlioz' autobiographical *Fantastic Symphony*, first performed in the year 1830, contains a complex of many ideas he gathered from the musical and literary atmosphere that surrounded him. In the detailed programmatic notes he wrote for it, it is clear that he took the idea of poisoning by opium in the first movement from De Quincey's *Confessions of an English Opium Eater*, which had appeared shortly before in a French translation by Alfred de Musset. The musical form of this movement, with its *Largo* introduction and the *Allegro agitato e appassionato assai* continuation, is in the Beethovenian symphonic tradition. Its principal claim to technical originality is the use of an *idée fixe*, or fixed idea (below), by which Berlioz conveys the idea of his beloved who is everywhere present and colors his every thought. The metamorphosis of the theme on its appearance in each of the movements fulfills a dual purpose—that of providing a semblance of unity in the sequence of genre pieces, and that of expressing, by its mutations, the necessary dramatic progress. The theme is varied in each of its reappearances and provides the listener with the necessary continuity to build up the image of a dramatic character through the associative process. All evidence, however, points to the fact that this specific programme was written later than most of the music, which was apparently conceived for quite another purpose.

Fantastic Symphony. Fixed Idea, or Leading Melody — Berlioz

Gérard de Nerval's prose translation of Goethe's *Faust* had appeared late in the year 1827 and was the direct inspiration for Berlioz' *Eight Scenes from Faust*. Since most of the movements of the *Fantastic Symphony* were being written at the same time, this alone would indicate a connection in the creative process. Berlioz was among the earliest to attempt a realization of Goethe's great drama in music. An opera by Spohr had appeared in 1816, but the well-known one by Gounod was many years later. A secular oratorio by Schumann, a *Faust Symphony* by Liszt and a *Faust Overture* by Wagner are but a few of the many subsequent works on this theme. The subject of Faust was in the wind, and the stages of London, Paris, and other continental cities rang with the echoes of the many versions of this subject in dramatic and ballet form. The Paris opera alone had accepted no less than three librettos that were waiting to be commissioned. It is known that Berlioz was angling for one of these, and this fact further fortifies the case for the common source of inspiration for the *Damnation of Faust* and the *Fantastic Symphony*. Since the desired commission was not forthcoming, those parts projected for a Faust ballet became instead the movements of the *Fantastic Symphony*.

The reveries and passions of the first movement are certainly Faustian in a general, if not specific, sense. Every Faust ballet of the time contained a gay dance sequence for the Auerbach Cellar scene, and the second movement of the *Fantastic Symphony*, called the Scene at the Ball, was probably first written for Auerbach's Cellar. The external and internal storms of the third movement, the Scene in the Country, bring out the benign as well as the malignant aspects of the Faustian conception of nature. The closest correspondence, however, comes in the climactic final movements where the relationship is quite unmistakable. The fourth, the grim March to the Scaffold, was probably composed first as the execution scene where Margaret pays the penalty for the dual crimes of matricide and infanticide. In the *Symphony*, it becomes a musical nightmare of the first order in which the hero (autobiographically Berlioz himself) marches in grotesque rhythms to his own doom. As other writers have pointed out, this scene may well have been suggested to Berlioz by the unfortunate execution of the gifted young poet André Chénier, who met death on the guillotine under Robespierre and thus became the martyred poet of the Revolution. In the final bars of this movement, the fixed melodic idea is sounded in the high piercing register of the clarinet. It is suddenly cut off to suggest the fall of the blade and the decapitation of the hero. After a dull thud and a roll of the drums, the grimacing crowds roar their bloodthirsty approval of the execution.

The last movements of both the *Eight Scenes from Faust* and the *Fantastic Symphony* have to do with the triumph of the exultant diabolical forces as they claim the souls of their victims. The endings to Berlioz' early works are often the most wild and dissonant parts. No anticlimactic calms after the storms, no carefully planned resolutions, no safe havens after the shipwrecks. The *Symphony* ends with a diabolical Witches' Sabbath, just as *Harold in Italy* does with an Orgy of the Brigands. The grisly scene here is both the climax and the unresolved end, and the movement that most fully justifies the title "fantastic." It is divided into three distinct sections. The first is introductory and begins with wild shrieks for the piccolo, flute, and oboe, accompanied by the ominous roll of the kettle-drums in bars 7 and 8, which is echoed softly by the muted horns in bars 9 and 10 to suggest distance. After a repetition, the tempo changes from Larghetto to Alle-gro and the *idée fixe* is heard (21–28). The ghostly appearance of the fixed melodic idea associated with Berlioz' beloved in this final movement was undoubtedly de-rived from the witches' kitchen scene of Goethe's drama where Faust has gone to have his form changed from that of old age back to young and lusty manhood, and where the conjuring up of the image of Margaret is a part of the process (Fig. 18:4). It is also related to the Walpurgis-Night scene where Margaret again puts in a brief appearance. Surely it is a novel notion that the winsome heroine, exem-plified in previous mutations as the embodiment of desirability, should now ap-pear at the witches' sabbath. Was she a witch all along and disguised only in his imagination in desirable human form? Or is this merely another manifestation of her "bewitching" power? The entrance at this point of his beloved on her broom-stick, accompanied by a pandemonium of sulfurous sounds, is therefore somewhat unexpected. The hero, obviously Berlioz himself, gives a shriek of horror (29–39) as he listens to her modulate from the previously chaste C major to the more lurid key of E flat. Her instrumental coloration, while still that of the pale clarinet, de-scends now in pitch to a new low and more sensuous register. After this shocking revelation, she executes a few capers and subsides for the time being as the intro-duction concludes with bar 101.

The second section is labeled Lontano ("in the distance") and begins with the tolling of the chimes recalling the opening lines of Hugo's ballad. After this signal for the unleashing of the infernal forces, the foreboding *Dies Irae* is sol-emnly intoned, first by the brass instruments in unison octaves. In bars 127–146, it is in dotted half notes; next, in bars 147–157, the rhythm is quickened into dotted quarters; then it becomes syncopated in triplet eighths (157–162) and ends with an abrupt upward swish of the C scale. With the appearance here in syncopation and in such surroundings of this ancient and honorable Gothic liturgical melody, a solemn part of every Roman Catholic requiem mass, Berlioz fulfills the promise of his programme that he will make a "burlesque parody" on the *Dies Irae*. Besides serving Berlioz as a symbol conjuring up all the fire-and-brimstone aspects of me-dieval Christianity, it also introduces at this point a form of macabre humor. This parody of a sacred melody caused considerable comment at the time. Schumann attributed it to romantic irony, one of the few forms of humor tolerated in a style practiced by artists who took life and themselves with deadly seriousness. Another explanation, however, seems more logical and is to be found by applying a remark that Hugo made in his Preface to *Cromwell*. "When Dante had finished his terrible Inferno," he wrote, "and naught remained save to give his work a name, the unerring instinct of his genius showed him that multiform poem was an emanation of the drama, not of the epic; and on the front of that gigantic monument, he wrote with his pen of bronze: Divina Commedia." Thus if Dante was justified in conceiving his Inferno as a comedy, albeit a divine one, then Berlioz could include the *Dies Irae* in this context. Even the devil is conceded to be a clever theologian, and in Goethe's drama he is found in the sacred precincts of the church, whispering in Margaret's ear as she listens to the choir chant the *Dies Irae*. This scene was also one Delacroix chose for the subject of a lithograph (Fig. 18:5); and the image of Satan saying mass at midnight in the Gothic setting of Hugo's poem relates all these works to the same idea.

The title of the final section, which begins with bar 241, is *Ronde du Sabbat*, the same as that of Hugo's poem, again showing the connection with that ballad. A dance fragment hinted at previously now becomes the "Rondo of the Sabbath" theme and a four-bar phrase forming a fugue subject. The first entrance is for the cellos and double basses (241–244); this is followed by the violas (248–251); next, for the first violins fortified by the bassoons (255–258); and the final entrance is scored for the woodwind section and horns. These successive entries, each with a different instrumental combination, mark Berlioz' departure from the academic tradition of the linear fugue. Here he introduces the element of instrumental coloration into the usually austere fugal exposition. Other color combinations follow with melodic and chromatic variants of the subject in a fugal development that has won the composer wide admiration. It must be noted that when Berlioz is writing his wildest images, his mind is always in command; and at the climax of such a work as this, he writes a fugue without either violating the rules or sacrificing his expressive intentions. After the fugue on the dance theme has come to its climax with the entire string section playing an extension of the subject (407–413), the *Dies Irae* makes a reappearance, and the two themes are woven together with great skill from bar 414 to the end. Some of Berlioz' enthusiastic admirers have called this contrapuntal section a double fugue. There is only one fugue, however, with the *Dies Irae* melody running concurrently. With the final blood-curdling shrieks and flying images, a composer, perhaps for the first time in music history, has written a fugue that fulfills its literal meaning—that is, a flight.

After this *Symphony*, the use of the *Dies Irae* became a symbol of the macabre, and it has been used countless times since. Liszt's *Totentanz* for piano and orchestra is a set of variations on it, while it appears again in Gustav Mahler's symphonies and in some of Rachmaninoff's variations on a theme of Paganini. With this movement, Berlioz also established a style that brought the demonic element—and a chain of harmonic and psychological dissonances—into music to stay. Both Moussorgsky's *Night on Bald Mountain* and Saint-Saens' *Danse Macabre* are cut from the same cloth. One writer has even called this movement of Berlioz' the first piece of Russian music. Some of Stravinsky's wilder moments in the *Fire Bird* and the *Rite of Spring* would certainly seem to bear this out. Anyone, in fact, who knows this movement well can hardly be shocked by the dissonances of modern music.

Berlioz was one of the first composers to build up his musical forms by the use of tone color. The only way to understand his music is to hear it in all the full richness of its instrumental sound, because his scores can never be transcribed successfully for piano or any other instrumental medium. In addition to the incomparable richness of his orchestral palette, the sheer quantitative weight he added to the ensembles of his day is nothing short of spectacular. Since he seldom composed in any but the largest forms, and delighted in the use of orchestral and choral combinations of extraordinary complexity, his works have received from his time to ours all too few performances. Even today it is difficult to assemble all the necessary forces, and the demands his works make on the time and effort of the performers are considerable. In his gigantic *Requiem*, for instance, he employs an immense principal orchestra, a chorus of 500, a tenor soloist, and four huge brass bands. The latter were placed facing the four points of the compass, so as to suggest vast space and to enhance their acoustical effect when they sound the call for Judgment Day. All this, plus such additional effects as a battery of 16 kettledrums, caused the newspapers to comment the day following the first performance, that Paris had not heard such a volume of sound since the fall of the Bastille.

There was always something of the conqueror about Berlioz as he marshaled his orchestral forces in such a composition. Each orchestra had its own conductor, and the choruses were signaled by commanders of lesser rank, with all of them taking their cues from the generalissimo himself, who appeared in the role of a musical Napoleon storming over the battlefield. Berlioz was the first of the great orchestra conductors and the prototype of the great maestros of our day. No wonder his contemporaries did not know how to take him and found both his personality and his compositions somewhat difficult to absorb. He always reminded them of something monstrous, and it remained for Heinrich Heine to find the most apt way of putting this into words. "Here is the wingbeat that reveals no ordinary songbird," he wrote, "it is that of a colossal nightingale, a lark the size of an eagle, such as must have existed in the primeval world."

During the romantic period there was a growing gulf between the realities of the early industrial age and the escapist tendencies in the arts. In recognition of the new technologies an École Polytechnique had been established in 1794 by the revolutionary government. Napoleon, however, yielded to the advice of David and others and allowed the establishment of a separate École des Beaux Arts in 1806. By thus educating engineers in one school and architects in another, the construction techniques of building tended to be divorced from the stylistic aspects of architecture. When the architects did begin to use cast iron, it was to build dream castles and neomedieval cathedrals; and when the musicians began to use the improved horns and trombones, it was to sound the call of Judgment Day and introduce a rain of neomedieval fire and brimstone into their symphonies. In general, then, the full significance of the new era remained for a later age to exploit.

IDEAS

The dynamics of the Revolutionary Period, with its social, political and industrial upheavals, confronted artists with the image of a rapidly changing world. The shift of responsibility and wealth from the aristocracy to the middle class brought about a corresponding change in the patrons for whom the buildings were built, the statues carved, the pictures painted, and the music composed. No longer were the arts produced mainly for a small sophisticated group of aristocrats; instead, they were addressed to a larger and more inchoate bourgeoisie. Finesse, subtlety, and intellectual grasp of complex forms could no longer be anticipated in audiences. Artists now had to charm, exhort, and astonish. Under the new system, an architect could not count on one patron for a single monumental project but had to cater to many clients with smaller buildings involving many different tastes and styles. Painters and sculptors began to work in a greater variety of forms, while poets and musicians likewise revealed the fragmentation of their worldview by writing shorter works and generally showing an inability to conceive or present their world as a systematic whole. Even when such composers as Berlioz did write symphonies, the results were no longer the all-embracing universal structures of Beethoven but sequences of genre pieces strung together by a literary programme or some recurrent motive that gave them a semblance of unity.

Among the important innovations of the time was an increasing emphasis on color in the various artistic media, both for its own sake and for its capacity to convey symbolic meaning. For the architects and sculptors, color was associated with the picturesque and local color. Poetry began to depend on the sounds of words and their appeal to the senses more than to the mind. Hugo's "Witches' Sabbath" with its patterns of repeated sounds and colors would be practically meaningless if this literary tone color were omitted. To Delacroix, more than line or composition, color was the dimension on which he depended for intensity of expression. Berlioz can be understood only when his musical ideas are heard in the original instrumentation. He is a composer who defies transcription. If the English horn solo in the Scene in the Country, the third movement of the *Fantastic Symphony*, were to be played by a flute or clarinet, Berlioz' expressive intention would vanish instantly. Such an example reveals the extent Berlioz relied on the tone color of specific instruments; and in his hands instrumentation becomes a musical dimension in itself, capable of carrying its own expressive weight independent of melody and rhythm. Both Delacroix and Berlioz based their styles principally on color.

New also was the idea that an artistic opus was not a self-contained whole but shared many relationships internally as well as externally with other works of art. This began with the attempts by certain individual artists to overcome many of the arbitrary limitations and technical rules of their separate crafts. The literature of the period was filled with musical allusions, and musicians for their part were drawing on literature with full force for their programme pieces. The architects were called upon to build dream castles out of the novels of Walpole, Scott, and Hugo; and it is difficult to think of Delacroix' painting or Berlioz' music without Vergil, Dante, Shakespeare, Goethe, and Byron coming to mind. The effect on music was a host of new and hybrid forms, such as the programme symphony and the symphonic poem. The tonal art had been associated from its beginnings with words, and programme music was by no means an invention of the 19th century. No other period, however, built an entire style on this mixture. There is also a considerable distinction between the setting of words to music, as in a song, or the musical dramatization of a play, as in an opera, and basing a purely instrumental form on the spirit of a poem or the sequential arrangements of episodes taken from a novel. Berlioz wrote overtures not only to operas but to such novels as Scott's *Waverly* and *Rob Roy*. Mendelssohn wrote *Songs Without Words* for the piano leaving the imagination to supply the text, and Berlioz' *Fantastic Symphony* and *Harold in Italy* became operas without words. In such later works as the dramatic symphony *Romeo and Juliet* and the *Damnation of Faust*, which are scored for soloists and chorus as well as orchestra, he invented the concert opera in which the costumes and scenery are left to the listener's imagination. This tendency continued until it reached a climax in Richard Wagner's music dramas, which he conceived as *Gesamtkunstwerke*, or complete works of art.

Other aspects of romanticism are to be found in the social attitudes of the time. After the American and French Revolutions had seemed to promise the imminent liberation of man, a reaction bordering on pessimism had set in when the results failed to live up to the overly optimistic expectations. Then when the Revolution of 1830 had overthrown the last of the old line of Bourbons, the French middle class was finally confronted with a king cast in its own image. When the bourgeoisie saw him in his frock coat, umbrella in hand, walking down the boulevard in the direction of the Bourse, they were somewhat dismayed to find that their monarch was—like themselves—stouter of figure than of heart and—again like themselves—engaged in the pursuit of causes more materialistic than ideal. A bit appalled at what they saw, is it any wonder that they sought psychological compensation in the dreams of the more dashing royal personalities

of the past, whose recklessness consisted of more hazardous adventures than buying and selling shares on the stock exchange? How could King Louis Philippe,
living in a palace replete with the bourgeois comforts of modern plumbing, compare in popular fancy with Joan of Arc's dashing dauphin, living dangerously
while being pursued by his remorseless enemies from one dank and drafty castle
to another?

The activities of Darwin's earthworms, for instance, were infinitely more useful than the sublime spectacle of one of Delacroix' lions in mortal combat with a
stallion. But how could the worms capture the popular imagination as the lions
did? A highly productive factory or an ingenious city sewer system made infinitely duller pictures and poetry than the interiors of Oriental harems and the
palm-lined shores of the River Ganges. While willing to use the fruits of the
Industrial Revolution as aids in the production and dissemination of their artistic wares, the artists of the time were quite convinced that the new technologies
were not making their world more beautiful. Thus the rift between usefulness
and beauty widened. Refusing to reconcile themselves to reality, the artists
sought ever more fanciful ways and means of avoiding the issue. Certainly they
knew what was going on in their world. As intellectuals, they were better educated and better informed than similar groups in other times had ever been.
When employing their escape mechanisms, they were fully aware of what they
were escaping from.

"Any time but now, and any place but here" became the battlecry of romanticism. The yearning for past periods—whether ancient Greco-Roman or
medieval times—is expressed in the various revivals. Since the classic and medieval revivals were accepted as official styles, and since they have lingered longer
than other aspects of romanticism, they have been dwelt upon in these pages at
greater length. The fuller vocabulary of romantic ideas, however, included the
"Back to Nature" movement, a longing by city dwellers for the lost paradise of a
simple idyllic country life; exoticism, with its fantasies of life in far-off places;
the cult of romantic individualism; and the rise of a new nationalism. Together
these separate strands weave themselves into the more complete pattern of the
romantic style.

Back to Nature

Rousseau had already sounded the clarion call of "back to nature" in the late
18th century. By so doing, he challenged the urbane, civilized, aristocratic image
of man with his projection of the noble savage whose rustic charm was
achieved by shunning society and communing with a nature unspoiled by human
hands. For his own part, Rousseau was perfectly willing to be received in courtly
circles, and his unsophisticated little opera *Le Devin du Village* (*The Village*

Fig. 18:17. Constable. *Salisbury Cathedral from the Bishop's Garden*. Oil on canvas. 34¼″ x 43⅝″. 1836. Copyright, Frick Collection, New York

Soothsayer) was performed for Louis XVI at Versailles with great success. His ideas were partly responsible for the rustic cottage, complete with a dairy and mill, that Marie Antoinette built for herself amid the formal gardens of the palace.

The back-to-nature idea took root and became one of the more popular 19th-century escape mechanisms with that segment of the population who lived in the cities and dreamed of an idyllic country life they had no intention of living. They delighted, however, in reading poetry full of nature imagery as well as folk ballads and fairy tales. They hung pictures on the walls of their apartments and town houses that were painted by the English landscapists and the French painters of the Barbizon Forest. Constable's *Salisbury Cathedral from the Bishop's Garden* (Fig. 18:17) will serve as an example, and the many peasant scenes by Millet are all too familiar. Beethoven's *Pastoral Symphony* and Wagner's *Forest Murmurs*, as well as dozens of piano pieces and songs, sounded the proper bucolic note in music. Weber's opera *Der Freischütz*, which had been the success of the 1826 season in Paris, brought out some of the darker aspects of nature. In it, much is made of the sinister powers of the night, and the forces over which it rules are effectively presented in the eerie Wolf's

Glen scene. Nature, here, as well as in Goethe's *Faust,* included malignant and benign elements, and both works unleashed terrifying elemental forces as well as magical and fantastic ones.

Exoticism

The heady perfumes of the Orient were wafted into the nostrils and thence to the fancies of romantic patrons, intellectuals, and artists. While shrewd business-men were opening up new foreign markets, and missionaries were going forth from Europe to try to bridge the Christian and pagan worlds, artists were busy capturing the popular imagination with scenes of exotic mysteries associated with far-off lands and peoples. As early as 1759, Arthur Murphy in the Prologue of a play called *Orphans of China* had proclaimed: "Enough of Greece and Rome: Th'exhausted store of either nation now can charm no more." So the Oriental world was added to the imaginative repertory, and its changing image in one guise or another has been mirrored in the arts up to the present time. Reflections of this early phase can be found in such operas as Gluck's *The Un-foreseen Meeting* or *The Pilgrims to Mecca* (1764) and Mozart's *Abduction from the Seraglio* (1785), with its setting in a Turkish harem, and in Mrs. Hughes' novel *The Royal Palace of Persia* (1790). Kew Gardens in London was studded with fanciful structures revealing a wide imaginative range. Some paths led to little rococo pavilions, others to Greek temples or Gothic chapels. Among them were a Moslem mosque, a Moorish palace, and a house of Confucius. A pagoda, built by the conservative Palladian architect Sir William Chambers (1726–1796), is the only one of these bagatelles to survive to the present day.

Only a short time later, Napoleon was fighting his Battle of the Pyramids (1798), and Gros was commissioned in 1804 to paint the *Pest House in Jaffa,* depicting an incident in Napoleon's campaign of 1799 in the Near East. In England, a tale called *Thalabor the Destroyer* (1799) by Robert Southey in-cluded chapters called "The Desert Circle" and "Life in an Arab Tent." Draw-ing rooms were hung with wallpapers depicting scenes of mandarin China, and fashionable hostesses were pouring tea at Chinese Chippendale tables. The prince regent of England, like Kubla Khan in Coleridge's poem, did

> A stately pleasure-dome decree:
> Where Alph, the sacred river, ran
> Through caverns measureless to man
> Down to the sunless sea.

Less poetically though no less fancifully, this was the Oriental pavilion the prince commissioned his architect to build at his favorite seaside resort of Brigh-ton. John Nash, who had previously built an exotic country house for a gentleman

Fig. 18:18. Nash. Royal Pavilion. 1815–1821. Brighton, England. Print, courtesy of Metropolitan Museum of Art, New York

who had lived in India, came up with an Arabian Nights fantasy in a style that was referred to at the time as "Indian Gothic." The exterior (Fig. 18:18) featured a multitude of minaret towers and several bulbous cupolas constructed over cast-iron frames. Under the large central dome was a spacious dining hall (Fig. 18:19), where each detail of the decorative scheme carried out the extravaganza, right up to the chandelier in the middle with its gaily painted cast-iron dragons holding lotus lamps in their mouths.

Schopenhauer's *World as Will and Idea,* based on the Oriental philosophy of the negation of the will, saw the light of day in 1819. Byron wrote his poetic drama *Sardanapalus* (1821), which he based on Alexander the Great's conquest of the east; Delacroix used one of the scenes for his picture, the *Death of Sardanapalus* (1827), while Berlioz took the last part for a cantata (1830). Hugo published a group of poems called *Les Orientales* in 1829; Louis Philippe established the French Foreign Legion in 1831; and Barye was modeling wild animal figures, such as his *Tiger Devouring a Gavial* (Fig. 18:20). The next year Delacroix returned from a visit to North Africa, where he had made many sketches, and set to work painting scenes, such as his *Algerian Women in Their Harem* (Fig. 18:21) shown in the Salon of 1834.

Fig. 18:19. Nash. Royal Pavilion, *Dining Room*. 1815–1821. Brighton, England. Print, courtesy of Metropolitan Museum of Art, New York

The colorful Japanese prints that found their way to Europe after Admiral Perry's voyage of 1852–1854 had an important effect on painting. Gautier published a book called *L'Orient* in 1860, which was based on his travels, and the following year an opera by Auber called *La Circassienne* was performed. At this same time, Delacroix was painting one of his last pictures, *The Lion Hunt*, which vividly portrayed the violent struggle of men and horses against the unbridled ferocity of wild animals. Gounod's opera *The Queen of Sheba* was produced in 1862 at about the same time Ingres was finishing his fleshscape *The*

Fig. 18:20. Barye. *Tiger Devouring Gavial*. Bronze. 1831. 7⅝″ high, 20″ wide. Metropolitan Museum of Art, New York

Fig. 18:21. Delacroix. *Algerian Women in Their Harem*. Oil on canvas. 5′ 9″ x 7′ 5″. 1834. Louvre, Paris (Alinari)

Turkish Bath (Fig. 18:22). The search for exotic settings eventually culminated in two of the greatest works in the lyrical repertory—Verdi's *Aïda*, written in 1871 for the Cairo opera at the time of the opening of the Suez Canal, and Bizet's *Carmen* based on a short story of Mérimée, which was first performed in 1875. Toward the end of the century, when the realistic Zola was referring sarcastically to Gautier because "he needed a camel and four dirty Bedouins to tickle his brains into creative activity," Gauguin was off in Tahiti painting exotic scenes on the spot—*Mahana No Atua* (*Day of the God*) (Fig. 19:7).

Romantic Individualism and Nationalism

This was also the age of the emancipation of the individual, and the era of the great man who climbed to the heights through his own efforts. Napoleon had stamped his image on the period with his pre-eminence in the realm of military glory and statecraft, thus giving rise to the idea of similar dominating figures in the smaller worlds of letters, painting, sculpture, architecture, and music. Artists

Fig. 18:22. Ingres. *Turkish Bath*. Oil on canvas. Diameter 42½".
c.1852–1863. Louvre, Paris (Archives Photographiques)

vied with each other for the top rung of the ladder in their respective fields. For
sheer virtuosity in letters it would be difficult to surpass Victor Hugo, who could
write with mastery in any style. Viollet-le-Duc and other architects could duplicate any building in the history of architecture; and the names of such bravura
performers as Paganini and Liszt as violin and piano virtuosos, respectively, are
legendary. All this was perhaps a positive assertion of the diminishing self in the
face of growing social collectivization. Each work of art had a personal quality
by being sifted through the imagination of distinctive individuals. It was no
longer enough for an artist to be a craftsman, no matter how high the degree of
his skill; he had also to be a great man, a prophet, a leader. It was consequently
an age of autobiography, confessions, memoirs, portraiture, and showmanship.
The will to biography, the necessity of living a "life," sometimes took so much
time it was actually a handicap to artistic production. More than in any other
period there was an obligation for the artist to be a personality in the worldly
sense in addition to his artistic activities. The place of the artist in society was

a matter of vital concern to such men as David and Beethoven, who combined the moralistic fervor of revolutionary thought with a sense of social responsibility. David's championship of the cause of art in the French legislature, and Beethoven's behavior toward his patrons as their social equal, reveal both men as modern artists who placed the aristocracy of genius on a higher plane than that of birth.

The great individual, however, could not exist in a social or political vacuum. Byron, Delacroix, and others lent their energies and talents to the cause of liberating the oppressed Greek people from the Turkish tyrant's yoke. Whether an artist conceived of himself in classical terms as a Prometheus or in the medieval vocabulary as a knightly champion of the weak against the strong was not too important. He simply needed a geographical sounding board, local color, and a linguistic medium suited to his creative needs. One could find it in folk tales and ballads of a particular locale; another in collections and variations of Spanish epics, Scottish ballads, German fairy tales; still others in the writing of Italian symphonies, Hungarian rhapsodies, and Polish mazurkas. In this light, nationalism, like the medieval revival, was a northern declaration of cultural independence from the Mediterranean tradition, tied up in the immediate sense in England and Germany with the opposition to Napoleon as a latter-day Caesar. Berlioz' nationalism is expressed in a more subtle way, but his operas without words, concert operas, and music dramas were as distinct a departure from the prevailing Italian operatic tradition as were those of Weber in Germany.

The championship of nationalism by artists can be seen as an extension of individualism. Napoleon had tried to ride the wave of a social revolution toward the shores of a new international empire. But that revolution had liberated too many individuals who were clamoring for expression, and his ship was wrecked on the rocks of nationalism. The immediate cause of the Gothic revival in England and Germany was the distrust of the French Revolution and opposition to the Napoleonic dream of a new Roman empire. The struggle against Napoleon thus became a vicarious re-enactment of the battles of the northern tribes against the encroachments of the ancient Roman empire, which was reasserting itself once more in disguised political, religious, and aesthetic forms. Both England and Germany claimed the Gothic style as their own, and to them it was a conscious departure from the Greco-Roman ideals of antiquity as well as their rebirth in the Renaissance, baroque, and neoclassical styles. In England especially, the Gothic revival was bound up closely with the wave of prosperity caused by a great industrial expansion, a glowing national pride, and a reaction against the Napoleonic empire that threatened their own. A reassertion of the separation of the Church of England from Rome took shape in the Oxford movement, which demanded veering away from Greco-Roman architectural forms as essentially pagan, and restoration of medieval liturgies that, in turn, needed appropriate settings.

In Germany, the Gothic revival took the form of a vision of past national glory associated with that country's entrance upon the European scene under Charlemagne, whom the Germans adopted as their national hero, Karl der Grosse. The relative security and eminence of Germany under the rule of the Holy Roman Empire continued intermittently up to the reign in the 16th century of the Hapsburg Charles V, the last of the powerful emperors. The past thus played an important role in the 19th-century revival of German power, based as it was on the memory of an empire dominated by the north. Stung into action by its abolition under Napoleon, German nationalism fermented during the 19th century until it matured into the heady wine of Bismarck's statesmanship, the aroma of which reminded Teutonic connoisseurs of the heroic bouquet of such ancient vintages as those of Attila, Alaric, and Frederick Barbarossa.

From the Renaissance on through the artistocratic baroque tradition and the 18th century, French art was closely bound to traditional Greco-Roman forms. During the Revolution of 1789 and its aftermath, a wave of anticlericalism led to the actual destruction of some medieval buildings to protest against church influence and herald the new freedom. The neoclassicism of the First Empire continued through the early years of the 19th century and, though weakened under the Bourbon restoration, had at least official approval right up to the Revolution of July 1830. Underneath the political surface, however, the destruction of medieval monuments had indirectly stimulated certain groups to preserve some parts of these works in museums. When the glories of their own medieval past were brought to the attention of some Frenchmen, at a time when the popular wave of neomedieval enthusiasm was gathering such momentum in England and Germany, they were bound to have consequences in France. Unlike Protestant England and Germany, France had never broken its ties with Roman Catholicism and its medieval past. Even Napoleon found it politically expedient to make a concordat with the Vatican and to be crowned in the sacred precincts of Notre Dame in Paris in the presence of the Roman pontiff.

Since the power of the French state was such that it was able to withstand foreign pressure even at the time of the Revolution and, later, to embark on the conquest of the continent under Napoleon, there was no national inferiority complex to be taken into account. Very significantly, it was not until French national power had been thoroughly subdued under the coalition that defeated Napoleon that the romantic style took a firm hold on the French mind and imagination. Even then, it endured officially less than a generation—that is, between the revolutions of 1830 and 1848.

CHRONOLOGY:
Paris, Late 19th Century

General Events
1830–1848	Louis Philippe, constitutional king
1837–1901	Victoria, queen of England
1839	Daguerre and Niepce published findings on photography; Daguerreotype process resulted
1848	February Revolution; Louis Philippe overthrown; Second French Republic; *Communist Manifesto* issued by Marx and Engels
1851	Great Exhibition of All Nations in London; Crystal Palace built by Paxton
	Louis Napoleon, president of Second Republic, made *coup d'état*, and became dictator
1852–1870	Louis Napoleon reigned as Emperor Napoleon III
1853	Admiral Perry opened Japan
1856–1866	*Physiological Optics* published by Helmholtz (1821–1894); *On the Sensation of Tone as a Physiological Basis for the Theory of Music* (1863)
1858–1868	Bibliotèque Nationale built by Labrouste
1859	*Origin of Species* published by Darwin
1863	*Life of Jesus* by Renan
1870–1871	Franco-Prussian War; Third French Republic established; Germany united as empire
1871	*Descent of Man* published by Charles Darwin
1874	First impressionist exhibit held
1889	*La Grande Exposition Universelle* held in Paris; Eiffel Tower was one of buildings
1892	*Pelléas et Mélisande* by Maeterlinck presented in Paris
1896	*Matter and Memory* published by Henri Bergson
1902	Debussy's opera on Maeterlinck's *Pelléas et Mélisande* produced in Paris

Painters
1808–1879	Daumier
1819–1877	Courbet
1832–1883	Manet
1834–1903	Whistler
1834–1917	Degas
1839–1906	Cézanne
1840–1926	Monet
1841–1919	Renoir
1848–1903	Gauguin
1853–1890	Van Gogh
1859–1891	Seurat
1864–1901	Toulouse-Lautrec

Sculptors
1827–1875	Carpeaux
1840–1917	Rodin

Architects
1801–1865	Joseph Paxton
1801–1875	Henri Labrouste
1809–1891	Georges-Eugène Haussmann
1832–1923	Gustave Eiffel

Musicians
1813–1883	Wagner
1822–1890	Franck
1833–1897	Brahms
1835–1921	Saint-Saens
1838–1875	Bizet
1842–1912	Massenet
1845–1924	Fauré
1860–1956	Charpentier
1862–1918	Debussy
1875–1937	Ravel

Writers and Philosophers
1798–1857	Auguste Comte
1799–1850	Honoré de Balzac
1809–1865	Proudhon
1812–1870	Charles Dickens
1820–1903	Herbert Spencer
1821–1867	Charles Baudelaire
1821–1880	Gustave Flaubert
1828–1926	Henrik Ibsen
1840–1902	Emile Zola
1842–1898	Stéphane Mallarmé
1844–1900	Friedrich Nietzsche
1850–1893	Guy de Maupassant
1859–1941	Henri Bergson
1862–1949	Maurice Maeterlinck
1870–1925	Pierre Louÿs
1871–1922	Marcel Proust

19

THE REALISTIC
AND IMPRESSIONISTIC
STYLES

PARIS, LATE 19TH CENTURY

While neoclassicism and romanticism were dominated by flights from reality, realism and impressionism tried to come to terms with the contemporary world. One measure of the force of social progress is the rapid rise and overthrow of the various forms of government in France during the period from 1789 to 1852. Between the absolute monarchy of Louis XVI and the empire of Napoleon III, Paris experienced a revolutionary reign of terror, a republic, the Napoleonic empire, a royal restoration, a constitutional monarchy, and a Marxian commune. While these upheavals were making headlines, even more powerful and radical changes were being initiated by the Industrial Revolution. The growth of factories employing the new machine methods of production meant the shift from an agrarian to an urban economy and the migration of large numbers of people from the farms to the cities. While the 18th-century worker had been able to weigh the tangible produce of his farm or take staisfaction in the completion of a pair of handsome shoes, his 19th-century counterpart exchanged the intangible elements of his time and labor for a precarious and fragmentary living.

671

The application of the new scientific knowledge to industrial progress opened up many new possibilities in the arts. Such new materials as cast iron facilitated the rapid construction of buildings and furnished the means whereby complicated decorative devices, hitherto made laboriously by hand, could be reproduced cheaply to satisfy the demand for the picturesque. Painting likewise was indebted to science for the development of chemical pigments. Synthetic products began to replace the old earth pigments and ground minerals and often resulted in greater brilliancy and intensity than the genuine product. Low-cost reproductions, such as the lithograph and other prints, made it possible for artists to find a wider distribution for their pictures and a new public. The facilities provided by the mechanical printing press brought about the mass distribution of newspapers, novels, and sheet music. Cast-iron instead of wooden frames for pianos meant that pianists could have larger and more durable instruments as well as ones that stayed in tune over longer periods of time. The invention of new valve mechanisms for brass instruments and the comparative standardization of their manufacture made it possible for composers to demand complex instrumental effects in their orchestrations with a reasonable assurance of getting them.

Neoclassical and romantic artists were quite as willing as everyone else to use the technological processes for the distribution of their pictures, poetry, novels, and musical compositions in order to reach as wide an audience as possible. And even the most ardent advocates of ancient and medieval glories, on occasion, emerged from the past to participate in present events. David had portrayed revolutionary incidents in his *Oath of the Tennis Court* and *Assassination of Marat*; Delacroix' *Massacre at Scio* (Chios) had told the story of the Greek struggle for independence, and his *Liberty Leading the People* (Fig. 18:1) had dramatized the Revolution of 1830. The emerging sense of modernity thus was clearly visible amid the classic or romantic yearning for the past and the unreal.

From the mid-19th century onward, governments were seeking constitutional formulas that would strike a just balance between social rights and material progress; religious denominations were trying to reconcile time-honored Scriptural truths with the new scientific knowledge; social theories were concerned with how political liberalism could evolve side by side with religious orthodoxy; and philosophies were attempting a new resolution between the static absolutes of idealism and the dynamic thought underlying the theories of evolution. Architects were wondering how their work could still remain in the realm of the fine arts and yet make use of the new materials and technological methods they now commanded. Sculptors, such as Rodin, were asking whether the traditional mythological and historical themes could be replaced by more contemporary subjects. The realistic and impressionistic painters were seeking a formula

Fig. 19:1. Daumier. *Legislative Body*. Lithograph. 1834. Art Institute, Chicago

for the incorporation into the accepted framework of the pictorial art of the new physical discoveries concerning the nature of light and its perception by the human eye. Novelists, such as Zola, were trying to establish an alliance between scientific and literary methods. Poets and playwrights, such as Mallarmé and Maeterlinck, were looking for a middle ground between the realities of the revolutionary age and the traditional limitations of poetic expression. And composers, such as Debussy, were endeavoring to harmonize the new acoustical discoveries involving the physics of sound with the accepted concepts of tonality and musical form.

In this process, governments and rulers settled down from high-flown heroics and histrionics into the drab but necessary routine of bureaucratic officialdom. The energies of artists were diverted from historical and exotic subjects into everyday life and seemingly trivial occurrences. The novels of Balzac and Dickens were concerned with social criticism. Political satire became the content of such pictures as Daumier's *Legislative Body* (Fig. 19:1), and Daumier's prints and journalistic cartoons were often highly critical of existing customs and conventions. Ugliness, violence, and shock techniques, however, were intended to arouse but not to insult or alienate potential patrons. Some artists, though, found life so disillusioning that their art became the sole compensation for the miseries of their existence. These painters and poets eventually severed their ties with their potential middle-class patrons altogether and retreated into a private world of art, where the painters painted pictures for a limited audience of other painters of similar persuasion and the poets put down their inspirations principally for the eyes and ears of other poets. They thus led the insecure lives of an underprivileged social group and tended to band together in desperate little societies within society. In general, however, the artists turned toward the new world of the great city for their material and inspiration. The artificial replaced the natural, and urban entertainments eclipsed the delights of nature. The usual was dominant over the unusual, and the here-and-now was definitely in ascendance over the there-and-then.

PAINTING

About the middle of the 19th century, the most important younger painters began to look about for a means of avoiding romantic flights of the imagination and academic glorifications of the heroic past. Gustave Courbet was in the vanguard of those who styled themselves "realists," defined painting as a physical language, and ruled out the metaphysical and invisible. The saints and miracles of the 19th century, according to Courbet, were mines, machines, and railroad stations. With a keen eye and a desire to record accurately what he saw about him, Courbet consciously set out to build an art on the commonplace. His painting was concerned with the present, not the past; with the momentary, not the permanent; with bodies, not souls; with materiality, not spirituality. His nudes suggested no nymphs or goddesses; they were merely the models who posed in his studio. The villagers attending the *Funeral at Ornans* (Fig. 19:2) do so out of a sense of duty. The priest routinely reads the committal service, and the grave digger casually awaits the moment to complete his job. No one betrays any great grief, and the skull and bone at the grave's edge add a realistic rather than a macabre touch. Courbet, however, sometimes became almost as passionate about the ugly as his predecessors had about the beautiful. Both Courbet and his younger colleague Edward Manet, who came under his influence, were sometimes betrayed into an emotional interest in their subjects in spite of themselves; at times they even tried to induce shock reactions in their audiences much in the manner of the novelists Balzac and Dickens.

The generation of painters that followed Courbet sought for even greater closeness to nature in order to develop an art based on immediacy of expression. Like the realists, they took their easels out of doors and tried to do as much of their painting on the spot as possible rather than to work in their studios from sketches. They were against painting a picture that carried any moral, any message, or any literary associations whatsoever, and they cultivated a calculated indifference toward pictorial content. Optical realism was pursued to the point of separating visual experience from memory and avoiding any associations the

Fig. 19:2. Courbet. *Burial at Ornans*. Oil on canvas. 10′ 3″ x 20′ 10″. 1849. Louvre, Paris (Archives Photographiques)

mind normally calls into play. In 1874, Claude Monet exhibited a picture called *Impression—Sunrise,* which gave the new movement its name. At first, *impressionism* was picked up as a term of critical derision. But the word has a certain appropriateness, implying as it does something unfinished, incomplete, an affair of the moment, an act of instantaneous vision, a sensation rather than a cognition.

It is impossible, of course, to substantiate any claim of a direct cause-and-effect relationship between science and art in this period or any formal connection between optical physics and painting. It is equally impossible to state that painters were unaware of or indifferent to such things as the invention of the camera, the scientific discoveries about the nature of light, and the new knowledge about the physiology of the eye. Joint researches of Daguerre and Niepce on the making of photographic images on prepared metal plates, which resulted in the Daguerreotype process, had been published as early as 1839. The revelation that visual imagery was primarily dependent on minute gradations of light intensities was bound to have an effect on painting. Physicists, such as Helmholtz and others, made discoveries about the component prismatic parts of white light, and pointed out that the sensation of color has more to do with a retinal reaction in the eye than with objects themselves. The color wheel also demonstrated that the eye fuses two separate hues of a wheel at rest into a third hue when the wheel is in rapid motion. And when all the colors of the spectrum are rotated, the eye sees them as tending toward white.

Painters also did some speculation of their own on the nature of the visual experience. Form and space, they reasoned, are not actually seen but implied

Fig. 19:3. Manet. *Rue de Berne*. Oil on canvas. 25¼″ x 31½″. 1878.
Collection of Mr. and Mrs. Paul Mellon

from varying intensities of light and color. Objects are not so much entities in themselves as they are agents for the absorption and refraction of light. Hard outlines, indeed line itself, do not exist in nature. Shadows, they maintained, are not black but tend to take on a color complementary to that of the objects which cast the reflections. The concern of the painter, they concluded, should therefore be with light and color more than with objects and substances. A painting should consist of a breakdown of sunlight into its component parts, and brilliance should be achieved by the use of the primary colors that make up the spectrum. Instead of a green mixed by the painter on his palette, separate daubs of yellow and blue should be placed close together and the mixing left to the spectator's eye. What seems confusion at close range is clarified at the proper distance. By thus trying to step up the luminosity of their canvases so as to convey the illusion of sunlight seen through a prism, they achieved a veritable carnival of color in which the eye seems to join in a dance of vibrating light intensities. As a result of this re-examination of their technical procedures, the impressionists discovered a new method of visual representation. Since, however, it was concerned so exclusively with the world of appearances, impressionism was more the ultimate phase of realism than a new style in itself.

Fig. 19:4. Monet. *Old San Lazare Station*. Oil on canvas. 23½″ x 31½″.
1877. Art Institute, Chicago

Manet's *Rue de Berne* (Fig. 19:3) was painted late in his career with the impressionistic theory in mind. In it, he builds a cityscape out of a configuration of interrelated planes. By his subtle use of color intensities rather than by linear perspective, he achieves the effect of recession and depth. In other versions of this scene, he painted some roadmenders in the foreground, and his choice of such a casual street scene is in keeping with the general preference for subjects that can be taken in at a glance rather than those that must be studied carefully and in detail. It also exemplifies the conscious cultivation of the accidental—the random scene in which emotional involvement with the subject is impossible.

More than any other painter, however, Claude Monet was the central figure of impressionism, and his picture the *Old San Lazare Station* (Fig. 19:4) is among his most typical works. The rendering of the humid atmosphere, the mixture of steam and smoke, the hazy sunlight filtering in from the open background and the transparent roof, the contrast between the open spaces and the closed forms of the engines and railroad cars are the things that concern him most. There is no hustle and bustle, no drama of arriving or departing people, no crowds or excitement, no interplay of men and machines, such as one might expect in such a setting. Instead, his people merely file from the waiting room toward the train, and the workmen go about their tasks in a matter-of-fact manner. The picture therefore becomes an atmospheric study in blues and greens.

Fig. 19:5. Monet. *Garden at Giverny*. Oil on canvas. 35″ x 39″. *c*.1899. Art Institute, Chicago

The full development of Monet's broken-color technique is even more clearly discernible in the *Garden at Giverny* (Fig. 19:5), his suburban home. In it, he breaks his light up into a spectrum of bright colors that delights the eye by forming shimmering patterns in and around the leaves and lilies. Water imagery repeatedly recurs in impressionistic painting. Its iridescence, its fluidity, its surface reflections, the perpetual play of changing light, make it an ideal medium for conveying the conception of the insubstantial, impermanent, fleeting nature of visual experience. This is but one of many versions Monet painted of the same subject, and his method of work reveals that the objects he painted were of less concern than the light and atmosphere surrounding them. In order to capture the moment he wanted, he would take up in a single day a succession of canvases—one showing the garden at dawn, another in full morning light, and a third in a late-afternoon glow. The following morning he would take up the dawn scene where he had left off the day before and, when the light changed, set it aside for the next canvas, and so on. With scientific detachment, he tried to maintain the constancy of his subject matter so as to focus the interest on the variables of light and atmosphere. Each version varies according to the season, day, or hour. Monet might even be called the "weather man" of painting were it not that, in spite of himself, his genuine involvement with nature usually overcame his objective detachment.

Impressionism is clearly an art of the urban man who sees himself in terms of temporal flow, mounting tensions, and sudden change. His volatile life is ruled by impermanent rather than permanent forces, and becoming is more real to him than being. Impressionistic painters purposely chose everyday subjects, such as street scenes, children at play, and dancing in a night café. When they did go to the country, it was to the suburbs in the manner of city folk on a holiday. As a result, the general effect of the style is bright, cheerful, and lighthearted rather than heavy or somber. They were intoxicated by light rather than life, and they saw the world as a myriad of mirrors that refracted a constantly changing kaleidoscope of color and varying intensities of light. They lived therefore in a visual world of reflections rather than substances, and one in which visual values replaced the tactile. In order to reproduce the fugitive atmospheric effects they desired, they had to work directly from nature. This led to a

Fig. 19:6. Seurat. *Sunday Afternoon on the Island of La Grand Jatte*. Oil on canvas. 81″ x 126″. 1884–1886. Art Institute, Chicago

Fig. 19:7. Gauguin. *Mahana No Atua (Day of the God)*. Oil on canvas. 26″ x 34½″. 1894. Art Institute, Chicago

speeding-up in the process of painting to a point where working with oils approached the more rapid technique of watercolor. The criticism of hasty work and careless craftsmanship that the impressionists incurred from their contemporaries was sometimes fully justified. In general, however, there was no lack of technical skill on the part of its most important practitioners when their intentions are fully taken into account. They wanted their paintings to seem improvised and to have an unfinished, fragmentary look. Beauty, like color, they felt was in the eye of the beholder, not in the picture itself. They intended to paint not so much what is seen but how it is seen. Instead of composing, which implies a placing together, they sought to isolate one aspect of experience and explore it to the utmost. Their art therefore becomes one of analysis more than synthesis, sensation more than perception, sight more than insight. As such the cool objectivity of impressionism represents the triumph of technique over expression.

In their total immersion in the two-dimensional world of appearances, the impressionists consciously neglected the other dimensions of psychological depth and emotional involvement. As a consequence, they soon began to chafe under the arbitrary limitations of such a one-sided theory. Nor were their audiences happy with the role of innocent bystander that had been assigned to

Fig. 19:8. Van Gogh. *Starry Night*. Oil on canvas. 29″ x 36½″. 1889. Collection, Museum of Modern Art, New York

them. Both artist and spectator had, in effect, resigned their active roles in the scheme of things for that of the aloof observer of life who lets the river of experience go by without attempting to divert its flow in any significant direction. In scarcely more than a dozen years after Monet had shown his *Impression—Sunrise*, the movement had worked itself into a dead end. Even though no one painted an *Impression—Sunset* to commemorate the event, impressionism in its pristine form was to all intents and purposes at an end with the last impressionist exhibit in 1886. Many of the discoveries that were made, however, survived in variously modified forms in the work of the postimpressionistic painters who had come under its influence.

Sunday Afternoon on the Island of Grand Jatte (Fig. 19:6) by Georges Seurat shows how the impressionistic theory was carried to a logical, almost mathematical, conclusion. Light, shadow, and color are still the major concerns, and the subject is also that of an urban scene, this time of a relaxed group of middle-class Parisians on a Sunday outing. Instead of informal casual arrangements, however, everything here seems as set as an old-fashioned family portrait. Instead of misty nebulous forms, such details as a bustle, a parasol, or a plug hat are as stylized and geometrical as in a Renaissance fresco. Instead of improvising his pictures out of doors, Seurat carefully composed his large canvas

Fig. 19:9. Cézanne. *Mont Ste.-Victoire*. Oil on canvas. 25⅝″ x 31⅞″. 1885–1887. Metropolitan Museum of Art, New York

in his studio over a period of years. Instead of hastily painted patches of broken color, Seurat worked out a system called *pointillism* by which thousands of dots of uniform size were applied to the canvas in such a calculated and painstaking way that the most subtle tints were brought under the painter's control. The whole picture, moreover, was subdivided into areas, and a scheme of graduating shades were blended into one another in order to achieve a unified over-all tonality.

Gauguin's *Mahana No Atua* (Fig. 19:7), or *Day of the God*, shows how the brilliant color of the impressionists can be adapted to make quiet, two-dimensional decorative designs. Van Gogh's *Starry Night* (Fig. 19:8), on the other hand, demonstrates how the same colors can be used to achieve intensely expressive effects. The deep purple sky, the yellow light of the stars, the green upward-curling silhouette of the cypress tree all stem from impressionism. The broken color, however, has here become a myriad of dark swirling vertiginous lines used as a means toward revealing an inner ecstatic vision.

In the 1870's, Paul Cézanne was also using the prismatic color palette of the impressionists. He soon discovered the expressive limitations of the theory, and his solution of some of the pictorial problems it posed became a turning

Fig. 19:10. Cézanne. *Mont Ste.-Victoire.* Oil on canvas. 27⅞″ x 36⅛″. *c.*1904. Philadelphia Museum of Art

point in the history of painting. For him, the superficial beauty of impressionism did not provide a solid-enough base on which to build a significant art. The delight in the transitory tended too much to exclude the more permanent values. Instead of severing connections with the past, he said that he wanted "to make of impressionism something solid like the art of the museums." Poussin was the old master he chose to emulate, and his expressed desire was to recreate Poussin in the light of nature. The cultivation of instantaneous vision, according to Cézanne, ruled out the participation of too many other important faculties. His pictures, unlike those of the impressionists, were not meant to be grasped immediately, and their meaning is never obvious. For Cézanne, a painting should be not only an act of the eye but also of the mind. If painting aimed only at the senses, any deeper probing of human psychology would be ruled out. Light is important in itself, but it can also be used to achieve inner illumination. Color as such is paramount, but color is also a means of describing masses and volumes, revealing form, creating relationships, separating space into planes, and producing the illusion of projection and recession. Primary colors produce brilliance, but judicious mixtures can run a whole gamut of subtle effects. Both light and color are therefore retained as the basis of his art, but not

Fig. 19:11. Cézanne. *Still Life: Basket of Apples.* Oil on canvas. 24⅜″ x 31″. 1890–1894. Art Institute, Chicago

to the extent of eliminating the need for line and geometrical organization. Cézanne's interests are not so much in the specific or the particular as they are in the general. Analysis is necessary for simplification and to reduce a picture to its bare essentials, but for Cézanne the primary process of the pictorial art is still that of composition and synthesis. His canvases therefore tend to be more austere than voluptuous, more sinuous than lush. His pictures have order, repose, and a serene color harmony, yet are capable of rising to high points of tension and grandeur. In one landscape everything may be cool and shadowy, while in another the heat of the southern sun seems almost to burn the canvas.

The forms he chose were those of his daily experience—apples, mountains, houses, trees—constants by which it is possible to measure the extent of his spiritual growth. Mont Ste.-Victoire, a rising rocky mass near his home in Aix-en-Provence, was for Cézanne a recurring motif. Just as Goethe wrote his *Faust* throughout his entire creative career, so Cézanne paints his mountain again and again until it becomes a kind of symbol of his ambitions and aspirations. The contrast of an early and late version provides an interesting index to his artistic growth. The first picture, subtitled *Landscape with Viaduct* (Fig. 19:9), dates between 1885 and 1887. The second version, called simply *Mont Ste.-Victoire*

Fig. 19:12. Cézanne. *Card Players*. Oil on canvas. 25½″ x 32″. *c*.1890–1892.
Stephen C. Clark Collection, New York

(Fig. 19:10), was done between 1904 and 1906. Both are landscapes organized
into a pattern of planes by means of color. Both show his way of achieving perspective not by converging lines but by intersecting and overlapping planes of
color. In the first version, there is a complementary balance between the vertical
rise of the trees and the horizontal line of the viaduct. In the second, these
details are omitted and a balance is achieved between the dense-green foliage of
the lower foreground and the purple and light-green jagged mass of the mountain in the background. In the earlier picture, such details as the road, houses,
and shrubs are readily recognizable. In the later one, all is reduced to the barest
essentials, and only such formal contours as the cones, cubes, and slanting surfaces remain. In the earlier, the mountain descends in a series of gently sloping
lines; in the later, it plunges precipitously downward. Both pictures, however,
are landscapes interpreted by the same sensitive and highly individual temperament. Both show Cézanne's lifelong desire to mold nature into a coherent
pattern in order to unite the inanimate world of things and the animate world
of the human mind.

In such a still life as *Basket of Fruit* (Fig. 19:11), Cézanne works in a more
intimate vein. The search for pure formal values, however, still continues. In one
of his letters, he remarked that nature reveals itself in the forms of the cylinder,

the sphere, and the cone. Here his cylinders are the horizontally arranged biscuits, his spheres the apples, and his cone the vertically rising bottle. They are balanced in this case by the forward-tilting ellipse of the basket and the receding plane of the table top. An almost imperceptible feeling of diagonal motion is induced by the distribution of the fruit from the upper left to the lower right, which is brought to an equally imperceptible stop by means of the pear-shaped apple at the extreme right. Such a simple geometrical arrangement of familiar forms imparts a feeling of comfort as well as one of order and clarity. Cézanne painted these still-life compositions so slowly and carefully that he usually found it necessary to use artificial flowers and fruits so that he could study their arrangement for weeks at a time. While he treats his cones and cubes as abstractions, his warm color saves them from frigidity, and he never fails to relate them in a subtle and expressive way to living forms.

Cézanne never overlooked the human values in his art, and the stolid peasants he found in the cafés of his native Provence often served him as models. His *Card Players* (Fig. 19:12) are every bit as impassive and monumental in their way as are his mountains. They are posed with the same stability and equilibrium as his still lifes; and their lines, volumes, masses, and textures are conceived with the same simplicity as one of his landscapes. Cézanne sets himself such severe limitations that his pictures fall mainly within the classifications of landscapes, still life, figure compositions, and portraits. Even within these categories, he keeps his themes constant so that each picture can be treated as a separate experiment. By such means he tried to bring form and stability into a visual world where everything was change and transition. If he succeeded only at times and failed at others, each result must be equated with the immensity of the task that he set for himself. Like all great masters, he realized in his mature years that he had made only a beginning, and he once remarked that he would forever be the primitive of the method he had discovered. His historical position may indeed be just this, but his work may be said to form the bridge between impressionism and modern painting.

SCULPTURE

Among the sculptural exhibits at the Paris Salon of 1877 was a statue of a nude youth entitled the *Bronze Age*. So astonishingly natural and lifelike did it seem that rumors began to circulate that the sculptor was trying to pass off as a statue a cast taken from a living model. In official quarters the rumors were given sufficient credence to result in the hasty withdrawal of the statue. The artistry of Auguste Rodin, however, did not have to wait long for recognition, and the following year, with official explanations and apologies, the statue was again on exhibition. A short while later it was bought by the state for place-

Fig. 19:13. Rodin. *Hand of God.* Marble. 29″ high. 1898. Metropolitan Museum of Art, New York

ment in the Luxembourg Gardens. Such was the gulf, however, between art and life, between a monument and a reality, that in academic circles a statue that looked too real or believable was considered a disgrace.

Like his forward-looking contemporaries in other fields, Rodin had veered away from the heroic and toward the natural. Though he admired Gothic sculpture and even wrote a book about it, his work contains no sermons in stone. Though he admired Dante and drew practically all his later subjects from an early project for the *Gates of Hell,* his conceptions show little of the escapism that motivated his immediate predecessors. For Rodin, the process of forming supersedes that of form itself. The *Hand of God* (Fig. 19:13) exemplifies this, both in the method of execution and in the subject itself. Out of an indefinite mass of uncut stone, symbolic of the formless void, the hand of the Creator arises. Divine omnipotence is suggested by the scale of the hand in relation to those of the human figures that are emerging from a lump of uncarved marble. The significance of the work was caught by the philosopher Henri Bergson, author of *Creative Evolution,* who called it "the fleeting moment of creation, which never stops." It is the implication that nothing is ever quite complete, that everything takes place in the flow of time, that matter is the womb which is continuously giving birth, that creation is a never-ending process rather than an accomplished fact—in short, the acceptance of the theory and philosophy of evolution—that gives Rodin's conception its daring quality.

Fig. 19:14. Rodin. *The Kiss*. Marble. Life size. 1896. Rodin Museum, Paris (Archives Photographiques)

Rodin always acknowledges his material frankly, seeks neither to disguise it nor to escape from it, and creates the feeling that his figures are just emerging out of their original stone or clay state. This is not, however, the mighty Michelangelesque struggle of man against his material bonds. Rather it is a sensuous love of material as such, a reveling in the flesh or stone, and a desire to explore all its possibilities and potentialities. If Michelangelo left his figures incomplete and still dominated by their material medium, it was largely because circumstances prevented his finishing them. With Rodin the incompleteness is a conscious and calculated part of his expressive design. Like the symbolist poets, the novelist Proust, and the dramatist Maeterlinck, Rodin went one step beyond mere description. For Rodin, as with his literary contemporaries, events were nothing in themselves. Only when conjured up later in memory did they acquire the necessary subjective coloration; and only then, paradoxically, could the artist treat them with the needed objective detachment. Rodin always preferred to work from a memory image rather than directly from a model in the flesh.

When he did work with a model, it was usually to make a quick sketch or an impression in soft clay. He could then allow his figures to take plastic shape in this preliminary stage at the moment of inspiration and thus promote the feeling that they were the product of improvisation. All the arduous labor of transferring them into marble or bronze was left until the forms had been refined in memory and had assumed a more subjective and personal quality.

Rodin defined sculpture as an art of hollows and projections; or, as he put it in less fastidious moments, the art of the hole and the lump. Light and shadow thus become the principal means of animating his material. His figures do not displace volume so much as they cast shadows, and they seem to exist more in time than in space. His choice of subjects also reveals this preoccupation with the transitory—*The Kiss* (Fig. 19:14), *Dawn, Eternal Spring-time, Awakening, The Wave, The Tempest,* and *Twilight.* The surface play of light, and his greater concern with the atmosphere that envelops his forms than with the figures themselves, links his art with that of the impressionistic painters. It sometimes seems that his intentions are really closer to the two-dimensional pictorial art, and that oil and canvas would really have been the proper medium for his transitory and impermanent visions. Through memory and introspection, however, Rodin was able to give his compositions some three-dimensional plausibility, and by the projection of some psychological depth into his work, he saved his art from becoming commonplace.

ARCHITECTURE

Throughout the 19th century there was a sharp division of thought about the work of an architect. Was he primarily an artist or a builder? A designer or engineer? Should he concern himself more with decoration or with structure? Was his place in a studio making drawings or in the field working with his materials? The champions of the pictorial viewpoint achieved such virtuosity that at practically a moment's notice they could produce a design based on any known building from the past. Late in the century, all the historical styles had been so carefully catalogued and documented that the range of choices was almost unlimited. What had begun as the revival of special periods had now been broadened to include all. The term for such a freedom of choice is *eclecticism,* and if a name is to be chosen for the style of the period this is the only one possible. The sole limitation on this eclecticism was the generally accepted appropriateness of the styles of certain periods to special situations. The classical was considered best for commemorative buildings and monuments, but classicism now could be anything from Mycenean Greek to late imperial Roman. Medieval was the preference for churches, but this might mean Byzantine, Romanesque, early or late Gothic. For public buildings, Renaissance was thought most suitable, though here again the choice could be from the 15th century on.

The industrial age, however, had produced new methods and materials that opened up entirely new possibilities. The potentialities of cast iron, for instance, had been perceived by engineers and industrialists long before architects began to speculate on the creative applications it could make to their art. The structural use of iron actually dates from the latter part of the 18th century, although at first it was found in bridges, cotton mills, and other utilitarian buildings and usually combined with brick, stone, or timber or else used as a substitute for one or more of them. Nevertheless, the first steps toward a revolution in the art of building had been taken. The century was eventually to see the spanning of broader widths, the enclosure of more cubic space, and projections toward greater heights than had hitherto been thought possible. The new materials and structural principles were both a threat and challenge to the traditional pictorial designers, and the more they were incorporated into building plans, the more progressive architecture became.

It has already been noted how iron columns and girders had been used quite openly by John Nash in the exotic Brighton Pavilion (Fig. 18:18), marking

Fig. 19:15. Labrouste. Library of Ste.-Geneviève. 1843–1850. Paris

Fig. 19:16. Labrouste. Library of Ste.-Geneviève. *Reading Room.* 1843–1950. Paris (Archives Photographiques)

one of the first instances of their use in a large residential building. In Paris, Gau also had used iron to reinforce the vaults of his Gothic-revival Church of Ste.-Clotilde (Fig. 18:16) but had masked it by stone facing. In his Library of Ste.-Geneviève, however, Henri Labrouste went one step farther and achieved an even more penetrating insight into the possibilities of the new material at his command. A first glance at its exterior (Fig. 19:15) reveals simply a well-executed Renaissance-revival building—as such it is indebted to a 15th-century Italian church in Rimini designed by Alberti—with the usual festoons of garlands adorning the space above its seriated windows. A closer inspection, however, shows that the first floor is conceived more as a solid space, while the bold arcade of windows above gives promise of light and air within. Since this is a library, there is a working relationship between the closed storage space for the books below and the open reading room above. This is as far as the exterior goes toward a unity of means and ends, however, and the stone on the outside gives no hint that the interior is constructed of iron.

By utilizing the strength of metal, Labrouste was able to replace the massive masonry ordinarily required for such a large reading room (Fig. 19:16) and at the same time provide for a maximum of open space and brilliant illumination. The roof is vaulted by means of girders, cast in the form of arches, spanning the room crosswise and dividing it into two parallel barrel vaults. An open foliated pattern related to the classical acanthus leaf is used as a decorative motif, and

Fig. 19:17. Labrouste. National Library. *Stacks.* 1858–1868. Paris (Archives Photographiques)

the vaults are supported by tall, thin, fluted Corinthian colonettes, also made of iron. Labrouste has thus managed his material so that he brings out its full structural possibilities. By allowing his iron colonettes to assume a form associated with carved stone, however, he compromises with tradition and lets the expressive potentialities lag somewhat behind.

What Labrouste began in the Library of Ste.-Geneviève, he brought to a brilliant fulfillment in his later masterwork, the stacks of the Bibliothèque Nationale (Fig. 19:17). This storage space for books is conceived as the very heart of the library, and it is now brought out into the open alongside the reading room itself. Though closed to the public, a full view of it is obtained through a glass-enclosed archway. All superfluous ornamentation is now omitted in favor of the function for which it was designed. Except for the bookcases and the glass ceiling, everything is of cast iron. By dividing his space into five stories, four above and one below the ground level, Labrouste provided for the housing of about a million volumes. The floors are of open grillwork, which permits a free flow of light to reach all levels. Frequent stairways provide rapid communication between floors, and the strategically placed bridges permit freedom of access between the two wings. As a composition, they present a pleasing visual pattern of vertical and horizontal intersecting planes. In both these libraries, it is evident that Labrouste has taken a bold stride toward the realization of the potentialities of the new materials and that his work as a whole represents a positive contribution to the development of a new architecture.

The same year that Labrouste was completing his first library, a new and original structure was going up in London that made no pretensions whatsoever of being either a Roman bath or a Renaissance palace. The London *Times* referred to it as Mr. Paxton's "monstrous greenhouse"; and, to be sure, it was conceived and carried out by a landscape gardener skilled in the construction of conservatories and nurseries. The occasion was the Great Exhibition of the Works of Industry of All Nations, where the latest mechanical inventions as well as raw materials were to be brought together with the finished products of industry. Machinery of all sorts was to take its place beside the manufactured arts and crafts that were being turned out by the new factories. The Crystal Palace (Fig. 19:18) that Joseph Paxton constructed to house the exposition was destined to eclipse the exhibits themselves and to find for itself a unique place in the history of modern architecture. His light and airy structure was rectangular in shape, 408 feet in width and—with a neat bit of symbolism to coincide with the year of the exhibition—1851 feet in length. It rose by means of a skeleton of cast-iron girders and wrought-iron trusses and supports, all bolted together with mathematical precision. Its walls and roof enclosed 33 million cubic feet of space in a transparent sheath of glass. The rapidity of its construction was no less remarkable than its form. The whole structure was accurately analyzed into a multiplicity of prefabricated parts, and so well planned was it that 18,000 panes of glass were put in place by 80 workmen in a week. Begun the end of September 1850, it was easily ready for the grand opening, May 1, 1851.

Fig. 19:18. Paxton. Crystal Palace. *Exterior.* Cast iron and glass. 1851′ wide. 1851. London. Lithograph from Nash, Haghe, and Roberts, *The Great Exhibition*

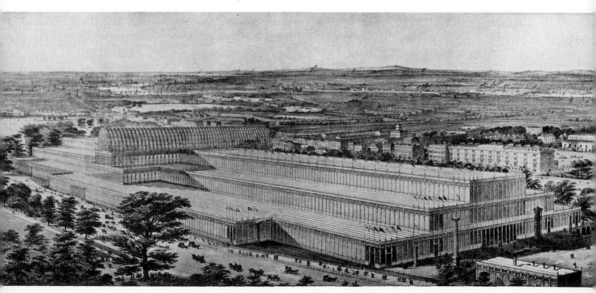

Fig. 19:19. Paxton. Crystal Palace. *Foreign Pavilion*. 1851. Lithograph from Nash, Haghe, and Roberts, *The Great Exhibition*

The building, contrary to expectations, turned out to be a thing of surprising beauty and brilliance, as inexpensive in its construction as it was daring in its use of materials. No applied decoration of any sort marred the forthright character of the exterior. And while the iron columns of the interior paid lip service to their classical ancestors, the enormous scale made such details incidental. At the inauguration ceremonies (Fig. 19:19), Albert, the Prince Consort, stood by Osler's crystal fountain and restated the purpose of the exhibition, which was to present "a living picture of the point of development at which the whole of mankind had arrived, . . . and a new starting point from which all nations will be able to direct their further exertions." Nothing seemed impossible to the machine age, and the engineers were indeed the prophets of the new order. Everything now seemed set for Victorian man to step out of his self-created pseudo-Gothic gloom into the new and shining age of industrial prosperity. Mr. Paxton and his greenhouse, however, had to wait more than half a century before the architects fully caught up with them.

Back across the channel meanwhile, Georges-Eugène Haussmann was replanning the city of Paris on a scale commensurate with its growth into one of the first great 19th-century industrial cities. The new method of cast-iron construction, the need for wide and long streets to facilitate the flow of traffic, and the accessibility of railroad stations were all taken into account in his designs. If the taste of his patron, Napoleon III, ran somewhat to festoons of floral garlands and bulbous terracotta statuary, these were only a camouflage for the really fundamental changes that were going on beneath the surface. The expositions devoted to the wonders of modern industry, which were held at regular intervals, reached a climax in the International Exhibition of 1889. Its Gallery of Machines, by employing steel and glass, achieved a span of 375 feet, the widest ever made up to that time. Even more spectacular, however, was the tower (Fig. 19:20) that soared more than 1000 feet above ground. Gustave Eiffel, an engineer who had made his reputation in bridges and industrial buildings, was entrusted with a contract for this unprecedented structure that he conceived as a bridge into the sky. It was to be built by means of an assembly of small machine-manufactured parts riveted together with precision down to a tenth of a millimeter. In just 17 months, he was able to boast that he had engineered a structure that would stand forever against earth, wind, and weather.

From its four foundation members, the Eiffel Tower makes a series of three spectacular upward leaps to a platform 984 feet above the ground, where all of its elegant lines converge. A lantern then carries the height still further to a point over 1000 feet in the sky. A spiral staircase and a system of elevators corresponding to the above stages allow visitors to mount as far as the base of the lantern. Except for a few nonfunctional decorations about the base, Eiffel's design is a

Fig. 19:20. Eiffel. Eiffel Tower. 984′ high to base of lantern. 1889. Paris

masterpiece of structural integrity and honest use of material. Before it was built, however, a violent protest in the form of a petition was received by the exposition authorities. "We the writers, painters, sculptors, and architects," it began, "come in the name of French good taste and of this menace to French history to express our deep indignation that there should stand in the heart of our capital this unnecessary and monstrous Eiffel Tower." What was to have been but a temporary exhibition building, however, turned out to be such a rousing success that it was assured a permanent place in the Parisian scheme of things. Uses quite unanticipated at the time it was built were subsequently found. Successively and simultaneously it has served as a lookout point, a weather observation post, a beacon tower for air traffic, a radio tower, and television sending station. It was at once the prototype of the modern steel skyscraper and a symbol of the modern metropolis.

LITERATURE AND MUSIC

The desire on the part of writers to come to terms with their own world rather than to explore the avenues of escape was responsible for the literary movements known as realism and naturalism. In some cases, writers cultivated a kinship with the scientific materialism that dominated the thought of the period following the February Revolution of 1848. In others, notably with Zola and Ibsen, they allied themselves with sociology and wrote their novels and plays much as a social worker might handle a case history. Somewhat earlier, Balzac had proved himself far too sophisticated a writer to see in the medieval period much beyond ignorance, poverty and rustic village life and was able to write glowingly of the beauty of factories and big cities. The subject matter of his novels was drawn from the complex moral and psychological trials of middle-class life in the large cities that he knew. This did not imply complete acceptance of the bourgeois image of man; on the contrary, it often meant violent opposition to his accepted values. Attitudes toward their writing varied with the temperaments of individual writers. Flaubert, for instance, felt compelled to withdraw from life in order to describe it with the necessary objectivity; and he was convinced that such scientific detachment alone qualified the artist as well as the scientist. Zola, on the other hand, could not write without a passionate self-identification with the oppressed subjects of his novels. In the spirit of a reformer, he found it a necessity to bring social sores out into the sunlight of public exposure in order to effect a cure. With him, the novelist becomes a social research worker, and the novel a documentary case history.

This scientific objectivity was obviously better adapted to the writing of novels than to poetry or music. Some realism, to be sure, can be found in the vivid instrumentation of Berlioz, and his opera *Benvenuto Cellini* had included a forging scene. Wagner's *Ring of the Nibelung* had a scene that calls for anvils to be hammered backstage, while the fire glows and sparks fly during the forging of a sword. In spite of its exotic setting, Bizet's conception of the character of Carmen was realistic enough to cause a certain sensation when it was first performed; and some time later the whir of sewing machines could be heard in Charpentier's opera *Louise*. In general, however, music as well as poetry found a far more congenial sphere of operation in the intangible realm of the imagination. Thus another movement arose in the 1880's under the leadership of the poet Mallarmé, which tried to give freer reign to the imaginative process through a new use of symbolism.

The art of the symbolist was one of the fleeting moment; everything rushes past in an accelerated panorama. With the metaphor as a starting point, a symbolist prose poem flows by in a sequence of images that sweeps the reader along on a swift current of words with a minimum of slowing down to ponder on their meaning. Like the impressionistic painters, the symbolists reveled in sense data, and, like the realistic novelists, they looked for their material among the seemingly inconsequential occurrences of daily life. But in their endeavor to endow such happenings with profundity, and in their effort to attach to them a deeper symbolic significance, they went one step beyond their colleagues. While the painters had found a new world in the physics of light, and the novelists another new world in the social sciences, the symbolists looked to the new discoveries in psychology. By purposely leaving their poetry in an inconclusive and fragmentary state, they were making use of the psychological mechanism of reasoning from part to whole. Since the poets did not define the whole, the reader's imagination was allowed full scope. Just as the impressionistic painters had left the mixing of color to the eye of the observer, and the relationship of the subject matter to the viewer's mind, so Mallarmé and the symbolists left the connection, order, and form of their verbal still lifes to be completed by the reader. They also found a new world to explore in "listening" to colors, "looking" at sounds, "savoring" perfumes, and in all such mixtures of separate sensations known to psychology as synaesthesia. Debussy's piano piece *Sounds and Perfumes on the Evening Air* is an attempt to capture this type of experience in the tonal medium. The symbolists pushed outward to the threshold limits of perception in order to develop more delicate sensibilities and stimulate the capacities for new and peripheral experiences. They moved about in a twilight zone where sensation ends and ideation begins. The very word *symbolism*, however, implies that their images are revelations of something surpassing the senses. And it is here that they parted company with the objective techniques of the realists and impressionists, who were largely content with careful description.

Maurice Maeterlinck made an interesting attempt to translate the aims of the symbolist poets into dramatic form. His *Pelléas et Mélisande,* a play first performed in 1892, uses a uniquely atmospheric method that he devised to effect a synthesis of the material world and the world of the imagination. In it, he denies the importance of external events and explores the quiet vibrations of the soul. His symbols function as links between the visible and invisible, the momentary and the eternal. The tangible fragments of common experience, the seemingly trivial everyday occurrences, however, furnish clues to the more decisive stuff of life. "Beneath all human thoughts, volitions, passions, actions," he writes in one of his essays, "there lies the vast ocean of the Unconscious, the unknown source of all that is good, true and beautiful. All that we know, think, feel, see and will are but bubbles on the surface of this vast sea." This sea, then, is the symbol of the absolute toward which all life is reaching out but can never quite grasp. What is heard is only the ripples on the surface. "The shallows murmur," as Maeterlinck puts it "while the deeps are dumb." A play by its very nature must unfold through the medium of speech, but Maeterlinck felt that "it is in silence that true life lies."

In his drama, the sea, the forest, the fountain, the abyss are the *dramatis personae* in a profounder sense than the human characters, who at best are but shadowy reflections of real people. In spite of the settings in which they appear, Maeterlinck's characters belong neither to the past nor to the future but hover in an extended now. They seem to have no spatial extension, no volume, but exist more as creatures of duration. They grope their way through the impenetrable forest of symbols that surrounds them and mysteriously controls their destinies. Daytime is never more than a shadowy twilight, and at night even the moon is veiled and its light pale. Maeterlinck is the master of the enigmatic, the indefinite, and paradoxical. Wise old Arkel is blind, but he is the only one in the cast who can "see" what is going on. Philosophical profundities flow more naturally from the child Yniold than from the more "mature" members of the family. And on her deathbed, Mélisande declares sonorously that she was never in better health. A book without a subject had once been projected by Flaubert, but it was never written. *Pelléas and Mélisande*, however, comes perilously close to being a play without a plot. So little is externalized that the progress of what plot there is seems to unfold within the characters. One overhears rather than hears the dialogue, and, in the ordinary sense, so little happens that a kind of dramatic vacuum is created which can be filled only by the imaginations of the spectators. Just as the eye must mix the colors in an impressionistic painting, so the observer's imagination in a Maeterlinck play must connect the metaphors, must unite the separate tableaux into a flow of images, must fill each pregnant pause with projections from his own experience, and must supply the emotional depth to its surface play of symbols.

Such a fragile theory is too flimsy a foundation on which to build a very substantial dramatic art, and it is not too surprising that Maeterlinck's audiences were somewhat baffled. A period that knew Zola's realistic novels and Ibsen's problem plays found it hard to enter into this shadowy world of the spirit. Maeterlinck's good fortune, even though he never quite realized it, was to find a composer who could fill his silences with the necessary nebulous sounds, who could give voice to the "murmur of eternity on the horizon," and who could write the music that provided the link from dream to dream. It was, indeed, as if the music of Claude Debussy had been created for the very purpose of providing the tonal envelope to enclose Maeterlinck's "ominous silence of the soul." Debussy was able to make the sea sing "the mysterious chant of the infinite." In his score, the references to the ocean on which all the characters are floating toward their unknown destinies are handled with special sensitivity. In one guise or another, its waters are present in practically every scene, either in the fragmentary form of a spring in the forest, a well in a courtyard, a fountain in a park, or the stagnant fetid pools of underground caverns. This ever-present water imagery is

Pelléas et Mélisande. Act II, Scene 1   Debussy

used as the symbol of the flowing, fleeting nature of experience. As an unstable medium without form of its own, it becomes the means of capturing vague atmospheric effects and reflecting subtle changes of mood. The course of Mélisande's life is conveyed by means of these changing waters. She comes from over the sea, is found by a dark pool in the forest, discovers her love for Pelléas at a fountain in the park, and as she dies she asks that the window be opened so that she can once more be with the sea.

Debussy was conversant with the literary figures and developments of his time, especially the work of Mallarmé and Pierre Louÿs. He had entered into their discussions and sought the technical means of translating their poetic theories into the medium of music. His style first took shape in the songs he wrote on texts by the symbolist poets, but Maeterlinck's drama provided him with the necessary lyric material to ripen it and bring it to maturity. Like the poets, his musical methods were in many ways the opposite of conventional operatic techniques. He followed Wagner in giving the orchestra the main task of carrying on the sequence of the drama; and, as a result, his work became more of a symphonic poem with running commentary by the singers than a conventional opera. With his characteristic insight, Debussy saw that melody, in the sense of a set operatic aria, impeded rather than promoted the dramatic progress. "I wished—intended, in fact—that the action should never be arrested; that it should be continuous, uninterrupted," he commented. "Melody is, if I may say so, almost anti-lyric, and powerless to express the constant change of emotion or life. Melody is suitable only for song (chanson), which confirms a fixed sentiment."

In thus considering recitative as the most important element of the lyric drama, he allies himself with his illustrious predecessors Lully and Rameau. But while their characters spoke in the highly inflected accents of baroque grandiloquence, Debussy's speak in cadences more closely approximating modern French. His prosody, in contrast to theirs, is more spoken than declaimed; and it comes closer to conversational than to theatrical French. "The characters in this drama endeavor to sing like real persons," the composer wrote; and by bringing their language closer to everyday speech, and allowing the flow of dramatic action to proceed without interruption, his opera assumes a plausibility seldom achieved in such a highly artificial medium. By using modes other than the traditional major and minor, his recitative takes on the flexible character of psalmodic chant. The rhythms are free, and the absence of regular accentuation allows the words to flow with elasticity. Debussy's motives parallel the literary symbols and are often just broken fragments of melody, which suggest rather than define atmospheric effects or are associated with the mood of a character. While used with greater subtlety, they nevertheless are much closer to Wagner's system of leitmotifs than Debussy was willing to admit. His harmonic method likewise was well suited to the rendition of the ambiguities and obscurities of the symbolist poets. His key centers lose their boundaries; progressions move about freely in tonal space; the predominance given to the tritone interval accents the indefinite drift; and everything is in a state of flux, always on its way but never arriving. Debussy's sensitivity to the timbre of sounds borders on the uncanny. He thought of Mélisande's voice as "soft and silky," and the woodwinds dominate the orchestral coloration with their peculiarly poignant and penetrating quality. Above all, performers must know how to make this intangible music live and breathe, how to render its rhythms with the proper elasticity, and how to fill its silences with meaning.

Debussy's evocation of Maeterlinck's pallid world is one of those rare instances of the indissoluble union of literature and music that make it impossible for later generations to think of them as separate entities. Debussy worked on the score over a period of ten years and was constantly worrying about the audience reaction to his fragile lyric drama. The play had not been a success, and in a letter dated August 1894, Debussy anxiously asks a friend, "How will the world get along with these two poor little beings?" In an obvious reference to the popularity of Zola's writing, he goes on to express his hatred of "crowds, universal suffrage, and tri-colored phrases." Even after the opera had been accepted for performance in 1897 and rehearsals had begun, he withdrew it again for another five years of revision. Contrary to expectation, however, the opera was a success and was widely performed. His elusive music ultimately proved its capacity to cast a spell over the most indifferent of audiences. After this it dropped out of sight for a while, but recent revivals have assured it a permanent place in the international repertory.

IDEAS

Any interpretation of the complex interplay of forces that underlies and motivates the divergent tendencies of the latter part of the 19th century faces the usual danger of oversimplification. Two of the most salient ideas, however, are chosen principally because they provide significant insights into the relationship of the several arts. These are: the influence of the scientific method on the arts and the interpretation of experience in terms of time.

Alliance of Art and Science

Artists in all fields were aware of the extraordinary success of the scientific method. Realism and impressionism brought a new objective attitude into the arts, together with an emphasis on the technical side of the crafts and a tendency for artists to become specialists pursuing a single aspect of their various media. Architects began to look toward engineers for the more advanced developments in building. A painting for an impressionist was a kind of experiment, an adventure in problem-solving. Cézanne thought of each of his pictures as a type of visual-research problem. In sculpture, Rodin was seeking for a new synthesis of matter and form. The literary realists were cultivating a scientific detachment in their writing and developing a technique that would enable them to record the details of their minute observations of everyday life with accuracy and precision. Zola, by means of his experimental novel, introduced a modified scientific technique to fiction. In addition to his poetic dramas, Maeterlinck wrote popular nature studies, such as his *Life of the Bee* and the *Magic of the Stars*. Debussy, when writing to a friend, spoke about some of his compositions as his "latest discoveries in musical chemistry."

Many of the actual discoveries of scientific research opened up new vistas in the various arts. Experiments in optical physics revealed secrets of light and color that painters could explore. New chemical syntheses provided more luminous pigments for their canvases. Increased knowledge of the physiology of the eye and the psychology of perception led to a re-examination of how an observer looks at a picture and what he perceives. New metal alloys and processes of casting were a boon to sculptors. The theories of evolution gave Rodin some poetic ideas on how form emerges from matter, the animate from the inanimate. Helmholtz' book *On the Sensation of Tone as a Physiological Basis for the Theory of Music* stirred Debussy and other composers to speculate on the relation of tone to overtone and consonance to dissonance, in their harmonic procedures.

The impressionistic painters were convinced that pictures were compounded of light and color, not line and form; the symbolists claimed that poetry was made with words, not ideas; and composers felt that music should be a play of varied sonorities rather than a means of evoking programmatic associations. By pursuing this general line of thought, Monet revealed a new concept of light and color and their interdependence; Rodin, an atmospheric extension of solid three-dimensional form; the symbolists, a new world of poetry; Debussy, a new concept of sound; and Paxton and Eiffel, by incorporating light and air into their designs, achieved a new architectural relationship between inner and outer space. This mechanistic phase, however, could lead just so far, and artists were soon trying to push beyond it into paths that would lead to deeper psychological insights. Each of the postimpressionists in his own way was probing to see how the new discoveries could be used as a means toward new modes of expression. Cézanne's path led into a new concept of pictorial geometry. Maeterlinck attempted to humanize science and describe it in poetical terms. In his case, the result was a kind of animism in which stones, fountains, and objects spoke a language and felt a soul life of their own. In an essay on the "Intelligence of Flowers," he tried to establish more sympathetic ties between man and nature.

In his stage fantasy *The Bluebird*, Sugar and Bread are among the live characters. Cézanne also felt the living force of the objects he placed in his still lifes, and in a conversation with a friend spoke warmly of the "soul" of a sugar bowl. The symbolists also tried to effect a synthesis between the phenomenal world and that of the creative imagination. Their metaphors were material in the sense that they received expression through the senses, but they hinted at the existence of a more profound ideational world and were definitely based on a view that life was something more than the sum of its molecular parts. Debussy also veered away from the exploration of the physical elements of sound toward the deeper psychological implications of tonal symbolism.

Continuous Flux

The arts of the late 19th century are also bound together by their common tendency toward the interpretation of experience in terms of time. Progress was an idea that was carried over from the late 18th century. Material progress continued to be an indisputable fact, but what was rapidly becoming apparent was that it did not go hand in hand with moral, spiritual, and aesthetic progress. With industrialization came a specialization in which men were concerned more with fragments than wholes. Industrial man was rapidly forfeiting to the machine his place as the primary productive unit. With this loss of control came a corresponding shift from a rational worldview toward an increasingly irrational one. With industrialization also came a capitalistic economy in which the lives of workers were controlled by intangible forces beyond themselves, such as the fluctuations in foreign markets and on the stock exchange. Two centuries previously, baroque man had been shaken by the Copernican revolution in which the notion of a static earth in the center of the universe was replaced by that of a freely moving satellite around the sun. Late 19th-century man was similarly rocked by the Darwinian and other evolutionary theories, which taught that creation was an ever-continuing process rather than an accomplished fact. As a result of such forces and ideas, the onward-and-upward notion of progress was revised downward to one of continuous flux and change.

The literary and visual realists concentrated on the momentary, the fragmentary, the everyday occurrence. Even when they planned their works in more comprehensive schemes, the effect was more that of a broad cross section than a coherent three-dimensional structure. For 20 years, Balzac worked on parts of his *Human Comedy*, Wagner on his Ring Cycle, Rodin on his *Gates of Hell*, and Proust on his *Remembrance of Things Past*. None, however, is a systematic, organic, or logical whole or a single perfected masterpiece. Instead of an all-embracing unity, they are easily broken down into a collection of fragments, motifs, genre scenes, scraps, and pieces. The late 19th century produced no grandiose metaphysical systems, such as those of Thomas Aquinas, Leibniz, Kant, or Hegel, each of whom tried to encompass all experience in a single universal structure.

The thinker who came the closest to making a coherent picture of this turbulent age was Henri Bergson, a lecturer at the École Normale in Paris. His point of departure was a remark made by the pre-Socratic philosopher Heraclitus, who had said that one cannot step into the same river twice. Bergson cited Heraclitus in support of his theory that time was more real than space, that the many were closer to experience than the one and becoming was closer to reality than being. Bergson was critical of the intellect because it tended to reduce reality to immobility. He therefore ranked intuition as a higher faculty than reason, because through it the perception of the flow of duration was possible, and through it static quantitative facts were quickened into the dynamic qualitative values of motion and change. Existence is never static but a transition between states and between moments of duration. Experience, he taught, is durational, "a series of qualitative changes, which melt into and permeate one another, without precise outlines. . . ." Art for Bergson is the force that sets man free and through which he can grasp "certain rhythms of life and breath," which compel him even against his will "to fall in with it, like passers by who join in a dance. And thus they compel us to set in motion, in the depth of our being, some secret chord which was only waiting to thrill."

Bergson was thus convinced that reality is mobility, tendency, or "incipient change of direction." Looking at or listening to a work of art is perceiving the mobile qualities of the objects or sounds presented. The aesthetic experience is essentially temporal and involves an "anticipation of movement," which permits the spectator or auditor in various ways "to grasp the future in the present." His theory of art is based on what he calls his "spiritualistic materialism" by which finely perceived material activity elicits spiritual echoes. All is based on the "uniqueness of the moment"; and perception of the temporal flow is synonymous with an awareness of the pulsation of life, something that is quite apart from the mechanical or inert matter. Past, present, and future are molded into an organic whole as "when we recall the notes of a tune melting, so to speak, into one another." Time, therefore, is "the continuous progress of the past, which gnaws into the future and which swells as it advances." But Bergson's concept of time is not clock time with its divisions into seconds, minutes, and hours, nor is it concerned with the usual groupings of past, present, and future. These are just arbitrary conveniences, like the points on a clock past which the hands move. Time cannot be spatialized and measured in such a quantitative way; it is a quality, not a substance.

The application of Bergson's theory of time to the arts of the late 19th century can be very illuminating. The philosopher often cited the motion picture as an example of what he meant by the perception of duration. The pictures in themselves are static, but through mobility the separate states are melted together by the mind into a continuous temporal flow. So also are the separate colors on an impressionistic canvas, the separate metaphors in a symbolist poem, the separate scenes in a Maeterlinck play, the separate chords in a Debussy progression, molded by the mind into a temporal continuum. In visual impressionism, the eye mixes the colors; in a symbolist poem, the mind supplies the connecting verbs for the nominal fragments; in a Maeterlinck play, the imagination makes the irrelevancies of speech and action into a dramatic sequence; and in Debussy's music, the ear bridges over the silences.

In all the arts, this ceaseless flux leads toward the improvisatory, the consciously incomplete; and each work tries to be a product of inspiration rather than calculation. With the visual impressionists, all pictorial substance is atomized into an airy mixture of color sprays, fleeting shadows, and momentary moods. Cézanne sometimes paints so thinly that parts of the canvas are actually bare, and at other times the texture is so thin as to be almost transparent. Rodin likewise leaves parts of the stone surrounding his figures uncut; and it is by no means an accident that some of the most important buildings of the time were open to the air and sky and were conceived as temporary exposition structures, such as the Crystal Palace, the Gallery of Machines, and the Eiffel Tower. In *Pelléas et Mélisande,* the characters are only outlined or sketched out, and what they really feel has to be inferred by the spectator. The imagination actually supplies the emotional depth to what is but a surface play of forms. In all instances the audience, through perception, imagination, and memory, actively participates in the creative activity.

Both the awareness of science and the accentuation of the temporal flow became important means by which the arts at the end of the century established the basis for the transition to the various modern styles. Cézanne has with justification been called the first great modern master; the functional architecture of Labrouste, Paxton, and Eiffel has become the foundation stone of contemporary architecture; Rodin's convex and concave surfaces and his preoccupation with the atmospheric problems of light and shadow have led to important new developments in sculpture; the fragmentary style of the symbolists anticipated the "stream-of-consciousness" and other techniques of modern literature; and Debussy's concept of relative rather than absolute tonality, together with his harmonic experimentation, have for their part pointed toward some of the significant musical developments of the 20th century.

CHRONOLOGY:
20th-Century Panorama

General Events

1891	Wainwright Building, St. Louis, first skyscraper
	Motion-picture camera patented by Thomas Edison; sound recording developed
1903	Aviation age begun by Wright brothers
1905	Einstein published articles on theory of relativity
	First motion-picture theater opened in Pittsburgh
1908	Model T (touring car) introduced by Henry Ford
1909	Wireless radio developed by Marconi
1914–1918	World War I
1917	Russian revolution began
1922	Fascist revolution in Italy
1929	New York stock market collapsed; depression began
1933	Nazi revolution in Germany
1936–1939	Spanish Civil War
1939	Television begun under commercial license
1939–1945	World War II
1945	First atomic bomb exploded
1950–1954	Korean War
1957	First earth satellite put into orbit by USSR; US satellite, 1958
1961	First manned satellite by USSR; US manned satellite, 1962

Architects

1856–1924	Louis Sullivan
1869–1959	Frank Lloyd Wright
1883–	Walter Gropius
1886–	Miës van der Rohe
1888–	Le Corbusier
1890–	J. J. P. Oud

Painters

1844–1910	Henri Rousseau (*le douanier*)
1866–1944	Vasily Kandinsky
1869–1954	Henri Matisse
1870–1954	John Marin
1871–1958	Giacomo Balla
1871–1958	Georges Rouault
1872–1944	Piet Mondrian
1879–1940	Paul Klee
1881–1955	Fernand Léger
1881–	Pablo Picasso
1882–	Georges Braque
1883–1949	Jose Clemente Orozco
1884–1920	Amadeo Modigliani
1886–1957	Diego Rivera
1886–	Oskar Kokoschka
1887–	Marc Chagall
1887–	Marcel Duchamp
1888–	Giorgio de Chirico
1889–	Thomas Hart Benton
1892–1942	Grant Wood
1893–	Joan Miro
1897–1946	John Stewart Curry
1898–	Charles Burchfield
1904–	Salvador Dali

Sculptors

1861–1944	Aristide Maillol
1876–1957	Constantin Brancusi
1883–1962	Ivan Mestrovic
1885–	Paul Manship
1888–	Hans (Jean) Arp
1898–	Henry Moore

Writers and Philosophers

1856–1939	Sigmund Freud
1856–1950	George Bernard Shaw
1863–1938	Gabriele d'Annunzio
1869–1951	André Gide
1871–1945	Paul-Ambroise Valéry
1874–1946	Gertrude Stein
1875–1955	Thomas Mann
1878–	Carl Sandburg
1882–1941	James Joyce
1885–1951	Sinclair Lewis
1887–1962	Robinson Jeffers
1888–1953	Eugene O'Neill
1888–	T. S. Eliot
1889–	Jean Cocteau
1897–1962	William Faulkner
1899–1961	Ernest Hemingway
1905–	Jean Paul Sartre

Musicians

1860–1911	Gustav Mahler
1862–1918	Claude Debussy
1864–1949	Richard Strauss
1866–1925	Erik Satie
1872–1915	Alexander Scriabin
1873–1943	Sergei Rachmaninoff
1874–1951	Arnold Schoenberg
1875–1937	Maurice Ravel
1876–1946	Manuel de Falla
1881–1945	Bela Bartok
1882–	Igor Stravinsky
1885–1935	Alban Berg
1891–1953	Serge Prokofieff
1892–	Darius Milhaud
1892–1955	Arthur Honegger
1895–	Paul Hindemith
1898–1937	George Gershwin
1899–	François Poulenc

20

CONTEMPORARY STYLES

THE 20TH CENTURY

Wars, revolutions, social upheavals, widespread displacement of people collectively and individually, scientific discoveries, technological innovations, and automation—all have proceeded at such a pace that 20th-century man has difficulty keeping up with himself. While new facilities for communication and new means of transportation are shrinking his globe, the vast expansion of knowledge is making it impossible for him to view his world as a whole. The completion of the Industrial Revolution and the accompanying necessity for specialization further fragment his vision. For him, clashes and discord are more usual than resolution and concord, disunity is ascendant over unity, and a multiverse has replaced the universe. In the quest for reality today's angry young man and modern organizational man exist in their lonely crowds—bombarded from all sides by the mass media of television, radio, motion pictures, newspapers, and magazines—and they cannot decide whether to conform or reform, suppress or express themselves, look within or without for enlightenment.

The 19th century, somehow, had been able to contain the forces of liberty and authority, democracy and dictatorship, individualism and collectivism, free enterprise and economic monopoly, scientific advances and orthodox religious beliefs, freedom of thought and anti-intellectual tendencies. The 20th century, however, has seen these smoldering disputes break out into open conflict.

707

The struggles of rival colonialisms were followed by revolutions in the wake of World War I that brought communism to Russia, fascism to Italy, nazism to Germany, civil war and dictatorship to Spain. There came a second world war, the Korean conflict, the cold war, and the emergence of a host of new nations from the disintegrating territories of old empires. These crises have been expressed in art movements as well as on the battlefields, for the arts are also forms of action. Artists, like social reformers and revolutionists, shout their battlecries, issue their manifestoes, and formulate their creeds and doctrines. But through the clangor, confusion, and multiplicity of styles, the voices of the new age can be heard.

While still within the 20th century, it is difficult to see the forest for the trees. Certain clearings in the woods, however, are already beginning to appear; and sizeable clumps, if not the whole forest, are coming into view. It is possible, for instance, to localize some movements in geographical terms, such as the Americans who fall into the regional schools. One knows certain aspects of the small midwestern town through Sinclair Lewis' novels, Illinois through Carl Sandburg's poetry, the Deep South through William Faulkner's books, and New England through Eugene O'Neill's plays. One sees Iowa through Grant Wood's eyes, Missouri through Thomas Benton's, Kansas through John Stewart Curry's, upstate New York through Charles Burchfield's, and New York City and the Maine coast through John Marin's. One can also hear the rhythms and melodies of these regions through the folk-song collectors and adapters. The early phases of expressionism can be identified with France and Germany prior to 1933; abstractionism with Russia and Holland up to 1921; futurism with Italy before World War I; cubism, the mechanical style, and surrealism with Paris; and the international style of architecture with Germany, France, and Holland. Yet any strict localization of arts, styles, and ideas is impossible in such a mobile period. The foremost architect of the century, Frank Lloyd Wright, found his ideas accepted in Europe and the Orient before his own United States discovered him. Ernest Hemingway resided abroad during his most productive years, and the materials for his novels were gathered in Paris, Italy, and Spain. While a whole generation of American artists have studied in Paris and other European centers, established European artists, because of political upheavals in their native countries, have come to the United States to continue their careers and teach.

From the temporal point of view, the 20th century has been marked by events that are often mirrored in its works of art. The aftermath of World War I brought about the bitter disillusionment that gave birth to the nihilistic movement called dadaism. The Mexican social revolution, which culminated in the 1920's, gave rise to the school of muralists that includes Rivera, Orozco, and Siqueiros. The depression of the 1930's brought forth many forms of violent protest. The Spanish civil war, which began in 1936, was responsible for Picasso's great mural *Guernica* and for Hemingway's novel *For Whom the Bell Tolls*. The ideational wars, the intellectual and scientific revolutions, which also affect the arts, do not obey such strict temporal laws, and their shadows are spread over broader intervals of time and place.

In approaching the art of the 20th century, one must keep many things in mind. All art has to be understood first and foremost in terms of its own frame of reference and what the artist is trying to do. The contemporary artist, contrary to the expectations of a large segment of his potential audience, does not necessarily aim to please. The customer, in his considered opinion, is not always right. His motives may be to delight or irritate, to exhort or castigate, to surprise or excite, to soothe or shock. A painter may deliberately plan a picture as a visual sock in the eye. A composer may intend his music as aural assault and battery. Judging from the reactions to some of Picasso's early exhibits and the riot that greeted Stravinsky's ballet *The Rite of Spring*, some artists have succeeded beyond their wildest expectations; it is also the audience's privilege to accept or reject.

The artist's honest convictions must also be taken into account. When a sculptor concludes that he lives in a misshapen and deformed world, he can hardly be blamed if he does not portray it in symmetrical contours. If a novelist feels that life is cruel and ugly, common candor would not permit him to suppress his views. If a composer is convinced that his age is marked by tension and discord, he would not be truthful if he disregarded dissonance and wrote in saccharine harmonies. As artists observe the current informality of dress and manners, they cannot be condemned because their works lack the formal qualities that characterized previous centuries. At times, an artist may find tight organization necessary for his purpose; at others, a deliberately contrived chaos. Sometimes a contemporary artist is concerned with conceptual meaning; often the act of painting or writing becomes an alternative. Just as some abstract painters have eliminated subject matter from their pictures, writers, such as Gertrude Stein and James Joyce, have at times written without a subject. In the absence of such a normal focus, their works become extremely difficult to read, and much of them must remain enigmatic. Some conservative composers, such as Rachmaninoff, continued to write in the lush emotional vein of romanticism. Others, such as Stravinsky and Hindemith, wrote music that is intentionally nonexpressive. Schoenberg, in order to avoid sounding romantic, often went to such extreme lengths that he became highly romantic about his antiromanticism. The problem of understanding such a complex picture is far from simple.

Modern materials and methods, as well as engineering and communication techniques, have opened up new possibilities in the arts. In architecture, glass and ferroconcrete have taken their places alongside bricks and mortar, while cantilevering has joined the post-and-lintel. The sculptor now uses the welding torch as well as the chisel, and his materials are aluminum and plastics as well as bronze and marble. Painters work on masonite surfaces as well as canvas and with the palette knife as well as the brush. And a new pictorial category of abstract and imaginary pictures has been added to the traditional classifications of historic paintings, genre scenes, portraiture, landscape, and still life. The graphic arts have been expanded to include many new media, among them silk-screen printing and color photography. The arbitrary distinction between the so-called "major and minor arts," fine arts and crafts, beauty and utility has narrowed to the point where architect and engineer, sculptor and furniture designer, a cathedral and a suspension bridge—once thought to be poles apart— have been brought together in the modern unity of form and function. Drama has expanded from the live theater to include the motion picture and television media. New concepts of language are being explored with words used as syllabic sounds in an abstract poetry, and composers are busy exploring the possibilities of electronically generated sound.

During no other century has it been possible to witness the construction of so many buildings, see so many paintings, read so much literature, or hear so much music. The facility of modern travel; the flood of picture books, paperbacks, and recordings; the proliferation of television, radio, and motion-picture performances have brought about a greater accessibility to the arts than any previous age has ever known. Through high fidelity recording, the entire literature of music—past and present—has become available, and every home is a potential concert hall. Through television, every living room can be both a theater and an opera house. And picture books and prints have become what André Malraux has called museums without walls. But, as with any positive advance in civilization, there is a corresponding negative aspect. The obverse side of the coin is seen in the exploitation of the arts for commercial purposes and in the attitudes of casualness bordering on indifference when great experiences are available with too little effort.

With the mass media there are so many publics, so many degrees of sophistication, so many levels of education, so many frames of national and international reference, that an artist can no longer be sure which audience he is addressing. Unlike past times when a direct relationship existed between artist and patron, the contemporary creator can only cast his art on the wave lengths of sight and sound and hope somewhere and somehow to reach a sympathetic segment of his anonymous audience. There is also a concomitant confusion in the choice of media. Knowing that a wider public may be reached, a novelist may well write a book with the expectation that it will be staged or filmed, a painter or sculptor produce works that will photograph well in a picture book, and a composer or performer adapt his style to make a successful recording.

The tempo of change has been so swift that 20th-century man cannot keep pace with his scientists and artists. The span of time between important innovations and their popular acceptance, often referred to as cultural lag, is found also in late 19th-century Paris. There the realists, impressionists, and post-impressionists were refused official approval by the academicians and had to exhibit in the *Salon des Refusés* (Salon of the Rejected). These painters had to wait for approval until the 20th century and perhaps, by way of compensation, are almost overly popular today. Similarly, the major breakthroughs in contemporary art had already occurred before World War II with the discoveries of Frank Lloyd Wright, Gropius, and Corbusier in architecture; Picasso, Kandinsky, and Mondrian in painting; and Schoenberg and Stravinsky in music. These artists now enjoy the status of old masters of modern art, while the younger generation of artists as well as the public is, quite understandably, passing through a period of consolidation and assimilation of the gains that have been made.

In sorting out the developments in contemporary art, one needs to remember that basically there are but two ways of looking at the world—from within or without, subjectively or objectively, through emotion or reason. These outlooks are by no means mutually exclusive since mind is necessary for emotional awareness, and without emotional drive even the most rational proposition would be empty and devoid of meaning. The arts in which emotional considerations are dominant can be classified under expressionism; those in which logical and analytical processes are uppermost, as abstractionism. Here a note of caution must be sounded, because all art is expressive to some degree, just as all art is abstract to a certain extent.

EXPRESSIONISM

Expressionism looks within to a world of emotions and psychological states rather than outward at a world of colored reflections. The expressionist is fully conscious of the visible world, but, leaving behind the classical idea of art as an imitation of nature, he closes his eyes to explore the world of the mind, spirit, and imagination. He would agree with Goethe's dictum that feeling is all, and he welcomed Freud's delving into the subconscious that revealed a new world of emotion in the dark drives, hidden terrors, and mysterious motivations that underlie human behavior. Beginning with his *Interpretation of Dreams* (1900), Freud's books and those of his associates were to affect profoundly the pictorial, literary, and musical expression of the 20th century. The expressionist is well aware that he inhabits a number of complex overlapping worlds, and he knows too that there are worlds to be explored which are not seen by the eye and which are not subject to logical interpretation. Expressionistic pictures are in psychological rather than natural focus, describing intangible worlds with new techniques and new symbols, discordant colors and distorted shapes. The clashing dissonances of expressionistic music are intended to arouse rather than soothe the listener, and expressionistic literature intends to startle the reader with subjective revelations of psychical, often psychotic, states.

As James Joyce phrased it, the artist should strive "constantly to *express*, to *press out again*, from the gross earth or what it brings forth, from sound, shape and colour which are the prison gates of our soul, an image of the beauty we have come to understand—that is art." To describe his reactions to physical, psychical, and spiritual events, the expressionist alters, distorts, and colors his images according to the intensity of his feelings. Expressionism, then, may range from quiet nostalgic moods, through sudden shock reactions and hysterical outbursts, to screaming nightmares. The results of such expressionistic excursions into the subconscious may be quite uneven, but the artists' passports to such nether regions are nonetheless valid. Over the years, expressionism has embraced such movements as neoprimitivism, dadaism, surrealism, social protest, and the warmly human spatial dreams of Frank Lloyd Wright's organic architecture.

Neoprimitivism

As the great conflagration of 20th-century expressionism burst into flame, the spark that set fire to that movement called neoprimitivism was the 19th-century discovery of the primitive arts of the South Sea islanders and the wood carvings of indigenous African tribes. As the term is used here, *neoprimitivism* is limited to the conscious adaptations by sophisticated artists of authentic specimens of primitive art. The first major artist to employ the colorful Polynesian patterns and motifs in his woodcuts and paintings had been Gauguin, and such pictures as his *Mahana No Atua* (Fig. 19:7), painted during his extended sojourn in Tahiti, clearly reflect the native influence. Examples of Polynesian craftsmanship, such as oars, arrows, and harpoons, had been collected by traders on their voyages and were shown in the Paris expositions of 1878 and 1889. Later, when expeditions went to the interior of the dark continent, wooden objects carved by African Negro tribesmen were brought back for display; and the ethnological museums, founded in Paris and Dresden to house these collections, commanded considerable interest among scholars, artists, and the general public. Articles and books on African sculpture soon began to appear, and in 1890 James Frazer began publishing *The Golden Bough*, a monumental 12-volume compendium of primitive customs and beliefs, folk lore, magical practices, and taboos.

With its complete negation of the notion of progress, primitive art seemed like the promise of a new beginning, while the animistic attitude of the primitive carvers who divined the spirit of their wood and stone and revealed it in the grain, textures, and shapes of their materials had particular appeal. German expressionists were fascinated by the strange weird forms and anti-intellectualism of African images; French artists, among them Matisse, found in their simplified geometrical forms a new wealth of decorative motifs and a justification for their abstract designs; and the Spaniard Picasso, who for a time had his African period, painted the *Young Ladies of Avignon* (Fig. 20:1), finished in 1907, that has been one of the pivotal pictures of modern art.

From his sketches, it is known that Picasso had started out to paint an allegory. A man in the midst of fruit and women was to have symbolized Vice, while his counterpart entering on the left with a skull in his hand was to have represented Virtue. But while his picture was in its preliminary stages, Picasso was impressed by an exhibit of pre-Roman Iberian sculpture, which, as in most primitive art, represented the human body as sharply angular and reduced to severe geometrical pattern. Thus, in his painting, the girl on the left who is pulling back some curtains is represented as a system of overlapping planes and geometrically arranged contours. A short while later, Picasso was also stimulated by Negro sculpture exhibited at the Trocadero Museum in Paris, and he started a collection of his own primitives, which included specimens from the west coast of Africa. The resemblance of the *Mask* from Itumba in the old French Congo (Fig. 20:2) to the head of the figure in the upper right of Picasso's painting is most striking. Just below, the head of the young woman and the profile of the figure on the left also show African influence. Drawings he made just before he finished the *Young Ladies* reveal his interest in the oval-shaped heads, the long noses, small mouths, and angular bodies that character-ized the sculpture of the Ivory Coast. Under these African and Iberian in-fluences, Picasso turned entirely from the pathos of his earlier period to a stricter formalism. In the case of this picture, he abandoned the original allegorical plan and blended the female figures, the drapery in the background, and the still life below into an abstract design. The color, with its spectrumlike blending of bright shades one into another, contributes the effect of an emotional cre-scendo, while the formal arrangement of the figures suggests the angular rhythms of a primitive dance. The title of the picture is relatively unimportant and seems to have been suggested by a friend as a joke.

The impact of primitive art was felt in other fields than painting. When the young Italian painter Modigliani came to Paris in 1906, he fell so completely under the spell of African Negro sculpture that for a while he traded the brush for the chisel. One of his sculptured works, *Head* (Fig. 20:3), is in the same Ivory Coast style that Picasso had adopted, and, in his paintings, he later

Fig. 20:1 (*above*). Picasso. *Les Demoiselles d'Avignon* (*Young Ladies of Avignon*). Oil on canvas. 96″ x 92″. 1907. Collection, Museum of Modern Art, New York

Fig. 20:2 (*left*). *Wooden Mask from Itumba*, former French Congo. 14″ high. Collection, Museum of Modern Art, New York

Fig. 20:3. Modigliani. *Head*. Stone. 22¼″ high. *c.*1915. Collection, Museum of Modern Art, New York

used stylized oval faces and elongated forms. The sculptors Brancusi and Henry Moore at various times also came under the African influence.

Knowledge of non-European musical systems had likewise increased rapidly during the late 19th century. The orchestrations of Debussy and Ravel had been influenced by the strange and exotic sounds of the gamelan orchestras from Java, which they heard at the International Exposition of 1889. By far the strongest of these influences, however, was American jazz music, which had its beginnings in New Orleans and Chicago and which was heard in Europe through the traveling Negro bands. In his group of piano pieces called *The Children's Corner* (1908), Debussy included a number called "Golliwog's Cake Walk." The Golliwog was an eccentric comic-strip character in the Paris newspapers who was born out of an ink blot. Obviously a popularization of the interest in primitivism, he delighted grown-ups as well as children with his antics. The cake walk was, of course, a favorite dance in the American Negro minstrel shows and one of the ancestors of the fox trot.

Stravinsky included a Moor in his ballet *Petrouchka* (1911), and the music he gives him is quasi-Oriental. Two years later, however, in the *Rite of Spring*, Stravinsky achieved the primitive musical counterpart of Picasso's *Young Ladies of Avignon*. Subtitled "Scenes from Pagan Russia," the opening Dance of the Adolescents uses repetitive rhythms and syncopated accents similar to those of American jazz. The sharply angular melodies, the complex polyrhythmic textures, the brutal accentuations, and the geometrical movements of the dancers are a masterly realization of the spirit of savagery.

The Rite of Spring. Dance of the Adolescents   Stravinsky

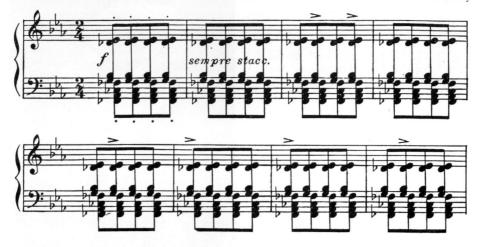

The primitive hypnotic repeated rhythms first exploited by Stravinsky are found, minus the jazz element, in the familiar Ritual Fire Dance from Manuel de Falla's ballet *Love the Sorcerer* (*El Amor Brujo*, 1915), and culminate in Ravel's *Bolero* (1928), in which the dance tune is repeated in the same key 18 times. The vast dynamic crescendo and heavy use of a battery of percussion instruments invariably incite an audience to a thoroughly primitive state of frenzy. The entrance of jazz idioms into serious musical forms is also one of the familiar patterns of contemporary music. Stravinsky published some ragtime music for piano in 1922, with a cover designed by Picasso; and George Gershwin's *Rhapsody in Blue* (1924) and his jazz opera *Porgy and Bess* (1935) have achieved a wide popular success.

Wild Animals, Blue Riders, and Operatic Uproars

The expressionist deals with intensities of feeling rather than intensities of light. For him, the heat of creation supersedes the coldness of imitation, and he presents subjective reactions instead of representing objective realities, reasserting the supremacy of the human imagination over the impersonality of nature. About the time Picasso was discovering primitive sculpture, other groups were forwarding expressionism in painting as a reaction to the cool atmospheric effects and objective detachment of impressionism. Van Gogh had pointed the way with his frenzied canvases, passionate pictorial outbursts, saturated colors, and evangelical fervor. Such a painting as *Starry Night* (Fig. 19:8), with the dark-green flames of the cypress trees, rolling rhythms of the hills, and cosmic explosion of the Milky Way, was enough to set imaginations on fire. The barbaric splendor of Gauguin's color harmonies was seized upon as a useful

Fig. 20:4. Matisse. *Blue Window*. Oil on canvas. 51½" x 35⅝". *c.*1911. Collection, Museum of Modern Art, New York

means for producing lively emotional responses, while the expressionists looked more distantly at the luminous colors of medieval stained glass and the imaginative inventiveness of Romanesque sculpture. Primitive arts of Polynesia and Africa played their parts here too.

The violent color clashes and visual distortions of the French painters of expressionistic persuasion earned for them the critical designation of *Les Fauves*, or the Wild Animals. The early work of Matisse was so classified, though in retrospect it is difficult to understand why. If there was ever anything "wild" about Matisse, it has to be found in his reveling in brilliant color for its own sake, a subtle resourcefulness of invention, and a quality of Oriental splendor, which make him a *fauve* but a *fauve* devoid of ferocity. To Matisse, expression did not apply to the content of his canvases or to the communication of an emotional message but rather to the entire formal management of his pictorial pattern. "Expression to my way of thinking," he once remarked, "does not consist of the passion mirrored upon a human face or betrayed by a violent gesture. The whole arrangement of my picture is expressive. . . ."

The *Blue Window* (Fig. 20:4), which he painted in 1911, shows his concern with formal aesthetic problems, vibrant color harmonies, and arabesquelike

Fig. 20:5. Kandinsky. *Improvisation No. 30 (On a Warlike Theme)*. Oil on canvas. 43¼" square. 1913. Art Institute, Chicago

decorative motifs. The picture is composed as an abstract still-life study merging subtly into a stylized landscape. The hatpins in the cushion on the left unite with the empty vase behind them; the flowers in the other vase grow into the foliage and the roof of the painter's studio outside; the Oriental idol in the axial center leads the eye to the vertical division of the casement window, while the lines formed by the contours of the lamp continue with those of the tree trunk in the garden. The bedroom table and its objects are thus united with the trees and sky beyond, and the interior and exterior elements become parts of one design. Depth and recession are suggested only by a slight lessening of the color intensities. In this picture, Matisse came close to realizing his dream of an "art of balance, of purity and serenity devoid of depressing subject matter."

Kandinsky is an international figure, who first painted in his native Russia, worked next in the impressionistic and postimpressionistic styles in Paris, and then joined the Blue Rider group in Munich that was exploiting the various possibilities of expressionism. Eventually, he arrived at the type of abstract expressionism known as nonobjective art (see also pages 745–746) in which painting is "liberated" from nature. His *Improvisation on a Warlike Theme* (Fig. 20:5) shows what he can express with lines, colors, and shapes. Commenting on this work, Kandinsky stated that its content is "what the spectator *lives* or *feels* while under the effect of the *form and color combinations* of the picture"

—which may or may not coincide with what the artist had in mind when he painted it. In this case, the artist mentions that he painted it "subconsciously and in a state of strong tension" in 1913 when rumors of war were rife. This, he added, explains the presence of the two cannons in the lower left and the explosive forms. Kandinsky, who published poetry, plays, and an autobiography, also recognized the affinity of his work to music. According to his own account, he strove to reproduce on his canvases the "choir of colors which nature has so painfully thrust into my very soul," and he believed that a painting should be "an exact replica of some inner emotion." Works that required "an evenly sustained pitch of inner emotional uplift sometimes lasting for days" he called "compositions." Spontaneous shorter works, sketches, and watercolors that "do not last the span of a longer creative period" he designated "improvisations."

Some of the earliest and most violent outbursts of musical expressionism are found in Richard Strauss' operas *Salome* (1905) and *Elektra* (1909). Taking off from Richard Wagner's *Tristan und Isolde*, Salome's "love death" is an operatic excursion into the realm of abnormal psychology. In *Salome*, Strauss lures his listeners with sensuous sounds and a rainbow of radiant orchestral colors, and at the same time horrifies them with the gruesome spectacle of Salome's amorous soliloquy to the severed head of John the Baptist. This simultaneous attraction and repulsion is bound to produce emotional excitement and elicit truly expressionistic reactions. The sensational nature of Oscar Wilde's libretto, together with the famous Dance of the Seven Veils, caused the opera to be banned in New York, Boston, and London. *Elektra* is a dramatically effective version of Sophocles' tragedy (as adapted by Hugo von Hofmannsthal) filled with emotional climaxes, blood-curdling shrieks, and lurid orchestral sounds.

Arnold Schoenberg's expressionistic song cycle *Pierrot Lunaire* (1912) explores the weird world of Freudian symbolism, and in his monodrama *The Lucky Hand* (*Die Glückliche Hand*, 1913) the dissonances of the musical score are reinforced by crescendos of colored lights. Something of a climax is achieved in Alban Berg's opera *Wozzeck* (1925), a musical dramatization of big-city low life, in which a ballet of beggars, drunkards, and street girls pursue the murderer as he vainly tries to escape from himself. Whereas Wagner had worked up his climaxes over a considerable period of time, generally starting low in pitch and volume and mounting upward in an extended melodic, harmonic, and dynamic crescendo, Schoenberg and Berg telescoped the process. Their music became all climax, with the extremes of low and high, soft and loud, following each other suddenly and by leaps instead of in a gradual progression. Dissonances with Wagner existed in chains of sequences that eventually resolved. With Schoenberg and Berg, dissonance exists freely for its own sake with little or no relation to consonance.

Fig. 20:6. Chirico. *The Disquieting Muses*. Oil on canvas. 37¾″ x 25⅞″. Private collection

Dadaism and Surrealism

In their Paris exhibits of 1911 and 1912, the Italian Giorgio de Chirico and the Russian Marc Chagall anticipated the development of dadaism and surrealism. The latter term, in fact, was coined at that time by the French critic and playwright Guillaume Apollinaire to describe the dream fantasies, memory images, visual paradoxes, and assorted incongruities of their pictures. Chirico's dreamscape *The Disquieting Muses* (Fig. 20:6) takes expressionism into an introspective world of free associations. "Everything," according to this artist, "has two aspects: the current aspect, which we see nearly always and which ordinary men see, and the ghostly and metaphysical aspect, which only rare individuals may see in moments of clairvoyance and metaphysical abstraction." On a visit to the Versailles Palace, as he says in his autobiography, he realized that "every corner of the palace, every column, every window possessed a spirit, an impregnable soul. . . . At that moment I grew aware of the mystery which urges men to create strange forms." His intention was to break down the barriers of childhood and adulthood, the sleeping and waking states, the unbelievable and

Fig. 20:7. Chagall. *I and the Village.* Oil on canvas. 75⅝" x 59⅝". 1911. Collection, Museum of Modern Art, New York

the believable, the illogical and the logical, the fantastic and the familiar. *The Disquieting Muses* is filled with an ominous silence and an all-pervading emptiness that are heightened by the mystery of deep perspective. Other Chirico pictures bear the deliberately ambiguous but evocative titles, couched in Freudian psychoanalytic terms, of *Nostalgia of the Infinite, Melancholy and Mystery of a Street,* and *Enigma of an Autumn Afternoon.* They are filled with sundials casting lengthened shadows, arcaded galleries, empty vans, modern factory buildings, and spacious city squares populated only with strange statues. These elusive fantasies are based on Chirico's memories of his youth spent in Greece and Italy, and they are painted with a meticulous academic brush technique.

   I and the Village (Fig. 20:7) grows out of Chagall's memories of Russia. In one of his childhood reveries he remembered the ceiling of his parent's crowded cottage suddenly becoming transparent. "Clouds and blue stars penetrated along with the smell of the fields, the stable and the roads," he writes, and "my head detaches itself gently from my body and weeps near the kitchen where the fish is being prepared." In *I and My Village,* as in a dream, one image is superimposed on another, the houses are topsy-turvy, the farmer going to the fields is right side up, the peasant woman upside down, and the cow seems to be dreaming contentedly about a milkmaid.

The melancholy empty spaces of Chirico's and Chagall's dream worlds find a remarkable parallel in Gustav Mahler's *Song of the Earth* (1911) and Thomas Mann's short novel *Death in Venice* (1913). In them, there is the same attempt to synthesize the contradictory tendencies of the time, the same juxtaposition of banal and fanciful elements, the same weary lyricism, a similar longing for the unattainable, the same elusive ideals hovering on the distant horizon.

Dadaism was the product of the disillusionment and defeatism of World War I. Anguished artists felt that the civilization that had brought about such horrors should be swept away and a new beginning made. Dadaism, consequently, was a nihilistic movement, particularly distrustful of order and reason, a challenge to polite society, and a protest against all prevailing styles in art. Dada artists worked out an ism to end all isms, painted pictures compounded of the contents of waste baskets, concocted nonsense for the sake of nonsense, wrote manifestoes against manifestoes, and their political expression was anarchy. Their bitter humor and iconoclasm, however, helped to clear the postwar atmosphere. Fortunately, dadaism did not last long and many of its artists were absorbed into surrealism (or superrealism), the logical successor movement in expressionism, which has been aptly called the "dadaism of the successful."

The surrealist manifesto of 1924 proclaimed that the style was based on "pure psychic automatism by means of which one sets out to express, verbally, in writing or in any other manner, the real functioning of thought without any control by reason or any aesthetic or moral preoccupation." Members of the group believed in the superior reality of the dream to the waking state, of fantasy to reason, of the subconscious to the conscious mind. André Breton, author of the manifesto, also spoke of the "convulsive beauty" of dreams, and

Fig. 20:8. Dali. *Persistence of Memory*. Oil on canvas. 9½" x 13". 1931. Collection, Museum of Modern Art, New York

Fig. 20:9. Klee. *Diana*. Oil on wood. 37½″ x 23⅝″. 1931. Collection of Mr. and Mrs. William Bernoudy, St. Louis

the surrealists developed a psychological symbolism in the manner of Freud's *Interpretation of Dreams*. The painter Salvador Dali associated himself with the group in 1929 and became one of its leading advocates. He described his pictures as "hand-painted dream photographs" and adorned them with symbols of various phobias, delusions, complexes, and other trappings of abnormal psychology. Like Chirico and Chagall, Dali was haunted by the mystery of time, and besides evolutionary, geological, and archeological concepts of time, his *Persistence of Memory* (Fig. 20:8) suggests images of dream time.

Today Paul Klee is generally accepted as one of the most significant pictorial talents of the century. Such pictures as *Diana* (Fig. 20:9) have caused many to dismiss him with a shrug, a scoff, or a smile. His disarming childlike innocence, however, is a highly deceptive simplicity and usually masks infinitely subtle meaning. His inventiveness outdoes even Picasso. He can delight the eye, tickle the fancy, or repel the observer with images straight out of nightmares. *Apparatus for Magnetic Treatment of Plants, Twittering Machine, A Cookie Picture, Moonplay, Idol for Housecats, Child Consecrated to Suffering, A Phantom Breaks Up*—so the titles run. The symbolism in his *Diana* will show the extraordinary complexity of Klee's art. The title identifies the figure

Fig. 20:10. Miro. *Personages with Star*. Oil on canvas. 78¼" x 97½". 1933. Art Institute, Chicago

as the mythical goddess of the chase, while the arrow is equipped magically with an eye to insure unerring accuracy. The broken contours of Diana's body suggest hurried flight through space, and the wheel under the goddess' foot is derived from Romanesque sculpture where it signified miraculous transportation. The color and surface treatment recall impressionism and Seurat's pointillism.

Klee consciously set out to look at the world through the eyes of a child in order to achieve a spontaneity untroubled by reason. "I want to be as though new-born, knowing nothing," as he put it. With Klee, as with Freud, the child was father of the man. By experimenting with hypnotic suggestion and psychic automatism, he gives his drawings the casual quality of doodles or the impulsiveness of improvisations. His mastery of line is so complete, however, that his work should never be confused with carelessness. By sticking mainly to small forms and to the techniques of watercolor and ink, pencil and crayon, he produces pictures with a refreshing unpretentiousness. He also has an element of genial humor that is notably missing in so much of modern art.

Joan Miro, like Klee, essayed an art of pure imagination existing outside logic or reason. His *Personages with Star* (Fig. 20:10) uses the technique of automatic drawing in a trancelike state and shows the influence of Kandinsky. While much of surrealism is preoccupied with morbid and abnormal psychological states, Miro lightens his fantasies with whimsy. His pictures have such fanciful titles as *Persons Magnetized by the Stars Walking on the Music of a Furrowed Landscape*, and they teem with abstract insects that buzz silently and geometrical worms that squirm statically.

The attempts by the surrealists to work in the arts of sculpture, literature, and music have not been successful, and significant parallels can be found only outside the movement. James Joyce and Gertrude Stein tried to establish a method for subconscious or automatic writing as a way to tap the reservoir of the subconscious mind. The result was the stream-of-consciousness technique, notably exemplified in Joyce's *Ulysses* (1922). The more irreverent iconclastic tendencies of surrealist painting have their musical parallels in such compositions as Erik Satie's three piano pieces of 1913. Entitled *Desiccated Embryos*, they have semisarcastic expression marks, such as that which calls upon the pianist to play a melody "like a nightingale with a toothache." There is also the biting satire of Prokofieff's brilliant fairy-tale opera *Love of Three Oranges* (1921) and the weird symbolism of Bela Bartok's legendary opera *Bluebeard's Castle* (1922). Paul Klee's world of childhood fantasy finds a charming lyrical counterpart in Maurice Ravel's opera *The Child and the Sorceries* (*L'Enfant et les Sortilèges*) of 1925. In Colette's libretto, a child breaks some bric-a-brac and toys in a temper tantrum. In a dreamlike sequence, the objects then come to life to seek revenge. A Wedgewood teapot and a china cup, appropriately enough, carry on a conversation in broken English while dancing a fox trot; a little old man pops up out of nowhere and sings multiplication tables and story problems with erroneous answers; two cats sing a hilarious meowing duet; and all that is left of the torn picture of the fairy princess in the story book is "a golden hair and the debris of a dream." Ravel's ingenious orchestration adds whistles, wood-blocks, and friction instruments to the usual ones and cheese graters for certain bizarre effects.

Neoclassical Interlude

No century would be complete without its bow before the shrines of Greece and Rome, and just as the Renaissance, the 18th and the 19th centuries did, the 20th century has its neoclassicism. While works with classical allusions abound in the present century, the neoclassic movement came into sharpest focus in the 1920's. The comparative calm before the storm of World War I had been riled by the emotional extremes of pictorial expressionism and such neo-primitive outbursts as Stravinsky's *Rite of Spring*. In the aftermath of war, order and clarity seemed more important than violent expression.

In 1917, Picasso had made a trip to Italy where he was impressed by the Pompeiian wall paintings and stimulated by meetings in Rome with Stravinsky and Serge Diaghileff, who were there with the latter's Russian ballet company. One direct result was their three-way collaboration on a ballet with song called *Pulcinella*, which was first performed in Paris in 1920. Stravinsky's score was based on the form of the classical dance suite of the early 18th century with

Fig. 20:11. Picasso. *Three Graces*. Oil and charcoal on canvas. 78⅞″ x 59″. 1924. Collection of the artist. Courtesy Museum of Modern Art, New York

music adapted from Pergolesi. Picasso's costumes were designed in the manner of the stylized *commedia dell' arte* characters of Pierrot, Harlequin, and so on, while his scenery included a backdrop filled with angular distortions showing a street in Naples with a view of the bay and a moonlit Mt. Vesuvius. In 1922, an adaptation of Sophocles' *Antigone* by Jean Cocteau was mounted in Paris. Picasso designed the scenery and masks, while the incidental music for harp and oboe was supplied by Arthur Honegger. An opera called *The Eumenides* by Darius Milhaud, based on Paul Claudel's translation of the tragedy by Aeschylus, was written in the same year. *Mercury* was the title of still another ballet brought out by the Diaghileff company in 1924, with music by Erik Satie and costumes and scenery by Picasso. Three years later, Stravinsky completed his opera-oratorio *Oedipus Rex*. Diaghileff again was the producer, and Jean Cocteau's text, based on Sophocles' tragedy, was translated into Latin so that it would be in a "petrified" language and thus would be reduced to mere syllabic material. The motionless stance of the actors was intended to make them as static as Greek columns, and the chorus was placed back of a bas relief where only their heads were visible. Such productions continued sporadically throughout the 1930's where Stravinsky is once more found collaborating with André Gide on a work for orchestra, chorus, and tenor called *Persephone* (1934).

Picasso's pictures in the 1920's, such as the *Three Graces* (Fig. 20:11), also reflect this neoclassicism and are characterized by elegance of line, sculpturesque modeling of bodies, and reduction of pictorial elements to the barest essentials. Others, such as *The Pipes of Pan* (1923), are beach scenes in which the figures appear statuesquely against geometrically organized backgrounds and chaste colors of white and blue. While his painting took another tack after the *Three Graces*, his many book illustrations continued to show classical influences. Picasso had long admired the linear technique of Ingres, especially the pencil drawings. Even in such an austere medium as etching, his illustrations for a new edition of Ovid's *Metamorphoses* (1930) and for Gilbert Seldes' version of Aristophanes' *Lysistrata* (1934) show his capacity for effective expression.

In the neoclassical interlude, the statues of Maillol and Despiau reassert the expressive importance of the nude figure, both in the round and in relief, while a musical counterpart is found in the ballet and many purely instrumental works. A list would include such works as Debussy's *Six Épigraphes Antiques* (1914) for two pianos, the first of which is an "Invitation to Pan"; Ravel's revival of the French classical piano suite in the *Tomb of Couperin* (1918); and Prokofieff's well-known *Classical Symphony*, which is consciously patterned after the symphonic style of the 18th century and has a finale in the Haydn manner. Stravinsky adopted the style in a way that is marked more by cerebration than inspiration in a work such as his *Duo Concertante* (1932), which contains movements labeled Eclogue and Dithyramb that pay his respects to the pastoral poets of antiquity.

One of the most consistent patterns of contemporary literature, especially in France, is the reinterpretation of Greek myths in highly sophisticated terms as a subtle device for pointing out modern moralistic or political parallels. This tendency runs regularly through the works of André Gide from his early *Prometheus Drops His Chains* (1899) to his autobiographical story *Theseus* (1946). It can also be found in Franz Werfel's antiwar play *The Trojan Women* (1914) and in Jean Paul Sartre's *The Flies* (1943). The latter was staged in Paris during the Nazi occupation, and the allusion to the plague of flies that sucked blood of Orestes in Aristophanes' bitter comedy could have escaped no one. Poets have sometimes found classical subjects a convenient way of leaving their works in a fragmentary state like antique ruins. Paul-Ambroise Valéry's trilogy of 1922, for instance, contains a poem called "Fragments of Narcissus." T. S. Eliot's *Sweeny Agonistes* (1932) in which the grandeur of the past is contrasted with the banality of the present, likewise is incomplete and bears the subtitle "Fragments of an Aristophanic Melodrama." Freud's use of the names of characters from Greek literature—Oedipus, Electra, Narcissus—as symbols of recurrent subconscious drives also found its way into literature.

James Joyce's novels *The Portrait of the Artist as a Young Man* (1916) and *Ulysses* (1922) use classical allusions as a frame of reference but avoid the logic and order of Greek forms. The author's admitted inspiration for *Ulysses* was Homer's *Odyssey*. With his adoption of the stream-of-consciousness technique, the classical molds became convenient devices to hold the nebulous dream-like sequences in some semblance of unity. They also provide the bewildered reader with a few recognizable straws to grasp when he begins to founder on the sea of such an unfamiliar style of writing. The entire action of *Ulysses* occurs in a single 24-hour period, though this unity of time and place is not Greek. The plot, however, does concern a wanderer who voyages through the terrors and temptations of the labyrinth of Dublin's streets while on his way home to his wife and son, which is reminiscent of Odysseus' search for Penelope and Telemachus. In the larger sense, the book is concerned with man's eternal search for a meaning for life. In Joyce's manuscript, the titles of chapters were based on quotations from the *Odyssey*, but these were omitted when it was printed. Most of the work is obscure and cryptic, but the juxtaposition of the heroic past helps to heighten the squalid picture of the present that he paints.

Social Protest

This Will Be the Last, Little Father (Fig. 20:12) is the title of the print by Georges Rouault that describes the heartbreaking farewell of a son as he leaves for war and almost certain death. Rouault's art is visionary, but his tragic clowns, comical lawyers, static acrobats, and active landscapes reveal his broad compassion for and passionate protests against human exploitation and degradation. His pictures often mirror the grimacing masks of those who presume to sit in judgment on their fellow men, and the insensitive countenances of people in positions of power who are indifferent to human suffering. His prints continue the great tradition established by Hogarth, Goya, Daumier, and Toulouse-Lautrec in the graphic arts. His series of 100 etchings and aquatints for two projected portfolios entitled *Miserere* (Have Mercy on Us) and *Guerre* (War), with text by a literary friend, occupied him intermittently in the years following World War I. Though the portfolios as such were never published, 58 prints have been issued separately. The title page of the war volume in which Figure 20:12 was to have appeared reads: "They Have Ruined Even the Ruins."

In his *Guernica* (Fig. 20:13), Picasso used expressionistic technique as a violent protest against a cruel and inhuman act by modern barbarians. What lighted the fuse that set off this pictorial explosion of carnage and terror was the first saturation air raid of the century—the macabre "experiment" by the German

Fig. 20:12. Rouault. *This Will Be the Last, Little Father*. Etching from *Miserere et Guerre*. 28⅛″ x 16⅞″. 1927. Collection, Museum of Modern Art, New York

air force carried out against the defenseless Basque town of Guernica, an incident in General Franco's successful rebellion against the legally elected government of the Spanish Republic. Picasso, a loyalist partisan, was in Paris with the commission to paint a mural for the Spanish pavilion of the World's Fair of 1937. Just two days after the news of the bombing reached Paris, he began work. The huge canvas, accomplished in a matter of weeks, took up one wall of the Spanish pavilion, where it made an unforgettable impression on the thousands who saw it. The attention it attracted and the measure of understanding accorded it have been in proportion to its value as one of the century's most important paintings.

Guernica is one of those rare incidents of the right artist painting the right picture at the right time. Its purpose was frankly propagandistic, its intent, to horrify. But besides recalling the apocalyptic visions of Romanesque *Last Judgments*, it is a work of sociological expression in the manner of Goya, and Daumier. The principal action begins in the lower right where a woman dashes forward, clutching her hands in an attitude of despair. The triangular composition then mounts to its apex at the point where the lamp, horse's head, and the

Fig. 20:13. Picasso. *Guernica*. Oil on canvas. 11′ 6″ x 25′ 8″.

eye of day with the electric bulb of night as its pupil converge. From this climax, the eye moves downward to the head of the dismembered warrior in the lower left. According to Picasso, the picture is symbolic, although much is still to be explained. The sculptured warrior grasping the broken sword in his severed hand represents the military. The horse with the spear in his back, the inevitable victim of every bullfight, signifies victimized humanity. Above, an arm reaches forward holding the lamp of truth over the gruesome scene. The bull, standing for brute force, is the only triumphant figure in this symbolic struggle between the forces of darkness and light, between barbarism and civilization.

730

Collection of the artist. Courtesy Museum of Modern Art, New York

Guernica appeared at a time when many earlier pictorial experiments could be combined. It employs all the exaggerations, distortions, and shock techniques developed by expressionistic drawing, but it omits lurid coloration in favor of the somber shades of mourning—black, white, and gradations of gray. The abstract design, the overlapping planes on a two-dimensional surface, and the absence of modeling, all derive from cubism (see p. 737). So also does the simultaneous principle of the day-and-night symbol; the head of the bull, which is seen both from the front and the side at the same time; and the sensation of inner and outer space by which the observer is at once both inside and outside the

731

burning buildings. The elongation of the heads to express headlong motion coincides with the photography of movement made with stroboscopic cameras. The screaming nightmarish subject matter is similar to that of surrealism, but the 100 preliminary sketches Picasso made before he began to paint show that it is a carefully worked-out composition rather than a hasty effort of psychic automatism. Picasso usually paints so rapidly and prolifically that he often has difficulty resisting the temptations of his own facile technique. Consequently, much of his work is uneven. Here, however, he worked in a disciplined and selective manner that shows his complete command of his medium. Thus, his successful synthesis in *Guernica* of all these divergent 20th-century techniques, as well as the vivid dramatization of his subject, has given powerful expression to the chaos and conflicts of this tortured century.

The eminent Jugoslav sculptor Ivan Mestrovic characteristically used the human figure to achieve a similar result with an even greater economy of means. *Job* (Fig. 20:14), after he has lost his family and flocks, sits down among the ashes and cries out, "Let the day perish wherein I was born, and the night in which it was said, There is a man child conceived." (Job: 3:3.) By this allusion to the age-old personification of human misery, and by the twisted and tortured posture of the emaciated body, Mestrovic created a symbol of the plight of mankind crying out to the heavens in a protest against needless suffering.

Fig. 20:14. Mestrovic. *Job*. Bronze. 4′ high. 1946. Collection of Syracuse University

Organic Architecture

The doors to a new architecture were pushed open by the new materials of glass, structural steel, and reinforced concrete as well as the processes of cantilevering and suspension. Modern architects have well pointed out the absurdities of people catching trains in Roman baths, working in Renaissance office buildings, banking money in Doric temples, hearing operas in baroque theaters, living in English Tudor houses, and going on Sunday to Gothic churches. Frank Lloyd Wright has aptly characterized this inheritance from 19th-century eclecticism as "façade making." Such style revivals were based on the assumption that architecture was a fine art concerned only with design and decoration, and that actual building should be left to stone masons. Fortunately, the 20th century has reunited designing and engineering, theory and practice, beauty and utility.

Wright always described his buildings by analogies to nature. His 18-story skyscraper at Bartlesville, Oklahoma, has a "tap-root" foundation, grows upward like a tree, with its floors and walls cantilevered outward like branches from its central trunk. Skyscrapers, he was convinced, did not belong in already-congested cities but in the open, where they could breathe and have room to cast decent shadows. Wright's philosophy of architecture was that of a liberating force, and his creative freedom allowed for decorative motifs to grow organically out of his basic designs, the relations of masses to voids, the fenestration, the colors and grains of wood, and the textures of stone. Through his masterly articulation, space for living and working comes to life and breathes. "Nothing," he observed, "is complete in itself, but is only complete as the part is merged into the larger expression of the whole."

Falling Water (Fig. 20:15), which Wright built for Edgar J. Kaufmann at Bear Run, Pennsylvania, is an expressive combination of reinforced concrete material, cantilevered construction, and a dramatic site. (*Cantilevering* is the method whereby the horizontal architectural member is extended, tablelike, outward over its vertical supports.) It was characteristic of Wright's warm sense of humanity that he should have begun his career building houses in the Chicago of the 1890's. For him, human needs were always foremost, and when building a house the first thing he thought about was the people who were to live in it. For him, a house must express a sense of shelter; after that the manner of living, the site, the region, the availability of materials, and so forth, could be considered. Wright's ingenious solutions for dwelling places have been highly influential, both in his own country and abroad. In this case, his client loved the waterfall and wanted to live near it. Falling Water therefore embraces both the stream and the waterfall; and by means of the cantilevered slabs that project from the rock embankment on which they rest, Wright carried the living space outward over the waterfall itself. Like all his other buildings it is intimately related to the site. The two ledges of natural rock below, for instance, are paralleled by the two concrete shelves jutting out into the open space above them. The horizontal planes of these porches, in turn, are balanced by the vertical volumes of the fireplace. The local stone used in this chimney mass is related both in color and texture to the natural rock of the river bank. The cantilevering here allows the several stories the independence to develop their own fluid floor plans. As on the outside, the inside space radiates around the central core, with advancing and receding areas promoting what Wright called the "freedom of interior and exterior occupation."

In the closing years of his notable career, this dean of American architects finally received a commission to construct a building in the nation's largest city—the Guggenheim Museum (Fig. 20:16), an art gallery for abstract painting and sculpture in New York City. To Wright, a museum should not be a group of boxlike compartments but a continuous flow of floor space in which the eye encounters no obstruction. To achieve this ideal, he designed a single, round, windowless room of reinforced concrete nearly 100 feet in diameter, with a hollow cylindrical center core surmounted by a wire-glass dome 92 feet above ground (Fig. 20:17). Spiraling upward around the room, traversing a distance of

Fig. 20:15. Wright. Falling Water. Reinforced concrete and stone. *c.*64′ deep x 62′ wide. 1937. Bear Run, Pennsylvania (Hedrich-Blessing)

Wright. Solomon R. Guggenheim Museum.

Fig. 20:16 (*above*). *Exterior*. Reinforced concrete. Diameter at ground level *c*.100′, at roof level 128′, dome 92′ high. Designed 1942, built 1957–1959. New York. Fig. 20:17 (*below*). *Interior*. Ramp over ¼ mile long.

a quarter of a mile, is a cantilevered ramp rising at a 3-percent grade and broadening from a width of 17 feet at its lowest level to almost 35 feet at the top. Throngs of spectators can be accommodated without congestion as they move easily up or down the ramp. The visitor can take the elevator to the top level and wind downward at leisure, or he can start at the bottom and walk up. He can inspect part of the exhibit at close range and at eye level or view three levels simultaneously across the open room.

An expressionistic work of art—because of the inflammatory nature of its subject matter, the violent color clashes of its painting, the twisted bodies of its sculpture, the lacerations of its literary soul, the strident dissonances of its music, and the individualistic approach of its architecture—cannot be disregarded by the public. The challenge to society was made and accepted, sides were chosen, and the heated discussions that followed led, in general, to a better understanding of the emotional basis of expressionism. Abstractionism has fared less well and been less intelligible—not too surprisingly, since it rests on a more rational basis.

ABSTRACTIONISM

Abstractionism implies analyzing, deriving, detaching, selecting, simplifying before distilling the essence from nature and sense experiences. The heat generated by the contemporary psychological and political revolutions of the 20th century was felt in expressionism, but the light of the new intellectual points of view is mirrored in the various forms of abstractionism.

In previous centuries, a picture was a reflection, in one way or another, of the outside world. In 20th-century abstractionism, the artist frees himself from the representational convention. Natural appearances play little part in his design that reduces a landscape or a group of objects to a system of geometrical shapes, patterns, lines, angles, and swirls of color that achieve his desired abstract image. Completely contrary to the expressionist's emotional response to his inner world, the abstractionist emphasizes the essential order of things as he understands them, abstracting his pictorial content from nature, eliminating the details and minutiae of the observed world, and refining the haphazardness of ordinary visual experience. His imagination and invention is concentrated on pictorial mechanics and the arrangement of his patterns, shapes, textures, and colors. From the semiabstract art of the cubists, in which objects are still discernible, abstractionism has moved toward nonobjectivism in which a work of art has no literary or associational meaning outside itself, and the picture becomes its own referent.

In the early years of the century, physicists were at work formulating a fundamental new view of the universe, which resulted in the concepts of space-time and relativity. In painting, for example, the cubist canon of multiple-visual viewpoints was developed, whereby all sides of an object could be presented at the same time. In sculpture, a new theory of volume was worked out, whereby open holes or gaps in the surface suggested the interpenetration of several planes, and the existence of other sides and surfaces not immediately in view. In architecture, the international style, using steel and glass, was able to incorporate in a structure the simultaneous experience of outer and inner space. Literature and music found new ways of presenting materials in the temporal dimension. In literature, the stream-of-consciousness technique merged objective description and subjective flow of images; and in music, the so-called "atonal" method of composition was formulated, by which fixed tonal centers were avoided in favor of a state of continuous flux and constant variation.

Such novel organizations of space and time demanded new ways of thinking about the world, new ways of looking at it, listening to it, and reading about it. Abstractionism thus includes such developments as cubism, futurism, the mechanical style, nonobjectivism, the 12-tone method of musical composition, and the strict functionalism of the international style of architecture.

Cubism

As a pictorial style, cubism made several significant departures from generally accepted practices. A strong shove in the direction of abstraction came from the large retrospective exhibit of Cézanne's paintings held in Paris in 1907, where the young painters who saw it were struck by the artist's pictorial architecture. In the catalogue, they noticed a quotation from a letter in which Cézanne remarked that natural objects can be reduced to the forms of the cylinder, the sphere, and the cone. Art, they reasoned, is not an imitation of nature in the usual sense but an imposition upon nature of geometrical forms derived from the human mind. As a result, cubist painting becomes a play of planes and angles on a flat surface. Cézanne's famous sentence, it should be pointed out, never mentioned cubes at all. His cylinders, spheres, and cones are rounded forms, presupposing curvilinear drawing; cubist drawing, on the contrary, is mainly rectilinear.

The Renaissance ideal had been the complete description of a pictorial situation from a single point of view; another vantagepoint would imply another picture. The cubist theory of vision is predicated on the fact that, in a fast-moving age, objects are perceived hastily and casually as, for instance, from a moving vehicle. The world therefore is seen fragmentarily and simultaneously from many points of view rather than as a whole from a single viewpoint. To continue to paint in the static Renaissance manner, the cubists thought, was incompatible with the dynamics of the modern age, and the results in any case would be a

Fig. 20:18. Picasso. *Accordionist*. Oil on canvas. 51¼″ x 35¼″. 1911. Solomon R. Guggenheim Museum, New York

falsification of the visual facts of their time. They therefore undertook a new definition of pictorial space in which objects are represented simultaneously from many visual angles, in wholes or in parts, opaque and transparent. Just as the Crystal Palace and the Eiffel Tower had pointed the way to the inter-penetration of the inner and outer aspects of architectural space, cubism undertook to move inside as well as outside an object, below and above it, in and around it.

One of the earliest examples of this new approach is Picasso's *Young Ladies of Avignon* (Fig. 20:1), where the faces of the second and third figures from the left are seen frontally while their noses appear in profile. The cubists were also convinced that pictorial space, limited as it is by the two dimensions of the flat canvas, was something quite apart from natural space. From the Renaissance onward, the accepted procedure had been to produce the illusion of three-dimensionality by some form of linear perspective derived from the principles of Euclidean geometry. The cubist painter, however, approaches his canvas as an architect in order to construct his picture. He accepts the limitations of his medium; and, instead of trying to create the illusion of depth, he builds his pictorial architecture on the straight lines of the triangle and T-square by which he defines the planes of his surface. The expression of volume, as achieved by the modeling of objects in light and shade, was also modified and so was the tactile feeling and structural solidity of Renaissance painting. Instead of representing objects in the round, the cubists analyzed them into their basic geometrical forms, broke them up into a series of planes, then collected, reassembled, tilted them at

Fig. 20:19. Picasso. *Three Musicians*. Oil on canvas. 80″ x 74″. 1921. Philadelphia Museum of Art

will into a new but strictly pictorial pattern of interpenetrating surfaces and planes. Cubist emphasis is on design and texture, and unity is found in the picture itself rather than in the objects represented. The technique in its earliest stages can again be observed in Figure 20:1 in the way Picasso renders the bodies of the figures on the extreme left and upper right. His *Accordionist* (Fig. 20:18) shows it in a more developed form after all the rules had been worked out.

Cubism has been associated mainly with Picasso and Braque in the decade between 1907 and 1917, but its paternity is not to be attributed to any one man. Actually, it is the collective brain child of the 20th century. In their early doctrinaire stages, cubist pictures tended to be rather cold, impersonal studies in abstract design, but modifications of this pure state began to appear, such as Picasso's *Three Musicians* (Fig. 20:19). The flat two-dimensional arrangement is retained, but the bright coloration gives the canvas a gaiety not found earlier. The three masked figures sitting at a table are the same *commedia dell' arte* figures that regularly recur on Picasso's canvases, cubist or otherwise, and that come from his love of circus and theatrical performances in which clowns and other performers dress in gay carnival costumes. The figure on the left playing a violin is a Harlequin, the central one with the clarinet is a Pierrot, while the more solemn monk on the right plays what appears to be an accordion.

Fig. 20:20. Picasso. *Woman's Head*. Bronze. 16¼″ high. *c*.1909. Albright Art Gallery, Buffalo

Just as the discovery of the rules of linear perspective had revolutionized the expression of the Florentine Renaissance, cubism brought about a new way of looking at things in the 20th century, and its influence was felt directly in architecture and sculpture, and indirectly in literature and music. Picasso's *Woman's Head* (Fig. 20:20) is a translation of cubist principles into the three-dimen-

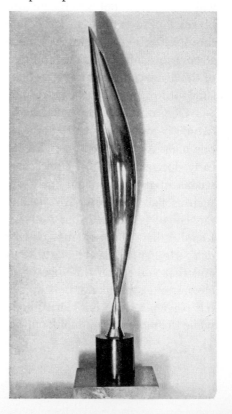

Fig. 20:21. Brancusi. *Bird in Space*. Polished bronze. 49¾″ high. 1925. Philadelphia Museum of Art.

sional medium of sculpture. It presents a geometrical analysis of the structure of the human face and emphasizes its most important planes and surfaces. By this process of disintegration, the head can be organized into a number of different facets, each of which can cast its own shadow and thus bring variety and a sense of movement to the composition.

Constantin Brancusi's *Bird in Space* (Fig. 20:21) presents one of the modifications of the stricter canons of cubism. His work is characterized by a direct and honest approach to the individual qualities of his materials. He accepts marble for its smoothness or roughness and metal for its hardness or softness. Whatever the material, he tries to divine its nature and realize its potentialities without forcing it to simulate something else. "What is real," Brancusi once remarked, "is not the external form, but the essence of things." In this case, he is dealing with a bronze that has such a high copper content it approaches the brilliance of gold. By molding it into a graceful curvilinear form and giving it a high polish, he releases the metal medium into a form of energy. It is the abstraction of a movement, a feather in flight. Brancusi has sometimes tried to increase the sense of motion in sculpture by placing his figures on slowly rotating turntables. In this way, his glistening surfaces catch the light and his forms seem to float through space.

The musical aspect of this new concept of space-time is found in the breaking up of traditional tonality as well as in the search for new musical resources and mediums of expression. Stravinsky, as a strict adherent of the principles of order, had said that "tonal elements become musical only by virtue of their being organized." The 12-tone system of musical composition that Schoenberg evolved about 1915 was an answer to the need for a new order and one of the stricter forms of tonal organization. Schoenberg, who preferred to be called a constructor rather than a composer, begins a work by setting forth a basic row of 12 different tones. This row can be played in normal order, upside down by melodic inversion, backward in retrograde motion, and upside down once more in retrograde inversion. Furthermore, it can be presented successively in sequences or simultaneously as in the various species of counterpoint. It can also be played vertically as in a chord or tone cluster or horizontally as in a melody. A row can be used either as a whole or broken up into several shorter themes or motives. It has been estimated that around half a billion different combinations are possible, which certainly is no limitation on its possibilities. The system provides a wealth of material as well as a certain freedom within an orderly framework. The 12-tone method has generally been referred to as atonality (that is, without tonality), but Schoenberg called it simply a method of composing with 12 tones that are related only with one another. Tonality is thus relative rather than an absolute, since there is no single tonal center. Tonality in the usual sense, however, is not excluded; rather, it is encompassed and transcended.

Futurism and the Mechanical Style

The movement known as futurism was begun in Italy under the leadership of the poet and dramatist Marinetti prior to World War I. Agreeing with Nietzsche, who said that history was the process by which the dead bury the living, Marinetti said in his *Manifesto* of 1909 that futurism was being founded to "deliver Italy from its plague of professors, archeologists, tourist guides and antique dealers." The futurists wanted to destroy the museums, libraries, academies, and universities in order to make way for their particular wave of the future. "A roaring motor-car, which runs like a machine gun," they said, "is more beautiful than the Winged Victory of Samothrace." Theirs was a vision of a state ruled by a mechanical superman, in which the people would be reduced to cogs in the gigantic wheel of a fully mechanized society. War was praised as "a motor for art," and their social thinking was completely antidemocratic. Mussolini frankly acknowledged his indebtedness to the group for some of the ideas and symbols that were later incorporated into his fascist movement.

"We go out. We swallow fog. The city is full of phantoms. Men cloaked in the mist walk silently. The canals exhale vapors." So goes in part a poem by Gabriele d'Annunzio, who was close to the movement. In architecture, futurists admired factories, skyscrapers, grain elevators, railway terminals, and triple-decked bridges. A manifesto on the "Aesthetics of Machinery" was written by one futurist painter to celebrate the beauty and spiritual qualities of gears, pulleys, pistons, locomotives, steam shovels, fly-wheels, and pinions. Above all, the futurists admired the motion, force, velocity, and strength of mechanical forms and in their pictures wanted more than anything else to include the dynamic sensation of motion. A galloping horse, they said, has not four legs

Fig. 20:22. Balla. *Swifts: Paths of Movement and Dynamic Sequences.* Oil on canvas. 38⅛" x 47¼". 1913. Collection, Museum of Modern Art, New York

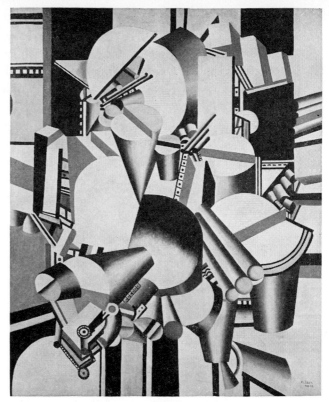

Fig. 20:23. Leger. *Mechanical Elements*. Oil on canvas. 83⅛" x 66⅛". 1918–1923. Private collection, Paris

but twenty. Giacomo Balla, in a picture called *Leash in Motion*, paints a dog with each of its legs in several positions spreading out fanwise. As a composite photographic painting of moving bodies, his *Swifts: Paths of Movement and Dynamic Sequences* (Fig. 20:22) shows the same principle applied to mechanical motion.

Futurist painting burst upon the international scene in 1912 with a Paris exhibition, but futurist music had no such equivalent until a concert in 1921. A musical manifesto had been issued in 1913, and a year later, in Milan, a program entitled "Network of Noises" had been presented, including such gems as *Awakening of Capital* and *Meeting of Automobiles and Aeroplanes*. An "orchestra" of 19 noise instruments, conducted by their inventor Luigi Russolo, consisted of three bumblers, two exploders, three thunderers, three whistles, two rufflers, two gurglers, one fricasseur, two stridors, and one snorer. Futurism was influential chiefly in the formation of the so-called "mechanical style." Its members were a bit too noisy and exhibitionistic to be enduring, and their productivity ran more to manifestoes than to significant works. As a result, their future was all too soon behind them.

By taking some ideas from the cubists and others from the futurists, Fernand Léger developed an individual style of his own. Such a picture as *Mechanical*

Elements (Fig. 20:23) has the visual hum of well-oiled machinery. Each part fits into its appointed place, and everything is neat and precise. Léger loved crank- shafts, cylinder blocks, and pistons, which he painted in gleaming primary colors of enamellike brightness. Taking Cézanne's statement about cylinders, spheres, and cones far more literally than the cubists did, he made his lines curvilinear rather than rectilinear, and he modeled his forms in light and shade. His buildings are structural steel skeletons populated by robots with spheres for heads, cylinders for legs, pipes for arms, and tubes for fingers. There is no room in Léger's world for sentiment, and such human forms as do occur, he introduces only for their "plastic value"; for this reason they remain "purposely inexpressive." In 1924, Léger made an abstract film called *Ballet Méchanique,* in which machine forms and motorized movements replaced human beings and their activities.

Stravinsky, meanwhile, had composed an *Étude for Pianola* in 1917, and the French composer Arthur Honegger, using the normal symphonic comple- ment, gave voice in 1924 to the triumphant song of the machine in a work called *Pacific 231.* Its name is an allusion to that year's model of an American locomotive, and the piece was designed to evoke the sounds of the railroad, com- plete with the grinding of the wheels and the shriek of the steam whistle. Per- haps the most successful musical realization of the mechanical style is found in the works of Edgar Varèse. Technically trained in two fields, Varèse is as much a physicist as a musician, and the titles of his works sound as if they came from a laboratory: *Intègrales, Density* 21.5 (the specific gravity of the platinum of the flute for which it was composed), and *Ionization.* The last is constructed in a series of interlocking planes of sound that suggest, but are not directly imitative of, the rhythms of modern city life. Varèse's expressed aim is to build a music that faces the realities of the contemporary industrial world rather than escapes from it.

Industrial Design and Utilitarian Music

When Walter Gropius was called upon to reorganize a German art school after World War I, he renamed it the Bauhaus and made it a technical school of design with special emphasis on the industrial arts and the study of modern ma- terials and methods. All the visual arts were included in the curriculum but with- out the traditional distinctions between fine and useful arts. By making furni- ture design and photography as respectable as sculpture and painting, Gropius hoped to break down the artificial cleavage between artist and craftsman. In the 19th century, Ruskin and William Morris had made a similar effort to bring the world of art and the world of work back together again, but in their romanticism they thought only in terms of handicrafts and shunned the machine. Gropius, however, regarded the machine as the normal tool of modern civilization, a tool to be mastered as any other and made to serve not enslave. His objective was a marriage of beauty and utility within the framework of the machine age.

The Bauhaus exploration of materials and industrial processes led to many new approaches in printing, pottery, metalwork, weaving, and stagecraft. Students were taught never to forget the purposes their products were designed to serve. A chair, in other words, was made to sit in, a lamp to give efficient lighting. As a result, the Bauhaus became the fountainhead of the new industrial design. Such innovations as tubular steel chairs, indirect lighting fixtures, and streamlined appliances were accepted for mass production and are parts of every household today. In order to counterbalance the utilitarian side, however, Gropius added the painters Kandinsky, Klee, and Lyonel Feininger to his distinguished faculty to uphold the expressive and creative aspects of drawing and painting. Their work in this sane atmosphere did much to dispel the current confusions that futurism and dadaism had created.

While the Bauhaus was primarily a school for the visual arts, the constructive new line of thinking was felt in other fields. A movement generally known as *Gebrauchsmusik*, which can be rendered either as utilitarian music or workaday music, got under way in Germany. The composers who adopted its principles tried to establish a new relationship between the producers and consumers of music wherever they were to be found. It was first identified with the composers Paul Hindemith and Kurt Weill, who wrote vocal music for school situations, marches for special occasions, and piano pieces for students and amateurs as well as for professionals. As such, *Gebrauchsmusik* tried to direct composers away from writing heroic symphonies in the grand manner and to encourage them to compose for everyday situations wherever music could serve a useful purpose. It also implied a coming to terms with the new media of radio, moving pictures, and the recording industry. Technical proficiency was considered more important than inspiration, and writing background music for films was felt to be just as respectable as composing grand operas.

Nonobjectivism

Abstractionism was carried to its logical geometrical conclusion by Piet Mondrian just as expressionism had reached its point of pure abstraction in the work of Kandinsky (see page 718). The pictures of these two artists are, of course, poles apart—the rational approach opposed to the emotional. But both artists are nonobjective in that the pictorial content of their canvases bears no reference to recognizable objects or to anything outside the actual pictures. All subject matter, all associational meanings, are studiously avoided. The picture with its lines, shapes, and colors is its own referent.

Mondrian's art, like Kandinsky's, evolved gradually from the concrete to the abstract. In his early years, Mondrian painted landscapes and quiet interior scenes in the tradition of his native Holland, and his later style (Fig. 20:24), though completely abstract, owes much to the cool geometrical precision of his great predecessor Vermeer. "The new style," said Mondrian, "will spring from the metropolis"; and he delighted in the criss-cross patterns of city streets, architect's blueprints, gaunt structural steel skeletons of skyscrapers under construction, and simple faces of buildings of the international architectural style. The new art, he continued, would not be individual, but collective, impersonal, and international. All references to the "primitive animal nature of man" should be rigidly excluded in order to reveal "true human nature" through an art of "balance, unity, and stability." This objective he strove to realize by using "only a single neutral form: the rectangular area in varying dimensions." His colors are likewise abstract—black lines of various widths against white backgrounds, relieved occasionally by a primary color "climax"—red, blue, or yellow —in as pure a state as possible. In his opinion, a work of art should be "constructed," and he approached a canvas with all the objectivity of a draftsman making a blueprint. The result of this pictorial engineering is the series of chaste, two-dimensional spatial studies for which he is best known. His visual patterns have a repose that rests on a precise balance of horizontal and vertical elements, and they are clean to the point of being prophylactic. His pictures are far more

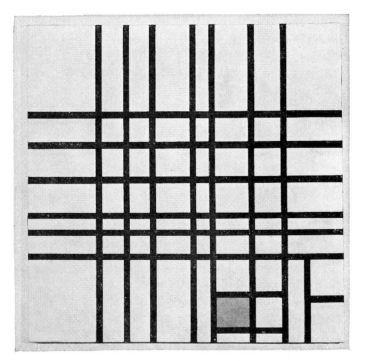

Fig. 20:24. Mondrian. N:12 *Blue Square*. Oil on canvas. 24" square. Collection of Harry Holtzman, New York

Fig. 20:25. Arp. *Relief.* Wood. 19¾" square. 1938–1939. Collection, Museum of Modern Art, New York

complex than they may seem to the casual eye; and they have had a great influence on modern design, especially of advertising layouts, posters, rugs, and linoleum.

Hans Arp, who was a member of both the dadaist and surrealist movements, is also associated with abstract sculpture. His *Relief* (Fig. 20:25) represents his abstract work in wood, which he cuts with a jig-saw. In the manner of the African Negro carvers, he accepts the nature of his material with its curved shapes, knots, grain, and other distinguishing characteristics, and then sets himself the problem of bringing out its beauty by varying its contours and by cutting and refining its surfaces and textures.

International Style Architecture

The skyscraper is among the earliest and boldest instances of modern architecture. It came out of the American Middle West as an answer to the need for commercial centralization. In the hands of Louis Sullivan, who put up the Wainwright Building in St. Louis in 1891, the skyscraper was a "proud and soaring thing," reflecting the pride of the businessman in his work. As such, skyscrapers have had more new engineering ideas and new materials put into their construction than any other modern architectural form. The principal drawback to skyscrapers, however, is their contribution to congestion in already-over-crowded areas. From a human standpoint, their value has thus far been less spectacular than their engineering.

Fig. 20:26. Gropius. Bauhaus Machine Shop. 1925–1926. Dessau, Germany

Sullivan's slogan that "form follows function" is subject to a variety of interpretations, but the line of thought it provoked led to an important re-evaluation of architectural forms in relation to human activities and to a re-examination of basic architectural methods, materials, and purposes. Modern building had to wait until structural steel was available in units of sufficient length and at a reasonable cost. As long as architecture remained an art of masonry, it had to use either the post-and-lintel or the arch-and-vault methods of construction. Cantilevering and suspension, both of which methods had long been known in principle, could be effectively employed on a large scale only with materials as strong as steel and reinforced concrete. Sullivan's disciple Frank Lloyd Wright, and the architects identified with the international style, accepted the principle that stone should behave like stone, wood like wood, and steel like steel and that design must be modified in relation to its materials and purposes. Their lines of development, however, have led in divergent directions.

The international style crystallized in France with the work of Le Corbusier, in Holland with J. J. P. Oud, and in Germany with Miës van der Rohe and Walter Gropius. Open structures, such as the Bauhaus Machine Shop (Fig. 20:26) and Lever House in New York (Fig. 20:27) with the neighboring Seagram building, are the lineal descendants of the Crystal Palace and the Eiffel Tower (Figs. 19:18 and 19:20). Walter Gropius in 1914 was building steel

Fig. 20:27. Skidmore, Owings, and Merrill. Lever House. 1952. New York

and glass factories that seem as modern now as when they first saw the light of day. When the Bauhaus moved from Weimar to Dessau in 1925, he designed its complex of studios, machine shops, administrative offices, and professors' houses into a single masterly space composition. As an exponent of the international style, he started with the open box as the basic unit of space, varied its volume, and grouped several in a related pattern of cubes. The Machine Shop (Fig. 20:26) shows how the building is treated as an open volume rather than as a closed mass. By the method of cantilevering Gropius allowed the building to project several feet outward over its site. The horizontal emphasis thus established is then carried out in the concrete base and repeated at the roof level. Between these parallel lines hang the glass-curtained walls that bear no structural weight. This transparency permits details, such as the spiral staircase and the skeletal structure of the interior, to remain open and visible from the exterior. By thus allowing the interior and exterior of the building to be seen at the same time, Gropius achieved the architectural equivalent of the cubist painters, who presented simultaneously the front view and profile of a human face or several different sides of an object. The Bauhaus group has proved to be one of the most important and influential buildings of its decade.

The steel, glass, and concrete creations of Gropius were absorbed into the international style, of which one of the most striking examples is Lever House in New York (Fig. 20:27). Here the pronounced vertical tendency of the earlier skyscrapers is offset by a horizontal base that becomes the pedestal on which the skyscraper is balanced. Here, too, the building is cantilevered outward beyond the substructure, a device that, together with the glass walls, contributes notably to the effect of spaciousness and openness, and its sparkling, spic-and-span exterior is as cleanly as the products its owners sell. By omitting the ground floor and reducing the supporting steel shafts to a minimum, the designers created an open passageway at the street level for pedestrians. Such steel stilts had been used first in residences designed by Le Corbusier, but Lever House is notable for their use on a large scale.

The international style is thus mainly identified with the cantilevered steel skeleton enclosed in a transparent sheath of glass. Frank Lloyd Wright sharply critized this emphasis on structural openness, characterizing it as "indecent architectural exposure." And Le Corbusier in his definition of a house as a "machine for living" reveals certain mechanistic limitations of the style in its approach to human problems. While the internationalists have succeeded in breaking down the distinction between architecture and engineering and reuniting art and utility, in their zeal they have sometimes failed to realize that the construction of bridges and viaducts is one thing and the building of dwellings, apartment houses, and offices for human living and working situations is something else. By their insistent use of the vocabulary of steel, glass, and concrete and of the principle of cantilevering to the point where each has become a stereotype, they have added these terms, for better or worse, to the architectural language of today. But, in employing new methods and materials just because they are new, the internationalists often have neglected to appraise critically the reasons for their use. Technological inventiveness alone is never an adequate foundation on which to build a permanent style. Now that the novelty has worn off and the devices have been repeated so often, the internationalists have the dubious distinction of having created clichés. It cannot be denied, however, that the international style is one of the few aspects of contemporary art to achieve wide popular acceptance.

Frank Lloyd Wright always worked harmoniously with nature; his buildings cling to the ground; his textures, colors, and materials are derived from mother earth. Le Corbusier and Miës van der Rohe's steel, bronze, and glass buildings, contrariwise, defy nature. With their steel stilts, they disdain the ground and dissociate themselves from the earth beneath. The architecture of tomorrow may well achieve a synthesis of Wright's warm, organic, natural designs and the more frigid, mechanized, abstract forms of the international style.

RELATIVISM

The only thing that is permanent is change. This seeming paradox points its finger at the very heart of 20th-century thought, whether expressed in philosophical, scientific, or aesthetic terms. No static unchanging absolute can possibly provide a satisfactory view of the moving world of today. Even the firmest dogmas of religious faiths and political doctrines are subject to far more commentary and modification from time to time than their followers would care to admit. The shift from a static world order to the present dynamic view of the universe, which began with Copernicus and Galileo, has swept all before it. Those who believe in orderly progress toward a definable objective interpret this flux as some form of evolution; those who accept it at face value, as most scientists do, believe simply in change. Both would agree with Nietzsche when he said that truth has never yet hung on the arm of an absolute; both must of necessity describe the world in relative terms. In his observations of physical phenomena, Albert Einstein saw that, in a world where everything moves, any calculation or prediction, to be valid, must be based on the relative position of the observer. Newton's absolute space, which was immovable, and his absolute time, which flowed on uniformly—both of which were "unrelated to any outward circumstances"—had to be discarded and replaced by the theory of relativity. All space, in the modern view, has to be measured by mobility and change of relative position, and all time by the duration of movement in the space traversed. The world thus becomes a spatio-temporal continuum, in which all matter, energy, and events are related in the four dimensions of space-time.

The study by anthropologists of the life and customs of primitive peoples has shown how ethical considerations are relative to tribal customs as well as social and economic conditions. In Tibet, for instance, a woman may have several husbands because one man may be too poor to support a wife. In some African tribes, on the other hand, a rich man may have as many wives as he can afford. The pragmatic philosophers William James and John Dewey took a long look at history and a wide view of the world and came to the conclusion that when an idea is useful and effective it is true; when it ceases to work, its truth is no longer valid and another solution must be found.

Such a relative world, in which all things appear differently to each person and each group, depending on educational, geographical, historical, ethical, and psychological backgrounds, can be understood only in terms of many frames of reference. Any absolutism—a totalitarian society such as Plato's *Republic*, for instance—insists on a maximum of conformity; a relativism—such as that of a modern democracy—allows for many different images of man. This relative world, moreover, is populated by men who see themselves in multiple images and express themselves in a multiplicity of styles. In it can be found Marx's proletarian man, speaking in some form of social protest and bent on bringing about the ultimate triumph of the working classes and masses. Darwin's jungle man is there, beating on his neoprimitive tom-toms and discoursing in existentialist vocabularies on the survival of the fittest. Nietzsche's superman, determined to impose his mighty will on an unwilling world, has been thwarted in two world wars. The voice of Freud's psychological man is heard coming from couches and canvases as he tries to share his surrealistic nightmares with the world at large. Mechanical man, the spawn of the Industrial Revolution and the machine age, walks robotlike at large, thinking mechanistic thoughts in his electronic brain and expressing futuristic principles in his mechanical style. There, too, is Einstein's scientific man of relativity, drawing abstract pictures of his space-time world in slashing angular lines organized by the multifocus perspective of cubism. Modern art as the mirror of this relativistic world thus assumes many shapes and reflects a multiplicity of human images.

Small wonder then that this world, which has produced scientists who analyze and synthesize and physicists who work with fission and fusion, has also given birth to revolutionists who want to destroy a social order so as to reconstruct it in a different way; to warring nations who hope to break down one international order so as to build up a new balance of power; to iconoclasts who feel compelled to shatter certain images men live by so that they can remake the world in their own image; and to artists who dissolve and distort tangible solid objects so as to shape them into new forms that exist solely in their imaginations and on their canvases.

In this relative world, then, the cubist disintegrates the objects in his paintings so that he can reintegrate them in patterns of his own choosing. Since each picture creates its own spatial relationships, space is relative to the mind and mood of the painter rather than an absolute as in Euclidean geometry. It is both impossible and undesirable to make any precise analogy between cubist principles and the mathematics of space-time. A relationship, however unsystematic it may be, can nevertheless be found in the cubist concept of the simultaneity of several viewpoints, in the presentation of objects from many sides at once, in the use of multifocus perspective, and in the symbolic emphasis on abstract geometrical forms. By representing bodies at rest or in successive stages of motion, a futurist or mechanical-style picture sets up a space-time continuum of its own. By showing a figure simultaneously from the front and side, clothed and in the nude, opaque and transparent as in an X-ray view, Picasso in the *Girl before a Mirror* (Fig. 20:28) creates his own pictorial theory of relativity. Similarly, Chirico in *The Disquieting Muses* (Fig. 20:6), representing ancient Greek statues in a space bounded by a medieval castle, a modern factory, and a futuristic

Fig. 20:28. Picasso. *Girl before a Mirror*. Oil on canvas. 63¾″ x 51¼″. 1932. Collection, Museum of Modern Art, New York

tower, creates a simultaneous image of time in which past, present, and future coexist in an extended now.

Concurrently with this new conquest of two-dimensional space, architecture developed many new ways of molding its three-dimensional equivalent. Frank Lloyd Wright ruled out such self-contained absolutes as the Greek temple in favor of an architecture specifically related to the changing aspects of human living and working space. He thus evolved the flexible floor plan with its advancing and receding areas and its freedom of interior and exterior occupation. The international stylists also came up with their version of the simultaneous perception of inner and outer space by means of the glass-curtain wall and the organizing of such multibuilding complexes as apartment houses and the United Nations group into systems of related cubes of varying volumes.

In music, the experience of dissonance is emancipated from its dependence on consonance, so that it demands neither preparation, anticipation, nor resolution. The absolutes of tonality, rhythmical regularity, and musical form have yielded to a host of tonal relativisms. Instead of an insistent reiteration of a single meter, a modern musical score can use polymetrical sequences in which a measure of ⅘ is succeeded by one of ⅞, then ⅖, ⅘, and so on. The same principle can be used simultaneously with several rhythms going on at the same time, as in the polyrhythmical textures of Stravinsky's *Rite of Spring*. Instead of organizing a work around a single key center, some composers have employed two tonalities simultaneously in the technique known as bitonality, while others have gone one step farther into polytonality. This, in turn, led to Schoenberg's method of composing with 12 tones that are related not to a central tonality but only to one another. Within the internal organization of the work, the sequence of tones known as the row can be played forward or backward, normally or upside down, simultaneously as in a chord, or fragmented into shorter motives. The 12-tone method emphasizes change and discourages repetition, and the principle of constant variation creating a perpetual state of tonal flux is its ideal.

In *Ulysses*, James Joyce found his answer by making a simultaneous cross section of the life of a city. In this labyrinthine literary space-time continuum, all events, whether memories of the past or premonitions of the future, flow together into a kind of extended present. As in a dream, there is no distinction between before and after. While the single day and night and city in which all takes place have some relation to the Greek unities of time, place, and action, there is no Aristotelean beginning, middle, or end to his structureless literary structure. The reader can begin at almost any place in the book and the continuity will not be broken. The series of fleeting images are simply recorded, and the door to the dream world of free association of words and thoughts is left open so that the reader can move in and supply the transitions between moods, the union of the fragments, and thus, in turn, create his own relative order; and its end, like the title of the final chapter of a Samuel Johnson novel, is a conclusion in which nothing is is concluded.

Many of the forms of expressionism are also relative to the individual psychology of the artist, just as a Frank Lloyd Wright building is relative to the need of the human situation. Expressionism presupposes the free associational techniques of psychological relativism. Somewhat like the romantic revolt of a century earlier, the expressionistic artist reasserts the primacy of the imagination over the intellect and takes flight from reality in order to find a superior reality in the world of mystery and fantasy. The tendency is anti-intellectual in the extreme, though the symbols and vocabulary are evolved by highly rationalistic procedures. The emotional content poured on their canvases, pages, and musical scores all takes place within the human imagination and hence is relative to the infinite number of unsolved conflicts and suppressed passions of many different private worlds.

Historical relativism has provided the modern artist with an unparalleled number of choices of styles and techniques from the past as well as the present.

The artist of the 20th century is the heir of all the ages. A Picasso exhibit or a Stravinsky concert can mean a bewildering assortment of styles. Inspiration for the one can be drawn from ancient Iberian sculpture, Oriental textiles, Romanesque wall frescoes, medieval illuminated manuscripts as well as contemporary sources. His media may include pencil drawings; collages constructed of cloth and paper; ceramics, and woodcuts as well as oils and watercolors. Sources for the other may be drawn from the free rhythms of Gregorian chant, the dissonant counterpoint of the 14th century, the operas of Mozart, or the polyrhythmic practices of the African aborigines. When Picasso said, "I do not search, I find," he implied that his freedom of approach was unlimited. He can accept for the moment any style that comes along without becoming its dogmatic prisoner. Both Picasso and Stravinsky have repeatedly demonstrated that a new work can be based on an aesthetic theory diametrically opposed to the one that preceded it. This does not mean, however, that they must repudiate or burn up that which has gone before. To these master craftsmen, historical relativism provides a complete freedom of choice without the necessity of sacrificing either their originality or their principles.

Philosophers of history, such as Spengler and Toynbee, through their sweeping historical panoramas have shown that the past still exists within the living present. From the point of view of historical relativity, tradition is usually a more potent factor than innovation, and at all times, including the present, evolution has been a stronger force than revolution. Most 20th-century ideas and problems are variations on old themes that have bothered men ever since the 5th century B.C. Those that in the past led to such sharp dissonances have never been resolved; instead, they have become outmoded, outgrown, temporarily forgotten, or are bypassed, circumvented in one way or another, or assume new shapes and forms. "Ideas have never conquered the world as ideas," as Romain Rolland remarked in his novel *Jean Christophe*, "but only by the force they represent. They do not grip men by their intellectual contents but by the radiant vitality which is given off from them at certain periods in history. . . . The loftiest and most sublime idea remains ineffective until the day when it becomes contagious, not by its own merits, but by the merits of the groups of men in whom it becomes incarnate by the transfusion of their blood." Much more important than the solutions or lack of them have been the emotional forces they have generated and the good fruits they have yielded, since all the ideas have ultimately been embodied in the buildings men erect to house their activities, the statues and pictures that reflect their human images, the words that express their innermost thoughts, and the music that gives voice to their strivings and aspirations in a constantly changing world.

INDEX

Certain features of a Glossary are combined with the Index. When a technical term is defined in the text, reference is made to that page; in other instances, a short definition (in parentheses) is given here after the entry. Figure references are cited in **bold face** type, so that terms may be clarified by looking at the illustrations. Each work of art has been listed by title as well as by artist and, in addition, is listed under the city and building in which it is presently located. (See, for example, the titles listed under Florence, Italy: Uffizi Gallery.) Each building is also listed under its city and under the architect, with a cross reference made from its title to the city of location. (See, for example, Parthenon, The. *See* Athens.) General events as well as birth and death dates of persons are given in the Chronologies at the beginning of chapters and have not been indexed.

Plato (*Continued*)
386; *Timaeus*, 40, quoted, 383; *see also* Neo-Platonism
Pliny the Elder, on mosaics, 77
Pliny the Younger, 122–123, 125, 167
Plutarch, on music, 82; on Pericles, 5–6; *Parallel Lives*, 122, 600, 609
Poetics, Aristotle, 37; quoted, 47
poetry, epic, 228–231, 233; of Florentine Renaissance, 358–359; Gothic and Romanesque, compared, 241; of Greek dramas, 35; medieval Latin, 310–311; 19th-century French, 650–652, 659; of Petrarch, 307–308, 317; realism in, 696, 697; Roman patrician, 123; Romanesque, 221, 222, 228–233, 242; romantic, 650–652; of symbolists, 697
pointillism, 682. **19:6**
Politics, Aristotle, 41
Poliziano, Angelo, 351, 352, 359, 383, 402, 403; portrait of, 348; *La Giostra*, 353
Pollaiuolo, Antonio, 344–345, 346, 357, 361, 363; *Hercules Strangling Antaeus*, **9:15**, 345
polychoral style of music, bridge to baroque, 477; Venetian development of, 435–440
Polyclitus, 6; canon of, 27, 30, 51–52; quoted, 51; *Doryphorus*, **1:26**, 27, 30, 44
Polygnotus, 6, 74; Aristotle on, 47
polyphony, beginning of, 210–211; and English counterpoint, 562; forerunner of, 219; Gothic, 277, 278–281; and laud singing compared, 312; northern, 399; 16th-century developments of, 400–401; Venetian developments of, 435–440, 444
Pont du Gard. *See* Nîmes
Ponte, Lorenzo de, 588
Porta, Giacomo della, 452; Church of Il Gésu, **12:2**, 453; St. Peter's dome, **10:21**
portal, defined, 9; Galilee, 190; Gothic, **7:2**, **7:11**, **7:13**
Portia and Cato (?), **3:11**, 107
portico, defined, 9; Greek, **1:9**; Roman, **3:15**, **3:19**, 105
Pórtico de la Gloria, Master Matteo, **133**
Portinari, Tommaso, 355
Portinari Altarpiece, van der Goes, detail, **9:27**, 355–357
portraiture, in Bayeux Tapestry, 226; in Byzantine mosaics, **4:21**, **4:22**; in etching, **14:16**; in miniature, **7:12**; in painting, **9:26**, **10:1**, **12:17**, **13:1**, **15:1**; Rembrandt's psychological depths in, 522, 526–527; in sculpture, **3:10**, **3:11**, **9:28**, **16:17**, **17:13**. *See also* equestrian statues; group portraits; self-portraiture
Poseidon, contest of, with Athena, **1:19**, 14, 23
Poseidon (?), **1:29**
Poseidon and Apollo, **1:18**, 23
post-and-lintel construction, 9, 10, 51; in Pergamon, 61
postimpressionism, **19:6–19:12**, 681–686
pottery, Pergamene, 77
Poussin, Nicholas, 502–505, 566, 629; and Cézanne, 683 and French academicism, 507, 514; and Lebrun, 506, 507; and Rubens, compared, 507; *Et in Arcadia*

Poussin (*Continued*)
Ego, **13:16**, 504–505; *Rape of the Sabine Women*, **13:15**, 503–504, 612
Pozzo, Andrea, 452; *St. Ignatius in Glory*, **12:8**, 457–459
Praxiteles, 629; *Aphrodite of Cnidos*, **1:34**, 32; *Hermes and the Infant Dionysus*, **1:27**, 30; sculpture of school of, **2:17**, 81
Prandtauer, Jakob, Abbey Church at Melk, **16:5**, **16:6**, 575
Prez, Josquin des. *See* Josquin des Prez
primitive art, **20:2**, 712–713
Prince, The, Machiavelli, 363, 366
Procession in St. Mark's Square, G. Bellini, **11:1**, details, **11:25**, **11:26**, 407–410, 437
Procession of Virgin Martyrs, **4:10**, 145
Procopius, on Hagia Sophia, 152, 155; on Theodora, 158
programme music, 660
Prokofieff, Serge, music of, 724, 727
Prometheus, Beethoven, 624–625
Prometheus Drops His Chains, Gide, 727
Prophet, Donatello, **9:13**, 342–343
Propylaea. *See* Athens
prosody, of Debussy, 700; defined, 39; of representative style, 559–560
protagonist, defined, 36, 37
Protestant church music, 534; developed, 539
Protestant churches, and the arts, 520, 521; and music, 447
Protestant Reformation, 395, 449
Protestantism, 519–520, 540–541, 565–566
prothesis, defined, 147. **4:11**, **4:12**
Proust, Marcel, 688
psalmody, 168, 169, 174; Protestant, 534, 539; responsorial, defined, 168; sacred eight tones of, symbolized, 208–210; staff notation for, 208
Ptolemy, in Gothic sculpture, 269
Puget, Pierre, 486; *Milo of Crotona*, **13:20**, 497; *Perseus Delivering Andromeda*, 497
Pulcinella, Picasso, Diaghileff, Stravinsky, 725
Purcell, Henry, 545, 549, 558, 559–563, 565; summary of, 563; *Dido and Aeneas*, 559–562, excerpts from, 560, 561; *King Arthur*, 562–563; *The Libertine*, 589
Pythagoras, in Gothic sculpture, **7:17**, 269; and meloldic intervals, 40; quoted, 49

Q, Initial, from illuminated ms., **5:18**, 202
quadrivium, the, 266–267, 277
quadruplum, 278
Quay at Amsterdam, Ruisdael, **14:1**, 518, 519
Quinault, Philippe, 511, 627
Quintilian, 122, 123, 130, 131; on music, 125

Rachmaninoff, Serge, 709
Racine, Jean, 486, 492, 627
raking cornice, **1:7**; defined, 11
Rameau, Jean Philippe, 700
Rape of the Sabine Women, Poussin, **13:15**, 503–504, 612
Raphael Sanzio, 362, 364, 367, 369, 370, 373; and the mannerists, 443, 446; teacher of, 382; *Portrait of Julius II*, **10:1**, 371; *Portrait of Leo X with Two*

The Dean

The Dean

The Best Seat in the House

John D. Dingell

with David Bender

Research Editor
Frederick D. Paffhausen

HARPER

An Imprint of HarperCollins*Publishers*

HarperCollins books may be purchased for educational, business, or sales promotional use. For information, please email the Special Markets Department at SPsales@harpercollins.com.

FIRST EDITION

Library of Congress Cataloging-in-Publication Data has been applied for.

ISBN 978-0-06-257199-1

18 19 20 21 22   LSC   10 9 8 7 6 5 4 3 2 1

For the Lovely Deborah

and to the memory
of my mother and father

CONTENTS

Part I

5

Part II

129

FOREWORD

———————

FOR THE MOST PART, WHEN I HEAR PEOPLE COMPLAIN ABOUT the gridlock in Washington and their wish to return to "the good old days," I dismiss them as being whiny and shortsighted. After all, the most popular show on Broadway in a good many years has been the musical version of the story of Vice President Aaron Burr shooting and killing former secretary of the treasury Alexander Hamilton.

So, no, these are not the worst of times. And, yes, life in Washington has always been complicated.

Having said all that, this wonderful book from my great friend John Dingell has made me nostalgic, too, for a time in Washington that was perhaps a bit more civilized and when *compromise* was not a dirty word.

John was and is a fiercely loyal Democrat, just as I was a Republican. But he based his views, and therefore his votes in Congress, on what he thought was best for the country and for the people he represented from his beloved state of Michigan. That often meant going against the party line, which also meant that, thanks to him and others, some very good bipartisan legislation was passed during my presidency, when both houses of Congress were controlled by the Democrats.

I particularly will always be grateful to John for his support for the Gulf War. I know he was under party pressure to vote

otherwise, but as he did so many other times in his long and storied career, he voted his conscience.

John could be a tough negotiator, but he was always fair and always willing to listen, which might be another lost art these days. And no matter what the outcome of our disagreements or agreements, he was always willing to then let me beat him at paddleball. (John asked me to be honest in the assessment of our relationship, so I felt the need to say I won more often than he did. At least that is my recall at age ninety-four.)

The Dingell and Bush families have a lot in common, including our commitment to public service, which both our fathers instilled in us, and which we both are grateful and proud that our children and grandchildren are continuing. I would be remiss in not adding that my respect for Debbie matches that which I have for her husband.

America, especially Michigan, is blessed that John and Debbie Dingell have called her home. They are the best examples of what public servants can and should be.

So, I hope you'll join John in his "Best Seat in the House," for a quintessential American journey you will love—and a journey from which, I hope, some of you will learn a thing or two about how to be a great American.

—*President George Herbert Walker Bush*

FOREWORD

DIGNITY. WHEN I THINK OF JOHN DINGELL, THAT'S THE WORD that comes to mind. It's how John walked, how he talked, how he carried himself. But more than anything else, it's how he treated people. John fought hard for his constituents. But a lot of members of Congress work hard. What set John apart was his deep belief that everyone deserves to be treated with dignity and respect.

My father used to say that a job was about a lot more than a paycheck. That it was about your dignity, your respect, your place in the community, your ability to look your child in the eyes and say, "Everything is going to be okay." John got that in his bones. And as a guy who came from an auto state, too, I could see that John fought not only for jobs, but for jobs that made it possible to live a life of dignity. Jobs that made it possible to own a home, not just rent it, to raise a family, to send your kids to college, to do more than just eke by.

John gets the essential truth of America: that it's all about possibilities. That what sets this country apart is that it doesn't matter where you're from, where you start out in life—everyone gets the opportunity to go as far as their God-given ability and their willingness to work will take them. Big dreams and limitless possibilities—that's who we are. And if we ever lose that, we will lose the soul of this nation.

My father used to say something else. He'd say it's a lucky man or

woman who gets up in the morning, puts both feet on the ground, and feels that what they are about to do that day still matters. John was a lucky man. Because for fifty-nine years, when he put his feet on the ground, no one doubted that what he was about to do mattered. Look at every piece of major legislation going back decades. From the Civil Rights Act of 1964, to Medicare and Medicaid, to the great battles to protect our air, water, and land, John was in the fight.

And, of course, no one stands taller in the long battle we've had in this country to make health care a right and not a privilege than John Dingell and his father. John's father introduced the first national health care legislation, in 1943, and for John and his father it was a cause they never abandoned. So, when President Obama signed the Affordable Care Act into law on March 23, 2010 (some sixty-seven years after the battle begun by John Dingell, *Senior*), it was only right that the man seated next to the president be the Dean himself.

We miss John Dingell in Congress. He knew that public service was an honorable profession. He knew it could change lives. And he knew that for our government to work, we had to find consensus. For John, *compromise* wasn't a dirty word. You wouldn't find anyone tougher or more principled, but you also wouldn't find anyone who better understood that for our system to work, we have to find consensus.

John Dingell's career in the U.S. House of Representatives will be studied for years to come. I know that historians will rank him among the giants of Congress. My hope is that those serving today will read this book, wake up, and remember what public service is all about.

—*Vice President Joseph R. Biden*

INTRODUCTION

"DINGELL, YOU'VE SEEN IT ALL."

When I was serving in the House of Representatives, I heard it over and over again: "You ought to write a book."

That suggestion came regularly from more than a few people, including colleagues from both sides of the aisle, former staffers, and a number of my longtime constituents back home in Michigan. I've even been encouraged to do so by a few presidents of the United States.

I always gave the same answer: "Too busy. I've already *got* a job. Maybe someday, after I retire."

Truth is, I never intended to retire. My father died in office and, at twenty-nine years old, I'd succeeded him in the House of Representatives.

Like him, I knew I had the best job in the world. I fully expected to go out the way my dad did—serving my people until the day came when the good Lord called me home.

But what they say is true: man plans, and God laughs. Turns out I did retire, only a month shy of sixty consecutive years in office. It's the record for length of service in congressional history. At this point, I'd also been "Dean of the House"—its longest-serving member—for twenty years (another record). I laughed when it dawned on me that the awards I was getting were for just showing

up to work. All that was missing was a gold watch inscribed "Turn out the lights when you leave, Dingell."

About six months before I announced my retirement, my wife, Debbie, and I were lying awake in bed in the early morning. The bedroom was still dark; the sun's first rays had yet to appear. The house was quiet, and everything was peaceful.

In that tranquil moment, it suddenly became clear to me that I was ready to call it a career. Most everything that my dad spent his life in the Congress trying to accomplish, and his unfinished goals that I had worked so long and hard to complete, had now been achieved. Sixty-seven years after he first introduced health care reform legislation, I'd helped get it signed into law. Our food was safer. Our air and water were cleaner. Endangered species were protected. We'd looked after the widows and the orphans and all those who, as my father always said, "needed a hand up, not a handout." I'd carried on his lifelong commitment to protect the unspoiled open spaces of our beautiful country. During my six decades in the Congress, tens of millions of acres of pristine land had been set aside for conservation and protected from development.

There were a few things left that I still wanted to do. I still wanted to see the FDA get more resources and an improved ability to make our food and drugs safer. I still wanted to lead the fight to protect Social Security, Medicare, voting rights, and civil rights. But these battles now belonged to younger men—and women.

I turned to Debbie, who was, as always in the early morning, lying next to me quietly checking her emails. In the soft glow of the light emanating from her iPad, she looked like an angel sent from Heaven. She was my gift from the good Lord.

"Deb?"

"Yes, John?" Sensing from my tone that this was not just an idle

question, she put down the iPad and looked at me quizzically, peering intently at me over her reading glasses.

"I'm finished."

"Finished with *what*, John?" she asked, a hint of concern in her voice.

"The job." And I proceeded to tell her what I had finally come to tell myself: that it was time to hang it up.

Debbie said nothing for what seemed like an eternity but was probably less than a minute. She never took her blue eyes off me. I could see they were misting up. Finally, she spoke. She asked me to think it over for a few more days before I said anything publicly, and I agreed. Still, I knew then that my decision was the right one. It was time.

Starting over is the hardest thing I've ever had to do. This book is not like anything I've ever done before. For most of my life, I've let the work speak for itself. Now I realize I have one job left. It's to explain why that work was so important—and why it still is.

AFTER EIGHTY YEARS OF LIVING IN WASHINGTON, DC, IF I'VE learned one thing, it's that elected officials are supposed to be there as servants of the public interest, not of their self-interest, or of partisan ideology. A lot of my most recent former colleagues, especially this crowd of spineless Trumpet Blowers, forget that—if they ever knew it in the first place. These gutless wonders are terrified that if they show any independence or integrity, they will get kicked out on their hind ends by even crazier members of their own party. The sad truth is that *both* parties have become captive to a mentality that rewards pandering over patriotism.

That's why I finally decided to write this book: to tell the truth

about why the Congress has become reviled by the American people, and what we can still do to fix it.

In my time, America has had its share of great leaders: Franklin Roosevelt, Harry Truman, Sam Rayburn, John McCormack, Lyndon Johnson, Ted Kennedy, Barack Obama, and Joe Biden—to name just a few. They weren't all Democrats. Republicans like George H. W. Bush, Jerry Ford, James Baker, Alan Simpson, Fred Upton, and Pete McCloskey all put country before party. I worked closely with most of them, and they all served with genuine dedication and a deep belief that America was greater than a collection of its special interests.

People today, especially younger generations, have become deeply cynical and distrustful of their own government. They have good reason to be. Young people find it almost impossible to believe, but the truth is that a twice-elected African American president wouldn't have been allowed even to *vote* in many states before Congress passed the Civil Rights Act of 1964. Of all the bills I've played a part in helping pass into law, that still remains the one I'm most proud of.

This book will provide a behind-the-scenes account of some of the great congressional accomplishments I've been privileged to play a role in achieving, and of the tough fights that made them possible.

When I entered the Congress, it was largely a place of comity and mutual respect across the aisle. Sure, there were demagogues like Joe McCarthy—I kept his picture up in my office for decades, as a daily reminder of how *not* to conduct myself in public office—but there are always a few of those types in every era. There was Huey Long in the 1930s, and there are more than a few around today. One of them is now president of the United States.

Maybe the good Lord has kept me here to tell the story of how government, like life, is cyclical. FDR is revered today, but there was a time—and I remember it well—when he was called "a traitor to his class," "a fascist," and "a warmonger." It's no coincidence that those are some of the exact same terms (and worse) still used by frothing critics of former president Obama, a good and decent man who, I believe, will be viewed by history as one of our most courageous presidents.

Obama's successor is another matter entirely. He is unfit to serve. He demeans the office of president of the United States, and he is a daily embarrassment to our nation.

Still, I remain convinced that the innate decency of the American people will prevail, even in the face of what anyone with half a brain can see is an existential threat to our republic itself. This crude and reckless man is not just the problem. He is the manifest symptom of a citizenry that has grown cynical about all our institutions, not just government. The clown doesn't cause the circus. He fills it with people desperate to believe that the free loaves of bread he's promised them aren't merely crumbs. Trumpism is a far bigger danger to the country than the man himself.

History is something that can't ever be understood while it's happening. It's only the perspective of time that allows us to see beyond the temporary passion of the moment and to judge our actions, good or bad, by their consequences, not just by our intentions.

There's a quote by the great English member of Parliament, Edmund Burke, that I kept on the desk of my House office for almost sixty years: "Your representative owes you, not his industry only, but his judgment; and he betrays [it], instead of serving you, if he sacrifices it to your opinion."

Following the public will is only one part of the job. Our main purpose is to work together to find solutions to the problems faced by the people we were sent there to serve. *Congress* literally means "a coming together." That's why *compromise* was once considered an honorable word.

Hucksters like Trump have conned and intimidated a majority of both houses of Congress into believing that they are no longer a coequal branch of government. Too many members of Congress now believe that "leadership" consists of following the latest polls and shamelessly regurgitating popular opinion, all in the service of their own self-interests (reelection and a high-paying job when they leave office). Working on behalf of the public interest and fighting for the greater good are quaint ideas to them, artifacts of a naïve, bygone era.

I offer you this book as evidence that nothing could be further from the truth.

I was a part of our government when it worked honorably and well together. In this book, I hope to show you why it did, and how, by coming together again for the common good regardless of partisan ideology or petty personality, we can preserve, protect, and defend our beloved constitutional republic.

The Dean

PROLOGUE

———————

MY DAD TAUGHT ME NEVER TO TRUST A FELLOW WHO TALKS too much about himself in the third person. After Richard Nixon lost the California governor's election in 1962, he declared, "You won't have Nixon to kick around anymore." Turned out we *would* have that SOB to kick around a hell of a lot longer, until they put him on that helicopter with a one-way ticket out of town. (Resigning when you're about to be impeached is like being the drunk at a party who has his hat and coat thrown at him and slurs, "I think I'll be going home now.")

Like Nixon, Trump is overly fond of talking about himself as if he were somebody else: "Trump/Russia story was an excuse used by the Democrats as justification for losing the election. Perhaps Trump just ran a great campaign?" J. K. Rowling, who wrote all those Harry Potter books that my grandkids read, asked the right question: "I wonder whether Trump talks to Trumpself in the third Trumperson when Trump's alone."

As I write this, more than three years after I left Congress, Donald Trump still occupies the Oval Office and calls himself the forty-fifth president of the United States. I don't call him that. He is what royalists call an "imposter to the throne."

I call him a grave danger to our country and to the world. Even worse, his legacy of Trumpism has the potential to threaten the survival of our fragile and increasingly divided nation. As my

friend Norm Ornstein and his coauthors Thomas E. Mann and E. J. Dionne write in their wise book, *One Nation After Trump*, "The most disturbing aspect of Trumpism—beyond whatever we come to discover about his and his campaign's relationship with Putin and Russia—is its dark pessimism about liberal democracy, an open society, and the achievements of the American Experiment."

Perhaps by the time you read these words, with the good Lord's blessing, Trump will have left us by way of resignation like Nixon, or by impeachment, or he might finally have been called out by his own party for creating too bad a stench around them in this election year.

The Twenty-Fifth Amendment to the Constitution, which I voted for in 1965, gives the vice president, leaders of Congress, and/or the Cabinet the responsibility to declare what is now self-evident: that this is a man fundamentally incapable of fulfilling even the most basic duties of the presidency. Yet, as of this writing, the swamp creatures surrounding him are too busy lining their own pockets to even notice that their Emperor is an empty suit (whose ties were made in China).

Moreover, should criminal action by the president be alleged by Special Counsel Robert Mueller, we may yet see the Supreme Court involved. It remains an open question as to whether a sitting president can be subject to criminal indictment. However, the Court has held that a president *can* be sued in a civil action while in office; we saw that with President Clinton. To this old Polish lawyer, that suggests criminal liability by any member of the executive branch, including the president, is also within the purview of the judicial. Trump thinks he is above the law. I believe that no judge or jury, truly fulfilling their constitutional duties, would agree.

Trump once boasted that he could "stand in the middle of Fifth

Avenue and shoot somebody and I wouldn't lose voters." He may be right about that with a relatively small number of crazy jackasses who voted for him even though they knew exactly who he was. Some of them are my former colleagues on the other side of the aisle. When it comes to Trump, most of them have been acting like monkeys with their hands over their eyes, ears, and mouths. Shame on them for making a deal with the Devil just to pass a tax cut for their wealthy friends and pack the federal benches with right-wing ideologues.

As for the millions of people who voted for Trump out of hope and not hate, I'd say the vast majority is made up of decent folks who were taken in by the lies of a con man. With the exception of Trump's true believers who swallow his crap like it's a chocolate dessert, most of the men and women who supported him in the election were hardworking, honest, and decent people who were, with good reason, frightened about their futures. I don't "deplore" them. I feel sorry for them, because they will suffer the most from this ignorant fool's heartless and cruel policies.

Like the last despot we had to break with, King George III, Trump not only thinks he's above the law, but he also believes his word (or tweet) *is* the law. The Supreme Court can't impeach a president, but I believe it *can* uphold a criminal conviction that would move Trump's presidency out of Mar-a-Lago and into a federal penitentiary. He might still retain his job, at least for a day or two, but they would immediately take away his phone.

That alone could save the republic.

PART I

CHAPTER 1

The Day of Infamy

The American people have a right to know and I, as a member of Congress on their behalf, demand to know who was to blame for the great catastrophe which befell our American fighting forces in the stronghold of the Pacific, which jeopardized the very existence of the United States of America.

—CONGRESSMAN JOHN D. DINGELL SR.,
HOUSE FLOOR SPEECH, DECEMBER 9, 1941

"JACK!"

I shot up off my ass and ran across the crowded floor of the House of Representatives toward the tiny, round man who'd called out my name. At his full height of four feet and ten inches, Chief Page John W. McCabe was almost as big around as he was tall. Though I was only fifteen, I towered over him by almost a foot and a half. Yet, like all the pages, I treated him with great respect and affection.

John McCabe was a kind man, but he did have quite a temper.

It was not unusual to hear him barking out commands. But on this day, there was a different kind of urgency to his tone that I'd never heard before. He sounded deeply troubled.

"Jack," he said, reaching up and grabbing my arm for emphasis, "you're on that radio fellow Fulton Lewis today. I want you to bird-dog him and see that he doesn't talk more than he should. And make sure he turns off his recording machine the minute the president finishes speaking."

"Yes, sir, Chief!"

It was Monday, December 8, 1941. The time was just before noon.

My father, Congressman John D. Dingell Sr., had appointed me to the House Page Program back in '38, when I was only eleven. Even before that I'd been helping him around his office, addressing envelopes and running errands all over the Hill. But to make it clear that his son was not expected to get any special treatment, my dad arranged for me to become a page boy on the GOP side, which is why John McCabe, who was the chief of the Republican pages, was my boss.

Back then, the House had only two office buildings. The "Old" Building (later named after legendary House Speaker Joe Cannon) dated back to 1908. The "New" Building (now the Longworth House Office Building) was finished in 1933, the year my father was sworn in as a freshman congressman from Michigan. Dad moved into a bare-bones office in the Old Building with a single typewriter and one electric fan.

Page boys carried messages and delivered draft copies of bills back and forth between House members. Back then, there was still a great sense of humor up on the Hill. Sometimes they would send us pages running for "bill stretchers" or "check stretchers." We didn't know there were no such damn things. I'd go into an office, and the

secretary would say, "Sorry, son, we don't have them here today, but if you go on down to so-and-so's office, they should have one." Some days, I'd spend about a half a day running around before I finally realized, "Balls of fire, I've been *had*."

Not that we didn't cause a great deal of trouble ourselves. The principal of the House Page School was a strict, humorless man named Ernest "El" Kendall. My fellow prankster pages George and Walter and I used to leave stink bombs in his office. If we ever got caught, the work would double, and our time off would disappear.

Truth is, I loved it all. It was a great place for a young man to learn how the government really worked. It was better than any social studies class in the country, and we all felt lucky just to be there.

Johnny, as my dad and the other members affectionately called McCabe, started out as a page boy himself, back in 1919, during the Wilson administration. A Republican from Indiana, he survived party leadership changes for decades, staying on the job because everybody on both sides of the aisle respected him. And he loved and protected all "his kids."

For some reason, I was one of McCabe's favorites. He used to take me hunting and fishing with him on weekends down at his place in Northern Virginia. It's where Dulles Airport is located now, but it was all farmland back then. There was so much of it surrounding the city that Washington, DC, was called "the little town in the woods."

———

BACK THEN, I KEPT A SHOTGUN IN MY LOCKER AT PAGE SCHOOL so I could sneak out and go down to McCabe's farm. I'd even clean out his chicken coops to have the pleasure of hunting with the

chief. Cleaning chicken shit was not exactly my idea of fun, but if doing it got you out in the woods to shoot squirrels and turkeys, hell, it was a fair trade.

I've always loved hunting. When the House wasn't in session, some of my fellow pages and I would go down into the Capitol basement with an air gun and a terrier to hunt rats. Damn things were about as big as house cats.

But on that December day, there would be no time for fun and games.

Less than twenty-four hours before, most of America had been enjoying a typical winter Sunday. Families went to church; folks took leisurely walks; kids were outside playing ball. It was a clear, chilly afternoon in Washington, DC. My ten-year-old brother, Jim, and I were walking home from Mass at St. Joseph's Church. Our apartment was in the old United Methodist Building at 110 Maryland Avenue, right across from the Capitol. Mother, Dad, and my five-year-old baby sister, Julé, were in Northwest Washington overseeing the construction of our new home.

We had recently been gifted with a black-and-white cocker spaniel named Colonel. We kids loved the dog, but the Methodist Building didn't feel the same affection for our new four-legged family member. Rather than make us give him up, our parents decided it was time we had our own house.

So, that's why our folks weren't with my kid brother and me when a man we didn't know ran up to us and shouted, "The Japs just bombed Pearl Harbor!"

Jim and I looked at each other in shock and started running back to our apartment. We took the steps two at a time and burst through the front door, not even taking time to close it behind us. I switched on the big General Electric radio on top of the kitchen

table, quickly turning the dial until we heard someone giving a live report of the first sketchy details of the attack, even as they were still coming in live over the air:

> This is John Daly speaking from the CBS newsroom in New York. Here is the Far East situation as reported to this moment. The Japanese have attacked the American Naval Base at Pearl Harbor, Hawaii, and our defense facilities at Manila, capital of the Philippines. The first disclosure of this news was made by Presidential Secretary Stephen Early by telephone at approximately 2:25 in Washington . . . "The Japanese have attacked Pearl Harbor from the air and all naval and military activities on the island of Oahu, the principal American base in the Hawaiian Islands." That was Secretary Early's message. A short while later he dictated another message. "A second air attack has been reported. This one has been made on the army and navy bases in Manila." And here's a last-minute Associated Press flash from Honolulu: "A naval engagement is in progress off Honolulu with at least one black enemy aircraft carrier in action against the Pearl Harbor defenses." Secretary Early informed all correspondents and then rushed to the White House to be with President Roosevelt.

Jim and I sat glued to the radio for the rest of the afternoon. Several broadcasters, like much of the country, were hearing of our base at Pearl Harbor for the first time. One pronounced Oahu as "O-how." Others referred to "Ha-VAY-ee" instead of Hawaii. Unlike most Americans, Jim and I knew exactly where Pearl Harbor was. We had stayed there with our dad about five years earlier, on one of his congressional trips.

A couple of hours later, our father came through the still-open door of the apartment, his eyes dark with anger. He looked at us wordlessly, but his expression made it evident that he had heard the news. Mom came in just behind him, cradling Julé, and quietly closed the front door. I knew exactly why my dad was so angry. He'd been warning all of us, and the whole country, for a long time about the possibility of this kind of sneak attack. Now he'd been proven right. Even so, I was still stunned by the reality of the attack itself. It was like the feeling you have when someone you love dies; you know it's true, but your mind can't immediately process how your life has changed forever.

The radio remained on all evening. All the popular shows— *Fibber McGee and Molly*, *The Fred Allen Show*, *The Jack Benny Program*—were preempted by news bulletins, each one more shocking than the last. Most of the U.S. fleet at Pearl Harbor had been destroyed. The USS *Arizona* alone lost more than a thousand men when it was hit directly by an aerial bomb.

Much later we would learn that the total number of American casualties at Pearl Harbor was 2,403 U.S. servicemen and civilians killed and 1,178 wounded. It was the deadliest attack on American soil since the British burned Washington, DC, to the ground in 1812.

People began to panic. Many thought the Japanese were going to invade Hawaii and maybe even the West Coast. Their fears weren't unfounded. The following year, Japanese submarines would, in fact, shell targets in California and Oregon and occupy the Alaskan islands of Attu and Kiska, far out in the Aleutian chain. On that dark December night, there was legitimate concern as to whether we could do anything to stop them.

First Lady Eleanor Roosevelt threw away the previously scripted

remarks from her regularly scheduled Sunday night radio address and somberly prepared the nation for what was to come:

> Good evening, ladies and gentlemen. I am speaking to you tonight at a very serious moment in our history. The Cabinet is convening, and the leaders in Congress are meeting with the president. The State Department and the army and navy officials have been with the president all afternoon. In fact, the Japanese ambassador was talking to the president at the very time that Japan's airships were bombing our citizens in Hawaii and the Philippines.

As Mrs. Roosevelt spoke, I carefully studied my father. His face was a mask of fury.

> I should like to say just a word to the women in the country tonight. I have a boy at sea on a destroyer. For all I know he may be on his way to the Pacific. Two of my children are in coast cities on the Pacific. Many of you all over this country have boys in the services who will now be called upon to go into action.

I looked across at my mother, who was clutching my baby sister tightly to her chest. She was already worrying about what dangers might lie ahead for me and maybe even for my younger brother.

> You have friends and families in what has suddenly become a danger zone. You cannot escape anxiety, you cannot escape a clutch of fear at your heart and yet I hope that the certainty of what we have to meet will make you rise above these fears.

The First Lady concluded with a hopeful call to the nation that was characteristic of her God-given gift of optimism:

Whatever is asked of us, I am sure we can accomplish it; we are the free and unconquerable people of the United States of America.

No one spoke. My mother, with tears in her eyes, put my brother and sister to bed. The phone rang. My father was informed that a joint session of Congress had been called for noon the next day. He and I exchanged a quick glance. We both knew what we'd hear when the president came to the Capitol: **War**.

After a night with almost no sleep, I got up early the next morning fueled by my dad's anger, and my own. Large crowds had been building up outside the Capitol Building all night. Soldiers with .50 caliber machine guns were stationed on the roofs of government buildings, including the Capitol. A perimeter fence had been erected hurriedly overnight to keep civilians a safe distance away.

Police, stationed heavily throughout the grounds, carefully checked and rechecked the identification of everyone going in. You had to have a special pass that day, and people were forced to wait for long periods on the Capitol lawn while the security process played out. The bizarre sight of wire cables and barriers around the Rotunda were a stark reminder of how our lives had changed completely overnight. I handed a grim-faced Capitol policeman my ID. Because I'd been a page for some time, I didn't have too much trouble getting through security. They all knew me on sight.

Sam Rayburn, who had held the Speaker's gavel for less than a year, gave orders for every member to be seated in the House

Chamber (where joint sessions were held due to its larger capacity) by noon. "Mr. Sam"—a nickname used only by those closest to him—was a small man (at best, he was five foot and a little change), with a hairless face and a cue-ball pate. But, make no mistake, this tiny Texan was a giant to everyone, from the most senior members of Congress to the lowliest of pages.

Calmly and firmly, he guided the House through its required procedures. The resolution for a joint session was passed promptly at noon; then everybody waited anxiously for the president's imminent arrival.

The chamber was packed. Even though there were soldiers at every doorway, there seemed to be a lot of people hoarding seats. Those with children had to hold the youngest ones on their laps.

As I made my way up to the Gallery after the chief gave me my orders, I heard the sharp crack of the Speaker's gavel. Rayburn called on all unauthorized people to give up their seats for the senators who'd soon be arriving. People gathered behind the railings on the floor as a clamor rose again and the Senate started to file in.

The five hundred seats in the visitor and press galleries were already full to overflowing. The Mutual Broadcasting System, Fulton Lewis's radio network, was set up in the center gallery between the two wings. It was well away from the press gallery, where the NBC and CBS radio broadcasters were stationed.

I moved carefully through the crowd toward Lewis. People were too excited to sit. Thankfully, I was taller than most, so I slid between them and navigated my way quickly through the throng. I paused for a moment when I caught my first glance of the full expanse of the floor: Members I'd come to know well over the years were rushing to their seats. Wives and children were everywhere. This was not like anything I had ever seen before in the chamber.

Perhaps this was what it had been like in 1917, when President Wilson had asked Congress to declare war on Germany. That was supposed to have been the "war to end all wars." Sadly, it was not.

It was no coincidence that Wilson's widow, Edith, was here today, too, in a maroon dress, seated stoically next to Eleanor Roosevelt. The First Lady was wearing her trademark silver fox furs, still demonstrating the elegance and grace that were now even more important to the country in this time of crisis. I saw both women from a distance as I continued to make my way up toward Fulton Lewis.

Microphones were secured on the rostrum where the president would speak. Dozens of newsreel cameras were pointed toward the still-empty spot. Majority Leader John McCormack of Massachusetts leaned down and whispered something into Rayburn's ear, then took his seat behind the House microphone on the Democratic side. When the justices of the Supreme Court took their seats, I knew we were close to the president's entrance into the chamber.

When I finally got to Lewis, I introduced myself and told him he could record only the president's remarks. Barely acknowledging me, he nodded slightly as he prepared to go live on the air. He already knew the rules. Like all the other broadcasters, Lewis had been firmly instructed to stop recording as soon as the president was finished speaking.

Up until that day, Fulton Lewis had been an intractable isolationist. Throughout the 1930s, much like today, radio was an outlet for conservatives who felt betrayed by what they considered liberal control of government. The emotions of millions of Americans were inflamed by the commentaries of broadcasters like Lewis, Quincy Lowe, and the anti-Semitic priest Father Charles Coughlin, all of whom regularly denounced FDR and his New

Deal policies. And Lewis had gone so far as to provide a radio platform for the great aviator Charles Lindbergh, a prominent leader of the virulently isolationist America First Committee. (Does that phrase sound familiar? It should.)

I understood why McCabe wanted me to keep a tight leash on Lewis. Yet the demeanor of many people in the chamber that day already made it clear that, overnight, political opinions had dramatically shifted. Watching Republican minority leader Joe Martin sticking his thick finger in the chests of longtime isolationists as they nodded in mute acquiescence was like watching a familiar movie unspooling in reverse.

––––––––

AT 12:30, RAYBURN'S GAVEL SOUNDED AGAIN, AND THE ROOM fell silent. By now, no space was unoccupied. People stood on chairs, sofas, and even the paper-thin wall panels. Over on the Republican side, in the section reserved for pages, I saw my buddies Walter Harris; Sam Epsy; fussily dressed Buddy Jones; tough, muscular John Jurgensen; egghead Donald Scobie; troublemaking John Slattery—all standing on the benches so they could see the president when he arrived.

I chuckled at the spectacle of them elbowing one another for position and quickly covered my mouth. Whenever one of us was caught sleeping on the job, McCabe would have someone wake you up by dragging the business end of a match across the sole of your shoe to the tip, where it would ignite right at your toes. The poor, shocked bastard would wake up to a crowd of us laughing at his hot foot.

It suddenly struck me that, as of yesterday, none of us was a kid anymore.

When the president was announced, the entire chamber rose as one to greet him with a standing ovation.

With his right arm tightly gripping the railing of the ramp that led to the rostrum, Franklin Roosevelt slowly made his way to the microphone. His inability to use his legs was an open secret to everyone but the American public. The president's son, James, who was wearing the formal, blue dress uniform of the U.S. Marine Corps, held firmly on to his father's other arm.

As my eyes locked onto the soldier-son aiding his dad up the ramp, I thought of the nights when I could hear my own dad struggling to draw breath from his tubercular, asthmatic lungs. I would sit outside his room to make sure someone was nearby if his coughing ever stopped suddenly. I thought of the courage it took for FDR to rally himself, polio be damned, and literally rise to the occasion.

The president arrived at the lectern, propped himself up on the reading clerk's stand, and opened his black notebook. I'll never forget the image of his tired, pale face. But his eyes were riveting. They shone with unmistakable fury. None of us had ever seen this naturally cheerful, optimistic man appear so grim. He looked exactly how my dad had looked the night before, when he'd returned home to our apartment: filled with rage yet determined not to let it get the better of him. My father knew he had to stay strong for the fight ahead.

As did FDR. He made his determination clear the moment he began to speak, his familiar mid-Atlantic accent resonating powerfully throughout the hushed chamber:

Yesterday, December 7th, 1941—a date which will live in infamy—the United States of America was suddenly and deliberately attacked by naval and air forces of the Empire of Japan.

Fulton Lewis was hunched over his microphone, listening intently to a man he had long reviled. The broadcaster's body language made it obvious to me that he understood that his role had fundamentally changed. His duty now was to bring the president's words to the country honestly, no longer through a filter of personal bias. "America First" was dead. Watching his rapt expression as the president spoke, I could tell Lewis realized, like all of us, that he was now an *American* first. Partisanship had given way to patriotism.

President Roosevelt continued:

The United States was at peace with that nation and, at the solicitation of Japan, was still in conversation with its government and its emperor, looking toward the maintenance of peace in the Pacific. Indeed, one hour after Japanese air squadrons had commenced bombing in the American island of Oahu, the Japanese ambassador to the United States and his colleagues delivered to our secretary of state a formal reply to a recent American message. While this reply stated that it seemed useless to continue the existing diplomatic negotiations, it contained no threat or hint of war or of armed attack. It will be recorded that the distance of Hawaii from Japan makes it obvious that the attack was deliberately planned many days or even weeks ago. During the intervening time, the Japanese government has deliberately sought to deceive the United States by false statements and expressions of hope for continued peace. The attack yesterday on the Hawaiian Islands has caused severe damage to American naval and military forces. I regret to tell you that very many American lives have been lost. In addition, American ships have

been reported torpedoed on the high seas between San Francisco and Honolulu. Yesterday the Japanese government also launched an attack against Malaya. Last night Japanese forces attacked Hong Kong. Last night Japanese forces attacked Guam. Last night Japanese forces attacked the Philippine Islands. Last night the Japanese attacked Wake Island. And this morning the Japanese attacked Midway Island.

I tried to pick out my father on the crowded House Floor below me. Looking down at where I knew his seat always was, near the front of the chamber, I could barely make out the top of his head. But I didn't need to see him to know exactly what he was thinking. Guam and the Philippines were both places that I had accompanied him to on his fact-finding trips. Dad's close friend Frank Murphy, now a justice on the Supreme Court, was then governor-general of the Philippines when we visited there. He had hosted us in his grand official residence. These were real places to me, not simply abstract points of color on a map. They had been attacked right along with Pearl Harbor. Our family knew people who were still there; many of them had kids my age. Were they safe? How would we even find out? In that instant, this attack became deeply personal to me, as if the Japanese aircraft had dropped their damned bombs directly on Washington, DC.

Although an angry bile had been rising inside me until I could almost taste it, I forced myself to stay focused on the president's words:

Japan has, therefore, undertaken a surprise offensive extending throughout the Pacific area. The facts of yesterday and

today speak for themselves. The people of the United States have already formed their opinions and well understand the implications to the very life and safety of our nation. As commander in chief of the army and navy, I have directed that all measures be taken for our defense. But always will our whole nation remember the character of the onslaught against us. No matter how long it may take us to overcome this premeditated invasion, the American people in their righteous might will win through to absolute victory. I believe that I interpret the will of the Congress and of the people when I assert that we will not only defend ourselves to the uttermost but will make it very certain that this form of treachery shall never again endanger us. Hostilities exist. There is no blinking at the fact that our people, our territory, and our interests are in grave danger. With confidence in our armed forces—with the unbounding determination of our people—we will gain the inevitable triumph, so help us God.

And then the inescapable conclusion:

I ask that the Congress declare that since the unprovoked and dastardly attack by Japan on Sunday, December 7th, 1941, a state of war has existed between the United States and the Japanese Empire.

Overwhelming applause and cheers followed Roosevelt as he turned and left the microphone. All around, you could see unashamed tears streaming down the faces of strong men in the chamber. Watching this extraordinary display of open emotion

from adults was something I had never seen before. My father taught me that grown men don't cry. Yet, somehow this seemed like the only right response.

All the while, my eyes stayed focused on the president's gaunt face as he slowly worked his way back down the ramp. In only six and a half minutes, he had summed up the national mood more viscerally than any newspaper or broadcaster could ever do.

FDR gave the American people the unvarnished truth: we were attacked suddenly and deliberately by a ruthless force that now had to be defeated. His clarity and forcefulness made it possible for us to accept the harsh fact that we would once again have to fight in a global war. Even more important, he had called us to the collective national belief that we could, we *must*, win that war.

I watched the newsreel operators turn off their machines, as House staff members directed NBC's and CBS's radio broadcasters to cut away to their home stations and pack up their equipment. Fulton Lewis looked over at me, expecting me to tell him that he must do the same. Ever so slightly I shook my head, silently giving him permission to keep his microphone on. This was history. He had to keep recording it. Where I got the courage to make that call, I don't know. I only know that I've never regretted it.

It was now 12:39 p.m. Chaos filled the chamber as soon as the president exited. Representatives were in a mad rush to vote for the war resolution and loudly declare their support for it. Speaker Rayburn told them to keep their seats until all the senators and the members of the Supreme Court had filed out. Lewis had a wonderful delivery, almost like a sports announcer's, and he colorfully described each of the senators as, shoulder to shoulder, they exited the House Chamber.

By name, he praised now-former isolationist senators such as

Bennett Champ Clark, Hiram Johnson, and George Norris (all of whom had voted against our entry into World War I in 1917), as if their collective change of heart was completely understandable. This was suddenly a new world; their old rhetoric no longer mattered.

People were stepping down from the chairs and sofas, but some still straggled about after the senators had left. Representatives moved past them to get up to the seats that the senators, Cabinet members, and Supreme Court justices had just vacated. Furniture set up for the president's address was quickly moved out. The Speaker took a seat on the only chair left behind the rostrum. He asked that "all who do not have the privileges of the floor . . . kindly retire from the chamber." Sternly, he added, "That means *everybody*." Laughter broke out. Lewis quickly noted that "There is still humor on such a grim occasion as this."

Speaker Rayburn, in full control, continued directing his House members to move with all due speed. "Please let it be done as quickly as possible." Soon, all that was left of the guests were a few small children that members were holding on their laps. The tension which filled the room during the president's speech had now been transformed into an urgency that drove members of Congress furiously back to their seats.

———————

WEARING A PURPLE DRESS AND MOVING TOWARD THE FRONT with particular purpose, as if she were moving into battle position, was Montana's lone representative, Congresswoman Jeannette Rankin. I heard Lewis narrate her march toward the front of the chamber: "She is here, strangely enough, back again in Congress once again for her first term since those days of the world war when she was one of those who voted against the declaration. [In 1917,

she had] walked down the aisle weeping, said that she hated to cast the vote . . . but that she had to do so."

Rankin had been seated in the back, and before she moved forward, I saw Minnesota's Harold Knutson, the only other serving House member who had voted against the last war, lean over her seat and wave his arms, as if he were pleading with her to vote for war. She was plainly unmoved by his arguments. Something about the way she carried herself suggested that she would not shed a tear after *this* vote.

When all the members were seated, Speaker Rayburn started the required parliamentary process of suspending the regular House rules in order for a resolution of war to be voted on immediately. Though seated, most House members were still loudly buzzing with nervous energy and excitement. The din made it virtually impossible for Rayburn to proceed.

The Speaker swiftly silenced the clamoring members with a loud slam of his gavel: "Gentlemen will suspend until business is in order!" The old and frail House Clerk, Alney Chafee, read the war resolution to the House Chamber in a strong voice that belied his age:

Declaring that a state of war exists between the imperial government of Japan and the government and the people of the United States and making provisions to prosecute the same.

Whereas the imperial government of Japan has committed repeated acts of war against the government and the people of the United States of America:

Therefore be it resolved that the state of war between the United States and the imperial government of Japan which has thus been thrust upon the United States is hereby formally declared; and that the president be and is hereby, au-

thorized and directed to employ the entire naval and military forces of the United States and the resources of the government to carry on war against the imperial government of Japan; and to bring the conflict to a successful termination all of the resources of the country are hereby pledged by the Congress of the United States.

As Chaffee carefully enunciated each word of the resolution, many eyes were turned toward Congresswoman Rankin, who had remained standing in the aisle with her hand raised high above her head. Below Chaffee's voice, we could hear her shouting repeatedly, "Mr. Speaker! Mr. Speaker!" Rayburn slammed his gavel and ignored her, while Chaffee kept reading. The moment the resolution was fully read, the Speaker called for someone to second the motion. Miss Rankin of Montana continued waving frantically for recognition, but he simply would not acknowledge her presence. She might as well have been in Butte.

"I object!" Rankin shouted, as soon as McCormack provided the required second to the motion. Rayburn barely paused, angrily declaring that "There can be no objection to a unanimous consent request." Then he quickly moved the proceedings forward with the motion by recognizing the tall, distinguished majority leader from Massachusetts, John McCormack.

Much later, both men would become my mentors. But on this day, I saw them only through the wide eyes of a very young man still wet behind the ears. I was awed by their ability to skillfully lead the House of Representatives through this crisis. In the hands of lesser men, the situation might have devolved into chaos. Rayburn and McCormack would not permit that.

Majority Leader McCormack made a simple statement that set

the tone for all the speeches to follow: "A dastardly attack has been made upon us. This is the time for action."

The Speaker then recognized Minority Leader Joe Martin, who read from prepared remarks. Because he had no microphone, Fulton Lewis had to annotate Martin's words in real time so that people listening at home could understand what the Republican leader was saying. When Martin declared, "[T]he president's request has my support," Lewis noted that applause came from both sides of the aisle. Martin then added, "I hope there will not be a single dissenting vote." Although he wasn't looking at her, he was clearly aiming his words directly at Rankin.

Immediately after Martin finished, members seated across the chamber started shouting "Vote!" The word echoed through the chamber like a chorus of barking dogs. With renewed calm, Rayburn implored the House to come to order. "It won't be long," he said. "Let us maintain order at this time particularly."

He then recognized a very right-wing member from New York named Hamilton Fish, with whom Martin had conferred on the floor before the speech. Fish would be one of many isolationists who publicly switched sides that afternoon, yet I was still young enough to be amazed—and appalled—by the self-serving rationale Fish employed to reverse himself so completely about intervention. This newfound amnesia was not unique to him; it had spread like a contagion among all his previously isolationist colleagues. Fish had finally realized that he could not swim against this tide any longer:

> Although I have consistently fought against our intervention
> in foreign wars, I have repeatedly stated that if we were at-
> tacked by any foreign nation, or if the Congress of the United
> States declared war in the American and constitutional way,

I would support the president and the administration to the bitter end. Whom the gods would destroy they first make mad. The Japanese have gone stark raving mad, and have by their unprovoked attack committed military, naval and national suicide . . . There is no sacrifice too great that I will not make in defense of America and to help us annihilate these war mad Japanese devils.

When Fish stopped speaking, Jeannette Rankin stood up and motioned again to Rayburn. In a strong, forceful voice, she insisted that he recognize her. He pretended not to hear her and asked instead for someone to turn off some overhead lights that were bothering him. Undaunted, Rankin kept calling for recognition. Neither the palpable hostility of her colleagues nor Rayburn's complete dismissal of her right to speak deterred her.

I heard my dad's booming voice shout, "Sit down, sister!" His words would have been even harsher had she been a man. Within seconds, McCormack and Rayburn recognized Congressman Sol Bloom, whose one-sentence speech effectively spoke for everyone other than Miss Rankin: "Mr. Speaker, speedy action, not words, should be the order of the day."

The proceedings continued as if they had been uninterrupted, momentum gathering toward the vote. Well-respected congresswoman Edith Nourse Rogers of Massachusetts took the microphone and, in the only speech delivered that day completely without notes, made it clear that Rankin was not speaking for all women. With passion in her voice, Rogers said, "American women, too, have been brave."

Maryland congresswoman Katharine Byron, who had filled the seat of her husband, Bill, after his death in a plane crash, declared

that "I am willing to give my sons to this country's defense." During her speech, I heard Fulton Lewis inform his audience that the Senate had already passed the resolution without debate.

As the next speaker, John Casey of Massachusetts, was recognized, I heard an angry hiss from behind me. Fulton Lewis, red faced and angrier than hell, was arguing heatedly with someone behind him. It was a congressional staff member who had told him to shut off his recorder. Seeming satisfied that he had shut Lewis down, the staffer turned and left.

I may have been only fifteen, but I knew that that self-important staffer didn't have the brains God gave a goat. I subtly nodded to Lewis to keep recording. He shot me a quick smile and relayed to his listeners that "one of the aides got excited and came up and said that we were not to continue to broadcast. We *will* continue to broadcast because he has no authority to cut us off."

The rest of the speeches were delivered in haste, as the House grew more and more restless to vote. I had never been caught up in this kind of crowd mentality before. Their collective anger, combined with a deep sense of urgency, was why my father had shouted at Jeannette Rankin. Over the past few years, he had watched with horror as the people of Poland had endured systematic persecution at the hands of the Nazis. Now was his chance to do something about it. It was, after all, the communities of Polish immigrants and laborers that had given my dad a home in America. They were his people.

Even though I believed that Congresswoman Rankin was wrong, I remember thinking that she was one tough woman in her dogged determination to make her voice heard no matter how many people hated her for it.

At 1:04 p.m., McCormack called for the vote. Rayburn started to end the debate, and Miss Rankin again stood up. "Mr. Speaker!" she shouted futilely once more.

SPEAKER RAYBURN: Those in favor of taking the votes will rise and remain standing.

MISS RANKIN: A point of order!

SPEAKER RAYBURN: Evidently a sufficient number. Those in favor of suspending the rules—

MISS RANKIN: Mr. Speaker, I would like to be heard!

She would not be heard. The roll call began. Congresswoman Rankin continued shouting for recognition well into the vote. The Speaker slammed his gavel. "Roll call cannot be interrupted by any motion or point of order." Exhausted and defeated, Rankin slumped down into her seat.

When the clerk got into the *B*'s, Fulton Lewis was finally moved out of the chamber and into the radio broadcast center, just off the floor. Sometime later, I would hear him report that "quite by accident we had transgressed one of the rules of the Congress. This became the first broadcast ever to be made of a session of Congress."

I scanned the floor. The mood was now somber and quiet. Every isolationist voted in favor of the resolution. One of them, plump, bearded George Tinkham of Massachusetts, did so while pointing piously at his heart. I heard forty-five-year-old Illinois congressman Everett Dirksen, in his deep, stentorian voice, powerfully intone, "Aye!" Decades later we would become colleagues when I was serving in the House and he was the Senate minority leader. After

casting his vote, Dirksen put his arm around Miss Rankin. Like Knutson, he seemed to be counseling her, advising her to change her mind. But it was all to no avail.

When her name was called, Jeannette Rankin stood straight up and unflinchingly declared, "No!" Her fellow House members made a sharp hissing sound. "As a woman, I cannot go to war," she continued bravely, "and I refuse to send anyone else." Rayburn pounded the gavel until the hissing finally stopped.

At 1:26 p.m., with 388 "yea" votes and only one "nay," the resolution had passed. We were at war with the Empire of Japan. In cathartic approval, the House members whooped and shouted through Rayburn's announcement of the final tally. The "high five" had not been invented yet, so two-handed clasped handshakes were joyously exchanged by members across the aisle.

When I entered the House Page Program nearly four years earlier, I had no expectation of ever being present for an event that would profoundly change the course of American history. And at only fifteen years of age, I would have found it completely unimaginable that I would someday be on that same floor casting votes that would also change our history.

No, all that was still to come. But on December 8, 1941, what I knew for certain was that I had just witnessed our republic at one of its finest hours. In the years that followed, as I continued my studies in history with the Jesuits, I learned that America has not always lived up to her greatness.

CHAPTER 2

A Nation of Immigrants

As a nation, we began by declaring that "all men are created equal."
We now practically read it "all men are created equal, except negroes." When the Know-Nothings get control, it will read "all men
are created equal, except negroes, and foreigners, and catholics."
When it comes to this I should prefer emigrating to some country
where they make no pretence of loving liberty—to Russia, for instance, where despotism can be taken pure, and without the base
alloy of hypocracy.

—ABRAHAM LINCOLN, LETTER TO JOSHUA SPEED,

AUGUST 24, 1855

ON THE EARLY AFTERNOON OF MAY 10, 1869, UNDER A BRIGHT
blue sky in Promontory Summit, Utah, the president of the Central Pacific Railroad, Leland Stanford, strode confidently toward
two sets of steel railroad tracks gleaming in the midday sun. After
six years of backbreaking labor performed primarily by eleven

thousand "imported" Chinese workers, many of whom lost their lives under brutal conditions ranging from avalanches to smallpox, the historic day had finally arrived. With one final symbolic act by Stanford, 1,776 miles of railroad track would be connected together into a single, transcontinental line. A journey by stagecoach from Omaha to Sacramento, the sole means of transportation then possible, took twenty days to complete. That same trip would now take less than a week.

Leland Stanford, a large, bearded man given to few words, was keenly aware of the historic importance of his moment in the Utah sun. As a former governor of California, he fully understood the political significance of his newfound role on the national stage and was basking in it. Even before the connection ceremony began, he had authorized this telegram to President Ulysses S. Grant in Washington, DC:

To His Excellency General U.S. Grant, President of the United States—We have the honor to report the last rail laid, the last spike driven. The Pacific Railroad is finished.

LELAND STANFORD
President
Central Pacific Railroad

Stanford approached the steel tracks. They were laid out end to end, each set of metallic bars not quite touching the other. One stretched 1,086 miles from the east, the other 690 miles from the west. All that remained to conjoin them permanently was for a single wooden tie to be driven into the ground with a final spike, thus

creating the nation's first transcontinental rail line from the Atlantic to the Pacific.

The two great Iron Horses, the Union Pacific's Number 119, facing west, and the Central Pacific's "Jupiter," pointed east, were uncoupled from their trailing cars and drawn together, engine to engine, the distance between them only the space required for that final tie to be hammered into place. Workmen carefully placed it into position, then moved quickly away, clearing a path for Leland Stanford to stride forward and strike it permanently into the Utah soil.

Stanford grabbed a heavy silver maul, expensively crafted for the occasion with a sharply pointed, shimmering tip. The smartly dressed captain of industry then took aim at a solid gold spike engraved with the words MAY GOD CONTINUE THE UNITY OF OUR COUNTRY AS THIS RAILROAD UNITES THE TWO GREAT OCEANS OF THE WORLD and, with one swing, drove the glittering gold nail firmly into the ground. Hundreds cheered, threw their hats into the air, and toasted the great achievement with champagne.

Newspaper photographers dutifully captured the scene in an explosion of flash powder that sent the soon-to-be iconic image of that glittering spike across the nation and around the world.

Yet, like most media events that would become the stock-in-trade of American politics over the next century, this day had been entirely staged to tell only a feel-good story. Truth is always the first casualty of theater. Almost everything about this story is, at best, what we used to dismiss as "spin" and what would now be called "alternative facts." Although the transcontinental railroad was now a reality, the widely accepted story about its completion is almost total fiction.

I still like my facts the old-fashioned way—when they're real. Here's what *actually* happened:

FACT: The spike was not really solid gold. Gold was far too soft, and Stanford too cheap. A gold-plated *iron* spike was *dropped*, not hammered, into a predrilled hole and quickly removed. Stanford only pretended to be striking the not-quite-real thing.

FACT: Stanford actually *missed* hitting the spike with his theatrical blow. No matter. Within seconds, a telegraph operator, poised at the ready, tapped out one word in Morse code: "Done." The entire nation soon believed exactly what this powerful man wanted it to believe—that he had successfully struck a blow for the industrial future. It was the first national "fake news" story ever broadcast live.

FACT: Stanford called his immigrant Chinese laborers "[a] degraded and distinct people [who] would exercise a deleterious effect upon the superior race." They were derisively referred to as subhuman "coolies," and because they were supervised by Stanford's business partner, Charles Crocker, they were dubbed "Crocker's pets."

FACT: Stanford, the Republican politician whose grandiose spending eventually garnered him a storied place in American history, was, in reality, one of the first great robber barons who openly bribed government officials.

Four years after the end of the bitter War Between the States, this media moment was manipulated to excite and distract a deeply

divided nation with "news" of a now-physical bond that would speed the opening of the western frontier.

America would become great again.

MY PATERNAL GRANDFATHER, JOSEPHUS, WAS BORN ON February 26, 1857, to Albertus and Marianna Dzieglewicz (*JENG-le-vitch*). His twin, a baby girl named Marianna after her mother, died in childbirth.

Josephus—after his baptism, it was shortened to "Josef"— entered the world in Bączal Górny, a tiny village about ninety miles southeast of Kraków, in what was once Poland. When he was born, Poland had not existed as a sovereign state for more than three generations.

At its high point in the early seventeenth century, the Polish-Lithuanian Commonwealth governed over 450,000 square miles and eleven million subjects. On May 3, 1791, just three years after our American Constitution was ratified in Philadelphia, the commonwealth adopted the first codified constitution in Europe. Unlike the United States, the difference for the Poles was they were not separated from their enemies by four thousand miles of ocean.

Completely surrounding this would-be constitutional republic were three entrenched dynastic monarchies reigned over by Leopold II of Austria, Frederick William II of Prussia, and Catherine the Great of Russia. To varying degrees, all of them feared that the dangerous scourge of democracy, if left unchecked, would spread like a populist plague to their own subjects.

In 1795, Austria, Prussia, and Russia agreed on the last of three partitions that effectively erased Poland from the map. In the words of the Polish Constitution's framers, their bold document

had become "the last will and Testament of the dying Homeland." The partitions rendered the proud Polish people, especially those under Russian and Austrian control (like my great-grandparents), impoverished, second-class citizens. For them, living conditions were brutal, while work was scarce or nonexistent.

Adalbertus and Marianna, a young couple with barely enough money to afford food for themselves, prayed fervently every day for the good Lord to bless their newborn son with a better life than their own, often traveling to nearby St. Nicholas's in Bączal Dolny, an imposing Gothic wooden church that had survived wars and countless political upheavals since the seventeenth century. Astonishingly, it stands to this day.

From their fellow parishioners, my great-grandparents began to hear incredible stories of prayers being answered half a world away, in the new land of America. Even in tiny Bączal Górny, tales of the American gold rush were told and retold in reverent tones, as if describing the Virgin birth. Letters from the brave few who had survived the dangerous crossing to America were read aloud by small clusters of townspeople, who passed them back and forth as if they were family heirlooms. The letters told of a place with vast open spaces, private ownership of property, and opportunities for honest work with good wages.

Adalbertus and Marianna began talking quietly together about how they, too, could somehow make their way to this modern-day Promised Land. They were aware of the disease and death they would face in crossing the Atlantic. The letters from those first Polish immigrants who'd made it to America provided stark accounts of the grave illnesses that befell many who undertook that dangerous journey. Yet, the Devil my young great-grandparents knew (a lifetime of despair for themselves and, even worse, for their chil-

dren) was by far more frightening than any demons that might await them on the open sea.

Hope is the soul's breath. Having been taught by the Jesuits that free will does not negate the Lord's plan, I have always believed that hope is one of God's greatest gifts to us. Our duty to ourselves, to one another, and to Him, is to use that gift to its fullest. In the words of the great poet Alfred, Lord Tennyson, "Come, my friends, / 'tis not too late to seek a newer world." Although they surely never read Tennyson's "Ulysses," this was the message my father's parents heard in their hearts.

Ironically, it was an American political event, one of the most shameful days in our nation's history, that would lead to the opportunity for my family to make its way to the United States. On March 6, 1857, when my infant grandfather Josef was just nine days old, the U.S. Supreme Court issued its now-infamous *Dred Scott* decision, declaring that "The Constitution of the United States recognizes slaves as property, and pledges the Federal Government to protect it. And Congress cannot exercise any more authority over property of that description than it may constitutionally exercise over property of any other kind."

The Supreme Court affirmed by a vote of 7–2 that "the negro might justly and lawfully be reduced to slavery for his benefit." This decision enflamed the growing hostility between "free states" and "slave states" (largely in the South) and placed the nation inexorably on the road to war with itself. My great-grandparents knew nothing about any of this. For them, all that mattered was survival and the imperative of finding their way to freedom in America, even as Americans were finding that the definition of "freedom" was now a source of great conflict.

Eleven years later, in 1868, the Fourteenth Amendment to the

Constitution overturned *Dred Scott*, allowing freed slaves to legally leave the cotton farms and plantations that had literally chained them to the land for generations. When these new American citizens gathered their families and migrated north, the vanquished Confederate states angrily realized that the slave labor on which they had always relied would now have to be replaced. This quickly became a crisis for the agricultural communities of the South, where seasonal crops such as cotton would wither and die, thus devastating the plantation owners' livelihoods.

The Texas state government, recognizing the need to act immediately to avert financial disaster, conceived and funded a plan to take advantage of the Polish people living half a world away in abject poverty. The Texas Bureau of Immigration directed the governor of Texas to fund the recruitment of Polish laborers to the Lone Star State. They used that state money to send recruiting agents to Europe armed with pamphlets that read (in Polish), "Texas, the Home for the Immigrant from Everywhere." Imagine the holier-than-thou outrage in today's nativist climate if tax dollars were used to *import*, rather than deport, foreign workers. The mind reels.

———————

AMONG THOSE AGENTS WAS MEYER LEVY, A POLISH MERCHANT from New Waverly, Texas, a small town located in the southeastern part of the state. Levy was an effective salesman, and it seems likely that his efforts, either directly or indirectly, helped persuade my great-grandfather to view Texas as the new Promised Land. Nowhere in the pamphlet was there any reference to the Negro slave laborers that he and his fellow Poles would be replacing. It probably wouldn't have mattered to them anyway. The dusty streets of New

Waverly may not have been paved with gold, but they glittered brightly in the imaginations of the hundreds of Poles who Levy and his Waverly Emigration Society, over the next decade, successfully persuaded to pack up their meager belongings and follow him back to Texas.

It was against this backdrop that my great-grandfather, then almost forty years old, booked passage on the *Celestial Empire*, a wooden sailing ship that departed Bremen, Germany, on May 20, 1872, with 454 passengers, all of them immigrants bound for America. On the ship's passenger manifest, Adalbertus listed himself as a laborer from Austria. The miserable trip took almost two months. The human stench in the decks below was almost unbearable. Sleeping conditions were painfully cramped, chaotic, and cold; there were only nine dry days during the entire crossing. Fourteen of his fellow passengers died before reaching the port of New York. Yet, somehow, one woman gave birth. Here's a vivid account of death and new life from a diary kept by a German man who'd made a similar crossing a few years earlier:

> A boy dide [*sic*] on the Atlantic, and another was born. I will never forget the funeral. The ships carpenter made a coffin of rough planks and filled it with sand in the bottom. Then he bored holes in the side to make it sink faster. But it did not sink fast, and as the wood in the coffin had a pale color we could watch it for a long time as it was slowly sinking.

Adalbertus Dzieglewicz was at the very beginning of what would, over the next four decades, dramatically expand into a massive wave of impoverished Poles flooding into the United States. Like the one million starving Irish who immigrated to the United

States during the Great Potato Famine of the late 1840s, they were fleeing their ancestral homeland in desperate search of food and work.

Calling themselves *za chlebem*, or "for-bread," immigrants, the Poles in this enormous influx of migrants, one that far exceeded in size even the Irish migration, numbered more than *three and a half million* by 1914. You have to remember that the entire population of the United States back then was still under one hundred million people, so as droves of Poles swarmed ashore, they created enormous economic and political challenges for their new country.

They could see this in the resentful eyes of those who preceded them, and even of fellow Poles who had arrived only weeks or months earlier. This painful (anti-)American tradition continues to this day—you're a "real" American only if you got here *first*; then you turn around and pull the rope ladder up right behind you, even if the people clutching on to it look just like you.

When he descended the gangplank in New York Harbor on July 15, 1872, my great-grandfather understood none of this. He couldn't speak English, and had he been asked as a condition of entrance to name "His Excellency General, the President of the United States" (still Ulysses S. Grant), he would not have understood the question or the language in which it was asked, let alone have provided the correct answer. Fortunately for him (and for me), all these new arrivals were addressed collectively by an immigration officer who communicated by shouting at the top of his lungs and pointing: "Put your bags here! Men this way!"

Initially, these immigrants only expected to stay long enough to make what little money they could and then return with it to their anxious families who'd stayed behind. Their worried loved ones back home could do little more than light candles and pray for

the safe return of their faraway husbands and fathers. Yet the harsh truth of this exodus was that these families were often separated for years and sometimes decades. Many never saw one another again.

My great-grandfather left behind his wife and three children, including his eldest son, my then-fifteen-year-old grandfather Josef.

What these Poles, who could barely read or write Polish (let alone English), would soon discover to their surprise and horror was that the contracts they had "signed" with a large X rendered them indentured servants to the plantation owners for a full three years. They were to be paid $90 in their first year (equivalent to $1,542 today), $100 in their second, and $110 in their third. The landowners were required to provide them with only a "comfortable cabin" and minimal food.

The laborers were also obligated to pay back their bosses for the cost of their passage to America, which they often did in installments that kept them working well beyond the three-year contract. In practical effect, the plantation owners treated these Polish immigrants as little more than white-skinned slaves.

THREE DAYS AFTER DISEMBARKING IN NEW YORK, ON JULY 18, 1872, Adalbertus (his first name now anglicized to "Albert") arrived in New Waverly, Texas. Thanks to Meyer Levy and the Waverly Emigration Society, hundreds of Poles had preceded him to the Lone Star State, where, despite the hardscrabble conditions, they were creating a Polish community. Many were even buying land that was, literally, dirt cheap.

My great-grandfather's name was the very first one listed on a petition asking a priest to come by horseback to New Waverly so

these devout Catholic workers wouldn't have to travel elsewhere to attend Sunday worship services.

What was originally intended to be only a short-term commitment for food and work resulted in something that Albert had not foreseen: a permanent life for himself and his family in the United States of America.

In the late spring of 1881, my grandfather Josef, then twenty-four years old, boarded the SS *Nurnberg*, a steamship also out of Bremen, bound for New York. Unlike with his father's harrowing journey, however, the *Nurnberg* sped across the Atlantic in only two weeks, arriving on June 18, 1881. Shortly thereafter, Josef made his way down to Texas, where he was reunited with his father for the first time in nine years.

I've often tried to imagine what they might have said to each other. What do you say to the now fully grown son you left behind as a fifteen-year-old, who stands before you as an adult? *"Jesteś taki duży"* ("You're so big")? More likely, though, knowing my family, Albert simply clasped him on the arm gruffly and said, *"Zabrać się do pracy"* ("Get to work").

Before leaving for America, Josef had married a young woman, Mary Knapp, my grandmother. Like his father before him, he also left her behind as he embarked on a journey that he might not survive.

Soon, though, both men were able to send money back for their families to join them in Bryan, Texas, another fast-growing Polish community in Brazos County, about sixty-some-odd miles west of New Waverly. By the end of 1881, the growing Dzieglewicz clan in Texas now totaled ten men, women, and children.

Only a year later, in 1882, Josef and Mary welcomed my uncle Walter into the world, the first of my immediate family born on

American soil. My aunt Julia and my uncle Victor followed in the next five years, as Josef and Mary steadily expanded their American-born brood.

Unfortunately for my grandparents, their timing couldn't have been worse. During the three years that Julia and Victor were infants, Texas suffered a historic drought. Nothing could grow or graze on the bone-dry land, and there was virtually no work for anyone, least of all for the new immigrants.

We have very little family lore handed down from those days, but there is one story that has been passed along for well over a century. It sums up the frustration and futility of my grandparents' time in Texas. Josef, a blacksmith by training in Poland, found himself reduced to driving a horse-drawn wagon through the bleak, dusty streets of Bryan. A scrawled sign on the side of his rickety wagon read WATERMELONS! 5 CENTS!

After seemingly endless days of riding around and around the barren town with scarcely a nickel to show for his labors, he yanked on the reins, pulled the horse over to the side of the road, and spilled out all the unsold watermelons into a ditch. Then he rode home, gathered up his young family and their meager belongings, said good-bye to his father and mother, uncles, aunts, and cousins, and pointed the wagon north. My grandmother was pregnant with my uncle Frank, who after almost four weeks of bumpy travel, was born in St. Joseph, Missouri, on January 6, 1890. They stopped there long enough to christen the new baby and then got back on the trail, still headed north.

About a month later, my exhausted family drove their buggy past the city line of Detroit, Michigan: population 205,876. The name "Detroit" had been chosen by an early French explorer to reflect its strategic location on the body of water, now the Detroit

River, linking Lake Erie and Lake Huron. The French called it *le détroit du Lac Érié*, literally meaning, "the strait of Lake Erie."

Most Polish immigrants immediately settled into an established and fast-growing community on the east side of the city. For reasons now lost to history, my grandfather took our family instead to the west side, which was only just beginning to see a few Polish families settling there. It ended up *not* being a wrong turn—just the opposite, in fact.

When the young Texas family climbed out of their wagon on that winter's day in Detroit, wrapped heavily in whatever warm clothes and blankets they had, they stared up in awe at the massive façade of what would soon be St. Casimir Church, ambitiously modeled after St. Peter's Basilica in Rome. It remained unfinished after almost a year of continuous construction.

My family craned their heads up at the majestic structure. Even though it was only half complete, St. Casimir's was already bigger than any church they had ever seen. Eyes wide in wonderment, Josef crossed himself and said to my grandmother, *"Bóg przywiózł nas domu"* ("God has brought us home").

In Michigan, Josef's early training and skills as a blacksmith were finally put to practical use. There would be no more watermelons to peddle. He spent most of that first year in Detroit working long hours to help finish the remaining construction on St. Casimir. Shortly before Christmas, on Sunday, December 21, 1890, St. Casimir's, the first Polish church on Detroit's west side, was officially dedicated. My grandfather, now fully "Americanized" as Joseph Adam Dingell, became known to his new friends and neighbors as a skilled worker who had chosen Detroit as his permanent home. The fantastic stories told in hushed tones back

in tiny Bączal Górny of America as a "land of miracles" had proven true.

For my family, there was another miracle yet to come. On Friday, February 2, 1894, my father, John David Dingell, was born. He was baptized by the Reverend Paul Gutowski, the first pastor of St. Casimir Church, whose construction my grandfather had helped finish with his own hands. On this blessed day, Joseph's rough hands tenderly presented his youngest son to Reverend Gutowski, who solemnly declared, "We anoint you with the oil of salvation in the name of Christ our Savior; may He strengthen you with His power, who lives and reigns for ever and ever."

My father would need that strength every day of his life.

[CHAPTER 3]

Go West

One cannot be pessimistic about the West. This is the native home of hope. When it fully learns that cooperation, not rugged individualism, is the quality that most characterizes and preserves it, then it will have achieved itself and outlived its origins. Then it has a chance to create a society to match its scenery.

—WALLACE STEGNER, *THE SOUND OF MOUNTAIN WATER*, 1969

IN 1871, THE YEAR BEFORE MY GREAT-GRANDFATHER SET SAIL in search of a better world on the western shores of the Atlantic, Horace Greeley, the nationally renowned editor of the *New-York Tribune* newspaper, received a letter from a young Massachusetts man beseeching him for career advice. Greeley, who had himself traveled west to Colorado during the Pike's Peak Gold Rush of 1859, sent back this now-famous reply:

Dear Sir:

So many people ask me what they shall do; so few tell me what they can do. Yet this is the pivot wherein all must turn.

I believe that each of us who has his place to make should go where men are wanted, and where employment is not bestowed as alms.

Of course, I say to all who are in want of work, Go West!

Yours,

Horace Greeley

My great-grandfather's decision to "Go West" from Poland to America certainly was not the kind of migration Greeley was addressing or even contemplating when he urged his Massachusetts-born correspondent to "Go West!" Yet his advice, to "go where men are wanted, and where employment is not bestowed as alms," was, and remains, the dream of all newcomers to America. My great-grandfather was not at all certain that he would be wanted in America. His dream, like that of immigrants to this day, was that he would find something, anything, better than the brutal conditions he and his fellow Poles had endured throughout their lives. Continuing to stay in Poland meant an unforgiving future that would be just as bleak for his children and for theirs.

It was that same powerful desire for a better life that impelled my grandfather Josef north to Detroit, after leaving behind only a wagon full of watermelons rotting by the side of the road. In the town where his own father had once found genuine refuge, Josef felt trapped and hopeless.

Adalbertus "Albert" Dzieglewicz died and was buried in New Waverly, Texas, in 1895, a year after my father was born in Detroit. He never met his grandson, a man whose extraordinary achieve-

ments in America would have been completely unfathomable to him. Yet, without the toughness and tenacity of my immigrant great-grandfather, my father's career would never have happened, nor my own. I literally wouldn't be here writing these words today, because no part of my family's history in America, including me, would have come about.

My father, like the grandfather he never knew, was a born leader. Just as Albert led the petition drive to bring a priest to their Polish community in Texas, my dad was never content with the status quo. Physically frail, but with a voice like a foghorn, he would grow into a man listened to and respected by his fellow Poles and, eventually, by three American presidents.

Yet the true miracle of my father was that he lived long enough even to *become* a man. In 1907, when he was only thirteen years old, his mother died. We were always told she died in childbirth with twins, but the death certificate, a document I'd never seen until preparing to write this book, says it was from stomach cancer. Either way, my dad's life changed completely when, just four months later, his father, Joseph, remarried. The new wife, Mary Opalewska, was a thick, muscular woman who my dad and his older brother, Uncle Frank, called "the Wrestler" (of course, not to her face, mind you; she could easily have broken them in two). She brought a pack of kids with her to their house, and in short order, my grandfather had no choice but to yield to his new wife's demands that *her* kids come first. My father and uncle quickly found themselves out on the street, having to fend for themselves while still in their teens.

My dad, who was only in the eighth grade at that point, had to leave Saint Casimir's School and find work. It was the end of his formal education, something he would compensate for throughout

his life by becoming a voracious reader. Out of necessity, he became his own best teacher. In order to survive, my dad took every job he could find. He sold newspapers on the streets of Detroit. At fourteen, he became a cabin boy on a Great Lake steamer. Then, still only in his late teens, he found work at the *Detroit Free Press*. With a boundless capacity for hard work, he accepted every task they gave him with enthusiasm. He sorted papers, delivered completed jobs, and fetched more than one cup of coffee.

A naturally gifted writer, my father was even given a few assignments as a cub reporter. That earned him membership in the International Typographical Union, a stroke of good fortune that would later prove crucial to his survival.

One of the toughest jobs my dad had at the paper was working as a printer's devil, the assistant apprentice to the Linotype operator. He mixed tubs of ink and fetched blocks of lead type for the printer to use as print "slugs" in the hot metal machines. Often, he was assigned to heat up and pour the molten lead, a risky practice that could leave burns or, if the hot lead squirted out, cost you an eye. It was dirty, dangerous work. The very term *printer's devil* was coined to describe the regular practice of dumping the used and broken pieces of lead into a big metal "hellbox," so they could be taken to the blast furnace to be melted down for reuse. My dad told me that he often left at the end of his shift covered in ink and bone tired after working twelve- to fourteen-hour days. There were no child labor laws yet; many of these kids worked until they dropped.

In my dad's case, that was literally what happened. After daily exposure to lead, he developed a persistent cough that wouldn't go away. One day he just keeled over, unable to stop hacking. A doctor examined him and told him that he was done at the paper. It wasn't

clear if it was the lead exposure or something even worse, but my dad's health declined quickly. He spent many feverish days in bed and, as my father always did, faced the problem head-on, pragmatically. He read everything he could about new treatments for lung illnesses. One of them became his best hope: a town out west with clean air, built near natural hot springs.

Now let me tell you the story of a train, a town, and a man named Tom who saved my dad's life.

In 1914, my father, John David Dingell, left Detroit on a train bound for Colorado Springs, Colorado. He was *not* following Horace Greeley's advice to go west in search of a well-paying job.

He was twenty years old and he was dying.

————————

MY DAD WAS HEADED WEST ON THAT TRAIN BECAUSE IT WAS his last hope of survival. By this point, his cough had been diagnosed as the white plague, so named because of the anemic pallor of its victims. It was also then called consumption, a highly contagious disease that was spreading across America like a scythe through wheat. Today we call it tuberculosis.

For most, consumption was a certain death sentence. The body literally consumed itself, and vital organs simply shut down. Because it was so contagious, those who had it were shunned like lepers, lest they spread it to healthy folks. Between 1910 and 1920, consumption, pneumonia, and scarlet fever had reached pandemic proportions in the United States. Millions died.

Somehow my father managed to scrape enough money together for a ticket to Colorado Springs. It was widely thought that the hot springs bubbling up from the ground there contained restorative minerals that could cure those afflicted with the white plague.

Grasping on to that slim reed of hope, thousands of sick and dying people from across the country did anything they could to get there and "take the waters."

My dad was too weak even to sit up in a chair for the two-day trip, but he couldn't afford the expense of a sleeper car. A kind porter took him into the baggage car and laid him out on an old mattress on the floor. He was barely conscious when the train slowly pulled into Colorado Springs at nine in the morning.

Tom Kelleher, a strapping young Irish cop, was patrolling the station when the train arrived. Like my dad, he was only twenty years old. Boarding the train, he saw an emaciated man lying on a mattress, gasping for air. One of his lungs had collapsed.

"What are you doing?" Kelleher asked my dad.

He was barely able to respond. "I'm sick," he wheezed out between spasms of coughing. "Can you get me to the Union Printers Home?"

As a card-carrying member of the International Typographical Union, my dad was eligible to receive care at the Union Printers Home, a castle-like structure built on a hill high above Colorado Springs. It was a place where he could go to die with some measure of dignity.

At least, that was his plan. But Kelleher would have none of it. He quickly sized up this pale, sickly Polish kid and realized he was in need of immediate care. "To hell with that. You're going to my mother's house."

Knowing that no ambulance would take my father, and ignoring the potential danger to himself, Kelleher summoned a police paddy wagon, also known as a Black Maria. Then, gathering up my small, frail father in his strong arms, the six-foot Irish cop hoisted

him onto the back of the paddy wagon and jumped in beside him. They drove straight to the Kelleher family home on Victoria Street, a house so new it was the only one in the neighborhood that had an *indoor* bathroom. Tom's mother, Mary, herself an immigrant like my father's mother, briskly set about the near-impossible task of nursing my father slowly back to health. Years later, my siblings and I would call her "Grandma Kelleher."

The doctor who arrived to examine my father, John Conway, was grim faced when he put down his stethoscope and told my twenty-year-old dad that he had six more months to live "at the outside." Dr. Conway's voice must have sounded like it was coming from some distant place as he explained his prognosis. "When it gets down in the lungs, son, if you're very lucky, the lungs will encapsulate and protect the rest of the body for a time. If you're unlucky, something will rupture and you'll hemorrhage and bleed out through the nose and mouth."

Even then, my father was a scrapper. He told Doc Conway (who would later become our friend and family doctor, and my godfather), "Doc, I'll piss all over your grave."

John Conway passed away in 1935. He lived long enough to see his young Polish patient become a member of the United States Congress. My father always told us, "Well, *I* didn't die, but all my doctors did."

After a number of weeks spent recuperating and regaining some of his strength in the Kelleher house, my father was given a bed in the majestic Union Printers Home, a Victorian-style castle built in 1892. It had a red sandstone and lava exterior and words engraved above its huge arched doors reading ITS BOUNTY UNPURCHASABLE. The UPH, as it was called, had been built and paid for

by the International Typographical Union to *guarantee* good health care for its members whenever they needed it. (Remember that point; I will be coming back to it throughout this book.)

I can only imagine my dad's eyes going wide with wonder when he first entered the grand hallway made of dark mahogany wood. Directly ahead of him was a great staircase of shining white marble. The UPH amenities included large sun porches, magnificent grounds designed by a landscaper who had maintained the gardens of the Taj Mahal, a working farm maintained by the patients, a pool hall, and an in-house barber for a shave and a trim.

Yet, for all the architectural grandeur of the UPH, I know exactly what made my father feel as if he had passed through the gates of heaven on earth: the library. At the top of that bright marble staircase was a reading room where he would have access to a collection of ten thousand books. For my father, this was like a personal gift from the good Lord above. Although he had only completed the eighth grade back in Detroit, my dad was an inveterate reader. He taught himself things that graduate students in law, medicine, history, economics, and philosophy don't know after years of study. Regardless of not having gone to high school, he was one of the most learned men I've ever known. Throughout his life, he had a unique ability to apply his philosopher's mind to solving practical problems. Dad saw the way things *could be*, while never losing sight of how they actually *were*.

One day, as he lay still in bed (something he was forced to do for most of the day as he slowly regained his strength), my father read a newspaper column titled "Where Will You Be Twenty Years from Now?" It was a story about how so many of America's greatest figures had risen from humble beginnings to great heights in government service, business, and the professions. It told how some

had even won election as members of Congress. He took out a pen and underlined "member of Congress."

My father put down the paper and stared out at the beautiful Colorado landscape. His gaze, however, went far beyond the horizon. Years later, he told me that at that moment he said to himself, "If I ever recover, that is what I want to be twenty years from now, a member of Congress." It was 1916. He was twenty-two years old.

———————

SHORTLY AFTER MY DAD FIRST ARRIVED IN COLORADO TOO weak to walk, Archduke Franz Ferdinand was assassinated in Sarajevo, in the Austro-Hungarian province of Bosnia and Herzegovina. In little more than one month, the First World War had broken out in Europe. At the beginning, this was considered a distant fight by most Americans, a viewpoint reinforced by President Woodrow Wilson's declaration that our nation would remain "neutral." Two years later, Wilson successfully won reelection on the slogan "He Kept Us Out of War." However, that pledge was broken less than a month after he was sworn in for a second term. On April 6, 1917, the United States declared war on the German Empire, thus joining the Great War.

My father had no intention, as he would later put it, "of sitting on my ass" in Colorado when his country was at war. By early June 1917, he'd recovered sufficiently to board a train back to Detroit, where he checked into Room 508 of the YMCA. (There was still no room for him in my grandfather's house.) He then went straight to his local draft board and tried to enlist. They told him, "Sorry, son. Boy Scouts, or even *women*, before we'd take you."

On June 26, the first fourteen thousand infantrymen landed in France as part of the American Expeditionary Forces under the

command of General John "Black Jack" Pershing. My father read about it in his old newspaper, the *Detroit Free Press*, and was madder than a boiled owl that he wasn't among them. He kept going back, though, trying every enlistment center in the city, all of which rejected him. He even went over to Canada, but they turned him down, too. At one point, he asked a friend to enlist for him, using my dad's identification. This gambit failed as well.

I'm holding his draft registration form in my hand. On it, my father describes himself as having "hazel eyes and light brown hair." He also lists himself as "tall," which is a pretty good measure of how desperate he was to get inducted. When he stretched himself all the way up to his full height, my dad was barely five feet, eight inches tall. The words that must have stung my father the most were written by a clerk in two separate places on the form: "Ill health." As hard for him as it was to accept, my dad understood that the potential risk he presented to the health of other soldiers was just too great for the military to let him join up.

Finally resigned to the reality that he would not see combat, my father went back to Colorado Springs. He did his part in the war effort by volunteering with the Red Cross. And he resolved to make a fresh start in the place that had given him back his life. Soon after he returned to Colorado, my dad landed a job with the Mountain States Telephone Company (formerly the Rocky Mountain Bell Company) as a salesman.

In 1918, he met and immediately began courting a very attractive coworker, a secretary named Grace Blossom Bigler. She had fair skin, delicate features, and honey-blonde hair. Dad always said she looked like a movie star, "even more beautiful than Mary Pickford." Grace was three months younger than her new suitor, and she also hailed from the Midwest, from a small town in Iowa called

Spencer. As the crow flies, Spencer is about six hundred miles due west of Detroit.

Grace and her family had moved out to Colorado when she was very young, and so she always thought of herself as a native Coloradan. Her father, Albert Bigler, was an ill-tempered man of Swiss heritage and considerable means. He owned two cantaloupe farms in Colorado, one near Pueblo and the other in Rocky Ford. Unlike my paternal grandfather in New Waverly, Texas, Grandpa Bigler chose fertile territory on which to grow and sell his melons.

Right from the start, Albert Bigler and his wife, Laura, didn't much care for my father. To them he was, in every respect, the wrong man for their lovely daughter. But the woman who would become my mother paid them no mind. She took an immediate shine to her dashing new beau with the Douglas Fairbanks mustache.

Much to the extreme disapproval of her family, the budding relationship between John and Grace grew serious. He started calling her "Honey," a name she never liked, except when spoken by my dad. As matrimony began to appear more and more likely, the Biglers began pressuring my mother to give him up. They didn't like Catholics. They didn't like Poles. They didn't like "wets"— Prohibition was adopted in 1920 as the Eighteenth Amendment to the Constitution; its many "conscientious objectors" were called "wets"—and they *definitely* didn't like Democrats.

My father was a Polish-Catholic Democrat who loved a cold beer, which he brewed himself. My Grandfather Bigler was a "dry," at least so he claimed. Peruna, the "health elixir" he drank for years, contained as much as 25 percent alcohol. But it didn't say so on the label, so he sanctimoniously called himself a teetotaler. The old dipso probably even believed he was.

MY FATHER NEVER SPOKE AN ILL WORD ABOUT HIS PROSPEC-
tive father-in-law. For a brief time, Grandpa Bigler even threw my
mother out of the house after she became engaged to my dad, and
completely cut her out of his will. Grandfather Bigler was a mean old
buzzard, yet my father always treated him the way Jesus prescribed
in the Gospel of Matthew: "Do not resist the one who is evil. But
if anyone slaps you on the right cheek, turn to him the other also."
My dad's devotion to his beloved bride-to-be meant that he kept his
famous temper in check. Her passion for him cost her dearly, not
just in dollars, but also in the loss of her family's unconditional love.
That was one thing she never had to worry about with my dad. His
commitment to her was as unshakable as his religious faith.

While my parents' courtship was growing more and more serious, significant political change was taking place in the United
States—most of it bad. The Roaring Twenties were also the Republican Twenties. The Ku Klux Klan began to reassert itself, after
a long period of dormancy. It began stirring up renewed religious
hatred against Catholics, Jews, immigrants, and especially "the dar-
kies." The Klan's opposition to "demon drink" was a prime force
in the passage of Prohibition. My dad fought back against the Klan,
particularly through his active membership in a Catholic fraternal
organization called the Knights of Columbus.

In 1920, Dad got promoted at Mountain States Telephone. He
was put in charge of payroll for one of the company's districts and
started packing a .38 caliber pistol wherever he went. Years later,
we talked about why he felt he needed it:

ME: Were you afraid someone would steal the payroll?
DAD: No. The Ku Klux Klan wanted to run a road grader over me.

ME: What did you do?
DAD: I told them to get the hell out of my way.

In 1922, my father met a man named William E. "Billy" Sweet, a Democrat running for governor of Colorado. Sweet promised him a job in his administration in return for help in managing the campaign. My father, who had never worked on a campaign before, played a big role in getting Sweet elected on an anti-Klan platform. After the election, he met with Governor-elect Sweet:

SWEET: Dingell, I said you could have any job you wanted. Name it.
DINGELL: How about conservation commissioner?
SWEET: I'm sorry, friend, but that's the one job that's already been promised. Is there anything else I can offer you?

My father respectfully declined Sweet's offer of a different job. Yet he'd been bitten hard by the political bug. Two years later, he decided to put his fate in his own hands by running for one of the three state legislative seats that represented El Paso County, where his home of Colorado Springs is the county seat. The top three vote getters, all Republicans in a heavily GOP county, each won a seat. My dad ran a strong race but narrowly came in fourth. It was a measure of his effectiveness as a campaigner that he ran significantly ahead of the statewide ticket, getting many more votes in the county than Governor Sweet, who was soundly defeated for reelection by Clarence Morley, the Klan-supported candidate.

Clarence Morley was soon indicted, convicted, and removed from office for financial crimes. If I've learned anything about greedy politicians—to be clear: I'm *not* talking about my many

friends, on both sides of the aisle, who are honorable and dedicated public servants—it's this: when they find themselves in positions of great power, the thieving bastards invariably overreach. Too much is never enough for them. The ancient Greeks called it hubris. I say they're just plain crooks.

Despite the unrelentingly cruel opposition of my mom's family, my parents continued their courtship for seven years. Finally, on April 27, 1925, Grace Blossom Bigler became Grace Dingell.

A little more than a year later, on a mild summer day in Colorado Springs, I made my entry into the world. The date was July 8, 1926. My name was never in doubt: I was to be John David Dingell Jr. Now I don't know if I was a colicky baby, but from very early on my personality was on full display. By the time I was two, my dad had taken a job with Williams Brothers, a natural gas pipeline company that kept moving him all over hell's half acre. In 1928, he was working in Greenville, Mississippi, when my mother wrote these revealing lines about me in one of her frequent letters to him:

> Mother has a terrible time with him. He stands up & fights her when she gets after him. I don't say much, for in my way of thinking, she doesn't know how to manage him & is always after him for something. When he is up with me he is an angel & we have big times.

Although my mother had cautiously reconciled with her parents, they used my father's absence to renew their efforts to break up the marriage. By "helping" with me while my mother was pregnant, they saw a chance to get their daughter back.

On February 22, 1928, my mother gave birth to their second child, Patricia Ann Dingell, who was called both Patsy and Pattie

Ann. She was born in Long Beach, California, where my maternal grandparents had a winter house. Not by accident, we were now even farther away from my father, who was still laboring hard to finish that pipeline in Mississippi.

While they were apart, my parents corresponded multiple times a week. What's clear from reading those letters now is how hard the physical separation was on both of them, particularly my mother. On September 25, 1928, she wrote my dad:

> Just two weeks ago I saw you going down Platte leaving me alone. And how lonesome I am. Sunday I was blue all day and yesterday. Today is just getting started. What shall I plan to do? The only thing I want is to be with you and that seems impossible. I don't want to stay here alone *unless* my dearest will be here in say six months. I don't suppose the folks will be back from Calif. before June 1 and I couldn't bear to be away from you that long unless it had to be.

Just three days later, she sent my father another longing letter:

> My heart just aches tonight and there are so many, many miles between us. Your sweet tender letter came yesterday and I admit it jarred me to the depths. I saw for the first time a blacker picture than has ever been painted. Yes, dear, I have decided there is something far greater than money—something we are and have been robbed of far too much—our sweet companionship. This must be absolutely the last separation. Dr. Conway said I would gain better if I was not so blue and lonesome. He was here yesterday and said I might be up for a short time *but not an hour*— I'd give an awful lot tonight for a loving embrace and the sweet

darling boy I promised to love and obey (?) to come and crawl in bed with me. Even if I have the kiddies there is a vacancy nothing can fill. I am doing my best to be ready to come when my month is up & half of it is gone now.

It's almost impossible to imagine now, but the 1928 election was only the *third* time women were eligible to vote for president. This was also the first time in history that a Catholic American had been nominated by one of the two major parties as its standard-bearer. New York's popular governor Al Smith was the Democratic nominee against Republican Herbert Hoover, a former secretary of commerce who had never held elective office. Smith's Catholicism was the hot-button issue in the campaign; many people were genuinely afraid that a Catholic president would take his orders directly from the Pope. It was a crock of shit, yet millions of voters believed it. My mother tried and failed to persuade my grandmother that this was just plain bigotry:

I have read those papers you sent from cover to cover—ads included—and found them very interesting. I enjoyed the "What's the Matter with Hoover" most. If for no other reasons than there stated—I'd be for Al. Did you read that over 70 percent of the soldiers in the Allied Armies were Catholics? The article then said "if the Pope intended to do anything he had the opportunity then." That is a keen argument. I read that article to Mother—from the Congressional Records—and as usual she said "I don't believe that." Jack, darling—it's no use wasting time and strength trying to show her anything about anyone. Once her mind is made up—right or wrong—she's RIGHT.

In all these years, I had never seen any of my mother's letters until only recently. Nine decades later, it gladdens my heart to learn that even at two years old, I already wanted to be just like my father:

I said to Son this morning "What are you going to be when you grow up" and he said "I am going to be just like Daddy dear"—so you see he is decided on two points. He is to be like you & a doctor.

My mother showed the depth of her love for my father every day of their lives together. Through her endless patience, tireless care, and by the sheer force of her will, she kept my father alive beyond what any doctor could do. To my dad, she was his Grace from God.

You know, dear, I never worry about you as to your actions for I trust you and love you with every drop of blood I have. The only time I worry is for fear you won't be well and rest and eat as you should. The reason I harp on that so much is because I love you so and I feel I must have you forever. As to our future, dear, it's up to you—all I ask is the pleasure to be with you . . . You know the one big reason why I wanted to go with you is so we could soon worship together as of one faith. Dearie this must be. I am so anxious to get the babies away. John should be being trained right now and Pattie must have it too. I have them lots of the day & enjoy them so. Pattie Ann is so dear and so good. Jack Jr. was pleased with his letter he picks it up and says "Dear Sonny Boy." He loves his Daddy Dear too. You have promised me another honeymoon (all over) and I will hold you to it. Sweetheart I long

for it. I long to be with you and steal a kiss as I pass by your chair. We have had a few hard bumps but they have only made our love more true, more lasting.

A few months after those letters, my mother's fervent wishes came true when the four of us were reunited in Greenville, Mississippi, where my dad was finishing up his work on the pipeline. Then, in December of 1928, we moved permanently up to Detroit.

The weather in Greenville had been mild, ranging from the high thirties to the mid-fifties. The opposite was true when we arrived in Detroit, just before Christmas. The temperatures in January and February were well below freezing. It was a hard adjustment for all of us, especially so for my infant sister. Patsy developed a severe case of strep throat. Her condition only worsened over the next three months, and on March 23, 1929, she died. It was the day after her first birthday.

My mother fell into a dark and despondent state of grief. In some ways, she never stopped mourning Patsy's loss for the remainder of her life. I'd never seen my parents more distraught. It was the only time I can ever remember when my father seemed totally helpless. My mother's parents strongly urged her to come back to California, but she would never again leave us.

Nineteen twenty-nine was also a devastating year for the whole country. On October 29, the stock market crashed. The ensuing panic wiped out millions of investors, and its effects were immediate. In Detroit, a city heavily dependent on the manufacturing of automobiles, production plummeted by 75 percent within a year, leaving tens of thousands of workers unemployed. Banks failed.

My father did anything and everything he could to make sure we always had food, clothing, and a roof over our heads. He sold

meat wholesale, and though Prohibition was still in effect, he brewed beer in our house. Some of the best brew I ever had was the beer my dad made. I even had my own child-size mug.

Every once in a while, a bottle exploded in the back room. We'd rush back to get it before the other bottles of beer burst, which would have made a hell of a mess. Not to mention wasting a perfectly good batch of beer.

My family, like most families in our neighborhood, shared what little we had with kith and kin. We took care of the friends and relatives who needed help. It was just what you *did*. My parents never turned anyone away, even "cousins" who would appear for one meal, stay a few weeks, then leave—never to be seen again.

And even though the whole neighborhood was as poor as Job's turkey, every Wednesday night, my father had his many friends over. They'd all drink his beer. Someone would roll back the rugs, and they'd play and sing and dance till about one o'clock in the morning.

In October 1931, our family grew to four again when my brother, Jim, was born. Having a new baby was a blessing for my mother.

———

IT WAS DURING THOSE EARLY DEPRESSION YEARS THAT MY dad also became head of the West Side Dom Polski (House of the Poles), a social organization. They'd sell insurance and (still-illegal) home-brewed beer, and they'd have absolutely wild parties on Friday and Saturday nights, complete with big damn street fights right outside the social club's place at a junction near Michigan Avenue, the main thoroughfare of the now-burgeoning Polish section of West Side Detroit.

I don't mean to suggest that the Great Depression was all beer

bashes and street fights. People needed all kinds of help, and too often they had nowhere to turn. The city, state, and federal governments were either overwhelmed or incompetent. Many people, especially in the Polish community, turned to my dad for advice. Given his knowledge of the law and of government bureaucracy, many believed he was a lawyer. He did what he could do to help people with their problems, or if what they needed was just someone to listen, he did that, too. These were the times when he'd grab a couple of bottles of his home brew out of the back room and go sit out on the front stoop with a friend or neighbor who was in trouble. My dad was as good a listener as he was a talker.

Years later, when I actually *was* a lawyer, there was a kind old judge at the Court of Common Pleas in Detroit who was a dear friend. He called me into his chambers one day. I thought it was about a lawsuit that I was trying before him.

"John, sit down. I want to tell you a story."

"Of course, Your Honor."

"John, your dad was being sued for his milk bill back in '32. The issue came up just before the election. I told the milk company that I was going to postpone the case. He did so much for everybody else, it was the least I could do for him."

I was flabbergasted. I knew the Depression was hell and that money was tight, but I didn't fully understand that it was that bad for us until that moment, twenty years after the fact. I called my mother and asked her how bad it had really been. "Well, Jack," she said quietly, "I packed my shoes with newspaper to make them last just a bit longer, so you kids could get new ones." I hung up the phone and just stared into the middle distance. We were *that* poor, yet both my mom and my dad almost always thought about everybody else before themselves.

Poor as we were, that's exactly why my father chose that time to make good on the vow he'd made to himself sixteen years before in that sickbed in the Union Printers Home in Colorado. People needed his help *now*. And time was something he knew he couldn't afford to waste. At thirty-eight, he was a young man in an old man's body.

He decided to run for Congress.

CHAPTER 4

Ring (in) with Dingell

The public institutions themselves, of peoples, moreover, ought to make all human society conform to the needs of the common good; that is, to the norm of social justice. If this is done, that most important division of social life, namely, economic activity, cannot fail likewise to return to right and sound order.

—POPE PIUS XI, QUADRAGESIMO ANNO,

MAY 15, 1931

I REMEMBER SATURDAY, OCTOBER 1, 1932, VERY WELL, THOUGH I was only a six-year-old whelp still pleading for my first big-boy outfit of kneesocks and knickers. That day, the New York Yankees and the Chicago Cubs were playing the third game of the World Series at Chicago's Wrigley Field. Even though my beloved Detroit Tigers had finished a disappointing fifth in the American League pennant race, I remained riveted by the Fall Classic.

For me, it was a young boy's joy of the national game. For most adults, the World Series provided a desperately needed distraction

from the grim reality of the Great Depression. The unemployment level was at a staggering rate of almost 25 percent, and the prospects for recovery seemed remote, perhaps impossible.

"Play ball!"

I sat curled up on the floor of our living room with my head propped up on my knees, so close to the radio that my mother finally said, "Son, get away from there, you'll hurt your hearing!" I moved away a little, but as soon as she left the room, I pressed my body right back up against the speaker.

What made that particular game so historic in baseball lore occurred in the fifth inning. Writing about it even today, I feel the same sense of excitement that made my heart race when, as a child, I listened to the live broadcast. With two men on base for the Yankees, and the score tied 4–4, the great Babe Ruth stepped up to the plate in Chicago's Wrigley Field. The catcalls and booing from Cubs fans were immediately replaced by cheers as Ruth took two quick-called strikes.

———————

PEOPLE WHO WERE THERE, INCLUDING DEMOCRATIC PRESIdential nominee, New York governor Franklin Delano Roosevelt, and, somewhere else in the stands, twelve-year-old John Paul Stevens (later to become a Supreme Court justice), watched in wonder as Ruth called time and stepped out of the batter's box. In a moment that spoke to Ruth's unshakable belief in his ability to control his own destiny, a moment that the country sorely needed in those dark days of the Great Depression, he extended his arm and pointed his bat toward the center field bleachers. His intent was clear: "I'm hitting the next pitch over that wall."

A moment later, the nation listened in disbelief as the an-

nouncer made the call: "There's the windup. Here's the pitch. It's a slow curve, low, and the Babe swings—and it's a long one, a long one going out right toward center. It's in there! Another home run for the Bambino! It's his second homer of the day!"

In the months and years that followed, the tale of the Babe's "Called Shot" was told and retold across the nation. It became a quintessential story of American resilience and determination. Miracles could happen.

The final score was a 7–5 win for the Bronx Bombers over the hapless Chicago Cubs (perennial losers even back then). The Yankees were now but one game away from sweeping the World Series, and I couldn't wait to hear the following day's broadcast. I was so excited, I barely slept that night.

But it was not to be. The next morning, my father, who was in the final month of his first campaign for Congress, said, "Boy, you're going to see a great man today." I looked up at him and, for a fleeting moment, I thought, "He's taking me to Chicago for the World Series, and I'm going to see Babe Ruth!" But then he said, "Governor Roosevelt is going to be our next president, and he's speaking here in Detroit." I instantly knew I wouldn't be watching or even listening to game four of the World Series. Trying hard to conceal my disappointment, I looked up at him with a forced grin and said, "That's great, Pop!"

I didn't know much about Roosevelt, except that he was a Democrat like us. Most people thought he would defeat Republican president Herbert Hoover by a wide margin, and I knew enough to understand that would also help my dad win his election, too. The best line about Herbert Hoover actually came from Babe Ruth, who, at the beginning of the 1932 season, was holding out for eighty thousand dollars a year. It would be the most money

ever spent on a single player. A sports writer told him, "Babe, that's more than Hoover gets for being president of the United States." To which Ruth famously quipped, "I had a better year than he did."

On that crisp October day, with the election just over a month away, I held tight to my father's hand as we made our way through the five thousand people packed into the Naval Reserve Armory. It was to be FDR's only big speech in Detroit during the entire campaign, so an overflow crowd of fifteen thousand more listened outside through loudspeakers hung from trees lining the park along the river. It wasn't a long speech, but I was too small to see the stage and quickly lost interest. I remember playing with some of the other little kids while the adults were listening intently to Governor Roosevelt. I stuck my tongue out at one little girl, and she hid behind her father. As far as we were concerned, this was an event for grown-ups. We were too young to understand why it seemed so important to them. But when the speech was coming to a close and the crowd was repeatedly cheering, my father reached down and hoisted me up onto his shoulders so I could actually *see* Roosevelt speak these closing lines:

> And so, in these days of difficulty, we Americans everywhere must and shall choose the path of social justice—the only path that will lead us to a permanent bettering of our civilization, the path that our children must tread and their children must tread, the path of faith, the path of hope and the path of love for our fellow man.

Although I was too young to understand most of what FDR said that day, with those final lines it felt like he was speaking directly to me. I *was* a child. When my father put me back down on the

ground, he was smiling proudly under his thin, black mustache. I smiled right back up at him, this time with real enthusiasm. The World Series would happen again next year. This was a once-in-a-lifetime experience, even for a little boy.

Eighty-six years have passed since my dad's first congressional campaign, yet I can sometimes still recall random images from it quite clearly. They come to mind without warning, people and places so sharply defined that they seem like photographs. But these scenes never came from any camera; the few photos still remaining from my childhood are all either black and white or sepia-toned. These unbidden memories are in vivid color. They appear in my mind's eye suddenly and with bright clarity, like a flashbulb exploding in the night. There's that first instant of light, where every detail is visible; then the glare fades back to pitch darkness, and the image disappears from view.

FLASH! My dad is standing on a wooden crate, making a speech on a street corner in Detroit. Tears of pride are running down the faces of the Polish men and women gathered around him, hanging on his every word.

FLASH! I'm on the back of a campaign truck emblazoned in red, white, and blue bunting. My dad's booming voice, amplified even louder by a bullhorn, is reminding people, in both English and Polish, that there are only three days left until Election Day. "Please vote on Tuesday! Proszę Głosować Wtorek!" With my right hand holding tight to my dad's leg, I'm using my left hand to wave the cardboard sign I carefully made myself. It reads, "Ring (in) with Dingell," the campaign's slogan.

FLASH! My dad, his arm around Mom's waist, is standing in front of a big green chalkboard on Election Night, his face expressionless. Campaign workers, clutching slips of paper, are running

back and forth between constantly ringing telephones and the board. Every few minutes, a number is crossed out on one of the four columns on the board and replaced with a different one. I'm sitting cross-legged on the floor at my parents' feet, my arms wrapped around my one-year-old brother, Jim, to keep him from wandering off into the chaos. He'd just started walking, so my mother had asked me to hold on to him tight. At one point, when she leaned down to kiss us both, I asked, "Mom, how come there's four different rows on the chalkboard?" She said, "Because there are four different neighborhoods where people are voting, dear." She smiled patiently, I guess realizing that I still didn't fully understand her answer. It would be a few more years before I knew what a political "ward" was.

Dad's Republican opponent was a former mayor of Detroit, Charles Bowles, who was backed by the Ku Klux Klan, a group that had powerful political influence in Michigan, just as they had when my father took them on back in Colorado.

I can still remember the night when I was maybe five or six years old, when the Klan burned a cross in front of our house. I was standing next to our front window and called out to my mother, "Mom, come look and see what some nice people are doing for us!" She rushed over and pulled me away from the window, yanking the curtains closed. I had no idea why.

Although my father always exuded confidence as a candidate, as he sat there on the headquarters floor when the votes were coming in, I overheard him quietly say to my mother, "It's going to be close."

My dad was right. It *was* close. On November 8, 1932, he barely edged out Bowles by a nail-biting margin of 48 to 46 percent. Four years after Al Smith's crushing defeat, my dad rode the crest of a

Democratic wave that swept across the nation, washing away Republicans and anti-Catholic bigots from coast to coast. Two other Polish Democrats, George Sadowski and John Lesinski—who, like my dad, were running in newly created congressional districts (after the 1930 Census, Michigan's big population growth gained it three new House seats)—won their races as well. FDR carried Michigan handily, on his way to a landslide national victory over Hoover.

Overall, the 1932 elections were a massive rejection of the GOP, with Democrats winning a record number of House races (ninety-seven), as well as picking up twelve Senate seats. Out of hope (and not a little desperation), a "new deal for the American people" promised by Roosevelt at the Democratic Convention was overwhelmingly embraced by the American people.

However, unlike his fellow Democrats, my dad couldn't claim victory on Election Night. His Republican opponent stubbornly refused to accept defeat and immediately demanded a recount. It took until the first week of December, a month after the vote, for Bowles to finally withdraw his challenge of the results. It is lost to history if his concession was gracious. It didn't matter. My father, John David Dingell, was a thirty-eight-year-old congressman-elect.

On December 20, 1932, two weeks after my father was finally able to claim his victory, my mother was baptized into the Catholic faith in St. Leo's Church in Detroit. As she'd promised in her letters to him when he was working so far away from her, this was something she'd wanted to do for years, to bring us all closer together as a family: "You know the one big reason why I wanted to go with you is so we could soon worship together as of one faith."

I can picture the steam coming out of my maternal grandfather's ears when he learned that news. Not only was his daughter now a Democrat *and* a Catholic, but my father had just been

elected to the House of Representatives as a "wet." Four months later, when the Twenty-First Amendment was passed by the Congress (with my father's enthusiastic "Aye!" vote) and liquor would soon be legal again in America, Grandpa Bigler told everyone that Dad was "single-handedly responsible for repealing Prohibition." The old hypocrite probably went out and bought an entire case of alcohol-filled Peruna "health elixir" just to calm his frayed nerves.

Over the next six years, my father won reelection easily. "One Good Term Deserves Another" was his slogan; he wrote it himself. (The very idea of a paid political consultant would have appalled my dad.) In 1940, during his fifth campaign, my father gave an uncharacteristically personal floor speech, evoking the memory of the youthful epiphany that gave him strength and purpose for the rest of his life:

> Recuperating from a long and severe illness, still confined to my hospital bed, I studied the political philosophy of Theodore Roosevelt and the works of Woodrow Wilson's political economy. I decided then and there that I would make my mark in the field of public service as the representative in Congress within twenty years.

It was just like my dad to exceed expectations, even his own. "Within twenty years" had been accomplished in only sixteen.

———————

IN EARLY 1933, DAD LOADED OUR WHOLE FAMILY INTO THE car, and we all drove down to Washington together. I was six and a half; baby brother, Jim, was just over a year old. I'll never forget walking into the Capitol Rotunda for the first time. It was the big-

gest damn building I had ever seen. "Wow!" I shouted loudly, my voice echoing off the huge curved walls. My mother quickly put her finger to her lips. "Hush, dear," she whispered urgently. "But, Mom," I whispered back, "I can't even see the top of the ceiling!"

Back then—and it's hard to believe this today—the Capitol Building was wide open to the public; there were no fences or concrete barriers and only a small Capitol Police force. My brother and I used the grounds as our park, playing stickball and setting off firecrackers, doing what kids do. I even got my haircuts at the Capitol Barber Shop. I was too young to shave, but my regular haircuts on the Hill cost a full two bits, the same price my dad paid for his haircut *and* a shave. (For those of you too young to remember the old Milton Berle song "Shave and a Haircut, Two Bits," two bits equaled twenty-five cents.) For little kids, the Capitol was like a giant playground where everybody treated us like family.

The quality of life for adults was also very different from what it is today. When my family arrived in the winter of '33, Washington, DC, was still popularly referred to as "that little town in the woods." It was also frequently called a "sleepy southern town." Now that we were living in a much smaller city (its population of five hundred thousand people was only a third the size of Detroit), we had the sense of joining a close-knit community comprised of elected officials and their families who had come together from all forty-eight states. They became our neighbors and new friends. The wives got to know each other, and the kids would play together and go to school with one another. Some of the unmarried members of Congress would start courting their future brides in DC. Unthinkable as it would be today, it was commonplace then for couples to get married even if they were from different political parties.

Political differences existed, of course. Yet the personal meanness that is now considered normal in today's public discourse was simply unacceptable in "polite company," a phrase that, sadly, has now lost all meaning in the coarseness of today's Capitol Hill culture. Certainly, there was a lot of harsh political rhetoric back then, much of it aimed at Roosevelt. Both the left and the right took turns calling FDR a "fascist." Because of his strong support of Roosevelt, my father got a lot of that same criticism. Yet the level of vituperation did not begin to compare to that of today's bitter personal invective, in which nothing is off-limits.

As his son, I became fighting mad whenever anyone said anything bad about my dad. He would just laugh it off. "Boy," he'd say to me, "you'll make a lot of enemies in this life by doing what you think is right. What they say about you isn't worth a rat's ass. The only thing that matters is that you stand up and fight for what you believe in. If some son of a bitch doesn't like it, just tell him to go to hell."

———————

MAKE NO MISTAKE, REGARDLESS OF THE SIZE OF THE DEMOcratic victory, the battle to pass FDR's sweeping New Deal programs was still going to be one hell of a fight. In 1932, the country was reaching the peak of the Great Depression. By now, nearly half the nation's banks had gone belly-up, and fifteen million Americans were out of work.

Thank God both FDR and my father were ready and eager for the fight ahead. Roosevelt, crippled by polio, and my father, with a lung collapsed from tuberculosis, had each overcome life-threatening challenges that would have crushed lesser men. They were unafraid of fear because it did not exist within them. They relished

the daunting challenge of bringing the country back from the brink of economic and social collapse.

You could see it in President Roosevelt's face when he'd throw back his head and there'd be fire in his laughter. You could hear it in my father's passionate advocacy of New Deal programs like Social Security, the National Housing Act, the Civilian Conservation Corps, the National Industrial Recovery Act, and, particularly, the Banking Act.

You'll recall that my dad was not a tall man, but throughout his life, despite his breathing problems, he had a rich, powerful voice. Whenever he rose to speak, his presence filled the House Chamber. His thoughtful arguments carried tremendous weight with his colleagues.

My dad and FDR also shared deeply held beliefs and values that extended far beyond their own self-interest. The principle that guided them both in public service was encapsulated in a simple, yet powerful term: *social justice*.

To them it meant that our country has a moral obligation to take care of all Americans equally, regardless of race, ethnicity, religion, or economic standing. They believed it was our government's duty to guarantee that everyone had the same opportunity to get ahead. The principle of social justice was the foundation of what would become FDR's New Deal.

When I was still young, I first learned the term *social justice* in school, from the Jesuits. In 1891, a generation before I was born, Pope Leo XIII issued a historic and, for its time, radical encyclical entitled "Rerum Novarum ("Of The New Things"). In it, he addressed the need to draw "the rich and the working class together, by reminding each of its duties to the other, and especially of the obligations of justice."

Forty years later, when the whole world was affected by the Great Depression, Pope Pius XI powerfully reaffirmed that obligation, this time framing it in economic terms that specifically included the phrase *social justice*:

> . . . it is contrary to social justice when, for the sake of personal gain and without regard for the common good, wages and salaries are excessively lowered or raised; and this same social justice demands that wages and salaries be so managed, through agreement of plans and wills, in so far as can be done, as to offer to the greatest possible number the opportunity of getting work and obtaining suitable means of livelihood.

From the very beginning of his time in Congress, the issue of economic fairness was uppermost in my dad's mind. He particularly saw banks as institutions with a fundamental responsibility to the American people, much like government itself. To my father, it was as plain as day that the banks had failed because their greed far outweighed their sense of obligation to the public good.

Only three months into his first term, on June 5, 1933, my father went down to the well of the House and gave a fiery speech that was like a match thrown on dry kindling:

> The good people of Detroit were ravished by a scoundrel system that has fed upon humanity like an ogre. This organized method of thievery, gross violation of confidence, the wrecking of fortunes, gambling, manipulations, and carelessness has grown consistently at a greater pace than the nation itself has grown. Each time that this curse of mismanagement and

banketeering descended upon an unfortunate community—
and frequently it struck twice in the same place—the toll was
greater, the devastation more shocking.

Banketeering was the kind of word my father was always able to
mint in the heat of the moment. It perfectly described the gravity
of the situation we were facing as a nation. These bankers were
nothing more than criminal profiteers. In powerful terms, Dad
summed up the problem.

He also conceived a bold idea to guarantee that such a total
economic catastrophe could never again happen.

It is my purpose upon being reelected to introduce a bill
which will authorize the federal government to acquire full
ownership of the banking system of the U.S., thus vesting
the ownership, control, and supervision in the hands of the
government for the benefit of the people. This is possible
without the outlay of any additional funds on the part of the
government through the Reconstruction Finance Corporation, which today owns one half of the outstanding preferred
stock of the national banks. It will be only a step further to
assume full control and ownership and thus stabilize an institution which should be for the benefit of the merchant,
manufacturer, and the average citizen. The banking system
should be a utility available to the citizens of this country.
It should be stabilized so as to give absolute security to the
depositor as well as to the borrower.

My father was *not* a Communist. Far from it. He was a pragmatist. He understood that in order to save capitalism, a system

in which he fervently believed, "the banketeers" needed to give up control over what he saw as "public utilities." Dad saw government ownership of the banks as the best way to save capitalism from total collapse. He was well aware that by the early 1930s, communism was increasingly seen as a legitimate alternative to our capitalist system. His mission was to stop communism in its tracks.

My father never achieved his goal of federalizing the banks. However, his beliefs served to inform the Glass-Steagall regulatory provisions of the Banking Act of 1933. (Years later, it would become my turn to defend those same regulatory provisions from the relentless attacks of both political parties.)

Dad often took us with him to sit in the Family Gallery while the House was in session, especially on those days when he'd be giving a speech. Those were exciting times for us. One of the things I recall vividly from watching the House as a small boy was that everybody on the floor often seemed to be just standing around looking bored. My father explained that they were all waiting for the Senate, derisively described by House members as "the other body," to convene. The "Cave of Winds" (one of my favorite nicknames for a legislative chamber that so often seems to *breed* blowhards) always took its own sweet time to come to order. Since representatives frequently found themselves sitting around playing with the buttons on their vests, waiting impatiently for the Senate to take up all the work that the House had previously passed and sent over there "to die" (as was all too often the case), members of Congress found creative ways to alleviate their boredom.

There was a wonderful old gentleman named Louis Rabaut who was first elected in 1935, two years after my dad. Also a Democrat from Michigan, Rabaut, of Belgian descent, formed a lasting friend-

ship with my family. Because he was the father of nine children at home, he had, of necessity, developed a great gift for entertaining a large brood, lest they become unruly. He had a tremendous love of singing that served his colleagues well during those times when the "other body" was maddeningly slow in mustering up a quorum. Louis would delight in distracting his fellow members, on both sides of the aisle, with impromptu singing performances. He'd go down into the well of the House and, one after another, bring up every state delegation and lead them in song.

———————

CAN YOU IMAGINE SEEING THAT KIND OF CAMARADERIE IN Congress today? Instead of joyous barbershop quartets, it would be a sad commentary on how discordant our rhetoric has become. On the House Floor, I used to watch my former colleague Republican Steve King of Iowa spouting off about some damn-fool idea. I couldn't hear his words. All that went through my head was one of my favorite arias from *Pagliacci*: "While in delirium, I no longer know what I say, or what I do . . . / You are a clown!"

Especially in those first hundred days of the New Deal, my father was an extremely busy man. Though we weren't able to spend a lot of time together, we had a very close relationship. Every one of the minutes I spent learning to hunt or fish with him was precious to me. Those trips also had a peculiar effect on me. From early on, when I was a child, my eyesight was very bad. Compounding that fact, I was also deaf as a stump in my right ear. No hearing at all on that side. Since my left ear worked well enough, from an early age I reflexively cupped it so I could pay attention better when my parents and teachers were speaking to me. The strange thing

was that when I went out hunting and fishing with my dad, I had twenty-twenty vision and could hear a deer rustling in the underbrush from fifty yards away.

Another thing I learned from my father was that your reputation was based on trust. Trust from your family. Trust from your colleagues. Trust from your constituents. That also meant your word was your bond. He used to say, "Don't ever lie. The reason you don't is you can't remember today what lie you told yesterday; nor will you remember tomorrow what lie you told today. Tell the truth and you will be able to stay on the facts all the time."

Throughout his career, my dad held himself to those high standards of honesty and trust. After having once been criticized for his ethics by a political opponent, here's how he responded in a speech on the House Floor (and remember, these are the words of a man whose formal education ended at eighth grade):

> My record, Mr. Speaker, whether in Congress or in private life, is like an open book. It is without blemish; it is clean and therefore unimpeachable. All efforts of political or scurrilous calumniators who would attempt to defile my good name will fail in their attempted defamation. I may be poor in the accumulation of worldly Goods which Fortune at any time May snatch from me, but I am rich in the reputation which attaches to my name and which will survive the calumniators long after they are buried in the paupers' field of Oblivion and are forgotten.

—————

LET ME TELL YOU JUST ONE STORY THAT UNDERSCORES MY dad's commitment to integrity and, of equal importance to him,

the *perception* of that integrity. One day a guy came into my father's office and tried to hand him an envelope with ten thousand dollars in cash. My dad didn't touch it. He said, "Sit down in that chair and put that on the corner of the desk right there in front of you." The fellow put down the envelope and sat. Then he proceeded to describe a problem that he wanted my father to fix for him. Dad listened quietly until the fellow was finished and then said, "Wait, one moment." He pushed a button, and his secretary, Fanny Sheldon, came into the office. With her present, Dad says to the guy, "Now tell me your story again." And the man does. Then my father said, "Pick up your ten thousand dollars, and if I ever see you anywhere again, the FBI's gonna knock down your door. Now get the hell out of here!" And Miss Sheldon handed the envelope back to the man so my father could honestly say he never touched it.

In 1938, I entered the House Page Program. My father told me it was a good opportunity and that I ought to do it. When my dad made a suggestion, I almost always listened. That time, thank God, I did. It had a lasting effect on the course of my life.

A whole bunch of us kids in the program were the sons or nephews of members of Congress. The pages at the time were all boys. Their average ages were usually between twelve and sixteen, sometimes a little older. Only eleven when I was appointed, I was the youngest one in my group. Most of the boys came from families of modest means. What we all had in common, though, was a great desire to learn everything we could about government, especially Congress. After serving as a page, many of the boys went home and stayed active in public service, often running for office themselves. Over the course of my career in the House, I would eventually serve with many former pages, like Paul Kanjorski, Jed Johnson, Bill Emerson, and Rush Holt. Even though

we were of different ages, there was always a special bond among us page alumni. Our deep feeling for the institution was like first love—you never forget the memory of falling hard that first time for someone or something you'll care deeply about for the rest of your life. It's the same feeling of connection shared by so many military veterans. So many page boys, including me, would later enlist in the service as a way of continuing to help our country. Tragically, so many of the boys I worked with in my five years as a page would lose their lives in World War II. From boyhood, they gave their lives to their country. Too many of them never lived to see what their great sacrifice achieved.

———————

I BEGAN HEARING THE FIRST RUMBLINGS OF WAR AROUND 1936. German troops had marched into the Rhineland. I wasn't yet old enough to fully understand what this might mean. But my father certainly did. He was deeply concerned about the rise of Hitler, particularly since so many of Dad's constituents had family back in Poland.

In August 1939, my parents took an ocean liner to Europe just as the war there was widening. A year earlier, Hitler's troops had invaded Austria and annexed the Sudetenland, in Czechoslovakia. My parents took that risky trip only because my dad had been invited to attend an important interparliamentary conference.

While they were in Europe, my dad wanted to visit the birthplace of his forebears in Poland. It would be the only opportunity he would ever have to visit his ancestral country. My parents stayed at the Europejski, a historic hotel in the center of Warsaw. Anthony Biddle, the U.S. ambassador to Poland, learned they were in Warsaw and invited them to lunch. My parents spent as much time as

they could in Poland before leaving for other parts of Europe. On September 1, 1939, nearing the end of their trip, they decided to return to Warsaw. When they got there, they called Ambassador Biddle at the embassy, and he practically shouted into the phone, "Get out now! The Germans are marching in!"

Biddle told my father he would see what he could do about getting him and my mother out. A few tense minutes later, Biddle called them back at their hotel. He'd managed to secure them the only two tickets left on the last train out of Warsaw.

There was panic and chaos in the streets, with people desperate to get out ahead of the Germans. Practically every window on that train was broken by rocks and bricks as it made its way across the border for the last time.

Fortunately, my parents made their way safely to Paris. (Mom later told me about going out onto the Champs-Élysées, where all the lights were out in case of German bombing raids.) They then went back to England, where they boarded an ocean liner bound for home. Mom said that they could see mines bobbing in the water of the English Channel as they stood on the ship's deck.

———————

BY CHANCE, THE U.S. AMBASSADOR TO THE COURT OF ST. James's, Joseph P. Kennedy, was on that same ship, along with his wife and large family. My parents dined with them one evening during the crossing. Kennedy, who would soon be removed from his post by FDR, had been a vocal opponent of the United States' entry into the war in Europe for a long time. My father didn't much care for him or his political views. (When JFK was running for president in 1960, the same anti-Catholic garbage about "Vatican control of the White House" that was used so effectively against

Al Smith in '28 was thrown at Kennedy, too. Harry Truman had the best line on the subject of a possible JFK presidency: "It's not the Pope I fear. It's the Pop.")

Back at home, my brother and baby sister, Julé, were very worried that our parents might not be coming home at all. At thirteen, I was only slightly less concerned. I knew my dad would never let anything happen to them, especially not to my mother. Finally, we were all able to relax when we received a ship-to-shore call assuring us that they were both safe.

My parents managed to get out of Europe just in time. Only a few years later, I was ready to go over there myself—in uniform.

CHAPTER 5

The Courage of a Lion

Boys, if you ever pray, pray for me now. I don't know if you fellows ever had a load of hay fall on you, but when they told me yesterday what had happened, I felt like the moon, the stars, and all the planets had fallen on me.

—PRESIDENT HARRY S. TRUMAN, SPEAKING
TO REPORTERS ON APRIL 13, 1945, THE
DAY AFTER THE DEATH OF PRESIDENT
FRANKLIN D. ROOSEVELT

ON DECEMBER 11, 1941, THREE DAYS AFTER CONGRESS PASSED a declaration of war against the Empire of Japan, Germany declared war on the United States. It was just five months since my fifteenth birthday. That meant I was still two and a half years away from being allowed to enlist in the military. There was never any question in my mind that I would join up. But in 1941, I was still too young, and there was no way my folks would let me go until I turned eighteen. So, while I waited for what seemed like forever—

time moves too slowly when you're young and too fast when you're old—I did everything I could to be ready in both mind and body while literally marking off the days on my calendar until I could sign up.

I knew my brother, Jim, likely wouldn't serve. He was five years younger than me. It would have to be a very, very long war for him to be old enough to join up, but I was sure it would still be going on when I came of age and could enlist. I hurried like hell to get through school. I spent December of '41 clean through to July of '44 finishing high school and doing my freshman year at Georgetown University. Damned if I wasn't going to be ready!

On July 8, 1944, I finally turned eighteen. That same day, I went down to the recruiting center to register and see how quickly I could enlist. I told the recruiter I wanted to go into the army *right now*. Turns out, it didn't quite work that way. The army would tell *me* when it needed me. I told the recruiter I wanted to be in the infantry, and he said, "Good, that's exactly what you're going to get." The army needed infantry troops, and by that time, they were scraping the bottom of the barrel. I knew as soon as my ticket came up, I was going to go, too.

So, I went back home and waited. And waited. For three months, I kept pacing in circles around the house like a caged animal. By the time the call finally came, on October 10, 1944, even my mother was about ready to see me get out of the house. (Although I knew that, in truth, she was worried sick and that it was the last thing she really wanted. I also knew that every day I was gone, she would pray for me to come home safely.)

Soon after, I shipped out. The army sent me to a place called Camp Blanding, near Jacksonville, Florida, for training. Camp Blanding is where I got sick. One of the cooks had meningitis. Thirty

thousand men were stationed at the camp, and 10 percent, three thousand of us, all got it, likely from just one infected cook. I was sick. Very sick. Absolutely weak and totally incapable of moving.

I would have died, except they gave us a brand-new wonder drug called penicillin. That did the trick. The penicillin killed the meningitis, and I recovered.

Then the army decided I needed to be in a "rehabilitation" unit. We had a choice of rehabilitation "assignments": twelve-hour shifts of KP (kitchen patrol) or twelve-hour shifts of range duty.

I took the range duty. They put me on a crew that was cutting down sixty-foot-tall pine trees, either for construction or for clearing the land, or maybe just because the army thought it would toughen us up. One of the things we'd do was "borrow" a sergeant's helmet and put it down right where a big tree was going to fall. Helmets make a great noise when you fell a tree right on them—it's sort of a hollow, thuddy boom.

I might have been over the meningitis, but I didn't have my strength back, and the damned rehabilitation unit wasn't helping. I went to the first sergeant and asked to see the company commander:

ME: Sir! I'm volunteering for overseas duty. I can't take this blasted rehabilitation. It's going to kill me.
COMMANDER: Son, you think overseas might be safer?
ME: Sir, the Germans might just miss.

But the army had other plans for me. Apparently, I'd impressed someone as a bright guy with leadership skills, and there was an opening at Infantry Officer Candidate School (OCS) at Fort Benning, Georgia. The army decided to try to make an officer and a

gentleman out of me, and I was eager for any opportunity that would give me the chance to do more for my country than being a lumberjack in uniform, cutting down pine trees instead of Nazis.

Soon after I was transferred to OCS, they started calling me Artillery John. I was firing a 75-millimeter gun on the gunnery range and wiping out all the targets on the range. Wanting a bigger challenge, I shifted fire to the mortar range next door.

Not long afterward, a very irate colonel appeared, demanding to know what was going on. "Someone's taking out all my friggin' targets!" And that was one of the least profane things he unleashed in a barrage of cuss words aimed directly at us cadets.

I'd like to say that I knew then a similarly colorful story about one of my heroes and his own experience firing artillery, but in point of fact, I didn't hear it until I was long out of the army. Harry Truman had been an artillery officer in World War I. A newsman who saw Truman's battery firing said he'd never seen guns fired so fast in his life. Nor had he ever heard so much foul, blasphemous language as he heard from young Harry. Of course, his swear words never made it into the newspapers. But there's no doubt that, as was the case with my father, Truman's command of cursing served him well throughout his life. If we'd used those words at home, our mouths would have been washed out with soap. But in combat, military or political, we used words like weapons. Damned good ones, too.

———————

I HAD BARELY STARTED AT OFFICER CANDIDATE SCHOOL AT Fort Benning, Georgia, on April 12, 1945, when President Franklin Delano Roosevelt died suddenly. It was not unexpected news to those few "in the know" in Washington, DC (one of whom, I would find out later, included my father).

FDR had suffered a fatal cerebral hemorrhage at his "Little White House" in Warm Springs, Georgia, while sitting for a portrait. Clutching the back of his head, he said, "I have a terrific headache," and collapsed. Coincidentally, Warm Springs was only fifty miles away from Fort Benning, where I was stationed on that momentous day.

America as we had known it for more than a dozen years changed completely in a single instant. For most people my age and younger, FDR was the only president we'd ever known. Later on, we'd see the pictures in *Life* magazine or the newsreel footage of thousands of people standing alongside the railroad tracks waiting for a brief glimpse of the train carrying his coffin as it passed by. Some would wave, but most of them just stared numbly, sad-eyed with grief. A great number were crying; you'd see handkerchiefs in their hands.

None of us knew what the hell the country was going to do without him. He had saved us from the Depression. He had saved us from the Communists. And he'd damn near won World War II. Everybody was in shock.

One little guy with tears in his eyes was asked by a newsreel reporter, "Why are you so sad about him?"

"He was my friend."

"Oh, did you know him?"

"No, but he knew *me*."

I had tears in my eyes, too, but I didn't cry. I was still my father's son.

My dad told me later that Vice President Truman heard the news of FDR's passing when he was with Sam Rayburn in the Speaker's little hideaway office on the first floor of the Capitol. Rayburn always used to have a few folks in for bourbon and branch water,

and they'd talk about whatever was on their minds. People called it "the Board of Education." It was around 5:00 p.m., and Truman had just arrived when he got a call to go right over to the White House. They didn't tell him why. He wasn't very close to FDR, so Truman thought he'd done something wrong. He put down his bourbon, grabbed his hat, and—this is something Sam Rayburn told me himself—grumbled, "Jesus Christ and General Jackson!" before heading out the door.

Mrs. Roosevelt broke the news to the vice president herself, "The president is dead." Truman was pretty shaken up, but he kept his composure. "Is there anything I can do for you?" he asked her. As my dad told it, she looked him right in the eye and said, "Is there anything we can do for *you*? For you are the one in trouble now."

After I heard the news of the president's death, I walked around in a daze for hours. It didn't seem real. I finally took a shower and was cleaning my rifle on my bunk when I looked up to see what seemed like the whole blasted platoon gathered at the foot of my bed!

One of them asked me, "Dingell, your dad knew Roosevelt. Did you know him?"

I didn't want any special treatment in the army, so I asked my dad not to write me using his congressional letterhead. And I didn't want any special breaks, so I never told anyone that my father was a congressman who was good friends with our commander in chief. How in the bare-ass hell did they *all* know?

I hesitated before answering. "My father knows . . . *knew* him well. I met him a few times."

"What kind of a guy is this new fellow gonna be?"

I didn't know what the hell to tell them about Truman. I barely knew him on sight. I kept cleaning my rifle, and finally I said, "I really don't know. I'll write my dad and see what he has to say

about him." So, I put down my gun and wrote a letter and asked my father if he could tell me what Truman would be like as the new president. I told him that a lot of the fellows in OCS were worried that he wouldn't be up to the job.

A week later a letter comes back. This one is on my father's official letterhead, so everybody at mail call knows what it is when the guy handing out the letters shouts, "John Dingell!" He threw the letter at me, and I grabbed it before anyone else could.

Once again, damn near the whole company was at the foot of my bed.

"All right, Dingell, what's your dad say?"

"I'll read it to you."

> Dear Son:
>
> Have no doubt about it. Harry Truman is a great man and he's going to be a great president. He's going to run the country well, because he's absolutely honest and truthful. As a Senator he saved the American public billions of dollars with his investigations into those damnable war profiteers. He exposed how they were delivering shoddy equipment to our military that put all you brave young men at risk. You can tell your buddies that their new president has the courage of a lion.
>
> Love, Dad

A few of them patted me on the back. Most of them were grinning. They felt good again. Now they were sure we had a new president who was as strong as Roosevelt and who was going to win this effing war—even if they didn't know my dad from Adam's off ox.

Soon, the word was all over the battalion: *It's gonna be all right! Dingell says so.*

IN THE SUMMER OF 1945, AFTER GERMANY HAD SURRENDERED, but while the war in the Pacific seemed destined to go on indefinitely, I graduated from Fort Benning Infantry OCS. I was part of Class 518. Just before graduation, all of us were put on notice that if the war continued, we would be in the first wave of a full-scale invasion of Japan, likely in November.

It made for a very somber ceremony.

On August 6 and then again on August 9, the United States dropped atomic bombs on the Japanese cities of Hiroshima and Nagasaki. President Truman's decision to use the atomic bomb to end the war almost certainly saved my life.

On August 10, 1945 (only days after President Truman authorized the atomic bombing of Hiroshima and the day after the second bomb was dropped on Nagasaki), I was commissioned as a second lieutenant in the U.S. Army. Five days later, Emperor Hirohito announced the surrender of Japan, effectively ending the Second World War.

Truman's decision to use two atom bombs on Japan remains a controversial issue. I've read quite a lot on the subject, and I've got more books about World War II than I can count. Having read so many arguments on both sides, I still believe Truman made the right choice. When I graduated Infantry OCS, they told us all we were going to be invading Japan that November. What they didn't tell us were three things I found out much later, when I was already serving in Congress: First, they'd ordered the manufacture of half a million Purple Hearts because the experts predicted there would be that many U.S. casualties. (Japanese casualty estimates were even higher.) Second, the invasion planners anticipated having even more atomic bombs available and using them. And third, the life

expectancy for those of us who would have been in that first wave of the invasion of Japan was approximately ten seconds.

Even though I was learning all this for the first time in a brightly lit briefing room, twenty years after the fact, those stark numbers still froze my blood ice cold. Reflexively, I crossed myself. There's no doubt in my mind that President Truman's gut-wrenching decision saved the lives of as many as one million American soldiers, and perhaps ten million Japanese men, women, and children.

One of those lives would almost certainly have been mine.

CHAPTER 6

Becoming a Man for Others

What is the use of living, if it be not to strive for noble causes and to make this muddled world a better place for those who will live in it after we are gone?

—WINSTON CHURCHILL, STANDING FOR
ELECTION TO THE HOUSE OF COMMONS,
OCTOBER 10, 1908

AFTER PAGE SCHOOL, MY PARENTS SENT ME TO GEORGETOWN Preparatory School, run by the Jesuits. (It angers me that the rotten behavior of a bad apple named Kavanaugh is all that you may know about my alma mater. One obnoxious punk's reprehensible behavior has sullied the reputation of a fine school. If I were younger, I'd kick his entitled ass to kingdom come.) They taught us about the importance of becoming "a man for others," where service is the highest calling. We were made to work extra hard because there was a war going on and they knew that many of us would likely be going off to fight in it.

Service is a major component of Jesuit belief and practice. The Jesuits instill in their students the importance of becoming a man (or a woman) for others. They played a significant part in shaping my values into the man I would become—committed to always trying to be of service to others, in or out of public life.

Service to others does not mean being servile. Service means putting another person's needs before your own. It requires empathy, the ability to walk in someone else's shoes to better understand their suffering, their pain. It requires self-sacrifice. True public service requires a willingness to put the good of the people before your own self-interest, to be willing to cast a vote that may lose you your next election and not regret it if you do.

After Japan surrendered on August 15, 1945, my service continued: the army shipped me down to Panama as a junior commissioned officer. I was kept busy there. Very busy. I counted it up after I came back to the States, and all told, I had twenty-seven different full-time jobs in Panama. That's a lot for anyone, let alone a nineteen-year-old butterbar. (Second lieutenants are patronizingly referred to as "butterbars" or "nuggets," because of the golden bar insignias on their uniforms.) I ran two PXs and a couple of NCO clubs. I ran the theater and the bowling alley. Swarms of god-awful termites gnawed on the bowling alley day and night. My buddies and I used to joke that we'd been spared active duty only to end up dying in a freak termite tragedy in a gutter lane in Panama. "Dear Congressman and Mrs. Dingell, we regret to inform you . . ." I was in charge of the payroll (gold for the Americans and silver for the locals) and was made the personnel officer, and since we were short of typists, I even taught classes in typing. I taught sex-ed, too, but drew the line at doing any "short-arm inspections." I was also the postal officer and the perimeter guard. And because I knew something

about army regulations and civilian law, I did triple duty as defense counsel, prosecutor, and judge in court martials. Just for the hell of it, I often ruled myself out of order—it usually got a laugh.

Not everyone appreciated my rulings at court martials, especially some of my superior officers. When I was a judge, I ruffled more than a few feathers from some of the asshole, throw-the-book-at-'em types. I wouldn't find a man guilty if I didn't think he *was* guilty. I stood up for what I believed was legally right, and I'd suffer the consequences for it. I'm very proud of how I handled things then. I applied what I learned from my dad. He was a tough little guy who didn't take any sass from anybody. He never gave two shits if somebody criticized him for doing what he thought was right (something you'll recall he taught me as a very young kid). By the time I was an "adult"—what was I, *nineteen*?—I didn't take any guff, either.

There was time in Panama for some fun things, too. I asked my dad to send me the heaviest bass rod he could find so I could go fly-fishing in the Chagres River. There was some great fishing down there, but you had to be careful—alligators and crocodiles were always close by, especially at night. When you saw those orange eyes in the dark, it was time to hightail it out of there or you might be a snack. (Today, those beady eyes would belong to a DC swamp creature, but we'll get to that later.) In case of any serious disagreements with the local wildlife, I was one of the few guys down there who always carried a .45 pistol in an armpit holster.

I also took some classes from the Armed Forces Institute to continue my education. I studied math and Spanish and a few other things that'd prove useful in Panama or later. Those subjects helped me stay sharp and ready for when I'd get to go home and back to school.

One day in 1946, I went to base headquarters to see my personnel

sergeant major. He had an *Army Regulations* manual in his hand and a big grin on his face. The rule he showed me said that all soldiers with a certain amount of time served could be discharged immediately. I read it, returned his salute as I left, and then checked around to confirm that it was in fact true. It *was*, and it applied to officers as well.

"Good thing I've got a clean shirt on," I thought to myself the next day, as I knocked on the door of the colonel's office. The colonel was a mean old SOB with a permanent scowl on his face. (Little wonder: he'd been broken in rank from a general all the way back down to a colonel for some kind of bureaucratic screw-up.)

"Good morning, sir."

"Dingell. What do *you* want?"

"Sir, I'm going home."

"You can't go home. I won't let you."

"This army regulation says I can."

I pointed to the open manual I'd brought with me. He didn't even bother to look at it.

"If you do, I'll give you a bad efficiency rating."

"Colonel, you can give me any efficiency rating you like, because civilians don't give a hoot in hell about those things."

And with that, I jumped on the earliest available plane and got my tired ass out of there.

On November 13, 1946, I was honorably discharged from the army. The colonel's threat to my efficiency rating turned out to be a pretty funny story. Just before my discharge, the army had introduced a new form, Number 67-1, intended to dramatically improve the efficiency assessment process and personnel effectiveness. Instead, the form itself was—and I'm quoting here from the army's review—"a total failure. Officers did not like either the relative scoring system or the forced-choice items." Turns out it was

the *form* that was inefficient, not me, and they shitcanned it only a few years later.

Although I was no longer on active duty, I stayed in the Army Reserve. While I was in Panama, my father filed the paperwork for my readmission back to Georgetown University. Academically, I was two years behind where I wanted to be. I needed to study hard to catch up and get back on track.

Don't get me wrong. Even though I was eager to return to school, I've never, not for a second, regretted my two years in the military. My army service did more to shape my values than any other experience in my life. During my time in uniform, I came to understand the meaning of discipline and respect, two qualities that are the keys to success in life. The army reinforced what my dad instilled in me from a very early age. We all have a fundamental obligation to serve our country and help one another—to be "a man for others."

Although he became a difficult problem for President Truman, there's no one who can argue that General Douglas MacArthur didn't love his country or revere the military. In 1962, two years before his death, he gave a speech at the U.S. Military Academy at West Point that still inspires me every time I read it:

> Duty, honor, country: Those three hallowed words reverently dictate what you ought to be, what you can be, what you will be. They are your rallying point to build courage when courage seems to fail, to regain faith when there seems to be little cause for faith, to create hope when hope becomes forlorn.

Like all my fellow veterans, I showed up to my first college classes in uniform. I didn't have any civilian clothes; there were

none to be had. We couldn't even get white shirts. Many of the guys would borrow their fathers' clothes. That wasn't an option for me. I was six foot three and still growing; my father was almost a foot shorter. I was shit out of luck.

The GI Bill put me through the remainder of my undergraduate education at Georgetown University, where I earned a bachelor's of science degree in chemistry. I lived with my parents in Washington and paid my own bills, supporting myself by getting a job at my old stomping grounds in the Capitol (where else?), as a supervisor of the elevator operators.

Sometimes, as I'd study, my dad would come up to me and whisper, "Shirtsleeves, shirtsleeves." I understood what he meant without further explanation; I'd heard it from him since I was a young schoolboy. It was his shorthand message that if I didn't get good marks, I'd wind up in the sort of job where I'd be wearing shirtsleeves, not a jacket. It was also his way of reminding me of where our family came from and how far I could go in life if I worked hard. Unlike him, I had the love and support of my parents.

Nothing made my dad prouder than when I became the first Dingell to graduate college. He never had that chance.

In the summer of 1948, between my junior and senior years, I got a job as a park ranger in Grand Lake, Colorado, which is at the northern end of Rocky Mountain National Park. To this day, I still consider it the best public service job I've ever had. Being a ranger meant I was outside every single day, surrounded by nature and wildlife—deer, elk, antelope, and more than a few bears. I was able to hike and climb, fish and track. Once, I made it to the top of three different mountains all in the same day, all of them over fourteen thousand feet tall.

Being in the wild was a tonic for my body and for my soul; I loved every second of it. No need for a suit and tie or dress shoes. I wore one pair of Levi's until they got so dirty they could stand up by themselves. Then I'd scrub them clean in the creek. Every so often, though, my buddies and I would clean ourselves up and invite some gals over for a square dance.

That summer at Grand Lake, a few of my fellow rangers and I stopped at an inn not far from the entrance to the park. And it was there that I saw the most gorgeous woman I'd ever seen. That I found the nerve to approach her is still amazing to me. She said her name was Helen Henebry, and she was from Denver. I asked her out; astonishingly, she said yes. We went out a few times and seemed to hit it off. Then, too quickly for my liking, the summer was over, and I had to go back to DC and resume hitting the books at Georgetown.

Helen and I stayed in touch by letter, and we picked up our relationship when I was back at Grand Lake the following summer, just before I started law school at Georgetown. We fell into a similar pattern when I was in law school—we'd write letters or talk on the phone every so often. As anyone who's ever endured law school will tell you, it's no cakewalk, but I worked my tail off and made it through.

One night, while I was doing my homework upstairs, I heard the phone ringing in the den. A second later, my baby sister, Julé, called up to me. She must have been around fifteen or sixteen years old, but she was already growing into a beautiful young woman. Sharp as a tack, she was also my mother's closest friend and confidante outside of our dad.

"Jack! Phone call. It's your *girl*friend." She shouted it so loud the whole neighborhood could have heard it, which I believe was

her intention. I ran down the stairs two at a time and grabbed the phone out of her hand, glaring at her as I did. She gave a little curtsy, turned on her heel, and skipped happily away.

"Hello?"

"Jack? It's Helen Henebry. I'm in Washington, and I'm wondering if you're free . . ."

I took her around DC and showed her all the sights, and got razzed by my friends at the Capitol: "Dingell, what's a beautiful girl like her doing with a mutt like you?" Before Helen went back to Colorado, I asked her to be my wife. She said yes.

In June of '52, shortly after I graduated law school, we were married in St. Paul's Chapel of the Immaculate Conception Cathedral in Denver. It was a small wedding, with mainly our families and a few close friends attending. My brother, Jim, was my best man.

Helen and I were trying to figure out where to settle as newlyweds, and I kept our options open by taking the bar exams in DC as well as in Michigan. I passed both. Now what? My folks had a house in Detroit, where they lived when the House was adjourned. But as congressional sessions grew longer every year, and since airfare was still very expensive, my folks were spending most of their time in Washington. The Dingell family house in Detroit—my boyhood home—was essentially empty.

Shortly after our engagement, I had lunch with my dad. "Son, if you can help us out a little with the mortgage, you and Helen can move in tomorrow." My life was about to go full circle. Helen and I would be starting our own family in the same red-brick house at 17585 Pennington Drive that I'd grown up in. (As a kid, I learned a trick to remember the address: $17 \times 5 = 85$. Mental arithmetic served me well throughout my life, especially when some rascal was trying use phony figures to lie to my committee.)

IN 1952, I WAS PRIVILEGED TO CLERK FOR A HIGHLY RESPECTED U.S. District Court judge in Detroit named Theodore "Ted" Levin. Judge Levin was a good friend of my dad's and a damned fine jurist. I don't think he had a single verdict overturned on appeal during the year I clerked for him. (Much later, I served in Congress with two of Ted's nephews, Sander "Sandy" and Carl Levin. Carl was elected first, in 1978, going right into the Senate. Sandy ran for the House four years later. We all served together for thirty years and they still remain two of my dearest friends.)

In 1953, Helen was pregnant with our first child. (John Dingell III was born later that year; we named him in honor of my dad.) With a young family to support, I needed to make more money than I could by clerking for Judge Levin. That meant going into private practice as an attorney. Hanging out a shingle with two partners, Paul W. Harty and Tex Austin—Tex wasn't his real name, but for obvious reasons, J. Connor *Austin* was always called "Tex"— our small law firm took pretty much any and all clients we could get. We did bankruptcies, divorces, wills, and just about everything else, including criminal defense. When an ambulance siren roared past the office, we made a game out of seeing who could make it to the door first. The damn thing would be long gone, but we always got a kick out of the pretend "chase." We built a very good practice and, even better, had a lot of fun doing it.

One of the cases we handled had us examining a bankruptcy plan. Our client thought the debtor's plan was using some shady legal maneuvers to hide assets from him. We looked into it, and lo and behold, there was at least *twenty million dollars'* worth of slack in the numbers. Now, this was in the 1950s, when that was a hell of a lot of money.

We called the court and got the case reopened. Then I called the client.

"Mr. Dingell, you've done a superb job working with this, and you have to be paid. Let's talk compensation."

After talking with my partners, I called the client back. "It was just a few days' work. How about two thousand dollars?"

I then learned an important lesson: when the person paying you hears your amount, laughs out loud, and quickly says, "You bet!" you've almost certainly left a lot of money on the table.

My legal work expanded in another way: I started working as an assistant county prosecutor as well as a defense attorney. In those days, it was common for lawyers to do both. I prosecuted all the cases that nobody else wanted.

It was about that time, in 1954, that I started to get my own feet wet politically. I'd attend events in Michigan on behalf of my father when he was in DC, and I'd watch his back. I saw to it that he didn't get guff from anybody about "forgetting the folks back home."

I wasn't thinking about politics as a career. But the good Lord had other plans for me. And we serve His will above all.

CHAPTER 7

Called Home

Representative Dingell could be called a true liberal. He fought the
liberal fight. He was very proud to be a friend of the working man.
He was proud to work in behalf of social legislation in the field of
education, health, and welfare. He has left his mark on the public
laws of this land. His fine work will live on in the lives of many
people, who will have a better life because of what Representative
Dingell did for them.

—SENATOR HUBERT HUMPHREY,
FROM HIS EULOGY FOR CONGRESSMAN
JOHN D. DINGELL SR., JANUARY 3, 1956

MONDAY, SEPTEMBER 19, 1955

It was an unusually warm morning in Michigan, the start of what
seemed like just another regular work week. Our statewide legal
system included what we called the "bench courts," which were
located anywhere from Berrien County, in the southwest corner

of the state to Iron County in the north. Bench courts could take you all over God's creation. As a twenty-nine-year-old kid with a wife and young son to support, I had to take whatever cases came my way. All I could do was give each one my best effort. That morning I was in the Taylor Township Courthouse. The docket contained nothing more exciting than dog-bite cases and small-dollar civil suits—business as usual. At least that's what I thought. . . .

After lunch, I walked into our law office drenched in sweat from the ninety-degree heat and immediately sensed something was wrong. One of my law partners—I think it was Tex Austin—gave me a strange look and quietly said, "John, you should call your mother in Washington."

The telephone number he handed me was for a hospital nurses' station. They put my mother on the line quickly. I sensed that she had been staying very near the phone, waiting for my call. "Jack, I think you'd better come here. Your dad's been admitted to Walter Reed Medical Center for his breathing. We don't think it's serious, but the doctors want to keep him here for observation."

I hung up the phone and looked over at my law partners, Tex and Paul. Concern was evident on their faces; they'd known since the first urgent calls started coming in a few hours earlier.

My mind was racing. I had to get down there. Mom, my brother, and my sister were all living in DC. Driving there was out of the question; it would take far too long. From memory, I called Pan Am, the major airline flying the Detroit-to-DC route that I usually flew, but it was completely booked. Grabbing the phone book, I found the number for Capital Airways, a smaller airline, and dialed it immediately.

The woman who answered the phone was sympathetic but

couldn't help. Capital Airways had no space available either. "I'm so sorry, Mr. Dingell."

Then I remembered Jennings Randolph. A former congressman from West Virginia, Randolph had entered the House with my father in 1933 but lost his seat in the Republican wave of 1946. He was now working as a senior executive at Capital. I asked to be connected to him. Not only was he a good friend of my dad's, but I had grown up with his son, Jay.

He got on the line right away, and I explained the situation. "Jennings, could you help me get down there?" Without a moment's hesitation, he said, "Of course. Hang on." A minute later he was back on the line. "Head out to the airport right now, John. There'll be a blue Stinson Tri-Motor waiting to take off as soon as you get there."

The four-hour flight to Washington was considered relatively quick in those days, yet each minute felt like an hour. I stared out the window and thought about my dad. At sixty-one, he was younger than most of his peers. Sam Rayburn was seventy-three, John McCormack was sixty-four, Harry Truman was seventy-one. Even President Eisenhower was four years older than my father. The difference was that my father's lifetime of poor health had worn him down for so long that he seemed far older than his actual age. All of us knew that without my mother, he would have been gone years ago. Her devotion to him was total. Every labored breath he took was drawn from her love for him. She was his reason for living, as he was hers.

Mom had said it wasn't "serious," yet I couldn't shake the feeling that this was more than just a routine examination. Something in her voice told me that I needed to get there as soon as possible. Couldn't this sorry-ass plane go any faster?

Finally, we landed at Washington National Airport in Arlington,

Virginia. My sister, Julé, and her fiancé, Pete, met me at the airport. It was normally about a thirty-minute drive to the hospital in Maryland, and we sped the whole way. The car screeched to a halt in front of the hospital. Jim was standing inside the lobby, ashen-faced. "We lost Pop," he said quietly. Julé began sobbing. "They just took him to the funeral home. Mom's with him." My brother's voice sounded far away. I held my trembling sister tight to my chest. "It's going to be all right," I whispered.

It suddenly hit me that I would never get to tell my dad goodbye. Only much later would I come to be at peace with that. All that mattered was he knew I loved him. Still do.

———

OUTSIDE MY FATHER'S FUNERAL MASS, A MAN NAMED SAM NAthanson approached me. Sam owned a string of newspapers out in the northwest corner of Detroit. He was a close friend of my father's, who I would later come to refer to, with deep affection, as "my Jewish godfather."

Offering deep condolences on my dad's passing, Sam got right to the point. "So, when are you going to announce for your father's seat in Congress? Get yourself out there, because everyone else is announcing!" It had been only ten days since my father's death. I didn't even want to *think* about politics. Sam held on to my elbow and made me look him directly in the eye. Gently but firmly, he said, "When you're ready, call me."

Michigan governor G. Mennen "Soapy" Williams, another family friend, announced that a special election would be held to fill the now-vacant Fifteenth Congressional District seat. The primary would be on November 8, less than two months away, with the general election on December 13. Up until now, things had been

going very well for me. I had a house in a good neighborhood in Detroit, a new family, and a growing law practice.

A week after the memorial, I went into my law office and was handed a thick stack of phone messages. All my friends were telling me that I had to run.

The morning of Dad's passing, I had been trying lawsuits in front of Justice of the Peace Billy Ford, later my colleague and good friend in the Congress. Billy was encouraging me to run as well. I went home and talked to my wife and a few other close friends.

It was my mother who cast the deciding vote. "Jack, your father would have wanted . . ." I didn't need her to say anything more. The next day, I announced my candidacy.

The first person I called was Sam Nathanson. He was as good as his word. He rattled off a long list of names of all the people he knew in the district; it seemed like almost every one of them was his "good friend" or owed him a favor. I owe most of my support in that first election to Sam and his friends, most of whom were also Jewish. We never spoke about it, but I knew my father had helped many of them get their families out of Europe. Helping his son was their way of doing something for *him*.

In a crowded field, I won the special election. At twenty-nine years old, I would now be returning to the place where I'd already spent much of my life, the Congress of the United States. Not as a page or a supervisor of the elevator operators, but as the newest member of the House of Representatives.

———

ON TUESDAY, JANUARY 3, 1956, MEMBERS OF THE HOUSE TOOK to the floor to pay their respects to my father. My mother, my wife, and my brother and sister were all seated in the Family Gallery.

I was on the House Floor, trying with tremendous difficulty to maintain my composure. I remembered my father's admonition "Men don't cry." As the youngest member of the Eighty-Fourth Congress, I would be called (affectionately) the "Baby of the House," at least until someone younger was elected.

Today, however, I desperately wanted to be the strong man my father expected me to be—the man he was.

Our close family friend from Michigan, the normally jovial congressman Louis Rabaut, was in charge of the floor for the memorial speeches. He allocated time to multiple members, two of whom, John McCormack and Carl Albert, would go on to become Speakers of the House, while Charlie Halleck, a Republican from Indiana, would later lead his party as House minority leader.

As a point of personal privilege, please allow me now to share excerpts from just a few of their remarks that day. I was struck then, as I am now, sixty-two years later, how each of these men somehow managed to capture a *different* aspect of my father's character or take note of his legislative legacy in a unique way. They hadn't compared notes in advance; they all just spoke from the heart.

However, none of them was more eloquent than my father's beloved friend and political soul mate, Majority Leader John W. McCormack, to whom Rabaut quickly yielded the floor:

PROCEEDINGS IN THE HOUSE

TUESDAY, JANUARY 3, 1956

MR. RABAUT [LOUIS RABAUT, DEMOCRAT FROM MICHIGAN]:
Mr. Speaker, today our thoughts turn to a beloved colleague who is not with us. John David Dingell was a close

friend of mine who will be sorely missed in this most crucial year in a troubled world.

John was a frail man in physique, but he was a fighter at heart. Never have I known him to hesitate to stand up for what he knew to be right. Never have I known him to compromise with conscience in the interests of expediency. As a member of the Ways and Means Committee, he was a champion of the little people and strove always to see that the low-income families were properly represented on the committee.

John's passing is a loss to his district, his state, and the nation, and I extend my deepest sympathies to his wife, Grace, and his three children, John Jr., James, and Julé.

I yield to our distinguished majority leader.

MR. MCCORMACK [JOHN W. MCCORMACK, DEMOCRAT FROM MASSSACHUSETTS]: Mr. Speaker, Representative John D. Dingell, of Michigan, died last September, but even now, months after, it is difficult for us to reconcile ourselves to the fact he is not with us. We are not unfamiliar here in the House of Representatives with the sudden onslaught of a bereavement it is difficult for us to face. But for me in the case of John Dingell, the pain is the deeper because we two enjoyed a kind of partnership of the spirit. This is true not only because we were veterans together in the Halls of Congress. It is true also because there was an understanding between us, in many ways an unspoken understanding, instinctive and genuine, that may have had its roots in our respective backgrounds and that flowered for him as well as for myself in the consummation of great events in which we both played some part.

These events had their impact on history.

John represented the Fifteenth Congressional District in Detroit from 1932—through twelve continuous terms in Congress—until his passing Monday night, September 19; a tribute surely to the esteem in which he was held by his constituents. It was an esteem which many of us shared with the people who elected and reelected him. But on the stage of dedication to the people of America, on the stage of mighty government reform in the public interest, I like to aggrandize to myself the belief that perhaps I knew him most intimately of all.

There were two major motivations in the life of John D. Dingell, of Detroit—this son of Polish immigrants emerging out of the teeming populations of a great industrial city to a position of leadership and responsibility under our system of government. What were these two driving forces in his life? One was his religious faith—in his case, Catholicism that lived in him and with him every moment of his life. It guided him, it propelled him, it edified him, and he lived by its truths and principles deep in his soul, as good citizens live by the laws and ordinances of their community.

This fellow Catholic was well and proudly conscious of it. I derived a sort of strength in my own beliefs from contact with him. I noted how it elevated his perspective and gave him that unique strength that in the long run gives such force and such influence to the unselfish and the sincere servants of the commonwealth.

The other motivating force in his life was his deliberate, his devoted, his unceasing identification of himself and all his activities with the people whom he served, the public interest

generally, and the American ideal. Being religious, he lacked fear, fear of pioneering, fear of untrod paths in legislation, in government reform. He lacked fear of entrenched power and entrenched privilege. And he lacked fear of change and fear of dumping into the past and the limbo of the forgotten, the deadweight of archaic but long-established forms and usages that straitjacketed progress and cried out for improvement. A divine providence seems to have created men like John Dingell—precisely like Dingell—to meet the challenge of a changing era and master it. Because change, as even the most backward alarmists of the twenties and the thirties now agree, had to come. It had to come.

But what men with John Dingell's patriotism, his religious depth, and his fierce dedication to the American tradition made possible, was change without doing violence to our free-enterprise system, and without impairing the constitutional structure of our government. For above his crusading dynamism for moving us out of the mire of the Great Depression, and above his passion for curing the ills of our time and raising the living standards of the common man, was his orthodox faith in the principles of the Founding Fathers. He was undeviating in his loyalty to the Constitution of the United States and the body of law that grew out of it. John Dingell would have fought with all his zeal and every ounce of his strength against any radicalism that attacked by so much as one jot or tittle the basic principles of our government.

With that conservatism and that persistent forward march to improvement, there worked in John Dingell's soul the free man's loathing for absolutism, dictatorship, communism or fascism, the monolithic state, and all the

trappings of the Caesars on the left and the Caesars on the right. For this deep and clear-eyed thinking man from Detroit, where all races were gathered together, the fantastic and fuzzy race theories of the dictators were but the application of sick ideas to serve the ends of personal power. And these ends were in themselves so sick and so askew and so unscientific and so ill-advised that they perished in wars that are now recognized as the greatest tragedy of history. Bigotry and dictatorship, going together, hand in hand, had to be swept off the world stage by men of religion and men of faith, by freemen.

Among their leaders was John D. Dingell.

These were the ideas that mattered in the life of the man I eulogize. They expressed themselves on the practical level, and they materialized into legislation no responsible and knowledgeable citizen would today dream of removing from the nation's statute books, no matter how stubbornly they fought against men like Dingell when this legislation was in process of enactment.

Just as John Dingell was not a halfway patriot, so he was not a halfway legislator. He stood steadfast with the New Deal. Nor did his enthusiasm diminish when those of little faith saw some advantage later in the opposite trend. Rather, John Dingell became as much a devotee of the Fair Deal as he had been a leader in the dynamic days of the New Deal.

He believed, and his faith was vindicated.

For twelve years he fought for a national health insurance plan. He was as unrelenting in this fight as he had formerly been in his advocacy of the Securities and Exchange reforms, the Reciprocal Trade agreements, the National

Labor Relations Act, and the Social Security program. His horizons encompassed and went beyond this type of legislation. He was always looking years ahead, and a leader in charting the course for a better life for his fellow men.

If the question were asked "What were the greatest rewards that came to John Dingell in his lifetime?" I can guess, I think, quite accurately, what his answer might have been. First, I think he would have said, it came to him in the knowledge that he had fought the good fight and never surrendered. He would have said he found his reward in the respect and the affection he read in the eyes of his constituents who, again and again, elected him to office. I think he would have said, in an extremely moving way, that his reward was especially immense in the esteem in which he was held by members of this House, in their affection, in their high regard for his character as a gentleman and a colleague. And ever so poignantly and gratefully, he would have said that his reward came from the country he loved so devotedly. It was here that he struggled all his life, and almost always on a rising plane of success. He came out of a parochial school where his grounding in basic education had been solid. He informed himself by reading courses in political science and economics. He had worked on a Detroit newspaper and in other fields. And his career found its fullest assertion in politics where he became our associate and our friend. Always the light that marked his path was his religion and the public interest.

They say there is no indispensable man. Maybe not. But I dread to think what our world and what our country would be like if Almighty God did not, out of His eternal

regard for the least of us, provide the generations with men of the faith and the stature of John D. Dingell.

MR. MACHROWICZ [THADDEUS MACHROWICZ, DEMOCRAT FROM MICHIGAN]: Mr. Speaker, the passing of our beloved friend and distinguished colleague, John D. Dingell, has brought much sorrow to all who knew him and to the millions who benefited from the many years of his fruitful and unselfish public service. If there was any characteristic which particularly stood out to mark John Dingell, I would say it was his intense desire and will to serve his country and his people well, by bringing justice to those who needed it most, the poor, the sick, and the underprivileged. He loved to fight for them, to champion their cause, and to make life more bearable for them. It was for that reason that he pioneered in the struggle for Social Security legislation in this Congress, much of which was either sponsored by him or in which he played an important part in its enactment.

Those of us who were privileged with his close friendship know under what terrific handicaps he was working. He had always been in poor health, and it was with a great effort and personal sacrifice that he was able to carry on the important duties of his office. But he had a deep sense of responsibility and a great faith in God to give him the strength and the wisdom necessary to perform his task. I know personally that whenever he was faced with a particularly difficult decision, he always turned to the Almighty God for guidance. And when he was convinced he was morally right, no power on earth was able to swerve him from his determination to stay with that decision.

To me, John Dingell's passing was a particularly heavy blow. I had known him and enjoyed his friendship for many years, dating back even to the time before he started his service in Congress. His friendship was one of the richest experiences in my life. From the first day that I became a member of this great body, over five years ago, I looked to him for help. He was more than a friend to me. He guided me through those difficult first years and gave me words of encouragement when they were needed most. I feel proud to have been able to work with him in the fulfillment of his legislative program, and to have been honored by his close friendship.

Outside of his public service, John Dingell's greatest interest in life was his family. More than once, he told me that he would not have been able to carry on without his life's companion, his beloved and loving wife, who stood by him and worked with him loyally and tirelessly during his entire public career. He fully understood and appreciated her great sacrifice and devotion.

We shall miss the leadership and the guidance of John Dingell in Congress, but I am confident that his work will be continued in the way he would have wanted it, by his most able and deserving son, John D. Dingell. He will carry on in the tradition and the pattern of his most distinguished father, who will be long and lovingly remembered by us here in Congress and by the people whom he served so well.

MR. HALLECK [CHARLES HALLECK, REPUBLICAN FROM INDIANA]: Mr. Speaker, it was with genuine and deep-felt

sorrow that I read in the press of the passing of my good
and very dear friend John Dingell. He was my friend, and
I was his friend. At the time of his passing, our length of
service in the House of Representatives was about the
same, although I believe John Dingell came to the House
of Representatives shortly before I did. Through my service here, I have become increasingly convinced that to
be a member of this great body is indeed a high privilege,
an honor, and a pleasure. It is an honor and a privilege because, by and large, the members of this body are persons
of capacity. If they are not people of capacity, they do not
get here. If they are not people of capacity, they seldom
stay here long. Together with capacity, they must have integrity, decency, honor, intelligence, and judgment. John
Dingell was one of the men who added much to the standing and the prestige of the House of Representatives. I say
also it is a pleasure to serve in this body for many reasons.
Probably the best reason is that friendships are made here,
friendships that have no concern at all with the center
aisle which divides the Republicans from the Democrats;
friendships which are little concerned with differing political or economic viewpoints; friendships that transcend
all such differences and which, in my opinion, afford the
happiest occasions of our work.

Mr. Speaker, we shall all miss John Dingell. But may I
say to his boy who succeeds him here: Welcome.

He follows a leader, and he becomes part of a distinguished tradition in this high position in the House of Representatives, which I am certain he will uphold with honor
and with dignity.

MR. CHENOWETH [JOHN CHENOWETH, REPUBLICAN FROM COLORADO]: Mr. Speaker, I wish to join my colleagues in paying tribute to the memory of our departed colleague, John Dingell. I was indeed saddened when I learned of his passing. While Mr. Dingell represented a district in Michigan, we in Colorado felt that in many ways he belonged to us. He had gone to Colorado Springs some years ago and after regaining his health had engaged in business in that city, where he made many friends, who mourn his passing.

I can recall that John Dingell maintained his interest in and his love for the West. Whenever any legislation came before this House dealing with irrigation and reclamation projects in Colorado or other matters of peculiar interest to the West, we always found a champion in John Dingell. He never lost his love and affection for the people of Colorado. I think at one time he advocated that the capital of the United States should be moved to Colorado.

Mr. Speaker, the passing of John Dingell is a great loss, not only to the people of Michigan and his district, but to the entire nation, and to me personally.

MR. EBERHARTER [HERMAN EBERHARTER, DEMOCRAT FROM PENNSYLVANIA]: Mr. Speaker, it is with deep sorrow and a feeling of great personal loss that I rise to pay tribute to the memory of my colleague and friend John Dingell. I know that these feelings are shared by all of us here, for his courageous spirit, his patience and understanding were an inspiration to all who knew him.

John Dingell was a staunch liberal and, throughout his career as a member of Congress, he fought continuously

for legislation benefiting the working man. During his first four years of Congress, he was a strong supporter of such important measures as the Securities and Exchange and Reciprocal Trade Agreements Acts [of] 1934, the National Labor Relations–Wagner Act of 1935, and the original Social Security Act of 1935. In succeeding years, he continued the fight to improve the laws and introduced new measures to provide for the welfare of the people.

In recent years, he has become associated widely in the public mind with a measure providing for national health insurance. Actually, this interest on his part dates back to 1943, when, together with Senators Robert F. Wagner, of New York, and James E. Murray, of Montana, he introduced into the House the measure to extend Social Security coverage known as the Wagner-Murray-Dingell Bill. This measure has been supported by Mr. Dingell during every Congress since 1943 and has received the enthusiastic support of the AF of L and CIO, but has never reached the floor for a vote.

I had the privilege of serving for a good many years on the same committee with John Dingell, and of observing at first hand the qualities that made him such a great legislator. He always carefully studied the legislation before the committee, and never failed to express his views both in committee and on the floor of the House, and he was one of those rare individuals who possessed both the courage to carry on a never-ending fight for the ideals in which he believed, and yet also showed a willingness to compromise when it became obvious that his goals could not be attained at that particular time. He realized that it is not always possible to achieve the ideal solution to a problem

immediately, that there are times when one has to accept something less—a step toward the ultimate goal one is seeking. This he was willing to accept for the moment, but he would never once forget the real aim for a substitute.

The mere fact that John Dingell was a member of Congress for so many years is enough to set him apart as being an unusual person, of course, but there is something much more distinctive about this man than simply his tenure in office or his political ability. He was a true statesman of the highest caliber. He possessed the intelligence to grasp and understand the most technical phases of legislation, the interest, wisdom, and courage to tackle very difficult problems, and the Christian love and depth of understanding to know and feel the problems that confront human beings.

Too often, human values get lost in the shuffle when we become embroiled in the tremendous task of legislating for one hundred sixty million Americans, and we may tend to look at a tax revision bill or a Social Security bill simply in terms of a lot of statistics, or of how much money it is going to mean to the Treasury. It was indeed an inspiration to me to observe a man who was always aware of his tremendous responsibility, and whose primary concern was the effect his decision might have on each individual American.

We have lost a good statesman, and we who served with him certainly feel his absence, but we can be grateful that, although he is no longer with us, his contributions and his ideals will remain forever, as a constant reminder of the potentialities of human beings so dedicated to the highest level of social, moral, and political principles.

It is most appropriate that we today pay verbal tribute to

one who has given so much to humanity; but I believe the greatest tribute we can pay to John Dingell lies not in the realm of spoken praise, but in ourselves pursuing the ideals for a better world for which he so valiantly fought.

MR. CELLER [EMANUEL CELLER, DEMOCRAT FROM NEW YORK]: Mr. Speaker, I wish to add my voice to the many that have eulogized our distinguished late colleague John Dingell. I knew him from the time he came to Congress, and learned to have an affectionate regard for him, as I am sure he had for me.

Just as cream rises to the top of the bottle, so he, in a short time, rose and grew in his ability and effectiveness as a member of the House. He won the admiration of all the members for his integrity of purpose, high aims, exemplary character, and excellence in parliamentary procedure. He rendered excellent service as a ranking member of the Ways and Means Committee. His words on the floor of the House always carried conviction.

Unfortunately, in the last few years, illness pursued him. May we say that the good Lord wished to see an end to the suffering he endured and bestowed upon him an endless sleep. Even when suffering with pain, he insisted on coming to committee meetings and to the floor of the House. He bore his pain unflinchingly and uncomplainingly. He was indeed a stoic.

John Dingell's constituents loved him and honored him and returned him to office many times. They placed upon him this accolade of distinction for having the courage of his convictions and for his devoted service. He is now suc-

ceeded by his son who, I am sure, will walk in the paths hewn out for him by his revered father. Like father, like son. The mantle of his office now falls upon him. From what I have already seen and know about him, he will keep the memory of his father alive in this House by distinguished service, honor, and integrity.

MR. RABAUT: And now, Mr. Speaker, it is my privilege to ask his son to take the floor, the son of a worthy sire and a son who carries his father's name, a son who succeeds to his father's place by the free will of the free people of his district in Michigan, John Dingell Jr.

MR. DINGELL: Mr. Speaker, I am deeply touched by this tribute paid to my beloved father and the respect and affection in which he was held by all of his brother members of the House, without regard for political creed. I shall always remember and treasure this day.

On behalf of my dear mother, and my brother and sister, and myself, I wish to extend to the members of the House my deep thanks and gratitude for the splendid tribute that has been paid to my father today.

My father loved and respected the House and all its members. If I can be half the man my father was I shall feel I was a great success.

Then, I buried my face in my hands and cried.

PART II

SHORTLY AFTER THE 2010 ELECTION, I WAS ASKED TO GIVE A welcoming speech to the newly elected members, a privilege accorded every two years to the "Dean of the House"—the member with the longest record of service, regardless of party. Good thing too, since the especially large sea of faces—ninety-four first-timers—that I saw staring back at me was made up overwhelmingly by freshly scrubbed and obviously jubilant Republicans. They outnumbered the Democrats by a margin of 85 to 9. If it had been a football game, they would have called it at halftime.

We had gotten our asses whipped badly in that election, largely as a result of the Tea Party's well-funded and relentless campaign of fear mongering around the passage of the Affordable Care Act (aka "Obamacare"). The Tea Baggers just flat out lied about how seniors would now have to face government "death panels" that would decide whether they were healthy enough to keep receiving medical care. If not, we Democrats would come in to their hospital room and personally unplug them from life support. Pure evil. And, yes, I know what that term *tea bagger* also means. (If you don't, look it up on the Google when your kids are out of the room.)

My staff finally explained it to me after I'd been using it in a lot of my speeches. I told them I didn't give a shit. Still don't. Frankly, I think it suits them just fine—hell, they *are* nuts.

Naturally they were in an exuberant mood when the old New Dealer came up to give a talk. I could almost hear them thinking *Good luck with those death panels, Grandpa.* I paid none of it any mind. They were now about to be members of the House of Representatives, an institution that both my father and I revered. My dad served there for twenty-two years, more than a third of his too-short life. Standing there that night, it was almost exactly fifty-five years since Sam Rayburn swore me in for the first time. I wondered how many of these freshmen even knew "Rayburn" was anything more than just a name on one of the House Office Buildings they would be assigned to in a few weeks.

My friend Robert Draper, the wise historian, author, and damn fine observer of politics and people, was also there that night. He wrote about it in his excellent book about the House of Representatives, *Do Not Ask What Good We Do.* Let me briefly yield the floor to him:

"It is an institution that is often demeaned," said the old man. (Thanks, Bob. I'm even older now.) *"Usually during campaigns. But it is an institution composed of people who pride themselves on being public servants. And I'm pleased to tell you that most of the members who come here do so to serve and look after people and do important things."*

Sensing that I now had their attention, at least for the moment, I decided to lighten the mood and let a little partisan air out of the room:

"When I was a young congressman, a fellow was once very impressed with this institution he'd come to work for. And an older colleague said to him, 'My friend, for the next six months you're going to be wondering

how the hell you got here. And then one day you're going to come out onto the House floor, look around—and wonder how the hell all those other fools got here.'"

That line always gets a laugh. It did that night too—even from those smug, we-won-and-you-lost Republicans, most of whom I could tell weren't even *born* when I entered the House in 1955. It was a sobering thought that made me want to go out and get a snootful. These young true believers, most of whom had run against the very *idea* of the federal government, were now about to be totally in charge of the House. It was going to be the largest Republican majority since 1928.

Still, I had a job to do and I did it the best I could. I had to hope that maybe I was wrong about these new folks. Perhaps they might yet come to understand why the people had placed in them their most sacred trust as citizens—their vote—and how important that responsibility was:

"At any rate, it's a wonderful institution, one I've been very proud to have had the privilege to serve in. Something like ten to fifteen thousand Americans, out of the two billion who have been a part of America, have had such a privilege to be a part of the most humanly perfect . . . institution on this planet."

Unfortunately for the country, I wasn't wrong about that crowd of new Republicans. Since then, more and more of these folks have been getting themselves elected to the Congress on a pledge to destroy it. They run on a platform to diminish the federal government until there's nothing left of it. Never mind that these same lousy hypocrites gleefully accept their government salaries and perks. This ain't your "dollar a year" bunch unselfishly putting the good of the people over their own pocketbooks. These greedy bastards rail against government programs that benefit needy folk,

all the while making sure their holier-than-thou hind ends remain comfortably perched on plush pillows stuffed with campaign cash.

———————

THAT LEGEND IN HIS OWN MIND, GROVER NORQUIST, SAYS HE wants to make the federal government small enough to hold down and drown it in a bathtub. What he and his Americans for Tax Reform crowd want to drown is not some abstract institution they call "big government." When they hold it underwater, they're drowning seniors, they're drowning veterans, they're drowning active-duty servicemen and -women and, yes, they're drowning children and families, and all the other folks who count on the federal government for their survival. I'd say shame on them, but you can't shame these characters. They're right out of *The Wizard of Oz*. They've got no brains and they've got no hearts. And they definitely haven't the courage to stand up to the flying monkeys who foot their campaign bills.

There was a time when Congress could and did work, and when it passed major legislation that earned bipartisan support to move the nation forward; where its business was done with hard fighting, but also with goodwill and mutual respect.

That was how it used to be.

In the first part of this book, we looked back at how my family and my dad in particular were part of that grand coming together—a century of progress beginning with the birth of my grandfather in Poland and the subsequent immigration of my family and millions of others like them to the new Promised Land: America. Despite unimaginable hardships—disease, poverty, and xenophobia—these new arrivals helped build this country into the greatest democracy on the face of the earth. As we saw in Part I,

there were major obstacles to overcome: slavery, a Civil War, the Great Depression, two world wars, religious and racial bigotry, the despoiling of our natural resources, and many more seemingly insoluble problems.

It's my fervent hope that in the second part of this book, you'll see how over the course of almost sixty years as a member of the House of Representatives—the People's House—we all did our best (and I include in that "we" so many of my principled colleagues on both sides of the aisle, as well as my extraordinary and dedicated staff) to continue that work and, sometimes, even improve on it.

Progress never follows a straight line. Over those six decades we made great strides in areas like civil rights, the environment, health care, economic justice, and government accountability. Yet for every step forward, every apparent victory, there's frequently a partial step back. That's never been more terrifyingly true than it is right now.

But my father understood something I did not when I entered the Congress as a green-as-grass member. Patience is more than a virtue—it's a necessity. Someone recently asked me what I would tell that young fellow if I could go back to 1955 and whisper in his ear.

"Slow down, Dingell!" And it damn well wouldn't be a whisper. I'd shout it at his freshman ass until he was deaf in *both* ears. As you'll see in these next chapters, getting things done right takes time, hard work, and a *lot* of patience.

As I boy, my dad and I often went fishing at "our spot" along the Detroit River, the waterway that marks the border between the United States and Canada. After years of industrial development, it was the last open space left along the river. For years, I tried to find some way to preserve its pristine beauty. In 2001, I finally thought of a plan. Working with the Canadian government, we agreed to

create the Detroit River International Wildlife Refuge. It's one of my proudest achievements and proof that patience is more than a virtue; in government, it's a necessity.

Today we hear from members of Congress, "I am against this; I am against that." Do we ever hear much about what they're *for*? The more important question is, What are they willing to compromise on? Because *compromise* is an honorable word. At least it used to be.

The last Speaker I served with, my good friend John Boehner, suffered grievously due to open hostility from the Tea Party members of his Republican Caucus who viewed *any* compromise as heresy. Even more disgraceful than their political opposition to Boehner was the personal disrespect they showed this kind and decent man. He deserved far better. It was no surprise to me in 2015, only months after I left the Congress, when he resigned both the Speakership and the Congress, not even finishing out his term.

On the day he announced he was quitting, John walked toward the microphone with a new spring in his step singing, *"Zip-a-dee-doo-dah, zip-a-dee-ay; My, oh, my, what a wonderful day!"*

I understood exactly how he felt, because I had come to share those same feelings of disgust. The institution we both loved had become a mean-spirited place that was almost completely devoid of bipartisanship.

In the second part of this book, I hope you will see that it has not always been thus.

Nor does it need to remain that way.

DURING MY TENURE, I SERVED WITH ELEVEN PRESIDENTS AND ten Speakers of the House, both Democrats and Republicans. From

Dwight Eisenhower to Barack Obama, from Sam Rayburn to John Boehner, I was privileged to view them from a vantage point that allowed me to observe them as people, not only as public figures.

Overall, I served in the House for fifty-nine years and twenty-one days. It remains the record for continuous service in the United States Congress, something that seems to impress a lot of people. I am not one of them. Quite frankly I don't give a rat's ass about records. Any damn fool can sit in a chair and take up space.

It's what you *do* with your time that matters.

CHAPTER 8

A Right, Not a Privilege

What if, perhaps, Obamacare is actually good and the GOP lit its hair on fire just to frighten the American people & score political points?

—TWEET FROM @JOHNDINGELL,
MARCH 23, 2017, 9:26 P.M.

IT WAS A HUMID THURSDAY EVENING IN EARLY AUGUST 2009. As had been my annual practice for more than fifty years, I'd scheduled a series of town hall meetings back home in my district during the summer congressional recess. For decades, these gatherings had almost always been routine question-and-answer sessions about issues ranging from Social Security benefits to local environmental issues. The turnouts were light; there were always some empty seats in the room.

There were a few notable exceptions. In times of great national unrest, like the civil rights and anti–Vietnam War upheavals in the sixties and early seventies, or during the Watergate summers of

'73 and '74, our town hall meetings were packed to overflowing. Although there were certainly occasions during those tumultuous periods when debate would become heated, people still showed respect for the process. Even if my answer was not what the questioners wanted to hear, they still listened politely.

This town hall was to be in Romulus, a working-class Michigan city of about twenty-five thousand people, best known for being the home of the Detroit Metropolitan Wayne County Airport. The venue was the Romulus Athletic Center, a city recreation center with a pool, a gym, and a banquet room that held a few hundred people, more than enough for the event. At least, that's what my staff had thought when they reserved it. Based on our long experience with these gatherings, they had no reason to believe it might be too small a space.

It was.

My first clue that this would not be a run-of-the mill meeting was when we pulled into the parking lot. A burly man immediately started running right toward our car waving a five-foot-tall cardboard figure of Barack Obama with a Hitler mustache penciled in on the president's face. Although we were fifteen minutes early, there was already an overflow crowd waiting to get inside. The line of people stretched outside the entrance and wove all the way around the building. My district director was on his cell phone next to me in the backseat. He was speaking with our advance person inside the hall. I couldn't hear the conversation, but judging from the urgent tone in his voice, I knew something was wrong.

"Okay, I understand," he finally said, clicking off the call. When he turned to me, I saw by his expression that things were definitely *not* okay.

"Sir, you are going to need to be careful. She says it's pretty un-

ruly inside there. We're going to drive around and bring you in from the back entrance."

I nodded wordlessly. I'd represented this town for years and couldn't remember a time when I hadn't been greeted warmly at a meeting in Romulus. Usually people asked to take a picture or stopped me on the way in to say something like "Thank you, Mr. Dingell. You really helped my uncle in the VA hospital." Now I had to sneak in through the back door? What the hell was going on?

I soon found out. The boos and catcalls started as soon as I entered the room and made my way to the lectern.

"They ought to put *you* in front of your goddamn death panel, old man!" was the first thing I heard clearly over the noise. That was followed by shouts of agreement. "Fuck yeah!"

"You tell 'em!"

"Tell Obama he can kiss my ass!"

I walked to the podium; they hadn't switched on the microphone yet. For a brief moment I thought about giving them all my middle finger, turning around, and walking right back out of there. Then my curiosity kicked in. What *was* going on here? I looked around the packed room and saw nothing but people standing anywhere they could find space. They were crowded into the aisles and pressed up against the walls. As I scanned the crowd, I quickly realized that most of the regular folks I knew from Romulus (or, for that matter, from anywhere else in my district) weren't out there. These were almost all entirely new faces to me. Who *were* these people?

"They're from out of state, Chief," my district director whispered in my good ear, reading my mind. I leaned toward him so I could hear him better over the din. My two other staff people stood worriedly between me and the crowd. There was little they could do if things really got out of hand, except rush me out of there.

But I wasn't going anywhere. Now I was *really* curious.

"What the hell do you mean, they're from out of state? How do you know that?"

"A buddy of mine just texted me from out in the parking lot and told me that most of the cars—well, they aren't from Michigan."

"What?" Even with my good left ear, I could barely hear him.

"Most of the cars aren't from Michigan," he said, cupping his hand over the side of his mouth so I could hear him better. "They're from Ohio, Wisconsin, Indiana. My friend says they're from all over the Midwest."

For a moment, I said nothing. I just thought to myself, "Why in the bare-ass hell would someone from Indiana want to come to *my* town hall?"

Then it hit me. This was all a right-wing setup. I'd heard stories about it happening to a few other House members, but it never even crossed my mind that it could happen here. This was an ambush organized by that evil Dick Armey and his lunatic Tea Party crowd. The Koch brothers were funding the whole damn thing in order to stop the Affordable Care Act from passing in Congress.

"Let's do this," I said to my district director. He started to say, "Are you sure you," but before he could finish, I placed my hand firmly on his shoulder and repeated in a voice that brooked no further discussion, "Let's *do* this."

I turned back to the audience and, not waiting for an introduction, I switched on the microphone myself.

"How is everybody today?" I said, smiling broadly.

That was the last uninterrupted sentence I would utter for the remainder of the night.

A man hurriedly pushed his wheelchair-bound son to the front of the room, just a few feet from the podium. Pointing directly at

me, he screamed, "This motherfucking bill doesn't do a goddamn thing for my son! You're an accomplice in his murder!"

I couldn't get a word in edgewise. Every time I tried to respond, the crowd kept egging him on, and he would just start shouting more epithets. Then, much to the relief of my staff, the Romulus Police came in to help settle things down. A few minutes later, they politely ushered the guy and his son out of the hall. This only incited the crowd more.

And that was the tone of the entire Romulus town hall. Folks weren't there looking for answers. Many of them had come in from other states just to make trouble. They'd accuse me of not having read the bill. Not read it? Hell, I'd helped *write* the damn thing.

Whenever we'd try to answer their questions or counter misinformation, we were shouted down and called liars—or worse. It was fact-free insanity.

Originally planned as an hour-long event, the whole damn thing lasted closer to five hours. It was one of the most depressing experiences of my public life. I felt like I was in Rome, not Romulus, and that I was a Christian being fed to hungry lions.

The next morning, I met with my staff. I thanked them for how well they'd handled themselves the previous night. Despite their anger at how I'd been treated, my people had kept their composure. They hadn't responded to the crowd's verbal abuse in kind.

That crowd hadn't been real "grassroots" opposition at all. What had happened at that town hall was what my staff told me was called "Astroturfing"—protesting by a *fake* grassroots crowd. As I had realized the night before, it was a right-wing hit job, bought and paid for from the get-go. But it was very effective.

The sad truth was that the right wing's fear mongering would gin up public anger against a bill that would do those very same

protesters a lot of good. Many of them desperately needed what the Affordable Care Act would ultimately provide, but demagogues like Rush Limbaugh and Sean Hannity, and their wealthy right-wing friends, were working shamelessly to convince them otherwise.

The media in 2009 and 2010 (and not just Fox News) bought into the storyline. With some exceptions, they treated these "town halls" as genuine expressions of citizen outrage against the Affordable Care Act. And that's what scared a lot of members of Congress when it came to voting for it. They also bought into the bullshit and believed that these were legitimate groups of angry voters just waiting to kick them out for supporting the ACA.

Fuck 'em. We won.

———————

MARCH 23, 2010, WAS THE DAY OF THE SIGNING CEREMONY FOR the Affordable Care Act.

The night before, my excitement was so great that I had trouble going to sleep. I felt like a kid on Christmas Eve.

The event had originally been scheduled to be held in the Rose Garden, but rain loomed, so it had been moved indoors to the East Room of the White House. I felt the rain coming in my eighty-three-year-old bones long before the young White House aides saw the forecast on their so-called smartphones. A few good changes come with age; the ability to predict rain is one of them.

They wanted me seated beside President Obama when he signed the bill, so I had to be there early. A young presidential assistant—was he even old enough to vote?—was assigned to show me the way to the East Room. I followed behind him politely, even though I knew the way from memory and could have walked there blind-

folded. I'd been navigating those halls since before that young man wasn't an itch in his father's crotch.

My name was engraved on a card at the end of the rectangular table positioned ten feet from the spot where President Barack Obama would soon be speaking. The Presidential Seal was still being affixed to his lectern when I settled into the leather chair they'd graciously reserved for me.

I picked up the card placed in front of me: THE HONORABLE JOHN D. DINGELL JR. I smiled to myself as I turned the card over in my palm. Junior.

My father, Congressman John D. Dingell *Senior*, would have loved that moment.

I looked around at the frenzied room, photographers scurrying in panic trying to get set up in a new position, literally elbowing one another out of the way, looking for the best angle.

Television lights were being hustled in from the Rose Garden, and I saw whispering going on as frantic television producers shouted new orders into the earpieces of their reporters and camera crews, demanding that they get the best view of this soon-to-be historic ceremony.

It was (barely) controlled chaos, a perfect metaphor for the long, arduous path we'd all traveled to arrive at this historic day.

President Obama, a man of extraordinary character, had kept his word to me and to all Americans by putting all his political capital on the line to pass health care reform in his first term.

"John," he'd told me without hesitation in one of our very first conversations after his election, "if passing this [the Affordable Care Act] makes me a one-term president, so be it. It will have been more than worth it."

As I sat amid all that hubbub, I was thinking about my dad. He

was the author and chief sponsor of the first universal health care bill ever introduced in the House of Representatives, back in 1943, at the height of World War II. Senators Robert Wagner (D-NY) and James Murray (D-MT) introduced my dad's bill over in their chamber.

One of the reasons my dad chose that period to introduce such a bill was because it had been discovered during the military's mandatory physical examinations of draftees that fully *one-third* of the eighteen million young men who'd been drafted were suffering from previously undiagnosed (and therefore untreated) illnesses that prevented them from serving their country. My sickly father, who two countries rejected for service in World War I, was outraged by this.

Dad saw this as a matter of national security. If our young men were not able-bodied enough to serve in the armed forces, we were jeopardizing the entire war effort. Although my father had FDR's blessing to introduce the bill, the commander in chief simply didn't have the time or the political capital to force it through the Congress while he was so intensely focused on the war effort itself.

Two years later (and shortly after FDR's death), President Harry Truman proposed what was essentially the Wagner-Murray-Dingell Bill, and he lobbied aggressively for its passage. He shared my dad's deep concern that inadequate health care was a serious threat to our nation's security.

The American Medical Association fought back hard, fully aware that the cost of any change to the status quo of what we now call "pay-to-play" health care would come out of its (well-lined) pockets. As opponents of health care reform continue to do to this day, the AMA lied, claiming that Wagner-Murray-Dingell would lead to un-American, "socialized medicine." They spent lots

of money on media ads against the bill, and their flunkies in the conservative newspapers gladly gave the AMA's falsehoods "free" coverage in their columns.

On October 12, 1950, my father called his secretary, Jeannette Cantwell, into his office. (After my father passed, I asked her to stay on with me. She would later become my first chief of staff.) He asked her to take down a letter to President Truman forcefully condemning the American Medical Association's dishonest campaign to defeat the bill. He warned the president that these "press-titutes" (my dad created some great words; my mother once said he knew swear words that hadn't been invented yet) were going to spread all manner of false and misleading information, parroting the American Medical Association's talking points; in other words, a fake news campaign. Good thing we don't have those anymore.

My father had a gift for seeing the future. He saw the likelihood of a Republican presidency in 1952, and his sense of urgency about passing health care reform stemmed from his concern that he might not be around in time to fight for it much longer. Sadly, he was right on both counts.

In 1957, I reintroduced my father's health care bill. Even if it never got a hearing, I knew it was important to keep planting the flag as a way of reminding my colleagues that, even in the face of overwhelming odds, lost causes were "the only causes worth fighting for." As the years went by, we passed some modest reforms, many of which had been parts of my dad's original bill. Universal vaccine programs for children, maternal and child health programs, programs providing for safer prescription drugs and expansion of the National Institutes of Health were among the things we accomplished. Yet they were still only incremental steps toward my dad's primary goal: universal health care for every American. So, in each

new Congress, I began my term by reintroducing the fundamental principle of my father's bill.

In 1960, I even penned a lyrical response to the AMA's intractable opposition to giving people more access to health insurance:

> *If you make a diagnosis*
> *Of the medical psychosis,*
> *That is now identifiable as AMA disease,*
> *You will find that hypertension*
> *Is induced by any mention*
> *Of a method whereby patients*
> *Can afford their doctor's fees.*

It's easy to see why President Kennedy would choose Robert Frost over me as the nation's poet laureate. (I got a lot of pleasure out of writing similar "Dingell jingles" for my constituents during the holidays. It's a damn sight better than the lump of coal that they've come to expect from our more recent congressional "Scrooges.")

I was roused from my reverie when the young presidential aide knelt next to me and said, "Excuse me, sir. I just wanted you to know the program is about to start." I turned and saw Vice President Joe Biden walking to the lectern. He would introduce the president. That's standard operating procedure at important signing ceremonies, and this would arguably be the most important one of the entire Obama administration.

My beloved young friend Joe Biden—all age is relative, Joe—stood to my left, speaking to a crowd of three hundred or so, all of whom had played some part in turning the Affordable Care Act from a bill into the law of the land.

Usually, I'm not one to get misty eyed, but on that day, in that

room, I found myself taking off my glasses to wipe my eyes. Probably just an eyelash . . .

The vice president told the room that "history is made when men and women decide that there is a greater risk in accepting a situation we cannot beat than in steeling our spine and embracing the promise of change." Amen.

Once again my thoughts were drifting. In my mind, I was back in 1965. John McCormack, a tall, thin man with spectacles and a shock of white hair, was the Speaker of the House. I've already told you how very close he was to my father. To me, he was both friend and mentor. He was a gentle, kind, and decent man with the soul of an Irish poet. Speaker McCormack motioned me aside. Then, his Boston accent heavy with emotion, he told me, "John, get in the chair."

"I'm presiding?" I couldn't believe it. I'd never imagined that I, a junior member from Michigan, would be in the Speaker's chair presiding over the House when Medicare passed. I'd assumed one of the most senior members (Hale Boggs, Carl Albert, Wilbur Mills, or McCormack himself) would have claimed the privilege on this historic occasion.

"In the chair," the Speaker said, emphasizing his words with a nod and a smile toward the Speaker's chair, high atop the rostrum. Then he turned and walked away.

Had my dad still been serving in the Congress, there's not a doubt in my mind that McCormack would have made sure John D. Dingell Sr. presided that day. My dad, though, now had a seat with an even loftier view, so John D. Dingell Jr. was given the honor of formally guiding Medicare through the House.

Gaveling Medicare into passage remains one of the proudest moments of my career.

In truth, I had two gavels. One I gave to Wilbur Cohen. Wilbur was then the undersecretary of the then-named Department of Health, Education, and Welfare. He'd worked with my dad to write and enact Social Security, and he'd worked with us to write and pass Medicare. Wilbur was deeply touched by the gift.

The other gavel, a giant block of beautifully carved walnut, remains one of my most prized possessions. The thing's so big that Al Kaline could have used it to pop a few balls out of old Tiger Stadium. It's amazing the emotions that can be tied to a piece of wood. That gavel brought into being so much of the hard work that, collectively, my dad and I had done for decades.

In 2009 and 2010, as we passed the Affordable Care Act, I thought it only fitting to make sure the person presiding over the House had that same gavel. When I handed it to Speaker Nancy Pelosi before the final vote, I gave her one condition for borrowing it: she had to give it back.

That memory brought my attention back to the event. It was the reason why we were all here. Joe had just finished his introduction, and I heard the people closest to the front laugh and gasp at something he said to President Obama. But I hadn't heard it.

I turned to then–Senate majority leader Harry Reid, who was seated next to me. "What'd Joe say?"

"He said 'This is a big fucking deal.' "

"HAH!" My laugh cracked like a rifle shot. Grinning broadly, I said to Harry, "Joe's absolutely right. It sure as hell is."

As President Obama began to make the speech before his signing the ACA into law, my mind once more drifted back again on this day of nostalgia. Three days after Speaker McCormack chose me to represent my father and see Medicare through the House came the bill signing. LBJ wanted Harry Truman, "the Daddy of Medicare,"

to be there. The doctors wouldn't let Truman fly to Washington, so Washington came to Truman. The Truman Library, specifically.

Thousands watched from outside. I was one of the three hundred fifty in the room. LBJ's Texas drawl was laced with emotion as he vividly described the importance of Medicare.

> No longer will older Americans be denied the healing miracle of modern medicine. No longer will illness crush and destroy the savings that they have so carefully put away over a lifetime so that they might enjoy dignity in their later years. No longer will young families see their own incomes, and their own hopes, eaten away simply because they are carrying out their deep moral obligations to their parents, and to their uncles and to their aunts. And no longer will this nation refuse the hand of justice to those who have given a lifetime of service and wisdom and labor to the progress of this progressive country.

Loud, hearty applause frequently interrupted the speech. This wasn't a victory lap, but it was a celebration of completing a major milestone in the journey. Medicare was intended, I knew, to be a stepping stone on the path to universal health insurance for every man, woman, and child in America. One day, people are going to ask, "Why the hell didn't my grandparents do this before?" Wherever I'll be that day, I'll be smiling.

When LBJ said, "Let us also remember those who sadly cannot share this time for triumph. For it is their triumph, too. It is the victory of great members of Congress that are not with us, like John Dingell Sr.," the full emotions of the moment hit me. I knew my dad was proud. I knew he was proud of all of us who had worked

to see part of his dream come true. I knew he was surprised his colleagues hadn't forgotten him and his hard work. And I knew he was proud of me and all that I'd done to help advance the cause.

Now I smiled and nodded my head as President Obama laid out the reforms the bill would enact, providing insurance to 32 million people who didn't have it before. In just my own district in Michigan, it would provide new coverage to more than 34,000 people and prevent almost 2,000 life-destroying bankruptcies. But the president couldn't get more than a sentence out without another ovation.

In that moment of joy and success, I remembered the losses, too. The many, many times we'd tried but didn't have the votes. Or the bill that was never able to move out of committee, despite being reintroduced at the start of every session.

Long after Lyndon Johnson and Harry Truman had passed on to their greater reward, there came a time when a young candidate, new to the national stage, won the presidency. Health care and health care costs were a major issue in the campaign. He ran on a pledge to do what no president before him had been able to achieve: ensure that Americans had universal access to health care coverage. The year was 1993, and the new president with the ambitious agenda was Bill Clinton. His initiative was called the Health Security Act.

Unfortunately, there were three major problems with President Clinton's proposal. The first one was timing: he waited too long to propose it. The bill was announced in September 1993 and not brought before Congress until late November. The two months between the announcement of his plan and the unveiling of the bill gave opponents a head start in spreading their lies about it on television. Worse yet, our hands were tied by a lack of information. We

couldn't counter those lies with the facts about the plan because we didn't *have* the facts. Not knowing what was in the bill, we couldn't fight back against the other side's well-organized campaign to kill it in the cradle.

The second problem with the Clinton plan was one common to many new administrations. New administrations often put their own people in charge, whether or not those people are qualified to do the job. As a result, they invariably ignore the counsel of members of their own party in Congress. This is especially the case after a hard-fought campaign that relies on a close-knit, often insular team of advisers to achieve victory. Those presidents-elect—I'm thinking of Kennedy in 1960, Nixon in 1968, Carter in 1976, Clinton in 1992, Bush in 2000, and our current occupant in chief—almost always place tremendous trust in their campaign teams, no matter their lack of experience in actual governance. Their defense is always hubris: "What's wrong with that? We *won*, didn't we?"

The third problem for the Clinton health care initiative was, by far, the worst. With little consultation, they chose a fellow named Ira Magaziner to head the task force. Magaziner was a business consultant of some repute, but he'd never worked on a legislative matter as intricate, complicated, or politically sensitive as health care reform. He had neither the executive branch experience nor the legislative skills essential to passing something as complex as health care coverage reform.

Aside from his inexperience, Mr. Magaziner had another significant flaw. He was a jackass who treated allies and enemies alike: badly. He ignored input and scorned criticism. As a result, the plan's allies dwindled and its enemies were angry and emboldened. Also, Magaziner kept power, information, and decision making to himself. Outside health care experts, as well as those of us in Congress

who were essential to getting any legislation passed, were treated like mushrooms—we were kept in the dark and fed bullshit.

I'm sad to say that Hillary Clinton, too, bears some responsibility for the failure of the health care plan during her husband's administration. She and Magaziner led a task force of more than five hundred people. It was a disorderly, chaotic process that gave the opposition far too long to mobilize against the bill, while supporters were left twiddling their thumbs.

The entire effort was, in short, a mess. Magaziner led a navel-gazing group that never saw that they were about to be run over by a bus "driven" by a fictional couple named Harry and Louise. Harry and Louise were characters played by actors—what a surprise—hired by the Health Insurance Association of America to appear in a series of very effective commercials that framed the debate as Big Government versus the little guy. The Clinton team was caught completely flat-footed by the depth of the opposition to its efforts. As a result, health care put supporters like me on the defensive from the get-go.

The Harry and Louise ad campaign, incidentally, cost about twenty million dollars, or (without factoring in inflation) roughly the amount the American Medical Association had spent four decades earlier to defeat the Wagner-Murray-Dingell Bill.

Out of the ashes of the failure of Clintoncare, though, came bipartisan consensus. My dear friend Teddy Kennedy worked with his dear friend Orrin Hatch to pass what's now called the Children's Health Insurance Program. CHIP now ensures that millions of children have health insurance. Teddy was a tremendous tower of strength during my efforts to pass the Patient's Bill of Rights in 2000. I got it through the House. The Senate may be just down the hall from the House, but those are the longest four hundred yards

in the world. The Patient's Bill of Rights never made it out of the Senate then. But I saw to it that much of that bill made it into the Affordable Care Act.

My attention came back to the room just in time to hear President Obama say, "To all of the terrific committee chairs, all the members of Congress who did what was difficult but did what was right and passed health care reform, not just this generation of Americans will thank you, but the next generation of Americans will thank you."

And I started thinking about all the health care fights in my past, and all the friends I'd wished were there celebrating with us, but who were there only in spirit.

I also thought back to a few days before, the last time I saw my friend and colleague Bart Stupak. I was the one tasked with reconciling Bart's pro-life convictions with the ACA and making sure that his sentiments didn't bring the bill crashing down around us. It took some convincing, but I was able to forge an agreement that Bart could live with.

"Where's Bart today?" I wondered, scanning the room to see if I could spot him. I'd always been something of a mentor to him, and even when we disagreed, we'd still find a way to work things out.

I was sad when I found out a few weeks later that Bart wasn't running for reelection. The conservative ideologues who succeeded him are nowhere near the legislators Bart Stupak was.

President Obama continued: "I'm signing this bill for all the leaders who took up this cause through the generations, from Teddy Roosevelt to Franklin Roosevelt, from Harry Truman to Lyndon Johnson, from Bill and Hillary Clinton to one of the deans who's been fighting this so long, John Dingell, to Senator Ted Kennedy."

Hearing Ted Kennedy's name took me back in memory once

again, this time to my family's past and to his family's past. Each of us entered Congress with big shoes to fill. I succeeded my father in the House, and he took his brother's seat in the Senate, two years after JFK was elected president. Each of us had also experienced challenges, some of them quite similar, with physical and mental health issues that profoundly affected our commitment to guaranteeing that no American should ever be denied access to quality medical care when they needed it. Just as it was for me and for my father, this was also the cause of Ted Kennedy's life.

Thinking about Teddy, it suddenly hit me that there was one thing that had changed significantly in that cause since my father introduced the first bill for universal health care in 1943. In that era, and for decades to come, *mental health* care was not included in the debate. It was still an issue that people grappled with privately, often with great shame.

I know, because I'm one of them.

My first wife, Helen, suffered greatly from bipolar illness throughout her life. Like most people in the 1950s and '60s, I had no understanding of its symptoms—wild mood swings, erratic behavior, irrational statements, paranoia. In the beginning, I thought it was just a side of her personality that I hadn't seen until after we were married. Frankly, it made me angry. I regret that very much now, but I think I was like most people dealing with symptoms of undiagnosed mental illness. You can't wrap your mind around the fact that a person you think you know so well is suddenly a total stranger to you, even though they look exactly the same. It took me a long time to realize that Helen's behavior wasn't a character flaw; it was a symptom of an illness that required serious treatment. When you break your leg, you know exactly what to do. You go to the doctor, get a cast put on, and give it time to heal. You certainly don't

expect it will get better on its own, and you don't keep walking on it. You can't, because it hurts. The insidious part of mental illness is that even though the brain is suffering, you don't see it. You tell yourself all this will pass. You pray every day that it will all return to normal.

Over two decades of marriage, and with four children, we tried everything to make it work. I took Helen to multiple doctors and therapists. She went through many years of treatment and many different medications. When we finally got divorced, I saw my world come down around my ears. I was given custody of the kids. Our two boys were in college, but the two girls were still young. Thank God I was able to raise them with the help of my sister, Julé. Without her, I don't know what I would have done. My baby sister is going to find the Lord waiting for her with open arms in Heaven.

Like Helen's bipolar disorder, drug addiction is now recognized by thinking people as a serious medical issue, not a personal weakness. Mental health issues used to be dismissed as character flaws. My generation had a hard time even talking about them. The stigma attached to all forms of mental illness led to silence and, as a result, even more suffering for those afflicted by it. That silent suffering extends to family members who bear the additional burden of caring for someone who does not understand their own illness.

From her own devastating personal experience, Debbie knows firsthand about the pain and the all-too-often tragic consequences of addiction. Her father was, for many years, an addict. Her baby sister, Mary Grace, was an addict who died of an overdose. Debbie grieves for both of them. She has seen the suffering of others like her who have lost loved ones to this horrible epidemic. She's cried with them, comforted them, and she has committed herself to protecting other families from having to experience the terrible feeling of untimely loss. She's been working with both Democrats

and Republicans to help find a solution to the opioid crisis that now threatens our entire nation. The opioid epidemic spares no one, regardless of geography, economic status, or political beliefs.

My experience with Helen's illness and Debbie's loss of her sister opened our eyes to mental health issues in a way that would not have been possible had we each not had those personal connections. We learned about it because we had no other choice. That knowledge left both Debbie and me determined to find ways to help others cope with what is a major, underfunded public health issue.

Patrick Kennedy, the youngest son of Senator Edward Kennedy, was a colleague of mine in the House of Representatives. Patrick won his first election to the Rhode Island state legislature at the tender age of twenty-one. When young Kennedy entered Congress six years later, on January 3, 1995, he became the "Baby of the House," the dubious distinction I'd cringed at having "earned" four decades earlier.

Ironically, it was the same day that I officially became the "Dean of the House," its longest-serving member. After the group swearing in, Patrick came over to me with a wide grin on his freckled face. Even with a shock of red hair, he was unmistakably his father's son.

"Congratulations, sir," he said, extending his hand. "Becoming Dean of the House is a really amazing achievement."

"Thank you, my friend," I said as we shook hands. "I'm just glad that when I see the green grass, I'm still looking down, not up."

"So," he said, "I think I have a two-year head start on you here. You were, what, twenty-nine when you first came in?" His blue eyes were twinkling mischievously at his good-natured jab.

"That's absolutely right," I shot back. "But as memory serves, your father was thirty when he won his first *Senate* election. Seems to me *you're* the one running behind."

He roared with laughter, and I gave him a friendly pat on the shoulder. "You'll do him proud," I said as we parted ways on the crowded House Floor. "Holy Mother of God," I thought to myself, "I am now the Dean. How is that *possible*?" I turned around and shouted back at Patrick, "Hey, Baby Congressman! Make sure you get your butt over to my office on a regular basis. You damn well better not be a stranger!"

"Yes, sir!" Patrick saluted smartly, but with respect. I liked that young fellow.

Like his father, he was a strong champion of universal national health care. Yet, unlike his dad, he had a certain reserve about him that was sometimes worrisome. He seemed like someone doing what he thought was expected of him, but who wasn't always comfortable in his own skin. I chalked it up to living in the shadow of a famous father (something I knew a little bit about), but it wasn't until he'd been in the House for three terms that Patrick publicly announced that he suffered from chronic depression and was under a doctor's care. He would subsequently enter rehab for an addiction to prescription medication.

Patrick's bravery in coming forward was an inspiration to millions of Americans who had previously suffered in silence in their struggles with mental illness. Teddy told me that he was deeply proud of him. By sharing his personal story honestly and humbly, Patrick finally found his own voice. This extraordinary young man even helped me understand more about my own family's experience with mental illness than I ever had before.

Patrick showed guts and wisdom far beyond his years. When he introduced a bipartisan bill with Republican congressman Jim Ramstad of Minnesota to guarantee mental health and physical health insurance parity, I signed on as a cosponsor, and said from the floor:

Mental illness and addiction disorders have long been recognized by the health care community as actual and legitimate health afflictions which may have a significant effect on an individual's life and well-being. It has long been accepted that these afflictions deserve treatment by professionally trained health care providers. As I think of all of the different diseases and afflictions recognized by our scientific and health care communities, I struggle to find a reason why someone who has health care coverage should confront discriminatory barriers to treatment simply because of the nature of the disease. Mental health and addiction disorders can be just as painful and debilitating as medical and surgical disorders. The strains of these illnesses affect individuals, families, and society as a whole.

The bill was signed into law by President George W. Bush in 2008. After its passage, I took Patrick aside and thanked him personally for his leadership. We didn't talk about why I was expressing my gratitude to him. The look in his eyes told me that he understood. I'm so glad that Teddy lived to see all this happen. He passed the following year, secure in the knowledge that his youngest son had finally found the cause of *his* life.

My eyes grew misty again, and I had to remove my glasses once more. Damn dust—they ought to clean this old room more often . . .

When President Obama finished speaking, the room swelled with cheers and sustained applause. Finally, he waved us all down and took his place at the long table. It was time for him to put pen to paper and enact the newest law of the land.

As he handed me a pen—he used only twenty-two of them, far

fewer than the hundreds LBJ used to sign Medicare into law—he smiled broadly and said, "Thanks, John."

"No, thank *you*, Mr. President." There was nothing else left to say.

———————

WE'RE NOW EIGHT YEARS REMOVED FROM THAT DAY, AND AS I write this, the Affordable Care Act remains the law of the land, despite the worst efforts of Donald Trump and his Republican lackeys to undo it. Turns out it's popular. The last poll I saw has it receiving approval from a majority of the American people. And that number will continue to grow, mark my words.

Retiring from Congress has its perks. I no longer have to deal with the machinations of the "other body." I've got more time to read, to follow the Detroit Tigers and the University of Michigan Wolverines; and there are a lot of good movies I finally have time to see.

The hardest adjustment has been being on the sidelines, knowing that I still have things to say yet no longer have an electoral platform to get my message out. After fifty-nine years of being in the thick of the fight, it ain't easy to sit on the bench when I see the country going to hell in a big orange handbasket.

Thank God that Debbie has her platform in Congress and that she has used it with boundless energy and keen intelligence. I pray that I will live to see the day when she is part of the majority. She will take the fight right to the Republicans and, to quote Harry Truman, she'll "take the starch out of them." They should get ready for her.

Still, it's especially hard to watch from the wings while the Republi-cons work overtime to destroy all we've achieved and more. Rather than seeking to make things better, my former colleagues on the other side of the aisle seem intent on driving things backward, to

return to an America that was less clean, less safe, less fair. In short, the America of the 1920s, when the GOP ruled the roost and almost ruined the country. As someone who lived through those days, I've seen this movie before. It's not worth the price of the popcorn.

But wait a minute. That's wrong. I *do* have one way to get my frustrations out and maybe do a little good along the way: the Twitter Machine. It continues to amaze me that this Twitter account my staff and I started for fun on a slow January day in 2010 is now read by so many people. Everywhere I go, people quote my Twitters back to me.

We often hear it said that the younger generation isn't engaged in politics, that they don't pay attention. That's not what I hear from their parents. They tell me about things of mine they saw on the Twitter because their kids sent it to them.

Children are 25 percent of America's population and 100 percent of its future. We need to get out of their way and let them lead.

In March 2017, as the Republicans tried yet again—and failed yet again—to repeal the Affordable Care Act, the Twit-in-Chief was pouting. "Who knew health care could be so complicated?" This was too much. I put down the TV remote and picked up my gray message-sending machine. (I know it's called an iPad, but to me it's like having a Western Union office in your house.) I learned later that sending out multiple messages in a row is called a "Twitterstorm." They don't tell you that on the Weather Channel.

Here's pretty much what I said that night (or at least tried to say when I could get the damn buttons to work):

Who knew health care could be so complicated? In 1943, my father was one of the first people to introduce comprehensive

health care reform in Congress, a single-payer system for all. The decade prior he fought like hell to pass Social Security and see it signed into law. And he did.

But his effort wasn't as successful in '43. The Wagner-Murray-Dingell bill to create a national health program ultimately died in committee. He never would get to see universal health care become law. He passed in '55 and I decided to run to replace him, vowing to keep up his work.

In 1957—and in every Congress thereafter—I'd reintroduce my father's bill and work to create a national program to take care of those in need.

I was a pup at the time, but I began working with my colleagues on Medicare legislation. Cecil King. Aime Forand. My dear friend John Moss. It took years to work through, but then-Speaker McCormack brought our bill to the floor in '65 and gave me the honor of gaveling its passage.

My Pop would have been proud.

It was an accomplishment, but it was not my end goal. I continued to reintroduce my father's bill every year. As pieces of it slowly became law.

Over the years we'd create the National Institutes of Health, the Children's Health Insurance Program, and many other efforts to improve care.

We took another shot in the '90s but again came up short. You know who knew damn well how complicated health care could be? @HillaryClinton.

Nevertheless, we persisted. It was an honor to work with so many great champions of our nation in helping to craft the Affordable Care Act.

Hearing after hearing, amendment after amendment. We took the time to hear concerns from all.

Republicans were invited, too. They declined.

Our bill aimed to bring certainty to an uncertain experience. You don't hope to have to use insurance, but if you do, it needs to be damn good.

So we fought to expand coverage. We worked to lower costs. We wanted the American people to finally KNOW what their plan actually included.

Before this, many had to decide between bankruptcy or death. Children hit lifetime caps. Cancer & being a woman were deemed preexisting conditions.

When the ACA was up in the House, leadership asked me to preside over part of the debate. I accepted with one term: "I'm bringing my gavel."

Was Obamacare perfect? Hell no. The only perfect law was handed down to Moses on stone tablets by God himself. Obamacare is an important start.

Millions now have coverage they never had before. Lifesaving screenings. Preventive care. Affordable rates & subsidies that SCALE with cost.

They spent nearly a decade doing everything they could to undermine the ACA, and now sanctimoniously declare it broken. With the current crop of Republicans in charge, you can always count on one thing: "It's the *hypocrisy*, stupid."

And these were the last bolts of lightning from my first Twitterstorm:

Hell, I don't even remember why I started telling this story, except to urge folks to call their Congressperson and demand more from them.

Actual reforms can be made to improve the Affordable Care Act. A rushed, reckless repeal bill is not that. Too many people will be hurt.

Well, that's that. Goodnight.

And with that, I went to bed. While I slept, my "storm" crisscrossed the country, and the next morning, my staff told me it had gone "viral"—which, they assured me, was a good thing. (When

you get to be my age, the last word you associate with good news is *viral*.) As you've probably figured out by now, I use the Twitter Machine a lot, even though I don't have the first clue about how the thing actually works. I also don't know how a microwave works, but I can still get it to cook my dinner. You don't have to know *how* something works to get the job done. You just have to have good people around you that you trust to do the job right. Throughout my career, I've been blessed with hundreds of talented staff people who made me look a lot smarter than I am. The trick is to seek out the brightest people you can find and then get the hell out of their way. My dad taught me that you can't do it all yourself. Someone should tell that to that jamoke in the White House—at least while he's still there.

The next day, I went out to lunch at my neighborhood Coney Island restaurant, and I'll be damned if a dozen folks didn't come up to my booth to shake my hand and thank me for fighting the good fight.

It was clear the press had picked up on my Twitterstorm. I heard from friends and former colleagues in Washington that it had helped draw attention to their efforts to stop health care repeal by reminding folks of how hard it was to have come this far and how long it took to do it.

It made me feel really good to hear that the sort of things I normally would have yelled at the TV might actually help prevent the Republicans from doing harm to millions of our most vulnerable citizens.

Now, as I write this, the health insurance fight continues. A new generation of young leaders is forging the charge for universal, single-payer insurance. To them, I say, as a veteran of every health insurance reform effort since Eisenhower, "Welcome to the fight

and remember the words of Voltaire: 'The perfect is the enemy of the good.'" Or, as my dad would have said, "Half a loaf is better than none." If some reform is all you can achieve, achieve what you can and save the rest for another day.

Achieving part of our goal is how we passed Medicare, the Children's Health Insurance Program, and the ACA. Achieving part of the goal is how my dad helped FDR pass Social Security. Stubbornly insisting that only the perfect bill was acceptable would have meant we'd have had none of those things.

Over time, small victories add up. If you can make just a little incremental progress every day, you'll wake up one morning and find that you've already gotten most of the hard work done.

Once, on the floor of the House, I asked Bob Eckhardt, my old colleague and friend from a conservative district in Texas, "Bob, how can a liberal like you keep getting reelected back home?" He told me something that's always stuck with me. Putting his arm around my shoulder, he leaned in and whispered, "John, you can do extraordinary things when you talk about them in ordinary ways."

The fight for social justice is even older than I am. And it's a fight that will need to be fought over and over again, as our current situation makes abundantly clear. Don't let that discourage you. As my philosopher father taught me at his knee, even in the darkest of times, hope's light is always beyond the horizon.

CHAPTER 9

Promises to Keep

JFK challenged us to realize that the freedoms granted to us as proud Americans should make no exceptions for race, color or creed.

—TWEET FROM @JOHNDINGELL,

NOVEMBER 22, 2013, 11:58 A.M.

IN 1957, PRESIDENT DWIGHT D. EISENHOWER INTEGRATED Little Rock Central High School. Arkansas governor Orval Faubus initially tried to use the Arkansas National Guard to block integration; Eisenhower federalized the Guard so it wasn't under Faubus's spell. The mayor of Little Rock asked the president for federal troops to protect the students from angry segregationists. Eisenhower sent in the 101st Airborne Division, the Screaming Eagles, the heroes of the Siege of Bastogne during the Battle of the Bulge in World War II.

Brooks Hays, a Democratic congressman from Arkansas, represented Little Rock. During the Central High segregation crisis,

Hays had tried to mediate the dispute between Faubus and Eisenhower. Angered by what they saw as his betrayal, the old Dixiecrat wing of the Democratic Party drafted a last-minute write-in candidate, a Little Rock School Board member named Dale Alford, to run in the general election against Hays. After a heated campaign, Alford won a narrow (and immediately disputed) victory. Ultimately, the House would have to decide whether or not to seat him.

"According to precedent, the chair will swear in all members at this time," Speaker Rayburn intoned from his perch atop the rostrum.

It was January 7, 1959, and the House was meeting to swear in the new members, elect a Speaker, and handle all the parliamentary business that is required at the beginning of every new session.

Before the Speaker could administer the oath to all the members, he noticed a tall, gangly Pole with thick-framed glasses and a skinny tie shoot up out of his seat. I was thirty-two, still a kid, tilting at every windmill.

"Mr. Speaker!"

"For what purpose does the gentleman from Michigan rise?"

"Mr. Speaker, upon my responsibility as a member-elect of the Eighty-Sixth Congress, I object to the oath being administered to the gentleman from Arkansas, Mr. Dale Alford. I base this upon facts and statements which I consider to be reliable."

There had been a whiff of scandal about the race, given Alford's late entrance, the relationship between Faubus's gubernatorial campaign and Alford's congressional campaign, and the fact that an Independent segregationist was about to join the Democratic Caucus despite beating the incumbent Democratic member. There were also questions about whether ballot boxes had been stuffed.

I thought the whole situation about Alford being seated was a

crock of shit. He beat a Democrat; we shouldn't have let him caucus with us. He was an unapologetic segregationist; we shouldn't have let him caucus with us.

I wasn't going to let a man like Alford get sworn in without a fight. However, I was still only a member-elect. Technically, the Eighty-Fifth Congress had not yet ended its term; that would officially occur only when the new members of the Eighty-Sixth took the oath.

I was the only one brash (foolish?) enough to challenge the all-powerful Sam Rayburn, even though I knew other members quietly shared my sentiments. This was probably a case of thinking more with my balls than with my brains, but I knew I was right. It took me years to learn that being right is not always being smart.

I was also a young man in a hurry. I had no way of knowing how long I'd remain in the Congress, so I was trying to finish up all my dad's work as fast as I could—and he wasn't around to tell me to slow down and take my time.

"Under the precedents, the chair will ask the gentleman from Arkansas not to rise to take the oath with the other members for the present at least," Speaker Rayburn said, visibly annoyed. "If the other members will rise, I will now administer the oath of office."

We were all then sworn in by the Speaker—everyone except Dale Alford.

Right after we all took the oath, the chair recognized the gentleman from Massachusetts. John McCormack was the majority leader and Rayburn's chief deputy. Like Rayburn, McCormack was someone I respected deeply and whose friendship I treasured. Both men had been dear friends of my father, and each now kept a paternal eye on me in his stead. Their approval meant everything to me.

"Mr. Speaker," McCormack said. "I offer a privileged resolution and move its immediate consideration."

The clerk read the motion. "Resolved, that the Speaker is hereby authorized and directed to administer the oath of office to the gentleman from Arkansas, Mr. Dale Alford."

They were going to swear Alford in and leave unresolved the question of whether he should be seated until after the Committee on House Administration could investigate the election.

McCormack spoke again: "Mr. Speaker, this resolution is in accord with existing precedents, and, Mr. Speaker, I move the previous question on the resolution."

One man spoke up, a second-term Democrat from Massachusetts, Tip O'Neill. "Mr. Speaker, may I make an inquiry on a point of parliamentary procedure?"

Scowling at the interruption, Speaker Rayburn told him to get on with it. "The gentleman will state it."

I was glad to have company in what Tip and I both knew was a quixotic effort. I was glad to have company in fighting the good fight. Years later, when Tip was Speaker and I was an Old Bull committee chairman, we remembered that day and toasted our brash "bravery" in that "epic" battle with Rayburn and McCormack.

"Mr. Speaker, when the previous order has been moved and there is no debate, under the rules of the House, are we not entitled to forty minutes of debate?" Tip asked.

The Speaker gruffly declared that the point was valid—but irrelevant—since we hadn't yet *adopted* the rules. So, "under the precedents, the forty-minute rule does not apply."

A voice vote was taken on the resolution, and the "ayes" had it even before Rayburn brought down his gavel. Alford was then sworn in to more than a little applause from my colleagues on both sides of the aisle.

After my opposition to Alford attracted widespread national at-

My dad at the Union Printers Home in Colorado Springs after his recovery from tuberculosis. Circa 1917. *(Courtesy of Julé Dingell Walowac)*

My parents, John Dingell Sr. and Grace Bigler, on one of their early dates in Colorado. Circa 1920. *(Courtesy of Julé Dingell Walowac)*

On my third birthday, outside our home in Detroit. July 8, 1929. *(Courtesy of Julé Dingell Walowac)*

My dad and me outside the residence of the governor-general of the Philippines, Frank Murphy. Frank was a close friend of our family and later became an associate justice on the United States Supreme Court. Manila, 1933. *(Courtesy of Julé Dingell Walowac)*

President Franklin D. Roosevelt signing the Social Security Act into law. My dad is the young fellow behind him with the mustache. August 14, 1935. *(Courtesy of New York World-Telegram and the Sun Newspaper Photograph Collection, Library of Congress)*

My dad holding my beautiful newborn baby sister, Julé. 1936. *(Courtesy of Julé Dingell Walowac)*

My dad in a photograph he took for his second reelection campaign. 1936. *(Courtesy of Julé Dingell Walowac)*

My parents, my younger brother Jim (center), my baby sister Julé, and me outside our family home in Detroit. Circa 1937. *(Courtesy of Julé Dingell Walowac)*

Students and teachers of the Capitol Page School. I'm in the front row, ninth from the right. 1939. (*Courtesy of the Capital Photo Service, Collection of the U.S. House of Representatives, Jim Oliver Collection*)

My parents on December 10, 1941, three days after the Japanese attack on Pearl Harbor. (*Courtesy of Bettmann via Getty Images*)

Back in DC as a newly minted second lieutenant. Our family dog, Colonel, still outranked me. August 1945. *(Courtesy of Julé Dingell Walowac)*

Speaker of the House Sam Rayburn swearing me in as a new member of the Eighty-Fourth Congress. December 1955. *(Courtesy of John and Debbie Dingell)*

With one of my heroes, President
Harry S. Truman. Circa 1958.
(Courtesy of John and Debbie Dingell)

Looking on (I am third from the left) as President John F. Kennedy signs the Federal Water
Pollution Control Act. It was one of the first major pieces of conservation legislation that
I sponsored into law. July 20, 1961. *(Courtesy of the John F. Kennedy Presidential Library and
Museum)*

Posing for an official photograph as a member of Congress. 1962. *(Courtesy of the U.S. House of Representatives Photography Office)*

With Speaker of the House John McCormack, Vice President Lyndon Johnson, and House Majority Whip Hale Boggs. Circa 1963. *(Courtesy of John and Debbie Dingell)*

At the signing of the Civil Rights Act by President Lyndon B. Johnson. I am on the far right. Directly behind President Johnson is twenty-four-year-old John Lewis, one of the most courageous leaders of the civil rights movement. He would later become my colleague and beloved friend in the Congress. July 2, 1964. *(Courtesy of PhotoQuest/Getty Images)*

With a wolf in my office in 1973. I was proud to be the chief sponsor of the Endangered Species Act that President Richard M. Nixon signed into law that same year.
(Courtesy of the U.S. House of Representatives Photography Office)

With President Jimmy Carter and his congressional liaison, Frank Moore (far left), in the Oval Office. I respectfully told him, "Mr. President, I can be friendly, or I can be frank, but I can't be both." April 20, 1977. *(Courtesy of the Jimmy Carter Presidential Library, White House Staff Photographer's Collection)*

As the chairman of the House Energy and Commerce Committee. Circa 1984. *(Courtesy of the Collection of the U.S. House of Representatives)*

Debbie and I were blessed to meet with His Holiness Pope John Paul II. 1987. *(Courtesy of John and Debbie Dingell)*

At a bill signing with President Ronald Reagan at the White House. I am standing directly behind the president. To my left is Senator Patrick Leahy of Vermont. It was my great privilege to serve alongside him in the Congress for forty years. January 6, 1988. *(Courtesy of Bettmann via Getty Images)*

Left to right: Debbie, President George H. W. Bush, First Lady Barbara Bush, and me at the White House Christmas Party. December 1990. *(Courtesy of the George H. W. Bush Presidential Library and Museum)*

With my great friend and partner in the fight for universal health care, Senator Ted Kennedy. December 16, 1997. *(Courtesy of Douglas Graham/Congressional Quarterly/Getty Images)*

My father pointedly questions Secretary of Commerce Jesse Jones about revising the tax code. Secretary Jones is the man sitting dejectedly on top of the table. January 1942. *(Courtesy of Associated Press)*

Like father, like son. Questioning a witness at an Energy and Commerce hearing. April 2008. *(Courtesy of AP Photo/Susan Walsh)*

On the Truman Balcony at the White House with President George W. Bush following a luncheon in honor of my fiftieth anniversary as a member of the House of Representatives. December 13, 2005. *(Courtesy of AP Photo/The White House, Paul Morse)*

Gratefully watching as President Barack Obama signs the Affordable Care Act into law. It was a historic milestone in the long struggle to guarantee health care for all Americans. March 23, 2010. *(Courtesy of Oliver Douliery/Sipa USA via AP Images)*

Sharing a laugh with President Bill Clinton. October 24, 2010. *(Courtesy of Bill Pugliano/Getty Images)*

Debbie and me as the grand marshals of Detroit's Thanksgiving Day Parade. November 22, 2012. *(Courtesy of The Parade Company)*

Alongside my beloved friend Vice President Joe Biden at a Capitol ceremony honoring me as the longest-serving member of Congress in U.S. history. June 13, 2013. *(Courtesy of AP Photo/J. Scott Applewhite)*

With the Lovely Deborah shortly after I announced my retirement from the Congress. February 24, 2014. *(Courtesy of AP Photo/Detroit News, Max Ortiz)*

tention, a prominent conservative columnist called me a "tool of Walter Reuther," the liberal leader of the United Automobile Workers. Hell, the unions had nothing to do with it.

It may have been a fool-hardy move to oppose my party leadership on something I had no chance of winning, but I was nobody's tool. I hadn't told anyone in advance what I was going to do, nor had I asked anybody for permission. Throughout my entire time in the Congress, my only allegiances were to the Constitution and to my conscience.

The investigation, by the way, found that games *had* been played with the ballots, but Alford remained in Congress and won reelection two years later. Despite our polar-opposite views on civil rights, however, he and I were able to form a civil working relationship during his four years in Congress.

I ENTERED CONGRESS THE YEAR AFTER THE SUPREME COURT ruled against segregated schools in *Brown v. Board of Education*. On December 1, 1955, less than two weeks before my election, Rosa Parks refused to give up her seat on a bus, sparking the Montgomery Bus Boycott that led to the modern civil rights movement.

At the very heart of the American experiment is the self-evident truth that "all men are created equal, that they are endowed by their Creator with certain unalienable Rights, that among these are Life, Liberty, and the pursuit of Happiness. That to secure these rights, Governments are instituted among Men, deriving their just powers from the consent of the governed." We have never achieved the complete fulfilment of that notion of universal equality. By fits and starts, we have come ever closer, but there are still miles to go. I was in Congress for fifty-nine years. In those years, I saw us draw

closer to our noblest of ideals, but I have also seen us slide back to days I'd thought were (justifiably) behind us, an era I'd thought had rightly and rightfully been consigned to the dustbin of history.

The extension and preservation of civil rights is a story of struggle. It is a story of activists exposing themselves to scorn and ridicule, risking (and at times losing) life and limb. It is a story of hope and of loss. In short, it is a microcosm of the American story itself.

On March 26, 1956, after I'd been in Congress three and a half months, I took to the floor to speak about civil rights and the Eisenhower administration's failures to act. I was speaking in support of H.R. 627, introduced by Emanuel Celler, a veteran Brooklyn Democrat who previously fought side by side with my father on this issue. Manny's bill was the precursor to the Civil Rights Act of 1957. I supported it strongly on the floor: "[It would do] much to help see to it that all citizens get the full rights which the Constitution says are theirs. It guarantees protection of citizens from violence on account of race or color, it outlines and prohibits discriminatory practices in employment, housing, education, and other fields. H.R. 627 guarantees the right of citizens to vote, and establishes a Commission on Civil Rights, a thing the President advocates."

Celler's bill was stuck in the Rules Committee, which was then chaired by a pro-segregation Democrat from Virginia, Howard W. Smith. I went back to the floor, railing against the inaction of both my fellow Democrats in the House and the Senate and a Republican president.

"Too long has this action waited and too long have our people waited to claim the full rights which the Constitution grants. We were assured early in January that specific recommendations would be forthcoming from the White House on this most critical subject. Yet, to date, a long, violent two and a half months later, nothing has

been done. The delay has caused us to reach a point where unless action is taken now, nothing will come out of this session of Congress because of filibuster by opponents of civil rights legislation."

I'm told by my Jewish friends that *chutzpah* is the term for the trait required to make a speech like that when you're a green-as-grass new member whose older colleagues sometimes still mistake you for a Page Boy. I didn't care. At the same time, I was also co-sponsoring antilynching legislation, measures to ban the poll tax, and efforts to bring fair hiring and fair federal employment practices to federal employment. (Did I mention I was in a hurry?)

Eisenhower was calling for "moderation with progress." I told my colleagues in Congress what I thought those words meant:

The position seems to be to wait, to let individual citizens, the churches, the Congress, and the Supreme Court struggle with these difficult problems facing the people of this country. The position of the president seems to be much like that of one who stands sympathetically by as an interested spectator while a husband and wife fight a bloody intrafamily battle.

I for one would welcome the help of the president in this fight to guarantee to all Americans the rights which we regard as inalienable. I renew my call upon the president to furnish the leadership which we need in this fight. However, it appears that it is not his disposition to lead, nor worse yet, even to follow.

I call upon the president to give the country that vigorous leadership which only a strong president can give. Nay, I demand that he give that leadership, and that he cease relying upon the actions of others, the Supreme Court, the Congress,

and citizens to carry out unassisted what is properly and constitutionally also a function of the chief executive.

In those days, being a northern Democrat and calling for civil rights legislation was a very liberal position, particularly for a member with so little time in the chamber. It'd be a bit like being hired as an intern by Ford Motor Company and immediately insisting on a complete redesign of the Mustang.

I was angry. I thought it outrageous that the president wasn't acting decisively. I even suggested a six-point plan of action to the Eisenhower administration that included ensuring full enforcement of existing civil rights legislation and adoption of vigorous new bills.

I learned later that a young minister named Martin Luther King Jr. was sending Eisenhower telegrams along similar lines, calling for more and stronger action from the White House. Following congressional passage of the Civil Rights Act of 1957 (a weak-tea compromise bill that ended up accomplishing very little), King continued to push the federal government for stronger action, including legislative improvements to the act that would take three more years to become law.

I was young and naïve. I thought my plan would rouse the administration to action and that we'd fix the problem then and there. I would like to think the Eisenhower administration listened and took my advice, but I was so new to Congress that it probably had no idea who in the bare-ass hell I was.

Events (as they often do) were what finally forced Ike to act. That's how the 101st Airborne ended up at Little Rock Central High School, and it's why Dale Alford wound up getting elected to Congress.

I was sponsoring civil rights bills left and right; one bill would have barred segregationist groups from using any property owned by either the federal government or the Washington, DC, local government. Another would have made lynching a federal crime. My civil rights work didn't go unnoticed; I found myself in demand as a speaker arguing for civil rights across the country, particularly during the late 1950s and early '60s. Opponents of civil rights spewed hate at me; I'm still not sure why they thought calling me every name in the book would get me to recant my views and adopt their disgusting, bigoted stance, but they tried.

They even came at me through the person who I respected more than anyone else in the House of Representatives.

THE SPEAKER OF THE HOUSE OF REPRESENTATIVES WIELDS enormous power over the House and its members. To be on the Speaker's bad side, especially if it's a Speaker of your party, has . . . well, consequences. One of the many functions of the Speaker is to serve as a mentor and a role model, particularly to the new members.

I, of course, was in a relatively unique position, as I'd known the House leadership since I was a boy because of Dad's service and my page service. Even so, when I entered the House, I still stood in awe of Sam Rayburn and John McCormack. All these years later, I still do. These two men played a large part in making me into the legislator I became. These two men were like fathers to me after my own departed this vale of tears for his reward.

When I entered the House, Speaker Rayburn immediately pegged me as a wild man, a bomb thrower, a radical. It's not for nothing that he'd sometimes refer to me as "Oh, that boy." My civil rights speeches and the Alford exchange cemented my reputation

to Speaker Rayburn. I was an annoyance, a pest, a gadfly, a thirty-two-year-old who thought I knew everything.

Yet, Speaker Rayburn helped to make me the man I became. He set an example for how to act, how to work with others when you could and against them when you had to. I learned how to lead in Congress by watching him.

Before my retirement, I gave an oral history interview to the House historian, speaking of my time as a page and of my early service in Congress. I think what I said then about Rayburn remains true. He "was a giant, but [one] who was rather aloof. If you look at the statue of Rayburn you'll find he was just a little guy. There's one in the front of the building here." We were doing the interview in the Rayburn House Office Building. When you see Rayburn there, "he's up on a pedestal. And you think, 'God, he's a shrimp.' But I always saw Rayburn as about 11 feet high. He had an enormous presence. And nobody ever called him anything other than 'Mr. Speaker.' Some of the more senior Members would call him 'Mr. Sam.' But he was a very good-hearted man. He was a Texas populist. And he understood how tough it was to live, and to make it."

On November 16, 1961, the good Lord called Samuel Taliaferro Rayburn home. He was (and remains) the longest-serving Speaker of the U.S. House of Representatives in history.

Speaker Rayburn was a legend. A hero. He left mighty big shoes for his successor to fill.

And that successor, John William McCormack, lived up to Rayburn's lofty standards. McCormack was from South Boston, and he had worked his way up in Boston Democratic politics all the way to the House. He was so white and pale that he was almost translucent. McCormack and my family went back to my dad's arrival

in Washington; McCormack and my dad sat next to each other on Ways and Means.

I'd known him since I was a boy. I never heard McCormack say a bad word about anyone or anything. His words, though, were his bond, and once given, it was never broken.

His love for his wife was legendary. I've heard, but can't confirm, that they ate dinner together every night, and that they never spent a night apart. I do know that he and Harriet loved each other madly. McCormack, more than any other Speaker or committee chair, saw something in me as a young member, and he taught me much about the legislative process and how to be an effective legislator.

THE EARLY 1960S WAS A TIME OF PERSONAL LOSS. MY MOTHER, Grace, joined her beloved husband, my hero, my father, on April 6, 1962. Unlike when my father died seven years earlier, when my mother died I was there to say good-bye; so were my brother, sister, and brother-in-law. Mother hadn't been well; in fact, she'd been in a coma. So, we were there to say good-bye. Then she woke up—and she was hungry. She wanted a cup of coffee, a hamburger, and a chocolate malted.

This was Washington, DC, in 1962—in the middle of the night. For those of you who are used to pocket telephones being able to get you anything whenever you damn well please, this was the old days. My brother, Jim, and I got in the car and drove around for what seemed like hours (but was probably only twenty to thirty minutes), trying to find a place that was open to get her exactly what she wanted and couldn't get in the hospital. And we were both praying that we'd get back in time.

We got back, and we got back in time. We all had a nice visit with her for about an hour, and then she was gone. Peacefully and quietly. She looked like an angel. And I know my dad was there waiting for her at the pearly gates.

LIKE THE 1928 ELECTION BEFORE IT, THE 1960 ELECTION BE-came a referendum on the role of religion in the public sphere. I grew up hearing stories of Al Smith's failed bid in 1928 to become the first Catholic president of the United States, and in 1960, I helped elect the first Roman Catholic president.

John F. Kennedy's oratorical talents are well known and well commented upon. It's hard to imagine today, but in 1960 there was still a large number of Americans who truly believed that a Catholic president would be wholly subservient to the wishes and whims of the Vatican, and that the United States would be a puppet nation, secretly ruled by the Pope (just as they had feared with Al Smith).

Kennedy was president from 1961 to 1963, an all-too-brief thousand days that came to be known as "Camelot." I was still a small-potatoes, young congressman then, but our paths crossed in the Capitol and on the campaign trail.

These fears of a religious "other" leading the United States to secret domination have never really gone away. My friend Barack Obama was accused both of having such a radical Christian minister that he couldn't fairly be president *and* of being a secret Muslim! Sometimes the same people made both those accusations on the same day.

We do not discriminate on the basis of choices that are fundamental to the pursuit of happiness. That includes religion and sexual

orientation. You might be born and raised Catholic but become Baptist. We should not discriminate against others, period. Full stop.

I used to keep a copy on my desk of then-Senator John Kennedy's Address to the Greater Houston Ministerial Association. Whenever someone sent me a letter attacking me for policy positions I'd taken that the Catholic Church disagreed with, I'd send them a copy of that speech. (The vast, vast majority of these letter writers were writing about abortion or birth control.)

In his speech, JFK said, in part:

I believe in an America where the separation of church and state is absolute, where no Catholic prelate would tell the president (should he be Catholic) how to act, and no Protestant minister would tell his parishioners for whom to vote; where no church or church school is granted any public funds or political preference; and where no man is denied public office merely because his religion differs from the president who might appoint him or the people who might elect him.

I believe in an America that is officially neither Catholic, Protestant nor Jewish; where no public official either requests or accepts instructions on public policy from the Pope, the National Council of Churches or any other ecclesiastical source; where no religious body seeks to impose its will directly or indirectly upon the general populace or the public acts of its officials; and where religious liberty is so indivisible that an act against one church is treated as an act against all. . . .

Whatever issue may come before me as president—on birth control, divorce, censorship, gambling or any other subject—I

will make my decision in accordance with these views, in accordance with what my conscience tells me to be the national interest, and without regard to outside religious pressures or dictates. And no power or threat of punishment could cause me to decide otherwise.

But if the time should ever come—and I do not concede any conflict to be even remotely possible—when my office would require me to either violate my conscience or violate the national interest, then I would resign the office; and I hope any conscientious public servant would do the same.

That speech sums up my views on the separation of church and state quite nicely, and much more eloquently than I ever would have been able to do. Religion can inform your morality and your decision making, but the national interest should come before religious interest.

The United States should, in short, be a nation where every religion is welcome, but where none is granted status or favor above another. That is what the Founding Fathers intended.

The Kennedy administration was full of bright, smart, predominately young, predominately well-educated people, so much so that it irritated some of the old-timers in Washington. Rayburn, for instance, is said to have quipped that he'd have felt a lot better about these bright young things if "just one of them had run for sheriff once."

John Kennedy's administration was full of tremendous promise and hope. Yes, it had some fantastic missteps, like the catastrophically stupid Bay of Pigs, but it also had successes, like his masterful handling of the Cuban Missile Crisis.

John Fitzgerald Kennedy's thousand days ended before many

of his promises could be fulfilled, when, on November 22, 1963, in Dallas, Texas, a gunman murdered him. You never forget where you were when you heard the news; I was at our home in Washington, packing up to go on a weekend vacation with my sons.

President Kennedy's death made Vice President Lyndon Johnson the thirty-sixth president of the United States. The national outpouring of grief that followed the assassination was like nothing I'd seen since the day almost twenty years earlier, back in Fort Benning, when we learned that President Roosevelt had died.

President Johnson channeled our national grief and mourning, and Congress, into action, passing bill after bill to further the aims and ambitions of Camelot. This legislative catharsis was at the core of the Great Society. I've told you about Medicare. Now let me tell you about the Civil Rights Act of 1964. Not by taking you through the ins and outs of crafting the legislation and securing the votes. No, let me tell you how a controversial bill impacts a hard-fought reelection in a new district.

CHAPTER 10

Toward Justice

More buffoonery from a President who thinks Civil Rights fight ended in the 60s. Proud of those who #TakeAKnee in fight against injustice.

—TWEET FROM @JOHNDINGELL,
SEPTEMBER 24, 2017, 9:40 A.M.

EVERY TEN YEARS, CONGRESSIONAL DISTRICTS ARE REDRAWN after the census. In many states, it's the governors and the state legislatures who are in charge of drawing the new maps. When one party controls an entire state government, you'll invariably see gerrymandered districts intended to guarantee that party wins as many federal and state legislative seats as possible.

When Republicans gained state houses in record numbers in 2010, one of the first things they did was to redistrict themselves into dominant power across the nation. Here's a little math about how that's worked as I write this in 2018: Republicans now have total control in *twenty-five* states, while Democrats have only

eight. It's the most one-sided domination of state governments in history.

I know a little something personally about the effects of partisan redistricting. In the 1960s, the Michigan legislature tried to pit me against another Democrat, in order to pick up a seat for the GOP. The original plan would have had me running against my dear friend, and fellow Pole, Lucien Nedzi. Lawsuits were filed, and that district plan was thrown out by the courts, which found there was too large a population disparity between districts for their taste.

So, a new map was drawn. My former district was carved up and reassigned. I was forced into a primary against another Polish Democratic congressman, John Lesinski Jr. Lesinski's father was one of the three Polish congressmen Michigan sent to Washington alongside FDR in 1932. Thirty-two years later, the sons of two of those men were squaring off to keep their seats in Washington.

Running against Lesinski was like running against myself. We'd practically grown up together. Both our fathers were in Congress from Detroit. Both were Polish-Catholic Democrats. Both of us ran for our fathers' seats when they died in the 1950s.

The vast majority of the district I found myself running in was, in point of fact, Lesinski's district. This was mainly an area of Southeast Michigan called Downriver. I'd never represented the people there, but I had worked there when I was in private law practice a decade before.

There was a great big damn steak cookout at a VFW picnic one day back in '64. The organizers knew that John Lesinski and I had to be there because this was a huge affair. The primary election between the two of us loomed in ten days.

I showed up early. I had a great organization, and my staff ran around putting up big signs all over hell's half acre. I had a friend

with a donkey, and we put Dingell saddle blankets on it, and every-thing else we could find with my name on it, including a hat. We stormed that place with our campaign troops like it was a battlefield.

Lesinski arrived. "Dingell, you're talking first. I've got more years in than you."

"Lesinski, we can go in any order you want, but if you want me to go first, I'll do it."

He probably wouldn't have had me go first if he'd known my speech boiled down to "Lesinski is a wonderful guy, but he can't make a speech which can be heard or understood, and this district needs somebody who can be understood down there in Washing-ton. We need someone down in Washington who'll lead. And we need someone in Washington who's got a good voting record."

I made my speech. Lesinski's standing amid a whole bunch of my people in fancy straw Dingell hats, and in the tree above are a whole bunch of Dingell signs. The name Dingell was everywhere.

He was, to be kind, a bit flustered.

He turned to shake hands with the nearest guy, a little, round Polish steelworker with an enormous, luxurious mustache. The guy's name was Stash Bendula.

While shaking hands with Lesinski, Stash wore this angelic smile. Everyone knew Stash, so Lesinski must have felt (somewhat) at ease.

"Mr. Lesinski!"

"Yes, Stash?" Lesinski replied with an equally big grin.

"Mr. Lesinski, I hope you lose."

————————

I CAST MORE THAN TWENTY-FIVE THOUSAND VOTES WHILE I was in Congress. By far the vote I'm most proud of was in 1964,

for the Civil Rights Act. I'd voted for civil rights before, back in '57, which was the first time Congress had passed any civil rights legislation since 1875, just three years after my grandfather first set foot on American soil.

People love to tell me how courageous and proud they are of my vote back in '64. The truth is, what I did was easy. It's nice to hear, but the truth is that the only real *work* I did was walk over to the House clerk and vote yes.

The people who had the real courage were the activists on the ground facing down guns, dogs, and racist sheriffs forcing them to their knees with fire hoses. They were the ones being arrested, beaten with bullwhips, and, in some cases, murdered.

It is people like my dear friend Congressman John Lewis who deserve everlasting praise. At the time of the Civil Rights Act vote, John Lewis was the twenty-four-year-old chairman of the Student Nonviolent Coordinating Committee, the civil rights organization that was literally on the front lines of the fight. In fact, his body still bears the scars of multiple beatings, including a near fatal one on the "Bloody Sunday" march from Selma to Montgomery that left him with a fractured skull. John Lewis, my dear and beloved friend, my former colleague—he's one of the real heroes. All I had to do was vote for what I knew was right.

Yet, that single vote almost cost me my seat in Congress.

My bid for reelection in 1964 was a tough, nasty, dirty, hard-fought race. The campaign became a canary in the coal mine for civil rights. Lesinski, my opponent in the primary, was one of the only Democrats from the North to vote against the Civil Rights Act. (He voted "no" when the House passed the bill in February 1964. After filibusters in the "other body," he voted "present" when the House passed the Senate's version.)

Lesinski's opposition to the Civil Rights Act got him censured by the Michigan Democratic Party, and it cost him the support of the unions. He did, however, get the support of some of the more conservative ethnic organizations and of some white homeowners' associations.

That 1964 race was the second time I had a cross burned on my lawn. It was also when my family and I had to sell the Detroit house on Pennington Drive that I grew up in. After the redrawing of the electoral maps, it was no longer in the new district.

In 1963 and 1964, many people would lean out of windows and shout the most vulgar, appalling, hateful things at my wife and me if they saw us walking down the street. It didn't happen every day, but it was always a shock whenever it happened. These were the people I had grown up around. These were the people I thought I knew. And these were the people that I was trying to represent honorably in the Congress.

When my constituents confronted me about my vote for the Civil Rights Act, which included a provision to protect voting rights under the Fifteenth Amendment, I'd ask them, "Why is it that a white American citizen should be able to vote and a black American citizen should not?" Few ever replied.

We campaigned like every day was Election Day. One of the issues I emphasized to voters was that the district needed a representative who would do something, who would lead, and I showed I could and did. Lesinski didn't have a record he could point to in response.

Campaigns were very different in those days. There weren't polls or TV ads or messaging consultants. There wasn't a 24/7 news cycle, either. Instead, the emphasis was on going out and talking to the voters personally.

And that's what we did.

We just went and took the district away from poor, old John Lesinski. We'd ride around in a sound car, and I'd talk to people while they were fixing their roofs or watering their lawns or doing all sorts of things. If we saw a picnic or a party going on in a backyard, we'd stop and talk. I talked to one guy who was lying underneath his automobile, repairing it.

Lesinski may have already represented the district, but we had the support of the organizations that would bring volunteers to any event we held. Unions played a major role in my reelection and they were a key cog in the machinery of the civil rights movement. For instance, my friend Walter Reuther, president of the United Automobile Workers, spoke at the March on Washington for Jobs and Freedom in August 1963. That's where Dr. Martin Luther King Jr. stirred the nation's conscience with his "I Have a Dream" speech. A. Philip Randolph, the legendary civil rights leader and longtime president of the Brotherhood of Sleeping Car Porters (who had personally lobbied FDR to ban discrimination against black people who wanted to work in the defense industry during World War II), organized the march with Bayard Rustin, another labor activist and leader. And it was the United Steelworkers (like my devoted supporter Stash, in my district), the UAW, and the AFL-CIO who really carried me in that election, just as they did in every one of my campaigns, before and after the march.

One of the things my friends in organized labor warned me about was the possibility of racially targeted literature drops. That's when a campaign leaflets an electoral district with flyers damaging to the opposing party. We had folks keep an eye out for these, just in case. We called our people the Dawn Patrol. We took the name from an Errol Flynn movie that I loved as a kid.

Sure as hell, the night before the election, I got a call that a literature drop by the other side was happening in two communities, one white, the other black. The Lesinski campaign was dropping a lot of ugly material designed to enflame bigoted voters in both the white and black communities. But I knew exactly what we could do. We had a phone tree set up for Dawn Patrol, and it went into action.

All of a sudden—and this is after dark, with only hours to go before the polls opened—we had folks out gathering up the hateful literature that had been dropped on both communities. On my orders, though, they didn't throw the filth in a Dumpster, but brought it back to my campaign headquarters.

"John, what are we gonna do with this crap?"

"This is wonderful," I said, looking over the flyers they'd collected.

"Are you okay, John? This is nasty stuff."

"I was hoping they'd do this. We're going to put it back."

"Put it back?!"

"Yeah. Put it back. Only, put the stuff that's supposed to go to the white neighborhoods in the black neighborhoods, and the stuff that's supposed to go to the black neighborhoods in the white neighborhoods."

The next day, we won one of those communities by a five-to-one margin, and the other by ten to one. Someone asked me "Dingell, how come you were so close in the five-to-one community compared to the ten-to-one one next door?"

I don't think that "They didn't give us enough literature; we ran out" was the answer they were expecting.

Time healed any hard feelings between Lesinski and me. Before he died in 2005, he and I had a meeting in Washington. It was

good to see an old friend, and I took him around the whole Capitol complex.

When the good Lord called him to his final rest, I was the one who announced his passing to the House:

"I knew Congressman Lesinski personally, and as a fellow Polish American, he taught me much about what it takes to be an effective member of Congress. I served with Congressman Lesinski as a colleague and faced him as a primary opponent; I know that he served the people of the Sixteenth District with great purpose and conviction. I salute the long and full life Congressman Lesinski led and his service in this House—he was a good and able public servant who will be much missed."

And I meant every word of it. What people don't understand is that while campaigns get heated, and sometimes personal, government is where you go to bury the hatchet in order to work with people you've opposed in elections or in bruising battles over policy—often both. People are understandably cynical about heated rhetoric that gives way to fulsome praise. I understand that. Yet, in previous generations, we knew that the good of the country demanded that we find a way to do it, so we did. That's the saddest part of the state of our governmental institutions today. We don't leave politics at the chamber door. And the one thing that effective governance requires is not agreement or even friendship—it's mutual respect.

One thing that people often forget about campaigns in those days—and this was particularly true in 1964—was how much crossover there was among supporters of other campaigns. I hired some campaign people away from Lesinski, and I think he hired some of mine away from me.

Even though it was a bitter, hard-fought, at times nasty cam-

paign, our staff, volunteers, and supporters remained friends. They'd go to the bar together or catch a Tigers game. There was a time for political animosity and a time to be social.

In a more contemporary sense, it'd be as if a die-hard Bernie Sanders partisan and a staunch Hillary Clinton supporter, during the 2016 primaries, had left their respective campaign offices for the night and headed out for a cocktail or two. That sort of thing doesn't happen very often these days, but it was the rule then.

And it should be the norm again.

The tumult and turbulence of the 1964 campaign echoed the times. The 1960s were a time of enormous social change, some of it tremendously positive (the Civil Rights Act, the Voting Rights Acts, the War on Poverty) and some of it tragically negative (assassinations, race riots, and the misguided war in Vietnam).

Thankfully, that civil rights activism lives on. We see it every day in those who are protesting the Trump administration and its regressive policies. We see it in the patients, caregivers, and their families who fill the Capitol and jam the switchboards and in-boxes when Republicans attempt to repeal the Affordable Care Act and undo the progress we've made on health care reform. We see it in the activists protesting for a woman's right to choose.

We see it in the people fighting against asinine measures like voter ID or denying people the right to vote after they've served their prison sentences for crimes. The impact of these voting restrictions falls disproportionally on minority voters, who tend to vote for Democrats rather than Republicans. Why, it's almost as if Republicans wanted to improve their chances of winning an election by suppressing voters who don't vote for their candidates . . .

To those of us who were there for the Civil Rights Act of 1964 and the Voting Rights Act of 1965, today's voter ID laws represent

merely a poll tax under a new name. Poll taxes and voter ID laws both require voters to pay money to the government in order to exercise their constitutional right to vote. Like poll taxes, voter ID laws also fall disproportionately onto minority voters, particularly the elderly (who often lack driver's licenses), regardless of how long they'd been registered to vote.

Voting is the most basic right of every American. Passage of the Voting Rights Act resulted in our taking serious steps toward abating the problems black citizens had experienced since Reconstruction. I think everybody now recognizes that such efforts did, in fact, save the country. However, the expanded franchise has been under almost constant attack in the courts and, sadly, in Congress, by Republicans angry about whom folks are voting for. Their shameful efforts to gut the Voting Rights Act seek nothing less than the restoration of an unfair America.

And as for Republicans' claims of voter fraud: in-person voter fraud in the United States is rarer than hen's teeth. Their voter ID laws are a solution to a problem that does not exist.

Still, we see the activist spirit of the 1960s living on in all those fighting for equality in any form. We see it as people fight for equal pay. When you get to be my age, few things shock you anymore. But the fact that men still earn more than women for performing the same job shocks me. Yes, we tried several times, including with the Equal Rights Amendment, which, I admit, I was initially wrongly against. We need to pay men and women, regardless of age, regardless of race, equally for the same job. It's the right thing to do, *and* it would generate far more economic benefits for the lower and middle classes than that boondoggle of a tax bill the Republicans rammed through Congress late in 2017.

We see the spirit of the activists of the civil rights era also in

the continued fight for gay rights and equality, in those fighting to affirm the rights of people to be who they are and love who they love, free from fear of discrimination.

Before I announced my support for gay marriage, I'd given it a lot of thought. I was catching up one day with an old, dear friend who I'd known for decades. Although we'd never discussed it, I'd also been aware for years that he was gay. He asked me about my thoughts on gay marriage, and when I told him I was still thinking the issue over, he started to cry.

With tears in his eyes, he said, "John, do you think I've chosen to be like this after all I went through?"

It was only then that I truly understood that this, too, was a civil rights issue. And I was well into my eighties. The next day I announced my support for gay marriage.

We see that same civil rights spirit in the people fighting for immigration rights and immigration reform. Immigration is something that, as I've shown, my family knows a little something about firsthand.

When my Dzieglewicz forebears came to the United States, they didn't speak the language. They didn't have advanced degrees or fancy skills. They, like most of the immigrants of their time, were simple farmers looking for a better life for themselves, their families, and their descendants. They had quite a lot in common with the farmworkers from Central and South America who crossed the border in search of a better life doing work that, frankly, none of the white people in the United States want to do (or wouldn't do for the pay offered).

The entire question of who gets to come to America is deeply personal to me. Under some of the theories being proposed by those opposed to immigration, it's possible that my ancestors, and

likely the ancestors of many of the people proposing such changes, wouldn't have been allowed off the boat in the first place.

The philosophy that "I've got mine, so screw the rest of you" has always struck me as fundamentally wrong, as fundamentally not American. We are a nation of immigrants. With the exception of our Native American brethren, who have been subjected to cruel, vicious ill-treatment by the government, everyone is from somewhere else. It doesn't matter if your family came over on the *Mayflower* or on a rickety tug like the *Celestial Empire*—your ancestors came here from somewhere else.

Immigration is at the core of who we are as Americans—the idea of the city upon a hill as a beacon to others, the notion that the streets are paved with gold and that anyone can pull themselves up by their bootstraps.

We shouldn't be building walls to keep immigrants out; we should be welcoming those who wish to leave their homelands and find their American dream. We shouldn't deport the Dreamers; we should legalize them and their parents—which is what President Reagan and we in the Congress did with the Immigration Reform and Control Act of 1986. That law gave legal status to something like three million people.

What all these activists have in common, whether they are advocating for immigrants or voting rights, for equal pay or for equal treatment, is a deep respect for the ideals of America, the notion that "all men are created equal" and that "equal justice under law" is more than words etched into the side of the Supreme Court Building. These activists share the notion that America must live up to the better angels of her nature.

───────────

CHAPTER 11

"We Borrow This Land"

Happy 100th to @NatlParkService and thank you for providing me
with the job of a lifetime as a ranger 70+ years ago.

—TWEET FROM @JOHNDINGELL,

AUGUST 25, 2016, 5:15 P.M.

MR. DINGELL: Mr. Speaker, I am very much interested in the
bill before the House. As a sportsman and fisherman and
out-of-doors man, I have been trying to do everything I
could to bring about a restoration of the purity of the
streams, the lakes, and the rivers of this country.

About four years ago I had a long discussion with the
president, and it was as a result of our understanding that
I introduced a resolution here which was the basis of a na-
tionwide investigation. . . . [T]hat report constituted the
basis of this legislation. I should like to see a stronger, restrictive, and a more specific bill brought into the House

today, but since that cannot be had at this time, I am, of course, willing to compromise, because I consider this bill to be a step in the right direction.

For perhaps sixty or seventy years . . . industry has assumed as a matter of right not only to take the pure water of our streams and lakes but to pollute and destroy the wholesomeness of these bodies by dumping industrial refuse into these lakes and streams and rivers. . . . I insist that these are God-given resources, to be enjoyed by all, and within restrictive limitations by certain special interests; I want these lakes and rivers and streams to be enjoyed by sportsmen and outdoors people today, and I want them to be enjoyed in later years after I have gone on by my children and my children's children; but unless there is a limitation, a very specific, a very definite circumscription in the law to prevent these vicious abuses, the beauty and the utility of our waters will be destroyed forever. Industries will not conform to the latest and newest idea about the elimination of pollution unless compelled to do so. Certainly, there will always be enough of them who will not, to defeat our objective. I am sorry that I must assume an attitude so uncompromising and forceful, but I think I am obliged to place the blame as I see it and as I know it to be.

[Claude Parsons, a Democrat from Illinois, asks for recognition to speak.]

MR. PARSONS: Mr. Speaker, will the gentleman yield?
MR. DINGELL: Yes.

MR. PARSONS: Would the gentleman be willing to accept this rather than nothing at all, to give us a start?

MR. DINGELL: To make my position clear, I think I mentioned earlier that I thought this is a step in the right direction, although the bill does not go as far as I would like to have it go, but I have made it clear that I would accept this bill as a beginning. I would like to see the bill amended in such a way that there would be a certain progressive time schedule for conforming to a carefully worked-out plan. Public sentiment will sustain severe penalties to force compliance.

The Dingell engaging in that debate was not me. It was my *father*, on the House Floor in 1940, seventy-eight years ago.

When my father thundered that "for perhaps sixty or seventy years . . . industry has assumed as a matter of right not only to take the pure water of our streams and lakes but to pollute and destroy the wholesomeness of these bodies by dumping industrial refuse into these lakes and streams and rivers," he was describing the arrogant indifference of industry toward our nation's waterways, which, for him, were a sacred trust inherited from our forebears (not to mention the Native Americans, who, shamefully, are almost always erased from modern accounts of our nation's history). My dad believed to the core of his soul that we only *borrow* the waters, the lands, and the air we breathe, and that it was his moral duty to be a responsible steward of these precious gifts that are lent to each generation by the good Lord's grace.

Dad was fighting for the creation of a "Division of Water Supply and Pollution Control in the United States Public Health Service." This new agency in the Public Health Service would be legally

empowered to stop the dumping of raw sewage, industrial waste, and other contaminants into our lakes, streams, and rivers.

Think about this for a moment. In February 1940, my father understood the destructive impact of industrial pollution on our nation's waterways that had started in the latter part of the nineteenth century. The Schuylkill River in Pennsylvania, for example, first caught fire in 1892, two years before my dad was even born. Oil from a refinery in Philadelphia leaked into the river, and some damn fool tossed a lit match into it, causing a tremendous blaze. In understanding the past, my dad also saw the future. In 1969, two major fires, one on the Cuyahoga River, which runs through Cleveland, and the other on the River Rouge, which is part of the district I represented in Congress, caused national outrage. There's no question that those incidents helped us pass the Clean Water Act of 1972.

One of my dad's great heroes was Theodore Roosevelt. When my father was reading day and night at the Union Printers Home in Colorado, the first president Roosevelt's books were among his favorites. He once confided to me that he saw something of himself in TR. Both had respiratory troubles when they were young, and both went west for their health. Teddy Roosevelt wrote, "I have always said I would not have been President had it not been for my experience in North Dakota." My dad would not have survived to serve in the House had it not been for his experiences in Colorado. Both men had a deep, abiding passion for nature and worked to preserve and protect the planet so future generations could experience what they had. Both men became conservationists because they had lived it.

From a very early age, my dad took me hunting and fishing. It was one of his great gifts to me. Spending time in nature is what

made a conservationist out of me, my father, and Teddy Roosevelt. When I became a father, I made sure my kids experienced nature the way I had. When I took those summer jobs with the Park Service in the late 1940s, my dad told me how envious he was that I'd be getting to spend so much time outdoors while he was stuck in stuffy offices and smoky committee rooms. By then, it was clear that although he desperately longed to spend time engaged in physical activity outdoors, as he had when I was younger, his body no longer permitted it.

When I entered Congress, it was only natural for me to continue that work, especially given my seat on the Merchant Marine and Fisheries Committee. That's where the heavy lifting on conservation happened. We were able to look after the air and water, to make things better for hunters, for fishermen, and for anyone else who cared for our nation's wild places.

Many people say the modern environmental movement began in 1962, when Rachel Carson published *Silent Spring*, the first widely read account of the dangers of too much pesticide use. I've been an environmentalist since long before it was cool.

As my father had before me, I worked for cleaner water. In 1961, Congress debated amendments to what's formally called the Federal Water Pollution Control Act but is better known as the Clean Water Act. Among other areas, these amendments would fund more sewage treatment plants and increase the ability of federal and state governments to work together to regulate water pollution.

It was a bill I knew well by the time it came up for a vote; my colleagues and I had worked hard to craft it so that it would have broad support.

I reminded my fellow members that:

these substances which are inserted into the waters of our land today are not the substances which we know or understand or, indeed, of which we have any understanding of proper and adequate treatment for removal. . . . Rather, these substances are not only often in their own right toxic but they may even permit the waters to harbor other toxic matters to the point where they cannot be purified so that they may serve as useful, decent water for our people to drink.

The bill passed the House and the Senate vote with wide bipartisan majorities. President Kennedy signed it into law, noting "the preservation of the quality of our water supply, adequate to satisfy the needs for all legitimate uses, is of vital importance." I continued to lead the fight for cleaner water, including the landmark Clean Water Act of 1972 and all the clean water legislation that came after it during my tenure in Congress.

The problem then is the problem now: people who do not care about the damage their actions do to the planet or what state they'll leave things in for future generations. We do not own this planet. We inherited it from the past and are borrowing it from the future.

I served on the Merchant Marine and Fisheries Committee for the next twenty years, ultimately chairing its Subcommittee on Fisheries and Wildlife Conservation. But I was really quite astonished that the most ambitious environmental legislation ever passed by Congress was championed by one of the least regarded presidents.

On January 22, 1970, my jaw dropped as I heard the following words in the president's State of the Union address:

We can no longer afford to consider air and water common property, free to be abused by anyone without regard to the

consequences. Instead, we should begin now to treat them as scarce resources, which we are no more free to contaminate than we are free to throw garbage into our neighbor's yard.

This requires comprehensive new regulations. It also requires that, to the extent possible, the price of goods should be made to include the costs of producing and disposing of them without damage to the environment.

My astonishment, as I elbowed my best friend, Congressman John Moss, was that these words were being spoken by Richard M. Nixon.

When he was inaugurated in 1969, Moss and I made a bet about how long Nixon would last in office. One of us—I'd like to say it was me, but my guess is that it was more likely the prescient John Moss—wagered that in five years Nixon would be out of office due to a scandal of his own making. When I bought Moss lunch in 1973, just as the Watergate scandal was breaking wide open, we looked at each other and just shook our heads. Bad as we knew he was, we were still amazed at how crooked Nixon turned out to have been. Unfortunately, by today's standards, he would be nominated for sainthood.

Today, Nixon is remembered for his misdeeds. Yet fairness demands that we remember his good deeds, too. Who would have guessed that the most sweeping environmental programs proposed since Teddy Roosevelt would be put forward by Richard Nixon? Nixon championed the Environmental Protection Agency and a host of clean air and clean water legislation, including the Clean Air Act of 1970.

Yet, for all the good that Nixon was doing for the environment, he was also expanding the war in Vietnam by unilaterally ordering the bombing of Cambodia, without informing Congress. In March

1970, after those bombing raids had become public knowledge, I strongly opposed them. A year later, I came out against the Vietnam War entirely. Looking back, of all the votes I cast in fifty-nine years, the one I most regret was in support of the 1964 Gulf of Tonkin Resolution that led to massive escalation of America's involvement in that misbegotten war. I remember walking over to the floor to vote and being uncertain, but after the debate, I believed President Johnson was making the right decision for our country, so I gave him my support. Lyndon Johnson did great things as president, but this was his greatest failure. His judgment about Vietnam was just plain wrong and so was mine. To the hundreds of thousands of families who lost loved ones in Vietnam, on both sides, my regrets aren't worth a damn. I can only tell you that when it came time to make a similar decision about the war in Iraq in 2002, I wasn't about to make the same mistake again.

Bad people do good things, and good people do bad things. Differences on one policy do not require differences on *all* policies. So, despite opposing him on Vietnam, I still worked with Nixon on the environment.

Looking for the good in everyone makes it possible to find allies in the strangest places. In his 1971 State of the Union address, exactly a year after his 1970 speech, this same Republican president told Congress that he wanted to:

[C]ontinue the effort so dramatically begun last year: to restore and enhance our natural environment.

Building on the foundation laid in the thirty-seven-point program that I submitted to Congress last year, I will propose a strong new set of initiatives to clean up our air and water, to combat noise, and to preserve and restore our surroundings.

I will propose programs to make better use of our land, to encourage a balanced national growth—growth that will revitalize our rural heartland and enhance the quality of life in America.

And not only to meet today's needs but to anticipate those of tomorrow, I will put forward the most extensive program ever proposed by a president of the United States to expand the nation's parks, recreation areas, open spaces, in a way that truly brings parks to the people where the people are. For only if we leave a legacy of parks will the next generation have parks to enjoy.

Nixon called on Congress to pass new laws and regulations on the environment. And that's just what we did. We passed laws to ensure cleaner air and cleaner water, to ensure the safety of endangered and threatened species. For years, I've told the story of how I wrote portions of the Endangered Species Act in my head when I'd drive to and from the Capitol complex every day, but a whole litany of scientists, lawyers, clerks, analysts, and others wrote far more of it than I did.

Far too many species were threatened then. Decades earlier, Teddy Roosevelt noted that "the extermination of the buffalo has been a veritable tragedy of the animal world." There was a time when 20 to 30 million bison roamed North America. By 1889, habitat loss and unregulated hunting reduced that number to barely a thousand. Thanks to concerted efforts to protect them from extinction, there are now nearly half a million of those majestic beasts thriving again on our continent.

Passing the Endangered Species Act, as with many of the other pieces of environmental law we passed in the early 1970s, was not a

partisan process. It was a genuine meeting of the minds that led to building a constructive consensus. It was not just liberals (a word we let those right-wing bastards demonize) versus reluctant conservatives. Rather, we liberals came together with conservatives who understood that "conserve" is the core concept of both conservation and conservatism. Today, small "c" conservatives are not even on the Endangered Species List; they're extinct.

The House voted for a version of the bill in September 1973, and I was tasked with seeing it through to final passage. In legislative parlance, I was "running the floor." It's a job that requires skill, strategy, knowledge of the rules, and the ability to make sure you have the votes to win. Ensuring you have all your votes locked down is like herding buffalo—you round them up, determine if you've got the number you need, and look out for those stragglers on the edges. It's the ones on the edges that the wolves go after.

A reasonably bright herding dog could have run the floor on the Endangered Species Act without any change in the result.

The bill passed the House and the Senate with a huge, bipartisan majority. Though the results looked lopsided, we had passed it on the backs of years of hard work and compromise, meetings and analysis, disagreements and agreements.

Since we passed the Endangered Species Act of 1973, I have heard many criticisms. From those who have offered concrete suggestions for how to improve the bill, I learned much and worked to enact improvements whenever possible, giving them credit where credit was due. When many initially denounced the law as federal overreach, I called them out publicly:

"The Endangered Species Act does not preempt the States from enacting endangered species legislation. Rather, it declares a na-

tional policy that endangered species should be protected, and it prescribes what amounts to a federal floor to regulate the taking of such species. The states are free (just as they are now) to adopt stricter rules except to the extent that these contravene specific federal permits or prohibitions, and to enforce these."

The Congress did not intend for the Endangered Species Act to be the ceiling of endangered species policy in the United States; we intended it to be the floor. Should states want to enact stricter legislation, we felt that this was their right, but the minimum standard for the United States as a whole should be the national minimum standard, not a Michigan minimum versus a Texas minimum, a California minimum versus a Maine minimum.

Objecting to the federal government setting a minimum national standard is a time-honored complaint. One of the reasons, however, that the Articles of Confederation failed (and the Constitution was written) was their lack of national oversight for matters that transcended state borders.

The Endangered Species Act is now itself endangered because the very idea of protecting species from extinction has become yet another political issue. The Environmental Protection Agency and the White House are now run by people who seek to dismantle environmental protections so businesses can exploit the nation's resources in their further pursuit of the almighty dollar. The norms that allowed us to achieve broad, bipartisan consensus are gone. And this is not just bad public policy. The consequences of what we are seeing now could last for generations, if not for the duration of all life on this planet.

One piece of environmental legislation that afforded me an opportunity to work closely with a friend in the other chamber

was the National Environmental Policy Act, or NEPA, on which I worked with my friend Senator Henry "Scoop" Jackson, an influential Democrat from Washington State. The most important principle of the NEPA proposal was that the federal government would have to include environmental concerns in all of its decision-making processes.

NEPA and the Endangered Species Act were passed because we used the legislative process (what is often referred to as "regular order") to build broad, bipartisan support for passage. We gathered the facts and were patient while experts reviewed them. At every opportunity, we shared credit with our colleagues, especially colleagues from across the aisle. In life and in legislation, you can achieve anything if you don't mind letting the other fellow take the credit for it. Scoop was contemplating a run for president in 1972; I encouraged him to take credit for NEPA. He deserved it. As for me, I didn't care. I was always proud to have the reputation of being a workhorse, not a show horse.

The process of passing legislation takes time—far more time than most people realize. Frankly, it takes far more time than I'd like it to. But haste makes waste—or, in this case, piss-poor legislation with more holes in it than a moth-eaten sweater.

Some years later, I introduced a package of bipartisan clean air amendments to the law, which passed the House by a vote of 401 to 21. It took fourteen hours of work to pass the thing. Many of my colleagues came up to me after the vote. They couldn't believe what they'd just seen. "Dingell, how in the world did you manage to get all that done in only fourteen hours?" I chuckled at their incredulity. "You're half right. It took me only fourteen hours to get those amendments passed on the floor. But it took me fourteen *years* to do the spadework that made it possible."

The 1973 oil crisis had a major, negative impact on the American economy. Oil and gas were in short supply in the United States; prices spiked. Gas stations were forced to ration gas; some of them ran out. In Congress, we were looking for solutions above and beyond the price controls and other things we'd tried that weren't cutting the mustard. The people at home demanded that we solve this mess. I was leading Democratic efforts on energy policy in the House then, and a New Yorker named Frank Zarb ran the Federal Energy Administration and was Jerry Ford's point man on the issue.

Frank had a full head of dark hair. (By then, I was starting to lose mine, and I found myself noticing anytime some son of a bitch who was my age still had all his hair.) He smoked a pipe, and had large eyes that seemed too big for his face. Frank favored dark pin-striped suits with wide lapels and patterned ties, the now cringe-worthy style of the 1970s. And I can barely even look at pictures of so many of my staff and colleagues with long, scraggly mutton-chops without bursting into laughter.

Frank and I were bitter enemies, and we fought like dogs and cats. Zarb wanted to remove price controls; I didn't. He had his positions and I had mine. Modesty precludes me from saying which one of us was right most often.

At one point, Frank had his people delivering press statements giving me hell. I had someone take our prepared answer and go down and start passing it out to the same reporters. The press then had two statements, and this effectively killed Zarb's story.

"Dingell, why the hell did you do that to me and put out that statement?"

"Zarb, you didn't think I was gonna let you *win*, did you?"

When Zarb came to the Hill, I always knew when he was approaching. It was impossible not to hear the loud *tap, tap, tap* of his

wedding ring as he banged it along the corridor on his way to my office. Then there'd be a booming knock on my private door, like the noise a baseball makes when it hits the sweet spot on the bat.

"Zarb! Stop denting the walls and get your ass in here."

There was a fairly hushed-up scandal in the Federal Energy Administration. One of the leaders in the Atlanta office was found to have taken all manner of favors from an oil and gas dealer. In exchange for a sweetheart deal on a used car, trips, and the use of an apartment owned by the oil dealer—the FEA official used the apartment for trysts with his mistress—the FEA man saw to it that the oil and gas dealer had oil and gas to deal, rationing be damned. The two men cooked up schemes to justify the extra allotments, including creating gas stations that existed on paper but not in reality.

The schemes and crooked dealings were eventually brought to light, and the FEA man got a slap on the wrist: a reprimand and reassignment. Zarb managed to keep the whole thing out of the papers. One of my investigators found out; I think it was a brilliant investigator named Michael Kitzmiller. (Life is filled with loss; Michael's is one I still mourn deeply.)

When he came before my subcommittee, Zarb found out that *I* knew what he knew. I let him and his agency have it. After I built up a good head of steam tearing into him and his office, he looked at me and simply said, "Well, Mr. Chairman, it looks like we really screwed up."

That wasn't the answer I was expecting. Hell, I had been prepared for a fight. Damn it, I'd been looking *forward* to another fight and to raking the man over the coals. But you can't do that when he admits he was wrong.

"Are you going to sit there and try to wrap yourself in the

truth?" That was the best I could come up with, though it did make the room erupt with laughter.

That day, my relationship with Frank Zarb changed. I invited him into my office after the hearing—only, this time, I meant to be friendly.

"We need to find a way to make this work."

"A compromise?"

"Yeah."

"How are we going to compromise?"

"I'll be damned if I know."

"I don't know that, either, but I'd say we will both know it when it comes."

"Compromise," Zarb's boss and my friend Jerry Ford used to say, "is the oil that makes governments go."

I'd be a bald-headed liar if I said that night we found the perfect compromise and ended the oil crisis by morning. We didn't. But what we did do was start to trust and understand one another. It's through trust and understanding that you can build consensus and cooperation. When you realize the other person has the same goal, you can start to find a path there together.

Zarb and I came to work together very closely and very well after that.

Even when we were friends, though, we'd bicker through the printed word. For example, one time his FEA put out a whole series of pamphlets for all ages (including coloring books) that pushed the Ford administration's positions and made Congress look like the bad guys. One of them was an elaborate fable about an unnamed nation and how the "First Citizen" and his efforts to reform energy were held up by delays in "the Assembly." My old friend Frank

swears it's a fable and a storytelling device to increase public awareness of the issue. And if you believe that, I've got a bridge for sale in Brooklyn I'll give you a good price on . . .

The administration—any administration—may have been able to publish such propaganda, but Congress holds the power of the purse. The flow of such documents dried up once I threatened to make sure that we in Congress would take a chainsaw to the FEA's public relations budget.

Frank used to come down to my office on the Hill and confide in me about the latest treacherous things the right-wingers were doing to undermine Ford's chances to be renominated in 1980. The bitter battle for the 1976 Republican presidential nomination, a fight that Ronald Reagan had come so close to winning, still chafed the asses of the Reagan crowd. And we now know that Zarb was absolutely right. The Reagan government-in-waiting did, in fact, sandbag Ford's presidency at every opportunity in order to get him out of their way. Jerry deserved far better than that.

As part of his efforts to heal our nation after Watergate and Vietnam, Jerry had given "a full, free and absolute" pardon to Richard Nixon for any and all crimes he may have committed prior to his resignation (turns out it was a long list). At the time, I thought it was one of the worst actions ever taken by an American president. Now I see it for what it was: the most courageous political act of the twentieth century.

Ford knew his pardon of Nixon would hurt his own election chances in 1976. He also knew the nation needed it in order to heal from Watergate and move on. Jerry Ford lost a squeaker of an election to Jimmy Carter in 1976. If there'd been two or three more days, Ford would have gotten enough votes in Ohio and Hawaii to swing the Electoral College in his favor, despite losing the popular vote.

Jerry told me years later that his biggest frustration was that just when he thought he had mastered the job as president, he lost it. There's some truth to that. He was able to work with the Democrats and the Republicans. In point of fact, he likely worked better with me and my Democratic colleagues than with the members of his own party. They liked nothing better than to knife him in the most underhanded ways because winning was more important to them than acting in the public's interest. (Knaves like Roger Ailes, Lee Atwater, and even Karl Rove seem like patriots compared to the gang of thugs and scoundrels that have now succeeded them. As I said on the Twitter about Trump's "Truth Isn't Truth" crazy hatchet man: "If you've ever wondered what ghouls and goblins do to keep busy on the 364 days a year that aren't Halloween, here's Rudy Giuliani all over your television set" [at least until he gets canceled due to poor ratings from his audience of one].)

When Zarb made his last appearance before my subcommittee after the 1976 election, he and Commerce Secretary Elliot Richardson gave me a gift, a board game called Energy Crisis. These moments of bipartisan levity and comity were common then, but they're all too rare now.

(Thinking about Elliot Richardson reminds me that we lack anyone with his integrity in this hyperpartisan executive branch. As Richard Nixon's attorney general during Watergate, he was ordered to fire the special prosecutor whose investigation was getting far too close for Nixon's comfort. Instead, Richardson and his deputy resigned. If any of this sounds familiar, it should. The resulting national uproar left Nixon with the choice of resignation or impeachment. The system worked. Pray God that it will again.)

The Carter people who replaced my friend Zarb weren't worth a pinch of owl shit. Whereas Zarb used to complain to me about

the jerks in his party, now I was complaining to Zarb about the new crowd of jackasses in mine. We found it darkly funny that each of us found his own party so hard to work with, but that Zarb and I, a Republican and a Democrat, got along like a house on fire. We could get past our partisan differences to do the people's work.

I had the Devil's own time getting the Carter people to see the big picture. Like their boss, they could see every damned tree, but they couldn't see the forest. President Carter summoned me to the White House once for a discussion about auto emissions.

"John, I want to have a discussion that's both friendly and frank."

"Mr. President, I can be friendly, or I can be frank, but I can't be both."

The conversation went downhill from there. I felt President Carter had gone back on his word to me about auto emissions. (He had.) I also made it a point to tell him that his staff wasn't worth a tinker's dam. Or, as Jimmy put it in his diary, I called his staff "incompetent and rude."

But I was eventually able to see to it that energy legislation got to President Carter's desk and that it was signed. Among other things, these bills helped strengthen the regulation of oil and gas and made our vehicles more fuel efficient.

There are those who are displeased with the intersection of my environmental work and my work relative to the American auto industry. Ford, General Motors, and, as it's now called, Fiat Chrysler Automotive were all major employers in my district. Their suppliers (and their suppliers' suppliers) were also major employers, and the various foreign automakers generally all had a significant presence in my district as well. This meant that I had to factor into my decision making the needs of the voters and workers I represented.

It also meant that I possessed something that many of my envi-

ronmentalist critics do not have: a deep and thorough understanding of how automobile manufacturing works. When the government mandates new design or emission standards, they cannot be met overnight. It takes years to design and test a new model, to ensure that it meets not only environmental but safety standards. Then there is the time required to retool the plants and retrain the workers on any new manufacturing steps required.

In short, these things do not and cannot happen overnight. They require a relatively fixed yet finite amount of time. As I once said to a Speaker who asked a bill to be ready for a vote in the full House in a certain number of days, "I can't make a baby in four and a half months by getting two girls pregnant at the same time."

I knew full well the time it would take for automobile companies to make the changes they'd need to make to achieve the various new standards we in Congress mandated. Part of my job as a member of Congress was to fight for the needs of my district. So many of the jobs in my (now former) district depended on automobile manufacturing, whether directly or indirectly.

By ensuring the companies had the time they needed to produce the new models and new innovations required under any improved fuel economy standards, I was ensuring that the people of my district, the people who'd sent me to Congress to fight for them, had someone looking out for their economic well-being.

———

AFTER THE BATTLES WE HAD IN THE EARLY FORD ERA, IT probably wasn't my wisest move to show up unannounced on Zarb's doorstep with a rifle and ammo. His wife, Pat, didn't know we were friends; she thought I was there for ill purposes. But Frank was my friend, and I wanted to take my friend out into the wild

places and help him clear his mind as he prepared to enter a new phase of his professional life. Turns out, he took to hunting like a duck to water.

He and I would hunt elk in Wyoming every year for two decades.

But Zarb wasn't the only bipartisan buddy I took hunting, a habit I began in earnest during the Carter era. Secretary of State (among other duties) James Baker hunted with me for years, as did my good friend Senator Alan Simpson (R-WY). We'd hunt deer, moose, boar, rabbits, duck, geese, woodchuck, bears—whatever was in season, we'd hunt it. Hunting was more than a way to relax and be in nature; it was also a way to form a bond between me and a number of friends and colleagues from the other party. We may have had political differences, but they weren't personal.

When you have close social relations with someone, it's damned difficult to hate him as a person. Oh sure, I've had policy differences with all three—and I think Baker did more than anyone else to see that the Supreme Court made George W. Bush the forty-third president rather than Al Gore—but it was never personal. We were friends before our political differences, during, and after.

And if these old Polish bones of mine had one more hunt in them, well, Alan, Jim, Frank, and I would be in the woods somewhere, just waiting to see if we were lucky enough to get a clean shot.

Those three are my dear, beloved friends, and they're among my favorite Republicans.

But they're not my favorite Republican. No, my favorite Republican is an ex-Republican. But she hasn't *been* a Republican since shortly after we got married . . .

CHAPTER 12

The Lovely Deborah

Visiting the lovely Deborah at work today and it appears this place
is still standing and getting by without me. Good on them.

—TWEET FROM @JOHNDINGELL,

JANUARY 12, 2015, 3:45 P.M.

"THE LOVELY DEBORAH," "THE SAWED-OFF BLONDE," "THE
Blonde Whirlwind," "Congresswoman"—I call Debbie Dingell all
those things and more. But the greatest joy of my life is that I am
also able to call her my wife and my best friend.

We first met on a plane from Washington to Detroit in 1977.
It was a rough, turbulent ride, the sort of flight that puts even the
most seasoned travelers on edge, but Debbie was having a particularly tough time. She was a very pretty, young GM executive, and I
was a bespectacled, thick-necked, middle-aged House subcommittee chairman.

I've never thought of myself as a particularly charming man;
bullshit is something I've never had any patience for, so words

like *gruff* or *quick-tempered* were the adjectives most often used to describe me back then. I never gave two shits about what people thought about me.

But when I looked over at the ashen-faced young woman sitting next to me, her hands tightly gripping the arm rests, I introduced myself and, to my surprise, found that I was easily able to make small talk with *her*. What the hell, no sense denying it, I was *flirting* with her. She was gorgeous and I was single. And she seemed genuinely comforted by my attention.

Wait, Debbie has something to say:

I was nearly in tears due to the turbulence of the flight. Then, the man sitting next to me introduced himself. As if I didn't know who he was from the moment he sat down. I was terrified of John Dingell. He was a towering, large man with an ability to ask a question that could literally destroy someone's career. His intense demeanor when he was going after someone could make you shake. And he was a Democrat, and I was—then—a Republican.

But, that wasn't the John Dingell I encountered. He was kind and concerned.

Right from the start, she was honest and direct, two qualities that earned my respect immediately, neither of which she has ever lost. She was candid about her great fear of flying, yet still able to warmly express her gratitude for my attempt to distract her from the misery of that awful trip.

We kept in touch socially, and every so often, when I'd see her around Washington, I'd ask her out. She'd always respond with a friendly "No, I don't think so," and we'd move on. That happened *fifteen* times, because I was nothing if not persistent.

John is making himself sound like some sort of a creep, which was not the case. He was always a gentleman about it. We'd see each other

at a function or a party, and he'd ask if I wanted to have lunch or go to dinner and see a movie. It was never aggressive or untoward, and it wasn't every time he saw me.

We were in many of the same social circles in Washington, so we ran into each other a lot, in addition to the times when we'd see each other on the Hill. He'd ask me out every three to four months. After the second or third time, we both knew I was going to say no, but he'd continue to ask me anyway, always with a twinkle in his eye. As he would tell me later, he wanted to be certain that I knew that if things ever changed, he wanted a chance, as he put it, "to court me."

Finally, I had the bright idea to ask one of our mutual acquaintances to let me know if there was ever something Debbie really wanted to attend.

Then, in the late spring of 1980, my source called me.

"Dingell!"

"Yes?"

"Debbie wants to see *Giselle* when it's in DC in June, but it's sold out."

"I'll find some."

"You like the ballet?"

"I do."

Whenever I tell this story, people always seem surprised to find out that I'm a ballet fan. I love the music and the precise grace of the dancers; the ease with which they make the impossible become possible; and the athletic skill, rigorous discipline, and talent it takes to make it all look effortless. Hell, it's like football, except with beautiful women and great orchestras.

However, my memories of that June night are of the stunning woman who sat next to me and of the weather. It was the sort of gorgeous summer night that's perfect for romance. I can't tell you

a damned thing about the ballet itself. It wasn't important. All that mattered was watching her blue eyes, wide with delight.

John, for the record, the ballet was incredible, even if you weren't paying any attention to it. I know that you weren't, because at intermission I distinctly heard you humming "I Only Have Eyes for You." It wasn't part of the score.

Long before I met John, my first professional job after college was working for a legislator, Senator Robert Griffin, a moderate Republican from Michigan (yes, there used to be moderate Republicans). After I left Senator Griffin's office, I went to work for General Motors. I have something of a family tie to GM; my grandfather Howard Fisher was one of the Fisher brothers whose company built automobile bodies for them. I spent nearly thirty years first in public affairs at GM and, subsequently, as the president of its philanthropic foundation.

John was significantly older than I was. He was divorced, and I was a young Catholic woman who went to Mass every Sunday and had dinner with about ten Jesuits every Friday night. Dating John Dingell just didn't seem like a good idea.

For a long time, I was cautious. We would go out only every couple of weeks, so sometimes it would be a month before I would see him again.

Over time, we were becoming closer friends, but it was not at all clear to me that it would ever lead to anything more. Because we were both Jesuit trained, our dinner conversations almost always turned into thoughtful discussions about a wide range of issues and ideas.

Remember, up until college, I'd only gone to school with other boys. Now, here I was, a middle-aged man, getting to know a brilliant, independent young woman who was born into an era that was completely different from the one that shaped my view of women.

If any man came into her life, he would have to measure up to

her expectations, not the other way around. This was eye-opening for me.

John's right. I always intended to have my own career and I didn't want to be in anyone else's shadow, which is why I was so reluctant to be seriously involved with someone in politics, especially someone so much older than me. It took me a while to realize that as big as his shadow is, he doesn't use it to block out the light of the people around him. He's always supported my career choices. Although it is true that I grew up in a different era for women than he did, he's now also seen, in a very personal way, the obstacles that women face in their professional lives.

I remember how angry he was when I told him a story about something that happened to me on one of my first job interviews, years before we'd even met. I was applying for a public affairs position (which I would eventually get) at GM, and the first question I was asked was, "Why would a woman want to work at General Motors?"

I was applying to work in public affairs at GM. I knew if I told the man who was interviewing me, "My grandfather helped build this company into the giant that it is, you sexist pig," I'd never have gotten the job.

I was working so hard not to lose my composure and just storm out, that I honestly don't remember how I responded to his blatant sexism. I probably mumbled some cliché like "Because I've always loved the American auto industry, and General Motors has always been my favorite automobile company." It was a demeaning experience that, to this day, informs my understanding of the difficulties that all women face in the workplace.

On a Saturday afternoon, not long after we started going out, Debbie was outside her home in Washington, DC, and she was mugged. She fought back and somehow got away. A trip to the

Emergency Room revealed that Debbie's cheekbone had been shattered in the attack causing her to suffer from chronic sinus and dental troubles ever since.

I was really shaken when I was mugged, and very, very lucky to have survived. But it wasn't over. During the attack, the mugger had managed to steal my keys before I could break free. So, of course, I had all the locks changed right away. A week later, just as my anxiety was finally starting to fade and life was beginning to feel normal again, I came home and discovered that my back door had been smashed in, as if someone had literally taken an ax to it. Obviously, it was the man who'd stolen my keys—and he was angry when he discovered they no longer worked. Now I was completely petrified. Would he come back? Instinctively, I called John. He said, "I'm on my way." A few minutes later, he arrived with another one of our friends. They each had wooden planks and hammers. John took out a box of nails and they quickly sealed up the back door. Then, after our friend left, John sat down on a chair in the living room with a pistol in his lap. From the steely look in his eyes, I knew that he would stay there until he was certain that I was safe. Which is precisely what he did. I sat across from him on the couch, my legs curled up beneath me and we talked all night long. We told each other everything about our lives, down to the most personal details. He told me about his first wife. I told him about my father and my baby sister. We talked about so many things and even though I was still trembling from the week's multiple traumas, I actually found myself laughing with John.

It's true. We ended up talking all night, about our dreams and our fears, our hopes and our wants—everything that mattered. And somewhere around 3 a.m. I thought to myself, "You fool! Twice now, the good Lord has sent you a sign that He wants you to take care of her. What more do you need, a bolt of lightning?" So, just before sunrise, I kissed her good-bye and told her, "I'm going to

come back to you in about a week or ten days, and I'm going to ask you a question, and I hope you will say yes."

The question, of course, was whether Deborah Insley would agree to become Deborah Dingell. I thank God every day that she did.

Debbie and I were engaged in 1981, and we were married later that year. Both of us know how difficult political life can be on a marriage. Because we understood that right from the start, I think our marriage has endured and thrived. We've always grown together—never apart. And she's done wonders for my reputation. People tell me that she has "softened my rough edges." Darn right she has. She's got that all-too-rare combination of empathy and compassion that is essential to being a great public servant—and pretty wonderful in a spouse. It turns out the Lord's plan was not just that *I* would take care of her; *her* strength sustains me every day.

Because his instinct to protect me is so strong, there are a few rare occasions where I don't tell John something right away. A year after he and I were married, we were at a dinner at Statuary Hall in the Capitol. John was seated at one side of the big table and I was at the other. One of the other guests—I'm not naming names, but he's a historical figure—repeatedly tried to put his hand up my leg and under my skirt. A female member of Congress saw this and switched places with me. My friends all heard the story, and when this man and I were ever at the same event—well, there was always someone right next to me, just in case he tried it again.

Around the same time, one of John's colleagues from the other chamber made unwanted advances toward me. Many of my female friends witnessed it happen and, from that point forward, they always had my back. They stayed close whenever he was in the same room with me, and he was never able to try anything again.

It was years before I told John any of this—not out of shame, but out

of fear, fear that continues to this day of what would happen if I outed either of those two powerful, disgusting men. Not to mention that I don't want to see my husband arrested for murder.

And I'm not alone in being afraid of what would happen if I named names. Far too many women endure such conduct and stay silent. We, not just as a Congress but as a people, need to say, "No more." We need to create an environment where there is no tolerance for such behavior.

I love Debbie—more than the air that I breathe. I love her enough to do what is probably the hardest thing for me in any situation: keep my big Polish mouth shut about the decisions she makes about her own life, both personally and professionally. That's another reason why our love has lasted so long: because it's based on mutual respect. Even when I'm concerned about a decision she's made, I give her my unconditional support.

And that's true. He has. I can count on the fingers of one hand the number of times that John's tried to tell me what to do. Partly that's because he knows I'm just as stubborn and strong-willed as he is, and so I'd tell him exactly why he was wrong and do it anyway.

Better than anyone I've ever known, John knows the difference between telling someone what you think they should do and telling someone what to do.

John knows that by supporting me in what, as he puts it, "I'm minded to do" means that I can develop my own reputation and not just be known as "John Dingell's wife."

One invaluable lesson that I learned from being by John's side when he was in office was the need for members of Congress and their families to get to know each other socially in an effort to build ties of friendship, to have politics be partisan without that partisanship becoming personal. That's why I worked closely with Marlene Malek (whose husband, Fred, was high-up in the administrations of two Republican

presidents, Richard Nixon and George H. W. Bush) to host bipartisan lunches for women in Washington.

My fellow political spouses and I were able to use our newfound friendships to achieve many good things such as raising millions for the Children's Inn at the National Institutes of Health. Caring for sick children is a cause that's dear to my heart, and I'm tremendously proud of all the bipartisan good that we've done throughout the years, at least outside of Congress.

I think Debbie is a superb congresswoman; frankly, in many ways she's already better at the job than I ever was. Mark this down: she is going to build a national reputation as a bridge-builder, because she has a tremendous talent for bringing people together. It's a rare gift and our country is as blessed as I am for the passion she brings to everything she does.

Debbie is a great advocate of all the causes my dad and I fought for in Congress: looking out for the less fortunate, championing civil rights, preserving the environment, and especially protecting health care. Yet although she does our family name proud, she charts her own course. This is why I believe she will become a great leader in the Congress.

I've been working on health care issues since before I ever met John. I founded the National Women's Health Resource Center in the 1970s, after I found out that clinical trials in medicine were almost exclusively conducted on men. The first policy issue that John and I ever worked on after our marriage was breast cancer research.

Like John, I was educated by the Catholic Church from childhood through graduate school. The nuns instilled in me a commitment to social justice, to looking out for the less fortunate, and to what the Bible teaches us: to whom much is given, much is expected.

When I was a young teen, I was lucky (blessed, really) to hear Dr.

Martin Luther King Jr. speak at an event near my home in Michigan. This was just a few weeks before his assassination. I remember the deep resonance of his powerful voice and the profound impact his eloquence had on me—and still does to this day: "Somehow we must come to see that in this pluralistic, interrelated society we are all tied together in a single garment of destiny, caught in an inescapable network of mutuality. And by working with determination and realizing that power must be shared, I think we can solve this problem."

Working together—regardless of political views, regardless of gender, regardless of race, regardless of faith—that notion has come to define who I am as a public servant, and I think it defined my husband's service and his father's service as well.

There are a few times when Debbie and I have agreed to disagree; the issue of guns and Second Amendment rights being the most significant. In June 2016, 170 Democratic members of Congress occupied the House Chamber in memory of the 49 lives lost in the mass shooting in Orlando, Florida. They literally sat down on the floor and refused to leave it for twenty-five hours. Debbie was one of the most powerful of all the speakers. She spoke during the middle of the night, and I was sound asleep. My staff told me about it first thing the next morning, only saying that she had made a speech. They didn't tell me anything more. My aide, Freddie, put the iPad down in front of me and just hit play. And there, on the screen, was Debbie:

> I've been on the floor for twelve hours. . . . I've never actually thought I would *sit* on the floor of the House of Representatives. And it's been a tough day . . .
>
> You know, when Orlando happened . . . I sat with [Senator] Amy Klobuchar, who I am working with on a domestic abuse gun bill, and said, "It'll never change."

The number of horrific shootings—we're all going to say, "Isn't this terrible?" We'll offer our prayers, and we'll go back to normal, whatever the "normal" is we've come to accept, and wait until the next shooting.

And yet today we showed that that's not what's going to happen.

And as so many of my colleagues have talked about, we don't focus on what's happening every day. We don't focus on the daily shootings or how our young people are beginning to accept that that's just what happens. And we don't focus on what's happening and who has access.

I feel this House is torn in a way that I feel torn. I'm married to a man—you all know how much I love John Dingell. He's the most important thing in my life. And yet for thirty-five years, there's been a source of tension between the two of us. He is a responsible gun owner. He believes in the Constitution. I respect that.

I don't want to take his gun away or anybody else's gun [away]. But [growing up] I lived in a house with a man that should not have had access to a gun. I know what it's like to see a gun pointed at you and wonder if you were going to live. And I know what it's like to hide in a closet and pray to God, "Do not let anything happen to me." And we [as a country] don't talk about it. We don't want to say that it happens in all kinds of households. And we still live in a society where we will let a convicted felon, who was stalking somebody [or in a case] of domestic abuse, still own a gun.

I have a million thoughts as I sit in front of you here today. I have constituents who get labeled, who are on a "do not fly" list and [that] may not be right. [Of course] I do not want

a terrorist to have access to a gun. How can we protect someone's civil liberties if you won't come to the table and have
the discussion about how you keep us safe?!

The point of this discussion is that we've got to stop going
to our corners. We've got to stop spouting talking points. But
we've got to come and figure out how we're going to make this
nation safer. How we're not going to accept the violence that
we're seeing every day. How we're not going to let people have
access to guns that shouldn't have access to guns. And we're
not going to do it until we start to change the dialogue, until
we come to the table and we have the discussion.

So we're here on this floor tonight to say, "Enough. Is.
Enough."

It took Newtown. I wrote an op-ed. People knew I didn't like
guns. I probably said, as a child, some really stupid things (although many of you would probably agree with me on what I
said). But I know now we can't stay silent any longer. We have to
do something. I've never seen us more united than we are today.

I love my husband with my whole heart and soul. He doesn't
know I'm . . . here right now. And I love my Republican friends.
I have many. I love you all. Can't you come to the table? Can't
we have a discussion? Can't we say, "Enough is enough"? Can't
we have a vote?

As I watched my wife pour her heart out sitting on the floor of
the House, I began to think about the courage it took for Debbie
to sit down for what she thought was right, even if she thought I'd
be angry.

I thought about all the votes I'd taken, all the bills I'd supported
to protect the Second Amendment rights of gun owners. I also

thought about the times when there were exceptions I chose to make in the interest of compromise. For example, although I disagreed with the assault weapons ban in President Clinton's crime bill, I liked the rest of the legislation enough to hold my nose and vote to pass it. At that same time, I also made the decision to resign from the NRA board, writing, "I find the conflict between my responsibilities as a member of Congress and my duties as a board member of the National Rifle Association irreconcilable."

There were a few other exceptions to my strong commitment to protect the rights of law-abiding gun owners. It may surprise you to learn that in the 1970s, I introduced a series of bills trying to ban the sale of Saturday-night specials, the small, cheap pistols whose only use is violence. They were too poorly made and too inaccurate to target-shoot or hunt with, but they were, for years, the weapon of choice for street criminals.

I thought about whether the gun debate had gotten too polarized, with each side too entrenched in its own position to even *consider* talking with the other. As Debbie had said with such passion the night before, "Can't we have a *discussion*?"

And I thought about the role I know I played in contributing to that polarization.

DEBBIE'S SPEECH STARTED AT LEAST ONE DISCUSSION: AFTER turning off the iPad, it was the one that I was now having with myself. I thought about the unspeakable tragedy of twenty very young children gunned down by a mentally ill man in Newtown. I remembered how, after that horror, my old hunting buddy [former secretary of state] James Baker and I had proposed bipartisan suggestions for action on gun control in a joint opinion column in

the *New York Times*. But gridlock in DC meant that nothing had happened. And nothing had happened after the mass shootings in a movie theater in Aurora, just as nothing has happened after fifty-eight people were killed after a concert in Las Vegas last year, the largest mass killing in American history—to date.

I believe those who want to repeal the Second Amendment are as wrongheaded as those who believe everyone should have a personal grenade launcher. We need to work together to address all the causes of gun violence, from poverty to mental illness.

Those of us who hold the Second Amendment dear need to remember that its language calls for "a well-regulated militia." You can't have something be "well-regulated" without regulations. That's just logic. And that's the one weapon we never seem to employ in this debate.

Do I know what the solutions are? Honestly, I don't.

But I do know we need to work together and act. We need to find consensus and legislate from the middle, working to address not just the questions of who should or should not have this or that gun, but the larger, harder questions of what causes the problems of gun violence.

The children, our future, are calling on us to act. We owe it to them, and to the memory of those whose voices have been silenced.

I'm proud to say that Debbie is one of the members of Congress trying to find consensus and common ground for sensible gun safety legislation. And I'm glad to see that she's working on it with Republicans like my old friend [Michigan congressman] Fred Upton.

After I watched Debbie's speech, twice, and roused myself from my thoughts, Freddie told me there was a call for me and handed me my iPhone, without telling me who was on the other end.

"Who the hell is this?"

"It's your wife."

"Fox? Is that you?" I asked, using yet another one of my many nicknames for her.

"Yes, John."

"I watched your speech."

Then there was what can only be described as a pregnant pause, the sort that's accompanied by an intake of breath through gritted teeth while waiting for an explosion of rage.

"I told you when you became a member of Congress that I wanted you to be a first-class Deborah and not a second-rate John."

"You're not mad?"

"We have agreed to disagree on this."

It's true. When I told John I was going to run for his seat after he decided to retire, he told me exactly what he had told his son Christopher when he first ran for the Michigan State Senate in 1986: "I want you to be a first-class you and not a second-rate me." Both Christopher (who is now an elected circuit court judge) and I have taken that advice to heart.

Over the course of our thirty-seven-year marriage, John and I have agreed that we will disagree on certain things. Guns are the most notable, but there are others, mainly the sort of domestic differences that all couples have—important things like where to squeeze the toothpaste tube or whether brownies should have nuts.

In a coincidence that surely was *not* a coincidence, just as I was finishing up writing those last words, my young assistant, Zach, came in to tell me that breaking news had just interrupted the regular program he was watching on CNN. Seventeen people (fourteen teenagers and three teachers) had been fatally gunned down at Marjory Stoneman Douglas High School in Parkland, Florida. The shooter was a mentally ill former student armed with an AR-15–style semiautomatic rifle. I put my head down and said a quiet prayer for

their souls. When I looked up, the first thing I saw was the daily calendar that sits on my desk: February 14. Another massacre, exactly eighty-nine years to the day after the famous St. Valentine's Day Massacre ordered by Al Capone. The difference between the two shootings hit me like a brass-knuckled punch in the gut. These were not gangsters murdering other gangsters; this was a *child* mowing down other children.

In the days that followed, I watched the grief on the faces of those surviving youngsters in Florida and watched as their pain turned into anger against what had happened to their friends, to their teachers. It was impossible not to be moved by their eloquence, their passion, and, most of all, by their determination never to let it happen again. They created a slogan, #NeverAgain, that they shared with each other on the Twitter. In protest, high school students in cities and towns across the country were walking out of their classrooms. Many of them headed straight to their state capitals to call for those legislators to act now. Congress was out of session, so hundreds of DC youngsters went directly to the White House. I watched the scenes on TV. Many of them were lying down on the sidewalk as if they'd been shot. Some news announcers called it a "Die-In." But when I heard people start to chant, "Hey, hey, NRA, how many kids did you kill today?" I turned off the television in disgust. That chafed my ass. I have many great friends, good men and women all, who are not "gun nuts." They are responsible gun owners, a right guaranteed to them by our Constitution.

Later that day, Zach came over to me and asked, "Sir, can I say something?"

I put down my newspaper, folding it on my lap, and adjusted my glasses so I was focused on him, not the *New York Times*. "You have my full attention."

"Mr. Dingell," he said, his voice filled with emotion, "with all due respect, sir, my generation has been left with one hell of a mess to clean up."

I was impressed by the courage it took for him to speak up at all, since he was well aware that his opinion might not sit too well with me. Zach knew full well of my strong belief in protecting the rights guaranteed to American citizens in the Second Amendment.

Before I could respond, an image flashed through my mind. It was the look on the face of Fulton Lewis on December 8, 1941, following President Roosevelt's "Infamy" speech, when a suddenly grown-up fifteen-year-old House page quietly nodded his head, giving Lewis permission to keep recording the proceedings in the chamber, despite the fact that doing so violated all the rules. I looked Zach up and down for a long minute, one that almost certainly made him uneasy. He must have been thinking, *Have I really pissed him off?* Nonetheless, he held my gaze directly, not backing down. Strong kid. We need more like him.

Finally, I broke the silence. My tone was even; there was no annoyance in my voice, because I felt none. "There's a verse from the Book of Isaiah, 'The wolf shall dwell with the lamb: and the leopard shall lie down with the kid: the calf and the lion, and the sheep shall abide together, and a little child shall lead them.'" I smiled up at Zach, readjusted my glasses, unfolded my newspaper, and then went back to reading about the world's troubles from the comfort of my recliner.

Although Zach is not a little child—he's twenty-damned-something, but at my age, anybody under seventy is still a kid—he understood exactly what I was saying to him: that he was right to act on his beliefs. Not that we are likely to see eye to eye on how to deal with gun violence; that may never happen.

Yet, I have to admit that he *is* right about the hard fact that we old lions have surely left those kids with a shit ton of problems. Seems to me it's well past time that we get the hell out of their way and let *them* get to work on solving them. They certainly couldn't screw things up any worse than those spineless Republicans and their brainless cheerleaders at Fox News. I'm not saying we Democrats aren't blameless—we should have done a much better job of standing up for our beliefs and showing some backbone ourselves, which is exactly what these kids are doing. Agree with them or not, I have to give them credit for taking up the fight, despite the long odds against them. Fact is, they don't give a hoot in hell about the odds. That's the gift of youth. They still see the world as it should be. Doesn't matter if the deck is stacked against them right now. They know that time is on *their* side. It's from that certainty that they gain their strength and, inevitably, their power to bring about change.

"Thank you, Mr. Dingell," I heard Zach say from behind my newspaper as he went out to the kitchen to fix lunch. I heard both relief and a new resolve in his voice.

"Thank *you*, my friend. I respect what you're doing. God be with you."

Because I love John so much, it's been possible for me to understand his lifelong advocacy of Second Amendment rights from his point of view. And I like to think that having heard the stories of what I went through as a child—and what my mother and my siblings went through—has given him another perspective on the issue of guns that he wouldn't have had if he didn't love me.

There's one thing I can tell you about John Dingell that no one can dispute: he is always open to other points of view. That's why he married a Republican. Of course, he also fully intended on converting me . . . ☺

CHAPTER 13

Mr. Chairman

This is a time when proper congressional oversight is key. Sadly, the House has been taken over by a goofy gang of knaves & know-nothings.

—TWEET FROM @JOHNDINGELL,
FEBRUARY 13, 2017, 11:29 P.M.

"DO I WANT TO GIVE UP BEING IN THE CONGRESS AND RUN FOR judge back home?"

I remember sitting in my office in 1980 and having that conversation with myself. I hadn't yet filed for reelection, and I hadn't raised much money. I was in a rut, going through the motions.

"Maybe Carter would appoint me to the federal bench? Nah. The Senate would never go along with that. Too many toes stepped on over the years and too many feathers ruffled."

As a young fellow, I was working my ass off on health care, on civil rights, on the environment, on infrastructure. On any damned issue that came up, I was charging into the fray and fighting tooth

and nail. Looking back, I wish I'd picked my battles better, focused on the things that needed to be done right then and there, like civil rights. Fighting the battles that needed to be fought, not the battles that I wanted to stir up.

Knowing when the time was right to make something into an issue was a hard skill to learn. You eventually learn to watch for when the bastards are distracted and then sneak things through when they're not looking.

The phone buzzed, pulling me out of my thoughts.

"Chief? Speaker O'Neill's on the line. He wants a word."

"Oh shit," I thought. This can't be good. Speakers call subcommittee chairmen only when they need something, or when you're going to get your ass chewed out. The way my day was going, I figured I'd done something to annoy Tip. Damned if I knew what, though.

"Mr. Chairman!" Tip O'Neill's Boston Irish accent boomed through the phone. I was surprised he'd even bothered with a call. He could have opened the door and shouted down the corridor, and I'd have heard him clear across the Capitol complex. He had a booming voice, just like my dad, except O'Neill was taller and heavier and in much better health.

Wait a minute. "Mr. Chairman"? Yes, I was a subcommittee chairman, but you're called "Mr. Chairman" only during hearings. Nobody calls a subcommittee chairman "Mr. Chairman" during a call. If it were anyone else, I'd have thought he had the wrong number . . .

"Yes, Mr. Speaker?"

"I wanted you to be the first to know. Harley Staggers just told me he's retiring. That means the chairmanship of Interstate and Foreign Commerce is yours, if you want it."

It was then when everything changed. My dark mood went away; I knew I'd run again. I knew I'd raise money. I knew I'd do everything I had to do. Why? Because if we kept the House, I'd get the chance to run a full committee. I'd be able to fight even better for the things I believed in. Only problem was, I didn't know how to run a committee.

"Thank you, Mr. Speaker. I'm honored."

It's like that moment in the deer blind when a trophy buck comes into your sights. You get only one good shot. You can't miss. I wasn't going to throw away my shot.

When I decided to write a book, I grabbed a legal pad and wrote some notes about what I wanted to say. One of the first things I wrote, and proceeded to underline, was *"this book will be about oversight."*

Congress has always had oversight. Oversight is something that you do with a real focus on whether the law is being properly implemented, whether the people are being properly served, and whether public money is being properly spent. It's not something that should be political, yet, unhappily, it has become political. What passes for "oversight" from Republicans of late is nothing more than political gamesmanship. They look into what will score them votes from their base and checks from their donors—truth, justice, and the American way be damned, so long as the votes and the checks come.

Oversight defined my tenure in Congress, and I'm deeply proud of the work done by all of us on the Energy and Commerce Committee (the first thing I did when I took over as chairman was to change the name. "Energy" gave us a lot more purview, a fact that was not lost on my fellow committee chairs).

I made no secret of the fact that I worked hard to expand my

committee's domain, having staffers scrutinize every bill introduced in the House to see if it touched upon the concerns of the Energy and Commerce Committee. If it did, and if I wielded the gavel, the bill was subject to our scrutiny. That meant we played an enormous role in shaping all manner of legislation. Someone once estimated that 40 percent of the legislation in one congressional session ended up having to go through my committee; one wag said that if it "moved, burns, or is sold," then it'd end up before me. There's a lot of truth to that.

My dear and beloved friend the late John Moss was the closest friend I had in Congress in all my fifty-nine years there. He was a Democrat from Sacramento, California. We sat next to each other on the Interstate and Foreign Commerce Committee for close to twenty years, first, when Oren Harris was chairman, and then, after Harris had gone to the federal bench, during Harley Staggers's tenure.

Neither Moss nor I ever had to ask what the other thought about a topic, or how he was going to vote. We each knew instinctively what the other was thinking, how he would vote.

Moss was a very big believer in transparency and openness in government. In fact, the Freedom of Information Act was his doing.

Staggers was the chairman of the Commerce Committee from 1966 to 1981; Moss and I were, quite frankly, the power behind the throne. I was usually the one Staggers went to when he needed the answer to a rules question, and Moss was the ideas and strategy go-to guy.

I'd always hoped Moss would eventually become Chairman Moss. If he had, I'd have been his deputy, responsible for keeping his enemies off his back, picking them off one by one, the way you take ticks off a dog. That would have made me enormously happy.

A good man, and a good friend, would have been in charge, and I'd have been able to fight the battles he couldn't be seen to fight. We'd have had a blast doing so, too.

Then, in 1978, my good friend John Moss didn't run for reelection. When Moss retired, I was widely seen as the number two man on the committee, the heir apparent should Staggers ever step aside.

My father was still the second-most senior member of the Ways and Means Committee when he died, so this was one of those times when I couldn't rely on what my dad had done, because he'd never done this.

So, I did what all smart members of leadership do when they don't know what to do: I went to see the House parliamentarian, William Holmes Brown. One of the most important roles on my staff was being the liaison with the parliamentarian. He let us know what we could and couldn't do. And that's how I got my reputation as one of the best interpreters of the rules and procedures of the House; I had a direct line to the arbiter, the ultimate arbitrator of the rules of the House.

"I'm going to be chairman of the damned committee," I told Brown. "How am I going to do the job I have to do?"

"John, there are two things you've got to do."

I've never forgotten this piece of advice. It changed everything.

"One: you have to be fair. Two: you have to *appear* fair."

"How the hell do I do that?"

"You will know, and when you run into trouble, you call us."

As a committee chair, I quickly learned that I was only as successful as my staff. Over the length of my sixteen years of service as chairman of the Energy and Commerce Committee, we literally had hundreds of different people who worked as staff members.

Each and every one of them was essential to the functioning and success of the committee. We had lawyers who specialized in all manner of areas. We had investigators who'd travel far and wide to find the facts. We had extraordinary administrative staff people who kept everyone organized. Collectively, our staff made the entire committee run like a well-oiled machine.

If I were to name every staffer who ever worked for me, this book would be the size of a telephone directory. To all my former staffers, I thank you. For your goodness, for your integrity, for your loyalty. I thank you for all you did to look after our people. Blessings on all of you, and may God be with you.

Then there were my colleagues in the majority and in the minority. In the majority, we had subcommittee chairs, each tasked with overseeing their own policy areas. In the minority, there were ranking members, with smaller staffs and sometimes parallel interests to the majority.

My job as chairman was to make the whole thing work, to have the majority staff focused and working on areas I wanted them to be working on, while ensuring that relations with the minority party remained smooth.

I took the parliamentarian's advice to heart; I treated everyone fairly and appeared to be fair.

One of the photos on my office wall was a daily reminder of the sort of chairman I would *never* allow myself to be. Whenever I was seated at my desk, a photo of the former chairman of the Senate's "Committee on Witch Hunts" (officially, the Senate Permanent Subcommittee on Investigations), Joe McCarthy of Wisconsin, stared back at me. McCarthy and his chief counsel, Roy Cohn, were, without question, two of the most amoral, indecent,

hate-filled men I have ever had the misfortune of meeting. (Cohn, by the way, later became Donald Trump's first political mentor.) McCarthy's photo was there on my wall as a warning, reminding me what a bad investigator looked like and who I didn't want to be.

My dad told me that he once debated McCarthy on *American Forum of the Air*, a 1950s radio discussion show, and cleaned McCarthy's clock. The host of the program, Theodore Granik, wanted a rematch, knowing that it would bring good ratings and ad money. My dad was game for it; McCarthy refused. I wish I could find a tape of that broadcast; it'd be great fun to listen to Dad excoriate McCarthy.

Speaking of Tail Gunner Joe, I told my dad once how McCarthy was questioning the patriotism of a young second lieutenant in the army who was a friend of a friend. McCarthy was convinced the boy was disloyal simply because he had a Polish name.

My dad was madder than I'd seen him in years. "If that shanty Irish SOB ever makes a remark like that about me, I'll break his bloody neck over the back of his chair."

And people thought *my* questioning of witnesses and the letters I sent to administrative agencies were aggressive . . .

One particularly effective tool for a committee chairman was sending letters to the administration. Legally, administrations answer letters from Congress; Congress also holds the power of the purse. My letters, known as Dingellgrams, became something of a local legend on the Hill. They were long and detailed, and asked tough, probing questions. They weren't the sort of letters that could be answered with a "yes" or a "no"; they required the administration to put research and thought and effort and time into a reply. In short, they were dreaded by their recipients.

Not responding to our written inquiries or, worse, giving false or misleading testimony rarely happened. Though, early in President Reagan's tenure, it did. Anne Gorsuch (mother of Supreme Court Justice Neil Gorsuch) was Reagan's first permanent administrator of the Environmental Protection Agency. During her tenure, there was this rather hideous scandal about how the EPA was handling, or mal-handling, the Superfund program.

My committee subpoenaed the EPA for all manner of records regarding the management of that program. The Reagan administration cited administrative privilege as justification for not turning over the records we'd asked for. When Anne Gorsuch heeded President Reagan's orders and refused to turn over the documents, the full House of Representatives voted to cite her for contempt of Congress. It was the first time a Cabinet member ever faced such a charge. And the vote, I should note, was 259–105, with 55 Republicans voting to cite a Cabinet member of their own party for contempt of Congress.

Gorsuch was ultimately forced to quit, and the Reagan administration agreed to turn over the documents we'd subpoenaed. Gorsuch's subordinate in charge of the Superfund program was convicted of lying to Congress and served time in prison.

With that as an example, we found that future letters from our committee, whether sent by a Democrat or a Republican, were answered with care and concern, and administrations would cooperate to the fullest extent. Nobody wanted to be the next person forced to resign or sent to the hoosegow.

One of the main oversight roles of a committee chairman is to ask questions and seek answers. Congressional oversight is fundamentally the search for truth, no matter how painful the consequences.

One area we scrutinized heavily was defense spending. We

found that General Dynamics, for instance, was paid more than one *billion* dollars in cost overruns. The company claimed that these were legitimate defense spending items, and thus that the taxpayers should reimburse the company for them. In reality, these items, which included country club memberships and high-priced travel for executives, were to national defense the way side pockets are to a cow: absolutely useless. They were merely an effort to fill corporate coffers at taxpayer expense.

My favorite example of General Dynamics's abuses comes from a hearing we held on February 28, 1985. I personally chaired the Subcommittee on Oversight and Investigations of the Energy and Commerce Committee. That's where we could, and did, rake people over the coals when they deserved it. Not to score political points and make a spectacle of things, not to see ourselves on TV—no, we raked people over the coals to search for the truth.

In this instance, I was questioning Gordon E. MacDonald, an executive vice president at General Dynamics.

One of the first things they teach you in law school is never to ask a question you don't already know the answer to. When I was questioning MacDonald, I had all manner of receipts and invoices and memos in hand. My investigators, as always, did outstanding work, and they'd ensured that I was as prepared as possible to make sure the truth was known.

MR. DINGELL: I have been looking here at the vouchers, and the vouchers on this are signed, Mr. MacDonald, by you, I observe—rather, approved by you here at the bottom— and the first one is "Fursten boarding at Silver Maple Farm $87.25," and there's a proper receipt. It says, "Receipt received from Silver Maple Farm, $87.25." Then I further come down,

and I see here, as I go through these vouchers, it says here, at
a later one, it says, "Silver Maple Farm, boarding for Fursten,
$42." Then another one, it says, "Dog boarding, $26.25." Is
Fursten a dog?

MR. MACDONALD: I don't know what document you have,
Mr. Chairman. May I see it, and I can answer it, maybe.

MR. DINGELL: Are the taxpayers paying for dog boarding?

MR. MACDONALD: I wouldn't think so.

MR. DINGELL: Well, would you prayerfully consider the files
and give us an answer whether or not the taxpayers are
paying for dog boarding? And who is Fursten?

MR. MACDONALD: I will give you an answer right now. I will
withdraw that $100 or whatever it was or $150 right now, sir.

MR. DINGELL: What I am trying to figure out is, are the taxpayers picking up dog boarding costs?

MR. MACDONALD: No.

David Lewis, the chairman of the board at General Dynamics, was seated next to MacDonald. He chimed in, in full damage-
control mode, all righteous indignation and outrage:

MR. LEWIS: Absolutely not. They certainly should not. I don't
know that they did approve that. I have no idea.

Whether Lewis meant it or was putting on a show in the hope
that we'd go easier on General Dynamics, I don't know. In any case,
I chose to continue with my line of questioning. That they withdrew the expense did not undo the fact that the corporate policy at
General Dynamics had thought it appropriate to bill the taxpayers
for the dog boarding in the first place.

MR. DINGELL: Well, this is the expense account of Dr. and Mrs. A. M. Lovelace, and they are all submitted. They were not from my files. "Fursten" is in a document that's approved by you. It's entitled "Expense Report Employee 3891, Department No. 110, 5/14/83," and the item on the second page says, "Fursten boarding at Silver Maple Farm, $87.25." And this is while the Lovelaces were at Kiawah Island.

Then I have here, a little further on, I have an item which says, "Dog boarding, $26.25," and again, this is on an expense account which bears your signature as having approved it.

MR. MACDONALD: Yes, but you can't tell in that document, Mr. Chairman, whether or not that was excluded from our overhead claim or not. You can't tell from that document.

MR. DINGELL: This, I am told, is in the travel account.

MR. MACDONALD: That doesn't matter. The whole travel account is not necessarily in the claim.

MR. DINGELL: Okay. I'm told it was in an allowable account.

MR. MACDONALD: It may have been. I'm not sure.

One of the things that my staff used to do when a particularly grueling hearing was over was to go over to the witness table and check for wet spots on the center of the chairs. I'm not joking. On more than one occasion, they found them.

MR. DINGELL: All right. Now, here we've got another item of $42.00. It says, "Silver Maple Farm, boarding for Fursten," and this is again signed by Lovelace, and it is "Dr. and Mrs. A. M. Lovelace, 3891, Department 110, period from 11/2 to 11/6/83." Now, this is obviously a piddling matter, but I have to wonder how much we are getting in the way of

submarines from you folks, and how much we are getting
in the way of dog boarding.

MR. MACDONALD: We don't charge that stuff to the government, Mr. Chairman.

MR. DINGELL: Well, I am going to have the GAO audit that
account and give us an answer so we can find out whether
you are charging us for dog boarding or whether you're
charging us for missiles and submarines.

The GAO is what's now called the Government Accountability
Office; at the time, it was the General Accounting Office. Regardless of the name, the function is the same: they're the auditors of
the federal government, and they answer to Congress, not to the
president, not to the Cabinet, not to any of the executive agencies,
but to Congress.

One thing I do wish I'd asked was "What kind of dog is Fursten?"
I never did find out. I wish I'd asked for a photo, too. I've always
liked dogs, and a photo of one is good to brighten up your day. (My
son Christopher and his wife, Cindy, give us photos of their dogs
every year at Christmas; they'd end up in one of our offices or here
at home in Michigan.)

The boarding of Fursten was just a small part of the improper
expenses we found. General Dynamics had also billed the government $18,650 for an executive's initiation into a local country
club. They'd billed the government almost $90,000 for a corporate
retreat at a South Carolina resort; and Fursten was once boarded
at taxpayer expense so his owners could go on a taxpayer-funded
retreat.

But General Dynamics wasn't the only defense contractor overcharging the taxpayer. Lockheed charged the Department of Defense

$640 apiece for toilet seat covers and $317 for what was effectively a plastic bucket to contain waste in a military aircraft's toilet. My investigators noted that the parts were effectively ones that could have been purchased from a hardware store at a fraction of the cost.

The same plane that needed the $317 waste bucket also had engine mountings that the analysts whom my staff and I consulted said were virtually identical on the right and left sides, yet, the left-side engine mount cost more than three times the right-side mount.

The Department of Defense eventually forced Lockheed, General Dynamics, and other contractors who were grossly overcharging the government to repay many of the expenses, and the contractors offered new, lower prices for many of the spare parts (though those new, lower prices still resulted in the government overpaying rather significantly).

It wasn't just defense spending where we caught people feathering their nests with taxpayer dollars. We found a number of universities playing similar games. While Stanford University was the most famous and prominent example, we found a lot of others doing things similar to Stanford, but Stanford was the most egregious.

Two hundred million dollars—that's the high-end estimate of how much money Stanford asked the American taxpayer to reimburse it. And the expenses were for things the taxpayers should never have been charged for. It all had to do with indirect grant costs. Indirect costs are things like utilities, equipment, and other expenses necessary for a grant project but that cannot be directly attributed to the grant.

We found all manner of improperly charged expenses, things that were claimed as being related to research but that were, in no way, shape, or form, conceivably related to research. For example,

the advancement of knowledge and the discovery of new innovations are not supported by a wedding reception for the president of the university.

The Energy and Commerce Committee's Subcommittee on Oversight and Investigations held its first Stanford University hearing on Wednesday, March 13, 1991. I began my remarks by making two points, to ensure that everyone knew both what the point of the hearing was and what the point of the hearing was not:

"What we are going to hear today is a story of taxpayers' dollars going to bloated overhead rather than to scientific research. It is a story of excess and it is a story of arrogance. It is compounded regrettably by lax government oversight. The government simply did not do its job."

I wanted my colleagues on the committee, as well as the scientists and researchers who I knew were following the hearing, to be clear that we were focusing on waste and abuse in the research funding system and how that waste and abuse, in turn, caused there to be less money available for research. We weren't seeking to cut off the flow of research dollars; we were seeking to increase the flow, to make more money available for research by not having taxpayers be responsible for yachts and antiques, which serve no legitimate research function.

I'd been chairing Energy and Commerce for a decade by then, and I'd dealt with my fair share of waste and abuse. Yet one thing that continued to make my blood boil was the "catch me if you can" attitude of Stanford (or anyone else), who, when caught, lied and denied.

"When the subcommittee first raised the question as to why the university had charged the taxpayer for a seventy-two-foot luxury yacht outfitted with wood-burning stoves and a Jacuzzi, Stanford

made a flat denial that it owned a yacht. A month later, it admitted that it owned a yacht but denied having charged its cost to the government. A month later, it admitted that, yes, it had charged some of the expenses to the government, but it claimed that it was an honest error and announced that it was immediately withdrawing those charges."

I'm a firm believer that if you've been caught doing something that raises a stink, even if you think your actions were the correct actions, you should admit your mistake, apologize, and be open and transparent about what you did and why. Denials and obfuscation never make anything better. Indeed, they just exacerbate the problem, as my friend Secretary Clinton found about her emails . . .

Returning to the Stanford matter, the inclusion of the yacht expense was claimed to have been an accounting error, one incorrectly included in the indirect cost pool used to calculate reimbursements. That would have been a believable justification if the mistake had happened once. But it happened for *eight consecutive fiscal years*.

This "accounting error" for the yacht, the *Victoria*, had cost the American taxpayer $184,000 over eight years.

Stanford was billing the taxpayers for all manner of things that had no research function, things that the university claimed were overhead expenses related to research and innovation. At the hearing, I told the room about some of the things my committee staffers and the government's auditors had found that had been charged to the government as research expenses, including:

- $6,000 to cedar-line closets at the Stanford president's residence;
- $2,000 a month for flowers at the president's house;

- $1,000 a month for laundry at the president's house;
- $1,200 for an early nineteenth-century Italian fruitwood commode;
- $7,000 for sheets for the president's bed;
- Several Pierre Deux Voltaire chairs at $1,500 each;
- $400 for flowers for a dedication of the horse stables at Stanford;
- $45,250 for a retreat at Lake Tahoe for the Stanford Board of Trustees;
- $185,000 in administrative salaries and expenses associated with operating a shopping center; and
- $63,931 for five years of operations and maintenance at the home of the former chancellor of Stanford, a house not owned by the university, a house not even on university property, a house owned by someone who retired in 1968 and died in 1985 (yet for which Stanford continued to bill the taxpayers from 1986 to 1990; they might still be billing the taxpayers, if we hadn't stopped them).

Stanford's initial response to the bevy of government audits was, by the way, an audit of its own, which claimed that the taxpayer had underpaid Stanford by $13 million. No one on my committee, their staff, or any of the government experts we subpoenaed deemed that audit to be credible.

Stanford hired the best experts in public relations, law, and accounting to challenge the investigations of the overcharging. There was just one problem, as I told the officials from Stanford sitting before the subcommittee: the university hadn't "decided whether the costs for the Mankiewicz PR firm and the lawyers would be charged to research overhead." In other words, Stanford was being

questioned about whether its expenses were proper, and it wanted to defend itself by continuing that same practice!

I was angry. When you're caught with your hand in the cookie jar, it's best not to try to steal more cookies when your hand is on the way out.

That Stanford University—an institution named for and founded by a nineteenth-century robber baron who used and abused immigrant labor to build the railroads that built his fortune—was one of the worst offenders at bilking the twentieth-century American taxpayer was, I thought, strangely fitting.

Leland Stanford probably would have loved that a university named for him had found a way to gild its own lily at someone else's expense. Stanford was the Koch brother or Mercer of his time, building his fortune on the backs of others, putting his name on things when it was necessary to use good deeds to mask the foul stench of shady dealings.

The U.S. government is among the largest funders (if not *the* largest funder) of scientific research in the world. I have no quarrels with this. I do, however, take exception when funds intended for research are instead used to buy antiques for the president's official residence.

I did get Stanford and other universities billing for such things to repay some money. Not as much as I'd have liked them to repay, but millions were returned. And the various administrative agencies who oversee such federal research programs tightened the rules to make it even clearer such expenses were no longer reimbursable.

As a chairman, I was a pale imitation of Harry Truman. When he was a senator, Truman saved the government billions of dollars with the waste, fraud, and abuse his committee uncovered. The

success of his committee is likely what caused FDR to nominate him as vice president in 1944. Hell, when giants are your heroes, falling short of their high standards is something you learn to live with.

Oversight takes many forms. Congressional investigations, hearings, phone calls, letters—and the best part is they all involve one thing: asking questions. Who? What? When? Why? How? And to what extent?

As a general rule, the state of oversight in Congress these days makes me want to vomit. Republicans are using "oversight" to fire up their base, raise money, embarrass Democrats, and, in the Trump administration, protect a rogue president. I'm talking to *you*, Devin Nunes.

There are still a few rare moments of genuine oversight. One of them was in May 2018, when the House questioned the U.S. Olympic Committee and USA Gymnastics about the rampant sexual abuse of young athletes, predominately by the gymnastics team's doctor.

Toward the close of the hearing, a congresswoman nearing the end of her second term, one Debbie Dingell, got a chance to question the witnesses before the Energy and Commerce Committee.

There have been far too many incidents and allegations of sexual misconduct in sport, including allegations involving individuals associated with each of the national governing bodies before us today, and honestly, I'm not reassured by your testimony because I don't hear a sense of urgency. I keep hearing "We're going to do it. We're going to get to this. We're going to do it." Well, what is out there? Who are these young people who need help who aren't getting there? So, I have some questions here.

We've heard today that the U.S. Center for SafeSport plays a key role in protecting the athletes from abuse. Given how important this mission is, I find it deeply concerning that apparently it took seven years for the U.S. Olympic Committee to get SafeSport off the ground. In fact, as early as 2010, the U.S. Olympic Committee Working Group for Safe Training Environments found that the Olympic Committee must do more to take a leadership role in protecting the athletes from abuse. By the way, that is what you are all saying today—that you are all working on it. And I hope that as you are working on it, you will be transparent, too.

A hearing on making sure our young athletes are safe from predators is the sort I'd expect to yield bipartisan consensus, a moment when Congress uses its oversight powers to ensure that egregious events never happen again. Yet, I was still surprised to see it actually happen. Oversight had become so politicized, so twisted by partisan games, that I wasn't sure any of them even knew how to do it. So, it warmed my old Polish soul to see my wife and her colleagues on Energy and Commerce holding folks' feet to the fire.

These moments of genuine bipartisan oversight are exceptions to the norm. Generally, the "oversight" we're seeing in Congress today is anything but. Instead of a search for the truth, we're seeing partisan witch hunts designed to fire up one side's base, damn the consequences.

And it's letting all manner of rascality go unpunished. If the foxes are in charge of the henhouse, well, don't be surprised if there aren't as many chickens left come the dawn . . .

_____

CHAPTER 14

Too Big Not to Fail

I warned repealing Glass Steagall would destabilize US financial systems. Banks have grown bigger & less accountable since repeal.

—TWEET FROM @JOHNDINGELL,

JANUARY 24, 2012, 9:51 P.M.

PROCEEDINGS OF THE UNITED STATES HOUSE OF REPRESENTATIVES AS REPORTED IN THE CONGRESSIONAL RECORD OF NOVEMBER 4, 1999

MR. DINGELL: Madam Speaker, I yield myself the remaining time for purposes of closing.

Madam Speaker and my colleagues, I think we ought to look at what we are doing here tonight. We are passing a bill which is going to have very little consideration, written in the dark of night, without any real awareness on the part of most of what it contains.

I just want to remind my colleagues about what happened the last time the Committee on Banking brought a bill on the floor which deregulated the savings and loans. It wound up imposing upon the taxpayers of this nation about a five-hundred-billion-dollar liability. That is what it cost to clean up that mess.

Now, at the same time, the banks, by engaging in questionable practices, wound up in a situation where the Fed and the Treasury Department had to bail them out, also at the taxpayers' expense. But it did not show.

Having said that, what we are creating now is a group of institutions which are too big to fail.

Not only are they going to be big banks, but they are going to be big everything, because they are going to be in securities and insurance, in issuance of stocks and bonds and underwriting, and they are also going to be in banks.

And under this legislation, the whole of the regulatory structure is so obfuscated and so confused that liability in one area is going to fall over into liability in the next.

Taxpayers are going to be called upon to cure the failures we are creating tonight, and it is going to cost a lot of money, and it is coming. Just be prepared for those events.

You are going to find that they are too big to fail, so the Fed is going to be in and other federal agencies are going to be in to bail them out. Just expect that.

With regard to the privacy, let us take a look at it. We are told about all the protections for privacy that you have here. If you want to have a good laugh, laugh at it, because here is the joke: the only thing the banks are going to be required to say with regard to what they are going

to do with regard to your privacy—and this is everything, from your health to your financial situation, to everything else—is "We are going to stick it to you."

The privacy that you are going to have under this legislation is absolutely nothing. And what is going to drive that is going to be a simple fact, and that is that the banks are all going to be competing with the most diligence, and the result will be that those protections are going to be manifested in a race to the bottom.

Consumers, investors, and the American public will have no protection to their privacy whatsoever under this bill. The only thing the banks have to say and the other institutions have to say is "We are going to stick it to you." Vote against the conference report.

The House of Representatives was debating the Conference Committee's report on the Gramm-Leach-Bliley Act, which repealed parts of the Glass-Steagall Act of 1933. Glass-Steagall placed significant barriers on the sorts of activities banks were and were not allowed to engage in.

There's no need to understand all the details and minutiae of Glass-Steagall. Here's all you need to know: whenever you go to a bank and it offers you a mortgage, or to trade stocks, or your car insurance company offers you a savings account, that's now possible only because of the repeal of Glass-Steagall.

I'd like to be able to say that repealing Glass-Steagall was a Republican idea, as they're usually the ones who want to repeal the twentieth century. In truth, the repeal had the enthusiastic support of a Democratic president, my friend Bill Clinton. In his 1996 State of the Union address, President Clinton declared, "The era of big

government is over. But we cannot go back to the time when our citizens were left to fend for themselves." The problem of the Glass-Steagall repeal was that it ended "big government" regulations that had been created precisely to remedy the failings of an era when citizens were left to fend for themselves.

Repealing Glass-Steagall allowed for the creation of full-service investment institutions. Supporters claimed, as supporters of regulatory repeal always claim, that consumers would see a savings windfall when banks were allowed to be brokerage houses, when insurers could be banks, when insurers could be brokers, or any combination of the three.

Big companies got the regulatory repeal they wanted, and they got to line their pockets through all the new revenue streams. Thanks to Gramm-Leach-Bliley and other administrative and legal changes, big banks were regulated the same way a casino or house of ill-repute is managed—and as we all know, the house always gets a piece of the action.

Consumers? Well, the promised windfall of savings never arrived.

Taxpayers? There'd be no way, we were told, that the entire financial system would collapse necessitating a massive taxpayer-funded bailout—that is, unless the entire economy went into a tailspin and we saw an economic crisis like we did in 1929.

Well, the economy did crash, in 2008, and when it did, many pundits acted as if there had been no way of forecasting this, that nobody had warned Congress that they were making a mistake in repealing Glass-Steagall.

I knew before I spoke that day in 1999 that it was a lost cause and that the bill repealing Glass-Steagall was going to pass. When the House had voted to pass it and send it to a Conference Committee a

few months prior, the vote was 343 to 86. So, I knew the vote would go against me that night, but I made my speech anyway. That's what you do. Even when you know the vote's going to go against you, you make damned sure everyone knows what you think and why, that you make your stand for the people and the public good.

Fifty-seven of my House colleagues listened to me that night. Three hundred sixty-two voted the other way. Most of the "no" votes were from my fellow Democrats, but one Independent (then-congressman Bernie Sanders of Vermont) and five Republicans (Tom Campbell of California, Joel Hefley of Colorado, Joe Barton of Texas, Mark Sanford of South Carolina, and John Mica of Florida) also voted "no."

I don't often toot my own horn—I prefer to give credit to as many people as possible—but I was right about what would happen if we repealed Glass-Steagall. I wish I'd been wrong. I wish that the banks, brokerage houses, and insurance companies hadn't driven the American economy off a cliff and forced the taxpayers to spend trillions of dollars to bail them out.

I wish corporate greed hadn't sent us into the worst economic crisis since the Great Depression.

I wish that corporations hadn't put short-term profits above long-term risk.

I know that corporations exist to make money for themselves and their shareholders. To create a situation in which corporate greed requires taxpayers to bail the companies out, though, is an unacceptable risk.

It's a good thing we in Congress closed this loophole and re-stored Glass-Steagall . . .

Oh, wait. We didn't. But we should have. We should have in 2008 and 2009 as a condition of all the bailouts. We should have

said, "Never again." But we did not. Even then, when they came to the taxpayer with hat in hand, seeking a bailout to cover losses their own deeds had caused, the big banks still got their way.

Looking out for the people—not the rich, not the powerful, but the average, everyday person. That's something that has always been done for as long as there's been a Dingell in Congress.

When my dad entered Congress in 1933, the United States was still in the midst of the Great Depression. About a month before FDR was sworn in as president, there was a series of runs on banks all over Michigan. A bank run is when people think a bank is about to become insolvent and go out of business, so they rush to make withdrawals to get cash in hand. Those of you who have seen the Frank Capra classic *It's a Wonderful Life* will remember the famous bank run scene.

That scene was set in 1932, a time before the Federal Deposit Insurance Corporation, before the Federal Reserve could intervene and force an undercapitalized bank to sell to a larger, more fiscally secure institution. In those days, if your bank failed and you hadn't gotten your money out, the odds were very good that you'd never see it again.

In 1933, my father took to the floor of the House to excoriate the bankers and the banking crisis. Why? Because he felt there was a movement afoot to force ordinary men and women to absorb the losses while the bankers escaped punishment, sanction, censure, or blame.

They gave my dad twenty minutes to speak. The short, tubercular Polish man with a booming voice walked to the lectern.

Mr. Speaker, ladies and gentlemen of the House, you are all aware of the financial storm which leveled the fortunes of

the people of Michigan. You may not, however, know that the losses involved nearly eight hundred thousand bank depositors in Detroit alone, and have largely destroyed in assets between seven and eight hundred million dollars. The paralyzing effect of this unheard-of bank failure cannot be described nor comprehended. Its effect touched every merchant, every manufacturer, and every parish and congregation in Michigan. Commerce and industry throughout the Middle West was [sic] jarred to the foundation, and trade recovery delayed. This financial quake swallowed the life savings of the industrious, provident worker. It has snatched from the widow and from the estate left for the benefit of the widow and her children the patrimony which a thoughtful and considerate husband left to provide for her future and for the education of his children.

This historical failure, without precedent in the history of banking, has caused a trail of broken hearts and suicides that cannot be estimated. Its killing effect can never be appraised. It has stifled progress and withered the confidence of the people of Michigan to the point of hopelessness.

This was not seven or eight hundred million dollars in 2018 dollars; this was seven or eight hundred million dollars in 1933 dollars. The modern equivalent would be tens (perhaps hundreds) of billions of dollars.

Dad, though, wasn't concerned just with the social effects of the banking crisis. He wanted to know why it had happened and whether any of those responsible had violated any laws or regulations such that they could see time inside a prison cell. Imprisoning those responsible might not have made the depositors whole from

their losses, but those deliberate, culpable acts that had caused such a panic should not have gone unpunished. And Dad felt that Congress was the one institution that could look into this.

> At any rate, the people of Michigan are entitled to know at least what has happened to their banks and what was the cause of the wrecking. Congress should go into this matter as the only agency that will not be hemmed in by petty local influences and as a body which will recognize no limitations, which can summon witnesses from beyond its own state borders, and as a tribunal which will render a decision solely and only upon its findings, irrespective of whom it might harm or favor. The president of the United States, in his Inaugural Address, has said that the money changers must be driven out of the temple, but here we have an example, forsooth, where they have been kicked from the temple into the sanctuary.

My father was, in short, calling for federal oversight and investigation of the banking system and the failures of the banking system. It was a problem that transcended state borders, and as such, only a government body that transcended state borders could investigate. If your jurisdiction stops at the boundaries of your state, you cannot pursue the truth adequately and fully.

I was six when Dad made this speech. I don't remember it, but when I heard about it years later, I filed away the notion that proper oversight requires the involvement of Congress and the current executive administration; that multistate investigations require investigators and investigations with multistate jurisdiction. In rereading the speech for this book, I was stunned to find out that two

years before my dad entered Congress, he had been corresponding with Congressman Henry Steagall, something he slipped into this speech almost as an aside. Even before he entered Congress, my dad was making sure he would be prepared to hit the ground running.

Here's the part of FDR's First Inaugural Address that my dad was referring to:

> The moneychangers have fled from their high seats in the temple of our civilization. We may now restore that temple to the ancient truths. The measure of the restoration lies in the extent to which we apply social values more noble than mere monetary profit.
>
> [. . .]
>
> Happiness lies not in the mere possession of money; it lies in the joy of achievement, in the thrill of creative effort. The joy and moral stimulation of work no longer must be forgotten in the mad chase of evanescent profits. These dark days will be worth all they cost us if they teach us that our true destiny is not to be ministered unto but to minister to ourselves and to our fellow men.
>
> Recognition of the falsity of material wealth as the standard of success goes hand in hand with the abandonment of the false belief that public office and high political position are to be valued only by the standards of pride of place and personal profit; and there must be an end to a conduct in banking and in business which too often has given to a sacred trust the likeness of callous and selfish wrongdoing. Small wonder that confidence languishes, for it thrives only on honesty, on honor, on the sacredness of obligations, on

faithful protection, on unselfish performance; without them it cannot live. Restoration calls, however, not for changes in ethics alone. This nation asks for action, and action now.

This struggle is one that is still going on in the United States and around the world—the notion that having the most toys makes you the biggest success. It's horseshit now, and it was horseshit then. I'm just glad I never lived to see a president elected who loves to talk about himself, his buildings, his golf courses, his airplane, his stupid hats, his bottled water, his steaks, his vodka, his . . .

FDR wasn't warning us of anyone specific; he was warning us of a type, the sort of person who thinks he's a success and a good person because he's rich. As a rich man himself, FDR knew that wealth does not define worth, that scoundrels can be rich and poor alike.

Dad helped to pass legislation like the Glass-Steagall reforms and the establishment of the FDIC to reduce the risk of future bank runs and to protect the consumer in the event that such runs happened again.

Laws like Glass-Steagall get to the very core of who we are as a nation, of the values we seek to uphold, and of the standards we set for our companies and ourselves.

It's also precisely in these regulations where the most mischief can be made, where the most harm can be done. Whether it is in banking or food safety, water quality or automobile emissions levels, this sort of statutory oversight has a direct impact on everyone's everyday life.

One particularly effective way I found to ensure proper oversight was to see to it that the producers and consumers came together to agree on the regulatory process. If we could find a way

to have the producers, and not the taxpayer, bear the cost of the regulations, all the better.

On July 12, 2017, the House voted to reauthorize the FDA's User Fee Programs for another five years. I helped create the user fee process. Under it, drug companies must pay the user fees when they submit a product for approval; these fees, in turn, help fund the FDA's operations.

Debbie rose to speak in strong support of the FDA Reauthorization Act of 2017. She reminded her colleagues that:

> We all have loved ones, friends, and neighbors who are suffering from life-threatening diseases and illnesses and who want hope that that next-generation treatment or therapy will still be available to them.
>
> It is our shared responsibility to support the FDA as well as countless researchers and patient advocates across the country who are working to bring new cures to market. This critical bipartisan legislation helps us achieve that important goal by reauthorizing User Fee Programs at FDA for five years.
>
> I want to thank Chairman Walden, Ranking Member Pallone, Chairman Burgess, and Ranking Member Green for continuing the long-standing tradition on the Energy and Commerce Committee of advancing this legislation in a bipartisan manner. Our work together on this bill should be a model for how we can cooperate on other issues in the future.

The bill passed the House by voice vote, and it passed the Senate 94–1. It was signed into law on August 18, 2017.

Working across the aisle to pass good, bipartisan legislation that benefits the people—that's how the Congress used to operate. And that's what the Congress should return to doing. I'm glad to see Debbie's working with her colleagues in both parties to do what previous generations of legislators have done so effectively: come together (again, that's the very meaning of the word *congress*) to do the people's business.

CHAPTER 15

Going Home

Enough partisan politics—compromise is honorable. Let's get back
to doing the people's work #SOTU

—TWEET FROM @JOHNDINGELL,
JANUARY 28, 2014, 9:21 P.M.

"LADIES AND GENTLEMEN, THIS IS YOUR CAPTAIN SPEAKING.
Delta Air Lines Flight Ninety-Six is on time for an arrival at Detroit
Metropolitan Airport at six thirty-seven this evening. At this time,
we've reached our cruising altitude, and the Fasten Seat Belt sign
has been turned off . . ."

I'd been hearing announcements like this twice a week for decades, on the flight to Washington or on the flight home, or on
flights anywhere else the House or my colleagues needed me to be.

Usually I read on a flight or rested my eyes. This time, though, I
was staring out the window, lost in thought. Washington, DC, was
now behind me. I was going home.

When I was a ten-year-old boy, I used to have a footrace with my

brother, Jim, down the long corridors of the Longworth House Office Building. The finish line was Dad's office, Room 1616. It wasn't a fair competition, since Jim was only five, and my legs were a lot longer. Sometimes I'd let him win, because when he burst through the door and shouted, "Pop! Pop! I beat Jack!" my dad would always wink at me while patting Jimmy on the head for his triumph.

The day before my flight home, I'd had a scooter race with Republican congressman Ralph Hall of Texas, who served with me on Energy and Commerce. It wasn't a fair race. I was three years younger than he was. The winner got to face the reigning champion of our scooter racing league, Congresswoman Tammy Duckworth of Illinois.

"Dingell," I thought to myself, "when in the hell did you get to be so damned old?" Just yesterday, it seemed, I was a hatless junior congressman watching John Kennedy, the youngest man ever elected to the presidency, being sworn in. (At thirty-four, I was eight years younger.) Hell, back then, I wasn't even old enough to be constitutionally eligible for president. Still, a man less than a decade older than me was getting sworn in as president of the United States.

I looked down at the newspaper folded in my lap. The date read Friday, February 21, 2014. On Inauguration Day in 1961, the current president, Barack Obama, hadn't been born yet. It suddenly struck me that I was thirty-five years older than he was.

That day on the plane, I was bundled up like an Arctic explorer. It was cold and windy in Detroit, and Debbie wasn't going to let me catch a cold, especially not on this trip. I had an important speech to make on Monday.

It was one I never thought I'd give. As much as I'd denied it previously, I'd always assumed that they would have to carry me out

from the House Chamber feet first. Up until the last few years, as the House grew into a hateful, obnoxious place (what people in the private sector call a "toxic work environment"), it never entered my mind to stop serving my constituents voluntarily. I was blessed to have had their trust in me for fifty-eight years. The idea of quitting was antithetical to me. It felt that I would be letting them down. Still, I knew it was time. I'd accomplished much of what my father had set out to achieve, and more. I was proud of what we'd done, yet it was increasingly clear to me that the future was going to be one long fight.

Monday's speech was billed as my annual State of the District address, when I gave the people back home a report of what to expect out of Congress in the upcoming year. (What to expect from *this* Republican-led bunch of gridlocked hyperpartisan bastards would be one word: "Nothing.") Often, I'd use this speech as an occasion to announce that I would be seeking another term.

Not this time.

That morning, word started to leak out that this might be more than my regular report to the people. Somehow, the press got wind of the story that I would be announcing my retirement. I even heard it on the car radio, on the way to the Crystal Gardens Banquet Center in Southgate, about twenty-five minutes from our home in Dearborn. "We have an unconfirmed report that veteran congressman John Dingell, the longest-serving member of the U.S. House of Representatives, will announce his retirement today after serving thirty consecutive terms. We'll be following this story closely as it develops. Stay with us for further updates, which we'll bring to you as soon as they come in." I reached over and turned off the radio. Looking back at Debbie, I said, with a dead-serious tone in my voice, "Why don't we just put the damned cat back in the bag? I'll get up

there and say, 'The reports of my retirement have been greatly exaggerated. What do you say? Do you want me to run again?' They'll all shout, 'Run, John, run!' What do you think, Fox?"

For a moment, she thought I meant it. The look on her face was a mixture of surprise and excitement. *Flabbergasted* was the word invented for that look.

I couldn't keep a straight face any longer. I started chuckling.

"Doggone it, John! For a minute there . . ." Her voice trailed off, and that same wistful look she'd had all morning returned. This was hard for her, too.

The banquet room was filled with friends and former staff, local officials, and even some of my old political rivals. It was, in short, a Dingell reunion.

I started my speech by telling my friends in the room of the systemic problems we faced as a nation and of the need to remedy them:

Americans must change and they must insist that those who seek office and power do so too. When that happens, things will start to turn for the better. We have much to be grateful for, and we owe it to ourselves, to each other, and to our fellow Americans to demand this of those seeking the privilege of power and office to make this change. Too many officeholders have rejected this and have refused to carry out their duty to the country, to each other, and to all of us, past, present, and future. Let us love our country, our system, its blessings, its riches, and the good it deserves and that it gives to each of us.

This Congress has been a great disappointment to

everyone—members, media, citizens, and our country. Little has been done in this Congress, with only fifty-seven bills passed into law. That is not Heinz packaged varieties; it is the laws passed by the Congress.

I reminded everyone of the need to work together to solve our problems. (When I wrote this part of the speech, I debated including those great words of Benjamin Franklin "We must indeed all hang together or most assuredly, we shall all hang separately." I've always loved that line, but this didn't feel like a day to reference hanging.)

No one can say to a fellow American, "Pardon me your end of the boat is sinking." We narrowly saved the auto industry; it thrives today, turning out cars that are superb, and the wonder of the world.

We narrowly escaped the Great Recession—note those words: I went through the Great Depression. There's only a couple of letters' difference in the two names, but a major difference in the impact on the country.

By now, the few folks in the room who somehow hadn't heard that I wasn't running for reelection were starting to realize that this wasn't one of my typical speeches.

For too long, bad politics has allowed this Congress to career from one manufactured crisis to another, whether it's a stubbornness to agree on a budget, a necessary raise of our debt ceiling, or any other matter that would restore certainty.

Then I got to the portion of the speech that contained the words I thought I'd never hear myself say:

> I would like now to invoke a point of personal privilege to talk a little about myself, which is something I am usually reluctant to do. There are plenty of people in Congress who love to talk about themselves, and I have tried very hard not to join their ranks over the years. But I am setting aside that rule today to share my personal plans for the future with you, my dear friends.
>
> Around this time every two years, my wife, Debbie, and I confer on the question of whether I will seek reelection. My standards are high for this job. I put myself to the test and have always known that when the time came that I felt I could not live up to my own personal standard for a member of Congress, it would be time to step aside for someone else to represent this district.
>
> That time has come.

I wish I could tell you how people reacted to my announcement, but I can't. It had taken every ounce of self-control I had to hold myself together long enough to say those words, and I still had the final part of my speech left to deliver. I've never been one for public displays of emotion. I didn't want this day to be remembered as "that time John Dingell made himself cry."

But there were a few important—and personal—things still left to be said:

> I am fully aware of the honor that has been bestowed on me every two years by the people of Southeast Michigan when

they gave me their votes to serve them in Washington. There is no greater privilege than a life spent in service, and I know how fortunate I have been to spend my life as a member of Congress. I have done my best for the people who live here—my neighbors, my friends, those who supported me, and those who didn't. The fabric of Michigan is the fabric of my life, and it has never frayed.

Public service is undervalued in our modern times, and I can understand that when I look at what our Congress has become. But it doesn't have to be that. I am hopeful that this fever breaks at some point, and Congress goes back to what it should be: the House of the People, standing up for the average man and woman. That's how I've always defined the job, and it's a damn good definition.

But for now, let me tell you how much I love you all. We have fought many battles over the years as we tried to do what was right for the families who live here. We've been through tough times and have emerged, battered and bruised but stronger for the fight.

Let me close with this: I am not leaving Congress. I am coming home to Michigan.

Thank you.

After the cat was irretrievably out of the bag, a smart reporter who I'd known for years immediately asked me the obvious question. It was a two-parter, and I knew it was coming before it was even asked.

"Who do you want to replace you? And do you think your wife, Debbie, will run?"

"The Lovely Deborah would make a hell of a congresswoman,

and she doesn't need any advice from me. I'll be glad to vote for her if she runs."

A few days later, it was official. Debbie declared her candidacy.

"I'm not running to replace John Dingell," she said. "I think he's irreplaceable. I want to keep fighting for the issues that have always been my passion, especially women and children."

And that's just what she's done. She fights like hell for what she thinks is right.

Later that year, I sat at her victory party waiting for the results. It's a very different experience when you're the spouse of the candidate, and not the candidate. (Now I know what I put Debbie through so many times.)

Even though I knew the odds were in her favor, I was on the edge of my seat until it was official. Giving a congresswoman-elect a celebratory kiss was a new experience for me.

So, I'd announced my retirement, but I still had work to do. I worked until my last day, including overseeing the people we'd hired to pack up my office. Many of my hunting trophies went to friends and colleagues on the Hill, to adorn their office walls. There was also paperwork to do, and some final legislative business.

Then I prepared to scooter off into the sunset. Debbie was to be the congresswoman. I'd stay out of her way. The last thing I wanted to be was one of those people who don't work in Congress anymore but who hang around the place bothering people trying to get things done.

A fractured hip kept me from being at Debbie's swearing in. I watched it on C-SPAN, but it wasn't the same. I was, however, a few days later, able to pose for the ceremonial photo every member takes with the Speaker.

My retirement plan was to nap, read, watch TV, and amuse myself with the Twitter.

Then an orange clown descended from a gaudy escalator, launching his presidential bid with a racist screed against minorities.

"There's no way in hell we'll be crazy enough to elect this orange son of a bitch."

EPILOGUE

The most precious possession of citizenship, which distinguishes the American from any other, is the heritage of tolerance and respect for the other fellow's opinion. There has never been a time when I failed to respond in defense of an oppressed minority or failed to accept the challenge of a bigot or an intellectual boor.

— CONGRESSMAN JOHN D. DINGELL SR.,
HOUSE FLOOR SPEECH, JUNE 10, 1940

AFTER A FITFUL NIGHT OF SLEEP, I OPENED MY EYES ON TUESday, November 8, 2016, with a disturbing image still lingering in my wakening brain. A tall, fleshy figure was coming at me with a gun aimed directly at my chest. Although my groggy mind couldn't quite summon up his face, I sensed he was a person very familiar to me. In that blurry state between sleeping and waking, try as I might, I couldn't quite manage to bring his features into focus. Yet my feeling of unease remained palpable, even as the image itself began to recede into my subconscious. I am rarely affected by my dreams, but this one I couldn't shake. I felt a cold chill, and for just a brief moment, I considered pulling the warm covers back up and going to sleep again.

Instead, I shook off the cobwebs, swung my feet over the side

of the bed, and put on my glasses. As the room came into clarity, I glanced at a faded black-and-white photo in a frame on my nightstand. It was a picture of my dad standing directly behind President Franklin Delano Roosevelt. FDR was seated at the center of a long table, surrounded by nineteen men and one woman, a pen poised in his famously mottled hand.

I knew the picture well. It was taken in the Cabinet Room of the White House in 1935, when President Roosevelt signed the Social Security Act into law. At forty-one, my father, then only a second-term congressman, was almost certainly the youngest person to witness that extraordinary moment. He had been invited there because he'd played an important part in crafting that historic legislation, the significant cornerstone of the New Deal.

You know the way you remember something the moment you stop trying to recall it? That's exactly what happened. When I saw my dad's image in that long-ago White House photo, the key detail of my disturbing dream that I had been unable to remember suddenly appeared in my mind's eye with crystal clarity: the menacing armed man walking quickly toward me was Donald Trump.

During the 2016 presidential campaign, Trump had infamously boasted that he could "stand in the middle of Fifth Avenue and shoot somebody" and not "lose any voters." That's why my dream had been so unsettling. The truth is, when I was wide awake, I had long believed he might well have been right.

As I pulled on my pants to face Election Day, I tried to push the ghoulish image out of my mind. The American people were too decent to be taken in by a third-rate television huckster who was, without question, the crudest, least-qualified, most dangerous presidential nominee I'd ever seen in over eighty years of close contact

with almost every major elected official. Hell, this guy made even Richard Nixon look stable.

"Get a grip, Dingell," I said aloud, heading toward the kitchen. Yet I couldn't quite avoid the feeling that something was about to go very, very wrong.

For the next ten hours, Debbie and I went to more than thirty polling places and to Clinton-Kaine headquarters around the Dearborn, Ann Arbor, and Detroit areas. We exchanged very few words in between those many stops. Each of us knew what the other was thinking. It was going to be an extremely close race. Nothing more needed to be said.

Over the previous two weeks, both presidential candidates had virtually moved to Michigan, with Trump holding his final rally of the 2016 campaign at 12:30 a.m. on Election Day in Grand Rapids, the home district of my old friend Jerry Ford (whom the good Lord had mercifully spared from having to watch what was happening to his Grand Old Party).

Outwardly, Debbie, wearing a bright blue dress that highlighted her eyes, was buoyant and optimistic. She greeted every volunteer and constituent with a hug and words of encouragement. But I saw in those eyes what the voters did not. Behind her warm smile was a combination of frustration and fury at what we both knew was going to be a statewide outcome that could go either way. When the results were finally certified weeks later, Trump had ultimately carried Michigan by fewer than 10,000 votes out of almost 4.8 million cast—the political equivalent of finding your entire month's rent by digging lost change out of your couch.

It should not have been that close. Hillary, who Debbie and I both love and admire, would have won a comfortable victory in Michigan if her campaign people had heeded Debbie's consistent

warnings that the state was in play, no matter what their piss-poor polls were telling them.

I learned early on from my father (who narrowly suffered his first, and only, election loss for that state legislative seat in Colorado two years before I was born) that the only "poll" that matters is the one that happens on the first Tuesday after the first Monday in November.

Debbie and I understood what the Clinton campaign refused to believe—that our people were hurting and they were angry. Sure, they saw Trump for who he was: a two-bit charlatan with a fancy suitcase full of bad ideas and stupid hats. But elections are won when people have someone to vote *for*, not just a bogeyman to vote *against*.

Debbie dropped me off at home in Dearborn, then drove into Detroit to watch the results at the Michigan Democratic State "Victory" Party.

While I slept through the endless prattle of television talking heads grieving on MSNBC, dumbfounded on CNN, and jubilant on Fox, Debbie was hugging dozens of crying men, women, and children, many of them patriotic Muslim Americans who were our friends and neighbors in Dearborn. They were now, literally, afraid for their lives.

"America will no longer settle for anything less than the best," Trump crowed just before 3:00 a.m. "We must reclaim our country's destiny." Although I was asleep when he said those words, that scene was forecast by my hellish nightmare.

I later learned that while I slept, my brilliant, prescient wife was giving voice to what despondent Clinton supporters needed to understand and reluctantly accept: "Tomorrow we've got to be part of pulling this country together. We need to remember that we are

Americans. And we've got to make sure, as Democrats, we are pulling the country together and leading us to a future that includes everybody."

The next afternoon, I was on a panel discussion at the Gerald R. Ford School of Public Policy at the University of Michigan. I wasn't nearly as eloquent as Debbie, when I said, "I think I speak for everyone, including my Republican friends here, when I say that I'm still trying to figure out what the hell happened."

Laughter broke the tension in the packed auditorium, and that moment allowed me to make a serious point that I thought was particularly essential for young voters to hear, as they hadn't been through this kind of gut-wrenching disappointment before: "We have a president of the United States who is arranging to make a peaceful transfer of power from one officeholder to another. This is an extraordinarily important thing, and it is one of the reasons that the United States is the oldest and the most successful of the democracies in the history of mankind."

As I write these words, almost two years have passed since that painful Election Night. In that time, we've learned a lot more about the disturbing details of the Trump campaign, particularly the still-unfolding revelations about the extent to which Russia deliberately attacked the integrity of our most sacred democratic institution, the electoral process. And we've learned a lot more—none of it good—about the disturbance to the American republic that is Donald J. Trump.

With Twitter (perhaps the only thing that Trump and I have in common), we can now all communicate in real time. I tweet a fair amount, and it's therapeutic for me. As a retiree, I find that yelling at the television never makes me feel any better. However, tweeting that "Donald Trump couldn't pour piss out of a boot if the

instructions were printed on the heel!" gives me a surprising sense of satisfaction.

As important as it is that we maintain perspective—and a little humor goes a long way in doing that—we cannot ignore the fact that these are grave and serious times. Hyperbole is impossible when we have a president who creates "alternative facts" and then expects us to accept them as gospel, simply because a bully now uses the presidency as his personal pulpit. "Alternative facts" used to be called lies. Renaming them doesn't make them any truer. I believe it was our beloved former president, Barack Obama, who said "You can put lipstick on a pig, but it's still a pig."

Donald Trump is a clear and present danger to the United States of America. Even more dangerous than Trump himself is the mindset (what psychologists call "authoritarian personality syndrome") that breeds "Trumpism" and allows it to flourish.

This phenomenon, documented by researchers the world over, is characterized by two main features: first, a belief in total obedience to authority; and second, aggression toward "the other," that is, people who differ from the mob mentality, that spreads like poisonous mushrooms growing wild in manure. Fear spreads in the dark, and Trump's black-hearted bullshit about Mexicans, Muslims, and anyone else he chooses to demonize is a fetid breeding ground for his authoritarian followers. It fertilizes their self-righteousness and reinforces their (non)sense of being victims of a "conspiracy" that threatens "real Americans" like them.

This hysteria is not new to Trump. It's not even new to America. I watched it spread under the Ku Klux Klan when I was a small boy, and I saw it continue as a dangerous undercurrent of American politics ranging from Charles Lindbergh, Fulton Lewis, and that

whole America First crowd; to the fearmongering of demagogues like Joe McCarthy and Roy Cohn; all the way up to the modern-day messiahs of malevolence, Rush Limbaugh, Sean Hannity, and the other horse's asses of the Apocalypse who populate right-wing radio.

The difference between all of them and Trump is that he is not a true believer in *anything* except himself. Some of these right-wingers are hucksters who shill for whatever makes them money; some really believe their own bullshit. Not Trump. He is more dangerous than all of them, because his only priority is his own survival. He will sacrifice anything and anyone to preserve and protect himself—not the Constitution he swore to uphold.

This is unprecedented in the history of our nation. We have a rogue president and a large enough minority of Americans who, like lemmings, will follow him over any cliff. The problem is, if we let them, those crazy bastards will take us all down with them.

Trump's dark and destructive rhetoric, the polar opposite of Franklin Roosevelt's inspirational call to Americans that "we have nothing to fear but fear itself," is a malignancy on the body politic. Trump appeals to those who share his authoritarian mind-set by lying so often that truth itself has become obsolete. He rails against government and the press as "enemies" of the American people, not the noble extension of our best impulses.

Despite what a few smart-ass young pups say about my being old enough to have actually *signed* the Declaration of Independence, I really wasn't there in 1809, when Thomas Jefferson retired after serving two terms as president. Yet I've spent my career in public life attempting, as did my father and as Debbie is doing now, to adhere to the essential principle of American government that

Jefferson articulated more than two hundred years ago: "The care of human life and happiness, and not their destruction, is the first and only legitimate object of good government."

With that core principle firmly in mind, I believe we must renew our commitment to what Lincoln called on the nation to do in 1862: "Nobly save, or meanly lose, the last best hope of earth."

What is generally lost to history is that Lincoln's plea came in the form of a message to the Congress at the height of our nation's deepest division, a Civil War that threatened to rend us apart as united states. Just before he described America as the world's "last best hope," the Great Emancipator warned, "Fellow-citizens, *we* cannot escape history. We, of this Congress and this administration, will be remembered in spite of ourselves. No personal significance, or insignificance, can spare one or another of us. The fiery trial through which we pass will light us down, in honor or dishonor, to the latest generation."

It was another great president, Franklin Delano Roosevelt, who called on the American people, and the people of the world, to be guided by what he called the "four essential human freedoms":

- The first is freedom of speech and expression—everywhere in the world.
- The second is freedom of every person to worship God in his own way—everywhere in the world.
- The third is freedom from want—which, translated into world terms, means economic understandings which will secure to every nation a healthy peacetime life for its inhabitants—everywhere in the world.
- The fourth is freedom from fear—which, translated into world terms, means a world-wide reduction of armaments

to such a point and in such a thorough fashion that no nation will be in a position to commit an act of physical aggression against any neighbor—anywhere in the world.

Today we are in the painful throes of what I call an Uncivil War. The great principles of Jefferson, Lincoln, and Roosevelt are forgotten, ignored, or disdained. In this twenty-first century (hell, in just in these last few years), Americans have witnessed our national descent into a fact-free society where objective truth is reviled.

The British novelist George Orwell prophetically forecast the era of "fake news" when he wrote *1984* all the way back in 1948: "War is Peace. Freedom is Slavery. Ignorance is Strength."

This Congress has ignored its constitutional responsibility to check the executive's authority to take the nation to war. This president doesn't even inform his own staff of the military threats he makes. They learn about them the way the rest of us do: in the middle of the night, when they get up to take a piss and see some damn fool's comment that's misspelled, misinformed, and may result in missiles being launched at us or by us.

War is not peace. It's all too often the result of greed and of politicians valuing party (translation: their own asses) over country.

Freedom is not slavery. No group of Americans gains greater freedom by oppressing another group of Americans.

Ignorance is not strength. It's dangerous.

My father, as I've said to you throughout this book, was a self-taught scholar of history and human behavior. Lying in a sickbed in the Union Printers Home in Colorado, uncertain if he would live to see his twenty-first birthday, he pondered the mysteries of life with a fierce intellect that belied his frail body. His lifelong illness gave him the strength of will, determination to help others, and

a toughness that informed his character and focused his mind on solving problems that seemed insoluble. He was a philosopher in the truest sense of that word. Dad had a basic approach to dealing with any tough situation that he taught to all his children. He called it "Dingell's Two Rules of Holes":

- The First Rule of Holes is this: When you're in a hole, *stop digging*.
- The Second Rule of Holes is this: *Never* break the First Rule of Holes.

I think a lot about my father these days as I watch events unfold that bear a striking resemblance to what he experienced when he was in Congress and I was still a young kid. American fascism, which Sinclair Lewis warned "would come wrapped in the flag and carrying a cross," is once again fashionable. Gerald L. K. Smith and Father Coughlin have given way to Alex Jones and Mark Levin. They represent another kind of "hole." Just listen to them on any given day, and you'll know exactly what kind I mean.

The American people now find ourselves in the political equivalent of the Grand Canyon of Holes. But this is one we didn't dig alone. Let's not kid ourselves; the Russians attacked our electoral system and they'll do it again without firing a shot. Worse, they were cheered on by a corrupt crew of right-wing bastards who rent politicians like cheap hookers and treat the Constitution like toilet paper.

I've come to believe that there needs to be a Third Rule of Holes.

The Third Rule of Holes is this: Grab the shovel and beat the hell out of the people who are using it to bury you. I'm speaking metaphorically, of course. Violence begets violence, but weakness

invites brutality. We must use every legal means possible to wield our political shovels, and we must give no ground when it comes to standing up to bigots and bullies, both foreign and domestic.

Complacency got us Trump. It will take courage and constant vigilance to undo the damage he's done. Trump, and all he represents, is a tumor growing on our republic. We can lance him off like a bad boil, but the disease will remain until we treat it at its core. The cancer of cynicism eating away at our country can be cured only when we trust one another again. No leader alone, no matter how charismatic, no matter how great his or her appeal, can fix what ails us as a nation. That is our unique work as free citizens. There is no more important a cause.

Now, before you say, "Dingell, you're a crazy old coot who's lost his marbles. Just sit in your chair and shut the hell up," let me tell you exactly what I mean.

My father taught me early on that you never back down to a bully. You walk right up to him and punch him in the nose. I can't tell you how many times I had to run alongside my dad when he was taking on people twice his size. He never backed away from a fight, no matter how big the other guy was. And I'll be damned if he wasn't right. Bullies are cowards. They win only when we let them scare us into not fighting back.

Just as my father was struggling for every breath when he arrived in Colorado Springs on that train more than a hundred years ago, America is facing its own life-or-death fight for nothing less than its very survival. Unlike with tuberculosis or influenza, medical treatment is not the solution—although, a good start would certainly be the immediate passage of universal health care for every man, woman, and child in the last civilized nation on earth that doesn't provide it as a right, not a privilege—though, the sickness

we face as a nation does resemble what nearly killed my father at the age of twenty, almost before his life had a chance to begin. Remember, before they called it tuberculosis, the popular name for my dad's illness was consumption, a term derived from the literal wasting away of the body's vital organs. Today, our body politic is consumed, not by a physical illness but by an equally deadly mindset that is steadily shrinking us from the world's greatest champion of human freedom into a shriveled remnant of what was, in my lifetime, the finest example of a constitutional republic on the face of the earth.

We live in an age when celebrity, no matter how it is achieved, has become the highest measure of political credibility; the marketplace of ideas has become a chaotic online bazaar that sells us every wild assertion, as if it were equal in value to all others, no matter how damn-fool crazy it is; where bigotry is no longer seen as shameful but instead is shouted from the presidential pulpit as brave resistance to "political correctness" (my mother would have washed my mouth out with soap for being "brave" enough to say much of that hateful stuff out loud); and where all our public institutions, not just Congress, are cynically reviled by Trump, Limbaugh, Hannity, and their acolytes in order that they might nakedly profit from the fears of the American people.

The wise American jurist Learned Hand once wrote of his "faith in the eventual supremacy of reason." In the political malady we are now suffering through as a nation, I can't predict with certainty that Judge Hand will be proven right.

But I promise you this: even at my age, I am not going down without a fight. In 1787, at the conclusion of the Constitutional Convention in Philadelphia, eighty-one-year-old Benjamin Franklin was approached by a woman who asked him earnestly, "Well,

Doctor, what have we got, a republic or a monarchy?" Replied the tired Franklin, "A republic. If you can keep it."

Franklin's words never rang truer than they do today.

As I've said, my father believed we need to take a long view of history. He didn't live to see the passage of either Medicare or the Affordable Care Act. Yet he prayed that his son might see them both come to pass. Although the process was long and difficult (and suffered many setbacks, some of which continue to this day), I was blessed by the good Lord to see them both signed into law.

So, please listen to me carefully when I say that I know that *I won't be here* to see if the United States survives this current crisis. A lot of damage has been done to our fragile republic. Repairing that damage won't take months or even years. It will take decades, if not generations, to pull our deeply divided nation together again. If it's the good Lord's plan to let me watch from above, I'll be watching it happen because of you. And your children. And their children.

I won't sugarcoat this—it's not going to be an easy fight. Taking on massive amounts of money and powerful interests that care only about consolidating their own power has never been easy. But I struck a lot of powerful nerves over six decades in Congress, and there's nothing more gratifying than taking these high-and-mighty bastards down a peg or two.

Many things have been said of me over the years, not all of them fit for polite company. I have been called "abrasive," "arrogant," "high-handed," and, by my friend, former president George W. Bush, "a pain in the ass," which I considered then, and still do, a high compliment. Like all ten presidents I served with before him, I did chafe his hind end on more than one occasion if I thought it was warranted. That is the constitutional duty of the legislative branch: to hold the executive branch accountable. The Founders, men of character and

vision, understood that a system of checks and balances was essential to preserving the republic, and that, above all, an unchecked executive would be the greatest danger to our freedom.

I'm told by my young friends that when you write something in all capital letters, you're yelling. So, let me shout this out:

WE HAVE ABDICATED OUR CONSTITUTIONAL SYSTEM OF CHECKS AND BALANCES IN THE UNITED STATES!

Understand this: I'm *not* saying this as a partisan. I'm talking about *anybody* in *any* administration, Republican or Democrat, who thinks they're above the law. If we really want to make America great again, we need to start by hauling their asses up to Capitol Hill in front of truly bipartisan oversight committees and make them swear to tell the truth under penalty of perjury. Believe me, it works. Remember, I've seen the wet spots on the chairs after they've finished testifying.

I could have gotten out of public service decades ago and made a lot of money. But it never occurred to me to do so—not when I still had the opportunity to serve the people of my district who trusted me to always protect what they valued, not greedy special interests. Sure, I was criticized, by both the right and the left, for working with all sides to find common ground. My friend Gerald Ford, an honorable man whom I believe history will judge with the respect he deserves, put it best when he said, "Compromise is the oil that makes governments go."

Speaking of making government go, let me make an observation about the recurring hue and cry for term limits on members of Congress. Term limits are a piss-poor excuse from people (usu-

ally nonvoters) too lazy to do the basic work of every American citizen. It's easy to complain about the government. The real work comes when you have to get up off your couch and do something about it. You know who wins if you don't? Not you. The winners are the damned lobbyists who *love* term limits on everybody but themselves. We've seen it in many state legislatures over the last several decades: six years, and you're out. All that's left behind are kindhearted lobbyists who are more than happy to show any freshman member the ropes, free of charge. "Why bother to write a new bill, Mr. Assemblyman? We've got the draft text right here." Talk to me about term limits when they're also for *lobbyists*.

You know how all this "term limits" business started, don't you? In 1947, the Republican Congress wanted to stick a knife into FDR when he was barely in the grave. They passed what would become the Twenty-Second Amendment to the Constitution, limiting all future presidents to serving no more than two terms. In the House debate, my dad was in fine fettle: "It is the inherent right of a free-born American citizen to vote for whomsoever he chooses and as often as a candidate presents his name, once or ten times. This right must not be abridged now or in the future."

Here's something that will put a smile on your face. Two years ago, just imagine if the answer to the question "Could Barack Obama run for a third term?" had been "Yes, he can!" Polls taken then were unanimous: he would have beaten Trump like a drum.

And we'd all be sleeping better at night.

LET ME CONCLUDE BY HUMBLY SUGGESTING THREE PRINCIples for restoring what has always made America great: her fundamental commitment to social justice.

1. Restoring Civility to American Life

When I was a wet-behind-the-ears kid in school, the nuns made sure we understood one principle above all else, the Golden Rule delivered by Jesus in His Sermon on the Mount: "Do to others whatever you would have them do to you." Various versions of that essential principle inform every major religion the world over.

Although our American system of government is based on the laws of man, there is no real distinction between the Golden Rule and what Lincoln reminded us simply at Gettysburg: "All men are created equal." American equality demands that we treat one another with the same dignity and respect with which we expect to be treated.

Previously, I described the harshness of our national discourse and the unfettered schoolyard epithets and hateful taunts that plague our political culture as an Uncivil War. We do not speak with each other; we shout past one another. Political disagreements are no longer "honorable"; they are viewed as personal betrayals. Friendships, even families, are torn apart.

The fundamental problem is that for the first time in my life, hate speech is widely seen as normal, not extreme.

Yes, we must be critical of individuals and ideas with which we strongly disagree. It is our duty to speak truth, especially to power. So, how do we restore national civility while preserving the First Amendment guarantees of free and unfettered speech?

My father's great friend U.S. Supreme Court justice Frank Murphy gives us the answer. In the landmark 1942 case *Chaplinsky v. New Hampshire*, Justice Murphy wrote:

There are certain well-defined and narrowly limited classes of speech, the prevention and punishment of which have never

been thought to raise any constitutional problem. These include the lewd and obscene, the profane, the libelous, and the insulting or "fighting" words—those which by their very utterance inflict injury or tend to incite an immediate breach of the peace. It has been well observed that *such utterances are no essential part of any exposition of ideas and are of such slight social value as a step to truth that any benefit that may be derived from them is clearly outweighed by the social interest in order and morality.* [Emphasis mine.]

I suggest that the first step on the road back to national civility is to hold all Americans, private citizens and public officials, to the Murphy standard. The uttering of statements that represent "fighting words" and are not a "step to truth" should have consequences. The standard should, of course, be a very high bar. Dissent must be protected.

Yet, when the level of our political discourse is reduced to chants of "Lock her up!" and when individual members of the press are called out by name in a public setting as "enemies," placing them at physical risk, I believe it's well past time to apply the Murphy decision to political rhetoric, including on social media like Facebook and Twitter.

I've said it many times: "My right to swing my arm ends where the other man's nose begins." The same is true of speech. My right to speak my mind ends when I knowingly lie or intentionally incite harm toward an individual or a group. We live in an age when vitriolic words are hurled instantly, often without restraint. The consequences are rampant incivility and increasing hostility toward and intolerance of those with whom we disagree. I respectfully submit that if the worst offenders face tangible consequences, the Murphy

decision will help us find our way back to a society that promotes dialogue, not demagogues, and that lifts our nation up to common ground rather than letting it continue its downward spiral into constant chaos.

2. Restoring Economic Fairness

My parents and the Jesuits taught me that the core principle of social justice requires constantly working toward a more humane, decent society. Economic justice is the essential component of social justice, one that requires us to help abate suffering and misfortune, both of which we have far too much in this land of plenty.

How do we do that in an era when greed is viewed as more than just good but now admirable? When economic inequality in the United States (and around the world) is higher than it's ever been since our nation was founded?

It was not supposed to be this way. Just before taking office as our first president, George Washington wrote in a letter to businessman Richard Henderson:

> America, under an efficient government, will be the most favorable Country of any in the world for persons of industry and frugality, possessed of a moderate capital, to inhabit. It is also believed, that it will not be less advantageous to the happiness of the lowest class of people, because of the equal distribution of property. . . .

(That popping sound you now hear reverberating throughout the land is from Trumpist heads simultaneously exploding

like firecrackers at these "socialist" words from the Father of our country.)

Almost fifty years after Washington wrote those words, the Frenchman Alexis de Tocqueville, after exploring our young nation and getting an outsider's perspective on emerging American politics and sociology, observed in *Democracy in America* that "nothing struck me more forcibly than the general equality of condition among the people."

Tocqueville also saw the future dangers inherent in the growing rise of the new industrial economy, writing, "[F]riends of democracy must keep an anxious eye peeled in this direction at all times." Essentially, he predicted the rise of the Gilded Age robber barons like our old friend Leland Stanford and his rich-as-Croesus cronies John D. Rockefeller, Andrew Carnegie, J. P. Morgan, and Cornelius Vanderbilt. They treated the economy as their personal piggy bank and bought political influence with the casual indifference of kids set loose in a candy store.

Over the twentieth and twenty-first centuries the names have changed, but the corruption has continued. Whether it was Henry Ford's vicious union busting in my father's day or the Koch brothers' efforts to turn our democracy into a private-sector plutocracy by eliminating government regulations that protect wages, workers' rights and safety, and the environment, the bottom line is always the same, *their* bottom line: profits before people.

Here's a fact that would have curled the hair on my head (if I had any left). It did make me damn angry, though, as it should you. As of two years ago, according to an Oxfam International report, just *eight men* (five of them Americans) controlled *half* of all the money in the world. Put another way, their personal wealth equaled the total assets of 3.6 billion people, many of whom were living on as

little as two dollars per day. When economic disparity is so great between a handful of people at the top and billions at the bottom, we all know how that story ends. Badly.

Economic inequality has always been an accurate predictor of political unrest and the collapse of countries and empires throughout all of recorded history. The turmoil we feel in our own society is not imaginary. It is real, and it is inextricably linked to the rest of the world in our global economy.

Technology has brought us together as one planet, even as the negative effects of it have increased our vulnerability. A few years *before* our last presidential election, one of Putin's top military aides, General Valery Gerasimov, wrote of using covert and propaganda tactics to turn a "perfectly thriving state" into a victim of "foreign intervention," causing it to "sink into a web of chaos."

So, how can we create economic fairness in our country, and promote it around the world, when we have entered an age when economic chaos is no longer just the result of unchecked greed but also an undisguised tactic of what can only be called "economic warfare"?

My answer is twofold. First, let us pray.

One does not need to be Catholic to draw inspiration and hope from a man I consider to be the "anti-Putin," His Holiness, Pope Francis. Like Pope Leo XIII and Pius IX before him, Pope Francis has made economic justice a central tenet of his papacy:

> The worship of the ancient golden calf has returned in a new and ruthless guise in the idolatry of money and the dictatorship of an impersonal economy lacking a truly human purpose. The worldwide crisis affecting finance and the economy lays bare their imbalances and, above all, their lack of real

concern for human beings; man is reduced to one of his needs alone: consumption.

His Holiness is also pragmatic, calling out "trickle-down economics" for the fraudulent failure it has always been and will always be:

> Some people continue to defend trickle-down theories which assume that economic growth, encouraged by a free market, will inevitably succeed in bringing about greater justice and inclusiveness in the world. This opinion, which has never been confirmed by the facts, expresses a crude and naïve trust in the goodness of those wielding economic power and in the sacralized workings of the prevailing economic system.

So, when I say "pray," I do not mean it as a religious exhortation to any one faith. All of us, including those who do not worship any god, can benefit from this man's wisdom. He calls on us to have true concern for one another, not just the almighty dollar. This is the essence of peace. And when peace reigns, chaos is defeated.

The second path to economic justice in the twenty-first century is one that I don't pretend to fully understand, yet I know it is a road we must accept, as we are already traveling down it at high speed. Millennials, and the generation that is following them, were born into the information age. Our transition to the information age is as profound as that from the agrarian age to the industrial age. Every aspect of our economic, cultural, and political lives will be determined by how we cope with this change. Buggy makers hated the Model T. That didn't make its prevalence any less inevitable. What the Model T *did* do was render whole segments of the

workforce obsolete. Those who resisted change suffered mightily. Those who faced the future with curiosity and innovation thrived.

I was in the House Chamber on May 25, 1961, when our new, young president, John F. Kennedy, called on a joint session of Congress to aspire to a great goal that, at the time, seemed impossible. Like my colleagues, I listened raptly when he said, "I believe that this nation should commit itself to achieving the goal, before this decade is out, of landing a man on the Moon and returning him safely to Earth." Remember that even back then, we were in a technological race with the Russians—and we were losing that one, too.

Kennedy would have none of it. He knew that Americans could come together around a goal greater than their own self-interest and achieve it. Tragically, he didn't live to see Neil Armstrong take that "one giant leap for mankind" on July 20, 1969.

That brings me to the second part of how I truly believe we can achieve a future where we restore economic fairness: by dreaming big again.

In his First Inaugural Address on March 4, 1933, President Franklin Roosevelt called on the American people to value their worth not by the size of their bank accounts, but by the happiness they created in their lives.

> The measure of the restoration lies in the extent to which we apply social values more noble than mere monetary profit. Happiness lies not in the mere possession of money; it lies in the joy of achievement, in the thrill of creative effort. The joy and moral stimulation of work no longer must be forgotten in the mad chase of evanescent profits. These dark days will be worth all they cost us if they teach us that our true destiny is not to be ministered unto but to minister to ourselves

and to our fellow men. Recognition of the falsity of material wealth as the standard of success goes hand in hand with the abandonment of the false belief that public office and high political position are to be valued only by the standards of pride of place and personal profit.

Throughout my life, that's how I've always judged success. I was there that day, a six-year-old boy playing with my dad's shoelaces. Of course, I didn't understand the meaning of the president's words, yet they've had a lifelong impact on me. And those everlasting truths were never more important than they are today.

We are once again at a crossroads in our relationship with the future. American ingenuity has given us great opportunities to improve the quality of life. With new technology there have also come new challenges, particularly around employment. Automation is replacing human labor at an ever-increasing rate. For too many, this is a frightening reality. They've seen whole sectors of the economy shrink, if not disappear altogether. Yet, as was true in 1933, fear is not the solution.

Two years after his First Inaugural Address, FDR faced down that fear with a plan to put America back to work. He created the Works Progress Administration to build the country's new infrastructure and rebuild the nation's spirit. Over an eight-year period, Roosevelt's WPA employed more than 8.5 million Americans on 1.4 million public projects. We built highways, bridges, and dams. We provided work to students through the National Youth Administration. Some of our nation's greatest artists, like Jackson Pollock and Willem de Kooning, launched their careers with endowments from the WPA. Most of all, we restored our national pride in a uniquely American way: we came together in the face of adversity.

In the spirit of President Roosevelt's bold decision to put millions of Americans back to work at the height of the Great Depression, and inspired by President Kennedy's call to greatness that dared us to touch the moon, let me suggest a new American challenge for the twenty-first century: by March 4, 2033, the one-hundredth anniversary of FDR's First Inaugural, let us resolve to repair our nation's crumbling infrastructure with a program on a scale and scope even greater than the WPA. Rebuild America is a program that could put as many as twenty-five million Americans to work over the next fifteen years. It will cost at least two trillion dollars. How do we pay for that? No less an expert than Bill Gates has a brilliant solution. Because so much of the job displacement we're suffering is a direct result of automation, Gates advocates a "robot tax": "Right now, the human worker who does, say, $50,000 worth of work in a factory, that income is taxed and you get income tax, social security tax, all those things. If a robot comes in to do the same thing, you'd think that we'd tax the robot at a similar level."

To which I can only add, "Amen!"

3. Restoring Integrity in Government and Politics

Throughout this book, I've talked about all the changes I've seen in our nation and its institutions during my six decades in public service. Yet the most profound change I've witnessed is also the saddest. It is the complete collapse in respect for virtually every institution of government and an unprecedented cynicism about the nobility of public service itself.

These are not just the grumblings of an angry old man lamenting the loss of "the good old days." In December 1958, almost ex-

actly three years after I entered the House of Representatives, the first American National Election Study (initiated by my beloved University of Michigan) found that 73 percent of Americans trusted the federal government "to do the right thing almost always or most of the time." As of December 2017, the same study, now conducted by the nonpartisan Pew Research Center, found that number had plummeted to almost a record low. *Only 18 percent* of adult Americans trusted the government to "do the right thing" on behalf of our country.

There are many reasons for this dramatic decline, and we've touched on a lot of them throughout this book: the Vietnam War, Watergate, Ronald Reagan's folksy but popular message that government was *not* here to help, the war in Iraq, and worst of all by far, the Trumpist mind-set that elections are rigged (if he doesn't win); that government is to be hollowed out from within, like a building filled with termites; and that traditional journalism is conducted by partisan purveyors of fake news. These jackasses who see "Deep State" conspiracies in every part of government are a minority of a minority, yet they are now the weakest link in the chain of more than three centuries of our American republic. Ben Franklin was right. The Founders gave us a precious yet fragile gift. If we do not protect it with constant vigilance, we will most certainly lose it.

As an armchair activist, I now have the luxury of saying what I believe *should* happen, not what I think can get voted out of committee. I'm still a pragmatist; I know that profound societal change happens incrementally, over a long period of time. The civil rights fights of the 1950s and '60s, of which I am proud to have been a part, are a great example of overcoming setbacks and institutional racism. Yet, one hundred fifty-five years after the Emancipation

Proclamation and less than two years after our first African American president left office, racism still remains a part of our national life.

Just for a moment, however, let's imagine the American system we might have if the better angels of our nature were to prevail.

The power of the pen as a magic wand is not to be underestimated. The Magna Carta, the Declaration of Independence, and the Constitution were all created by hands wielding quills, not swords. What I write here is for the restoration of an American republic that our children, their children, and their children's children might someday bring about because they will dare to dream of its possibility. Our Founders dared to dream. In the face of overwhelming odds, they envisioned breaking away from British tyranny. And they made it so.

Here, then, are some specific suggestions—and they are only just that, *suggestions*—for a framework that might help restore confidence and trust in our precious system of government:

An electoral system based on full participation. At age eighteen, you are automatically registered to vote. No photo ID, no residency tests, no impediments of any kind. Advances in technology can make this happen effortlessly. Yes, voting should be restricted only to American citizens. This would also require strict protections against foreign meddling in our electoral system.

The elimination of money in campaigns. Period. Elections, like military service—each is an example of duty, honor, and service to country—should be publicly funded. Can you imagine if we needed to rely on wealthy donors to fund the

military? I know there are those who genuinely believe in privatizing everything. They are called profiteers.

Public service should not be a commodity, and elected officials should not have to rent themselves out to the highest bidder in order to get into (or stay in) office. If you want to restore trust in government, remove the price tag. I am fully aware that the Supreme Court has declared that "money is speech." That's horseshit. The day my wallet starts talking to me, I might reconsider that view. Until then, I believe that the pernicious influence of money on our elections must be removed.

The end of minority rule in our legislative and executive branches. The Great Compromise, as it was called when it was adopted by the Constitution's framers, required that all states, big and small, have two senators. The idea that Rhode Island needed two U.S. senators to protect itself from being bullied by Massachusetts emerged under a system that governed only four million Americans.

Today, in a nation of more than 325 million and 37 additional states, not only is that structure antiquated, it's downright dangerous. California has almost 40 million people, while the twenty smallest states have a *combined* population totaling less than that. Yet because of an eighteenth-century political deal, those twenty states have forty senators, while California has just two. These sparsely populated, usually conservative states can block legislation supported by a majority of the American people. That's just plain crazy.

The math is even starker when you look at places like Wyoming and Vermont, each of which has fewer people in

the entire state (575,000 and 625,000, respectively) than does the Twelfth Congressional District of Michigan, which I last represented and whose more than 700,000 residents Debbie fights her heart out for every single day. Yet, her efforts are often stymied simply because it is understood that even should a good bill make it through the hyperpartisan House, it will die a quiet death in the Senate because of the disproportionate influence of small states. With my own eyes, I've watched in horror and increasing anger as that imbalance in power has become the primary cause of our national legislative paralysis. In primaries, the vocal rump of a minority of obnoxious asses can hold the entire country hostage to extremist views. This insanity has sent true public servants fleeing for the exits.

The Electoral College has the same structural flaw. Along with 337 of my colleagues, I voted in 1969 to amend the Constitution to abolish it. Twice in the last eighteen years, we've seen the loser of the popular vote become president through the Electoral College formula, which gives that same disproportionate weight to small states, each of which gets two automatic votes for its two senators.

My friend Norm Ornstein sees a demographic shift coming that will effectively transform us into two countries. He tells me that "in 2050, 70 percent of Americans will be living in just fifteen states. That 70 percent will then have thirty senators, and the remaining 30 percent of the people, mainly those living in the smallest and poorest states, will have seventy senators."

How do we fix this? Practically speaking, it will be very difficult, given the specific constitutional protection granted these small states to veto any threat to their outsize influence.

There is a solution, however, that could gain immediate popular support: abolish the Senate. At a minimum, combine the two chambers into one, and the problem will be solved. It will take a national movement, starting at the grassroots level, and will require massive organizing, strategic voting, and strong leadership over the course of a generation. But it has a nice ring to it, doesn't it? "Abolish the Senate." I'm having blue caps printed up with that slogan right now. They will be made in America.

The protection of an independent press. This is where the Founding Fathers got it exactly right. Jefferson said, "Were it left to me to decide whether we should have a government without newspapers, or newspapers without a government, I should not hesitate a moment to prefer the latter."

Trump has said of reporters, "I would never kill them, but I do hate them. And some of them are such lying, disgusting people."

My father started out life as a cub reporter for the *Detroit Free Press*. He always believed journalism was a tremendously honorable profession. We cannot restore respect to our institutions of government until we put an end to the systematic attacks on journalism that have become increasingly prevalent. The playbook is simple: Lie. Repeat the lie. Then attack the journalists who expose those lies as being liars themselves—or, in modern parlance, "promoters of fake news." The Nazis' propaganda minister Joseph Goebbels replaced journalism with state-run propaganda and created a political climate based on fear and falsehoods.

As I write this, the *Washington Post* has just won a Pulitzer

Prize for its coverage of Russian interference in the 2016 elections. The Fourth Estate is not a branch of government, but none of the branches of government can be trusted to function honestly without an unfettered free press vigilantly holding it accountable.

We began this with Thomas Jefferson. He should have the last word: "Our liberty depends on the freedom of the press, and that cannot be limited without being lost."

———————

AS A YOUNG MAN, I SERVED IN THE ARMY DURING WORLD War II, and my father was a member of Congress. I learned from him and, later, from my own experience that history always repeats itself unless we remember it with clarity and conscience.

Now I am an old man. My age bears with it a responsibility to share what I've witnessed so that future generations avoid making the same mistakes. My advice always begins with the truth, which is why would-be despots and demagogues try so hard to discredit it. They hate it like the Devil hates holy water.

The conduct and outcome of the 2016 presidential election has put the future of our country in mortal peril. After a lifetime spent in public service, I never believed that day would come. Yet it has. And we now find ourselves on the precipice of a great cliff. Our next step is either into the abyss or toward a higher moral ground.

Since before the Civil War, we've been told that "Providence watches over fools, drunkards, and the United States." Yet the good Lord also granted us free will. The direction we choose to follow is ours alone to make. We ask only that He guide our choice with His wisdom and His grace.

It's up to you, my dear friends.

ACKNOWLEDGMENTS

AFTER I DECIDED TO RETIRE FROM THE CONGRESS AND RETURN to Michigan, one of Debbie's closest friends, Marjorie Fischer, invited us out to dinner with her new husband, a kind and gracious gentleman named Roy Furman. We learned that Roy, a highly respected New York investment banker and award-winning Broadway producer, also had a strong interest in government and politics, having served as finance chairman of the Democratic National Committee during President Clinton's first term. He suggested that if I wasn't yet prepared to write a book, I should at least consider sitting down for a series of oral history interviews that could be included with my papers at the University of Michigan. I was noncommittal. "That's an interesting idea," I said, certain that nothing would ever come of it.

Less than a week later, Roy introduced me to a writer named David Bender, whose idealism immediately reminded me of a New Dealer. He'd been Roy's chief of staff at the DNC and had gone on to become an author and political commentator. I couldn't say no to Roy without being impolite, so I agreed to sit down with David for a few recorded interviews. After our second session, David made a strong case for turning our interviews into a book proposal. "Who else," he asked me, "can describe what it was actually *like* to be in the House Chamber when FDR addressed a Joint Session of Congress the day after Pearl Harbor and was in the Chamber when he gave his 'Infamy' speech?"

Never having written anything longer than a piece of legislation, I remained highly skeptical that writing a book was something I could do, let alone one that anybody would care to read. David was undaunted. He came back with a book proposal based on our interviews and, much to my amazement, there was interest from a number of major publishers. With David's commitment to work with me on it, and with my brilliant young friend and former assistant Fred Paffhausen signing on as our research editor, I agreed to give it a shot.

Which is how, at the age of eighty-nine, I discovered that it's never too late to do something you've never done before—all that's required is a willingness to take a leap of faith. That *was* something I knew I could do. I've always had faith that the good Lord would guide my hand, as He has done throughout my life.

Early on in the process, I realized that writing a book was far more similar to drafting legislation than I'd thought. Each is an effort that requires trust, collaboration, careful attention to detail, and the ability to make informed decisions about what's important enough to be included in the final version. In both, there are numerous people whose hard work usually goes unseen by the public. When I served in the Congress, I always made sure to share the credit for any successful effort—be it the passage of a bill or conducting an oversight hearing—with my colleagues and my staff. But whenever something failed, I always took sole responsibility. The same holds true with this book. Whatever you may enjoy about it is entirely due to the efforts of the people who supported, encouraged, and helped me to write it.

First among them is my wife, Congresswoman Debbie Dingell, whose belief in me is exceeded only by my love for her.

Other members of my family also contributed greatly to this endeavor. First among them was my youngest sibling, Julé Dingell Walowac, who generously opened up her treasure trove of family photographs and letters that have enriched this book tremendously. But her gift to this project pales in comparison to the unconditional love that she's given to me and my children. I honestly can't imagine what we would have done without her. I love you, Baby Sister.

Along with Julé, my brother Jim granted an interview that brought back so many wonderful, long-forgotten memories of our boyhood together. Thank you, my beloved brother, for your contribution to this book and, far more important, for the bond of brotherhood that we will always share.

Special thanks to my son, Judge Christopher Dingell, and his loving wife, Cindy, who helped me in so many ways with this book. Chief among them was their love, encouragement, and patience with their old dad. On good days and bad, they are always there for me. Know that I love you both and pray that the good Lord always grants you the same strength that you give me every day.

To all my children—John III, Christopher, Jennifer—know that your Pops loves you now and always. Jeanne, I miss you every day and I know that you are at peace with Our Heavenly Father. My grandchildren are a gift and a treasure to me. Gabrielle, Romy, and Robin—I love you and wish for you long, healthy lives filled with friends and good fortune.

Great thanks also go to my former chief of staff John Orlando for his role in helping to make this book possible. One of the ablest public servants I've ever known, John was kind enough to offer his wise counsel and keen editor's eye to help ensure that my thoughts were expressed clearly and factually. John, you are a treasured

friend. Thank you for your many kindnesses to me and Debbie throughout the years. We are forever in your debt.

My beloved friend and former House colleague President George Herbert Walker Bush (or "41," a "nicknumber" that I gave him at the same time I dubbed his son President George W. Bush "43"), you are one of the kindest and most decent men I have ever known in public life. Mr. President, I am deeply grateful to you for your gracious words in the foreword to this book.

I was blessed to serve in the Congress with Joe Biden for forty-two years, from his entrance into the Senate in 1973 to my retirement from the House in 2015. His extraordinary gift for friendship is well known. Joe, thank you for your kind words. Let me offer you a few of my own: You're a young man who has a lot more to offer our beloved country. Know that you will always have friends in Debbie and me, whatever your future may hold.

My profound thanks go to two men without whom this book would consist only of my illegible scrawling on a yellow pad.

I have known my research editor, Freddie Paffhausen, since he was knee-high to a grasshopper. I've watched him grow into a learned and accomplished young man, wise beyond his years and sharp as a tack. He is destined for great things.

Fred, I'm profoundly grateful for all that you've done for me, and I don't just mean for your work on this project. Although without your efforts, *The Dean* would have remained only an honorary title, and not a book of which we can be very proud. I thank you for the crucial part you played in making it possible. Paffhausen, know that you've always got a friend in John Dingell. May God always hold you in the palm of his hand.

And to my coauthor, David Bender, a gifted wordsmith who has enriched my life with his irrepressible optimism, passionate patrio-

tism, and wise counsel on all things political. An activist since the age of twelve, he reminds me daily that youthful idealism need not give way to cynicism, no matter how dark the day. I treasure the time we've spent together discussing the past, present, and future of our beloved country.

David, you have my everlasting gratitude. I would never have begun this book without your encouragement and support. It's because of your determination that we took this journey together. We started it as colleagues; we finish it as friends. Know that you are loved and may God be with you always.

To Gary Morris of the David Black Literary Agency, whose belief in this book right from the very beginning, turned it into a reality, I thank you greatly for your kindness and unwavering support.

I am particularly grateful to the team at HarperCollins, chief among them, editor Jonathan Jao (my congratulations to you on your new son), John Jusino, Sarah Haugen, and Emily Taylor. You saw this through to the end and, somehow, we are all still here. Please know that I consider myself very fortunate to have had this book in your talented hands.

So many others played a part in the birthing of this book: Christopher Schuler, Sam Harwood, Amy Paffhausen, Christina Fayz, Leigh Greden, Raymond Karpinsky, Steven Zax, Rodrigo Baptista, and Maggie Rousseau. I thank you all for your efforts.

Thanks also to Maryrose Grossman of the John F. Kennedy Presidential Library and Museum, Latoya Devezin of the Jimmy Carter Presidential Library and Museum, and Mary Finch of the George H. W. Bush Presidential Library and Museum for your tremendous help in identifying and securing many of the photographs included in this book.

A long career in public service does not lend itself to material

wealth. Instead, you grow rich with friends. To the many great friends that I was (and still am) blessed to have over my fifty-nine years in the Congress, I hope you will accept my humblest and deepest apologies that I cannot mention all of you by name. Please forgive your friend John Dingell.

To the vast majority of my colleagues in the House or the Other Chamber who placed the public good above party or personal interest, I thank you for the privilege of serving with you. Many of those I knew as a younger member, giants like Sam Rayburn and John McCormack, and, later, close friends like John Moss, Thad Machrowicz, and Lucien Nedzi—all of you will forever hold a special place in my heart.

Jim Baker, Alan Simpson, and Frank Zarb are more than three of my favorite Republicans. I treasure the time we were able to spend together, especially in the wild. Great thanks also to Jim and to Thomas "Mack" McLarty for their kind words about this book.

I want to give special thanks to two committee chairs, Herbert C. Bonner of North Carolina and Leonor Kretzer Sullivan of Missouri, for their patience and kindness in helping a young member learn the legislative ropes.

While writing this book, wonderful memories came flooding back of so many people, from chiefs of staff to interns, from volunteers to voters. I have been fortunate beyond measure to have had the support and friendship of so many good, decent, and dedicated people throughout my career in the Congress. I thank you all for your kindness to me and for your service to our beloved country.

Finally, to the people of southeast Michigan, please know that you have my everlasting gratitude for the trust you placed in me. My staff and I worked hard every day to ensure that what we did

in Washington, DC, would make your lives better and our country stronger.

I hope I did you proud.

John D. Dingell
October 5, 2018

Additional Thanks

From David Bender

When Roy Furman, for whom I have great respect and deep affection, asked me if I would be interested in meeting Congressman John Dingell about doing an oral history project with him, my immediate reply was, "Who *wouldn't* want to meet John Dingell?" As a lifelong student and practitioner of American politics (it should be noted that practice does not always make perfect), I'd admired John Dingell since I was twelve years old. Having been born less than two weeks before John entered Congress, I grew up watching him fight for so many of the things that informed my worldviews: civil rights, voting rights, conservation, and, most of all, universal health care.

We don't agree on every issue, but as I have come to learn from him, finding common ground on which to come together is the literal meaning of the word "congress." And when John and I do disagree, there has never been a time when we've failed to learn something from each other in the process. He will insist that he learns more from me, but since this is the only place where I have the floor, let me assure you that five minutes spent with John Dingell

is the equivalent of a master's class in politics and history. He embodies what we call "the wisdom of the elders"—teaching simply by being himself. And every minute that we've spent together has also taught me that the old virtues of courtesy, kindness, and compassion are not old at all. Like John Dingell, they are timeless.

John, I thank you and Debbie for the privilege of being part of telling the Dingell family story. And to Roy Furman, Gary Morris, Jonathan Jao, Sarah Haugen, John Jusino, and Emily Taylor, thank you for making *The Dean* come together and guiding it safely into port. To Frederick D. Paffhausen, research editor par excellence, I can only say that were George Washington looking for an even better right-hand man, I would recommend you in a heartbeat. Thank you, my dear friend.

Finally, to Jaime Capone and Phil Buchbinder, Ray Karpinsky, David Permut, Wilson Cruz, Sam Harwood, Cari Beauchamp, Jake Flynn, the Abrams family, the Weidman family, David Crosby, Judy Balaban, Maura Clare, Ramsay Thurber, and especially Kirk and Anne Douglas, I know how lucky I am for your friendship and for your love.

From Frederick D. Paffhausen

Congressman Dingell likes to tell people "I've known Freddie since he was in the egg." That's true. I grew up knowing him and his son Christopher. Much of what I know about how to treat people, the nobility and value of public service, that public interest outweighs self-interest—that all comes from the two of them. I do my best to make them proud.

After the congressman's retirement in 2015, I had the privilege of serving as his assistant from 2015 to 2018. I was honored when he and David Bender asked me to serve as research editor for *The*

Dean. I was flattered and—to be truthful—more than a little nervous. But, I remembered what David told me shortly after we first met: "There are books in you." I hope my efforts merit the trust and faith they placed in me.

Gentlemen, it's been an honor and a privilege. I thank you both for letting me play a part. To borrow a line from the congressman, know that you two will always have a friend in me. I love and treasure you both.

I wouldn't have been able to help on this book without the assistance and love of my mother, Amy, and my sister and brother-in-law, Elisabeth and Michael Hipke. Thank you all for your understanding, your help, and for letting me ignore everything else to focus on *The Dean*.

You would not be reading these words were it not for some truly great teachers who inspired me throughout my academic career: John Wukovits, Dennis Hamilton, John Schulte, Elaine Clark, Eamonn Long, Sid Bolkosky, Claude Summers, Frank Wayman, Suzanne Bergeron, and Patricia Smith. Thank you all. I couldn't have worked on this book without the skills I learned from you.

To Lisa Nocerini, thank you for understanding when I needed to miss meetings or when I needed extra time to meet deadlines.

Sarah Helm, Chelle Silas, Dave Green, Jeannette and Matt Quirk—all of you provided much needed distractions, outreach, support, and friendship. For that, each of you has my gratitude.

But, most of all, thank you to Christina Fayz. Thank you for being you, for letting me reschedule plans to write, and putting up with all the times I'd reach out at strange hours to tell you the cool thing I'd just edited or discovered. Your support was a lit candle during self-doubt's darkness. There are no words to say how much I love you. With you, all things are possible.

ABOUT THE AUTHORS

JOHN D. DINGELL is an American politician and was a member of the United States House of Representatives from December 13, 1955, until January 3, 2015. During his fifty-nine-year House career, Dingell rose to the powerful chairmanship of the Energy and Commerce Committee. During his tenure, he played a hugely influential role in the passage of landmark legislation, ranging from civil rights and health care to environmental and consumer protection. A lifelong Democrat, John Dingell holds the record as the longest-serving member in congressional history, with 21,572 days in office. He lives in Dearborn, Michigan, with his wife of thirty-seven years, Congresswoman Debbie Dingell.

DAVID BENDER is an author, broadcaster, filmmaker, and a lifelong political activist who has worked for five decades on multiple presidential campaigns. He has cowritten books with actor Kirk Douglas, musician David Crosby, and broadcaster-businessman Merv Griffin, and was the West Coast contributing editor at *George*, the political magazine founded by John F. Kennedy Jr. Bender lives on airplanes.

DATE DUE

This item is Due on
or before Date shown.

DEC – – 2018